How to use this book

Heinemann Advanced Science: Biology has been written to accompany your AS and A2 biology courses, and contains all the specification material you will need during your period of study. The book is divided into seven sections of associated material which have been made easy to find by the use of colour coding.

At the beginning of each chapter a Biology Focus explores the real-life context of an area of the science to come. You may use this to whet your appetite for the chapter that follows, or read it when you have made some progress with the science to emphasise the relevance of what you are doing. However you use it, I hope it will make you want to read on!

In addition to the main text, the chapters of the book contain two types of boxes.

The *blue information boxes* contain basic facts or techniques which you need to know. This often includes key facts you will have already met at GCSE – the boxes then carry these ideas forward to AS or A2 level. Information boxes are sometimes referred to in the main text, and can be read either as you meet them or when you have finished reading the chapter.

The *pink headed extension boxes* contain more advanced information which is not referred to in the main text. You do not need to address the content of these extension boxes until you have really got to grips with the rest of the material in the chapter or are studying the subject at A2 level.

When you have completed the work in a chapter of the book, there are questions to help you find out how much of the material you have understood and to help you with your revision. The summaries at the end of each chapter provide further help with revision, while at the end of each section of the book there is a selection of AS and A2 level questions.

Throughout the book the Institute of Biology's recommendations on biological nomenclature have been followed.

This book has been written to be an accessible, clear and exciting guide to AS and A2 biology. I hope that it will help to maintain your interest in the subject you have chosen to study, and that it will play a valuable role in developing your knowledge of biology – and with it, an increased understanding of all life on Earth.

Acknowledgements

I should like to thank the team at Heinemann who helped get this new edition into print, particularly Lindsey Charles who has been stalwart in her support and Eva Fairnell who entered the fray late but has worked with dedication to make everything hang together. Finally, I should like to thank my husband Patrick, my sons and my mother for their constant support, help and encouragement.

Ann Fullick, 2000

Dedication

For William, Thomas, James and Edward

CONTENTS

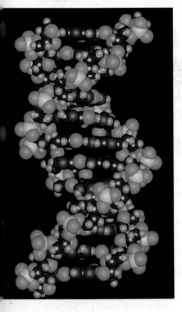

1 BUILDING BLOCKS OF LIFE

2 SYSTEMS OF LIFE

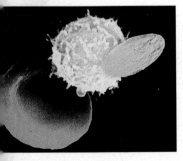

HEINEMANN
ADVANCED
SCIENCE

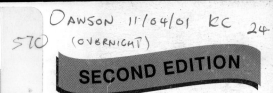
Dawson 11/04/01 KC 24
570 (OVERNIGHT)

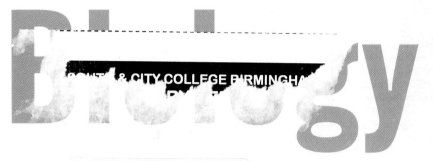

Biology

ANN FULLICK

Heinemann

Heinemann Educational Publishers
Halley Court, Jordan Hill, Oxford, OX2 8EJ
a division of Reed Educational & Professional Publishing Ltd
Heinemann is a registered trademark of Reed Educational &
Professional Publishing Ltd

OXFORD MELBOURNE AUCKLAND
JOHANNESBURG BLANTYRE GABARONE
IBADAN PORTSMOUTH NH (USA) CHICAGO

© First edition Ann Fullick, 1994
© This edition Ann Fullick, 2000

First published 2000

ISBN 0 435 57095 1

04 03 02 01 00
10 9 8 7 6 5 4 3 2 1

Edited by Eva Fairnell

Designed and produced by Gecko Limited, Bicester, Oxon

Original illustrations © Heinemann Educational Publishers, 2000

Printed and bound in Spain by Mateu Cromo

Tel: 01865 888058 www.heinemann.co.uk

3 | ENERGY SYSTEMS

4 | CONTROL SYSTEMS

5 | REPRODUCTION AND GENETICS

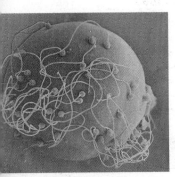

6 | POPULATION BIOLOGY

7 | MICROBES AND BIOTECHNOLOGY

1 BUILDING BLOCKS OF LIFE

Introduction

Biology is the study of living things. There is an enormous range of organisms, from the microscopic amoeba to the massive blue whale, from mosses to the giant redwood, including bacteria, fungi and many other weird and wonderful organisms along the way. But all living organisms have some features in common. Just as a house is made of bricks and timber, so living organisms are made up of smaller 'building blocks' which we call **cells**.

In this section we shall be looking closely at cells, magnifying them many thousands of times to find out their innermost secrets. We shall discover ways in which they are all similar, and ways in which they differ. These differences are important for cells that carry out particular tasks within the body of a whole organism.

As cells carry out their functions, they often need to move substances in and out of their cytoplasm. They can do this in a number of ways. Some cell transport mechanisms use energy, while others happen without an energy input. Within the cell, there are literally hundreds of different chemical reactions taking place at any one time. To prevent chemical chaos, these reactions must be tightly controlled. Cells manage their chemistry using enzymes, proteins that are vital to the functioning of all living things. In this section we shall look in detail at how enzymes are made and how they work.

Cells often work together in tissues and organs, and in order to interact in this way cells must recognise each other. If we can develop an understanding of how the cells of our body recognise not only each other but also 'outsiders' it will help us later as we look at the problems of infectious diseases and how they can be overcome.

Cells themselves are made up of even smaller 'building blocks'. Most of these chemicals of life are large, carbon-containing molecules. They make up the structure of our cells, control the workings of our bodies and carry information from one generation to the next. Understanding cells and the chemicals of

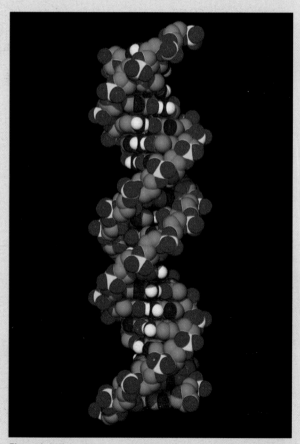

Figure 1 DNA is a large molecule containing the instructions for the way each cell is organised – it is the blueprint of life.

which they are made is an important step in the study of biology.

FOCUS IT'S A DOG'S LIFE

Millions of people keep dogs or cats, and most of the time both the pets and their owners are happy. But animals, just like people, can get ill, and a visit to the vet is often the only answer.

Looking at cells

Some illnesses are relatively easy to diagnose by examining the animal, taking its temperature and discussing the symptoms with the owner. If the problem is not so easy to spot, the vet may turn to the microscope.

The cause of an animal's illness may be in the cells of the body, and the only way to see what is going on is to prepare a slide of the tissue that is causing problems and have a look under the microscope. This may be done by the practice vet, or by a veterinary pathologist who specialises in animal diseases. They know what normal healthy cells from different areas of the body should look like, and so they can see if something is going wrong. For example, if an animal develops a lump, the growth can usually be removed during an operation. A thin slice of tissue from the growth is examined to find out whether the cells have turned cancerous.

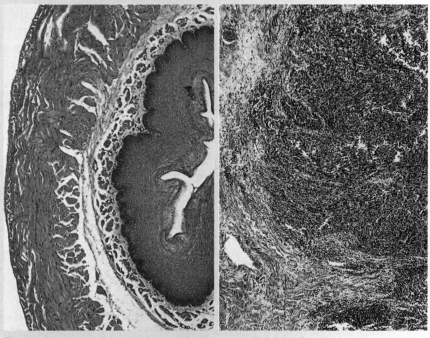

Figure 1 Cells taken from the oesophagus of a healthy dog (left) look very different from the cancer cells found in a tumour taken from another, less fortunate dog.

Figure 2 Sore patches like these are no fun for any dog, but a close look at the skin cells will soon pinpoint the problem so that treatment can be given.

Skin problems

A surprising number of dogs (and other animals) develop bald patches. These may be red and itchy, or red and sore, or just an area of hair loss. The causes include parasites such as fleas, fungal or bacterial infections, allergies to house dust mites and hormone problems. These different causes have different effects on the cells of the skin, even though the overall effect on the animal may look quite similar. By examining some of the skin cells under the microscope, a skilled vet can see exactly what is causing the baldness and give the appropriate treatment.

1.1 The units of life: Cells

Biology is the study of life. The planet which we inhabit teems with a great variety of living animals and plants, all interdependent on each other and on the environment in which they live. Biologists are concerned with studying the internal and external mechanisms of life, including the balances within individual cells, in whole organisms and between the members of specific ecosystems. To begin to understand an animal or plant, alone or as part of an interconnected system of organisms, we need to know what it is made up of, and this is where we shall begin – with cells.

What is a cell?

The idea of cells is familiar to most of us. Radio, newspapers and television often discuss cells in relation to cancer, test-tube babies, drug testing and other topics. But in spite of this, most people have only a vague idea of what a cell is.

Cells were first seen over 300 years ago. In 1665 Robert Hooke, an English scientist, designed and put together one of the first working optical microscopes. Amongst the many objects he examined were thin sections of cork. Hooke saw that these sections were made up of many tiny, regular compartments which he called **cells**.

It took many years of further work for the full significance of Hooke's work to emerge. In 1676 Anton van Leeuwenhoek, a Dutch draper who ground lenses in his spare time, used his lenses to observe a wide variety of living unicellular organisms in drops of water. He called these organisms 'animalcules'. By the 1840s it was recognised that cells are the basic units of life, an idea that was first expressed by Matthias Schleiden and Theodor Schwann in their 'cell theory' of 1839.

In the years since 1839 knowledge about cells has progressed a very long way, helped by developments in technology which have made ever-increasing detail available.

How we see cells

There are some cells which can be seen very easily with the naked eye. Unfertilised birds' eggs are single cells. The largest single cell in the world is an ostrich egg. But of the vast majority of cell types little or nothing can be seen without some kind of magnification.

The light microscope

Ever since it was first developed, the **light** or **optical microscope** has been the main method of observing cells, and in spite of the development of newer instruments like the electron microscope, it is still of immense value.

Making the image clearer

Living, untreated cells can be observed under a light microscope, but the image is not easy to see. Instead, slides are made of tissues or individual organisms. These are very thin slices of biological material which have been specially treated and stained so that particular features are easier to see.

How does a light microscope work?

A specimen or thin slice of biological material is placed on the stage and illuminated from underneath. Figure 1.1.1 shows how the objective lens produces a magnified and inverted image, which the eyepiece lens focuses at the eye.

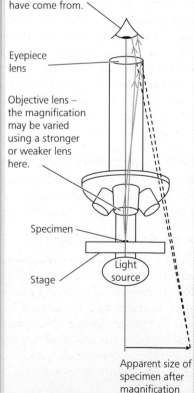

The eye receives diverging rays of light from the eyepiece lens. The brain builds up a large image of the object based on where the rays of light seem to have come from.

Eyepiece lens

Objective lens – the magnification may be varied using a stronger or weaker lens here.

Specimen

Stage

Light source

Apparent size of specimen after magnification

Figure 1.1.1 Light passes through the specimen and on through the lens to give you an image which is greatly magnified – and upside down.

It is important to remember when looking at stained cell samples that the cells are usually dead, and that the processes of fixing the material so that it does not decay and then slicing and staining it are potentially destructive. It is impossible to tell whether the features seen on such slides are present in the living cell, or are the result of these processes.

The information we get from the light microscope can be improved by using the light in different ways. **Dark field illumination**, where the background is dark and the specimen illuminated, can be useful for showing tiny structures inside cells. **Phase contrast microscopy** uses the fact that different parts of the cell refract light differently. A special *phase plate* in the microscope allows light from different regions to form interference patterns which result in very sharp contrasts. This is particularly useful for observing transparent objects such as living cells.

Advantages of the light microscope

One of the biggest advantages of using a light microscope is that living plants and animals or parts of them can be seen directly. This is of considerable value in itself, and it also allows us to check whether what we see on prepared slides is at all like the living thing. However, it is not usually possible to magnify living cells as much as dead tissue.

The other big advantage is that light microscopes do not necessarily cost a lot of money. Any biologist working in a hospital, industrial or research laboratory will have a light microscope readily available.

Disadvantages of the light microscope

The biggest problem with the light microscope is the limited detail it can show. A minimum distance is necessary between two objects for them to be seen clearly as separate. If they are closer together than this minimum distance they merge. This distance is known as a microscope's **limit of resolution** – the smaller the limit of resolution, the greater is the **resolving power** of the microscope and the more detail it can show. For the optical microscope the limit of resolution is approximately $0.2 \ \mu m$. In comparison, the unaided eye can resolve down to about 0.1 mm, as figure 1.1.2 shows.

The limit of resolution for any system depends ultimately on the wavelength of the radiation passing through it, so the resolution of a light microscope with the very best quality lenses is limited by the wavelength of light. A magnification of 1500 times is about the greatest that a light microscope can give with a clear image. At this magnification the average person would become over 2.5 kilometres tall so it might seem quite adequate – but to see the details of the inside of a cell a further technological leap is needed.

The electron microscope

In the 1950s the **electron microscope** was developed. This microscope has made great advances in biological knowledge possible. Instead of relying on light with its limit of resolving power, an electron beam is used. The image is formed as electrons are scattered by the biological material, in much the same way as light is scattered in the light microscope. The electrons behave like light waves, but have a much smaller wavelength. Resolving power is increased as the wavelength gets smaller, and as a result the electron microscope can resolve detail many thousand times better than the light microscope.

Preparation of specimens

Samples of material are prepared for examination under an electron microscope in a way which is quite similar to that for the light microscope, although the details are different, as table 1.1.1 shows.

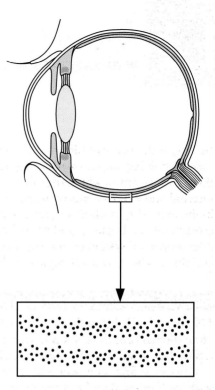

Figure 1.1.2 The resolving power of your eyes means that a mass of dots on the page looks like a clear line – because you can't resolve the dots individually. In the same way, what you can see through the light microscope is limited by the resolving power of the microscope itself.

Magnification and resolution

The two features of any microscope that determine how clear the image is are the **magnification** and the **resolving power**.

The **magnification** is a measure of how much bigger is the image you see than the real object, for example, 40×, 1500× or 500 000×.

The **resolving power** or **resolution** is a measure how close together two objects must be before they are seen as one. For example, the resolution of the naked eye is around 0.1 mm – two objects less than this distance apart cannot be seen as separate objects. The resolution of a light microscope is around $0.2 \ \mu m$ and that of the electron microscope is about 1 nm.

Treatment of specimen	For light microscopes	For electron microscopes
Fixation – the material has to be preserved in as life-like a state as possible and hardened for sectioning.	Living specimens are not fixed or subjected to most of the other stages. For non-living specimens a mixture of ethanol and glacial ethanoic acid is often used (proportions 99:1).	Specimens always fixed. Often glutaraldehyde or a mixture of glutaraldehyde and osmic acid are used – osmic acid also stains lipids black.
Dehydration – water is removed from the specimen to be replaced with the embedding medium.	Immersion in increasing concentrations of ethanol or propanone.	Immersion in increasing concentrations of ethanol or propanone.
Embedding – supports the tissue for sectioning.	Tissue embedded in wax.	Tissue embedded in resin such as araldite.
Sectioning – produces very thin slices for mounting.	Sections cut on a microtome with a metal knife to produce sections a few micrometres thick.	Sections cut on an ultramicrotome with a diamond or glass knife to produce sections 20–100 nm thick.
Staining – gives contrast between different structures and makes structures easier to see.	Coloured dyes are used to reflect visible light.	Heavy metals such as lead and uranium are used to reflect electrons.

Table 1.1.1 The preparation of specimens for light microscopy and electron microscopy

Seeing the image

Complex electronics produce an image on a television screen which can then be recorded as an **electron micrograph** or **EM**. This can have a magnification of up to 500 000 times. Our average person becomes over 830 km tall!

The most common type of electron micrograph you will see is produced by a **transmission electron microscope** (TEM), which gives us tremendous detail in two dimensions of the insides of cells. The **scanning electron microscope** (SEM) produces spectacular three-dimensional images of the surfaces of cells and organisms by recording electrons that are reflected off the surface of the object. The SEM does not give such high magnification or resolving power as the TEM, but its three-dimensional pictures of intact organisms or organelles give us a wealth of information about their surfaces. Figure 1.1.3 shows both kinds of electron micrograph.

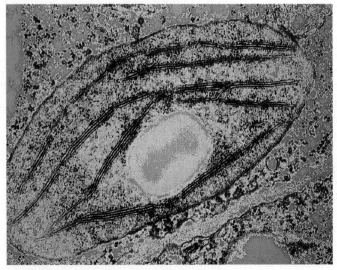

False-colour transmission electron micrograph of a chloroplast

False-colour scanning electron micrograph of a human egg surrounded by sperms (yellow)

Figure 1.1.3 The electron microscope has revealed, amongst other things, how our cells divide, the secrets of how plants provide us with energy and the start of a human life.

Advantages of the electron microscope

The amount of detail that can be seen using an electron microscope is immense. This is its biggest advantage. Many structures have been seen for the first time since electron microscopes were developed. Others that were known to exist from light microscope studies have been shown to have complicated substructures inside them which have helped us to understand how they work.

Disadvantages of the electron microscope

There are several disadvantages to the electron microscope. One is that air in the microscope would scatter the electron beam and so make the image of the tissue fuzzy. This means that all the specimens are examined in a vacuum – and so it is impossible to look at living material.

This leads to the second problem. How realistic a picture do we get from tissue which has been processed in many ways, including being sliced extremely thinly and put in a vacuum? Objects that we see in a micrograph that are purely the result of the production process are known as **artefacts**. The problem comes in telling what is an artefact and what is genuine cell content, and there has been considerable argument among scientists about this over the years.

Finally, electron microscopes are very expensive, fill a room, have to be kept at a constant temperature and pressure and need to maintain an internal vacuum. As a consequence, relatively few scientists outside research laboratories have easy access to such equipment.

Observing cells

You have probably looked at cells using a light microscope. With increasing practice and developing skills you may find that more becomes visible. As mentioned before, cells can be observed either unstained or stained.

There is one particular problem to bear in mind when you are working with microscopes. Unless you are looking at living material, or have the use of a scanning electron microscope, all the cells that you see appear flat and two dimensional. But cells are actually three dimensional – spheres, cylinders, strange asymmetrical shapes – so try to exercise some imagination in your consideration of cells and view them as complete living things.

In both the animal and plant kingdoms there is a very wide range of different types of cells, each carrying out different functions. But for both animals and plants, there are certain features of their cells which turn up again and again – so much so that we can put them together in a **typical cell**. Remember that this typical cell does not really exist, but it acts as a useful guide to what to look for in an animal or a plant cell.

The typical animal cell

A typical animal cell is shown in figure 1.1.5. It is surrounded by a membrane known as the cell **surface** or **plasma membrane**. Inside this membrane is a jelly-like liquid called **cytoplasm**, containing a **nucleus**. The cytoplasm and nucleus together are known as **protoplasm**. The cytoplasm contains much of what is needed to carry out the day-to-day tasks of living, whilst the nucleus is vital to the long-term survival of the cell.

When the light microscope was the only tool biologists had to observe cells, they thought that the cytoplasm was a relatively structureless, clear jelly. But the electron microscope changed all that by revealing that the cytoplasm was full of all manner of complex and detailed structures, now known as **organelles**. This detailed organisation is known as the **ultrastructure** of the cell. The cell's ultrastructure is explained below.

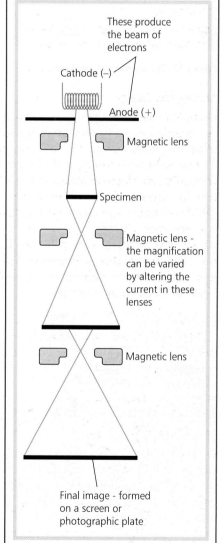

How does an electron microscope work?

Electron beams are focused by magnetic lenses, as figure 1.1.4 shows. A series of magnifications results in a final image which cannot be seen with the eye, but is formed on a screen or photographic plate.

Figure 1.1.4 What goes on inside an electron microscope.

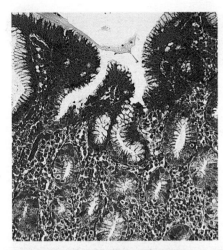

Light micrograph of section through the stomach lining showing gastric pits (white) surrounded by epithelial cells

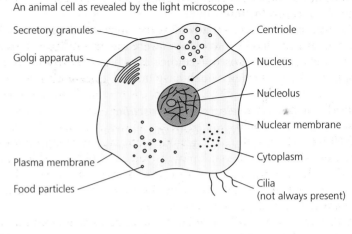

An animal cell as revealed by the light microscope ...

Secretory granules
Golgi apparatus
Centriole
Nucleus
Nucleolus
Nuclear membrane
Plasma membrane
Cytoplasm
Food particles
Cilia (not always present)

... and by the electron microscope

Golgi apparatus — Mitochondrion — Lysosome — Cytoplasm
Centriole
Vacuole (small, not permanent)
Ribosome
Rough endoplasmic reticulum
Plasma membrane
Nuclear membrane — Pore — Smooth endoplasmic reticulum — Nucleolus

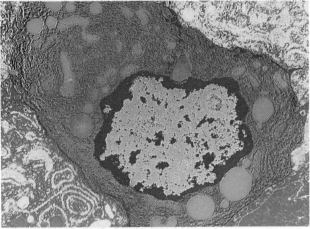

False-colour transmission electron micrograph of a single epithelial cell

Figure 1.1.5 Many regions of an animal cell which under a light microscope appear to have no particular features, or to be blurred areas, are revealed as complex structures by electron microscopy.

The structure of each organelle is closely related to its function within the cell. The basic ultrastructure of the typical animal cell gives rise to an enormous variety of animal cells suited for the different functions that arise within the animal kingdom.

The ultrastructure of the animal cell

Membranes

One of the most important structures in any cell is its membranes. The cell surface membrane (plasma membrane) acts as a boundary to the cell itself, and there is also a multitude of internal (intracellular) membranes. Much work has gone into producing a model of the structure of membranes. Over the years improvements in technology have made possible different, improved models until we have reached the level of understanding that we have today. We shall be considering the functions of membranes in almost every part of the cell in turn, but will leave the details of its structure until we know more about the chemicals which make it up.

The nucleus – the information centre

The **nucleus** is usually the largest organelle in the cell and can be seen with the light microscope. In experiments nuclei have been removed from some large amoebae. They can survive for a short time, but then die. No cell replication occurs. So although most of the reactions important to life go on in the cytoplasm, the nucleus is vital to organise and direct these reactions and to bring about reproduction.

Electron micrographs show us that the nucleus, which is usually spherical in shape, is surrounded by a **nuclear membrane** or envelope. This is a double membrane containing many holes or pores. In order to control events in the cytoplasm, the nucleus needs to communicate with it. That is the reason for the pores – they enable chemicals to travel easily in and out of the nucleus.

Inside the nuclear membrane is the **nucleoplasm**. This consists of two main substances, **nucleic acids** and **proteins**. The nucleic acids are **deoxyribonucleic acid (DNA)**, which is the basic genetic material, the blueprint for the cell to be passed on when it divides, and **ribonucleic acid (RNA)**, which translates the genetic code into instructions for making proteins in the cytoplasm of the cell. When the cell is not actually dividing the DNA is bonded to the protein to form **chromatin**, which appears as tiny granules.

Within the nucleus will be at least one **nucleolus**, an extra dense area of almost pure DNA which appears to be involved in producing RNA. When the cell is about to divide, the genetic material associates into long chains. These rapidly become more coiled, shorter and denser, readily taking up stain and becoming visible under the light microscope. These chains are called **chromosomes**, which means 'coloured bodies'. It can be seen that chromosomes have distinctive shapes and occur in pairs. Each species of living organism has a characteristic number of chromosomes in the nucleus.

The endoplasmic reticulum – manufacture and transport

This spreads throughout the whole cytoplasm. It is a three-dimensional network of cavities, some sac-like and some tubular, bounded by membranes. The network links with the membrane around the nucleus.

The outside of much of the endoplasmic reticulum (ER) membrane is encrusted with granules called **ribosomes**. Because of this it is known as **rough endoplasmic reticulum** or **RER**. The function of the ribosomes is to make proteins. The function of the rough endoplasmic reticulum is to isolate and transport these proteins once they have been made. Some of the proteins, such as digestive enzymes and hormones, are required outside the cell which has made them, so they have to be **secreted** or moved out of the cell. Many other proteins are needed within the cell itself.

The rough endoplasmic reticulum has a large surface area, giving space for the synthesis of all the proteins needed, and making possible their storage and transport both within the cell and from the inside to the outside. Any cell which secretes large amounts of material (such as those producing the digestive enzymes in the lining of the gut) will have a large amount of rough endoplasmic reticulum.

Not all endoplasmic reticulum is covered in ribosomes. **Smooth endoplasmic reticulum (SER)** is also involved in synthesis and transport. However, in this case it is the synthesis and transport of fatty molecules known as steroids and lipids. A large quantity of smooth endoplasmic reticulum is found in the testes and the liver, for example. By looking at the amount and type of endoplasmic reticulum in a cell we can get an idea of its function.

The Golgi apparatus – packaging the products

The **Golgi apparatus** can be seen using a light microscope, although it simply looks like a rather dense area of cytoplasm. It was first spotted almost 100 years ago by the Italian scientist Camillo Golgi, but it is only since the arrival of the electron microscope that we have been able to see it clearly. The Golgi apparatus is made up of stacks of parallel, flattened membrane pockets. They

Separating organelles

To find out more about a particular type of organelle, we may need to separate it from the rest of the contents of the cell. To do this we use a technique called **differential centrifugation**.

- A tissue sample is cut into small pieces in ice-cold buffer solution. The low temperature slows down cell reactions and the buffer makes sure that the different chemicals released when the cells are broken up do not react with each other.
- The sample and buffer are put into a blender (homogeniser) which breaks up the cells, releasing the contents.
- The mixture is filtered to remove cell debris. Organelles are small enough to pass through the filter.
- The filtrate is placed in a centrifuge and spun at high speeds. The organelles separate out at the bottom of the tube, below the rest of the filtrate liquid (the supernatant). Different organelles separate out at different speeds of rotation and after different lengths of time, depending on their density and shape. At a particular speed, sediment containing a specific organelle can be collected, as shown in table 1.1.2.

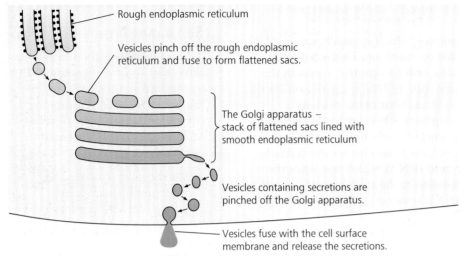

Rough endoplasmic reticulum

Vesicles pinch off the rough endoplasmic reticulum and fuse to form flattened sacs.

The Golgi apparatus – stack of flattened sacs lined with smooth endoplasmic reticulum

Vesicles containing secretions are pinched off the Golgi apparatus.

Vesicles fuse with the cell surface membrane and release the secretions.

Figure 1.1.6 A production line for cell secretions – the Golgi apparatus takes the raw materials, assembles them, packages them and transports them to the surface of the cell.

Centrifuge setting	Time/ min	Organelles that separate out
800–1000	5–10	Nuclei
10 000–20 000	15–20	Mitochondria Lysosomes
50 000–80 000	30–50	Rough ER
80 000–100 000	60	Plasma membranes Smooth ER
150 000–30 000	>60	Individual ribosomes

Table 1.1.2 The sediment in the tube contains different organelles depending on the speed of rotation and the length of time in the centrifuge

Once separated, light or electron micrographs can be prepared of the organelles, or they can be used in experiments to investigate the detailed biochemistry taking place inside them.

link with, but are not joined to, the rough endoplasmic reticulum. It has taken a long time to discover exactly what the Golgi apparatus does. Radioactively labelled materials have been followed through the system to try and find out. Figure 1.1.7 shows the result.

It seems that protein is transported from the rough endoplasmic reticulum in small vesicles. These pinch off from the rough endoplasmic reticulum and fuse to form the pockets of the Golgi apparatus. Then carbohydrate is combined with the proteins to form glycoproteins, the main substances secreted from the cell. Mucus is one example of a glycoprotein. The Golgi apparatus also appears to produce materials for plant cell walls and insect cuticles.

Lysosomes – digestion and destruction

Some of the vesicles pinched off the rough endoplasmic reticulum come to enclose digestive enzymes and form another organelle known as a **lysosome**. When food is taken into the cell of a single-celled animal such as *Amoeba*, it must be broken down into simple chemicals that can then be used. When organelles get worn out they need to be destroyed. Lysosomes carry out these functions.

Lysosomes appear as dark, spherical bodies in the cytoplasm of most cells and contain a powerful mix of digestive enzymes. They frequently fuse with each other and with membrane-bound vacuoles containing either food or an obsolete organelle. The enzymes then break down the contents into smaller molecules that can often be reused. The word 'lysis' from which they get their name means 'breaking down'.

Lysosomes can also self-destruct – they are sometimes known as 'suicide bags'. If an entire cell is damaged or running down the lysosomes may rupture, releasing their enzymes to destroy the entire contents of the cell. Problems can arise if this starts to happen before the proper time, as in diseases like rheumatoid arthritis, when the cartilage self-destructs.

Vacuoles – dealing with food and fluids

Vacuoles are not a permanent feature in animal cells. These membrane-lined enclosures of cell sap are formed and lost as needed. Many simple animals form food vacuoles around the prey they engulf. White blood cells in higher animals form similar vacuoles around pathogens which are engulfed. Contractile vacuoles are an important feature in simple animals living in fresh water as they allow control of the water content of the cytoplasm. But apart from these examples, vacuoles are not a major feature of animal cells.

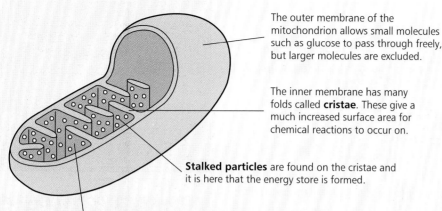

The outer membrane of the mitochondrion allows small molecules such as glucose to pass through freely, but larger molecules are excluded.

The inner membrane has many folds called **cristae**. These give a much increased surface area for chemical reactions to occur on.

Stalked particles are found on the cristae and it is here that the energy store is formed.

The matrix of the mitochondrion contains enzymes to carry out the reactions of respiration, and its own genetic material so that a mitochondrion can reproduce itself.

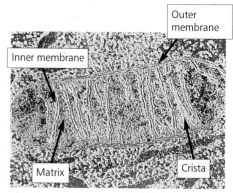

A transmission electron micrograph of the interior of a mitochondrion

Figure 1.1.7 The mitochondrion – a vital organelle whose structure is closely related to its function.

Mitochondria – the cellular power station

The name **mitochondrion** means 'thread granule'. This describes what mitochondria look like under the light microscope – tiny rod-like structures in the cytoplasm of almost all cells. In recent years biologists have been able to sort out not only their complex structure but also their functions.

Mitochondria are the 'powerhouse' of the cell. Here, in a series of complicated biochemical reactions, energy is released from the respiration of food. This energy is in a form which can be used for all the other functions of the cell and indeed the organism. Just as the amount and type of endoplasmic reticulum can give us valuable clues to the function of a particular cell, so can the number of mitochondria present. Cells which require little energy to carry out their functions, for example fat storage cells, have very few mitochondria. Any cell which does an energy-demanding job, such as muscle cells, will contain large numbers of mitochondria.

Mitochondria have a double membrane. They contain their own genetic material, so that when a cell divides, the mitochondria replicate. Mitochondria also replicate at times other than cell division, for example when the long-term energy demands of a cell increase. Figure 1.1.8 shows their internal arrangement which is perfectly adapted for their function.

The cytoskeleton

Work in recent years has shown that a **cytoskeleton** is a feature of all eukaryotic cells (see pages 13–14). This skeleton is a dynamic, three-dimensional web-like structure that fills the cytoplasm. It is made up of **microfilaments**, which are protein fibres, and **microtubules**, which are tiny tubes about 20 nm in diameter. They too are made of protein and are found, both singly and in bundles, throughout the cytoplasm. The cytoskeleton performs several vital functions. It gives the cytoplasm structure and keeps the organelles in place. Many of the proteins involved are closely related to actin and myosin, the contractile proteins in muscle (described in more detail in section 2.6) and the cytoskeleton is closely linked with cell movements and with transport within cells. Figure 1.1.9 shows the cytoskeleton.

Centrioles, cilia and flagella

A pair of **centrioles** is found near to the nucleus, made up of bundles of nine tubules. These centrioles pull apart during cell division to produce a spindle made of microtubules which are involved in the movement of chromosomes.

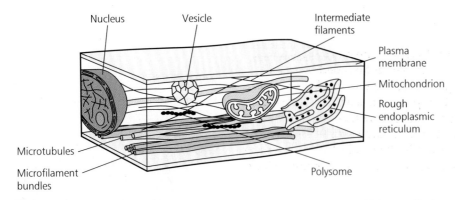

Figure 1.1.8 The cytoskeleton forms a tangled web of structural and contractile fibres that hold the organelles in place and enable cell movement to occur.

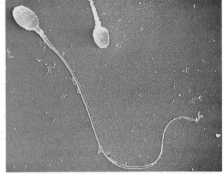

Single flagellum on spermatozoon

Cilia and **flagella** are quite common features of cells. They are very similar to each other in structure, as figure 1.1.9 shows, but cilia, with a length of 5–10 μm, are shorter than flagella, with an average length of about 100 μm. Cilia are also found in much greater numbers.

The importance of both structures is that they lash backwards and forwards. In flagella this action is used to produce movement of a cell or organism, but in cilia it may be put to other uses. For example, great borders of cilia waft mucus and other substances along the tubes of our bodies, whereas a single flagellum helps move a spermatozoon to an egg.

The typical plant cell

In many ways the typical plant cell, shown in figure 1.1.10, bears a strong resemblance to the typical animal cell. In common with animal cells, plant cells have many membranes and contain cytoplasm and a nucleus. You will find rough and smooth endoplasmic reticulum spreading throughout the cytoplasm, and Golgi apparatus as well. Mitochondria release energy from the respiration of food which is as vital to the working of the plant as it is to the animal cell. However, of the organelles found in animal cells, plant cells do not have centrioles. More importantly, there are several more organelles peculiar to plant cells, which are described overleaf.

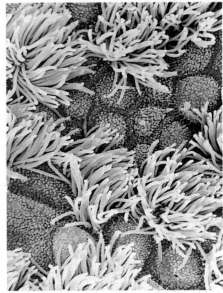

Mass of cilia in respiratory tract

Nine pairs or doublets of microtubules around the outside

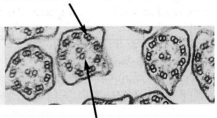

Central pair of microtubules

Internal structure of cilia

Figure 1.1.9 It is not known exactly how cilia and flagella move. They all have this 9 + 2 arrangement of microtubules in the centre.

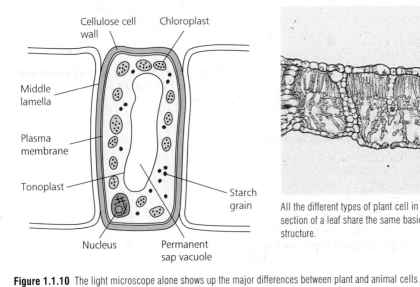

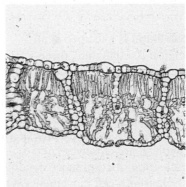

All the different types of plant cell in this section of a leaf share the same basic structure.

Figure 1.1.10 The light microscope alone shows up the major differences between plant and animal cells.

The ultrastructure of the plant cell

The plant cell wall

Animal cells can be almost any shape. Plant cells tend to be more regular and uniform in their appearance, largely because each cell is bounded by a rigid **cell wall**. We can visualise a plant cell as a jelly-filled balloon inside a shoe box. The cell wall gives plants their strength and support. It is made up of insoluble cellulose fibres which are meshed in a matrix of carbohydrates called pectates and hemicelluloses. The cell wall can become impregnated with suberin in cork tissues, or with lignin to produce wood. Unless it is affected by these substances the cell wall is freely permeable – it does not act as a barrier to anything which might enter the cell in solution.

The vacuole

A **vacuole** is a fluid-filled space in the cytoplasm surrounded by a membrane. Vacuoles occur quite frequently in animal cells, but they appear only when needed, and then disappear. In plants the vacuole is a permanent feature of the structure of the cell, with an important role to play. The vacuole of a plant cell is surrounded by a membrane called the **tonoplast**. It is filled with **cell sap**, a solution of various substances in water. This solution causes the movement of water into the cell by a process called **osmosis** and the result is that the cytoplasm is kept pressed against the cell wall. This keeps the cells firm and contributes to keeping the whole plant upright. Osmosis and the role it plays in plants will be considered in more detail in section 1.4.

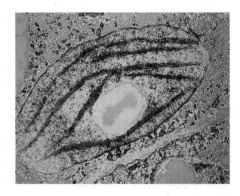

Chloroplasts

Of all the differences between plant and animal cells, it is perhaps the presence of **chloroplasts** in plant cells which is the most important, because they enable plants to make their own food. Chloroplasts have a structure similar in some ways with that of mitochondria. Chloroplasts are large organelles, the shape of biconvex lenses with a diameter of 4–10 μm and 2–3 μm thick. They contain their own DNA and have a double membrane. Also like mitochondria, chloroplasts have an enormously folded inner membrane which gives a greatly increased surface area on which biochemical reactions take place.

Figure 1.1.11 shows the structure of a chloroplast. The membranes are arranged in stacks called **grana**. This is where **chlorophyll** is found. Chlorophyll is a green pigment which is largely responsible for trapping the energy of light and so making it available for the plant to use. In a matrix surrounding the membrane stacks, called the **stroma**, are all the enzymes needed to complete the process of photosynthesis and provide the plant with its food. This food is stored as **starch grains** in the chloroplast.

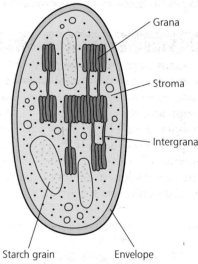

Figure 1.1.11 The structure of a chloroplast is shown in this electron micrograph.

Eukaryotic and prokaryotic cells

Animals, plants, fungi and protoctists (single-celled organisms such as *Amoeba*) all have cells containing the structures we have just looked at. These organisms are known as **eukaryotes** and are made up of **eukaryotic cells**.

There is another group of organisms, probably the most ancient on Earth, which do not fall into this category. These are the bacteria, the photosynthetic blue-green bacteria, and the viruses, collectively known as the monerans – and they have a very different structure. Organisms such as bacteria are called **prokaryotes** and are made up of **prokaryotic cells** which lack much of the structure and organisation of the eukaryotic cells. They do not have a membrane-bound nucleus – the genetic material is a single strand coiled up in the centre to form the **nucleoid**. Sometimes there are small additional pieces of genetic material within the cell called **plasmids**. The cytoplasm contains enzymes, ribosomes and food storage material, particularly glycogen granules and lipid droplets. However, there is no endoplasmic reticulum, no Golgi apparatus, no mitochondria and no chloroplasts. Respiration takes place on a special piece of the plasma membrane called a **mesosome**. Those prokaryotes which can photosynthesise have a form of chlorophyll but no complex structures to hold it. Figure 1.1.12 shows a typical prokaryotic cell.

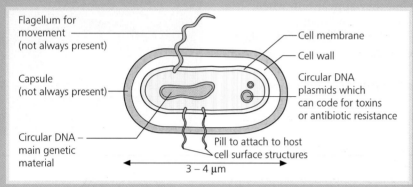

Flagellum for movement (not always present)

Capsule (not always present)

Circular DNA – main genetic material

Cell membrane

Cell wall

Circular DNA plasmids which can code for toxins or antibiotic resistance

Pill to attach to host cell surface structures

3 – 4 μm

Figure 1.1.12 The structure of a bacterial cell. It is likely that our cells evolved originally from prokaryotic cells such as these.

By looking at the features of a typical plant and animal cell we have familiarised ourselves with the main working parts of the most fundamental unit of life. Now we can move on to look even more closely at these basic units of existence – to the chemicals which work together to make up a living thing.

SUMMARY

- Living organisms are made up of individual units called **cells**.
- Cells can be observed using a light microscope (which magnifies up to × 1500) or an electron microscope (up to × 500 000). Cells may be altered by the various preparations which make them visible under a microscope.
- **Eukaryotic** cells comprise a **nucleus** and **cytoplasm** enclosed by a **cell surface membrane**. The **ultrastructure** of a cell consists of the organelles visible with the electron microscope.
- A typical animal cell has the following organelles:
  a **nucleus** – which controls cell function
  rough endoplasmic reticulum – a network of membrane-bound cavities linking with the nucleus
  ribosomes – structures on the rough endoplasmic reticulum involved with protein synthesis
  smooth endoplasmic reticulum – involved with the synthesis of steroids and lipids

Golgi apparatus – stacks of flattened membrane pockets, involved in the synthesis of glycoproteins

lysosomes – vesicles which digest food and worn-out organelles

vacuoles – temporary membrane-bound pockets of cell sap, such as food vacuoles formed around prey

mitochondria – rod-shaped organelles with a double membrane, the inner one greatly folded, involved in the release of energy from food by the process of respiration

cytoskeleton – a system of **microtubules** and proteins which maintain the internal structure of the cell

centrioles, **cilia** and **flagella** – concerned with movement in the cell. Centrioles pull apart and form a spindle of microtubules during cell division. Cilia and flagella have a similar 9 + 2 arrangement of microtubules. Banks of cilia waft substances past them, while flagella aid the swimming motion of a cell.

- The organelles can be separated out by differential centrifugation.

- A typical plant cell is similar to an animal cell except:
  it has no centrioles
  it has a rigid cellulose **cell wall** which is freely permeable; this supports the cell
  it has a permanent **vacuole** filled with cell sap, involved with water balance in the cell
  it has **chloroplasts** – structures similar to mitochondria, which contain chlorophyll and are responsible for photosynthesis.

- **Prokaryotic** cells do not have this high level of organisation. Their genetic material is grouped in a **nucleoid**, and sometimes on **plasmids**. Respiration takes place on a piece of membrane called a **mesosome**.

QUESTIONS

1 Draw up a table to summarise the appearance of a typical plant cell under
  a the light microscope
  b the electron microscope.

2 a Name the structures marked **i**, **ii**, **iii** and **iv** in figure 1.1.13. For each, give a brief explanation of its function.
  b What is the main function of this type of cell? Which features of the cell suggest its function?

3 Write a brief account of the impact of the development of the electron microscope on the study of cell biology.

Developing Key Skills

Your Head of Science is planning a presentation to year 11 pupils to give them a taste of the type of material they will study if they decide to follow AS and A2 Biology courses. You have been asked to talk briefly about Cell Biology. Plan a 3 minute presentation to emphasise the importance of the subject and its relevance to everyday life.

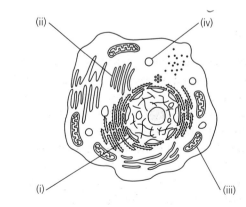

Figure 1.1.13

WHEN MOLECULES GO WRONG

Our bodies of made up of chemicals – we are a vast jelly of molecules and ions all working together. Some of these are tiny, such as water molecules (H_2O) and sodium or chloride ions (Na^+ and Cl^-). However, many molecules in our cells are huge and complicated, and the way they work depends not just on the atoms that make up the molecule, but also on the arrangement of these atoms forming the overall shape of the molecule. If anything goes wrong with these molecules of life, then the whole of the organism will feel the effects.

Growing old gracefully?

As human beings go through life, they age. At 17 the skin already is less soft and elastic than in a newborn baby. By 70 it is inevitably much less soft and also, to a greater or lesser extent, sagging and wrinkled. Why does this happen? The answer lies at least partly in the structure of the collagen molecules which are an integral part of the structure of the skin. In youthful skin the molecules form shapes called triple helices, an elastic arrangement which stretches and gives as the skin is compressed or moves. With age the structure of these molecules changes, and they become more rigid, more brittle and more likely to tear.

Figure 1 Our collagen molecules change shape as we get older, and the results are plain to see!

More deadly changes

Changes in the collagen molecules in our skin cause only cosmetic problems, but sometimes changes in our molecules can be a matter of life or death. Collagen fibres are also found combined with bone tissue, giving tensile strength rather like the steel rods in reinforced concrete. In the genetic condition known as brittle bone disease (osteogenesis imperfecta), the collagen and bone do not combine and as a result the bones break extremely easily. In severe cases, a child cannot be cuddled for fear of breaking bones, and coughing can shatter a rib.

In cystic fibrosis, another genetic disease, a membrane protein does not have the correct structure. The protein does not function, and this means that the cell cannot produce mucus properly – it makes too much and the mucus is too thick and sticky. In the past cystic fibrosis has led to an early death, although in recent years the life expectancy of sufferers has increased greatly, and there is hope of effective treatment as a result of genetic engineering. Brittle bone disease and cystic fibrosis are just two examples of the vital importance of the chemicals making up our bodies – the molecules of life.

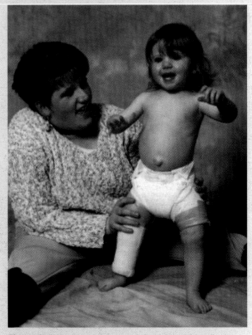

Figure 2 Brittle bone disease, caused by a problem in the collagen molecule, makes life very difficult both for the affected child and for their family.

1.2 The molecules of life: Carbohydrates, lipids and proteins

Cells are the fundamental units of life. But cells are themselves made up of a vast array of molecules, some very simple, some extremely complex. To understand how cells function, and so in turn to understand the way whole living organisms function, we need to have a grasp of the building blocks which make up the units of life.

Organic compounds in living things

We have looked at the ultrastructure of cells and seen the range of organelles that work together to continue the processes of life. But what are these organelles made of? What is the composition of cytoplasm? Around 65% of cells is water – we shall consider later why this is. There are also other important groups of molecules, many of which are **organic compounds**. This term is explained in the box below. There are three main types of organic compounds found in living cells – **carbohydrates**, **lipids** and **proteins**. We shall look at each in turn.

Organic molecules

Almost all material in a cell which is not water is made up of organic molecules. Organic compounds all contain carbon and hydrogen atoms. Most organic molecules also contain oxygen atoms, and some include nitrogen, sulphur and phosphorus.

Each carbon atom can make four bonds, so has the potential to join up with four other atoms – we say it has a **valency** of four. This is shown in figure 1.2.1. Carbon atoms bond very strongly to other carbon atoms. This means that many carbon atoms can join together to build very large molecules. Long chain molecules can be formed, with hydrogen and oxygen atoms bonded to the carbon atoms in the chain. Branched chains, or rings, or any number of three-dimensional shapes are also possible. Often a relatively small molecule (a **monomer**) will be joined to many other similar monomers to make a very large molecule called a **polymer**.

This ability to make large molecules is what makes carbon such an important element. The very many types of organic molecules provide the great biochemical variety and complexity needed in living things.

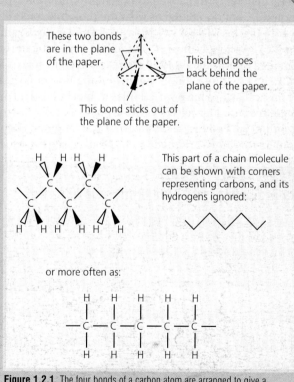

These two bonds are in the plane of the paper.

This bond goes back behind the plane of the paper.

This bond sticks out of the plane of the paper.

This part of a chain molecule can be shown with corners representing carbons, and its hydrogens ignored:

or more often as:

Figure 1.2.1 The four bonds of a carbon atom are arranged to give a tetrahedral shape. This means that organic molecules have a complicated three-dimensional structure. As this becomes extremely difficult to draw and confusing to look at, organic molecules are often drawn 'flat'.

Carbohydrates

The main job of carbohydrates within an organism is to provide energy. Carbohydrates are also involved in storing energy, and in plants they form an important part of the cell wall.

The best known carbohydrates are the sugars and starches. **Sucrose** is 'sugar' and **glucose** is the energy supplier in sports and health drinks, while **starch** is found in flour and potatoes. But the group of chemicals known to the biochemist as carbohydrates is much wider than this.

All carbohydrates are made up of carbon, hydrogen and oxygen. They fall into three main types, depending on their complexity. These are the **monosaccharides**, **disaccharides** and **polysaccharides**.

Monosaccharides – the simple sugars

In these simple sugars there is one oxygen atom and two hydrogen atoms for each carbon atom present in the molecule. A general formula for this can be written:

$$(CH_2O)_n$$

n can be any number, but is usually low. The **triose** ($n = 3$) sugars such as glyceraldehyde are important in the biochemistry of respiration. These sugars have the formula $C_3H_6O_3$. The **pentose** ($n = 5$) sugars are most important in the structure of the nucleic acids which make up genetic material. Ribose is a pentose with which you will become familiar. It has the formula $C_5H_{10}O_5$. The best known monosaccharides, including glucose, are the **hexose** sugars with $n = 6$. They have the general formula $C_6H_{12}O_6$.

These general formulae tell us how many and what types of atoms there are in the molecule, but do not tell us what the molecule looks like and why it behaves as it does. To do this we look at displayed formulae, for example those shown in figure 1.2.2. Although these do not follow every kink in the carbon chain, they do give an idea of how the molecules are arranged in space. This three-dimensional structure is very important in understanding how biological systems work.

Monosaccharides have varied roles in biochemistry. For example, glucose is the main fuel used by cells to provide energy, whilst fructose gives fruit its sweet taste, aiding in seed dispersal. Another role of monosaccharides is to form the monomers for large carbohydrate molecules (see disaccharides, polysaccharides).

α–glucose

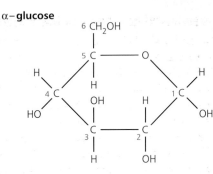

β–glucose

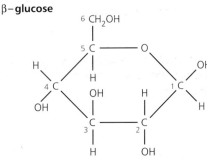

Fructose

Figure 1.2.2 Hexose sugars often have a ring structure. The arrangement of the atoms on the side chains can make a great difference to the way in which the molecule is used by the body. This is why the carbon atoms are numbered. Look carefully at the differences between α-glucose and β-glucose. These two molecules are known as **structural isomers**.

Stereoisomerism – the same but different

A triose sugar such as glyceraldehyde, with only three carbon atoms, sounds a fairly simple molecule. But the three-dimensional arrangement of the bonds means that there are two different forms, which are mirror images of each other. These are shown in figure 1.2.3. However hard you try you cannot superimpose the image of D-glyceraldehyde onto the image of L-glyceraldehyde. This phenomenon is called **stereoisomerism**, and the two forms of glyceraldehyde are called **stereoisomers**.

Glyceraldehyde is the standard molecule with which all others are compared in order to determine whether they are the D or L form. It is important to know which is which, because biological systems are sensitive to the difference between stereoisomers. For example, it is largely only the D forms of sugars and the L forms of amino acids that are found in living things.

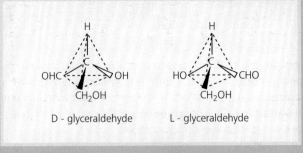

Figure 1.2.3 The stereoisomers of glyceraldehyde – the two forms cannot be superimposed. They are mirror images of each other.

Disaccharides – the double sugars

The molecules of disaccharides are made up of two monosaccharide monomers joined together. Sucrose is the result of a molecule of α-glucose joining with a molecule of β-fructose. The two monosaccharides join in a **condensation reaction** to form a disaccharide, and a molecule of water (H_2O) is removed. The bond between the two monosaccharides which results is known as a **glycosidic link**, shown in figure 1.2.4.

This joining of monosaccharides gives a different general formula for disaccharides, and indeed for chains of monosaccharides of any length:

$$(C_6H_{10}O_5)_n$$

When different monosaccharides join together, different disaccharides result. Table 1.2.1 shows some of the more common ones.

Disaccharide	Source	Monosaccharide monomers
Sucrose	Stored in plants such as sugar beet and sugar cane	Glucose + fructose
Lactose	Milk sugar – the main carbohydrate found in milk	Glucose + galactose
Maltose	Malt sugar – found in germinating seed such as barley	Glucose + glucose

Table 1.2.1 Some common disaccharides

Figure 1.2.4 The forming of a glycosidic link. The reaction between two monosaccharides results in a disaccharide and a molecule of water. Although these examples look relatively simple, remember that isomers of all different sorts are possible. Also, a link between C1 and C4 of two monosaccharides will result in a different disaccharide from a C1–C6 link between the same two monosaccharides.

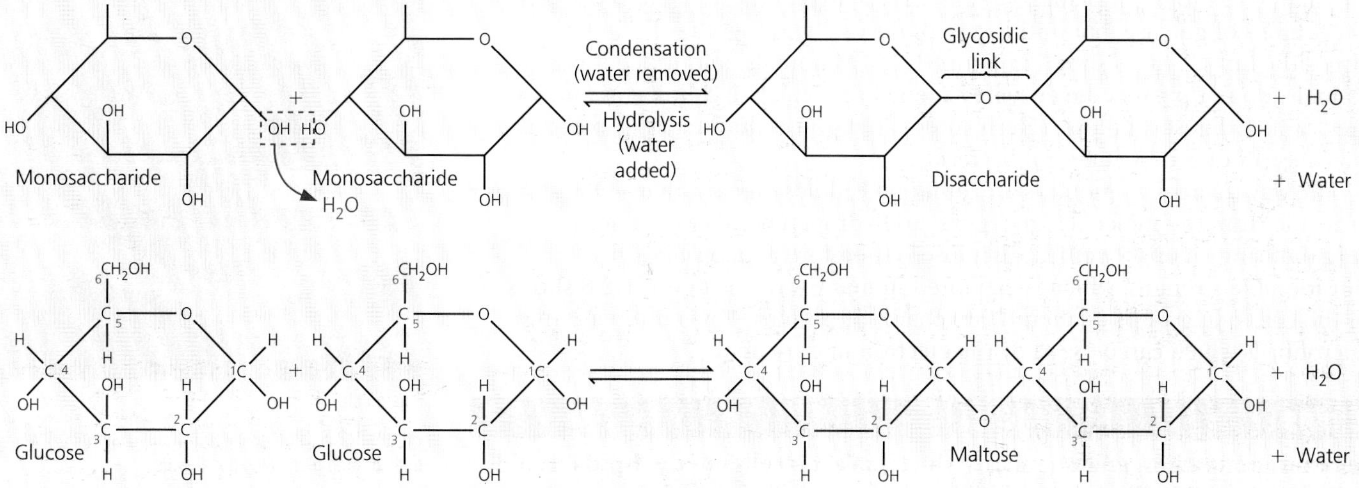

Polysaccharides

The most complex carbohydrates are the polysaccharides. The sweet taste which is characteristic of both mono- and disaccharides is lost when many single sugar units are joined to form a polysaccharide. Polysaccharides generally result from the linking of glucose monomers in different ways, and they form very compact molecules which are ideal for storing energy. The glucose units can then be released when they are needed to supply energy. Polysaccharides are physically and chemically very inactive, so their presence in the cell does not interfere with other cell functions. Figure 1.2.5 shows polysaccharide stores in both plant and animal cells.

Starch is one of the best known polysaccharides. It is particularly important as an energy store in plants. The sugars produced by photosynthesis are rapidly converted into starch, which is both insoluble and compact, but can be broken down rapidly to release glucose when it is needed. Storage organs such as potatoes are particularly rich in starch.

Starch is made up of long chains of α-glucose. It is a mixture of two compounds in which these chains have different structures. **Amylose** is an unbranched polymer in which the glucose monomers are joined purely by α-1–4 glycosidic bonds. As the chain lengthens the molecule spirals, kept stable by hydrogen bonding of the hydroxyl groups in the centre (see page 28). **Amylopectin** is also mainly made up of chains of glucose monomers joined by α-1–4 glycosidic bonds, but there are a few α-1–6 glycosidic bonds at which the chains branch. Branching chains provide more terminal glucose molecules, which can be broken off rapidly when energy is needed. This is why starchy foods such as pasta are good for us when we are doing sport. The starch provides a source of energy which is released rapidly when needed from the amylopectin, but more slowly over a longer period from the amylose, keeping us going throughout the period of exercise.

Glycogen is sometimes referred to as 'animal starch'. It is the only carbohydrate energy store found in animals. Chemically it is very similar to starch, also being made up of many α-glucose units. The difference is that in glycogen there are more 1–6 glycosidic links mixed with 1–4 links. Glycogen is found mainly in muscle tissue and particularly in liver tissue, which is very active and needs a readily available energy supply at all times. The highly branched structure of glycogen allows glucose to be released quickly when needed, to provide a source of energy.

Cellulose is an important structural material in plants. As we have seen, it is the main constituent in plant cell walls. Like starch and glycogen, it consists of long chains of glucose, but in this case β-glucose held together by 1–4 glycosidic links. This is shown in figure 1.2.6. Mammals, and indeed most animals, do not possess the enzymes needed to break β-1–4 linkages and so they cannot digest cellulose. (Herbivores can digest cellulose because of enzymes produced by their gut bacteria.)

The way that the monomers are joined in cellulose means that –OH groups protrude from the molecule, giving rise to hydrogen bonds which hold neighbouring chains together. Cellulose is therefore a material with considerable strength, which is exploited in many ways, as figure 1.2.8 shows. In the cell wall, groups of about 2000 chains of cellulose form interweaving microfibrils which can be seen by the electron microscope.

Lipids

Another group of organic chemicals which make up cells are the **lipids**. Lipids include some of the highest profile chemicals in public health issues – **cholesterol** and **fat**. The media constantly remind us of the importance of a low-fat diet and the dangers of high cholesterol levels. But are fats really harmful, and what *is* cholesterol?

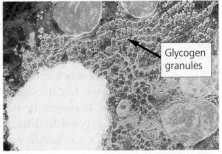

Liver cell

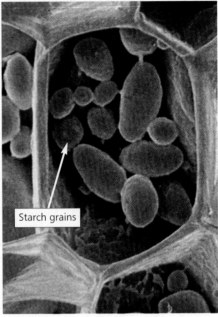

Potato cell

Figure 1.2.5 Storage carbohydrates play important roles in both plant and animal cells.

Figure 1.2.6 These seemingly small differences in the molecules of starch, glycogen and cellulose make all the difference to where they are found and what they do.

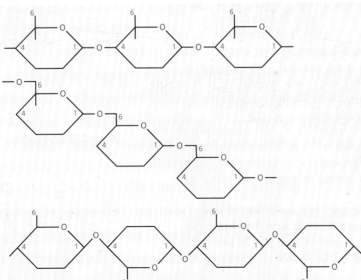

Starch : α-1 – 4 linkages with a few α-1–6 linkages

Glycogen : α-1 – 6 linkages with some α-1–4 linkages

Cellulose : β-1 -4 linkages

Lipids are an extremely important group of chemicals which play major roles in living systems. They are an important source of energy in the diet of many animals and the most effective form for living things to store energy – they contain more energy per gram than carbohydrates or proteins. Many plants and animals convert spare food into fats or oils for use at a later date. Combined with other molecules lipids also play vital roles in cell membranes and in the nervous system.

All lipids dissolve in organic solvents but are insoluble in water. This is important because it means they do not interfere with the many reactions which go on in aqueous solution in the cytoplasm of a cell.

As in carbohydrates, the chemical elements that make up lipids are carbon, hydrogen and oxygen. In lipids, however, there is a considerably lower proportion of oxygen than in carbohydrates.

Figure 1.2.7 Cellulose forms the basis of some major human industries. We use cellulose to make paper and cellophane, as well as using derivatives to produce explosives and films. Cellulose in the form of pure cotton is worn throughout the world.

Fats and oils

One of the main groups of lipids are the **fats** and **oils**. They are chemically extremely similar, but fats (for example, butter) are solids at room temperature and oils (for example, olive oil) are liquids. Fats and oils are made up of combinations of two types of organic chemicals: **fatty acids** and **glycerol** (or propane-1,2,3-triol).

Glycerol has the chemical formula $C_3H_8O_3$, which can be shown more clearly as in figure 1.2.8.

There is a wide range of fatty acids. Over 70 different ones have been extracted from living tissues. All fatty acids have a long hydrocarbon chain – a pleated backbone of carbon atoms with hydrogen atoms attached – and a carboxyl group (–COOH) at one end. Fatty acids vary in two main ways. The length of the carbon chain can differ, although in living organisms it is frequently between 15 and 17 carbon atoms long. More importantly, the fatty acid may be **saturated** or **unsaturated**.

In a saturated fatty acid each carbon atom is joined to the next by a *single* bond. The example shown in figure 1.2.9 is stearic acid.

In an unsaturated fatty acid the carbon chains contain one or more *double* carbon–carbon bonds. An example shown in figure 1.2.10 is linoleic acid, which is an essential fatty acid in the diet of mammals, including ourselves, as it cannot be synthesised within mammalian metabolic pathways.

Figure 1.2.8 Displayed formula of glycerol.

Figure 1.2.9 Displayed formula of stearic acid.

$CH_3(CH_2)_{16}COOH$

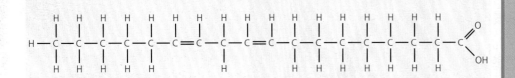

Figure 1.2.10 Displayed formula of linoleic acid.

A fat or oil results when glycerol combines with one, two or three fatty acids to form a **mono-**, **di-** or **triglyceride**. A bond is formed between the carboxyl (–COOH) group of a fatty acid and one of the hydroxyl (–OH) groups of the glycerol. A condensation reaction takes place, involving the removal of a molecule of water, and the resulting bond is known as an **ester link**. This type of reaction is called **esterification** and is illustrated in figure 1.2.11.

It is the combination of fatty acids in a triglyceride that determines what it is like. Saturated fatty acids give solid fats like butter and blubber, whereas unsaturated fatty acids give liquids such as olive oil.

Phospholipids

Inorganic phosphate, PO_4^{3-}, is present in the cytoplasm of every cell. Sometimes one of the hydroxyl groups of glycerol undergoes an esterification

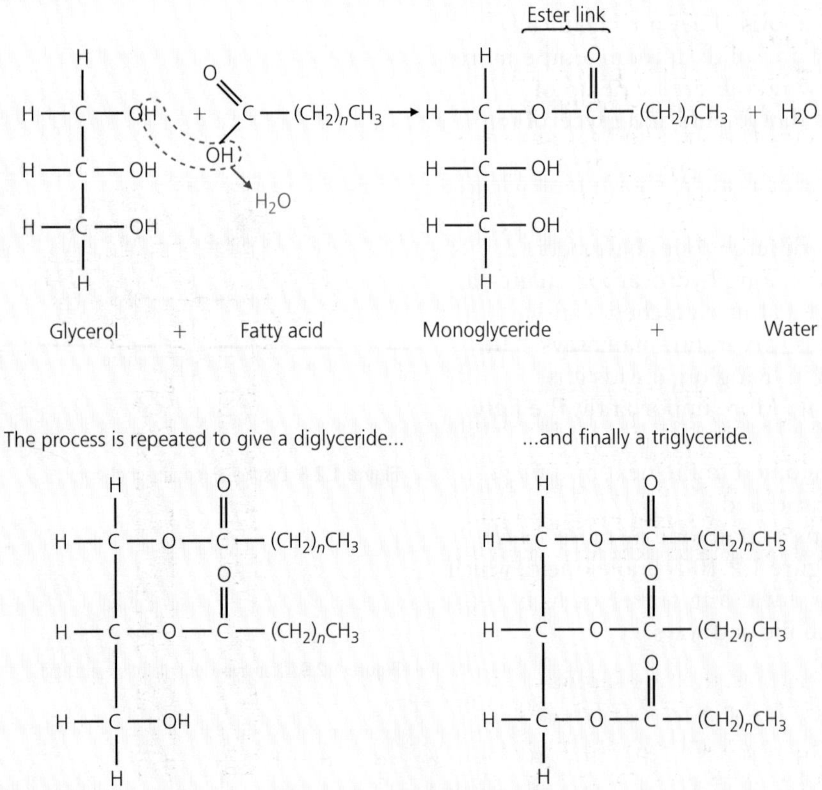

Ester link

Glycerol   +   Fatty acid   Monoglyceride   +   Water

The process is repeated to give a diglyceride...   ...and finally a triglyceride.

Figure 1.2.11 Esterification – and the molecules that result.

Biochemistry and affairs of the heart

Recent medical research seems to indicate that high levels of fat, particularly saturated fat, in our diet are not good for our long-term health. Fatty foods are very high in energy, and so a diet high in fats is likely to result in obesity. Worse than this, however, is the implication that saturated fats – found particularly in animal products such as dairy produce and meat – can cause problems in the metabolism leading to fatty deposits in the arteries. In the long term this can lead to all sorts of problems, including heart disease and death. Unsaturated fats, found mainly in plants, do not seem to have this effect and so people are being encouraged to replace saturates in their diets with unsaturates whenever possible.

But there is a further twist to this tale. Unsaturates themselves can be further divided into **polyunsaturates** and **monounsaturates**. Most of the fatty acids in polyunsaturates have two or more double bonds in their carbon chain. It seems that these do not have the damaging effects of saturated fats. The majority of the fatty acids in monounsaturates have only one double bond in the carbon chain – and these seem to have a positively beneficial effect, helping the body to cope better with saturated fats. The story is a long and complicated one, which will doubtless take many years to unravel (see section 7.3).

reaction with phosphate instead of with a fatty acid, and a simple **phospholipid** is formed. The phosphate element of the phospholipid may go on to react further and combine with other chemicals to form substances such as choline phosphoglyceride, needed for the formation of neurotransmitter substances and thus the successful functioning of the nervous system.

As we have seen, fats and oils are insoluble in water – they are not polar molecules. This makes them useful as inert storage materials, but limits their use elsewhere. Phospholipids are important because the lipid and phosphate parts of the molecule give it very different properties. The lipid part is neutral and is insoluble in water – it is known as **hydrophobic** or water-hating. In contrast, the phosphate part is highly polar and dissolves readily in water – it is **hydrophilic** or water-loving. This structure is shown in figure 1.2.12. It means that part of the molecule can be dissolved in fatty material such as the membrane, whilst the other part interacts with substances dissolved in water. Phospholipids are a vital component of cell membranes, and as such are present in almost all living things.

Waxes

Waxes are lipids made up of very long chain fatty acids joined to alcohols by ester links. The difference between fats and waxes is that there is only one fatty acid joined to each alcohol in a wax, as the alcohols only have one hydroxyl group, whereas glycerol has three. Waxes are very insoluble and are largely used by both plants and animals for waterproofing. Some waxes produced by insects to protect their cuticles from water loss can withstand extremely high temperatures without melting.

Steroids

Steroids are not typical lipids – apart from the fact that they are insoluble in water, they have little in common with the others. But steroids are of great biological importance, particularly as hormones in both animals and plants. Steroids are made up of very large numbers of carbon atoms arranged in complex ring structures. Figure 1.2.13 gives an example.

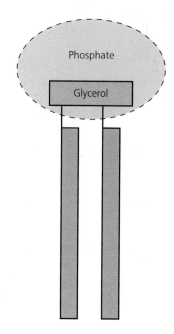

Fatty acid chains

Figure 1.2.12 The fatty acid chains of a phospholipid are neutral and insoluble in water. The phosphate head carries a negative charge and is soluble in water.

Proteins

About 18% of the human body is made up of protein – a high proportion second only to water. Our hair, skin, nails, the enzymes which control all the reactions in our cells, the enzymes which digest our food and many of the hormones that control our organs and their functions are made of protein. Protein molecules are also responsible for the contraction of muscle fibres, protection from disease in the form of antibodies, the clotting of blood by fibrinogen and prothrombin, the transport of oxygen in our blood by haemoglobin and much, much more. Proteins are extremely important molecules with a variety of functions throughout the living world. An understanding of how protein molecules are made up and the factors that affect their shapes and functions gives an insight into the biology of all living things.

Like carbohydrates and fats, proteins are made up of the elements carbon, hydrogen and oxygen, but in addition they all contain nitrogen. Many proteins also contain sulphur, and some also have phosphorus and various other elements. Proteins are very large molecules known as **macromolecules**. They are polymers, made up of many small units joined together. These small units are called **amino acids**. Amino acids combine in long chains to produce proteins in the same way as monosaccharide units join together to form polysaccharides. However, whilst each polysaccharide is made up of one or two different types of monosaccharide, there are about 20 different naturally occurring amino acids that combine to form proteins – so the potential variety of proteins is vast.

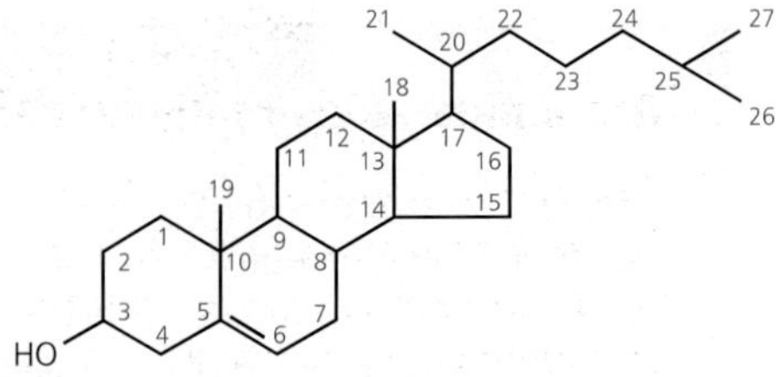

Figure 1.2.13 One of the best known steroids – cholesterol. A high blood cholesterol level can mean heart trouble ahead.

Amino acids – the building blocks of proteins

All amino acids have the basic structure shown in figure 1.2.14 of an **amino** ($-NH_2$) group and a **carboxyl** ($-COOH$) group attached to the same carbon atom.

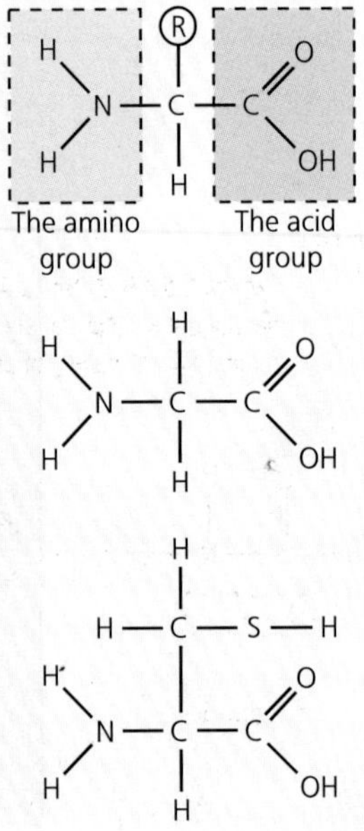

General structure of an amino acid

Glycine (R = H)

Cysteine (R = CH_2SH)

Figure 1.2.14 The R group varies from one amino acid to another. In the simplest amino acid, glycine, R is a single hydrogen atom. In a larger amino acid such as cysteine, R is a much more complex group.

The carboxyl end (–COOH) of an amino acid is acidic in nature. It will ionise in water to give hydrogen ions. However, the amino end (–NH$_2$) is basic in nature. It attracts hydrogen ions in solution. In acidic solutions an amino acid acts like a base, and in alkaline solutions it acts like an acid. In the mainly neutral conditions found in the cytoplasm of most living organisms it can act as both. This ability means an amino acid is said to be **amphoteric**. The R group also affects how the amino acid behaves – some R groups are more acidic in nature than others. The combination of all these things means that different amino acids can be separated by a sophisticated form of electrolysis which takes place in silica gel or on paper and is called **electrophoresis**. This is explained further on page 29.

Proteins from amino acids

When looking at how amino acids link to form long chains, we can ignore the R group and concentrate entirely on the amino and carboxyl groups. To make the diagrams easier to follow, the central carbon atom with the hydrogen atom and R group attached is shown simply as a striped circle, as in figure 1.2.15.

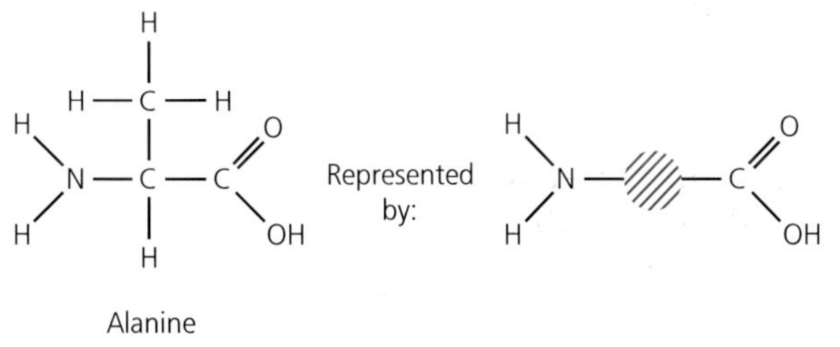

Alanine

Figure 1.2.15 Simple representation of alanine.

Amino acids join together by a reaction between the amino group of one amino acid and the carboxyl group of another amino acid. They join in a condensation reaction and a molecule of water is lost. The bond formed is known as a **peptide link** and when two amino acids join, a **dipeptide** is the result, as in figure 1.2.16. More and more amino acids can join together to form **polypeptide** chains, which may be from around ten to many thousands of amino acids long. A polypeptide can fold or coil or become associated with other polypeptide chains to form a **protein**.

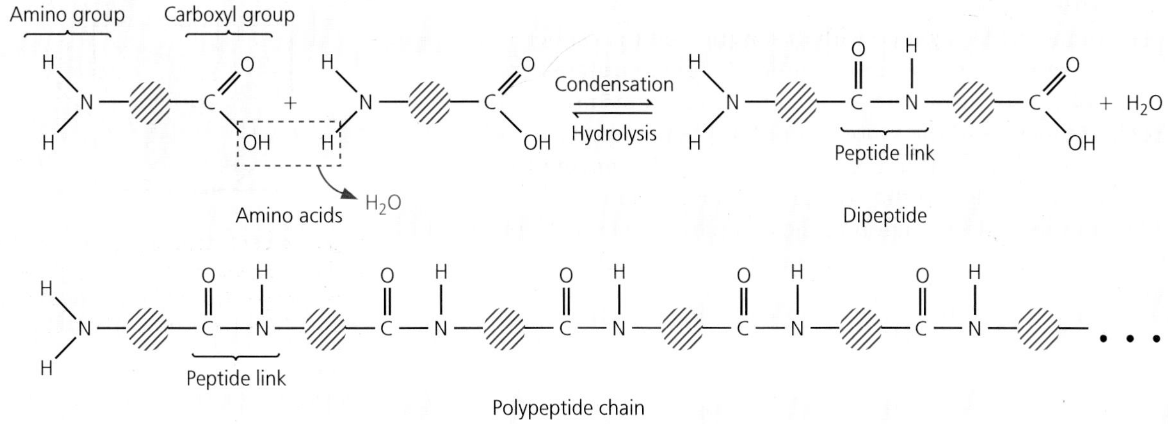

Figure 1.2.16 Amino acids can be joined in a seemingly endless variety of orders to produce an almost infinite variety of polypeptides.

Protein structure

Proteins are described by a **primary**, a **secondary**, a **tertiary** and a **quaternary structure**, illustrated in figure 1.2.17.

The primary structure of a protein describes the sequence of amino acids which make up the polypeptide chain. But this is only the beginning of the story. The secondary structure describes the three-dimensional arrangement of the polypeptide chain. In many cases it forms a right-handed (α-) helix or spiral coil with the peptide links forming the backbone and the R groups sticking out from the coil. Hydrogen bonds hold the structure together. Most fibrous proteins have this sort of structure. In other proteins, the polypeptide chains fold up into β-pleated sheets, again with the pleats held together by hydrogen bonds. Sometimes there is no regular secondary structure and the polypeptide forms a sort of random coil.

Some proteins are very large molecules indeed, consisting of thousands of amino acids joined together. The globular proteins (described below) such as the oxygen-carrying blood pigment haemoglobin and enzyme proteins are so large that they need a further level of organisation. The α-helices and pleated sheets are folded further into complicated shapes. These three-dimensional shapes are held in place by hydrogen bonds, sulphur bridges and ionic bonds. This organisation is the **tertiary structure** of the protein.

And finally, some enzymes and haemoglobin are made up of not one but several polypeptide chains. The **quaternary structure** describes the way these polypeptide chains fit together.

Fibrous and globular proteins

Proteins fall into two main groups – fibrous and globular proteins. **Fibrous proteins** have little or no tertiary structure. They are long parallel polypeptide chains with occasional cross-linkages making up fibres. They are insoluble in water and are very tough, which makes them ideally suited to their mainly structural functions within living things. They are found in connective tissue, tendons and the matrix of bones (collagen), in the structure of muscles, in the silk of spiders' webs and silkworm cocoons and as the keratin making up hair, nails, horns and feathers.

Globular proteins have complex tertiary and sometimes quaternary structures. They are folded into spherical (globular) shapes. They are relatively soluble in water, which is important for the way they function in the body. Globular proteins make up the immunoglobulins (antibodies) in the blood. They form enzymes and some hormones and are important for maintaining the structure of the cytoplasm.

Conjugated proteins

Sometimes a protein molecule is joined with or **conjugated** to another molecule, called a **prosthetic group**. For example, the **glycoproteins** are proteins with a carbohydrate prosthetic group. Many lubricants used by the human body, such as mucus and the synovial fluid in the joints, are glycoproteins, as are some proteins in the cell membrane. **Lipoproteins** are proteins conjugated with lipids and they too are most important in the structure of cell membranes. Haemoglobin, the complex oxygen-carrying molecule in the blood, is a conjugated protein with an inorganic iron prosthetic group.

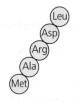

Primary structure – the linear sequence of amino acids in a peptide

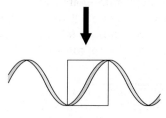

Secondary structure – the repeating pattern in the structure of the peptide chain, for example an α-helix.

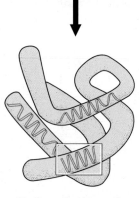

Tertiary structure – the three-dimensional folding of the secondary structure

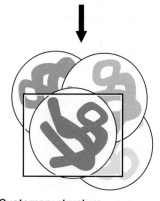

Quaternary structure – the three-dimensional arrangement of more than one tertiary polypeptide

Figure 1.2.17 It is not only the sequence of amino acids but also the arrangement of the polypeptide chains which determines the characteristics of a protein.

Haemoglobin and insulin – globular proteins

Globular proteins are large molecules and often have both tertiary and quaternary structures. One of the best known globular proteins is haemoglobin. This huge molecule is made up of 574 amino acids arranged in four polypeptide chains, and these are held together by disulphide bonds. Each chain is arranged around an iron-containing haem group, as shown in figure 1.2.18. The arrangement of the molecule allows it to perform the vital function of carrying oxygen in the blood.

Another globular protein is insulin. This molecule contains only 51 amino acids, but it too shows a globular structure which is important to its function. Unlike haemoglobin, insulin does not contain a prosthetic group.

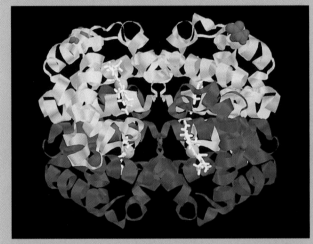

Figure 1.2.18 Computer modelling techniques give us detailed models of large molecules such as haemoglobin.

Collagen – a fibrous protein

Collagen is an unusual protein. It comprises three polypeptide chains up to 1000 amino acids long whose primary structure is repeating sequences of glycine with two other amino acids, often proline and hydroxyproline. These particular repeating sequences do not allow the chain to form an α-helix or a β-pleated sheet but instead the chains are arranged in a unique triple helix, held together by a large number of hydrogen bonds. These collagen fibres, which are single molecules, can be up to several millimetres long.

Collagen is formed as a precursor molecule, procollagen, so it does not clog up the secretory cell that makes it. Procollagen is then converted to collagen by enzymes at the site where it is needed.

Collagen is a fibrous protein that gives strength to tendons, ligaments, bones and skin. It is probably the most common structural protein found in animals. Collagen is extremely strong – the fibres have a tensile strength comparable to that of steel. This strength is due to the triple helix structure of the collagen molecule.

The properties of proteins

The secondary, tertiary and quaternary structures of proteins can be relatively easily damaged or **denatured**. Although the strong covalent bonds between the amino acids in the polypeptide chains are not readily destroyed, the relatively weak forces holding the different parts of the chains together can be disrupted very easily. As the functions of most proteins rely very heavily on their three-dimensional structure, this means that the entire biochemistry of cells and whole organisms is very sensitive to changes that might disrupt their proteins, such as a rise in temperature or a change in pH which will distort the internal balance of charges.

The large size of protein molecules affects their behaviour in water. Because they have ionic properties due to their carboxyl and amino groups, and also to many of the R groups, we might expect them to dissolve in water and form a solution. In fact, the molecules are so big that they form a colloidal suspension (see section 1.4, page 47) and play an important role in holding molecules in position in the cytoplasm.

Holding together

Peptide chains are held in the secondary, tertiary and quaternary structures of proteins by different sorts of bonds. Proteins often change their shape and then return to normal. What sorts of bond will allow this to happen?

Ionic bonds

These are electrostatic attractions between oppositely charged ions, and they play an important part in holding parts of polypeptide chains together.

Hydrophobic interactions

Some parts of protein molecules are repelled by water. In the aqueous surroundings of the body, this tends to force them to the inside of the molecule where other bonds can form to hold the shape in place.

Hydrogen bonds

Tiny negative charges are present on the oxygen atoms of carboxyl groups, and tiny positive charges are found on the hydrogen atoms of amino groups, OH– groups and indeed any polar group. When these charged groups are close enough to each other, the opposite charges attract, forming a **hydrogen bond**. Hydrogen bonds are weak compared with covalent bonds, but a large number can hold a structure very firmly. They are easily broken and reformed, for example by varying pH conditions, and are of great importance in biological molecules.

Sulphur bridges

Sulphur bridges are formed when two cysteine molecules are close together in the structure of a polypeptide, as shown in figure 1.2.19. An oxidation reaction takes place between the two sulphur-containing groups, resulting in a strong covalent bond known as a sulphur bridge or disulphide link. Sulphur bridges are much stronger than hydrogen bonds.

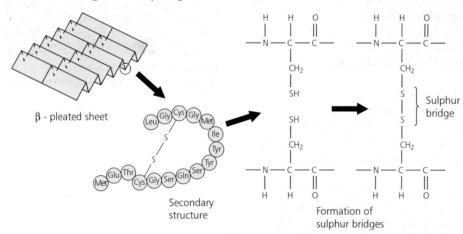

Figure 1.2.19 Sulphur bridges are strong bonds that maintain the shapes of the proteins in our bodies.

Blow-drying and perming

A simple demonstration of the difference in strength between hydrogen bonds and sulphur bridges is shown by blow-drying and perming hair. When you blow-dry your hair you break the hydrogen bonds in the protein and reform them with your hair curled in a different way. Next time you wash your hair it returns to its natural style as the original hydrogen bonds reform. If you have a perm, the chemicals of the perm solution break the sulphur bridges between the polypeptide coils and reform them in a different place. It is an involved procedure and the effect on that piece of hair is permanent.

How to unravel a protein

There are many different tools used by scientists to discover the molecular structure of proteins. Some of the techniques that have played a large part in helping us to understand them are described here.

Primary structure – chromatography

The relatively simple technique of **paper chromatography** is quite effective at separating amino acids. A piece of filter paper is soaked in water and then dipped into the mixture of amino acids dissolved in a different solvent. As the solvent moves up the paper, the amino acids are distributed between the water in the filter paper and the solvent moving up the paper to different degrees, depending on their solubility in water. Different amino acids will therefore move different distances up the paper. At the end of the process the paper is dried and sprayed with ninhydrin, a dye which reacts with the amino acids to form a coloured product and so reveals their position on the paper. We can work out which amino acids are present by calculating their R_f values (see page 30) and comparing them with those of known amino acids.

An important refinement of this technique is known as **two-way chromatography**. Paper chromatography is carried out as described above, but once the paper has been dried it is turned at right angles. It is then subjected to chromatography again using a different solvent before drying and spraying with ninhydrin. This provides a two-dimensional map of the molecules, giving a much better separation of the different amino acids.

Primary structure – electrophoresis

Chromatography can be used to separate amino acids quite successfully, but **electrophoresis** gives even better results. In chromatography, the amino acids are separated by their solubility in water. In electrophoresis the separation is the result of their mass and overall charge. Known amino acids are placed on a special support medium in a buffering solution (to keep the pH constant) and an electric current is passed through it. The amino acids move on the medium at different rates according to the charge on their R group, as figure 1.2.20 shows. Once the medium has dried the amino acids can be revealed using a ninhydrin spray. The distance each amino acid has travelled under these known conditions can then be measured.

This technique can be used to find out exactly which amino acids make up a particular protein. First the protein is broken down into its component amino acids. This is done using protease enzymes which break the peptide links in the protein. After electrophoresis the distance the amino acids have travelled can be measured and compared with how far known 'marker' amino acids have travelled under the same conditions.

The precise order of the amino acids in a particular protein can also be worked out. This involves special enzymes which break peptide links one at a time, starting from either the amino or the acid end of the molecule. One terminal amino or acid group at a time is labelled (tagged), removed and identified by chromatography or electrophoresis. The new terminal amino or acid group is now tagged and the process repeated. It is a very time-consuming process – when Frederick Sanger did it for the first time in 1958, working out the sequence of amino acids in the relatively small protein insulin, he was awarded the Nobel Prize!

Secondary and tertiary structure – X-ray crystallography

X-ray crystallography is a relatively simple technique. X-rays are fired into a crystal of the pure protein. The X-rays are reflected by the atoms of the protein

Figure 1.2.20 The amino acids revealed. Electrophoresis enables us to work out the amino acids present in a protein.

molecules and this scattered pattern is recorded on a photographic plate. The crystal is then turned round and the process repeated many times around the structure to build up a complete record. Interpreting the resulting images is very skilled work, now largely done by computers. X-ray crystallography has revealed regular and predictable protein molecule shapes – most frequently helices and globular shapes.

R_f values and how to use them

Once we have carried out chromatography or electrophoresis and separated the amino acids that make up a protein, we need to work out their R_f values and compare them with the R_f values of known amino acids in the same solvent. This is how we can identify the different amino acids in the protein. But what is the R_f value? It is the ratio of the distance moved by the amino acid to the distance moved by the solvent alone. The R_f value is a value between 0 and 1 and it is calculated as follows:

$$R_f \text{ value} = \frac{\text{distance travelled by solute (amino acid)}}{\text{distance travelled by solvent}}$$

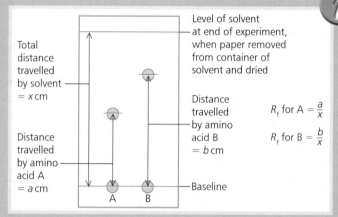

Figure 1.2.21 In this example the R_f values for amino acids A and B have been worked out.

Food tests

There are a number of simple laboratory tests which show up the presence of some of the very common biological molecules we have met in this chapter.

Because carbohydrates, proteins and lipids make up most of the food we eat, these tests are known as food tests. They are summarised in table 1.2.2.

Food test	Substance identified	Reagents and procedure
Iodine test	Starch	A drop of orange iodine/potassium iodide solution is added to a test substance. In the presence of starch, a distinctive blue-black colour appears as a starch–iodide complex is formed.
Benedict's test	Reducing sugars, e.g. glucose, fructose, maltose	Blue Benedict's solution (containing copper sulphate) is heated with the test reagent. With a reducing sugar the copper(II) ions are reduced to copper(I) ions and a bright orange precipitate appears. A low concentration of reducing sugar gives a greenish colour.
Benedict's test	Non-reducing sugars, e.g. sucrose	A disaccharide such as sucrose will give a negative result with Benedict's solution – sucrose is a non-reducing sugar. However, if a test substance containing a non-reducing sugar is boiled with dilute mineral acid, the glycosidic links are broken and monosaccharides (reducing sugars) result. The solution is neutralised and then the Benedict's test is repeated, when the familiar orange precipitate will appear.
Emulsion test	Lipids	The test material is broken into very small pieces, mixed with alcohol and shaken well. Any lipid present will dissolve in the alcohol. This solution of lipid and alcohol is poured off and mixed with water, and the mixture is shaken vigorously. If lipid is present, the mixture forms a white, milky emulsion as tiny lipid drops are suspended in the water. If there is no lipid, the mixture stays clear.
Biuret test	Protein (peptide bonds)	A test substance is mixed with blue Biuret solution, which is a combination of copper sulphate and sodium hydroxide, and heated gently. The solution turns lilac/purple if protein is present, and stays blue if it is not.

Table 1.2.2 Some tests for biochemical molecules that are frequently carried on food samples

Of the three most commonly found biological molecules – carbohydrates, lipids and proteins – proteins are present in the largest amounts. They are also the largest of the three types of molecule, and have the most complex structures. But where do they come from? How do cells know what proteins to make? The answer to that lies with another group of the molecules of life – the **nucleic acids**.

SUMMARY

- **Organic compounds** contain carbon and hydrogen atoms, usually with oxygen and sometimes with other atoms. Carbon atoms bond strongly to each other forming large complex chain and ring structures. Important organic compounds include **carbohydrates**, **lipids** and **proteins**.

- **Carbohydrates** provide energy and are divided into **monosaccharides**, **disaccharides** and **polysaccharides**.

- **Monosaccharides** have the general formula $(CH_2O)_n$. They include the trioses ($n = 3$) such as glyceraldehyde, pentoses ($n = 5$) such as ribose and hexoses ($n = 6$) such as glucose. Glyceraldehyde is a molecule which has **stereoisomers**, and other stereoisomers are named L or D by comparison with the structure of glyceraldehyde.

- **Disaccharides** are made up of two monosaccharide units joined by a condensation reaction and have the general formula $(C_6H_{10}O_5)_n$. Sucrose is a disaccharide.

- **Polysaccharides** are polymers of glucose and are used for food storage. They include starch, glycogen and cellulose.

- **Lipids** store energy and occur in cell membranes. They include **fats and oils**, **phospholipids**, **waxes** and **steroids**.

- **Fats** are solids at room temperature and **oils** are liquids. Fats and oils are made up of fatty acids and glycerol. Fatty acids may be saturated or unsaturated. Glycerol forms ester links with one, two or three fatty acids to form mono-, di- or triglycerides, respectively.

- **Phospholipids** are formed when one hydroxyl group of glycerol esterifies with a phosphate group. Phospholipids have a hydrophobic fatty acid chain and a hydrophilic phosphate part, and are important in cell membranes.

- **Waxes** are made up of fatty acids joined to an alcohol with one hydroxyl group, and are used as waterproofing. **Steroids** such as cholesterol have complex ring structures and are important as hormones.

- **Proteins** contain nitrogen in addition to carbon, hydrogen and oxygen. They are large macromolecules which are polymers of **amino acids**.

- There are about 20 naturally occurring amino acids that combine to form proteins, each with a carboxyl group and an amino group but with different R groups.

- Amino acids join by peptide links to form **dipeptides** (two amino acids) and **polypeptides** (up to thousands of amino acids). Polypeptides fold up to form proteins.

- The **primary** protein structure is the order of amino acids in the polypeptide chain.

- The **secondary** structure is the arrangement of the polypeptide chain into a helix or pleated sheet.

- The **tertiary** structure is the three-dimensional shape formed by folding of the secondary structure.
- **Quaternary** structures occur when two or more polypeptide chains associate to form a protein.
- **Fibrous** proteins, such as collagen, have no tertiary structure but form tough fibres.
- **Globular** proteins have tertiary and sometimes quaternary structures and include enzymes.
- **Conjugated** proteins are joined with another molecule called a prosthetic group.

QUESTIONS

1 a i   How do fats and oils differ?
    ii   Which chemical elements are found in fats?
    iii What is meant by an *unsaturated* fatty acid?
    iv   Name two cell structures in which fatty acids occur.
    v   Give an example of another type of lipid, and one example of its role in living organisms.
  b Compare the structure of lipids with the structure of polysaccharides.

2 Discuss how the properties of amino acids and proteins are suited to their variety of roles in living systems.

3 Produce a table suitable for inclusion in a revision guide summarising the three groups of macromolecules discussed in this chapter. It will need to contain as much information as possible, yet be compact and easy to read, understand and remember.

Developing Key Skills

Many hair and skin care products advertise themselves using scientific jargon. Products are often said to contain important biological molecules that will be absorbed and will really improve or rejuvenate the body tissues.

a) Carry out a survey of hair and skin care products used by you, your friends and your family as well as products you see advertised on television and in magazines. Present your findings using IT. Give as much information as you can about the biological molecules used in the products – vitamins, proteins, lipids, glycerides, collagen etc. Name the products in which the molecules are found and the effect they are claimed to have. Which biological molecules are most frequently used in hair and skin care products?

b) Why do you think that manufacturers make such claims about their products? Use your biological knowledge – and section 4.7 on the structure of the skin – to help you decide which, if any, of these ingredients might fulfil the claims made for them.

FOCUS DNA FINGERPRINTING

In 1984 Alec Jeffreys, a researcher at Leicester University, developed a technique that has had far-reaching effects on forensic science and the fight against crime all over the world. This was **DNA fingerprinting**, also known as genetic fingerprinting or DNA profiling. Our DNA is unique to each of us. On our chromosomes is all the information that makes us who we are, but there are also regions of DNA which code for nothing at all. These are known as **hypervariable regions**. They vary greatly in length from one person to another, and they are made up of repeating base sequences known as **core units**.

Using special enzymes known as **restriction endonucleases**, our DNA can be chopped up into fragments which show our hypervariable regions. Electrophoresis is used to separate the DNA fragments according to their size. Specific DNA probes, molecules that may be radioactive or fluorescent and which bind to particular sequences of DNA, are then mixed with the DNA fragments. On photographic film the labelled fragments produce a pattern that is effectively unique to each one of us. The probability of two people having identical sets of fragments is calculated to be 5×10^{-19}, which is effectively zero!

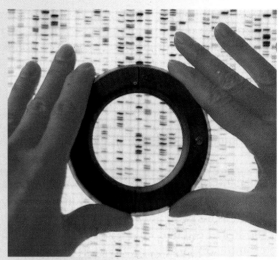

Figure 1 We all have unique patterns to our DNA. DNA fingerprinting allows them to be seen.

Pinning down parents

People who are closely related will have more DNA regions in common than people who are not related at all. One use for genetic fingerprinting has been to settle disputes over the parenthood of a child. For example, a man may claim a child is not his so that he does not have to support it, and DNA profiling can be used to show whether he is the father. The first use of this in the UK was to show that a young Ghanian boy was genuinely the child of a particular couple and therefore entitled to stay in Britain with his parents.

Tracking down criminals

The greatest success story for DNA fingerprinting has been in the battle against crime. Tiny amounts of material from the human body, such as blood, skin, semen or hair, can be used to produce a DNA profile of a suspect. A rapist usually leaves semen in or on his victim and a murderer is likely to be involved in a struggle and leave tissue fragments behind. A DNA profile can be prepared from these, which can be used to identify the person who committed the crime, and can also be given as evidence in court. In recent years the technology has been developed further so that the tiniest piece of genetic material can be replicated before testing it, using a reaction called the DNA polymerase reaction. Forensic scientists can now return to evidence collected from women who were raped and murdered 20 or more years ago, and produce enough DNA to run reliable tests. The culprits who committed the crimes are being found and brought to justice years later – genetic fingerprinting is a very powerful tool indeed.

Figure 2 For many years the family of Cynthia Bolshaw had to live with the knowledge that the man who raped and murdered her had 'got away with it'. Now, 17 years after her death he is behind bars, thanks to DNA fingerprinting.

1.3 The molecules of life: Nucleic acids

All living things have a biological drive to reproduce. From the tiniest microscopic organism to the largest mammal, replacement individuals must be made before the original wears out. But how is this reproduction of a living thing brought about? Somewhere within each cell must be a pattern, a set of instructions for the assembling of new cells – to form offspring, and also to form identical cells for growth. Over the last 50 or so years scientists have made enormous strides towards understanding the form of these instructions. In the unravelling of the secrets of the genetic code, we have come closer than ever before to understanding the mystery of life.

How cells reproduce

The processes that form new cells from an original are controlled by enzymes, which as we know are proteins. It is enzymes that control the biochemistry of the sort of cell that will form – whether it will be a muscle cell or a skin cell, for example. But what determines which enzymes will be produced in a cell, and how are the enzymes made?

This information is carried by molecules called **nucleic acids** in the cell. One kind of nucleic acid is **DNA**, or **deoxyribonucleic acid**, which makes up the chromosomes in the nucleus of the cell. DNA carries a code in its molecules which is read by another nucleic acid – **RNA** or **ribonucleic acid**. RNA is involved in protein synthesis, a production line which turns out enzymes to carry out the instructions and build a new cell.

Years of research and vastly expensive technology was needed to bring to light the sequence of events summarised in these few words. The first step in understanding this fascinating piece of molecular biology is to understand the structure of the main molecules involved.

The structure of DNA and RNA

DNA and RNA are both polymers. The chemical structure of the simple monomer units making up both DNA and RNA is very similar, though the polymer molecules themselves are quite different. The monomers are called **nucleotides**. Each nucleotide has three parts – a five-carbon or **pentose sugar**, a **nitrogen-containing base** and a **phosphate** group.

The pentose sugars

The sugar will be one of two very similar pentose rings. Ribonucleic acids contain the sugar **ribose**. Deoxyribonucleic acids contain the sugar **deoxyribose**. The only difference between these two sugars is that deoxyribose, as its name suggests, contains one oxygen atom less than ribose. Figure 1.3.1 shows their structures.

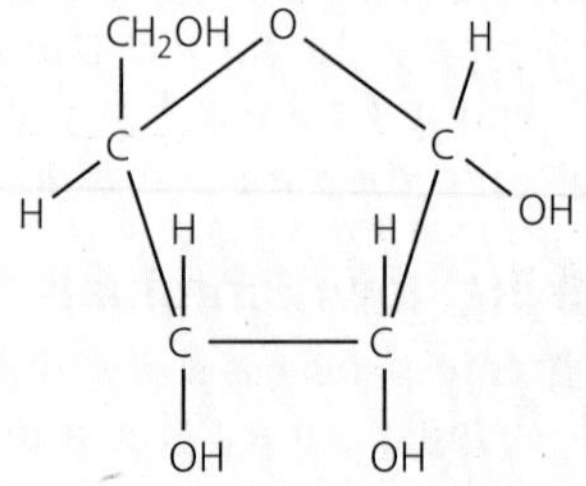

The nitrogen-containing bases

There are two types of bases found in nucleic acids. The **purine** bases have two nitrogen-containing rings, while the **pyrimidines** have only one. Each nucleic acid molecule contains combinations of four different bases with equal numbers of purines and pyrimidines. In DNA the purines are **adenine** (**A**) and

Ribose

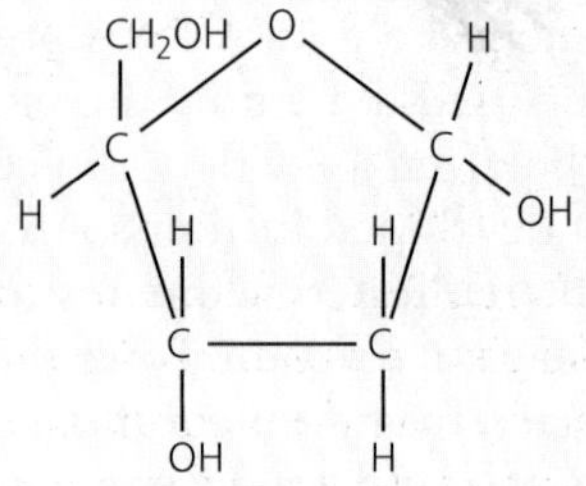

Deoxyribose

Figure 1.3.1 The formulae of these sugars shows that deoxyribose has one oxygen atom less than ribose.

guanine (**G**) and the pyrimidines are **cytosine** (**C**) and **thymine** (**T**). In RNA the purine bases are the same as in DNA but the pyrimidines are cytosine and **uracil** (**U**). These rings, shown in figure 1.3.2, have the chemical property of being bases because of the nitrogen atoms they contain.

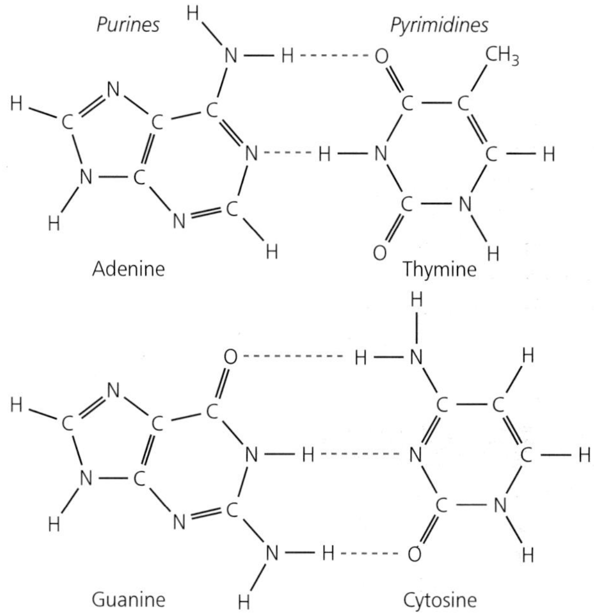

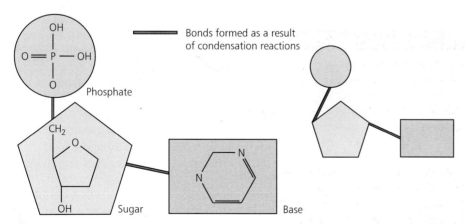

Figure 1.3.2 Look carefully at the shapes of these molecules – the importance of the way they pair will soon become clear.

Phosphate

We met phosphate groups (usually derived from phosphoric acid) when we looked at phospholipids. A phosphate group makes up the third component of a nucleotide. It gives nucleotides, and the nucleic acids that they make up, their acidic character.

Putting it together – the nucleotide and nucleic acids

Figure 1.3.3 shows how the sugar, the base and the phosphate are joined to form the nucleotide monomer.

Figure 1.3.3 The three parts of a nucleotide are joined by condensation reactions. Two molecules of water are removed in the process.

To form DNA, nucleotides containing the bases A, T, C and G join together to make chains which can be millions of units long. RNA is made up of long chains of nucleotides containing A, C, G and U. Knowledge of how these units join together, and the three-dimensional structures that are produced in DNA in particular, is the basis of our understanding of molecular genetics. The structure of DNA is taken as common knowledge now, yet the story of how it was worked out is very recent history.

The story of the double helix

Gregor Mendel's ideas of genetics were years ahead of their time. Once they had been accepted and absorbed by the scientific community, the next step was to discover what 'genes' actually were. It was almost 100 years after Mendel's time before the answers were found. For many years there were arguments between biologists about which of the many complex chemicals in cells might be the one that carried the genetic information. By the late 1940s most people agreed that it must be DNA. It was known to occur in almost every living cell. It was usually contained in the nucleus. It was a large and complex molecule. But how did it work? To understand the genetic code, the structure of DNA itself had to be understood, and so far no one had managed to work that out.

All sorts of threads of information were available. In 1951 Erwin Chargaff analysed DNA from a wide range of species. He found that in every case the proportions of cytosine and guanine were the same. In the same way he found that the proportion of adenine was always the same as that of thymine. But there was no relationship between the two groups.

At King's College in London, Maurice Wilkins and Rosalind Franklin were working on the X-ray crystallography of DNA. This proved to be rather difficult. It was very hard to get pure crystals of DNA to work with, as DNA does not crystallise easily, and the pictures were so complicated that interpreting them proved a further major hurdle. One such picture is shown in figure 1.3.4.

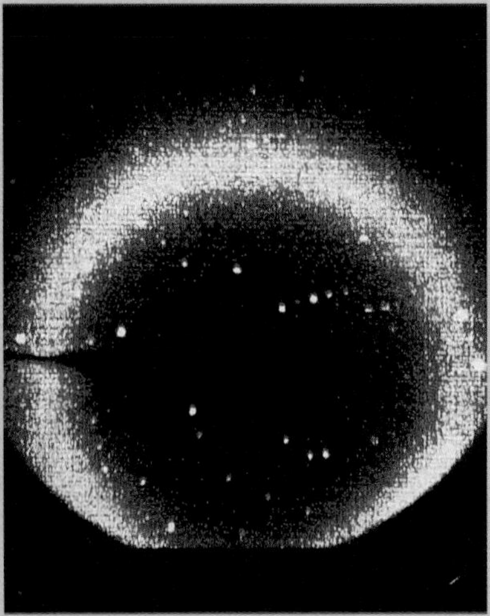

Meanwhile at Cambridge James Watson and Francis Crick were trying a different approach. They gathered all the available information about DNA and kept trying to build a model that fitted with all the facts. They worked with space-filling models and also with simpler representations of the known components of DNA. Any model they produced had to explain all the available data about the structure of the molecule and how it behaved. By a process of assimilating information from other researchers, long discussions and hours of manipulating the models, an idea emerged which seemed to work.

What finally took shape was the now famous **double helix**. The patterns from the X-ray crystallography suggested a helix measuring 3.4 nm for every complete turn. The idea of a double or parallel helix emerged – but how was the structure maintained? Watson noticed that if in every case cytosine was paired with guanine, and thymine with adenine, hydrogen bonds would hold them together. The two sets of base pairs (cytosine/guanine and thymine/adenine) are roughly the same size and fit within the measured dimensions of the molecule. Two purines would be too large to fit and two pyrimidines too small as hydrogen bonds would not hold them tightly enough together. The realisation that the bases are always paired in this way was a major breakthrough in understanding the structure of the DNA molecule. This model explained the relationship between the bases shown by Chargaff's results.

The base pairs occupied a length along the helix of 0.34 nm – meaning that ten of them would neatly make up one complete twist of the helix (3.4 nm) as measured by the team at King's College London. And best of all, the two complementary chains of DNA could 'open up' along the line of hydrogen bonds between the base pairs. They could then replicate to produce two identical double helices, making possible the vital role of DNA in reproduction. A Nobel prize was the reward for this masterly piece of molecular detection – and the DNA double helix is the basis of all our modern molecular genetics.

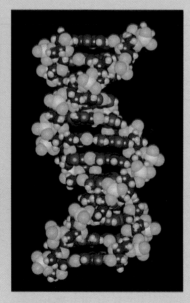

Figure 1.3.4 Working out a model of the large three-dimensional molecule that produced this picture proved to be no easy task.

Figure 1.3.5 To the untrained eye this model may not seem much easier to understand than the X-ray crystallograph. Within this complex arrangement of atoms is the whole basis of genetics.

How DNA replicates

The complex model of DNA in figure 1.3.5 does not help most of us to understand how it functions. However, when the structure is looked at more closely it becomes easier to see how the DNA molecule works.

To be sure that the genetic code is passed on to each new cell, DNA needs to **replicate** – it needs to produce another molecule exactly the same as itself. Figure 1.3.6 shows how it does this. The hydrogen bonds holding the two strands of the helix together break, so the strands are no longer joined. Nucleotides that are present free in the cell come in and pair with the nucleotides in the 'unzipped' strands – again, A pairs with T and G with C. These nucleotides are then joined by condensation reactions, controlled by the enzyme DNA polymerase, to form a new complementary strand which is hydrogen bonded to the original strand. The result is two double helices, identical with the original.

Figure 1.3.6 We can understand how DNA functions by looking at a small piece of it.

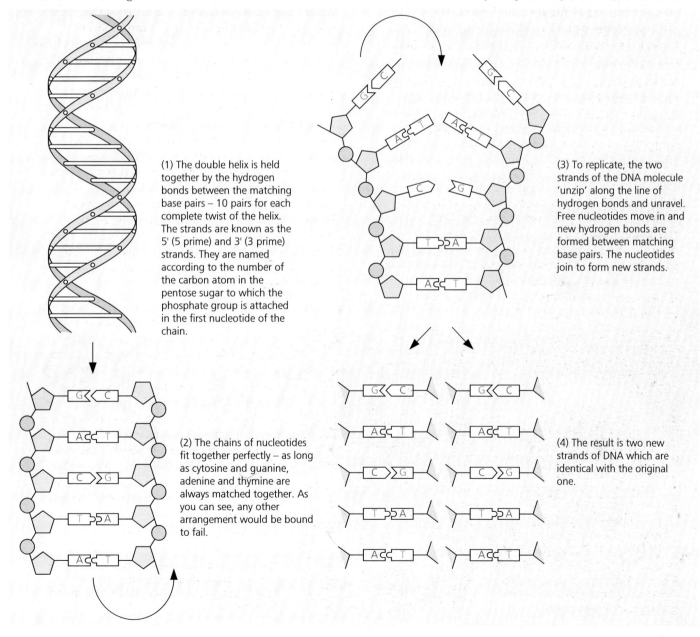

(1) The double helix is held together by the hydrogen bonds between the matching base pairs – 10 pairs for each complete twist of the helix. The strands are known as the 5' (5 prime) and 3' (3 prime) strands. They are named according to the number of the carbon atom in the pentose sugar to which the phosphate group is attached in the first nucleotide of the chain.

(2) The chains of nucleotides fit together perfectly – as long as cytosine and guanine, adenine and thymine are always matched together. As you can see, any other arrangement would be bound to fail.

(3) To replicate, the two strands of the DNA molecule 'unzip' along the line of hydrogen bonds and unravel. Free nucleotides move in and new hydrogen bonds are formed between matching base pairs. The nucleotides join to form new strands.

(4) The result is two new strands of DNA which are identical with the original one.

Conservative and semiconservative replication

Several years after Watson and Crick had produced their double helix model for the structure of the DNA molecule, there were two main ideas about how it could replicate. One was known as **conservative replication**. It said that the original double helix remained intact and in some way instructed the formation of a new, identical double helix made up of new material. The other was known as **semiconservative replication**. This assumed that the DNA 'unzipped' and new nucleotides aligned along each strand. This would mean that each new double helix contained one strand of the original DNA and one strand made up of new material. As the result of a very elegant set of experiments by M. S. Meselson and F. W. Stahl, semiconservative replication became the accepted model.

The experiments of Meselson and Stahl

In the late 1950s M.S. Meselson and F.W. Stahl performed a classic series of experiments which showed very clearly that semiconservative replication was the way DNA worked. Their experiment depended on the use of an **isotope** of nitrogen. Nitrogen 15 is a 'heavy isotope' – it has one more neutron in its atoms than the more common nitrogen 14. Both isotopes have the same number of electrons and protons and therefore react in the same way. Isotopes, particularly radioactive ones, can be used to 'label' biological molecules and follow their progress through an organism. In this experiment, the nitrogen 15 isotope used was not radioactive, but its density helped Meselson and Stahl to find out what happens when DNA replicates.

(1) Meselson and Stahl grew several generations of the gut bacteria *Escherichia coli* in a medium whose only source of nitrogen was the isotope nitrogen 15, in labelled ammonium chloride $^{15}NH_4Cl$. The bacteria were grown on this medium until all the bacterial DNA was labelled with nitrogen 15.

(2) The bacteria were then moved to a medium containing normal $^{14}NH_4Cl$ as their only nitrogen source, and the density of their DNA was tested as they reproduced.

(3) If DNA reproduces by conservative replication, some of the DNA would have the density expected if it contained nothing but nitrogen 15 (the original strands), and some of it would have the density expected if it contained nothing but nitrogen 14 (the new strands). If DNA reproduces by semiconservative replication then all the DNA would have the same density, half-way between that of nitrogen 15- and nitrogen 14-containing DNA.

The DNA was all found to have the same density – and so Meselson and Stahl concluded that DNA must replicate semiconservatively.

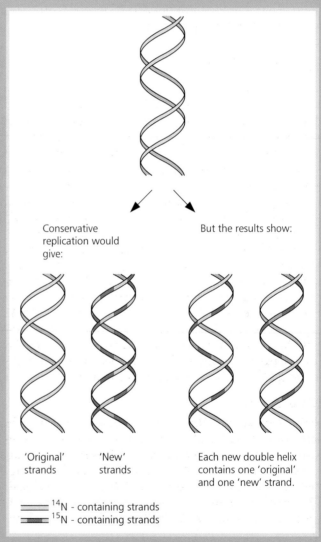

Conservative replication would give:

But the results show:

'Original' strands   'New' strands

Each new double helix contains one 'original' and one 'new' strand.

—— ^{14}N - containing strands
▬▬ ^{15}N - containing strands

Figure 1.3.7 After Meselson and Stahl produced their evidence, support for the idea of conservative replication melted away.

How DNA controls cell division and cell function

Now we have seen the structure of DNA and the way in which it replicates, the next question must be *how* does it act as the genetic code? Each different type of living organism must have a distinctive genetic message which produces, for example, sea urchin cells rather than daffodil cells. Added to that, within each type of living organism are millions of individual cells, each of which is unique and which must therefore have its own unique genetic message. There will often be a variety of types of cells within an organism, containing different structures and enzymes and performing a range of jobs. The information needed to give this enormous variety is found within the DNA. The sequence of the base pairs in the molecule is used as a code. The code determines which amino acids are joined together to form proteins.

Proteins are the key to how the genetic code works. Almost all enzymes are proteins, and enzymes control the synthesis and biochemistry of everything in the cell and in the larger organism. So DNA carries its instructions for the make-up of a cell in the form of instructions for particular proteins. Once the proteins (usually enzyme proteins) are made, they in turn construct the rest of the cell.

The genetic code

Proteins are made up of amino acids. There are about 20 amino acids that occur in proteins, but joined together in different combinations they make up an almost infinite variety of proteins. The amino acids which are put together to make a protein are arranged as a result of the genetic code.

In a double helix of DNA, the components which vary along the structure are the bases. Thus it was deduced that it is the arrangement of the bases which carries the genetic information. There are only four bases, but there are at least 20 possible amino acids. This means that one base obviously cannot code for one amino acid. Even two bases do not give a large enough selection of amino acids – the possible arrangements of four bases into groups of two are 4×4 $=16$. Thus at least three bases are needed to code for one amino acid.

A **triplet code** gives $4 \times 4 \times 4 = 64$ possible combinations – more than enough for all the possible amino acids. By the early 1960s it had been shown that it was indeed a triplet code of bases which was the basis of the genetic code. Each sequence of three bases along a strand of DNA codes for something very specific. Most code for a particular amino acid, but some 'nonsense triplets' do not code for an amino acid at all – they signal the beginning or the end of one particular amino acid sequence. A sequence of three bases on a molecule of DNA or RNA is known as a **codon**.

Cracking the code

Once the structure of DNA had been worked out many scientists, including Francis Crick, started work on the genetic code. The codons of DNA are difficult to work out because the molecule is so vast, so most of the work has been done on the codons of a type of RNA called messenger RNA. This RNA is formed as complementary strands to DNA, but its molecules are much smaller, usually carrying the instructions for a single polypeptide. Once the RNA sequence is known, the DNA sequence is simple to deduce.

A dictionary of the genetic code

The result of all this work on sequencing DNA was a sort of dictionary of the genetic code as shown in table 1.3.1. Much of the original work, done in the 1960s, used the gut bacteria *E. coli*, but all subsequent studies suggest that the code is very similar throughout the living world.

First base	Second base				Third base
	U	C	A	G	
U	UUU Phe	UCU Ser	UAU Tyr	UGU Cys	U
	UUC Phe	UCC Ser	UAC Tyr	UGC Cys	C
	UUA Leu	UCA Ser	UAA c.t.	UGA c.t.	A
	UUG Leu	UCG Ser	UAG c.t.	UGG Try	G
C	CUU Leu	CCU Pro	CAU His	CGU Arg	U
	CUC Leu	CCC Pro	CAC His	CGC Arg	C
	CUA Leu	CCA Pro	CAA Gln	CGA Arg	A
	CUG Leu	CCG Pro	CAG Gln	CGG Arg	G
A	AUU Ile	ACU Thr	AAU Asn	AGU Ser	U
	AUC Ile	ACC Thr	AAC Asn	AGC Ser	C
	AUA Ile	ACA Thr	AAA Lys	AGA Arg	A
	AUG Met*	ACG Thr	AAG Lys	AGG Arg	G
G	GUU Val	GCU Ala	GAU Asp	GGU Gly	U
	GUC Val	GCC Ala	GAC Asp	GGC Gly	C
	GUA Val	GCA Ala	GAA Glu	GGA Gly	A
	GUG Val	GCG Ala	GAG Glu	GGG Gly	G

Table 1.3.1 The triplet code which underpins all work on genetics. The code shown is that for messenger RNA, the most commonly used because it is simplest to work out
U uracil   C cytosine   A adenine   G guanine
c.t. These codons code for the termination of polypeptide chain synthesis (stop codes).
*   Under some conditions this codon codes for the initiation of polypeptide chain synthesis (start code).

Even this analysis of the genetic code did not answer all the questions. It appears that the code is **degenerate** – that is it contains more information than it needs to. If you look carefully at the 'dictionary' you will find that often only two of the three nucleotides seem to matter in determining which amino acid results. A possible reason for this is as follows: if each amino acid had only one codon, then any accidental change in the genetic code (**mutation**) would cause havoc. With the code as it stands, an error is more likely to produce another amino acid which may make little or no difference to the functioning of the final protein. There is even a chance that a change could still result in the same amino acid. Mutations are relatively common – the degenerate code at least partly protects living organisms from their effects.

How proteins are synthesised in the cell

DNA is contained within chromosomes in the nucleus of the cell. Proteins are synthesised on ribosomes, which are found on the rough endoplasmic reticulum in the cytoplasm. Nuclear DNA has never been detected in the cytoplasm, so the message about the order of amino acids in a protein cannot be carried direct. Messages are relayed from the nuclear DNA to the active synthetic enzymes on the ribosomes by ribonucleic acids (RNA).

Economy or freedom of choice

Another question was raised about the genetic code: do codons overlap or not? Take any sequence of RNA bases, for example UUUAGC. This could code for two amino acids:

phenylalanine (UUU) and serine (AGC)

On the other hand, if the codons overlap, it could code for four amino acids:

phenylalanine (UUU), leucine (UUA), a nonsense or stop codon (UAG) and serine (AGC)

An overlapping code would be very economical as relatively short lengths of DNA could carry the instructions for many different proteins. However, the amino acids which could be coded for side by side would be limited. In the example given, only leucine out of the 20 or so available amino acids could ever follow phenylalanine, because only leucine has a codon starting with UU–.

Some mutations which cause recognisable diseases (for example sickle cell disease) have been shown to change only *one* amino acid in a protein chain, rather than three. This is evidence against an overlapping code as a change in one codon would affect three amino acids in that model. As a result of all the evidence available, and the simple common sense of the argument, the model of a *non-overlapping* code is now fully accepted.

What does RNA do?

As we have already seen, RNA is closely related in structure to DNA. However, it contains a different sugar, ribose, and a different base, uracil instead of thymine. It consists of a single helix and does not form enormous and complex molecules like DNA. The sequence of bases along a strand of RNA is related to the sequence of bases on a small part of the DNA in the nucleus.

RNA carries out three main jobs in the cell:

1   It carries the instructions about which amino acids will be in a polypeptide from the DNA in the nucleus to the ribosomes where proteins are made.

2   It picks up specific amino acids from the protoplasm and carries them to the surface of the ribosomes.

3   It makes up the bulk of the ribosomes themselves.

To perform these three different functions, three distinct forms of RNA exist. These are **messenger RNA**, **transfer RNA** and **ribosomal RNA**.

Messenger RNA

Messenger RNA (**mRNA**) is formed in the nucleus in a similar way to the replication of DNA. Figure 1.3.9 shows the process. A part of the DNA double helix 'unzips' and the RNA nucleotides pair up with those on one of the DNA strands. They are joined to form a strand of mRNA. Whereas a double helix of DNA carries information about a vast array of proteins, a piece of mRNA usually carries instructions for just one polypeptide. The mRNA is formed on the 5' strand of the DNA. The bases that line up are complementary to those on this DNA strand.

Parts of the DNA are said to be **transcribed** on to strands of mRNA. This means that the mRNA carries the same code as the DNA. The process is brought about by an enzyme called **DNA-directed RNA polymerase**. The name of this enzyme is usually shortened to **RNA polymerase**, though the full

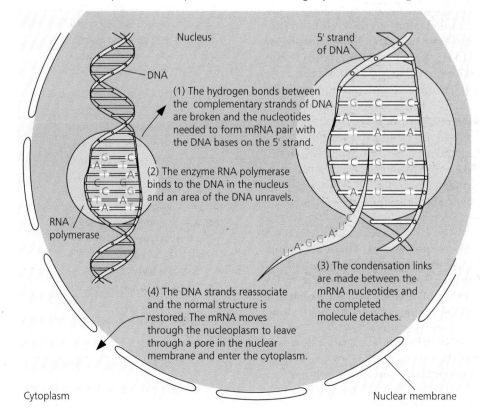

Figure 1.3.8 The transcription of the DNA message. Any mistakes in this process result in the wrong proteins being made, which can have fatal consequences for the cell or even the whole organism.

name does tell us precisely what it does. It polymerises the nucleotide units to form RNA in a way which is determined by the DNA. Just as in the DNA, the bases of the mRNA form a triplet code and each triplet of bases is known as a codon.

The relatively small mRNA molecules pass easily through the pores in the nuclear membrane, so carrying the genetic message from the nucleus to the cytoplasm. They then move to the surface of the ribosomes, transporting the instructions to the site of protein synthesis.

Transfer RNA

Transfer RNA (tRNA) is found in the cytoplasm. It picks up particular amino acids from the vast numbers that are always free there and carries them to the ribosome where they are joined to form a protein. Each amino acid has its own specific tRNA molecule. tRNA molecules have a structure closely related to their function, as figure 1.3.9 shows.

Ribosomal RNA

Ribosomal RNA (rRNA) makes up about 50% of the structure of a ribosome and it is the most common form of RNA found in cells. It is made in the nucleus, under the control of the nucleoli, and then moves out into the cytoplasm where it binds with proteins to form ribosomes. The ribosomes are made up of a large and a small subunit. They surround those parts of the mRNA which are being used to make a protein, and then move along to the next part of the mRNA. Their job is to hold together the mRNA, the tRNA and the enzymes controlling the process of protein synthesis.

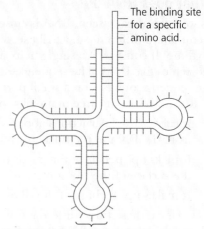

The binding site for a specific amino acid.

The anticodon - these three bases determine which piece of mRNA the tRNA will join to. This in turn decides the exact order of the amino acids in the resulting polypeptide chain.

Figure 1.3.9 There are almost 60 different tRNA molecules found in the cytoplasm of cells – more than enough to carry all the necessary amino acids to the surface of the ribosomes ready for synthesis into protein molecules.

Protein synthesis – what happens?

The genetic code of the DNA of the nucleus is transcribed onto messenger RNA. This mRNA moves out of the nucleus into the cytoplasm and becomes attached to a ribosome. Molecules of tRNA carry individual amino acids to the surface of the ribosome. tRNA molecules complementary to the codons in the mRNA strand line up, and enzymes link the amino acids together. This process is called **translation**. Its job done, the individual tRNA molecules return to the cytoplasm to pick up another amino acid. The ribosome moves along the molecule of mRNA until the end is reached, leaving a completed polypeptide chain. The process is illustrated in figure 1.3.10. The message may be read repeatedly to make many strands of the same polypeptide.

Protein synthesis, like many other events in living things, is a continual process. However, it makes it simpler to understand if we look at the two main aspects of it separately. The events in the nucleus involve the *transcription* of the DNA message onto the mRNA molecule. In the cytoplasm that message is *translated* into polypeptide molecules and hence into proteins.

Mass production

A common sight within the cytoplasm of cells are **polysomes**. These are groups of ribosomes joined by a thread of mRNA, and they appear to be a form of mass production of particular proteins. Instead of one ribosome moving steadily along a strand of mRNA to produce its polypeptide and then repeating the process, ribosomes attach in a steady stream to the mRNA and move along one after the other producing lots of identical polypeptides.

Mutation

Thus the genetic code carried on the DNA is translated into living cellular material by the synthesis of proteins. The nucleic acids are vital to the process,

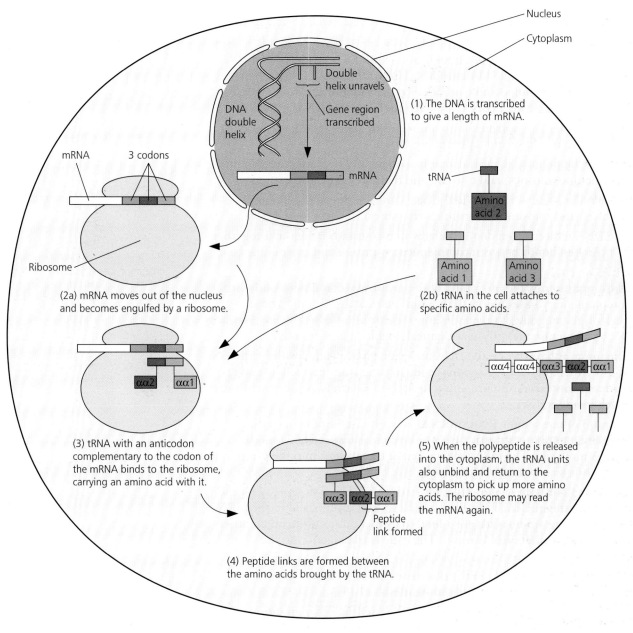

Nucleus

Cytoplasm

Double helix unravels

DNA double helix

Gene region transcribed

(1) The DNA is transcribed to give a length of mRNA.

mRNA

3 codons

mRNA

Ribosome

(2a) mRNA moves out of the nucleus and becomes engulfed by a ribosome.

tRNA

Amino acid 2

Amino acid 1

Amino acid 3

(2b) tRNA in the cell attaches to specific amino acids.

αα2   αα1

(3) tRNA with an anticodon complementary to the codon of the mRNA binds to the ribosome, carrying an amino acid with it.

αα4 αα4 αα3 αα2 αα1

αα3 αα2 αα1

Peptide link formed

(4) Peptide links are formed between the amino acids brought by the tRNA.

(5) When the polypeptide is released into the cytoplasm, the tRNA units also unbind and return to the cytoplasm to pick up more amino acids. The ribosome may read the mRNA again.

Figure 1.3.10 The stages of protein synthesis.

as both the carriers and the translators of the genetic code. If a single codon is changed by a mutation, then the likelihood is that it will code for a different amino acid, so the whole polypeptide chain and indeed the final protein will be altered. Such a tiny alteration at this molecular level may have no noticeable effect at all, but equally it can have devastating effects on the whole organism. Examples include some human genetic diseases where the blood proteins are not manufactured correctly or where certain enzymes do not function properly. Yet when the complexity of the process is considered, it is perhaps surprising that it does not go wrong more often. The precision of the various stages and of the enzymes such as DNA polymerase associated with them, the unvarying association of the base pairs with each other and the degenerate nature of the triplet code are just some of the factors which ensure that for most organisms, most of the time, the genetic messages in DNA are faithfully converted into the systems of life through the mechanism of protein synthesis.

SUMMARY

- All cell processes including cell replication and the reproduction of individuals are controlled by enzymes. The synthesis of these protein enzymes is determined and controlled by the **nucleic acids**: **deoxyribonucleic acid** (**DNA**) and **ribonucleic acid** (**RNA**).

- DNA and RNA are polymers with a **nucleotide** monomer made up of a pentose sugar, a base and a phosphate group.

- In DNA the pentose sugar is deoxyribose acid and the bases are adenine and guanine (purines) and cytosine and thymine (pyrimidines).

- In RNA the sugar is ribose and the bases are adenine and guanine (purines) and cytosine and uracil (pyrimidines).

- The DNA molecule is a double helix with two strands being held together by hydrogen bonds between complementary purine and pyrimidine base pairs.

- DNA replicates by the unzipping of the two strands, and nucleotides with complementary bases pair with those in the existing strands. These nucleotides are joined by condensation reactions catalysed by the enzyme DNA polymerase and two new identical double helices result.

- The order of bases along the DNA molecule gives a code for the synthesis of proteins. Three bases (a **codon**) code for one amino acid. The code is read and converted into proteins in a process known as **protein synthesis** which involves RNA.

- A strand of **messenger RNA** (**mRNA**) is synthesised in the nucleus, complementary to a strand of DNA. The code is **transcribed** onto the mRNA molecule. The mRNA passes out of the nucleus into the cytoplasm and onto a ribosome.

- **Transfer RNA** (**tRNA**) molecules have triplets of bases that pair with the codons on the mRNA. They each carry a specific amino acid to the mRNA molecule. The amino acids are joined to form a polypeptide, in an order determined by the mRNA strand. The code is **translated** into the polypeptide.

- **Ribosomal RNA** (**rRNA**) in the ribosomes holds together the mRNA, tRNA and enzymes during protein synthesis.

- A change in a base along the DNA or rRNA molecule is a **mutation**. This may lead to a change in an amino acid in the polypeptide chain.

QUESTIONS

1 DNA and RNA are the information molecules of the cell. Explain clearly the differences in the basic structure of these two molecules.

2 **a** How does DNA replicate?
   b What is the evidence for this?

3 The genetic code is said to be a *triplet code*. What does this mean and why is it important?

4 The DNA is contained within the nucleus of a eukaryotic cell. The proteins for which it codes are needed within the cytoplasm. Explain the roles of the following in the translation of the genetic code into an active enzyme in the cytoplasm.
   a DNA
   b messenger RNA
   c transfer RNA
   d ribosomal RNA
   e polysomes

FOCUS DEADLY HELPERS

The membrane of a cell is its gateway to the world, the route through which everything moves to get into or out of the cell contents. The make-up of this vital membrane is very complex, with many different receptor sites and carrier molecules embedded within the structure. These make sure that only those molecules that are required by the cell get into it, and only those molecules that the cell needs to remove are allowed out. However, in the natural world there are many 'clever chemists' – animals and plants producing poisons that block receptors or fool carrier molecules, causing distress, paralysis or death in their victims. Human biochemists are taking the game one step further, and using these poisons from living organisms to produce drugs which might save human lives.

Figure 1 This deadly South American poison arrow frog may provide a source of pain relief.

Frogs and scorpions ...

The brightly coloured South American poison arrow frogs produce a deadly poison on their skin as a defence. For generations, local people have used this poison to tip their arrows and kill their prey. Now scientists have discovered that the poison contains a molecule which stimulates receptors in the neurones, providing pain relief which is more effective than morphine, and is not addictive. A synthetic version of the poison molecule, hopefully free from side-effects, is undergoing clinical trials.

The human immune system works to protect us from disease, but sometimes we need to suppress its activity, for example, following a transplant operation. Scientists have shown that blocking potassium channels in the membranes of certain cells suppresses the immune system. However, all the chemicals they tried that blocked these channels also caused side-effects such as convulsions. Then researchers found that a small polypeptide in the venom of the Costa Rican scorpion blocked exactly the right potassium channels, and so new immunosuppressant drugs are being developed based on scorpion venom.

... snails and spiders

Marine snails of the genus *Conus* produce a venom which contains a whole range of toxic molecules. One of these toxins has been shown to block receptor molecules on the nerve endings particularly associated with pain. Scientists are producing modified versions of some of the poison molecules released by marine snails in the hope of producing a drug to control the severe pain of some cancer and AIDS patients.

Figure 2 A protein molecule taken from the venom of the Chilean pink tarantula seems to prevent the inflow of calcium to damaged nerve cells. Following a stroke, this protein protects the patient from death or brain damage until the blood flow is restored.

Cellular processes

You now have a picture of the basic make-up of the cells and major groups of chemicals found in living things. The next stage is to consider how these different elements interact in the processes of cellular life.

But before moving on, there is one other chemical which needs careful consideration. Water makes up the largest proportion of all cells – in fact your body mass is at least 60% water. It is a molecule of enormous biological importance which has many vital roles.

Water, water everywhere ...

Around two-thirds of the surface of the Earth is covered by water. It is believed that the conditions for the beginnings of life developed in the oceans many millions of years ago, and that much of the subsequent evolutionary process took place in water. In fact, each cell can be regarded as a membrane-bound drop of the primaeval broth of those early seas.

Even those species which dwell completely on the land need a water-based environment both for their reproductive cells and for the development of embryos. This environment is provided by the eggs of reptiles and birds, and in the more complex reproductive arrangements of the mammals.

Water is the medium in which the chemicals of life are dissolved, and in which all the reactions in living cells take place. It is the basis of the transport systems found in most complex organisms. It is one of the reactants in the process of photosynthesis, on which all life depends. And water is a major habitat – it supports more life than any other area of the planet.

The chemistry of water

The ability of water to play its wide variety of roles, and the reason for its importance in biological systems, is due to the basic chemistry of the molecule. The simple chemical formula of water is H_2O, which tells us that two atoms of hydrogen are joined to one atom of oxygen to make up each water molecule, as figure 1.4.1 shows.

The water molecule is slightly polarised. This means it has a very slightly *negative* end – the oxygen atom – and a very slightly *positive* end – the hydrogen atoms. This separation of electrical charge is called a **dipole**,

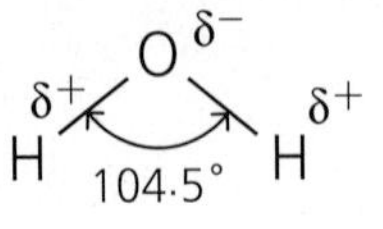

Figure 1.4.1 The water molecule.

and the tiny charges (represented as δ+ and δ–) give the water molecule its very important properties. One of the most important results of this charge separation is the tendency of water molecules to form **hydrogen bonds**, shown in figure 1.4.2.

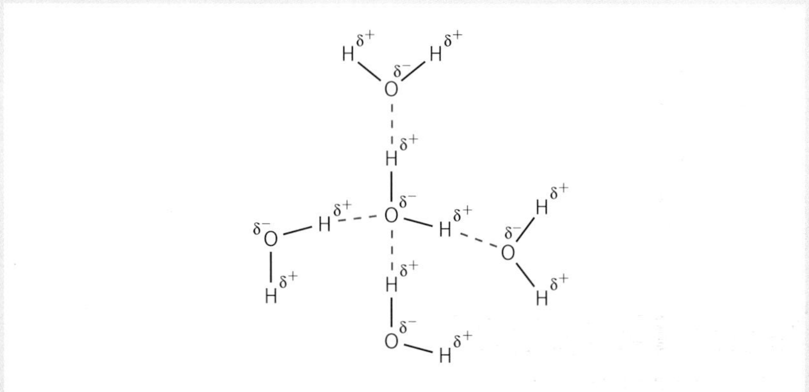

Figure 1.4.2 The slightly negative oxygen atoms attract the slightly positive hydrogen atoms of other water molecules and the weak electrostatic attraction between them is called a **hydrogen bond.** This means that the molecules of water 'stick together' more than might otherwise be expected, because although each individual hydrogen bond is weak, there are a great many of them. The ultimate effect of this is to give water particular properties which make it the perfect medium for life.

Why is water so important?

A variety of the properties of water are important in biological systems. Some of the most important ones are given here.

(1) An unusual and excellent solvent

Many other substances will dissolve in water. The fact that the water molecule has a dipole, with slightly positive and negative parts, means that **polar** substances with positive and negative regions, and particularly **ionic** substances such as sodium chloride (salt), made up of positive and negative ions, will dissociate (separate) and dissolve in water. Polar substances will not dissolve in organic solvents. Once the ions or polar molecules have dissolved in water they become surrounded by water molecules which keep them in solution, as figure 1.4.3 shows.

Water can also act as a solvent to many **non-polar** substances. As all the chemical reactions that go on within cells take place in aqueous solution, the ability of water to act as a solvent is vitally important for the processes of life.

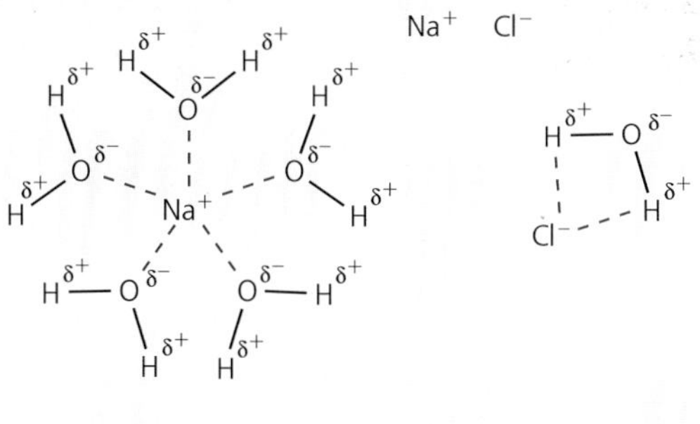

Figure 1.4.3 Once salt has dissolved, the ions become surrounded by water molecules which hold them in solution.

Does it dissolve in water?

You know that if you stir a spoonful of sugar crystals into water they disappear – they dissolve. The molecules of the sugar are **polar** – they have positive and negative regions. They become surrounded by the water molecules with their tiny dipoles and form a **true solution**. But not all substances dissolve completely in water like this. Some form **colloids**, whilst others exist as **suspensions**.

Colloidal solutions are formed when the solute particles are much bigger than those of the solvent, but they do not separate out under the influence of gravity – they are distributed evenly through the solvent. Many of the plasma proteins of the blood are in colloidal solution, and cannot pass through the capillary walls.

In **suspensions** the solute particles are so large that they separate out under the influence of gravity unless the suspension is constantly moved and stirred. The blood itself also falls into this category – if it is left to stand the cells and platelets sink to the bottom.

(2) The change of density with temperature

As water cools to below 4 °C the molecules take on an arrangement which occupies more space than the arrangement at room temperature. When freezing takes place at 0 °C, this new arrangement becomes rigid, so *ice is less dense than liquid water*. This makes water unique. The fact that ice floats on water means that living things can survive in ponds and rivers when the temperatures fall below freezing. The ice acts as an insulating layer, helping to prevent the rest of the water mass below from freezing. If ice formed from the bottom up, freshwater life would only be found in those areas where the water never freezes. Ice also thaws quickly because it is at the top, nearest to the warming effect of the sun.

(3) Slow to absorb and release heat

The **specific heat capacity** of a substance is a measure of the amount of energy needed to raise the temperature of a fixed amount of that substance by 1 °C. The specific heat capacity of water is high – it takes a lot of energy to warm it up. This makes water, particularly large bodies of water like lakes, seas and oceans, a thermally stable environment. Therefore the very wide variety of aquatic organisms do not have to contend with their surroundings getting quickly hotter or colder depending on the weather. This thermal stability is also seen within the water-based protoplasm of individual cells, and allows the biochemistry of life to be carried out at fairly constant rates.

(4) Taking large amounts of energy to turn from a liquid to a gas and from a solid to a liquid

The **latent heat of vaporisation** is a measure of the energy needed to overcome the attractive forces between the molecules of a liquid and turn it into a gas. For water the amount of energy needed for this is very high, because the hydrogen bonds holding the molecules together have to be broken before it can become a gas. Although each hydrogen bond is very weak, there are a great number of them. There are two major values of this to biological systems. One is that there is a large amount of water left on the surface of the Earth – it does not all vaporise and disappear into the atmosphere. The other is that the evaporation of water uses up a large amount of heat energy, and so can be put to good use as a cooling mechanism. The sweating mechanism of the mammals has capitalised on this particularly.

The **latent heat of fusion** of water is also high – it takes a great deal of energy to melt ice. Conversely, water needs to lose a lot of energy to form ice. This means that, in most circumstances, the contents of cells are unlikely to freeze. This is very important because the formation of ice in cells, with the accompanying increase in volume, is almost always damaging if not fatal.

(5) A high surface tension

The hydrogen bonds between water molecules tend to pull them down and together where water and air meet, giving water one of the highest known surface tensions, illustrated in figure 1.4.4.

(6) An amphoteric molecule

The water molecule is **amphoteric** – it acts as both an acid and a base. An acid gives up (donates) electrons to form H^+ ions. An alkali gains (receives) electrons to form OH^- ions. Water molecules can do both, as the following reaction shows:

$$2H_2O \rightarrow H_3O^+ + OH^-$$

Figure 1.4.4 Surface tension is of great importance in plant transport systems, and also affects life at the surface of ponds, lakes and other water masses.

This ability of water molecules to both donate and receive electrons means that it is the perfect medium for the biochemical reactions occurring in cells. It acts as a **buffer**. A buffer helps to prevent changes in the pH of a solution when an acid or an alkali is added, by neutralising any excess H^+ or OH^- ions that are introduced. Thus the water in cells minimises any changes in pH which might result from products of reactions in progress, and so prevents any interference with the smooth running of the metabolism.

Figure 1.4.5 The fox needs water to drink, and the stable cellular environment of all these living things depends on the unique chemistry of water. Its 'skin' supports the pondskater and water makes possible the transport systems and photosynthesis of plants.

Armed with an understanding of the unique role of water in biological systems, we can now begin to consider the most basic processes of life. A vital step in the beginning of life was the evolution of the **cell membrane**. The processes of life are closely bound up with the structure of the membranes of the cell, so this is where we shall begin.

Cell membranes

The functions of membranes

Membranes are ubiquitous in cells. The cell surface membrane acts as the boundary of the cell – anything that enters or leaves the cell must pass through it. If there was no barrier between the contents of a cell and its surrounding medium, there would obviously be no difference between the cytoplasm and the medium. Equally, if the cell surface membrane was completely permeable to all the molecules and ions in the external medium, the chemical make-up of the cytoplasm would be the same as that of its surroundings. But in fact the make-up of the cytoplasm of a cell is very different from the constituents of the surrounding fluid. This is a clear indication that the cell surface membrane controls and regulates what gets into and out of the cell. This is the most important function of membranes. Both polar and non-polar substances must have access to the cell, and the entry and exit of substances from specialised membrane-bound areas of the cell such as the nucleus, mitochondria and chloroplasts must be controlled.

Membranes perform many other functions too. Cells, even plant cells, are not rigid structures. A cell may need to change shape very slightly as the water content changes, or it may need to change shape quite dramatically as when a single-celled organism finds and engulfs food. The membrane must be flexible enough to allow this to happen. We have seen that chemical secretions made by the cell are packaged into vesicles, so the membrane must be capable of breaking and fusing readily.

How does the structure of the membrane allow it to perform these various functions?

The structure of the membrane

It has taken a number of years of research to arrive at our current model of the structure of cell membranes. In time there may well be further refinements, but the overall picture seems unlikely to change dramatically. The membrane is made up of two main types of molecules – **lipids** and **proteins** – arranged in a very specific way.

The lipid part

The lipids are of a particular type called **polar lipids**. These are lipid molecules with one end joined to a polar group. The phospholipids, already met on page 22, are a good example with a phosphate group as the polar part.

When polar lipids come into contact with water, the two parts of the molecule behave differently. As we have seen, the polar area is **hydrophilic** (water-loving) and is attracted to the water. The lipid tails are **hydrophobic** (water-hating) and move away from the water. If the molecules are tightly packed this gives a **monolayer** as shown in figure 1.4.6.

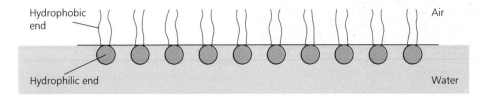

Hydrophobic end

Air

Hydrophilic end

Water

Figure 1.4.6 Polar lipids form a monolayer at an air–water interface.

However, a surface between air and water is a fairly rare situation in living cells. Much more usually the environment is entirely water based, and in that situation a **bilayer** is formed by the lipid molecules with the hydrophilic heads pointing out into the water while the hydrophobic tails are together in the middle. This structure, shown in figure 1.4.7, is the basis of the cell surface membrane or **unit membrane**.

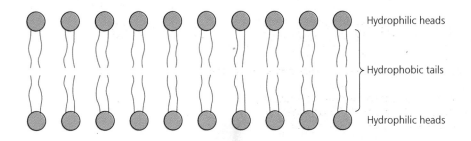

Hydrophilic heads

Hydrophobic tails

Hydrophilic heads

Figure 1.4.7 This bilayer structure forms the backbone of the cell membrane.

A lipid bilayer alone would allow the passage of organic molecules which are fat soluble, but there are many ionic chemicals needed in cells. Ionic compounds dissolve in water but cannot dissolve in or pass through lipid. This, and the microscopic appearance of the cell membrane, is explained by the presence of proteins in the bilayer.

The protein part

The unit membrane is regarded as a fluid lipid system, with protein parts floating within it like icebergs. This is called the **fluid mosaic model** of the membrane. Generally the proteins have a hydrophobic part which is buried in the lipid bilayer and a hydrophilic part which can be involved in a variety of activities. Some of these proteins travel about freely, others are fixed in place. Some of them penetrate all the way through the lipid, others only part of the way. Thousands of different proteins have been found associated with the membrane. What do they do?

One of the main functions of the membrane proteins is to let substances into and out of the cell. They form **pores** – some permanent, some temporary – which allow different molecules and ions to pass in or out. Some protein pores are **active carrier systems** – they use up energy to move materials into or out of cells. Others are simply gaps in the lipid layer which give access to ionic substances in particular. Figure 1.4.8 shows the routes for substances through the membrane.

Some proteins are not pores but can act as specific receptor molecules, for example, making cells sensitive to a particular hormone. Others act as enzymes, particularly on the internal cell membranes. Still other proteins are

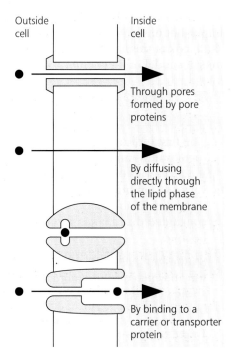

Figure 1.4.8 Three of the main routes through the membrane.

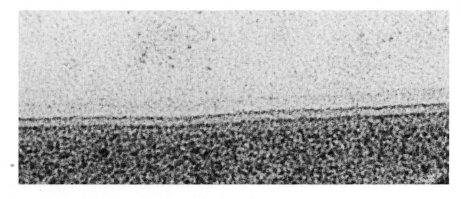

Transmission electron micrograph showing the two layers of the membrane

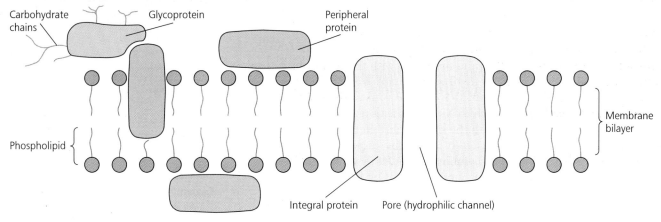

Figure 1.4.9 Whether acting as the boundary of a cell or as a major element of its internal make-up, the complex structure of the membrane is closely linked to its wide variety of functions. This model of the floating proteins in a lipid sea is known as the fluid mosaic model and was first proposed by Jonathon Singer and Garth Nicholson.

glycoproteins, with a carbohydrate part added to the molecule. These are very important on the surface of cells as part of the cell recognition set-up and we shall look at them in more detail in section 1.6. Figure 1.4.9 shows the fluid mosaic model of the membrane.

Where does our picture of the membrane come from?

The first indications that lipids are important components of cell surface membranes came at the end of the nineteenth century when E. Overton made a series of observations on how easily substances passed through various membranes. As a result of these observations, along with the fact that lipid-soluble substances enter cells more easily than any others, he concluded that a large part of the cell surface membrane structure must be lipid.

Studies on the behaviour of membranes when cells join together, and the way in which most membranes seal themselves if they are punctured with a fine needle, led to the idea that cell membranes are not rigid structures but are much more like a fluid.

In the early twentieth century I. Langmuir demonstrated the lipid monolayer we have mentioned, and developed equipment for collecting lipid monolayers, known as the Langmuir trough.

In 1925 two Dutch scientists, Gorter and Grendel, set out to measure the total monolayer film size of lipids extracted from human red blood cells (erythrocytes). They estimated the total surface area of an erythrocyte and found that the area of monolayer they measured was about twice the estimated area. As a result they concluded that the cell membrane was in fact a lipid bilayer. We now know that their results were wrong on two counts – they did not extract all the membrane, and they miscalculated the surface area of the erythrocytes, thinking they were discs rather than biconcave. In spite of this, their conclusions were correct – by an amazing coincidence the two errors cancelled each other out!

By 1935 H. Davson and J. F. Danielli had produced a further model of the membrane which is broadly the basis of our current ideas. They suggested a membrane with a lipid centre coated on each side by protein.

This hypothesis was backed up in the 1950s by electron microscope work by J. D. Robertson. He found ways of staining the membrane which showed it up as a three-layered structure – two distinct lines with a gap in the middle. When the membrane was treated with propanone to extract the lipid, the two lines remained intact, suggesting that these were the protein layers and that they played an important role.

More recently still, techniques such as X-ray diffraction and freeze-etching, which allows us to see both the surface and the inside of the membrane structure, have been used to add to our knowledge of the structure of cell membranes. The combination of all this work and thought resulted in the fluid mosaic model devised by J. Singer and G. Nicholson of a lipid sea with many and various proteins floating in and on it, a structure which is compatible with the enormous variety of functions associated with this ubiquitous organelle.

Figure 1.4.10 New techniques like freeze-etched electron microscopy have helped to unlock the secrets of cell structure. This technique allows us to visualise clearly the pores in the nuclear membrane, as shown above.

Diffusion

In physical terms, diffusion is the movement of the molecules of a liquid or gas from an area where they are more highly concentrated to an area where they are at a lower concentration. They move along a **concentration gradient**. This occurs because of the random motion of molecules – the more tightly packed they are, the more likely they are to move apart. The end result of diffusion is a uniform concentration of the molecules. Although the molecules do not stop moving once they reach a uniform concentration, the movement no longer causes a change in concentration. Figure 1.4.11 illustrates the process of diffusion.

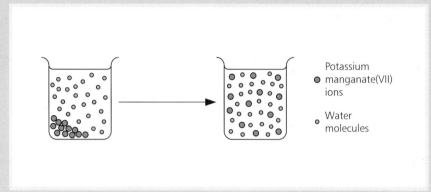

Potassium manganate(VII) ions

Water molecules

Figure 1.4.11 If the beaker is left to stand, the random motion of both the water and the manganate (VII) ions will ensure that they are eventually evenly mixed. In the real world, a state of equilibrium is rarely reached because other events intervene. For example, particles of blood spread through the water by diffusion will soon be sensed by a shark and act as a signpost to the potential prey.

Diffusion and osmosis

How does the membrane exercise its control over the passage of substances into and out of the cell?

Some substances, particularly those which dissolve very easily in lipids, simply pass through the membrane as though it was not there. Other very small molecules, water in particular, seem to pass freely in and out of cells through minute hydrophilic pores in the membrane. In both these cases the molecules move by **diffusion**.

Osmosis – a special case of diffusion

Diffusion takes place when there is no barrier to the free movement of molecules or ions. Water molecules have complete access to the cytoplasm of the cell through the membrane. This means that as a result of random motion, the water molecules will tend to move into or out of the cell along a concentration gradient.

The situation becomes more complicated when other substances are also considered, because although water can move freely across the membrane of a cell, other substances cannot. The membrane is **partially permeable**. Some molecules cannot cross the membrane, others can but only slowly, some move quite rapidly and some (like water) enter freely.

We can make a model of this situation using an artificial membrane which is permeable to some molecules – in particular water – and impermeable to others such as sucrose. There are many experiments which show the movement of water in these circumstances, and one of the simplest is illustrated in figure 1.4.12.

Fick's law

A number of factors affect the rate at which diffusion takes place across a membrane. These include:

- the surface area available for diffusion. The bigger the surface area, the higher the rate of diffusion, so folded membranes with very large surface areas allow diffusion to take place quickly.
- the concentration gradient of the substance diffusing. The bigger the difference in concentration on each side of the membrane, the faster diffusion occurs. Maintaining the gradient, for example by transporting substances away once they have diffused, allows rapid diffusion to continue.
- the size of the particles. Smaller particles diffuse faster than bigger particles, and there is a limit to the size of particles that can pass through the membrane. Very large particles cannot pass through at all.
- the distance over which diffusion is taking place – the thickness of the membrane.

We can use this information to calculate the rate at which substances of a given particle size will diffuse at a given temperature. This relationship is known as **Fick's law**:

$$\text{Rate of diffusion} = \frac{\text{surface area} \times \text{concentration difference}}{\text{thickness of membrane}}$$

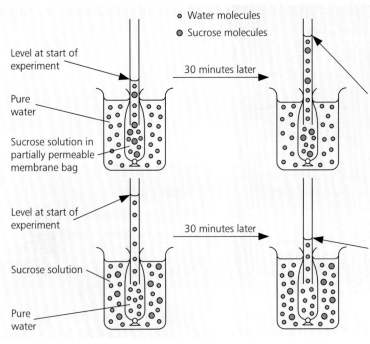

Water molecules
Sucrose molecules

Level at start of experiment

30 minutes later

Pure water

Sucrose solution in partially permeable membrane bag

Random motion of the water molecules leads to a net movement of water *into* the membrane bag along the concentration gradient of water molecules. Random motion of the sucrose molecules would lead to a movement of sucrose molecules *out of* the bag along the concentration gradient of sucrose molecules if the bag was freely permeable. This cannot happen because the pores in the membrane are too small to allow sucrose molecules through, so the sucrose stays inside the bag and water continues to move in, causing the level in the capillary tubing to rise.

Level at start of experiment

30 minutes later

Sucrose solution

Pure water

Random motion of the water molecules leads to a net movement of water *out of* the bag along the concentration gradient of the water molecules. Sucrose molecules cannot cross the membrane and so stay in the external solution. As a result the water level in the tubing falls.

Figure 1.4.12 When water is moving freely across a membrane through which the other molecules involved cannot move, we say that the water is moving by **osmosis**.

This simple model of osmosis gives us a picture of what is happening in a cell. The cell membrane is partially permeable. If the solution bathing the cell has a *lower* concentration of dissolved substances (**solutes**) than the solution inside the cell, there will be a concentration gradient of water molecules *into* the cell. If the opposite is true and the solution bathing the cell has a *higher* concentration of solutes than the cell contents, water will move *out* of the cell. In the context of living cells, the movement of water by osmosis and its control is very important. In animal cells in particular, it is vital that water does not simply move continually into the cells along a concentration gradient, because the cells would eventually swell up and burst.

Terms of osmosis

Osmosis may be defined as the net movement of solvent molecules from a region where they are at a higher concentration to a region where they are at a lower concentration *through a partially permeable membrane*.

When describing osmosis, certain terms are commonly used. These include:

- **Solvent** – the substance in which molecules or ions of other chemicals are dissolved. The only solvent in living systems is water.
- **Solute** – the chemical dissolved in a solvent. (For example, in a salt solution, water is the solvent and salt ions are the solute.)
- **Partially permeable membrane** – a membrane which allows solvent molecules to pass through it freely, and some other molecules to pass through as well, although in a selective way.
- **Osmotic concentration** – the concentration of a solution, taking into account only those dissolved substances which have an osmotic effect. Many large molecules found in the cytoplasm do not affect the movement of water and so are ignored when calculating osmotic concentration.

- **Isosmotic** – solutions with the same osmotic concentration. There would be no net movement of water between two isosmotic solutions separated by a partially permeable membrane.
- **Osmotic pressure** – if a solution is separated from pure water by a partially permeable membrane, the osmotic pressure is the hydrostatic pressure which would have to be applied to prevent any movement of water across the membrane. It can only be measured in a special instrument called an osmometer and as such is not a very useful measure in itself.
- **Solute potential** – the potential of a solution to cause water movement into it across a partially permeable membrane as a result of dissolved solutes. As a solute is dissolved in water, in osmotic terms it effectively reduces the concentration of water molecules and so lowers the **water potential** (see box 'Terms of osmosis in living cells'). It is always given a negative sign, and is measured in kilopascals (kPa). The symbol for solute potential is Ψ_s.

Osmosis in living cells

It is most important to animal cells that the net movement of water in or out is kept to a minimum. The problems of too much water moving out of a cell, although not as dramatic as those associated with too much going in, are equally damaging to the organism. The cells shrivel and the concentrated cytoplasm loses its internal structure and ceases to function. This is called **plasmolysis**.

In plant cells the situation is rather different because of the presence of the cellulose cell wall. Although it is freely permeable, it exerts an inward pressure on the cell and so has an effect on osmosis. Think of a balloon. You can tell by looking at it how far it is blown up. Keep blowing it up and eventually it bursts. Now imagine fitting a balloon inside a shoe box, sealing down the lid and then blowing up the balloon. The balloon will inflate so far, but the point will come when you cannot force any more air into it because of the inward pressure of the walls of the box. The outward appearance of the box will be little altered whether the balloon is completely empty or fully inflated. This gives you some idea of the difference between animal and plant cells. The outer box represents the cellulose cell wall.

Terms of osmosis in living cells

Most work on osmosis in cells is done on plant cells. They are generally larger and easier to see with the light microscope than animal cells, and also changes are easier to see and measure than changes in animal cells. In order to consider osmosis in living cells, we need to introduce some more terms.

- **Water potential** – the potential for water to move *out* of a solution by osmosis. Water potential has the symbol Ψ. Pure water has the highest possible water potential. Water molecules will always move from pure water into any solution on the other side of a partially permeable membrane. This maximum water potential is given as zero. *All* solutions have a lower water potential than pure water, because their concentration of water molecules must obviously be lower than that in pure water, and so Ψ always has a negative value. Water always moves from a region of higher water potential to an area of lower water potential. This means we can redefine osmosis as:

The movement of water molecules from an area of higher water potential to an area of lower water potential through a partially permeable membrane.

In a plant cell the water potential is the result of two elements:

- **Solute potential** – the potential of a solution to cause water movement into it across a partially permeable membrane as a result of dissolved solutes. It reflects how much the solute molecules have lowered the water potential of the cell sap. But this alone does *not* give the water potential of the cell because another factor is involved.
- **Pressure potential** – the influx of water by osmosis into a plant cell immersed in pure water is affected by the inward pressure of the cell wall. As water moves into the cell, the vacuole expands and pushes out the protoplasm. This means an inward pressure is exerted by the cell wall as the cell contents expand and press outwards. (Think of the balloon in the box.) This pressure is known as the pressure potential. It is usually a positive figure and has the symbol Ψ_p.

During osmotic experiments cells are often immersed in solutions of varying concentrations. When working with animal cells, these have the following definitions:

- **Hypotonic solution** – a solution in which the osmotic concentration of solutes is lower than that in the cell.
- **Isotonic solution** – a solution in which the osmotic concentration of solutes is the same as that in the cell.
- **Hypertonic solution** – a solution in which the osmotic concentration of solutes is higher than that in the cell.

If the cytoplasm of a plant cell contains more solutes than the surrounding fluids, water will enter the cell by osmosis – but not indefinitely. The inward pressure of the cell wall builds up as the cytoplasm swells until the pressure cancels out the tendency for water molecules to move in by osmosis. At this point the cells are full and rigid, in a state known as **turgor**. This is the normal and desirable state for plant cells. Figure 1.4.13 shows osmotic effects in plant and animal cells.

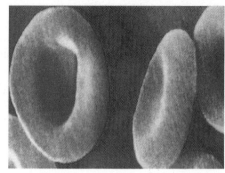
Normal red blood cells in isotonic solution

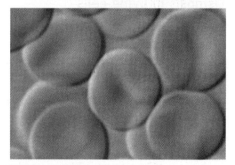
Red blood cells in hypotonic solution

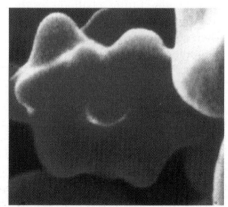
Red blood cells in hypertonic solution

Figure 1.4.13 The effects of osmosis on plant and animal cells. Remember that these situations are almost entirely confined to the laboratory – they do not usually happen in living animals and plants. Even when a plant wilts, for example, it is not because of plasmolysis but because the entire cells, wall and all, have shrunk due to lack of water. But seeing these extreme effects of osmosis helps us to understand why living things have so many complex systems designed to control their water balance.

Plant cells in a solution with a higher water potential than the cell sap – turgor

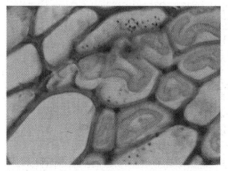
Plant cells in a solution with a lower water potential than the cell sap – plasmolysis

The water potential in a plant cell

The water relationships in a plant cell can be summed up using the ideas met so far. The water potential of a cell is the sum of the solute potential of the cell sap and the pressure potential of the cell wall. Thus:

Water potential = solute potential + pressure
of cell   of cell sap   potential
(Ψ, usually –ve)   (Ψ_s, always –ve)   (Ψ_p, usually +ve)

Combining the changes we can see in actual cells with the changes we know are occurring in Ψ, Ψ_s and Ψ_p, we can develop the picture shown in figure 1.4.14 of what happens when plant cells are immersed in different solutions.

Figure 1.4.14 The changes which take place in plant cells as they pass from full turgor to plasmolysis as a result of osmosis.

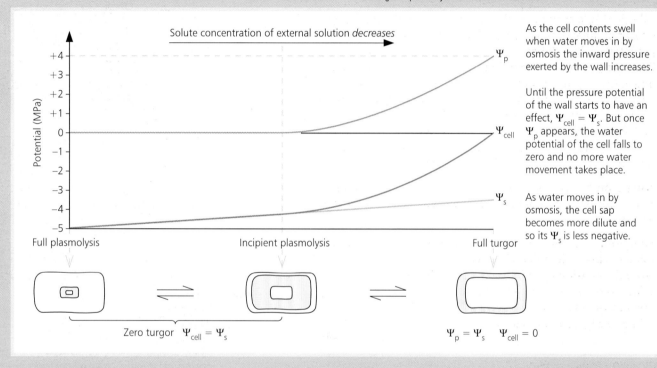

As the cell contents swell when water moves in by osmosis the inward pressure exerted by the wall increases.

Until the pressure potential of the wall starts to have an effect, $\Psi_{cell} = \Psi_s$. But once Ψ_p appears, the water potential of the cell falls to zero and no more water movement takes place.

As water moves in by osmosis, the cell sap becomes more dilute and so its Ψ_s is less negative.

As we have seen, many of the substances which pass into and out of the cell are not lipid soluble and are too big to fit through the minute pores available to water. Also, water movement by osmosis depends largely on the relative concentrations of various solutes in the cytoplasm of the cells and in the surrounding fluids. Thus it is of prime importance that solutes can cross the cell surface membrane in the right proportions. This may at times even mean moving them *against* a concentration gradient – and through a system which is naturally impenetrable to ionic substances. How is all this made possible?

Membrane 'ferries'

In general, membranes are very specific about the substances which can cross them. Usually only water molecules have free access to cells along a concentration gradient. There seem to be two main ways in which other substances are transported across the cell membrane. Both involve membrane proteins. One does not use up energy and is called **facilitated diffusion**. The other needs energy supplied by the cell and is called **active transport**.

Facilitated diffusion

This depends on carrier molecules floating on the surface of the membrane – for example, red blood cells seem to have a carrier to help glucose move into the cells rapidly. The carriers are found on the *outside* surface of the membrane structure when a substance is to be moved *into* the cell or organelle, and on the *inside* for transport *out* of the cell. The protein carriers are specific for particular molecules or groups of molecules. Once they have picked up a substance they rotate through the membrane, carrying the new molecule with them. Once on the other side of the membrane, the carrier releases the substance. The movement through the membrane takes place because of the change in the shape of the carrier once it is carrying something. The process can only take place along a concentration gradient – from a higher to a lower concentration of a molecule. Facilitated diffusion simply helps diffusion to occur in a situation where it would otherwise be impossible because the molecule involved could not pass-through the cell membrane – it provides a route through the membrane for that molecule, as figure 1.4.15 illustrates.

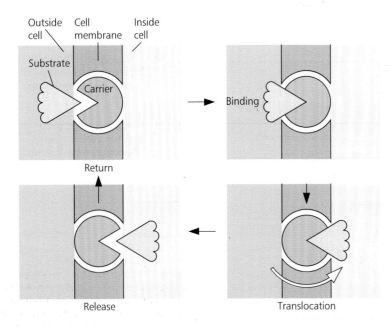

Figure 1.4.15 Facilitated diffusion acts as a ferry across the lipid membrane sea. But this is a boat with no oars, sail or engine – it can only work when the tide (the concentration gradient) is in the right direction.

Active transport

Diffusion and facilitated diffusion both rely on a concentration gradient in the right direction. But what happens if a chemical needs to be moved *against* a concentration gradient? This often happens, and cells have several ways of dealing with the problem.

One is simply to 'mop up' the chemical as soon as it arrives inside the cell, either by immediately starting to metabolise it or by using another carrier molecule to remove it from the pool of free ions and molecules. Another is to chemically change the molecule immediately it enters the cell. These two methods effectively change the concentration gradient so that the substance continues to move into the cell by diffusion. The third alternative is to use a transport system which can move substances *against* a concentration gradient. To do this needs energy, and so the process is known as **active transport**.

The transport of the molecule needed by the cell is linked with that of another particle – often a sodium ion. One of the best known examples of active transport is the **sodium pump** found in the membranes of nerve cells, amongst others. This pump actively moves potassium ions into the cell and sodium ions out. As we shall see in section 4, this is vital for the working of the nervous system.

The carrier often spans the whole membrane, as figure 1.4.16 shows. It may be very specific, only picking up one type of ion or molecule, or it may work for several relatively similar substances. In this case, the particles have to compete with each other for a place on the carrier, so the one which is present in the highest concentration usually wins.

The energy needs of the cell are met by the molecule **ATP** or **adenosine triphosphate**. This is explained more fully in section 3.1. The carrier system in the membrane involves the enzyme **ATPase** which breaks down a molecule of ATP into **ADP** or **adenosine diphosphate**. This breakdown releases energy which is used to move a substance against a concentration gradient. The energy may be used to move the carrier system in the membrane or to release the transported substances and return the system to normal. Active transport is a one-way system, so that substances are only moved in the direction required by the cell – they cannot move back down the concentration gradient which has just been overcome.

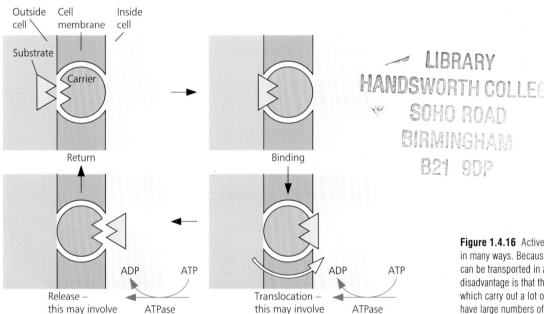

Figure 1.4.16 Active transport – a far superior 'ferry' in many ways. Because it has its own power, molecules can be transported in any direction at any time. The only disadvantage is that the energy must be provided – cells which carry out a lot of active transport generally also have large numbers of mitochondria.

Evidence for active transport

Active transport requires energy in the form of energy-rich ATP. This is produced in the process of cellular respiration, as explained in section 3.4. Much of the evidence for *active* transport is concerned with linking these two processes together, showing that without ATP active transport cannot take place:

(1) Active transport only takes place in living, respiring cells.
(2) The rate of active transport is affected by temperature and oxygen concentration. These also have a big impact on the rate of respiration and so on the production of ATP.
(3) Many cells known to carry out a lot of active transport contain very large numbers of mitochondria – the sites of cellular respiration and ATP production.
(4) Poisons which stop respiration or prevent ATPase from working also stop active transport. For example, cyanide inhibits ATP production. It also stops active transport. However, if ATP is added artificially, transport starts again.

The combination of diffusion, facilitated diffusion and active transport means that the cell surface membrane acts as an excellent 'barrier' between the contents of the cell and its surroundings. The concentrations of ions and molecules within the cell can be maintained at levels very different from those of the external fluids. Yet there is still communication between the two environments – materials can be exchanged between them in a variety of ways. The same role is performed by the internal cell membranes, providing a range of microenvironments within the cell, each suited to different functions and yet all in communication. The partially permeable nature of the cell membrane is a major contributor to the processes of life.

Cell 'eating' and 'drinking'

We have considered how the membrane allows ions and molecules to pass into and out of the cell. But there are times when larger particles need to enter or leave the cell. Millions of simple animals, along with cells in the bodies of most large multicellular creatures, need on occasion to take in large particles. White blood cells ingest bacteria, and amoebae engulf their prey. Membrane transport systems cannot do this type of job – but the membrane itself can.

Endocytosis and exocytosis

Endocytosis is the term used when materials are surrounded by and taken up into membrane-lined vesicles. This can occur at a relatively large scale, for example when bacteria are ingested. In this case it is called **phagocytosis** – 'cell eating'. Endocytosis also appears to happen at a microscopic level, when minute vacuoles taking in the external medium are formed. This is called **pinocytosis**. Recent work with the electron microscope shows that pinocytosis is very common, even in some mammalian cells.

Exocytosis is the term for the emptying of a membrane-lined vesicle at the surface of the cell or elsewhere. For example, in cells producing hormones, vesicles containing the hormone fuse with the cell surface membrane to release their contents.

Intake of materials – endocytosis
Large particles – phagocytosis
Liquids – pinocytosis

Outside cell

Vesicle within cell

Release of substances from vesicle – exocytosis

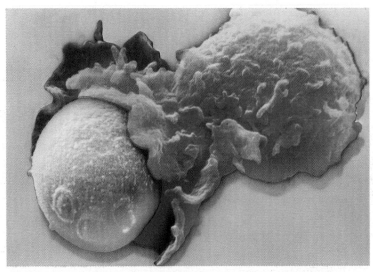

Figure 1.4.17 The properties of the membrane allow cells to take in large particles or release secretions. The scanning electron micrograph shows a lymphocyte engulfing a yeast cell.

These processes, about which you will find out more in later sections of the book, are made possible by the fluid mosaic nature of the membrane. It is capable of flowing around a particle, sealing up on the surface and fusing with internal membranes in ways in which a rigid structure could not do – another example of the way the structure of the membrane is intimately related to its functions.

SUMMARY

- Water is the medium in which all cellular reactions take place. Water has unique chemical properties, generally due to its ability to form hydrogen bonds between the slightly positive hydrogens and slightly negative oxygens of adjacent molecules:
  Water is a good solvent.
  Ice is less dense than liquid water.
  Water has a high specific heat capacity.
  Water has a high latent heat of vaporisation and a high latent heat of fusion.
  Water has a high surface tension.
  Water molecules are amphoteric.

- Cell surface membranes provide a **partially permeable** barrier between the cell contents and the external medium, allowing some materials to pass freely but not others.

- Cell surface membranes consist of a **phospholipid bilayer** with the hydrophilic ends of the molecules pointing outwards and the hydrophobic ends together in the centre. **Proteins** float in the lipid bilayer. This is the **fluid mosaic model**.

- **Diffusion** is the movement of a substance from an area of higher concentration to an area of lower concentration by random movement of the molecules or ions of the substance.

- **Osmosis** is the movement of water molecules from a region of higher concentration of water to a region of lower concentration through a partially permeable membrane.

- The **water potential** of a system is the difference between the potential of water in that system and the potential of pure water at the same temperature and pressure. Pure water has a water potential of zero, and all other water potentials have negative values. Water moves from a solution of higher water potential to an area of lower water potential.

- Osmosis in living systems is the movement of water from a region of higher water potential to a region of lower water potential.

- Water potential Ψ combines the effects of the **solute potential** Ψ_s (the osmotic effect of the solutes in the cell) and the **pressure potential** Ψ_p (the hydrostatic pressure, for example that exerted by the plant cell wall):

$$\Psi = \Psi_s + \Psi_p$$

- The proteins in cell surface membranes allow molecules other than water to cross the membrane through pores, by **facilitated diffusion** or by **active transport**.

- In **facilitated diffusion**, specific protein carriers pick up a molecule or ion. This changes the conformation of the protein and causes it to rotate through the membrane. It releases the molecule or ion on the inside of the cell. Facilitated diffusion takes place *along* a concentration gradient.

- **Active transport** moves molecules or ions through the cell surface membrane *against* a concentration gradient. The specific carrier protein picks up a molecule or ion and rotates, again releasing it on the other side. The process involves energy, which is provided by the conversion of **ATP** to **ADP**, catalysed by **ATPase**.

- **Endocytosis** is the taking up of materials in membrane-bound vesicles. **Phagocytosis** involves large vesicles, for example around a bacterium, and **pinocytosis** is on a smaller scale, taking in minute vacuoles of medium.

- **Exocytosis** is the emptying of a membrane-bound vesicle at the surface of the cell, as in secretions.

QUESTIONS

1 Water is a molecule of great biological importance. Explain why this is the case, using three of the main properties of water to illustrate your answer.

2 **a** Describe the fluid mosaic model of the structure of the cell membrane.
b How has the development of the electron microscope helped in the production of this model?

3 Osmosis is a physical process which has a great effect on the biology of both plants and animals. It occurs in cells as a result of the properties of the cell membrane.
a What is osmosis?
b How does osmosis affect animal cells?
c How does osmosis affect plant cells?

4 List, with a simple explanation, the main ways in which substances may be transported across the cell membrane.

Developing Key Skills

You have to design a poster which is to form part of a major display in the science labs explaining the impact of different drugs on the human body. Choose **either** cyanide **or** the new drug derived from Costa Rican scorpion venom described on the focus page at the beginning of this chapter. Using the example you have chosen, show how membrane transport works, how it can be affected by drugs and how this in turn can have a major effect on the whole body.

FOCUS INDUSTRY AND ENZYMES

Enzymes are biological catalysts. Unlike most inorganic catalysts, they work at low temperatures, normal pressures and in a very easily achieved range of temperature and pH. They have much to offer industry and their potential was recognised many years ago.

Dog's faeces and pigeon droppings

Leather has always been regarded as useful and important in Europe. However, the original process by which the hides were treated before tanning was particularly revolting as a mixture of dog faeces and pigeon droppings was rubbed into the hides to soften them. At the very end of the nineteenth century the distinguished German chemist Otto Rohm discovered that it was proteases (enzymes that break down protein) in the dog faeces that softened the leather. By 1905 he had developed a new process for softening the hides using proteases extracted from the pancreases of cows and pigs. He must have earned the undying gratitude of leather workers everywhere!

Figure 1 Being a leather worker in the nineteenth century must have been one of the worst available jobs!

Fast food

The food industry has traditionally made much use of enzyme technology. The enzyme rennin is used to clot milk in cheese-making, and enzymes from yeast have long been used in both the brewing and the baking industries. Cellulases and pectinases are used to clear hazes in fruit juice production. Newer applications of enzyme technology include the use of trypsin to pre-digest baby foods, proteases in biscuit manufacture to lower the protein content of the flour, and a variety of enzymes to make sweet syrups from starch.

Enzymes have wide applications in other industries too. They are used in detergents to digest particular types of dirt, particularly the protein elements of blood and sweat. Enzymes are also being developed that will nip off the 'pilling' – little bobbles that form on cotton and woollen clothing when they are washed – and leave the fabric smooth.

Enzymes in medicine

More and more enzymes are being put to use in medical fields, particularly in the area of diagnostic tests. Glucose oxidase is the enzyme found on the 'dip-sticks' used for testing urine to see if it contains glucose. The enzyme is present on the stick mixed with peroxidase and a blue dye. If there is no glucose in the urine then the dye stays blue. However, if there is glucose present the enzyme oxidises it, releasing hydrogen peroxide which in turn reacts with other chemicals present on the stick to turn the dye from blue to green to brown, depending on the glucose level. Enzyme-linked immunosorbent assays (ELISAs) are another enzyme-based technique used in medicine to detect antibodies to particular infections.

With improvements in technology and advances in genetic engineering making 'designer enzymes' possible, the use of enzymes in industry and medicine can only increase in the future. (There is much more about the use of enzymes in industry in section 7.)

Figure 2 The enzymes that attack protein dirt on clothes also attack people's skin. Before these tiny capsules were developed to contain the enzymes, many workers in detergent factories suffered from allergic reactions.

1.5 Enzymes

Inside every cell, hundreds of chemical reactions are occurring simultaneously on the complex infrastructure of the cytoplasm. In a science laboratory it is a matter of skill and coordination to produce the desired products from a single reaction. The process is usually relatively inefficient, with material wasted along the way and many attempts needed to produce the desired end products. How is the efficiency and control of living cells achieved?

Enzymes – the enablers

Under the conditions of temperature and pH found in living cells, the majority of the reactions needed to provide cells with energy and produce new biological material would naturally take place very slowly indeed – too slowly for life to exist. But within cells is a group of molecules which speed up chemical reactions without changing the conditions in the cytoplasm. These are the **enzymes**.

What is an enzyme?

An enzyme is a globular protein which speeds up one or more biological reactions. Within any cell a great range of chemical reactions is going on at any one time. Those reactions which build up new chemicals are known as **anabolic** reactions. Those which break substances down are **catabolic** reactions. The combination of these two processes results in the complex array of biochemistry which we call **metabolism**. Most of the reactions of metabolism occur not as single events but as part of a sequence of reactions known as a **metabolic chain** or **pathway**.

Anabolism + catabolism = metabolism

A **catalyst** is a substance which speeds up a reaction without changing the substances produced, and without itself being changed. Enzymes are powerful biological catalysts. Each enzyme will only catalyse a particular reaction or group of reactions – they show varying levels of **specificity**. For metabolism to proceed at an appropriate rate, every reaction needs catalysing. To achieve this each cell contains several hundred different enzymes controlling a multitude of reactions.

How do we know about enzymes?

In modern biology and medicine, knowledge of enzymes is very much taken for granted. But our present knowledge has developed over a long period of time, with much information being relatively new.

In 1835 it was noticed that the hydrolysis of starch was brought about more effectively by malt than by sulphuric acid. This suggested that there was a catalyst present in the living malt which was more effective than the inorganic acid. Also, for a long time it was suspected that there was a biological catalyst in yeast which brought about the fermentation of sugar to alcohol, though nobody could prove it. Initially called 'ferments', it was in 1877 that the name **enzyme** (literally 'in yeast') was first used for these theoretical chemicals.

1897 brought a major landmark in enzyme research. Eduard Buchner extracted from yeast cells the enzyme responsible for fermenting sugar, and showed it could work independently of the living cell structure.

The first pure, crystalline enzyme, extracted from jack beans, was produced in 1926 by J. Sumner. It was the enzyme urease, which catalyses the breakdown of urea. Sumner showed that the crystals were protein and concluded that enzymes must be proteins. Unfortunately no one believed him!

In 1930–36 the protein nature of enzymes was firmly established as the protein-digesting enzymes pepsin, trypsin and chymotrypsin were extracted from the gut and crystallised by J. Northrop.

Work has continued since then, with more and more enzymes being extracted and a variety of techniques being developed to look at their structure.

Name that enzyme

Most enzymes have several names:

- a relatively short **recommended** name, which is often the name of the **substrate** (the molecule that the enzyme works on) with '-ase' or 'kinase' added, for example sucrase, creatine kinase
- a longer **systematic** name describing the type of reaction which is being catalysed, for example ATP:creatine phosphotransferase

- a classification number, for example EC 2.7.3.2.

It is easy to tell what some enzymes do, such as urease, ribonuclease and lipase, from their recommended names. But some enzymes are still known by old and distinctly uninformative names, such as trypsin and pepsin.

How do enzymes speed up reactions?

To answer this question, we first need to understand what is happening in a chemical reaction. Reactions involve breaking and remaking chemical bonds. In order to react, molecules first need sufficient energy – they have to get over an 'energy hill', known as the **activation energy** for the reaction. Imagine pushing a large boulder up a steep hill. Once the boulder gets to the top (achieves activation energy), it will roll down the other side quite easily.

Increasing the temperature is one way of increasing the rate of chemical reaction. It increases the numbers of reactant molecules which have sufficient energy to react. However, living cells could not survive the high temperatures needed to speed up many cellular reactions to the required rate, and the energy demands needed to do this would be enormous. Instead, enzymes solve the problem by lowering the activation energy needed for a reaction to take place (they make the hill smaller). Figure 1.5.2 uses an energy diagram to show this.

Figure 1.5.1 The chemicals in the cardboard tube and the oxygen in the air form a potentially explosive mixture. But it is not until heat from the lighted fuse supplies the activation energy that the sparks begin to fly.

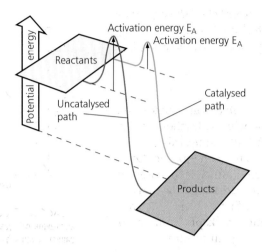

Activation energy E_A
Activation energy E_A

Reactants

Catalysed
path

Uncatalysed
path

Products

Figure 1.5.2 This energy diagram shows the difference in activation energy between a catalysed and an uncatalysed reaction.

Apart from speeding up reactions, enzymes have another important function. They control and regulate the sequences of reactions occurring in metabolic chains. We shall be returning to this later in this section.

The characteristics of enzymes

All enzymes share certain characteristics. By considering these in turn we can learn a great deal about how enzymes work.

1 All enzymes are *globular proteins*. Within these large molecules is found an **active site** which is the part responsible for the functioning of the enzyme. Anything which affects the three-dimensional shape of a protein molecule affects its ability to function.

2 Enzymes only change the *rate* of a reaction. They do not alter the end products that are formed, or affect the equilibrium of the reaction, that is, the ratio of reactants to products. This shows that they act purely as catalysts and not as modifying influences in any other way.

3 Enzymes are present in very small amounts. This reflects their great *efficiency as catalysts*. Minute amounts of enzymes can speed up reactions enormously. In order to explain this more fully, we need to introduce the idea of **molecular activity** or **turnover number**. This is a measure of the number of substrate molecules transformed per minute by a single enzyme molecule. The number of molecules of hydrogen peroxide broken down by the enzyme catalase in one minute is 6×10^6! A more usual turnover number would be thousands of molecules per minute rather than millions – catalase, extracted from liver cells, is the fastest known enzyme. It has been calculated that the enzyme urease can break down in one second an amount of urea that would hydrolyse spontaneously in 3 million years! Enzymes generally increase reaction rates by factors from 10^8 to 10^{26}.

4 Enzymes are *specific* to the reactions that they catalyse. They are unlike inorganic catalysts which can frequently be used to catalyse a wide range of reactions, although often at extremes of temperature and pressure. Some enzymes will only catalyse one particular reaction. Others are specific to a particular group of molecules of similar shape, or to a type of reaction which always involves the same groups. Many enzymes show great **stereospecificity** – they will only catalyse reactions involving either L- or D-isomers. This suggests that a site in the enzyme has a particular shape into which a specific substrate will fit.

Enzymes in and out of cells

Many of the enzymes found in animals and plants work inside the cells that make them, controlling all the reactions going on there. These are known as **intracellular enzymes**. However, some enzymes are secreted by cells to have their effect outside the boundaries of the cell membrane. These are **intercellular enzymes**.

5 Enzyme-catalysed reactions are affected by the *amount of substrate* which is present. Take a simple reaction in which the substrate A is converted to the product Z. If the concentration of A is gradually increased, the rate of the enzyme-catalysed reaction:

$$A \rightarrow Z$$

will increase – but only for so long. Then the enzyme becomes **saturated** and a further increase in substrate concentration will not further increase the rate of the reaction. The graph in figure 1.5.3 illustrates this. This observation reinforces the idea of an active site in an enzyme. Once all the available active sites are involved in the reaction, further increases in the concentration of substrate molecules will not increase the rate any further. (In rate experiments like this, every other factor – temperature, pressure, pH and the enzyme concentration – must be kept the same, so that any changes can only be the result of the change in substrate concentration.)

6 The rate of an enzyme-catalysed reaction is affected by *temperature* in a characteristic way. The effect of temperature on the rate of any reaction can be expressed as the temperature coefficient, Q_{10}. This is given as:

$$Q_{10} = \frac{\text{rate of reaction at } (x + 10)\,^{\circ}\text{C}}{\text{rate of reaction at } x\,^{\circ}\text{C}}$$

Between about 0 and 40 °C, Q_{10} for any reaction is 2. In other words, in that temperature range every 10 °C rise in temperature produces a doubling of the rate of reaction. Outside this range, however, Q_{10} for enzyme-catalysed reactions decreases markedly, whilst Q_{10} for other reactions remains relatively unchanged. The rate of enzyme-catalysed reactions falls and by about 60 °C the reaction has stopped completely in most cases, as figure 1.5.4 demonstrates.

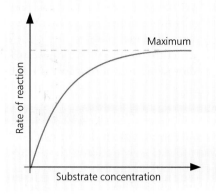

Figure 1.5.3 The effect of substrate concentration on an enzyme-catalysed reaction. The enzyme becomes saturated with substrate and the reaction rate levels off.

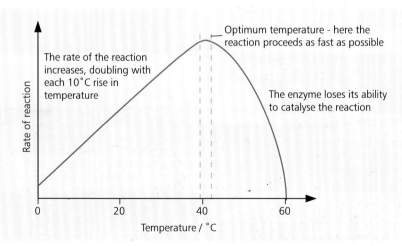

Figure 1.5.4 The effect of temperature on the rate of a typical enzyme-catalysed reaction. All factors other than temperature must be kept constant.

We know that at temperatures over 40 °C, most mammalian proteins lose their tertiary and quaternary structures – they unravel or **denature**. As enzymes denature, they lose their ability to catalyse reactions. This confirms our idea of an active site in the three-dimensional structure of the globular protein.

There are a few enzymes that do not denature at such low temperatures. The enzymes of thermophilic bacteria, found in hot springs at temperatures of up to 85 °C, can obviously function at higher temperatures. They are made of unusual temperature-resistant proteins.

7 pH has a major effect on enzyme activity. pH is known to affect the shapes of protein molecules as hydrogen bonds and sulphur bridges are broken or formed. This again confirms the importance of the three-dimensional structure. Different enzymes work in different ranges of pH, as figure 1.5.5 shows. pH may also affect the substrate molecule.

Enzyme mechanisms

We have seen a great deal of evidence suggesting that the function of an enzyme is closely tied in with its three-dimensional structure. Now we shall take a closer look at models for enzyme action, and also at more evidence to support the picture.

Enzymes catalyse reactions by lowering the activation energy for the reaction. To bring this about the enzyme forms a **complex** with the substrate or substrates of the reaction. Thus we have a simple picture of enzyme action:

Substrate + enzyme → enzyme/substrate complex → enzyme + products

Once the products of the reaction are formed they are released and the enzyme is free to form a new complex with another substrate molecule.

The lock and key mechanism

How does this relate to the structure of the enzyme? The basic picture is summed up in the **lock and key mechanism** shown in figure 1.5.6.

Induced fit

The lock and key mechanism fits most of our evidence about enzyme characteristics. It illustrates how enzymes can become saturated when the concentration of substrate molecules rises above a certain level. It also explains how any change in the protein structure, such as those brought about by changes in pH or temperature, could affect enzyme action by altering the shape of the active site.

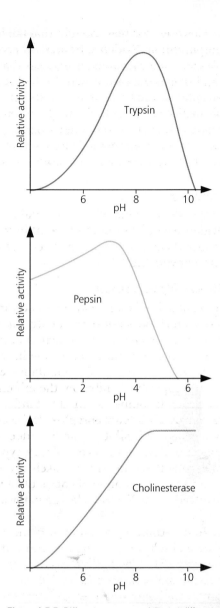

Figure 1.5.5 Different enzymes work best at different pHs. Again, all other factors must be kept constant. Interestingly, the optimum pH for an enzyme is not always the same as the pH of its normal surroundings. It is thought that cells may control the activity levels of their intracellular enzymes by minute changes in pH.

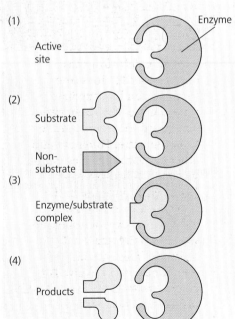

(1) Within the structure of each enzyme is an area known as the **active site**. It may involve only a small number of amino acids. It has a very specific shape, which gives each enzyme its specificity, as only one substrate or type of substrate will fit into the gap.

(2) Here we can see the difference between the shape of the enzyme substrate and another biological molecule. Only a molecule of the right shape can be a substrate for the enzyme.

(3) The enzyme and substrate slot together to form a complex, as a key fits into a lock. In this complex the substrate is enabled to react at a lower activation energy. This may be due to bonds within it being deformed and stressed in the complex, so making them more likely to react.

(4) Once the reaction has been catalysed, the products are no longer the right shape to stay in the active site and the complex breaks up, releasing the products and freeing the enzyme for further catalytic action.

Figure 1.5.6 The lock and key mechanism – the basis of our understanding of enzyme action.

However, it is now thought that the lock and key mechanism is a slight simplification. Evidence from X-ray crystallography, chemical analysis of active sites and other techniques suggests that the active sites of enzymes are not the rigid shapes once supposed. In the **induced fit theory**, which is generally accepted as the best current model, the active site is thought of as having a distinctive but flexible shape. Thus, once the substrate enters the active site, the shape of that site is modified around it to form the complex. Once the products have left the complex the enzyme reverts to its inactive, relaxed form until another substrate molecule binds, as illustrated in figure 1.5.7.

Inhibitors

Our understanding of enzymes and how they work can be increased by evidence gained from **enzyme inhibitors** which stop enzymes from working or reduce their catalytic power. There are two main types of inhibition, **reversible** and **irreversible**.

Reversible inhibition

Reversible inhibition of enzymes occurs when an inhibitor affects an enzyme in a way which does not permanently damage it, so that when the inhibitor is removed, the enzyme can function normally again. Reversible inhibition is quite a common feature of metabolic pathways, as we shall see. There are two major forms of reversible inhibition – **competitive** and **non-competitive**.

In competitive inhibition, the inhibitor is similar in shape to the substrate molecule. It competes with it to bind at the active site of the enzyme, forming an **enzyme/inhibitor complex**. If the amount of inhibitor is fixed, the percentage of inhibition can be reduced by increasing the substrate concentration. As the two molecule types are competing, the more substrate molecules there are, the less likely is it that inhibitor molecules will bind to the active site. An example of competitive inhibition is found in the enzymes involved in the Krebs cycle, the pathway for cellular respiration, described in section 3.4.

In non-competitive inhibition, the inhibitor may form a complex with the enzyme itself, with the enzyme/substrate complex or with a prosthetic group (see page 71). The inhibitor is not competing for the active site but joins to the enzyme molecule elsewhere. This is confirmed by the fact that the concentration of the substrate makes no difference to the level of inhibition – only the concentration of inhibitor affects that. What appears to happen in most cases is that the presence of the inhibitor on the enzyme or enzyme/substrate complex deforms the active site so that it can no longer catalyse the reaction.

Figure 1.5.8 shows the differences between competitive and non-competitive inhibition.

Irreversible inhibition

In irreversible inhibition the inhibitor combines with the enzyme by permanent covalent bonding to one of the catalytic groups. This changes the shape and structure of the molecule in such a way that it cannot be reversed – the enzyme is inactivated permanently. Irreversible inhibition tends to occur more slowly than other forms of inhibition, but its effects are much more devastating and it is never used within the cells to control metabolism. Arsenic, cyanide and mercury are poisonous because they exert irreversible inhibition on enzyme systems. Some of the nerve gases used in chemical warfare also work in this way. They combine with and completely inactivate acetylcholinesterase. The normal function of this enzyme is to destroy the neurotransmitter acetylcholine as soon

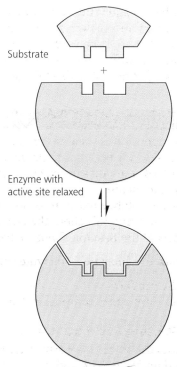

Substrate

+

Enzyme with active site relaxed

Enzyme/substrate complex showing the induced form of the active site, fitting snugly round the substrate

Figure 1.5.7 The induced fit theory of enzyme action proposes that the catalytic groups of the active site are not brought into their most effective positions until a substrate molecule is bound onto the site, *inducing* a change in shape (conformation).

An example of competitive inhibition

Succinate dehydrogenase removes two H^+ ions from succinate, an intermediate compound of the Krebs cycle (explained in section 3.4), to form fumarate. Fumarate and other similar molecules inhibit succinate dehydrogenase. However, an increase in the concentration of succinate reduces the level of inhibition and allows the reaction to continue. This type of inhibition is used to give very precise controls on the rates at which metabolic pathways progress.

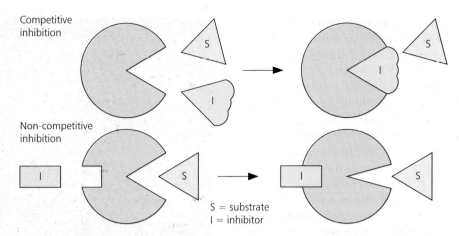

Competitive inhibition

Non-competitive inhibition

S = substrate
I = inhibitor

Figure 1.5.8 Competitive inhibitors bind at the active site, unlike non-competitive inhibitors.

as a message has been passed from a nerve to a muscle. When the enzyme is inhibited the muscles go into prolonged spasms and death results as breathing and swallowing become impossible.

Feedback control

How do cells control the hundreds of reactions going on inside them? There are many factors involved. Membrane compartments keep reactants apart. Variations in pH can be used to change the rate of enzyme-catalysed reactions, and the amount of substrate available is another mechanism at work. One of the most important methods of control is that exerted by the **regulatory enzymes**.

Regulatory enzymes are often **allosteric enzymes**. 'Allosteric' literally means 'another place'. These enzymes have another site, separate from the active site, to which another molecule can bind and act either as an inhibitor or as an activator. This ability to be activated as well as inhibited makes allosteric control different from non-competitive inhibition. Regulatory enzymes are usually found within metabolic pathways. The regulatory enzyme is found near the beginning of the pathway and is acted on by one of the end products of the chain. This is known as **end product control** or **feedback control**, shown in figure 1.5.9. There are some important examples of this in the respiratory pathways (see section 3.4).

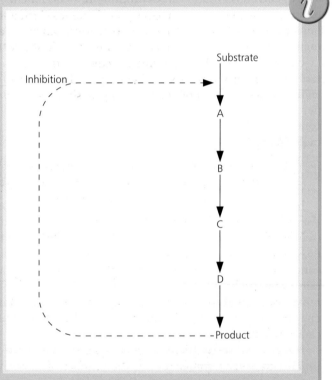

Substrate

Inhibition

A

B

C

D

Product

Figure 1.5.9 Feedback control gives a simple and effective way of controlling the rate of several reactions at once.

Enzyme cofactors

Many enzymes need a non-protein part to function properly. These non-protein components can be one of several types of ion or molecule and are given the general term **cofactors**. Sometimes cofactors are unchanged at the end of a reaction, but sometimes they are changed and then regenerated by another process. When an enzyme is linked with its cofactor to form a complex it may be referred to as a **holoenzyme**. The protein enzyme alone is known as the **apoenzyme**.

Simple inorganic ions are one type of cofactor. They may bind to the enzyme/substrate complex in a way that makes it function more effectively, for example, salivary amylase works better in the presence of chloride ions. Equally, they may form an integral part of the enzyme molecule.

Prosthetic groups are another type of cofactor. The word 'prosthetic' is derived from the Greek meaning 'added on, giving additional power'. These are organic molecules which are very tightly bound to the enzyme itself. A good example is haem, which is a flat ring molecule containing iron. Haem is the prosthetic group for a number of enzymes, including cytochrome oxidase which is involved in cellular respiration (see section 3.4), catalase and peroxidase. Haem is a permanent part of the structure of these enzymes.

Coenzymes are cofactors which are complex non-protein organic molecules loosely associated with an enzyme. They transfer chemical groups, atoms or electrons from one enzyme to another. Many of them are vitamins or derivatives of vitamins. Nicotinamide adenine dinucleotide (NAD) is a coenzyme which is very important in cellular respiration and other metabolic pathways.

Ribozymes

Throughout this section the assumption has been made that all enzymes are proteins. However, in very recent years Thomas Cech and his colleagues at the University of Colorado have shown that RNA can act as a biological catalyst. Small sections of a variety of tRNAs, mitochondrial RNAs and nuclear RNAs have been shown to have enzymatic activity and are known as **ribozymes**. The study of biological catalysts has been opened up by this discovery – in years to come our present view of enzymes may be shown to have been far too narrow.

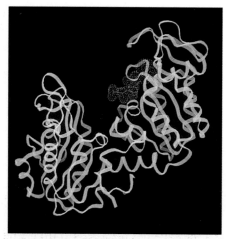

Figure 1.5.10 The shape of the active site of an enzyme (seen clearly above) is vital in determining which reactions the enzyme will catalyse.

SUMMARY

- The biochemistry of a cell is known as **metabolism**, made up of **anabolism** (building up complex molecules) and **catabolism** (breaking down complex molecules). Metabolism is controlled by enzymes.

- Enzymes lower the **activation energy** of a reaction, making it possible for more molecules to react under normal conditions of temperature, pH, etc.

- Enzymes have certain properties in common:
  Enzymes are globular proteins with an active site within their three-dimensional structure.
  They are **catalysts** – they speed up reactions without affecting the products or position of equilibrium, and are not affected themselves by the reaction.
  Enzymes are very efficient – small quantities may speed a reaction greatly. The **turnover number** reflects the number of substrate molecules transformed per molecule of enzyme.
  They show varying degrees of **specificity**, from stereospecificity (acting on only the D- or L-form of a substrate) to those which catalyse a type of reaction involving a particular group.
  The action of enzymes is affected by substrate concentration to a maximum rate where they become **saturated**.
  The rate of an enzyme-catalysed reaction increases with increasing temperature until the enzyme starts to **denature** – it loses its tertiary and quaternary structure and then no longer catalyses the reaction.
  Different enzymes work in different ranges of pH. pH affects the shape of protein molecules and therefore their active sites.

- The **lock and key mechanism** of enzyme action says that the substrate ▼ molecule fits into the three-dimensional shape of the active site to form an enzyme/substrate complex. This holds the substrate in such a way that the activation energy is lower, and the products are then released.

- The **induced fit theory** is a refinement of the lock and key mechanism which says that the active site has a flexible shape which is modified around the substrate molecule once bound. On release of the products, the inactive shape is resumed.

- Enzymes are inhibited in two ways – by **reversible inhibitors** and by **irreversible inhibitors**.

- **Reversible inhibitors** may be **competitive** or **non-competitive**. **Competitive inhibitors** are similar in shape to the substrate and bind to the active site to form an enzyme/inhibitor complex, blocking the site for substrate molecules. Increasing the concentration of substrate increases the rate of the reaction. **Non-competitive inhibitors** form a complex with another part of the enzyme but still affect the active site. The rate of reaction is not affected by substrate concentration – only by inhibitor concentration.

- **Irreversible inhibitors** such as some poisons change the shape of the enzyme permanently by covalent bonding.

- **Regulatory enzymes** in a metabolic pathway regulate that pathway. **Allosteric enzymes** have a site separate from the active site to which an inhibitor or an activator can bind. These are involved in feedback control.

- **Cofactors** are non-protein parts that enable certain enzymes (**apoenzymes**) to function. The enzyme and cofactor together form a **holoenzyme**. Cofactors include inorganic ions, **prosthetic groups** such as haem which are organic molecules tightly bound to the enzyme molecule, and **coenzymes** which are organic molecules more loosely associated with the enzyme.

QUESTIONS

1 What is an enzyme and why are enzymes important?

2 a What are the main characteristics of an enzyme?
  b How are enzyme-catalysed reactions affected by
    i temperature
    ii substrate concentration?
  c How do enzymes work?

3 a Explain the main types of enzyme inhibition
  b Apart from their role as an investigative tool, what is the importance of enzyme inhibitors in biochemical pathways?

4 Give four examples of enzyme technology in industry. What do you think would be the main difficulties of setting up an industrial process which relied on enzyme catalysis?

Developing Key Skills

A new 'super-biological' detergent has been developed using genetically engineered enzymes. These enzymes digest protein, fat and carbohydrate dirt and are effective at wash temperatures of only 30°C. The only problem is that if they are used at temperatures of 50°C they will completely denature and the washing efficiency of the detergent is severely reduced.

Design a 1 minute television advert to sell the new detergent. You need to identify all the advantages of the product whilst making sure that the use of higher temperatures is discouraged in a positive way.

FOCUS XENOTRANSPLANTATION

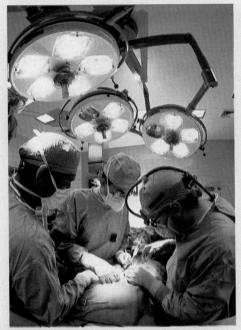

Figure 1 Any major new technique in medicine raises many issues, some scientific and others ethical – not just can it be done but should it be done? Transplants themselves raised such questions when they were first carried out.

The transplant of organs from one person to another was one of the major medical achievements of the twentieth century. Transplanting hearts, lungs, kidneys, livers and even combinations of organs has prolonged the lives of thousands of people. Unfortunately, the demand for organs is far greater than the supply available from dead human donors, and so scientists are working hard to find alternative sources. One area of research that has received a lot of media attention is **xenotransplantation**, the transplant of organs into people from other species of animal, particularly baboons and pigs.

The problem of rejection

What are the medical and scientific advantages of using other animals to provide organs for transplant into humans? The single biggest potential advantage is that if animals can be bred to provide organs, patients will no longer die waiting for a suitable donor. But the problems are many. Even when transplants are carried out from one human to another, there is a risk that the recipient will reject the donated organ. People who receive a transplanted organ have to take drugs for the rest of their lives to suppress their immune system and prevent it from destroying the new organ. This leaves them very susceptible to everyday infections. Much research into animal-to-human transplants has already been carried out, for example, a baboon heart has been transplanted into a tiny baby who survived for three weeks, and pig cells have been transplanted into the brains of people with Parkinson's disease. However, the problems of rejection when the transplanted organ comes from a different species are enormous.

Now scientists are working on producing animals that are genetically engineered to carry neutral human antigens on the cells of specific organs such as the heart or the kidney. In theory, these organs would be even less likely to be rejected than an organ from another human being. The technology exists to produce such organs for transplant in the very near future.

Ethical questions

There are a number of ethical concerns in the area of xenotransplantation. Animals cannot give consent, so they cannot be called donors – they are organ sources. There is also a serious risk of disease being transferred from the source animal to the human recipient.

Huge amounts of money are being ploughed into an area that many people doubt will ever provide a successful alternative to human organ donors. Others would argue that using animals for xenotransplants is little different from eating meat, and see this as a way forward that will save untold numbers of human lives in the future.

Figure 2 Source animals – most probably pigs – would need to be raised in a very unnatural sterile environment, and disease-causing organisms could still be present in their cells. Many people question whether we should contemplate such animals as a source of organs for human transplants at all.

1.6 | Cell recognition

The organisation of organisms

Many living organisms, both plant and animal, consist of single cells. For them, simple diffusion is adequate for supplying the oxygen needed for cellular respiration and for removing the waste products of metabolism. Osmosis can supply all the water required. The surface area of the cell compared to its volume (the **surface area : volume ratio**) is relatively large for small organisms, as figure 1.6.1 shows, and complex methods of gaining oxygen and water or getting rid of waste are not required.

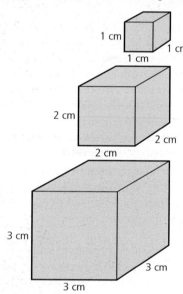

1 cm
1 cm
1 cm

Surface area = 6 cm^2
Volume = 1 cm^3
Surface area : volume ratio = 6 : 1

2 cm
2 cm
2 cm

Surface area = 24 cm^2
Volume = 8 cm^3
Surface area : volume ratio = 24 : 8 = 3 : 1

3 cm
3 cm
3 cm

Surface area = 54 cm^2
Volume = 27 cm^3
Surface area : volume ratio = 54 : 27 = 2 : 1

Figure 1.6.1 As the linear dimensions of an organism increase, the ratio of surface area:volume decreases. This sets limits on the lifestyle of an organism, or forces evolutionary change to overcome the restrictions which result.

Single-celled organisms have evolved to survive in a huge variety of places, but there is a limit to the capabilities of any organism that is just one cell. One of the many advantages of multicellular organisms is that they can, in some cases, grow remarkably large. However, being bigger causes some problems of organisation. As the surface area : volume ratio falls, it becomes less and less possible to supply all the needs of the cells by a simple process of diffusion. In multicellular organisms, cells become **differentiated** – they specialise to carry out particular functions. Some transport oxygen, some digest food, some provide movement and some are involved in reproduction, for example. Throughout a multicellular organism we find groups of cells that all have a similar structure and function, and these groups of similar cells are known as a **tissue**. Tissues are found in almost all multicellular organisms – examples include squamous epithelium, ciliated epithelium, liver cells and muscle cells in animals, and xylem and phloem in plants.

In turn, several different tissues may combine to form an **organ**. In an organ the different tissues work together to allow the organ to carry out particular functions that benefit the whole multicellular organism – for example, in an animal, a heart pumping blood around the body or a liver detoxifying the

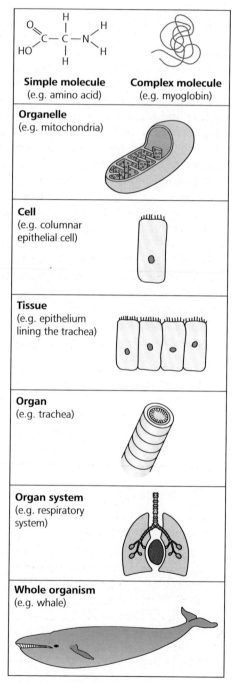

Simple molecule (e.g. amino acid)   Complex molecule (e.g. myoglobin)

Organelle (e.g. mitochondria)

Cell (e.g. columnar epithelial cell)

Tissue (e.g. epithelium lining the trachea)

Organ (e.g. trachea)

Organ system (e.g. respiratory system)

Whole organism (e.g. whale)

Figure 1.6.2 Large multicellular organisms such as people, whales and trees contain literally billions of cells. There are many different levels of organisation working to make sure that every cell gets everything it needs and that the whole organism functions properly.

blood and processing the digested food, or in a plant, a leaf photosynthesising to provide food for the whole plant.

Finally, organs combine together to work as an **organ system**, carrying out major processes for the body such as digestion or reproduction.

Recognition of cells by other cells

It might seem that for unicellular organisms, cell recognition would not be important. However, they need to sense the presence of potential food, and those which undergo a primitive form of sexual reproduction need to recognise the cells of others of the same species.

For larger organisms, the surface area:volume ratio is such that simple diffusion is not adequate to supply all the necessities of life. Cells within a multicellular animal or plant become increasingly specialised, differentiating further and further away from the generalised cell to perform very individual functions, be it causing movement, obtaining food or oxygen or carrying nerve impulses to allow for coordinated action. In such an organism it is obviously important that individual cells recognise each other as members of the same living entity, and also that they recognise other cells performing the same function so that they can operate as a tissue. It is also important to be able to recognise foreign cells, not simply potential prey but also invaders such as bacteria and viruses within the organism. This aspect of cell recognition is particularly important for animals. Their motile way of life and relatively vulnerable cells make them particularly open to attack by invading organisms. Plants, without the need to move about, can produce much stouter external barriers to prevent invasion.

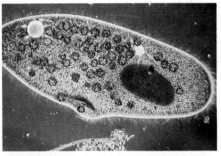
Light micrograph of *Paramecium*, a single-celled organism

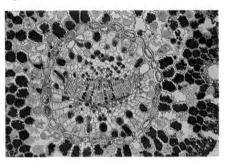
Light micrograph of a section through a cedar leaf, showing the many different types of cells that make up the leaf

Figure 1.6.3 The more cells there are, the more important cell recognition becomes.

Evidence for cell recognition

Sponges are the most primitive of the multicellular animals. Until 1765, they were thought to be plants. They are made up of many simple cells grouped together, and do not move about. Their cells show some differentiation into different types concerned with food extraction and water flow, but they do not have high levels of organisation.

In the early years of this century E. Wilson split sponges into their individual cells by passing them through sieves (sponges have no nervous system and so cannot feel pain!). The individual cells began to show amoeboid movement, and continued to move until they encountered another cell. Aggregates of sponge cells formed, clearly demonstrating cell recognition, and these aggregates went on to develop into new animals. So even in simple organisms we see evidence of cell recognition, and this recognition plays a vital role at all levels of organisation.

Figure 1.6.4 For a long time thought of as plants, sponges are in fact simple animals. These primitive organisms clearly display cell recognition.

How do cells recognise each other?

As we have seen, protruding from the outer surface of the cell surface membrane are many proteins, in particular **glycoproteins**, protein molecules with a carbohydrate component. These chains of sugar molecules can be very varied, and they seem to be important in cell recognition in several ways. Similar sugar recognition sites may bind to each other, holding similar cells together. When tissues and organs are forming in embryonic development this kind of recognition and binding is of great significance.

The immune system

Apart from the association and differentiation of cells in the developing embryo, perhaps the most striking example of cell recognition in living organisms is the **immune system**. The immune system enables the body to recognise foreign material – that is, anything which is not part of itself – and to produce the appropriate response to remove it from the system as quickly and efficiently as possible. Various aspects of the immune system are accepted as normal parts of life. We speak of being immune to a particular illness. We are vaccinated against a wide variety of diseases. But the immune system is extremely complex. We shall look here most closely at the humun immune system, since this is of greatest relevance to us in terms of the prevention of disease.

How does the body recognise foreign material?

The protein and glycoprotein markers on the surface of cell surface membranes are known as **antigens**. Each organism carries its own unique set of antigens – some of them common to every member of a particular species, others specific to a particular individual within a species. The more closely related two individuals are, the more antigens they are likely to have in common. But the only individuals who will have matching antigens are genetically identical twins.

The term antigens, which refers specifically to the markers on the membranes, is often used loosely to refer to the whole cells that carry the antigens.

Lymphocytes

The body recognises the presence of a foreign antigen by means of **lymphocytes**. Lymphocytes are white blood cells, made in the white bone marrow of the long bones. Every individual possesses a wide range of lymphocytes. Each lymphocyte is capable of recognising *one* specific antigen. There are two types of lymphocytes involved in the immune response. **T-cells** (activated by the thymus gland) are involved in what is called the **cell-mediated response**. **B-cells** (activated, it is thought, by the cells of the bone marrow, liver and spleen) are involved in the **humoral response**.

The cell-mediated response

T-cells congregate at the site of an infection and mount a direct attack on the foreign organism or tissue. The T-cells present in the blood have receptor proteins attached to their cell surface membranes. When a T-cell comes into contact with a **complementary antigen**, an antigen it recognises on another cell, the antigen is bound to the receptor proteins and the cell destroyed. As a result of this reaction, the T-cell undergoes a rapid series of cell divisions to produce a **clone** of identical T-cells all capable of recognising and destroying the same type of antigen. These cells are sometimes known as **killer lymphocytes** or **killer T-cells** because they destroy the invading material.

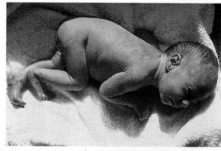

Figure 1.6.5 In a newborn infant, lymphocytes cannot immediately recognise foreign tissue or perform any other useful function – they have to be activated. Once we understand how cell recognition is activated, we should be able to suppress it and solve many of the problems of rejection associated with the technique of transplantation.

The humoral response

B-cells in the lymph glands and around the body make substances to be carried around which attack the invader. Just like the T-cells, B-cells have receptor proteins on the cell surface membrane. However, when B-cells detect a complementary antigen and bind it to their receptor protein, the effect is very different. Like the T-cell, the B-cell undergoes a rapid series of cell divisions, but *two* different types of new cells result – plasma cell clones and memory cells. The majority of these new cells are **plasma cell clones**. These have the ability to produce large amounts of **antibodies**, special proteins which are released into the circulation and which bind to the antigen, causing its destruction in one of several ways. The B-cells and the plasma cell clones are not themselves directly involved in the destruction of the antigen. Plasma cell clones only live for a few days but can produce up to 2000 antibody molecules per second.

Memory cells are also produced by the divisions of the B-cell. These are important in allowing the body to respond very rapidly to a second invasion by the same antigen. Once you have had a disease, you do not usually catch it again. This is because when you encounter the disease-causing antigen again, your body can produce antibodies against it so rapidly that it is destroyed before the symptoms of the disease develop. It is the memory cells that make this possible. As yet no one is entirely sure how memory cells provide this **immunological memory**.

Figure 1.6.6 summarises the immune response and compares the cell-mediated response and the humoral response.

Where do lymphocytes come from?

Lymphocytes are manufactured by special cells called **stem cells** in the white bone marrow of the long bones of the body. Stem cells are cells whose only function is to reproduce and make more new cells of one very specific type. Bone marrow transplants provide stem cells for people whose bone marrow has been destroyed by radiation, either during cancer treatment or following a nuclear accident such as that at Chernobyl in Russia.

T-lymphocytes or T-cells move from the bone marrow to the thymus gland in the neck, where they continue to mature under the influence of hormones produced by the thymus gland itself, until they are released into the blood. (**T**-lymphocytes come from the **T**hymus.)

In mammals, the B-lymphocyte stem cells are formed in the embryo in either the bone marrow or the liver. The B-lymphocytes or B-cells made by these stem cells move to the lymph glands around the body and this is where they continue to mature. (**B**-lymphocytes come from the **B**one marrow.)

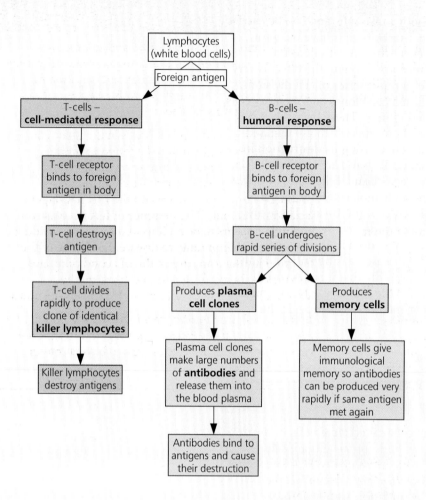

Phagocytes

Phagocytes are another type of white blood cell. They are formed as **monocytes** which mature into phagocytes. These are amoeba-like cells which can move out of the capillaries into the tissues. Phagocytes act as scavengers, cleaning up cell debris, and also engulf and remove antigen–antibody complexes, digesting and destroying them. The pus that forms in a spot or infected cut is made up largely of dead phagocytes.

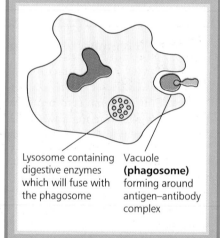

Lysosome containing digestive enzymes which will fuse with the phagosome

Vacuole **(phagosome)** forming around antigen–antibody complex

Figure 1.6.7 Phagocytes engulf the whole antigen–antibody complex.

How antibodies destroy antigens

Antibodies are large protein molecules produced by plasma cell clones in the humoral response. They are collectively known as the **immunoglobulins**. They contribute to the defence of the body against the invasion of foreign material in a variety of ways.

1 Antibodies reduce the ability of most **pathogens** (disease-causing organisms) to invade the host cells.

2 Antibodies bind to antigens and **agglutinate** or clump together which helps to prevent their spread through the body.

3 The antigen–antibody complex is readily engulfed and digested by **phagocytes** – another type of white blood cell – which travel through the circulatory system ingesting foreign material. The box on this page describes how this happens.

4 The antigen–antibody complex may stimulate other reactions within the body, such as the destruction of the membrane of the antigen if it has one, or the release of the chemical histamine by the invaded cells, causing inflammation.

Types of immunoglobulins

Although immunoglobulins are all different, each being specific to one antigen, they all have the same basic structure. They are globular proteins made up of four polypeptide chains, two *light* or short chains and two *heavy* or long chains. Five different types of immunoglobulin have been isolated, each of which appears to have a slightly different function.

IgM is the first type of immunoglobulin to appear in the blood in response to an antigen. It is produced for a week or two and seems to be involved in the **primary response** of the body to an antigen – that is, the way it responds the first time it meets an antigen.

IgG is the main immunoglobulin type found circulating in the blood – it makes up about 80% of immunoglobulin. IgG is the workhorse of the immune system, conferring most of the benefits of immunity and being very heavily involved in the **secondary response** of the body to an antigen – the way it responds on repeated exposures to a particular antigen. IgG cannot be synthesised during the first couple of months of human life, and so newborn babies are dependent on immunoglobulins which they have received across the placenta and continue to receive through their mother's milk to protect them from a wide variety of diseases.

IgA is found in relatively low levels in the blood, but is the main immunoglobulin to be found in body secretions such as tears, saliva, nasal drippings, colostrum (the special antibody-rich form of milk produced during pregnancy and the first few days of lactation) and milk. The presence of IgA in colostrum and milk appears to be an important way of providing the infant with immunity to disease. IgA is one of the few proteins that can survive the pH conditions and enzymes of the stomach and intestines and be absorbed into the body with its biological activity intact.

IgD and **IgE** are found in relatively small amounts. The functions of these two immunoglobulins are not yet clearly understood. IgE seems to have a role in allergic reactions.

Different types of immunity

Natural immunity

Normally, where the body comes into contact with a foreign antigen, the immune system is activated and antibodies are formed which result in the destruction of the antigen. This is known as **natural active immunity**. The other natural type of immunity is that passed between mother and offspring, where preformed antibodies are provided to the infant either before or after birth, providing it with temporary immunity until its own system becomes active. This is called **natural passive immunity**, and tends to be quite short-lived because the antibodies are used up and are not replaced.

Figure 1.6.8 Natural passive immunity ensures that young mammals survive until their own immune system becomes active.

Induced immunity

The value of immunity to disease has long been recognised and we have managed to induce it artificially in a number of ways. Beginning with Edward Jenner's observation that those who had suffered from cowpox were less likely to suffer smallpox, the development and introduction of vaccinations has been a major preoccupation of the medical profession. Smallpox, diphtheria, polio and tuberculosis have all been major killers in their time, but have now been either eradicated (smallpox) or greatly reduced in incidence, in the developed world at least.

Acquired passive immunity is given when antibodies are formed in one individual, extracted and injected into another individual. This does not confer long-term immunity, but can be valuable if someone is suspected of having been exposed to a dangerous antigen. A good example of this is in the treatment of tetanus, also known as lockjaw. Tetanus results from a toxin, produced by a microorganism, which causes all the muscles to go into spasm (or tetanus), making swallowing and breathing impossible and so causing death. People who may have been exposed to the tetanus microorganism, for example from a deep cut whilst gardening or whilst working with horses, are injected with antibodies against tetanus extracted from the blood of horses. This prevents the development of the disease in the short term, but does not give prolonged immunity.

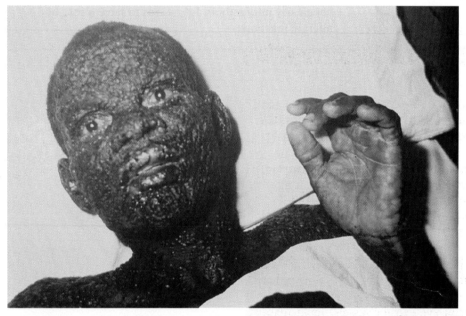

Figure 1.6.9 Smallpox has been officially eradicated from the globe by an intensive vaccination programme.

In **acquired active immunity**, small amounts of antigen (known as the **vaccine**) are used to produce immunity in an individual. The antigen is not usually the normal live microbe, as this might have fatal results. It is made safe without reducing its ability to act as an antigen. This can be done in a number of ways. If a toxin produced by the microorganism causes the symptoms, a **detoxified** form that cannot produce the symptoms will be injected. Sometimes dead viruses or bacteria are used as vaccines, and in other cases **attenuated** organisms (living but modified so they cannot produce disease) are used. The body will then produce antibodies against the antigen, and appropriate memory cells will be formed. Should the individual subsequently come into contact with the active antigen, the body will destroy the antigen without experiencing the symptoms of the disease it causes. Figure 1.6.10 illustrates the process.

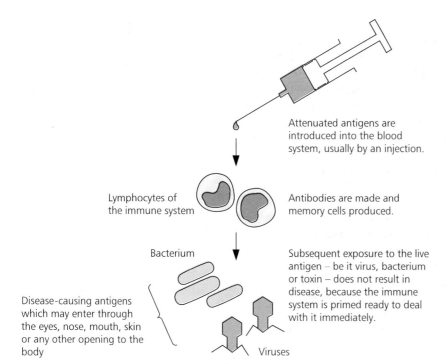

Attenuated antigens are introduced into the blood system, usually by an injection.

Lymphocytes of the immune system

Antibodies are made and memory cells produced.

Bacterium

Subsequent exposure to the live antigen – be it virus, bacterium or toxin – does not result in disease, because the immune system is primed ready to deal with it immediately.

Disease-causing antigens which may enter through the eyes, nose, mouth, skin or any other opening to the body

Viruses

Figure 1.6.10 The implications of this artificial manipulation of the immune system are enormous. The introduction of vaccines worldwide gives hope that some of the epidemics seen in the past, leaving millions dead and crippled, may one day be consigned to history.

Blood groups

The ABO system

A specialised and unique aspect of the immune response is seen in the human blood. There is a variety of different **blood groups**, but the one most familiar to us and in most common usage is the **ABO system**. There are four possible blood groups within this system.

On the surface of the red blood cells of any individual are molecules which act as antigens. In this case they are mucopolysaccharides known as **agglutinogens** and there are two different ones, **A** and **B**. There are two antibodies (**agglutinins**) in the blood plasma called **a** and **b**. These antibodies are not made in direct response to an antigen as normal antibodies are – they are present regardless of any exposure to the antigen. If red blood cells carrying a particular agglutinogen come into contact with plasma containing the complementary agglutinin, the reaction between them causes the red blood cells to **agglutinate** (stick together). This means that they can no longer do their job and are likely to block capillaries or even larger vessels. Table 1.6.1 shows the agglutinogens and agglutinins present in the different blood groups.

Blood group	Agglutinogen (antigen on red blood cell)	Agglutinin (antibody in the plasma)
A	A	b
B	B	a
AB	A and B	–
O	–	a and b

Table 1.6.1 The ABO system of blood groups

In the UK group O is the most common blood group (46% of the population), with group A a close second (42%). Groups B (9%) and AB (3%) are much less common, although within specific ethnic groups the proportions may vary quite markedly.

Why does blood group matter?

Imagine an accident victim with blood group A who has haemorrhaged severely and needs several pints of blood. Figure 1.6.11 shows which blood groups are compatible. Blood from donors of groups B or AB cannot be given to the victim. Group A blood has the plasma antibody b. If this comes into contact with antigen B on the surface of red blood cells, the plasma would cause cell agglutination.

Donor \ Recipient	O (Antibodies a and b)	A (Antigen A, antibody b)	B (Antigen B, antibody a)	AB (Antigens A and B)
O (Antibodies a and b)	✓	✓	✓	✓
A (Antigen A, antibody b)	✗	✓	✗	✓
B (Antigen B, antibody a)	✗	✗	✓	✓
AB (Antigens A and B)	✗	✗	✗	✓

Figure 1.6.11 Correct matching of the blood makes the difference between life and death when a blood transfusion is needed.

For most of the population most of the time, blood groups have little importance. As long as your blood remains within your own body system and you avoid major blood loss or the need for surgery, it is quite possible that no one will know your blood group. But blood group information becomes vital when blood needs to be given from one person to another. Blood donors' blood groups are checked and the donated blood is clearly labelled. Before undergoing surgery or giving birth, or in any situation where the possibility of a blood transfusion arises, the blood group needs to be ascertained.

When a blood transfusion is given, it is the cells of the donated blood that will be affected by any adverse reaction. The blood of the recipient is usually present in much greater amounts and so any adverse reaction is relatively minor. But if the donated blood agglutinates as it flows into the recipient's system, then difficulties can arise.

Blood group O can be given to anybody in a transfusion. Because it carries no antigens on its red blood cells it cannot stimulate an agglutination reaction. It is often referred to as the **universal donor**. On the other hand, group AB blood cannot be given to anyone other than an AB recipient, because all the other blood groups contain antibodies in their plasma which would cause some level of agglutination. However, people with blood group AB can receive any type of blood as their plasma contains no antibodies – so group AB is known as the **universal recipient**.

The rhesus factor

The **rhesus factor** is an agglutinogen (antigen) which is found on the surface of some red blood cells whatever their ABO grouping. In fact, 85% of us possess this particular feature of our red blood cells and are known as **rhesus positive.**

The remainder, who do not have the agglutinogen, are **rhesus negative.** Normally neither rhesus positive nor rhesus negative blood possesses rhesus agglutinins in the plasma. Rhesus positive blood never forms rhesus agglutinins, otherwise it would coagulate itself. But in certain circumstances, rhesus negative blood will form plasma agglutinins, usually during pregnancy if a rhesus negative mother carries a fetus that is rhesus positive.

In theory this should not matter at all. Every fetus is genetically different from its mother. By some suspension of the immune system which we do not fully understand, this foreign genetic material is allowed to grow and thrive in the uterus for some 40 weeks without being attacked and destroyed. The placenta forms a barrier between the cells of the mother and the cells of the fetus so that an inappropriate immune response is not triggered. However, the placenta leaks. This leakage is usually only slight in the first pregnancy, but a few fetal red blood cells will get into the bloodstream of the mother. If they are of a different ABO blood group they will probably be destroyed. However, if mother and fetus have the same ABO group or a compatible one, the fetal blood cells will survive long enough to stimulate the production of rhesus antibodies in the mother's plasma.

In subsequent pregnancies the placenta gets progressively more leaky. The build-up of maternal agglutinins to any further rhesus positive fetal blood cells is much larger and more rapid. These agglutinins can cross the placenta. The red blood cells of the fetus are then attacked and agglutinated. In the past this led to many babies dying, either before they were born or shortly afterwards. In more recent years, once the rhesus incompatibility was recognised, affected babies were given transfusions as soon as they were born. Now blood transfusions are carried out whilst the fetus is still within the uterus.

It is worth noticing that rhesus incompatibility only matters in one direction – that is, if the mother makes antibodies against the fetus. If the developing baby is rhesus negative and the mother rhesus positive, the same thing will happen in reverse. But the amounts of antibodies the fetus makes against its mother's blood are so tiny that their effect is not noticed.

In order to prevent the necessity for intrauterine blood transfusions, women who are rhesus negative and have carried one rhesus positive child are usually given an injection shortly after the birth. This contains anti-rhesus agglutinins and is known as anti-D. It prevents the antibody-forming process, which means that a second fetus is at no higher risk than the first.

Transplants and the immune system

In recent years medical advances have highlighted the immune system in a new way. The development of the transplantation of organs and tissues from one person to another has led to much work being done on the immune system and its suppression. However closely the tissues of a donor organ – for example, a kidney – are matched to the tissues of the patient who is to receive the transplant, a perfect match is not possible unless the donor is an identical twin. This means that, to a greater or lesser extent, the immune system of the recipient will set out to destroy or **reject** the donated organ.

The problem is how to prevent the recipient from rejecting the transplanted organ without reducing the ability of the immune system to the extent that the patient dies from a succession of infections which the body cannot fight. Rejection is prevented by a cocktail of **immunosuppressant drugs** which endeavour to get the balance right. Transplant patients have to take these drugs for the rest of their lives.

The immune system is capable of 'holding off'. As we have already mentioned, during the development of the fetus the mother's immune system does not destroy this foreign genetic material. At an even earlier stage of reproduction, sperm are allowed to travel and live within the female reproductive tract for days at a time without triggering an immune reaction. Once scientists can understand how these suspensions of the normal immune response are brought about, they may be in a position to develop a more specific and effective way of preventing rejection.

SUMMARY

- Unicellular organisms have a large surface area:volume ratio and can gain the materials they need by diffusion. However, they need to recognise potential food and recognition may also be necessary for sexual reproduction.

- Multicellular organisms have a variety of specialised cells so cell recognition is needed for the organism's organisation, and also to deal with invasion by foreign cells.

- Cells are recognised by glycoproteins on their cell surface membranes. In a foreign organism, these glycoproteins are called **antigens**. The **immune response** enables the body to recognise and remove foreign antigens.

- **Lymphocytes** are white blood cells that each recognise one particular antigen. There are two types of lymphocytes – **T-cells** and **B-cells**.

- T-cells bring about the **cell-mediated response** to invasion by a foreign antigen. A T-cell binds to and destroys its complementary antigen and then divides to produce a clone of **killer T-cells** which all destroy the same antigen.

- B-cells bring about the **humoral response** by producing **plasma cell clones** and **memory cells**. Plasma cell clones produce **antibodies** which bind to the antigens and destroy them. Memory cells convey **immunological memory** so that the next encounter with the antigen results in rapid production of plasma clone cells.

- Antibodies are proteins known as **immunoglobulins** which prevent pathogens entering host cells, cause antigens to **agglutinate** (clump together) so facilitating their digestion by phagocytes, and stimulate histamine production.

- **Natural active immunity** results from activation of the immune system. **Natural passive immunity** results from absorbing antibodies from another individual. It is passed from mother to child before and shortly after birth, and is short lived.

- Immunity may be induced artificially. **Acquired passive immunity** results from the injection of ready-made antibodies, for example to tetanus. **Acquired active immunity** is gained in response to injection with a vaccine containing an attenuated organism or detoxified toxin which stimulates the immune response without producing symptoms of the disease.

- The **ABO blood system** groups people according to antigens or **agglutinogens** (A and B) found on the red blood cells, and antibodies or **agglutinins** (a and b) found in the blood plasma. The blood groups are A, B, AB and O.

- In a blood transfusion, donated blood with particular agglutinogens cannot be given to a recipient who has complementary agglutinins, as the donated blood would agglutinate. Group O is the **universal donor** since it lacks any agglutinogens, and group AB is the **universal recipient** since it lacks any agglutinins.

- The **rhesus factor** is an agglutinogen found on the red blood cells of **rhesus positive** people. If a **rhesus negative** mother carries a rhesus positive child, she may develop agglutinins in her plasma to any fetal red blood cells that leak through the placenta. Subsequent pregnancies with further rhesus positive fetuses may result in the mother's agglutinins causing the fetal blood to agglutinate.

- Patients who receive transplanted organs have to take **immunosuppressant drugs** to prevent the donated organ being rejected.

QUESTIONS

1 Why is cell recognition important in
   a simple organisms
   b complex multicellular organisms?

2 When the body is invaded by a foreign organism, it responds by identifying and destroying the invader. This is brought about by the lymphocytes in a two-pronged attack involving a *cell-mediated response* and a *humoral response*.
   What is
   a the cell-mediated response
   b the humoral response?

3 Explain the differences between
   a natural active immunity
   b natural passive immunity
   c acquired active immunity
   d acquired passive immunity.

4 What is meant by the human ABO blood system? What is the importance of the blood groups in the context of a blood transfusion between one individual and another?

Developing Key Skills

A prestigious radio current affairs programme is to run a debate on xenotransplantation. They will consider the technical difficulties, the possible benefits and the ethical arguments for and against the process. Decide whether you will speak for or against the new technology and prepare a brief speech to support your view.

1 Name the organelles described below.
  a Usually rod-shaped, 1 μm wide and up to 7 μm long; have a double membrane; the inner membrane is folded to form cristae.
  b Rounded organelle approximately 25 nm in diameter; consists of RNA and protein.
  c Disc-shaped structure, about 1 μm wide and up to 5 μm long; contains a system of thylakoids.
  d Hollow, cylindrical structure; consists of nine triplets of microtubules.
  e Contains the genetic material of a cell; surrounded by a double membrane. **(5 marks)**
  (Edexcel, June 1999)

2 The drawing shows part of a cell as seen under an electron microscope.

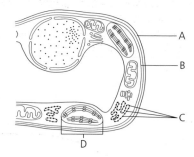

  a Identify structures **A** to **D**. **(4 marks)**
  b Describe how a sample of whole chloroplasts could be obtained from leaf tissue. **(3 marks)**
  (AQA, specimen 2000)

3 The figure shows a diagram of a cell surface membrane.

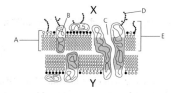

  a i Name **A** to **E**. **(5 marks)**
   ii State the width of a cell surface membrane. **(2 marks)**
  b i On which side of the membrane, **X** or **Y**, is the cytoplasm of the cell? **(1 mark)**
   ii Give a reason for your answer based on the evidence in the figure. **(1 mark)**
  c State the function of **three named** components of the cell surface membrane. **(6 marks)**
  The properties of the components of cell surface membranes determine whether molecules can pass through membranes.
  d Explain why cell surface membranes are impermeable to most biological molecules. **(4 marks)**
  (OCR, specimen 2000)

4 a Describe the structure of the cell surface membrane. **(6 marks)**
  b Discuss the functions of membranes, both within and at the surface of cells. **(10 marks)**
  (OCR, March 1998)

5 a State **three structural** features of prokaryotic cells. **(3 marks)**
  b Describe the functions in eukaryotic cells of lysosomes, ribosomes, and centrioles. *(In this question, 1 mark is available for the quality of written communication.)* **(7 marks)**
  (OCR, specimen 2000)

6 Sucrose is a disaccharide. It is also a non-reducing sugar.
  a Benedict's solution is used to identify non-reducing sugars. Complete the flow chart to show the steps you would carry out in order to get a positive result.

  Add **(i)** ....

  (ii) ....

  Add Benedict's solution then heat in a water bath

  Red-brown precipitate indicates a non-reducing sugar
  (2 marks)

  b A sample of sucrose was incubated with the enzyme sucrase. This hydrolysed the sucrose. A chromatogram was produced by loading chromatography paper with sucrose, with sucrose which had been incubated with sucrase, and with sucrase. The diagram below shows this chromatogram.

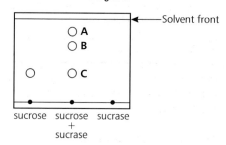

   i Calculate the R_f value of sucrose. Show your working. **(2 marks)**
   ii Explain the presence of the three spots labelled **A**, **B** and **C**. **(2 marks)**
   (AQA, specimen 2000)

7 a What type of molecule is shown in the diagram below? **(1 mark)**

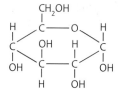

b If two of the molecules shown are linked together, what products result? **(2 marks)**

c Draw a diagram to show how two such molecules would join. (You need only draw the relevant parts of the molecule.) **(2 marks)**

d What name is given to the type of chemical bond formed when the two molecules are joined, as you have shown in (**c**)? **(1 mark)**

e i What biochemical term would be used to describe large numbers of such molecules joining together? **(1 mark)**

ii If many of the molecules shown are linked together, suggest a name for the product. **(1 mark)**

(OCR, June 1998)

8 a Describe the structure of an amino acid and the formation of a peptide bond in a cell. **(7 marks)**

b Explain the primary, secondary and tertiary structure of proteins, referring to the types of bond holding the molecule in shape. **(9 marks)**

(OCR, June 1998)

9 PrP is a protein normally found in brain tissue. The diagram shows part of the structure of a PrP molecule. The dotted line represents the middle part of the molecule which has been left out of this diagram.

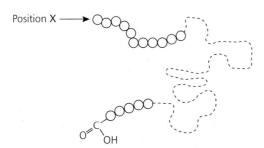

Position X

a i Name the monomers which make up this molecule. **(1 mark)**

ii Name **one** chemical element which would be found in this molecule but not in a polysaccharide molecule. **(1 mark)**

iii Give the formula of the chemical group that would be found at position **X** on the molecule. **(1 mark)**

PrP molecules are found on the outside of the cell surface membranes of nerve cells. The precise function of PrP is still unknown but it is thought that its tertiary structure enables it to act as a receptor molecule.

b Describe:

i the secondary structure of a protein **(1 mark)**

ii the tertiary structure of a protein. **(1 mark)**

c i What is meant by a *receptor molecule*? **(1 mark)**

ii Explain how its tertiary structure might allow a protein molecule to act as a receptor molecule. **(2 marks)**

d It appears that when a cow gets BSE something causes the PrP molecules to become sticky so that they clump together. With an electron microscope, string-like fibrils composed of clumps of PrP can be seen in the brain tissue of cattle affected by BSE. Explain why the string-like fibrils of PrP can be seen in the brain tissue of cattle with an electron microscope but not with a light microscope. **(2 marks)**

e It is not know what makes the PrP molecules stick together. One hypothesis is that an unknown infectious agent may bring about a change in the secondary structure of the PrP molecule. This could explain the fact that the PrP molecules in fibrils are resistant to the action of protein-digesting enzymes which bring about the hydrolysis of PrP from healthy animals.

i Describe what happens during *hydrolysis of PrP*. **(2 marks)**

ii Suggest how a change in the secondary structure of the PrP molecule could explain the fact that PrP in fibres is resistant to the action of protein-digesting enzymes. **(2 marks)**

(AQA, specimen 2000)

10 a Diagram **A** shows an enzyme, and **B** is the substrate of this enzyme.

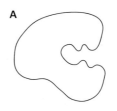

A   B

Draw a diagram to show how a competitive inhibitor would affect the activity of the enzyme. **(2 marks)**

b The graph shows the effect of changing substrate concentration on the rate of an enzyme controlled reaction.

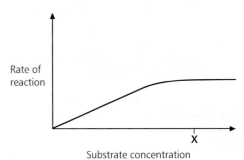

Rate of reaction

Substrate concentration

Explain why increasing the substrate concentration above the value shown at **X** fails to increase the rate of reaction further. **(2 marks)**

c Explain how adding excess substrate could overcome the effect of a competitive inhibitor. **(2 marks)**

(AQA, specimen 2000)

11 An investigation was carried out to determine the effects of temperature on the action of sucrase (invertase) on sucrose. Various tubes containing equal volumes (and the same concentration) of enzyme and sucrose solution were warmed to the required temperature in water-baths before mixing. Then the solutions were mixed and the time taken for the enzyme to hydrolyse all the sucrose to monosaccharides at each temperature was taken as a measure of the rate of the reaction. The results are given overleaf.

Temperature /°C	Time for complete hydrolysis of sucrose/minutes
5	24
10	15
20	8
30	4
40	5.5
50	18
60	98

a Using this information, plot a graph to show how the **rate** of reaction varies with temperature. **(6 marks)**

b Comment on the results as seen between 10°C and 30°C **(2 marks)**

c Explain briefly what is happening to the enzyme molecules between 40°C and 60°C. **(2 marks)**

d Using the information shown on your graph, calculate the Q_{10} value for the rate of reaction between 15°C and 25°C. **(3 marks)**

e In this experiment, the sucrase and the sucrose solutions were originally at room temperature. They were placed in separate test tubes in a water-bath for 10 minutes, to ensure they had reached the required temperature, after which they were mixed together and the timing started. Suggest, with a reason, what might have happened when investigating the enzyme action at 60°C if the enzyme and substrate had been mixed together in the tube and the tube then placed in the water-bath. **(2 marks)**

(OCR, March 1998)

12 a i Name **one** *fibrous* and **one** *globular* protein. **(2 marks)**

ii Outline the **difference** in structure between a *fibrous* and a *globular* protein. **(4 marks)**

The figure shows the effect of temperature on the rate of an enzyme reaction.

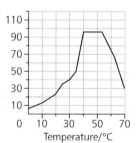

b With reference to the figure, describe and explain the effect of temperature on the rate of enzyme action. **(5 marks)**

c With reference to molecular structure, explain the specificity of enzymes. *(In this question, 1 mark is available for the quality of written communication.)* **(8 marks)**

(OCR, specimen 2000)

13 a Describe the types of bonding which hold protein molecules in shape. **(9 marks)**

b Discuss how the molecular structure of haemoglobin is related to its function. **(7 marks)**

(OCR, March 1999)

14 An experiment was carried out to determine what happens to amino acids after they are absorbed by animal cells. The cells were incubated for 5 minutes in a medium containing radioactively labelled amino acids. The radioactive amino acids were then washed off and the cells were incubated in a medium containing only non-radioactive amino acids. Samples of the cells were taken at 5, 10 and 45 minutes after the start of the experiment and the sites of radioactivity in the cells were determined. The results are given in the table below. The figures show radioactivity in certain cell organelles expressed as a percentage of the total radioactivity within the cells.

Organelle	Percentage of total radioactivity		
	At 5 minutes	At 10 minutes	At 45 minutes
Rough endoplasmic reticulum	80	10	5
Golgi apparatus	10	80	30
Secretory vesicles	0	5	60

a i Name **one** type of molecule synthesised from amino acids in cells. **(1 mark)**

ii Explain why the radioactivity is associated mainly with the rough endoplasmic reticulum after the first 5 minutes of the experiment. **(2 marks)**

iii Explain the changes in the pattern of radioactivity in the cell during the remaining 40 minutes of the experiment. **(3 marks)**

iv Suggest why the totals in the tables are less than 100%. **(2 marks)**

b If the experiment is continued for a further period of time, most of the radioactivity will be found outside the cell. Name and describe the process which brings about this result. **(3 marks)**

(Edexcel, June 1999)

15 Give an account of the structure and replication of deoxyribonucleic acid (DNA). **(10 marks)**

(Edexcel, June 1999)

16 The diagram shows part of a DNA molecule.

a i Name **J** to **M**. **(4 marks)**

ii What do the dotted lines represent? **(1 mark)**

b State **three** ways in which the structure of messenger RNA differs from DNA. **(3 marks)**

c Explain why exact replication of DNA is necessary. **(2 marks)**
Part of a DNA molecule is shown below.

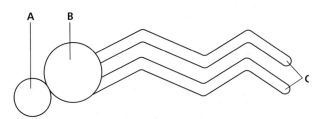

d Show by means of a diagram what happens to this part of the DNA during replication. **(4 marks)**
e Name the enzyme involved in **replicating** the DNA molecule. **(1 mark)**

(OCR, specimen 2000)

17 a Give **two** ways in which active transport differs from diffusion. **(2 marks)**

b The diagram represents a phospholipid.

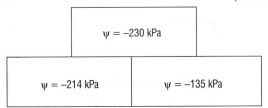

  i Name the parts of the molecule **A**, **B** and **C**. **(3 marks)**
  ii Describe the role of phospholipids in controlling the passage of molecules through the cell membrane. **(1 mark)**
c i The diagram shows the water potentials (ψ) of three cells in contact with one another. Copy the diagram and use arrows to show the net direction of water movement between **all three** cells. **(1 mark)**

$\psi = -230$ kPa

$\psi = -214$ kPa $\psi = -135$ kPa

  ii If solute were added to a cell, what effect would this have on the water potential within the cell? **(1 mark)**

(AQA, specimen 2000)

18 The graph shows the expected and actual results of an experiment to investigate the uptake of glucose by human red blood cells.

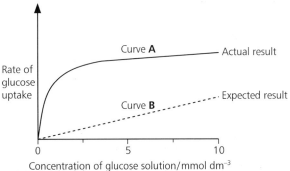

Rate of glucose uptake

Curve **A** — Actual result

Curve **B** ---- Expected result

Concentration of glucose solution/mmol dm^{-3}

a Curve **B** shows the result that would be expected if glucose enters the red blood cells by simple diffusion.
  i State Fick's Law. **(1 mark)**
  ii Explain how Curve **B** demonstrates one aspect of Fick's Law. **(1 mark)**
b Curve **A** shows the results obtained from the red blood cells. It shows that these cells took up glucose by facilitated diffusion. Explain the shape of the curve at glucose concentrations:
  i less than 2 mmol dm^{-3} **(1 mark)**
  ii greater than 5 mmol dm^{-3}. **(1 mark)**

(AQA, June 1999)

19 a Explain why blood of group A cannot safely be given to a person who is blood group B. **(3 marks)**
b Copy and complete the table by using ticks to show the transfusions which can be carried out safely and crosses to show those which cannot be carried out safely. **(2 marks)**

		Blood group of donor			
		A	B	AB	O
Blood group of recipient	A				
	B				
	AB				
	O				

c Describe how you would use solutions containing antibodies anti-A (a) and anti-B (b) to confirm that a sample of blood is group AB. **(2 marks)**

(AQA, March 1999)

20 Distinguish between the following pairs of terms.
  a *Antibodies* and *antibiotics*. **(2 marks)**
  b *Active immunity* and *passive immunity*. **(2 marks)**
  c *T lymphocytes* and *B lymphocytes*. **(2 marks)**

(OCR, June 1999)

SYSTEMS OF LIFE

Introduction

The important processes of life, such as feeding, respiration, excretion and reproduction, take place in animals and plants alike. In single-celled organisms the processes of life all happen within the cell. However, bigger multicellular organisms need specific systems to enable them to carry out the processes of life.

Plants and animals have very different requirements and the organ systems they have evolved are specially adapted for their different roles. In this section we shall be considering some of these complex organ systems, and discovering how animals and plants have solved some of life's difficulties, particularly the common ones of support, supply, transport and movement.

One of the most obvious features of multicellular plants is that they cannot move from place to place. This means that they have to find everything they need to survive in the area where they are growing. In this section we shall find out more about the systems that allow them to survive in this situation. Very large plants have to transport substances far further around their bodies than animals do. How do they do this – and how do they support such massive bodies? The answers lie in the systems found in the roots, stems and leaves of the plants we see all around us. The leaves are the main organs of photosynthesis, the site of the chemical process on which all life depends. An understanding of the way these diverse systems work together will underpin our study of the biochemistry going on within a plant later in the book.

Animals have some of the same pressing needs as plants, but their bodies are usually mobile and they have to find and eat their food. These needs are therefore met in rather different ways. In this section we shall look at respiratory systems, and how they enable animals to exchange the gases needed for respiration. Again, an understanding of the structure of these systems helps when we look deeper into the chemistry of respiration.

Considering systems used to solve the problems of transport, support and movement builds up a firm base from which we can move on to look at issues of energy and control in living organisms.

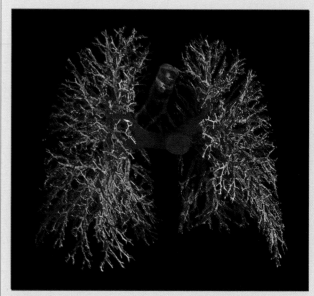

Figure 1 If an organ system such as the lungs fails then life becomes impossible.

DO PLANTS MATTER?

Plants are of vital importance to us all, because they harness the energy of the Sun by photosynthesis and make it available to us in the form of food. They also absorb carbon dioxide and produce oxygen in this process, maintaining the balance of the gases in the atmosphere. The ways in which we use plants are many and various, and they have had far-reaching effects on human history for thousands of years.

Plants provide food and drink ...

Around the world much of the staple diet of the human race comes from plants. Cereal crops, pulses, nuts, fruits and berries are all the products of plant reproduction, whilst other foodstuffs come from stems, roots, leaves and storage organs. Plentiful food supplies have allowed nations to expand and prosper, whilst food shortages such as the Irish potato famines in the nineteenth century changed the course of history for a whole country. Many drinks are also plant products. Some, like tea, coffee and alcohol, have become more than just a drink – they are bound up in the way societies work. The tea trade with China brought that great civilisation to its knees when opium (another plant product) instead of silver was brought into the country as payment for tea.

The enjoyable effects of alcohol are offset by the wake of human suffering that its abuse causes through violence, crime and ill health. The introduction of alcohol to groups such as the native Americans and the Aborigines helped destroy these ancient cultures.

... materials and drugs

Plants have other uses as well as providing us with food and drink. Hemp, flax, jute, manila and sisal are all plant fibres used in fabrics and ropes. The most important plant fibre is cotton. It was in part the great split between the Northern and Southern States of America over the use of slavery in the growth and production of cotton that led to the American Civil War.

Plants provide us with an enormous range of drugs. Many of these have healing properties, and have enabled people to live longer in different places of the world. The search for new active chemicals from plants continues all the time. Some drugs, like the nicotine in tobacco, are accepted for social use in spite of the many deaths from smoking-related illnesses. Other plant-based drugs are illegal almost all over the world, and the supplying of these drugs underpins many a dubious economy whilst their use destroys countless lives.

Plants are vital to the health of the Earth. They are intimately involved in almost every strand of human existence and the study of plant systems and the way they work leads us as biologists to an ever greater understanding of these life-giving organisms.

Figure 1 Plants are decorative, but their importance on Earth is far greater than this.

Figure 2 When cotton was king, slaves were bred like farm animals – and eventually the world rebelled...

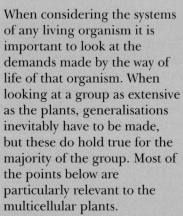

2.1 Systems in plants: Roots

As organisms increase in complexity, becoming multicellular, evolving distinct methods of providing for their energy needs, perhaps moving around, then the levels of organisation within the organism must also become more complex. In unicellular organisms the single cell must perform all the functions necessary for life. In multicellular organisms there is scope for specialisation of function. Groups of cells become organised into systems dealing with only one or two particular aspects of life – perhaps obtaining energy, perhaps reproducing the species – whilst at the same time becoming dependent on different systems to provide their other needs. These **systems of life** will be considered in this section.

Plant organisation

The living world can be divided in many ways, but two major groups are the **plants** and the **animals**. Plants are **autotrophic** (self-feeding). They can utilise the energy of the Sun to drive reactions involving water and carbon dioxide, with glucose as the immediate end product. The glucose can then be broken down by the process of **cellular respiration**, producing ATP as an energy supply for the other reactions of the cell, or used for the synthesis of amino acids and lipids. This process of using the Sun's energy to synthesise sugars and so provide an energy supply for the cell is known as **photosynthesis**, and is described in detail in section 3.2. Most organisation in plants is related in one way or another to this feature of plant life.

Figure 2.1.1 Multicellular organisms need oxygen and food, must get rid of waste, and have to reproduce themselves. They have evolved specialised systems made up of highly modified cells to carry out these functions.

The needs of plants

When considering the systems of any living organism it is important to look at the demands made by the way of life of that organism. When looking at a group as extensive as the plants, generalisations inevitably have to be made, but these do hold true for the majority of the group. Most of the points below are particularly relevant to the multicellular plants.

(1) Plants need to be anchored in some way to give a base for the photosynthetic part of the plant and to allow the plant to take advantage of a particular habitat.
(2) Plants must be able to capture as much sunlight as possible for photosynthesis.
(3) Plants must be able to obtain all the water, carbon dioxide and minerals that they need, and also get rid of any toxic waste products.
(4) For sexual reproduction to occur, male and female sex cells must be brought together and the seeds protected and nurtured as they develop and then dispersed to give the maximum possible chance for the species to continue.

Most multicellular plants show some differentiation into at least two, and often three, distinct permanent regions. One area is involved in anchorage and often also in the uptake of water and minerals. Another region may act as a support for the third, which consists of the major photosynthetic organs. These divisions are more commonly referred to as **roots**, **stems** and **leaves**, shown in figure 2.1.2. Many plants also develop further specialised reproductive areas (flowers, spore capsules, fruit, etc.) at certain times of year. These will be considered in more detail in section 5.

The root system

The need for roots

Plants need to trap as much energy from the Sun as possible to make food by photosynthesis. In order to do this they generally have a very large surface area. This in turn makes them very vulnerable to water loss by evaporation. To reduce this water loss the plant is protected from dehydration by a waxy covering. This means that water cannot be absorbed through the exposed surfaces of the plant and so alternative methods of obtaining water have evolved – most commonly, the **roots**. These are structures which contain **vascular** (transport) tissue.

Some plant groups such as the liverworts and mosses (see section 6.1) do not have a waterproofing layer of wax over their leaves. This means that they can absorb water over the entire plant surface and do not have a true vascular root system. Instead they have a system of **rhizoids**, simple root-like structures whose major role is that of anchoring the plant. If you have ever tried to prise moss off a wall, you will know that they are very successful at this. This lack of vascular tissue restricts the distribution of liverworts and mosses to moist or wet habitats.

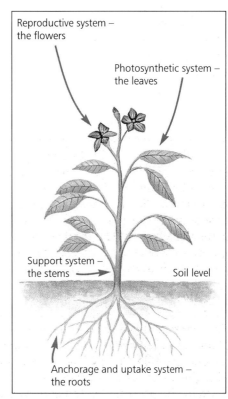

Figure 2.1.2 The main systems in a generalised plant. They are all interlinking and interdependent to give a coordinated and successful organism.

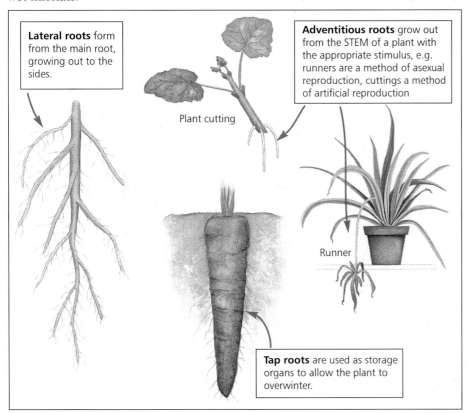

Lateral roots form from the main root, growing out to the sides.

Plant cutting

Adventitious roots grow out from the STEM of a plant with the appropriate stimulus, e.g. runners are a method of asexual reproduction, cuttings a method of artificial reproduction

Runner

Tap roots are used as storage organs to allow the plant to overwinter.

Figure 2.1.3 Root systems come in a variety of shapes and forms to enable them to perform their variety of functions.

True root systems

Most land plants have a **true root system**. This contains cells specialised for the uptake and transport of water and minerals from the soil. The root system of a plant is usually very large – often at least as extensive as the visible plant above it. The more extensive the root system of a plant, the larger will be the surface area available for the uptake of water and minerals from the soil. Large root systems are also very effective at anchoring plants. Figure 2.1.3 shows the different types of roots.

Roots are very important to the structure of the soil. The extensive network of plant roots traps soil, binding it together and helping to prevent erosion by wind or rain.

Structure of the root system

The cells which make up true root systems are specially adapted for their functions. One of their most striking features is that, under normal conditions, they do not contain chloroplasts or the green pigment chlorophyll which is usually associated with plant cells. As little or no light penetrates the soil, photosynthetic pigments would be of no use to root cells. There are several different types of cells within the root system, each adapted to its particular function. To enable them to work effectively they are arranged in a distinctive way.

The root system involves a complex, branching network to give a large surface area, and to maximise this surface area the roots are covered in microscopic **root hairs**, extensions of the outer cells. Plants cannot move around to find minerals in the soil, but the growth of these roots and root hairs allows them to exploit the soil minerals over a wide area. They are the equivalent of a 'foraging strategy' for plants. The outer layers of cells are permeable to water. Within the roots the tissues can be divided into two main types. Much of the root – indeed, much of the plant – is made up of supportive packing tissue. This largely consists of the most common type of plant cells, known as **parenchyma** cells. These cells do not need particular specialisation to carry out their supportive role, but they can be modified in a variety of ways to make them suitable for other functions such as storage and photosynthesis.

The remainder of the root consists of vascular tissues, the **phloem** and **xylem**. The phloem is living tissue which carries the dissolved products of photosynthesis around the plant. Root cells need energy to grow, divide and live. Glucose is made in the leaves, converted to sucrose and transported by the phloem to areas of the plant where it is needed. The flow within phloem tissues can go either up or down the plant. The xylem carries water and dissolved minerals from the soil to the photosynthetic parts of the plant and the movement within xylem tissues is always upwards under normal circumstances. Xylem starts off as living tissue, but increasing amounts of **lignin** (woody material) are laid down in the cell walls to make the tissue stronger and more supportive, and the living contents of the cells die. This means that most of the functioning xylem in a plant is dead. A simple picture of the structure of a typical root is given in figure 2.1.4. Figure 2.1.6 builds on this basic picture of the root to show us exactly where the different tissues are found, what they look like and what they do.

The flowering plants contain two groups – **monocotyledons**, in which the embryo has one seed leaf, and **dicotyledons**, in which it has two. This will be considered in more detail in section 5.3. Figure 2.1.6 shows the structure of a dicotyledonous root.

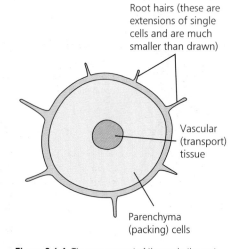

Root hairs (these are extensions of single cells and are much smaller than drawn)

Vascular (transport) tissue

Parenchyma (packing) cells

Figure 2.1.4 The arrangement of tissues in the root system.

The root system of a plant can thus be seen to be a collection of a variety of cells, many of which have evolved to carry out very specialised functions. As you have seen, the large quantities of packing cells and the arrangement of the vascular tissue in the centre of the root are particularly important in the role of support. But how do the various elements of the system come together to perform the other major function of the roots – the uptake of water and mineral ions from the soil?

The root system at work

The uptake of water

An adequate supply of water is of prime importance to a plant. It is needed for photosynthesis. It is also important to maintain turgor in the cells, ensuring support of the tissues by the parenchyma cells, and to prevent wilting so that the leaves are positioned correctly for photosynthesis. (Note that wilting is *not* simply loss of turgor – when a plant wilts whole cells shrink. However, unless the wilting continues for a long time, no permanent damage is done.) Water is also important for the transport of organic solutes and mineral salts around the body of the plant.

There is a thin film of water containing minute traces of dissolved minerals around soil particles. This water is absorbed mainly by the younger parts of the roots, where the majority of the root hairs are found as the epidermis is still present. These microscopic hairs increase the surface area of the roots enormously, and they also come into very close contact with the soil particles. At its simplest, uptake of water by the roots depends on the water potential gradient (see section 1.4, page 57) across the root from the soil water to the xylem. Water moves from the soil into a root hair cell along a water potential gradient by osmosis. This makes the root hair cell contents more dilute than those of its neighbour, and water again moves by osmosis and so on across the root, as figure 2.1.5 shows.

The picture is in fact rather more complicated than this simple model suggests. The water potential gradient across the root from the piliferous layer to the cells closest to the xylem is the result of two factors – firstly, water is continually moved up the xylem, lowering the water potential of the xylem contents, and secondly, the xylem contents have a more negative solute potential than the soil water. The water does not simply flow from one cell to another – there appear to be three alternative routes which may be taken, as shown in figure 2.1.7. The **vacuolar pathway** allows water to move by osmosis along a

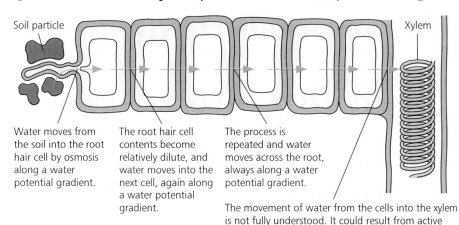

Water moves from the soil into the root hair cell by osmosis along a water potential gradient.

The root hair cell contents become relatively dilute, and water moves into the next cell, again along a water potential gradient.

The process is repeated and water moves across the root, always along a water potential gradient.

The movement of water from the cells into the xylem is not fully understood. It could result from active transport or could be simply the result of physical processes such as evaporation from the leaf surface.

Figure 2.1.5 A simple model of the movement of water into the root of a plant.

Exodermis

The **exodermis** may or may not be present. It may be under the epidermis, or may replace it entirely. Its function is to protect the root system from the entry of pathogens and it can appear very similar to the endodermis.

Root hair

A **root hair** is an extension of a single epidermal cell which is known as a **root hair cell**.

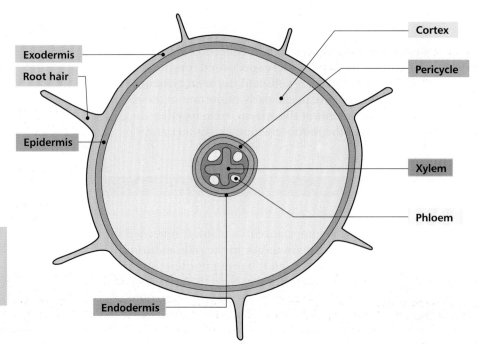

Cortex

Pericycle

Exodermis

Root hair

Epidermis

Xylem

Phloem

Endodermis

Epidermis

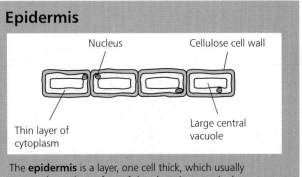

Nucleus

Cellulose cell wall

Thin layer of cytoplasm

Large central vacuole

The **epidermis** is a layer, one cell thick, which usually covers the entire surface of the plant, but may be lost as the plant grows older. The epidermis is made up of specialised parenchyma cells. In the root, these cells may produce hair-like extensions known as **root hairs** and the epidermis then called the **piliferous (hair-producing) layer**. The root hairs greatly increase the surface area available for the uptake of water and minerals.

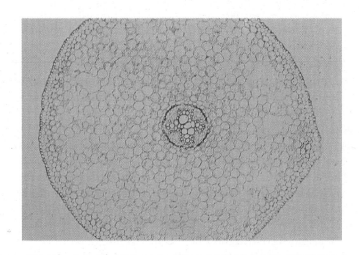

Endodermis

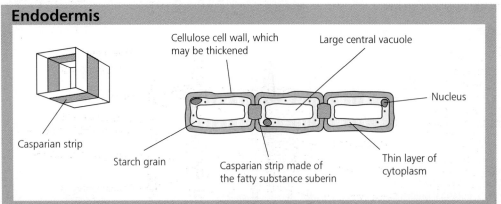

Cellulose cell wall, which may be thickened

Large central vacuole

Nucleus

Casparian strip

Starch grain

Casparian strip made of the fatty substance suberin

Thin layer of cytoplasm

The **endodermis** is a layer of cells surrounding the vascular tissue of the roots. It is particularly noticeable in roots because of the **Casparian strip** which develops. The Casparian strip is a band of fatty material called **suberin** which runs around each cell, and its possible role in the regulation of the movement of water and minerals across the root is discussed on page 98. The starch grains found in the endodermis cells may be important in the way that roots respond to gravity (**geotropism**).

Figure 2.1.6 This section through a young (primary) dicotyledonous root shows the main elements of a typical root system. The details may vary in monocotyledons or in older plants, but the main types of cells found in roots, along with the modifications they show for their particular function, are displayed here.

Cortex

The parenchyma cells of the **cortex** are unspecialised, rounded cells. Their main function is as packing tissue between more specialised parts, and they make up a substantial part of the root. Parenchyma cells have air spaces between them, but become very tightly packed when they are fully turgid. Because of this they play a useful role in providing support. The cortex parenchyma is also used for food storage. This is particularly important in those plants which use storage organs as away of overwintering, such as potatoes and carrots. Large amounts of starch are then packed away in organelles called **amyloplasts**. This ability to store food has been utilised by humans for thousands of years to provide a valuable food source.

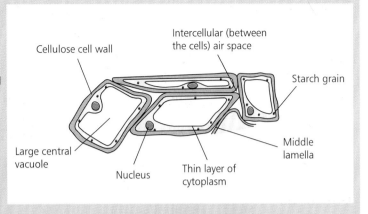

Pericycle

The cells of the **pericycle** are again parenchyma cells, similar to the cells of the cortex, acting as packing tissue between the endodermis and the vascular tissue. The cells of the pericycle can divide to form new lateral (side) roots if given the appropriate stimulus.

Xylem

The **xylem** has two main functions in the plant – the transport of water and mineral ions, and support. In roots it is the transport function which is the most important. Xylem is made up of several different types of cells, most of which are dead when they are functioning within the root. The xylem vessels are long tubular structures made by several cells fusing end to end by the breakdown of their end walls. There is no equivalent of the phloem sieve plates – xylem vessels are just hollow tubes. The first xylem to form is called **protoxylem**. It is capable of stretching and growing because its walls are not fully lignified. However, once growth has stopped **metaxylem** is formed. The walls are fully lignified and the cell contents die. Water moves out of the xylem into the surrounding cells either through unlignified areas or through specialised **pits**. In the root the xylem is positioned centrally, allowing it to perform a supportive role by helping the plant cope with the tugging strains imposed on it by the leaves and the stems as they bend in the wind. The only living cells found in xylem tissue are **xylem parenchyma** which stores food, holds deposits of tannins and various crystals and is involved in the transport of various substances. There are two other dead elements found with the xylem – **tracheids**, elongated lignified single cells more common in primitive plants, and **fibres**, important for additional mechanical strength.

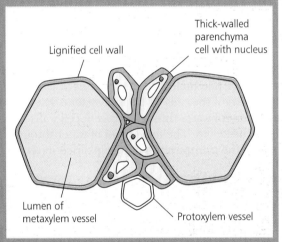

Phloem

The **phloem** makes up a system of tubes which transport organic solutes such as sucrose around the plant. It supplies the root system with the raw material for cellular respiration. Phloem tissue is basically made up of **sieve tubes**, cells which have fused end to end at **sieve plates** to form continuous tubes. As sieve tubes have no nucleus when mature, they are supported and kept alive by **companion cells**. Sieve tubes and companion cells form the functional unit of the phloem. The phloem is supported by **phloem parenchyma cells** – these look very like other parenchyma cells but are elongated to fit alongside the phloem cells. Also giving mechanical support and protection are **fibres** and spherical **sclereids**. These are dead because their walls are heavily lignified.

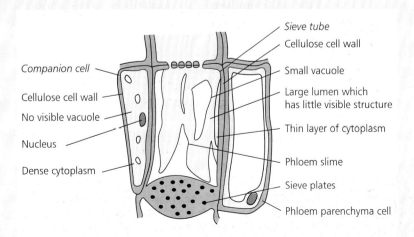

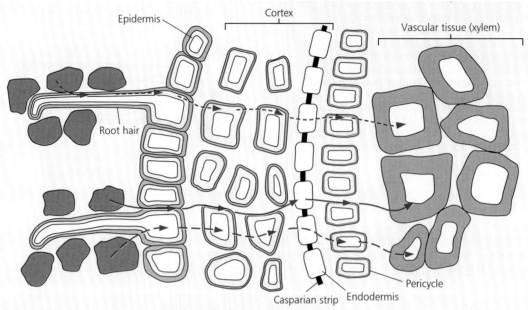

Epidermis | Cortex | Vascular tissue (xylem)

Root hair

Casparian strip | Endodermis | Pericycle

- - - - ▶ Symplast pathway – the plasmodesmata form a continuous pathway between cells, and water passes through by diffusion.
——▶ Apoplast pathway – water passes freely through the cellulose cell walls.
- - ▶ Vacuolar pathway – water moves through the vacuoles by osmosis from the cytoplasm.

water potential gradient from the soil water to the xylem across the vacuoles of the cells of the root system. In the **symplast pathway** the water moves along the same water potential gradient, but this time across the interconnected cytoplasm (**symplast**) of the cells of the root system. The **apoplast pathway** is the movement of water through adjacent cell walls (the **apoplast**) from the root hair cell to the xylem. The movement of water through this pathway is largely the result of the transpiration pull, explained in section 2.3.

Figure 2.1.7 The cells of the roots are organised into a system which is very efficient at taking up water from the soil.

A closer look at water movement in the root

To understand the pathways for the movement of water through the root system needs a closer examination of the cellular situation.

The vacuolar pathway

The soil water has a higher water potential (it is a more dilute solution) than the cells of the piliferous layer. As a result water moves across the cell wall and cytoplasm into the vacuole of the root hair cell by osmosis. It then moves from vacuole to vacuole across the root until it reaches the cells next to the xylem, moving down a water potential gradient which is set up as follows. As water moves up the xylem it is replaced. This replacement water is drawn from the neighbouring parenchyma cells. It seems that water must be moved from the cells next to the xylem into the xylem by active means, or it may just be by the suction created by evaporation at the top of the plant. As yet no one is sure exactly how this movement of water into the xylem vessels is brought about. As water leaves these cells, their water potential becomes more negative and so water enters them from the vacuole of neighbouring cells, which in turn develop a more negative water potential and so moves water from *their* neighbours. This continues right across the root system, and as a result, a continuous movement of water is seen from the soil solution to the xylem across the vacuoles of the root cells.

The symplast pathway

The cytoplasm of adjacent plant cells is connected by strands called **plasmodesmata** which go through pores in the cellulose cell walls. Figure 2.1.8 shows these connections. Water moves from the soil across the cytoplasm (the **symplast**) of adjacent cells along the water potential gradient from the root hair cells to the xylem.

The apoplast pathway

Because of the loose, open-network structure of cellulose, up to half of the volume of the cell wall can be filled with water molecules. As water is drawn into the xylem, attraction between the molecules ensures that more water is drawn across from the adjacent cell wall, and so on. As water is taken into the root hair from the soil, the mineral ions dissolved in it move too. The water and minerals move across the cells of the root in the cell walls until they reaches the endodermis. The Casparian strips of suberin stop any further progress through the cell walls. Any water and minerals that are to continue the journey have to enter the cytoplasm temporarily to avoid the Casparian strip. As minerals often need to enter the cytoplasm against a concentration gradient, active transport must be involved. This seems to be a method of controlling the amounts of water and minerals which move from the soil into the xylem. In spite of the barrier of the Casparian strip, the end result of the apoplast pathway is again a continuous stream of water across the root to the xylem.

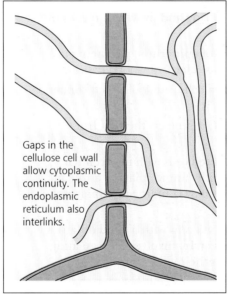

Gaps in the cellulose cell wall allow cytoplasmic continuity. The endoplasmic reticulum also interlinks.

Figure 2.1.8 Plasmodesmata connect adjacent cells through the cell wall.

The uptake of minerals

Along with its functions of support, anchorage and water uptake, the root system has also developed to absorb minerals from the soil. Although plants can synthesise their own carbohydrates by photosynthesis, they also need other molecules such as proteins and fats. To produce these they require certain minerals such as nitrates, and these they must extract from the soil.

Minerals dissolved in the soil water are carried in an unselective manner in the apoplast pathway of water uptake and move through adjacent cell walls. This means that the parenchyma cells of the root cortex are bathed in a very dilute solution of mineral ions because they are surrounded by the soil water held in the cellulose cell walls. Any ions which are needed may be moved across the cell membrane by diffusion if the membrane is freely permeable to the ion, or by facilitated diffusion or active transport.

On reaching the impermeable Casparian strip, mineral ions can no longer move through the cellulose wall. They may pass into the cytoplasm of the cells either by diffusion along a concentration gradient, or by active transport if they are being moved against a concentration gradient. In these ways the root system takes up mineral ions, including those which are required for the functioning of the plant as a whole. The water and minerals are then supplied to the other major systems of the plant.

SUMMARY

- As organisms become larger and more complex, they develop specialised systems to carry out particular functions.

- Multicellular plants need systems to carry out the functions of: anchorage; capture of sunlight for photosynthesis; taking in the water, carbon dioxide and minerals they need; sexual reproduction.

- Land plants commonly consist of stems, roots and leaves. **Roots** carry out the functions of anchorage and obtaining water and mineral salts from the soil. They may also store food for overwintering and provide a means of reproduction.

- The overall root structure is an outer layer of **epidermis**, **parenchyma** (packing) cells in the **cortex**, and central **vascular** (transport) tissue.

- **Epidermal** cells are specialised parenchyma cells, some of which contain hair-like extensions called **root hairs**.

- The **exodermis** may or may not be present; it protects the root from pathogens.

- The **cortex** parenchyma cells are unspecialised cells with intercellular spaces which disappear when the cells are fully turgid, playing a role in support. In some plants these packing cells may contain **amyloplasts** to store starch for overwintering.

- **Endodermal** cells are specialised parenchyma cells with a band of fatty **suberin** around them called the **Casparian strip**, involved in regulating the movement of water and minerals across the root.

- The **pericycle** contains unspecialised parenchyma cells between the endoderm and the vascular tissue of the phloem and xylem.

- **Phloem** vessels transport organic materials around the plant. **Sieve tubes**, long cells which fuse at **sieve plates**, have no nuclei and are supported and kept alive by **companion cells**. Phloem parenchyma cells which are elongated to fit alongside the sieve tubes support the phloem vessels.

- **Xylem** vessels transport water and mineral ions up the plant and help support the plant. They are long tubular vessels in the centre of the root, called **protoxylem** when first formed which mature into **metaxylem**. Metaxylem is **lignified** (lignin is impermeable) so its cells are dead. Living xylem parenchyma cells store food and hold deposits.

- Water passes into the root hair cells from the soil along a water potential gradient. It passes to the xylem in the centre of the root by three pathways:
  the **vacuolar pathway**, by osmosis along a water potential gradient, through the vacuoles of the root cells

the **symplast pathway**, by osmosis through the interconnected cytoplasm of the root cells

the **apoplast pathway**, by attraction between the water molecules, through the cell walls of the root cells, controlled by the Casparian strip of the endodermis.

- Minerals in the soil water are also taken up and are held in solution in the water in the plant cell walls so are available to cells and can enter by diffusion, facilitated diffusion or active transport, depending on the mechanisms available for each ion.

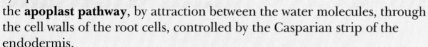

QUESTIONS

1 **a** Describe the main functions of a plant.
   b With reference to your answer to **a**, explain the need for cells to be arranged into tissues and organs in multicellular organisms.

2 The structure of a root is closely related to its functions.
   a What are the main functions of a plant root?
   b Describe the structure of a typical plant root and explain how this structure may be modified for the root to perform a variety of functions.

3 Explain the role of plant root cells in the uptake of:
   a water
   b minerals.

Developing Key Skills

Research the impact of one plant on human society. Trace the history of your chosen plant back as far as possible, and find out about the ways in which the use of the plant, or its products, has affected social, political and economic history. You should use a variety of resources, including IT. The biology focus on page 91 will give you some ideas for suitable plants to choose.

Plants have colonised much of the land surface of the planet, surviving in a great range of conditions. In some of these habitats it is easy to carry out photosynthesis with no particular stress on the system, but to photosynthesise on a sand dune, in a desert or in the Arctic is a very different proposition. Leaves have to reach a successful compromise between the need to collect sunlight and the need to prevent water loss from the plant.

Everyday adaptations

The plants we see around us all have some adaptations to maximise the amount of photosynthesis they can carry out. Deciduous trees photosynthesise when conditions are good in the summer, then shed their leaves and become dormant during the winter. Conifers have adopted a different strategy. They photosynthesise all year long using leaves that are reduced to thin 'needles'. These small leaves have thick cuticles and lose little water, are almost immune to damage by winds and can survive very cold conditions. All the plants in our gardens and in the fields each have their own ways of coping with the conflict between energy gain and water loss.

Figure 1 In spring, the woodland violet produces 'sun' leaves which are relatively small and bright green, and use the bright sunlight reaching them. Later, when the tree canopy develops overhead, the violet grows 'shade' leaves which are bigger and darker green, because they contain more chlorophyll. These leaves can make the most of the dim light now reaching the woodland floor.

Figure 2 Some plants, like these giant water lilies, have leaves that float on the surface of water. These can become huge, because water loss and support are not a problem, but they need special air spaces in the structure of the leaves to keep them buoyant.

More exotic leaves

Plants growing in more extreme conditions have had to make dramatic adaptations to survive and succeed. Cacti have reduced their leaves to thin spines, relying on their fleshy swollen stems to carry out photosynthesis with minimum water loss. Plants that grow in cold conditions such as ice plants often have thick, waxy cuticles and may also contain a chemical that acts as an antifreeze, helping prevent the cells from freezing and being destroyed.

As well as being organs of photosynthesis, leaves can be modified for storing food or water. In tropical rainforest plants, leaves are often large and brightly coloured, probably helping to attract pollinators. Leaves can also be minute, or covered in hairs and tightly rolled – adaptations common in environments with a very high salt level, which puts extreme water stress on a plant. So leaves are not all green and flat – they can be multicoloured, multi-purpose organs which are vital to a plant in many different ways.

2.2 Systems in plants: Stems and leaves

The root system of a plant is highly specialised to perform its particular functions. The other major plant systems, the stem and the leaf, show similar levels of organisation.

The stem system

Functions of the stem

The needs of plants were discussed on page 92. The primary function of a stem system in fulfilling these needs is support. Stems hold the leaves above the ground and support them in the best position for obtaining sunlight for photosynthesis. They also support flowers to maximise the likelihood of pollination and thus sexual reproduction – sometimes this means drooping stems, sometimes stems are erect. The stem system must be flexible in order to withstand buffeting by wind and rain, and yet have the strength to remain upright. In extremes of heat plants wilt, which helps prevent excessive water loss by reducing the surface area of the leaves in direct sunlight. However, they need to be able to revive rapidly as soon as conditions are suitable again. Thus the support system has to fulfil a variety of complex and in some cases conflicting needs.

The other major function of stems is the movement of materials about the plant. The products of photosynthesis are carried from the leaves where they are formed via stems to the buds, flowers, fruit and roots where they are needed. Water moves through the stems in a steady stream from the roots up to the leaves, and the mineral ions needed for the synthesis of complex chemicals are transported in this stream.

Most stems are green – they contain chlorophyll. They carry out a small amount of photosynthesis, but this is not a major function.

Not all plants have stems. The liverworts have a simple thallus structure and the mosses have leaves which arise directly from a pad of rhizoids (see section 6.1 for more details). Neither of these groups has specialised transport tissues, and both grow close to the ground. However, the majority of land plants possess stems.

The functions of stems

As in the root system, the cells of the stem carry out a variety of functions and have become specialised.

(1) Stems provide support for the main body of the plant.
(2) Stems support leaves in positions such that they capture as much sunlight as possible, and reproductive organs in positions to maximise pollination and aid seed dispersal.
(3) Stems must be flexible and able to withstand the pulling and bending forces exerted by the wind.
(4) Stems allow the transport of water, sugars and other dissolved substances around the plant.
(5) In some plants stems form the means by which the plant stores food for overwintering.
(6) In some plants stems can form adventitious roots.
(7) In some plants stems form a means by which the plant reproduces.
(8) In some plants, such as the cactus, the stem forms the main photosynthetic organ and also stores water. The leaves have been reduced to spines to cut down water loss.

Figure 2.2.1 Stems link the leaves, the roots and the reproductive systems and provide support.

Structure of the stem system

The cells which make up a stem system are adapted for their various functions. Many of the cells have structures similar to those of the root, but their arrangement is different. Unlike the root, the outer layers of the stem should not be permeable to water, in order to prevent unwanted water loss. A waxy, waterproof layer is produced over the surface of the epidermis which is known as the **cuticle**. The outer layers of the stem may contain some chloroplasts in modified parenchyma cells, ensuring that as much food as possible is produced. The bulk of the stem is made up of supporting and packing (parenchyma) cells with the transport tissue arranged around the edge in **vascular bundles** to provide both support and flexibility in the young stems which need it.

Figure 2.2.2 gives a simple picture of the main regions of a typical stem, whilst figure 2.2.3 shows in detail the types of cells and their functions. The example used is the stem of a young, dicotyledonous plant. Although the details of arrangement vary in monocotyledons and older plants, the basic cell types and principles of arrangement of stem systems can be seen here.

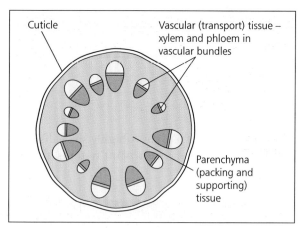

Figure 2.2.2 A stem appears very different from the root, although many of the same tissues are involved. The different distribution of the tissues allows the stem to carry out its supportive functions and yet resist the effects of the weather.

Pith

The centre of the stem is made up of **pith**. The cells are unspecialised parenchyma. They may store starch or fatty material if part of the stem forms a storage organ for overwintering, e.g. in crocus corms.

Endodermis

The **endodermis** is a single-celled layer that is difficult to identify unless the section is specially stained to show up the starch grains which are stored within it.

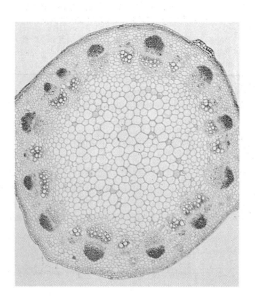

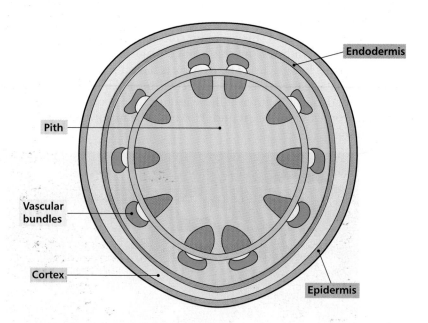

Figure 2.2.3 The main elements of a stem system. The arrangement of tissues enables the functions of support and transport to be carried out.

Epidermis

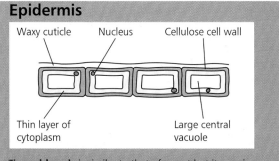

Waxy cuticle Nucleus Cellulose cell wall

Thin layer of cytoplasm Large central vacuole

The **epidermis** is similar to that of a root but it remains throughout the plant's life. The cells secrete **cutin**, a waxy substance which helps to prevent water loss from the stem surface and to protect against the entry of pathogens. Epidermal hairs may be formed, sometimes as an extension of a single epidermal cell as in root hairs, and sometimes involving several modified epidermal cells. These hairs perform a variety of functions. Some form a layer trapping moist air and helping to prevent water loss. Others are hooked and help climbing plants grip their supports. Others are protective – stiff and bristly, or loaded with irritant chemicals such as on stinging nettles.

Cortex

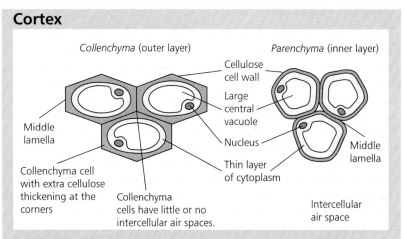

Collenchyma (outer layer) *Parenchyma* (inner layer)

Cellulose cell wall

Large central vacuole

Middle lamella

Nucleus

Middle lamella

Thin layer of cytoplasm

Collenchyma cell with extra cellulose thickening at the corners

Collenchyma cells have little or no intercellular air spaces.

Intercellular air space

The **cortex parenchyma** cells in the stem act as packing cells, as in the root. The **collenchyma** consists of cells similar to parenchyma, but more specialised in mechanical support. The increased amounts of cellulose, particularly at the corners of the cells, and the lack of air spaces between cells, means that they are effective in providing support regardless of their level of turgor. The outer cells of this layer may contain chloroplasts so that photosynthesis can take place.

Vascular bundles

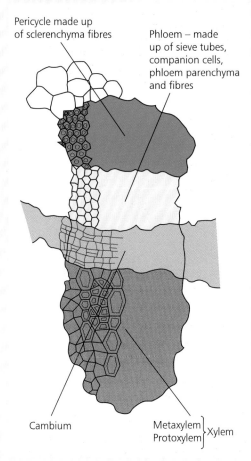

Pericycle made up of sclerenchyma fibres

Phloem – made up of sieve tubes, companion cells, phloem parenchyma and fibres

Cambium

Metaxylem
Protoxylem } Xylem

The **vascular bundles** contain the transport tissue of the stem. The xylem and phloem have the same structure and function as in the root system, with xylem carrying water and dissolved minerals up the stem and phloem moving dissolved organic substances around the plant. In contrast to the root, the transport tissue in the stem system is arranged around the outside in young dicotyledons. This contributes greatly to the support function of the stem. The xylem itself is lignified and the phloem contains strengthening fibres. In addition, the **sclerenchyma** present has a purely mechanical function. The walls are greatly thickened with deposits of lignin. This kills the cells, but gives them both tensile and compressive strength – they can resist stretching and squashing by the wind without breaking or buckling. The **cambium** is a band of unspecialised cells which divide, giving rise to more specialised cells which form both the xylem and the phloem.

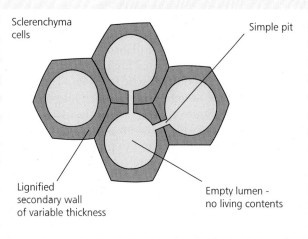

Sclerenchyma cells

Simple pit

Lignified secondary wall of variable thickness

Empty lumen - no living contents

The relationship between structure and function

The arrangement of the tissues in the stem system, with large amounts of parenchyma for packing and support and the additional mechanical strength supplied by collenchyma and sclerenchyma, enables the stem to support the body of the plant. At the same time it maintains the flexibility needed to change the orientation of the leaves and flowers to follow the Sun, and to withstand the stresses imposed by the wind.

In monocotyledonous plants the vascular bundles are not arranged around the edge of the stem but are scattered more generally through the parenchyma. They still provide effective support. Plants which live for a very long time or grow particularly large may add to their support systems with **secondary thickening**, involving the laying down of **lignified** or woody tissue which gives a great deal of additional support and strength.

The presence of the vascular tissue within the stem system provides for the transport of materials. The way in which the movement of water and solutes is brought about will be considered in more detail in section 2.3.

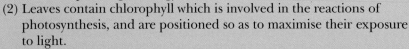

The functions of leaf systems

(1) Leaves capture light energy.
(2) Leaves contain chlorophyll which is involved in the reactions of photosynthesis, and are positioned so as to maximise their exposure to light.
(3) Leaves supply water and carbon dioxide to the site of photosynthesis.
(4) Leaves have a transport system to remove the products of photosynthesis so that they can be carried around the plant.

The photosynthetic system

All life depends on the photosynthetic system of plants. Without the oxygen- and sugar-producing capabilities of plants, animal life as we know it could not exist. Leaves have evolved to become photosynthetic factories. They contain specialised cells and have a high level of organisation which allows them to take full advantage of the prevailing conditions in order to synthesise food. In this section we shall consider how leaves provide a system arranged to make available the raw materials for photosynthesis, and to provide the 'chemical plant' required for the process itself. The biochemistry of photosynthesis will be considered later.

Of the needs of a plant already discussed, the leaf system's primary function is to capture sunlight and also take in carbon dioxide in order to carry out photosynthesis. The photosynthetic organs of the plant are highly organised to ensure that the needs for photosynthesis are met.

Structure of the leaf system

Figure 2.2.4 Leaves show a wide variety of adaptations for different extremes of environment. In spite of this variety, the underlying organisation of most leaves is the same.

In general, the leaves of plants offer as large a surface area as possible to the Sun. They tend to be relatively thin, so that sunlight can reach all the photosynthetic tissue. Transport tissue supplies water to the cells of the leaf and removes the products of photosynthesis. This transport tissue frequently has another role – it supports the thin leaf and thus helps to expose it to the sunlight. These features can be seen clearly by considering both the external and the detailed internal structure of a leaf, in figures 2.2.5 and 2.2.6.

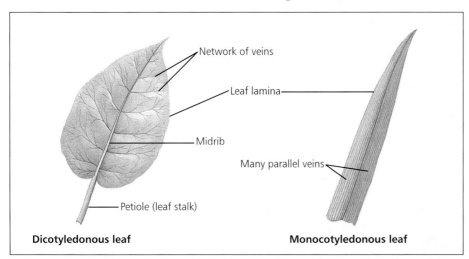

Network of veins

Leaf lamina

Midrib

Many parallel veins

Petiole (leaf stalk)

Dicotyledonous leaf

Monocotyledonous leaf

Figure 2.2.5 The external appearance of a leaf shows the overall arrangement with the transport tissues supporting the rest.

The leaf system at work

The relationship of structure and function

The structure of the leaf in figure 2.2.6 shows how the various tissues are arranged to allow them to function with maximum efficiency. The photosynthetic cells are closely packed near the upper surface of the leaf, closest to the Sun. The details of their functioning and the biochemistry of photosynthesis will be considered later. But the remainder of the leaf has other important functions including the transport of water, minerals and the products of photosynthesis in the xylem and phloem, as well as the support of the photosynthetic tissue of the leaf lamina. An important transport role is gaseous exchange between the cells of the leaf and the external atmosphere.

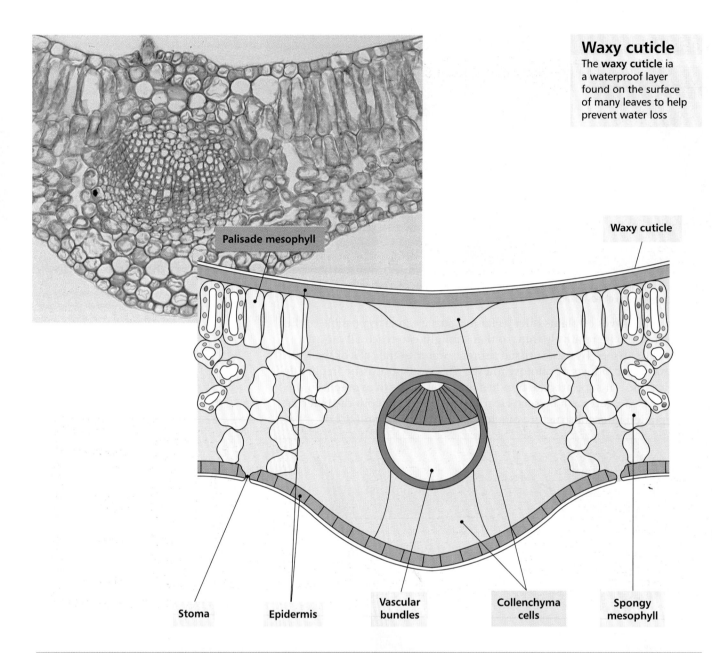

Waxy cuticle

Palisade mesophyll

Stoma

Epidermis

Vascular
bundles

Collenchyma
cells

Spongy
mesophyll

Epidermis

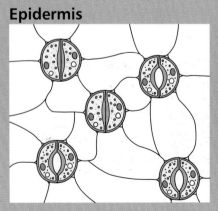

The **epidermis** of a leaf is made up of the same type of
simple, unspecialised, flattened cells seen in root and
stem epidermis. Those on the top surface of the leaf
are referred to as **upper epidermis** and those on the
underneath surface as **lower epidermis**. They secrete
cutin, forming a waxy cuticle which helps prevent water
loss through the leaves. However, gases such as carbon
dioxide, oxygen and water vapour need to both enter and
leave the leaf for photosynthesis and respiration. **Stomata**
allow this to happen. These are specialised pores with
guard cells on either side of the opening. Stomata are
found particularly in the lower epidermis, and in some plants
stomata also occur in the epidermis of the stems. Stomata
can be either open or closed, depending on the prevailing
conditions, and they therefore help control water loss from
a plant.

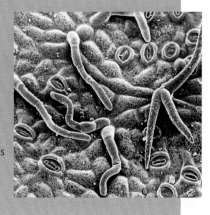

Figure 2.2.6 The specialised cells and their functional arrangement can be clearly seen in a section through a dicotyledonous leaf.

Collenchyma

Collenchyma cells may be found in the leaf, sometimes above and often as part of the **midrib** (main vein). With their areas of cellulose thickening they give mechanical strength and support.

Vascular bundles

The **midrib** contains the vascular bundles and is the main vessel of transport. A large system of smaller vessels branch out from the midrib. Water and mineral salts are conducted to the leaf in the xylem and the products of photosynthesis are removed in the phloem. The vessels, and in particular the midrib, are also important as a support for the thin lamina of the leaf.

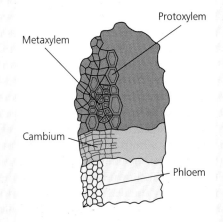

Palisade mesophyll

Palisade mesophyll is the main photosynthetic tissue of the plant. The cells are frequently columnar and contain large numbers of chloroplasts, tightly packed together. Within the palisade mesophyll cells the chloroplasts can move about, probably by cytoplasmic streaming (mass movement of the cytoplasm). In strong sunlight chloroplasts are fairly evenly distributed throughout the cytoplasm, as they can all receive enough light to photosynthesise effectively. At lower light levels, chloroplasts move closer together at the top of the cell to obtain maximum radiation. This maximises the chances of the chlorophyll pigment receiving enough light fo photosynthesis to occur. Palisade mesophyll cells are a very specialised form of parenchyma cell which has been modified through evolution to carry out photosynthesis.

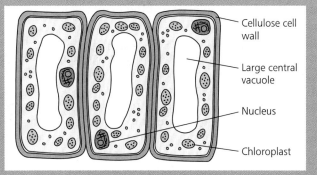

Spongy mesophyll

Spongy mesophyll is the second main photosynthetic tissue after the palisade mesophyll. It is lower down in the structure of the leaf and so less likely to receive enough light to photosynthesise effectively. There are fewer chloroplasts in spongy mesophyll cells than in palisade ones. Spongy mesophyll cells are again modified parenchyma, are smaller and have more irregular shapes than palisade mesophyll cells. Large **intercellular air spaces** in the spongy mesophyll, particularly around the stomata, are of great importance for effective gaseous exchange – in photosynthesis the uptake of carbon dioxide and the removal of oxygen, and also the evaporation of water from the leaf. They therefore have an important role in water balance and the transport of materials round the plant.

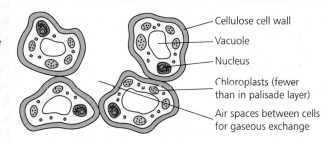

Gaseous exchange in the leaf

The cells of the spongy mesophyll are irregularly shaped and arranged with large air spaces between them. The surfaces of these cells are moist. This and the large exposed surface area means that gaseous exchange can occur freely between the cells of the leaf and the air spaces by a simple process of diffusion. During the day carbon dioxide (required for photosynthesis) moves by diffusion *into* the cells and oxygen (the main waste product of photosynthesis) moves *out*. Water passes by evaporation from the cells into the air spaces.

The inside of the leaf and the air spaces there are not a closed system. The impermeable waxy cuticle on the surface of the leaf acts as a barrier to gaseous diffusion, and particularly to the evaporation of water. A particularly thick waxy cuticle can virtually eliminate evaporation. Gases move into and out of the leaf through the **stomata**, specialised pores found mainly in the epidermis on the underside of the leaf, shown in figure 2.2.7. The pores open to allow the uptake of carbon dioxide by the leaf. The intercellular spaces are saturated with water vapour so evaporation of water takes place while the stomata are open.

Open or closed?

There is a constant state of conflict in the needs of a plant. For photosynthesis to occur successfully at its maximum rate carbon dioxide must move into the leaf and oxygen out of it, so stomata must be open. A steady flow of water and minerals up from the soil into the aerial parts of the plant then results from the evaporation of water from the leaf cells. On the other hand, water is often in relatively short supply. In dry climates or in drying conditions such as strong wind an enormous amount of water would be lost from the leaves if free evaporation were possible, so that the plant would suffer damage or death. How is this conflict resolved?

Stomata are not simple pores. The pore is bordered by two **guard cells**, specialised epidermal cells. They are sausage shaped and, like other epidermal cells, contain a sap vacuole. Unlike other epidermal cells they contain chloroplasts, and the cellulose of their walls is unevenly distributed. Figure 2.2.8 shows how stomata open as a result of turgor changes.

It appears that as water moves into the guard cells from the surrounding epidermal cells, the turgidity of the guard cells increases. The stomatal pore opens as a result of the uneven bending which takes place because of the unevenly thickened cellulose walls and the cellulose hoops around the guard cells. But what causes the osmotic situation of the cells to change so that water moves into the guard cells? As yet there is no definitive answer, although there are several hypotheses.

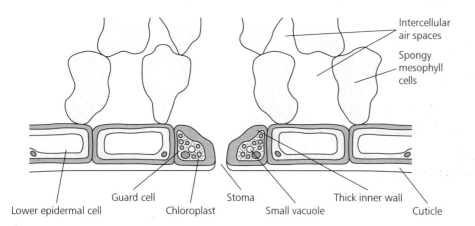

Figure 2.2.7 Stomata provide a route for gases in and out of the leaf, connecting the intercellular spaces with the outside world.

Intercellular air spaces

Spongy mesophyll cells

Lower epidermal cell   Guard cell   Chloroplast   Stoma   Small vacuole   Thick inner wall   Cuticle

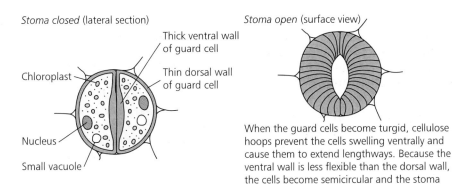

Stoma closed (lateral section)

Thick ventral wall of guard cell

Thin dorsal wall of guard cell

Chloroplast

Nucleus

Small vacuole

Stoma open (surface view)

When the guard cells become turgid, cellulose hoops prevent the cells swelling ventrally and cause them to extend lengthways. Because the ventral wall is less flexible than the dorsal wall, the cells become semicircular and the stoma opens.

Figure 2.2.8 The mechanics of stomatal opening and closing.

The best current theory on stomatal opening suggests that the osmotic movement of water is the result of some active ion transport. Levels of potassium ions have been observed to increase in the light to a degree which would affect water movement into the cells. It can be shown that the potassium ions are brought into the cell by active transport because metabolic poisons stop not just stomatal opening but also the accumulation of potassium ions. If this active transport stops in the dark, closure of the stomata would be brought about by the rapid diffusion of the potassium ions out of the cell along a very steep concentration gradient, followed by water movements due to osmosis. This theory provides an explanation for both the opening and the closing of stomata, is possible in all plants whether there are chloroplasts in the guard cells or not, and has some experimental evidence to support it. Until a better explanation is put forward, it seems that potassium ions are the key to the control of gaseous exchange in plants.

SUMMARY

- The **stem** system fulfils the role of support of the leaves and flowers of a plant, and also the transport of water, mineral ions and organic substances around the plant. It may also store food for overwintering, form adventitious roots, provide a means of reproduction or form the photosynthetic organ of the plant.

- The stem consists of an external **cuticle**, **vascular** tissue arranged in bundles, and central **packing** tissue. In dicotyledons the vascular bundles are arranged around the edge of the stem; in monocotyledons they are scattered through the parenchyma.

- **Epidermal** cells secrete cutin to form the cuticle in order to cut down water loss from the stem surface. They sometimes have epidermal hairs for various specialised functions.

- **Cortex** parenchyma cells act as packing cells. The cortex also contains **collenchyma** cells, which are tightly packed and strengthened with thickened cellulose at their corners, and provide support. Some photosynthesis occurs in the stem cortex.

- The **endodermis** is a single-celled layer with stored starch grains.

- Vascular bundles contain an outer **pericycle** made of strengthened **sclerenchyma** cells for support. The **phloem**, which transports organic solutes, and **xylem**, which brings water and mineral ions, are also strengthened. The cells of the **cambium** divide and differentiate to form xylem or phloem cells.

- The central **pith** contains unspecialised parenchyma cells.
- The **leaf** system fulfils the function of photosynthesis. Leaves capture sunlight and also supply carbon dioxide and other requirements to photosynthetic cells. The products of photosynthesis are transported from the leaves to the stem and around the plant.
- The overall structure of the leaf includes a **lamina** which is usually thin with a large surface area, and **vascular** tissue organised in a network of veins in dicotyledons and parallel veins in monocotyledons. Dicotyledons also have a **petiole** (leaf stalk) and central **midrib**.
- The **epidermal** cells of a leaf secrete cutin to form a cuticle. The lower epidermis particularly contains pores called **stomata**, surrounded by **guard cells**, which can open or close to allow gaseous exchange.
- The **palisade mesophyll** cells are columnar and tightly packed. They contain many chloroplasts and are the main photosynthetic cells of the leaf.
- The **spongy mesophyll** cells are smaller and more irregularly shaped and have large intercellular spaces between them, important in gaseous exchange. These connect with the stomata. Some photosynthesis takes place in these cells.
- **Collenchyma** cells provide support to the vascular tissue, particularly around the midrib.
- **Vascular bundles** in the midrib and veins contain **xylem**, **phloem** and **cambium** as in the stem, with a sheath of **parenchyma** or **sclerenchyma**.
- Stomata open to allow carbon dioxide into the leaf, and as a result water vapour passes out of the leaf. The guard cells elongate and open the stomata as a result of increased turgor, probably brought about by active transport of potassium ions.

QUESTIONS

1 a Describe the structure of a plant stem and how it is adapted to its function of transport.
  b Suggest how stems may be modified to perform functions other than the major function of transport.

2 a How is the structure of a dicotyledonous leaf related to its photosynthetic function?
  b How do stomata control gaseous exchange within the leaf?

3 Plants are found in a wide variety of habitats. Explain how adaptations of the stems and leaves can help plants to survive in a variety of adverse situations.

4 Plants leaves show many adaptations for survival in a wide variety of conditions, including extremes of heat and cold, shortage of water, loss of water, high salt levels and attack by herbivores.
  a Explain why leaf survival is so important to a plant.
  b Find out about as many different leaf adaptations as you can, using a variety of resources. Use ICT to make a table summarising your findings. This table should include the adaptation, details of the environment in which it allows the plant to survive and the way in which it is effective.

Developing Key Skills

Plant leaves show many adaptations for survival in a wide variety of conditions, including extremes of heat and cold, shortage of water, loss of water, high salt levels and attack by herbivores.

a) Explain why leaf survival is so important to a plant.

b) Find out about as many different leaf adaptations as you can, using a variety of resources. Use ICT to make a table summarising your findings. This table should include the adaptation, details of the environment in which it allows the plant to survive and the way in which it is effective.

TRANSPORT = LIFE

The transport system of any plant is vital, supplying water from the roots to the leaves and carrying the products of photosynthesis to the rest of the plant. Anything that interferes with the transport system of a plant threatens the life of the plant.

Cuddly killers

In recent years people have increasingly come to realise that we cannot simply keep taking materials from the natural world without careful management to replace what has been removed. The idea of sustainable growth and development is being embraced all over the world. This process can be seen clearly in the management of woodlands in the developed world, and there is increasing pressure for countries of the developing world to manage their woodlands in this way. Trees are harvested in careful rotation, and new trees are planted to replace those that are felled. However, some of the animals that also live in woodlands do not always co-operate with the management programme. Rabbits and deer are very partial to some young bark as part of their diet, particularly in the winter when other food may be in short supply. They tend to nibble a complete ring of bark away. The bark contains the transport tissues which carry water, minerals and food substances around the plant, so this removal kills the young tree. To help solve this problem, plastic protection strips are put around the base of the tree, and rabbits and deer are culled, but a complete solution is not easy.

Invisible assassins

Not all tree killers are cuddly. In the UK, the USA and Europe, elm trees have become a rare sight. They have been attacked indiscriminately by a killer that is invisible on the outside of the tree. Dutch elm disease is caused by the fungus *Ceratocystis ulmi* which is spread from tree to tree by bark-boring beetles. The beetles tunnel through the live tissue in and below the bark and can damage a tree, but they do not kill it. However, if they carry the spores of the Dutch elm disease fungus, the tree is doomed. The fungus spreads and grows through the transport tissues of the tree, blocking xylem and phloem alike. First the leaves die and fall off and then, deprived of its food-manufacturing system, the whole tree dies. New ways of fighting the fungus include using chemical messages to attract the beetles to decoy trees where they are killed by insecticide, and attacking the fungus itself with a bacterium which makes an anti-fungal chemical. We can only hope they will be successful.

Figure 1 We all love to see animals like this in the wild, but they threaten the woodlands we enjoy and depend on.

Figure 2 Any cures will come too late for most of the elms in the countries stricken by Dutch elm disease. These trees have already died, their transport systems hopelessly clogged by invasive fungal threads.

2.3 Transport systems in plants

Within a living organism substances need to be moved from one place to another. A chemical may be synthesised in one place for use somewhere else; materials need to be taken in from the external environment; waste products of reactions must be removed. Between an individual cell and the external environment, or a cell and its close neighbours, there is a variety of methods by which transport may occur. These include diffusion, osmosis, active transport and endo- and exocytosis.

For unicellular organisms, and multicellular organisms with a large surface area:volume ratio, the transport of substances in these ways is quite adequate. However, as organisms become larger and more complex in shape and design, the distances to be travelled become too large for these simple methods of transport. Specialised transport systems have evolved to carry substances rapidly around larger organisms.

Transport systems

Within any large organism, plant or animal, a transport system will be organised to carry out its functions as effectively as possible. Most major transport systems have certain features in common:

1   A system of vessels in which substances are carried. These are usually tubes, sometimes following a very specific route, sometimes widespread and branching.

2   A means of ensuring that substances are moved in the right direction.

3   A means of moving materials fast enough to supply the needs of the organism. This may involve a manipulation of physical processes (for example, actively changing concentrations of solutes to ensure a diffusion gradient) or a mechanical method (for example, the pumping of the heart).

4   A suitable transport medium.

5   Mass flow may be involved – bulk transport brought about by a pressure difference of some sort. In a mass flow system all the moving material travels at the same rate.

Both plants and animals need transport systems. Plants produce food in the leaves and must then transport the products of photosynthesis around the entire organism. They obtain water and minerals via the roots, and these too are needed by all the cells. Animals obtain food and oxygen in very specific systems within their bodies. They produce carbon dioxide in every cell. Transport systems are needed in animals to distribute food and oxygen to the active cells and to remove all the waste products.

Transport systems in plants

Routes for transport

Carbon dioxide enters plants and moves into the cells by diffusion. It is used up in photosynthesis, so a constant concentration gradient is maintained between the inside of the cells and their environment. Thus diffusion occurs continuously and a more specific transport route is not needed. The oxygen produced by photosynthesis is similarly moved out of the plant if it is not used in respiration.

When it comes to the transport of water, minerals and the products of photosynthesis, specific transport routes are required. An integral part of plant roots, stems and leaves is the vascular system, with xylem and phloem making up the transport routes. In general the xylem carries water and minerals up from the roots to the other areas of the plant, whilst the phloem carries the soluble products of photosynthesis from the leaves to the other cells. The xylem generally transports substances upwards, while substances can move both up and down in the phloem. The structures of these transport tissues were discussed earlier.

Evidence for the movement of water through the xylem

How do we know that water moves up the plant through the xylem? Evidence can be obtained in several ways:

1   If the cut end of a shoot is placed in a solution of eosin dye, the dye is carried to the vascular tissue of the leaves and appears in the xylem vessels, as figure 2.3.1 shows.

2   Ringing experiments involve killing with a steam jet a complete outer ring of bark, including the phloem vessels, but leaving the xylem intact. The upward movement of water through the plant is unaffected.

3   Radioactive isotopes can be introduced in minerals into the water available to the plant. Their path through the xylem, transported by water, can then be followed using autoradiography (see the box below).

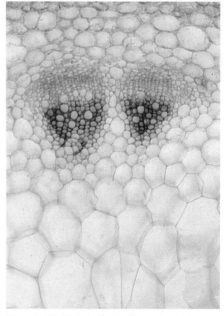

Figure 2.3.1 When sections of the stem and leaves are examined under the light microscope, eosin dye can be seen in the xylem vessels only.

Autoradiography

Autoradiography is a very useful technique for following the movements of various substances around plants. It involves the following steps:

(1) The plant is exposed to a **labelled** substance – a substance containing a radioactive isotope (for example carbon 14 in the carbon dioxide supply to investigate the movement of the products of photosynthesis).

(2) The radioactive label is taken up as the plant metabolises.

(3) The movement of substances can then be traced in several ways. An autoradiograph is produced when the plant is left against photographic film. The labelled substance causes the photographic film to shadow, and so the areas of the plant in which it has accumulated can be seen.

Figure 2.3.2 An autoradiograph of a geranium leaf showing labelled material in the veins.

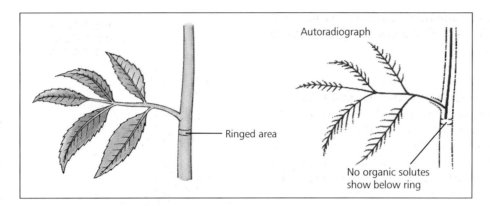

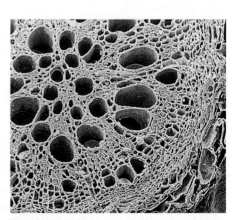

Figure 2.3.3 Phloem is the route for the transport of organic solutes. If the phloem is destroyed, no transport takes place.

Evidence for the movement of solutes in the phloem

Similarly, evidence can be obtained for the movement of solutes in the phloem:

1 The movement of solutes in the phloem can be observed by exposing the plant to carbon dioxide containing carbon 14. This labels the sugars produced by photosynthesis. Autoradiography can be used to follow the route of labelled sucrose around the plant. If the experiment is repeated in a plant with a ring of dead tissue, so that the phloem cells are no longer functioning, no radioactively labelled sucrose appears below the damaged area, as figure 2.3.3 shows.

2 A remarkably simple but very effective way of showing that organic solutes are carried by the phloem involves the use of aphids such as greenfly and is shown in figure 2.3.4.

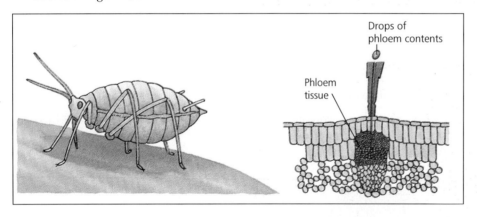

Figure 2.3.4 Aphids penetrate plant stems with their pointed mouthparts called stylets. Examination of the penetrated stem with a microscope shows that the stylet enters the phloem cells. T.E. Mittler in California realised that if the insect is removed from the mouthparts, a liquid oozes out of the end of the stylet. This is some of the contents of the phloem, and when analysed can be shown to contain sugars and other organic solutes.

Movement of substances in plants

The movement of substances around plants is usually referred to as **translocation**. Plants do not have mechanical systems to force materials along the narrow tubes of the xylem and phloem, but have evolved ways of manipulating a variety of physical processes to their advantage.

The movement of substances up from the roots to the leaves is well understood on the whole, though the mechanism by which organic solutes are transported in the phloem is much less clear.

Transport in the xylem

Translocation of water

The vessels of the xylem system are very narrow, dead tubes. They have a lumen diameter of 0.01–0.2 mm, and so have a great resistance to movement

Figure 2.3.5 The structure of the xylem is well suited to its function.

through them. Yet water has been shown to move up through the xylem vessels at speeds of 1–8 m h^{-1}, and to heights of up to 100 m above the ground in trees such as the giant redwood. How is this achieved?

Transpiration

The movement of water in the xylem of plants depends on **transpiration**. Transpiration is the loss of water vapour from the surface of the plant, mainly from the leaves, as figure 2.3.6 shows. This loss of water has the effect of 'pulling' water up through the xylem, as will be explained later.

When a liquid turns into a gas, it absorbs energy. The energy needed to turn a liquid into a gas is known as the **latent heat of vaporisation** and is high for water. When water evaporates from the surfaces of a plant, the latent heat of vaporisation is supplied by the Sun. Thus the energy for the transport of water and minerals in a plant comes from the Sun, without involving photosynthesis.

The amounts of water lost by a plant due to transpiration can be surprisingly large. A sunflower may transpire 1–2 dm^3 in a day, whilst a large oak tree can lose up to 600 dm^3 per day. Water moves from the xylem cells into the mesophyll cells of the stem and leaf along the vacuolar, symplast and apoplast pathways, with most using the apoplast route. (These routes were described when considering the movement of water across the root *into* the xylem.) Evaporation of water takes place from the cellulose walls of the spongy mesophyll cells into the air spaces. Water vapour then moves through open stomata into the external air along a diffusion gradient. Even on a windy day, each leaf has a layer of still air around it. The thickness of this layer varies with the wind speed. The water vapour diffuses through this still layer before it is swept away by the mass of moving air. Figure 2.3.7 illustrates the effect of wind speed on transpiration.

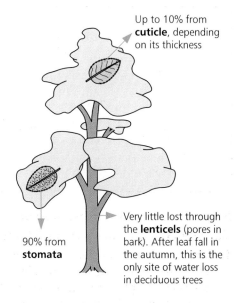

Up to 10% from **cuticle**, depending on its thickness

90% from **stomata**

Very little lost through the **lenticels** (pores in bark). After leaf fall in the autumn, this is the only site of water loss in deciduous trees

Figure 2.3.6 The main sites of transpiration from the surface of a plant.

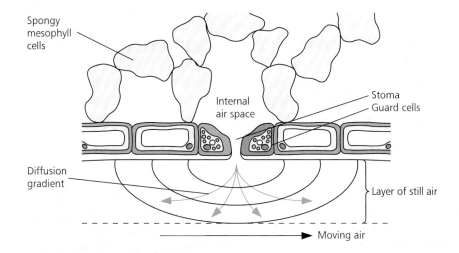

Spongy mesophyll cells

Internal air space

Stoma
Guard cells

Diffusion gradient

Layer of still air

Moving air

Figure 2.3.7 The thickness of the layer of still air around a leaf affects the rate of transpiration. The thinner the layer, the more rapidly is water lost, because the diffusion gradient is greater.

Factors affecting transpiration

Water loss from a plant occurs mainly as a result of the opening of the stomata for gaseous exchange, to provide the carbon dioxide needed for photosynthesis. The result of transpiration is that water is moved through the plant, carrying minerals with it. Evaporation of water from the leaf surfaces may also help to cool the plant. Yet in spite of these advantages, it appears that water loss is a major problem for plants, because there is rarely an abundance of available water.

Demonstrating transpiration

Loss of water from the surfaces of a plant can be demonstrated by enclosing the pot of a potted plant in a sealed plastic bag. This prevents the evaporation of water from the soil surface interfering with the experiment. The plant is then sealed in a bell jar. As transpiration proceeds, a colourless liquid collects on the inside of the bell jar. Cobalt chloride or anhydrous copper(II) sulphate paper can be used to show that this liquid contains water.

It is not easy to measure amounts of water transpired from a plant. We can more readily measure the uptake of water by a plant, which gives us a measure of transpiration because most of the water taken up by a plant under normal conditions is transpired, with a minute fraction being used for other purposes. Uptake of water is demonstrated using a **potometer**, as shown in figure 2.3.8.

Figure 2.3.8 Potometers provide a way of investigating uptake of water and the factors which affect it. Care must be taken to avoid air entering the apparatus.

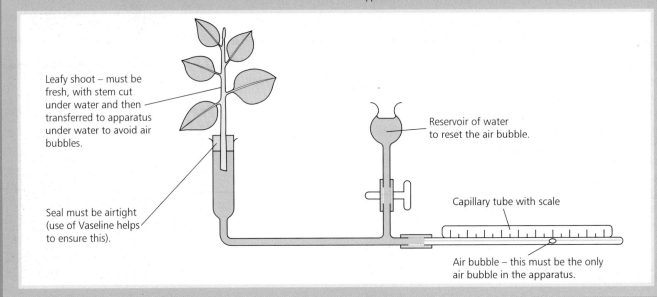

Leafy shoot – must be fresh, with stem cut under water and then transferred to apparatus under water to avoid air bubbles.

Reservoir of water to reset the air bubble.

Capillary tube with scale

Seal must be airtight (use of Vaseline helps to ensure this).

Air bubble – this must be the only air bubble in the apparatus.

The rate of water loss from the leaves of a plant may be affected by a variety of factors. In many instances plants have features to minimise water loss, such as curled, hairy and grooved leaves which trap layers of still, moist air around the stomata.

The following factors affect transpiration:

1 Light has a major effect on transpiration, as figure 2.3.9 shows. Stomata usually open in the light for photosynthetic gas exchange, and close in the dark. Thus transpiration rates increase with light intensity until all the stomata are open and transpiration is at a maximum.

2 Temperature is the next factor affecting transpiration after light. At a given light intensity, an increase in temperature increases the amount of evaporation from the spongy mesophyll cells, and also increases the amount of water vapour the air can take before it becomes saturated. Both of these factors increase the water potential gradient between the air inside and outside the leaf, increasing the rate of transpiration.

3 Air movement or wind increases the rate of transpiration because it reduces the shell of still air around the stomata and so increases the water potential gradient between the leaf and the air.

4 Air humidity is the concentration of water vapour in the air. A high air humidity lowers the rate of transpiration because of the reduced water

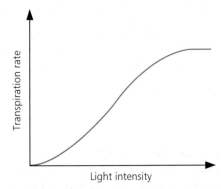

Figure 2.3.9 Light has a major effect on transpiration. Stomata usually open in the light for photosynthetic gas exchange, and close in the dark. Thus transpiration rates increase with light intensity until all the stomata are open and transpiration is at a maximum.

potential gradient between the leaf and the air. Very dry air – low humidity – has the opposite effect.

5 The availability of water from the soil has an effect too. If there is little soil water, the plant is under water stress and transpiration is reduced.

The transpiration stream

When water is lost by transpiration from the leaves of a plant, this affects the contents of the xylem, a continuous column of water. Water evaporating from the surface of one spongy mesophyll cell results in the osmotic movement of water across from the next-door cell, and so on to the xylem itself.

When molecules of water leave the xylem to enter a cell by osmosis, this creates tension in the column of water in the xylem, which is transmitted all the way down to the roots. This is due to the **cohesion** of water molecules. Because of their dipolar nature, water molecules are held together by hydrogen bonds. As a result the column of water has high **tensile strength** – it is unlikely to break.

The water molecules also **adhere** strongly to the walls of the narrow xylem vessel and (more importantly, it is thought) to the millions of tiny channels and pores within the cellulose cell walls of the apoplast pathway through the leaf. **Adhesion** is the attraction between unlike molecules. The adhesive force is sufficient to support the entire column of water. Thus the combination of adhesive and cohesive forces allows the whole column of water to be pulled upwards. More water is continuously moved into the roots from the soil to replace that lost from the leaves by transpiration. Figure 2.3.11 shows the transpiration stream.

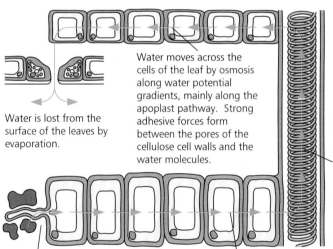

Water moves across the cells of the leaf by osmosis along water potential gradients, mainly along the apoplast pathway. Strong adhesive forces form between the pores of the cellulose cell walls and the water molecules.

Water is lost from the surface of the leaves by evaporation.

As water molecules are lost by evaporation and moved out of the xylem, cohesion between the water molecules means that the whole column of water in the xylem is pulled upwards.

Water moves into the root hair from the soil by osmosis.

Water is moved across the root by osmosis to maintain the continuous column in the xylem.

Figure 2.3.10 The maximum column of water that can be raised relying on the pressure of atmospheric air alone is about 10 m. The giant redwood tree regularly raises water to over 30 m.

◀ **Figure 2.3.11** The transpiration stream is set up as a result of physical processes, and a pressure of around 4 000 kPa, moving the water upwards, can result. This is enough to supply water to the tops of the tallest trees.

Root pressure

Transpiration is not the only method by which water is moved through the xylem. Transpiration seems to be a passive process, yet there are aspects of water transport which are affected by metabolic inhibitors and lack of oxygen. During the night, when transpiration rates are extremely low, drops of water may be forced out of the leaves of some plants in a process known as **guttation**. If a plant is cut off from the root, root sap will continue to ooze from the root xylem. These observations are thought to be the results of root pressure.

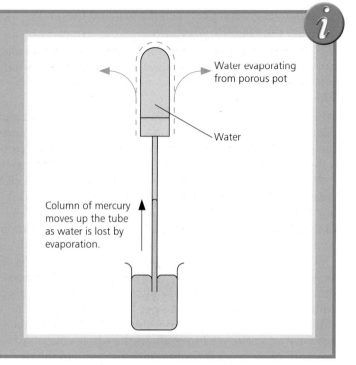

Artificial transpiration

A vacuum pump can cause a column of water to rise 11 m or a column of mercury to rise 760 mm. Yet trees regularly pull columns of water up 20 m and more. Figure 2.3.12 shows an experiment which demonstrates neatly the effect of evaporation on a column of liquid, carried out by Josef Bohm in 1893.

Adhesive forces between the water molecules and the pores of the porous pot are strong enough to support this enormous column of water, and cohesive forces between the water molecules stop the column breaking under the strain. This gives us our best model so far of the transpiration stream.

Water evaporating from porous pot

Water

Column of mercury moves up the tube as water is lost by evaporation.

Figure 2.3.12 Drawn by evaporation, the column of mercury rises to over 1 m. It has been calculated that if there was water in the system, the column could be pulled to a height of more than 1 km – far greater than the height of any living plant.

Root pressure seems to be produced by the active secretion of salts into the root cells, increasing the movement of water by osmosis. The pressure generated is about 100–200 kPa. This contributes to the movement of water in the xylem of many plants, particularly in situations where the transpiration rate is low.

Translocation of ions

The route by which mineral ions are taken in from the soil and moved into the xylem involves partially permeable membranes and active transport against concentration gradients. Once the ions reach the xylem, they are carried along in the transpiration stream in a mass flow system, being delivered by the extensive vascular network to the tissues where they are needed. They may be moved out into the cells by either diffusion or active transport, depending on the permeability of the cell membrane and the relative concentrations of the solutes.

Transport in the phloem

Translocation of the products of photosynthesis

The leaves of a plant produce large amounts of glucose. This is needed throughout the entire organism. Experiments such as those mentioned on page 116 show that the phloem is involved in the movement of organic solutes, and that the translocation is active. Sucrose makes up 90% of the solutes found in the phloem fluid, the rest being amino acids, organic phosphates and nitrates, etc. Sucrose is the form in which the products of photosynthesis are transported around the body of the plant. When it reaches the cells it may be converted back to glucose for use in respiration, or to starch for storage. Translocation is an energy-requiring process which moves substances, particularly sucrose, between the leaves (known as the **sources**) and the other parts of the plants where they are needed (known as **sinks**).

Whilst the process of transport in the xylem of plants is relatively well understood, the way in which solutes are moved in the phloem is much less certain. The flow rates are known to be about 0.2–6 m h^{-1}. In many species the distances moved are large, up to 100 m. There is relatively little phloem compared with the often extensive xylem vessels. The tubes of the phloem are very narrow, with a high resistance to movement which is increased by the presence of sieve plates. However, large quantities of solute can be moved. A large tree may transport 250 kg of sucrose down its trunk in a year, and this movement of materials in the phloem is an active process.

The mechanism of phloem transport

The soluble products of photosynthesis seem to enter the sieve tubes by an active process. The sucrose content of most plant cell sap is only 0.5%, yet sucrose makes up 20–30% of the phloem sap content. Active transport must therefore be involved to move the sucrose against this sort of concentration gradient. Specialised parenchyma cells known as **transfer cells**, shown in figure 2.3.14, appear to be involved in transporting the sucrose into the sieve tubes.

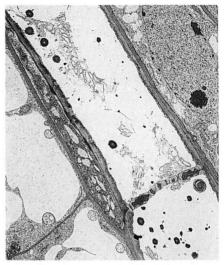

Figure 2.3.13 The structure of phloem gives us some clues about the way it works.

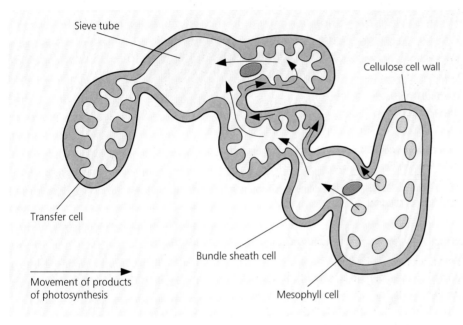

Movement of products of photosynthesis

Figure 2.3.14 Regular infoldings of the cell wall and membrane give transfer cells a large surface area for active transport. They contain many mitochondria and so have the supply of energy needed to be metabolically active.

Transfer cells are also found in roots, storage organs and growing shoots, where they are involved in helping to move solutes such as nitrates from the sieve tubes into the cells that need them.

The mechanism for the movement of substances along the sieve tubes themselves is still very much open to debate. Experiments have shown that killing the phloem prevents the movement of solutes, and that sugars and amino acids travel through the system too quickly to be relying on diffusion alone, so it seems reasonable to assume that an active process is involved. More evidence for this is the observation that translocation is reduced by lack of oxygen and by respiratory inhibitors. The companion cells with their mitochondria can supply the energy needed for this active process. However, there is no entirely satisfactory explanation of how the translocation of solutes in phloem occurs.

A mass flow system of some sort seems to be involved, but the fact that different solutes move at different speeds and sometimes in different directions mean this cannot be the whole story.

Plants, although they can be very large, have relatively slow metabolisms. As a result, transport systems relying mainly on physical processes are sufficient to supply all their needs. In animals, with their more active lifestyles and greater energy demands, the situation is not quite so simple, as section 2.5 will show.

Phloem transport theories

Münch's mass flow theory

In 1930 a purely physical explanation for the mass flow of substances through sieve tubes was proposed by Münch. The model in figure 2.3.15 shows the principle behind it.

Initially, water moves into both containers by osmosis. As X contains a much more concentrated solute solution than Z, water will move into X more rapidly and so there will be a flow of solution from X to Z. The hydrostatic pressure that this creates forces water out of Z. The flow will continue until the concentrations of the solutions in X and Z are the same.

The pressure flow hypothesis

The modern application of Münch's model is known as the **pressure flow hypothesis**. In a plant, X is the phloem in the leaves where the sucrose concentration is high due to photosynthesis and the transfer cells actively load the sieve tubes. Z is the area of phloem where the sucrose is unloaded and used by the cells. Water can move into the phloem by osmosis at any point, and the return route for the water to the cells is through the xylem. Unlike the physical model, the flow can be continuous because sucrose is continually being added at one end and removed at the other.

A variety of ideas has been put forward to try and extend this model, none of which are supported by much evidence. The pressure flow hypothesis certainly explains much of what is seen, but there is doubtless more to be discovered in this area. Some of the most recent and exciting research suggests that there are proteins present in the phloem cells closely related to the actin and myosin which make up muscles (see section 2.6, page 163). It has been proposed that the contraction of these proteins may be involved in translocation in the phloem, but much more work is needed before the hypothesis can be accepted.

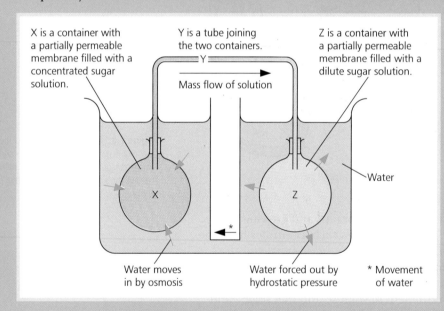

X is a container with a partially permeable membrane filled with a concentrated sugar solution.

Y is a tube joining the two containers.

Z is a container with a partially permeable membrane filled with a dilute sugar solution.

Mass flow of solution

Water

Water moves in by osmosis

Water forced out by hydrostatic pressure

* Movement of water

Figure 2.3.15 Münch's model for mass flow in sieve tubes.

SUMMARY

- **Transport systems** have evolved to carry substances rapidly around multicellular organisms. They generally consist of a system of vessels, a means of ensuring that transport occurs in the right direction, a means of moving substances quickly and a transport medium. The mass flow mechanism may be involved.

- In plants, specific transport systems are the **xylem**, which transports water and mineral ions up from the roots, and **phloem**, which transports the soluble products of photosynthesis from the leaves around the plant.

- Evidence for the movement of water and ions in the xylem is given by the uptake of eosin dye, ringing experiments and autoradiography using labelled mineral salts.
- Evidence for the movement of organic compounds in the phloem includes autoradiography on plants exposed to labelled carbon dioxide combined with ringing, and the use of aphid stylets to penetrate the phloem and subsequent analysis of the liquid carried there.
- Movement of water in the xylem depends on **transpiration**, the loss of water vapour from the leaves through stomata which open to allow carbon dioxide to diffuse in for photosynthesis.
- Transpiration is affected by light, temperature, air movement, air humidity and the availability of water from the soil. Plants may develop specialised features to reduce the rate of transpiration, by increasing the size of the envelope of still air around the leaf.
- The **transpiration stream** is the continual movement of water up through the xylem vessels caused by the **cohesion** of water molecules and the **adhesion** between water molecules and pores in the cellulose cell walls of the apoplast pathway. The entire column of water moves upwards, pulled by transpiration from the leaves.
- **Root pressure** contributes to transpiration under conditions when the transpiration rate is low, and involves the active secretion of salts into the root cells.
- Mineral ions are transported by mass flow in the xylem and are carried into and out of the plant cells by diffusion, facilitated diffusion and active transport, depending on the mechanism available for that ion.
- The sugar products of photosynthesis are transported as sucrose in the phloem, with small amounts of amino acids and other organic compounds.
- **Translocation** is an active process, moving substances between the **sources** (leaves) and the **sinks** (parts of the plant which need sucrose or other substances).
- Transport in the phloem involves active transport, with **transfer cells** loading sucrose into the sieve tubes against a concentration gradient. **Münch's mass flow theory** and the **pressure flow hypothesis** provide models for the mechanism of transport in the phloem.

QUESTIONS

1 a Produce a table comparing the structure and functions of xylem and phloem tissues within a plant.

b Explain the value of radioisotopes in determining the functions of these two transport systems.

2 a Describe an experiment which could be used to measure transpiration.

b Comment on any precautions which need to be observed in the setting up of the apparatus and on the limitations of the apparatus for measuring transpiration.

c How and why would **i** lowered light intensity and **ii** increased air movement affect the results of the experiment?

3 Trace the path followed by a molecule of water from the soil through the root, stem and leaf of a vascular plant until it enters the atmosphere, naming the tissues and cells along the route.

BABIES IN BOTTLES?

The breath of life

As a fetus develops inside its mother's body, its oxygen needs are supplied from her through the placenta. The lungs of a fetus are filled with fluid, and they take up a relatively small volume in its chest. Breathing movements are 'practised' by the developing baby whilst it is still in the uterus, but of course no air can be taken in. However, as soon as the baby is born it must take its first breath.

To accomplish this first breath, the newborn infant has to exert a force 15 to 20 times greater than that needed for a normal inhalation. As a result the lungs are enormously stretched, and the elastic tissue they contain never again returns to its original length. **Lung surfactant** is a special chemical which stops the alveoli of the lungs from collapsing. As long as plenty of lung surfactant is present, the baby will then establish a breathing rhythm which will continue for the rest of its life.

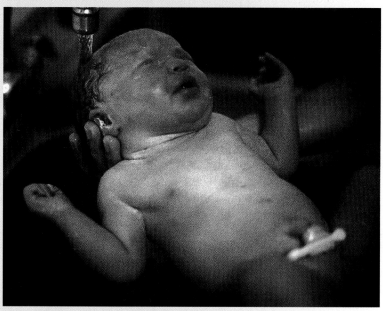

Figure 1 The first inspiratory effort a baby makes is very hard work, brought about by a powerful contraction of the diaphragm.

Born in a hurry

Full-term babies have lungs coated in lung surfactant ready for breathing. However, this chemical only begins to be manufactured in the lungs from about the 28th week of pregnancy. Babies born at 28 weeks or earlier do not have lung surfactant to allow them to breathe properly, and for many years this struggle for breath was one of the main reasons why very premature babies died. In recent years, artificial lung surfactant has been produced. A tiny amount of this sprayed into the lungs of a very premature baby coats the alveoli just like natural surfactant, making breathing easier and preventing lung damage. Because of this development, babies born as early as 23 or 24 weeks into a pregnancy now stand a chance of survival.

The latest research takes things even further. The physical ventilation of tiny lungs not yet ready to be used can cause severe problems later on. It seems that chemicals known as **perfluorocarbons** (PFCs) may be able to prevent this in the future. PFCs can be used to carry oxygen into the lungs with much less need for ventilation. This reduces the risk of permanent lung damage and increases the chance of tiny preterm babies not only surviving, but also having a normal, healthy life.

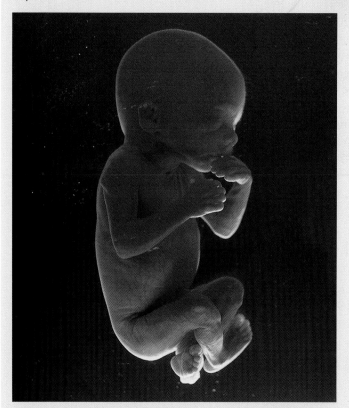

Figure 2 Dogs and mice have been kept alive for some time taking all their oxygen from PFCs. Perhaps the time will come when, just as described in the book *Brave New World*, human babies will develop in artificial uteruses, their oxygen supplied by the PFCs in which they float.

2.4 Respiratory systems

As we have seen, complex multicellular organisms have systems within them specialised to fulfil particular needs. **Respiratory systems** have evolved to enable organisms to obtain oxygen and to remove carbon dioxide from their bodies in a process known as **gaseous exchange**. Oxygen is vital for almost all living organisms as it is needed for efficient cellular respiration, the process by which energy is released from foods. Cellular respiration is described in detail later, but can be summarised by the equation:

Glucose + oxygen → energy + carbon dioxide + water

Carbon dioxide is formed as a waste product of this process. Carbon dioxide is toxic and so cannot be allowed to accumulate in cells or tissues – it has to be removed.

For unicellular and simple multicellular organisms, obtaining oxygen and getting rid of carbon dioxide happens by diffusion along concentration gradients. As organisms become larger their surface area to volume ratio gets smaller, and simple diffusion through the body surface is no longer sufficient to supply all cells with their requirements.

Figure 2.4.1 A cheetah needs a large amount of oxygen to satisfy its needs. The cheetah's surface area : volume ratio means that diffusion through its skin cannot supply all the oxygen it needs, so it has a specialised respiratory system.

Features of respiratory systems

A respiratory system is an area specialised for gaseous exchange between the organism and the environment. Oxygen and carbon dioxide are transported to and from the respiring cells by a transport system. Gaseous exchange takes place by diffusion at the **respiratory surface**. For effective diffusion to take place, all respiratory surfaces have certain features in common:

1 A large surface area gives sufficient gaseous exchange to supply all the needs of the organism. The surface area of the respiratory surface has to compensate for the relatively small surface area:volume ratio of the organism as a whole.

2 Permeable surfaces allow the free passage of the respiratory gases.

3 Thin surface structures allow effective diffusion from one side of the surface to the other.

4 Moist surfaces ensure that the gases are in solution and so can diffuse rapidly.

5 In many animals, a rich blood supply to the respiratory surfaces allows the transport of the respiratory gases between the respiring cells and the site of gaseous exchange.

Respiratory systems in plants

As plants get larger, their surface area:volume ratio gets smaller. However, there are no specialised systems within large and complex multicellular plants for obtaining oxygen and getting rid of carbon dioxide. The stomata connected with the large air spaces in the spongy mesophyll layer in the leaf, along with lenticels (slit-like openings in woody stems), ensure that any necessary gas exchanges occur smoothly. The large surface area of cells in the spongy mesophyll along with their moist surfaces do meet some of the requirements for a respiratory system as they are well adapted for gaseous exchange. But large multicellular plants do not need specialised respiratory systems in the way many animals do.

There are several reasons for this. One of the most important is that plants use up carbon dioxide in photosynthesis, thus removing much of this toxic waste product of respiration. Oxygen is a waste product of photosynthesis and is thus immediately available for cellular respiration. Another important factor is that the oxygen demand of plant tissues is relatively low. Most multicellular plants do not move around and the energy requirements of their tissues are not high. This means that the demand for oxygen for cellular respiration is small, and relatively low levels of carbon dioxide are produced by the process. Diffusion is sufficient to meet the needs for gaseous exchange for both cellular respiration and photosynthesis.

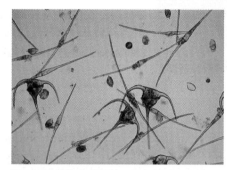

Figure 2.4.2 Protoctista have a large surface area : volume ratio. This means they can obtain sufficient oxygen and get rid of their carbon dioxide waste without specialised respiratory systems – simple diffusion is enough.

The need for respiratory systems in animals

Animals do not photosynthesise, so they have no internal system of generating oxygen or removing carbon dioxide. Animals are generally active for at least part of the day – plant eaters must find sufficient food to eat and avoid predators whilst meat eaters need to capture their prey or find carrion, and both must carry out digestion. They also need to carry out all the normal cellular processes common to plants and animals. Thus the oxygen demands of animals for cellular respiration are relatively high, and they consequently produce large quantities of carbon dioxide. As a result of the surface area:volume ratio, diffusion through the outer surface alone is insufficient for most animals except the very small, and so specialised respiratory systems have evolved.

Respiratory systems in land animals

In terrestrial life there is a perpetual conflict between the need for oxygen and the need for water. The conditions which favour the diffusion of oxygen into an organism also favour the diffusion of water out. Animals need a large, moist surface area for gaseous exchange, and yet they need to limit the water loss from this same surface as much as possible. Air-breathing vertebrates have solved the problem by developing **lungs**. Some lungs are quite simple and merely add to the area for gaseous exchange already provided by the body surface, for example in frogs. Other animals cannot use their outer surface for respiration at all and so are much more dependent on efficient lungs. Mammals have one of the most complex respiratory systems, which demonstrates the general features of most respiratory systems. We shall here look at the example of the human respiratory system in detail.

The structure of the human respiratory system

Most of the human respiratory system is found within the protective walls of the chest. The system is linked with the outside world by a tube which may be entered through either the mouth or the nose. Figure 2.4.4 (pages 128–9) shows the human respiratory system.

The human respiratory system at work

In looking at the human respiratory system we shall consider the following questions in turn:

1 How is air brought into the respiratory system, to reach the respiratory surfaces?

2 How is gaseous exchange brought about at the respiratory surfaces?

3 How is the process of breathing controlled and regulated to meet the varying demands placed upon it?

(1) Breathing – bringing the air in

The lungs are the site of gaseous exchange, but they play only a passive part in getting the gases there. The chest cavity is effectively a sealed unit, with only one way in or out – through the trachea. **Breathing** is the way in which air is moved in and out of the lungs, passing through the trachea, bronchi and bronchioles.

What does breathing involve?

Simple observation tells us that there are two parts to the process of breathing – taking air into the chest (**inhalation**) and breathing air out again (**exhalation**). Breathing involves a series of pressure changes in the chest cavity which in turn bring about movements of the air.

Inhalation is an active, energy-using process. The diaphragm, normally dome shaped, contracts and as a result is lowered and flattened. The external intercostal muscles contract to raise the rib cage upwards and outwards. This results in the *volume* of the chest cavity increasing, which in turn means the *pressure* in the cavity is lowered. As the pressure within the chest cavity is now lower than the atmospheric pressure of the air outside, air moves through the trachea, bronchi and bronchioles into the lungs to equalise the pressures inside and out.

Normal exhalation is a largely passive process. The muscles of the diaphragm relax so that it moves up into its resting dome shape. The external intercostal muscles relax and the internal intercostal muscles contract so that the ribs move down and in. The elastic fibres around the alveoli of the lungs return to their normal length. As a result of all this the volume of the chest cavity decreases, causing an increase in pressure. As the pressure in the chest cavity is now greater than that of the outside air, air moves out of the lungs, travelling along the same passageways as on the inward journey. Figure 2.4.3 shows the mechanism of breathing.

There are times when passive exhalation is not enough. On the occasions when we want to force the air out of our lungs more rapidly than passive exhalation allows, the muscles of the abdomen contract. This increases the pressure in the abdomen, forcing the diaphragm upwards further and so increasing the pressure in the chest cavity. This is known as **forced exhalation**.

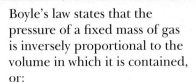

Boyle's law

Boyle's law states that the pressure of a fixed mass of gas is inversely proportional to the volume in which it is contained, or:

$$P \propto 1/V$$

Thus as volume increases, pressure is lowered. Conversely, as the volume decreases, the pressure in the system increases.

2

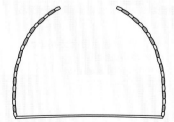

Inhalation:
Ribs lift up and out as external intercostal muscles contract.
Diaphragm contracts and flattens.
Volume increases, pressure falls.

Exhalation:
Ribs drop down and in as internal intercostal muscles contract.
Diaphragm relaxes and arches.
Volume falls, pressure increases.

Figure 2.4.3 These movements of the ribs and diaphragm result in pressure changes which in turn cause the movement of air in and out of our lungs.

Nasal cavity

The nasal passages have a relatively large surface area, but no gaseous exchange takes place here. The passages have a good blood supply, and the lining secretes mucus and is covered in hairs. The hairs and mucus filter out much of the dust and small particles such as bacteria that we breathe in. The moist surfaces mean the level of water vapour in the inspired air is increased and the rich blood supply raises the temperature of cold air. The entry of air into the lungs therefore has as little effect as possible on the internal environment there.

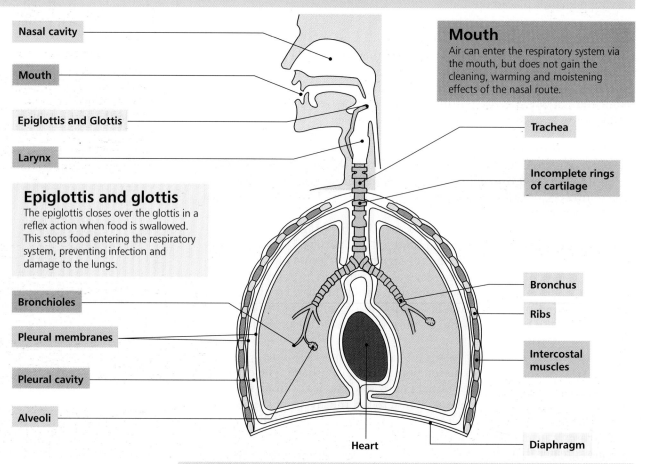

Nasal cavity

Mouth

Epiglottis and Glottis

Larynx

Mouth

Air can enter the respiratory system via the mouth, but does not gain the cleaning, warming and moistening effects of the nasal route.

Trachea

Incomplete rings of cartilage

Epiglottis and glottis

The epiglottis closes over the glottis in a reflex action when food is swallowed. This stops food entering the respiratory system, preventing infection and damage to the lungs.

Bronchioles

Pleural membranes

Pleural cavity

Alveoli

Bronchus

Ribs

Intercostal muscles

Heart

Diaphragm

Trachea

Columnar epithelial cell – these line the trachea and the bronchi.

Cilia – these all beat *away* from the lungs.

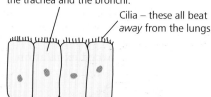
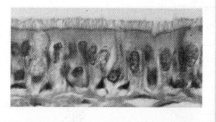

The trachea is the major airway leading down into the chest cavity. It is lined with **columnar epithelial cells**. In the layers below the epithelium are **mucus-secreting cells**. The cilia of the columnar epithelial cells beat to move the mucus and any trapped microorganisms and dust away from the lungs. The inhalation of tobacco smoke stops the cilia beating.

Larynx

The larynx makes use of the flow of air in and out of the respiratory system to produce sounds which in humans are developed into the spoken language.

Incomplete rings of cartilage

These cartilage rings support both the trachea and the bronchi and prevent them collapsing. The rings are incomplete to allow the easy passage of food down the oesophagus which runs behind the trachea.

Bronchus

Within the chest cavity the trachea divides to give two bronchi, one leading to the left lung and one to the right. The bronchi are very similar in structure to the trachea, but are slightly narrower. The left bronchus divides into two, the right bronchus into three.

Figure 2.4.4 The human respiratory system and the associated organs are well adapted for gaseous exchange, for ventilating the respiratory surfaces and for preventing excess water loss.

Ribs

The ribs form a protective bony cage around the respiratory system.

Diaphragm

The diaphragm is a broad sheet of muscle which forms the floor of the chest cavity. Movements of the diaphragm are important in the physical process of breathing.

Pleural membranes

The pleural membranes surround the lungs and line the chest cavity.

Pleural cavity

The pleural cavity is the space between the pleural membranes. It contains lubricating fluid which allows the membranes to slide easily during the breathing movements.

Intercostal muscles

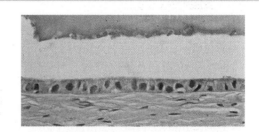

The intercostal muscles are found beween the ribs. The **external intercostal** muscles contract to raise the rib cage upwards and outwards during inspiration, while the **internal intercostal** muscles contract to bring the ribs closer together and lower the rib cage during expiration.

Bronchioles

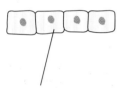

Flattened cuboidal epithelium – the flattened shape gives an increased surface area and a smaller distance for gases to diffuse.

Bronchioles are much smaller than the bronchi and there are many more of them. Larger bronchioles have cartilage rings, unlike those with a diameter of 1 mm or less. These small bronchioles collapse quite easily. Their main function is as an airway, but a little gaseous exchange may occur here. As the bronchioles get smaller the lining epithelium changes from columnar to **flattened cuboidal**, making diffusion of gases more likely.

Alveoli

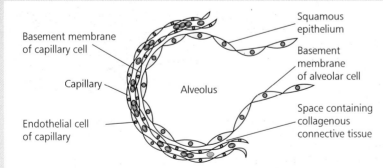

The alveoli are the main respiratory surfaces of the lungs where most of the gaseous exchange takes place. Alveoli are made up of **squamous epithelial cells** which facilitate diffusion as they have a large surface area and are thin, reducing the distance for gases to travel. The capillaries which run close to the alveoli also have a wall which is only one cell thick, creating the best possible conditions for gas exchange. Between the capillary and the alveolus is a layer of elastic connective tissue which holds them together. The elastic elements in this tissue help to force air out of the stretched lungs. This is known as the **elastic recoil** of the lungs.

Components of lung volume

A certain amount of air is always present in the respiratory system, simply filling up the spaces when no air is flowing. Other than this, the volume of air which is drawn in and out of the respiratory system can be very variable. There are different components of lung volume which have the following specific names for ease of reference:

(1) The **tidal volume** (V_T) is the volume of air that enters and leaves the lungs at each natural resting breath.

(2) The **inspiratory reserve volume** (**IRV**) is the volume of air that can be taken in by a maximum inspiratory effort, over and above the normal inspired tidal volume. In other words, this is the extra air that you can take in when you breathe in as deeply as possible after a normal inhalation.

(3) The **expiratory reserve volume** (**ERV**) is the volume of air that can be expelled by the most powerful expiratory effort, over and above the normal expired tidal volume. This is the extra air breathed out when you force the air out of your lungs as hard as possible after a normal exhalation.

(4) The **vital capacity** (**VC**) is the sum of the tidal volume and the inspiratory and expiratory reserves. It is the volume of air which can be breathed out by the most vigorous possible expiratory effort following the deepest possible inhalation.

(5) The **residual volume** (**RV**) is the volume of air left in the lungs after the strongest possible exhalation. It has to be measured indirectly.

(6) The **total lung capacity** (**TLC**) is the sum of the vital capacity and the residual volume.

(7) The **inspiratory capacity** (**IC**) is the volume that can be inspired from the end of a normal exhalation – in other words, the sum of the tidal volume and the inspiratory reserve volume.

Figure 2.4.5 illustrates these volumes.

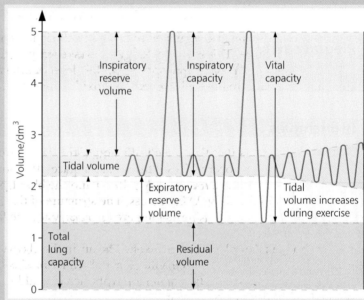

Figure 2.4.5 Different people's lung volumes vary – men usually have greater lung volumes than women, and athletes have larger lung volumes than non-athletes due to their training. This diagram gives the *average* figures.

Breathing rhythms

The body constantly needs oxygen to be delivered and carbon dioxide to be removed, so breathing continues throughout our lives. The pattern of our breathing will alter under differing conditions of exercise, stress, fitness, etc., but in normal circumstances a rhythm of some kind will be maintained.

The **tidal volume**, the amount of air naturally breathed in or out, is usually about 500 cm³ in a normal person at rest, or about 15% of the vital capacity of the lungs. The rate of breathing can be expressed as the **ventilation rate**, and this is a measure of the volume of air breathed in a minute:

Ventilation rate = tidal volume × frequency of inspiration (per minute)

The ventilation rate is a useful measurement which is affected by two things – the amount of air taken into the lungs at each breath and the number of breaths per minute. For example, the tidal volume can increase from 15% to 50% of the vital capacity during heavy exercise – a great deal more air is then passing through the system. The frequency of inspiration shows similar increases during exercise – you can easily measure this yourself.

Measuring the volume of inhaled or exhaled air

A piece of apparatus known as a **spirometer** is used to find out information such as the vital capacity of a person's lungs, or to measure the inspiratory or expiratory reserve volume. Spirometers come in a wide variety of shapes and sizes, but they all work in the same way – that is, as a gasometer.

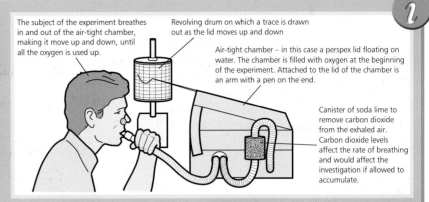

The subject of the experiment breathes in and out of the air-tight chamber, making it move up and down, until all the oxygen is used up.

Revolving drum on which a trace is drawn out as the lid moves up and down

Air-tight chamber – in this case a perspex lid floating on water. The chamber is filled with oxygen at the beginning of the experiment. Attached to the lid of the chamber is an arm with a pen on the end.

Canister of soda lime to remove carbon dioxide from the exhaled air. Carbon dioxide levels affect the rate of breathing and would affect the investigation if allowed to accumulate.

Figure 2.4.6 The volume of gas inhaled and exhaled under a variety of conditions can be measured using a spirometer.

The ventilation of the lungs is regulated to bring in sufficient air to allow effective gaseous exchange. This exchange of gases must supply all the oxygen required by the tissues of the body appropriate to their level of internal respiration, and must also remove all the carbon dioxide which is formed as a waste product.

(2) Gaseous exchange

Fick's law (page 53) tells us that the rate of diffusion of the gases involved is a function of the surface area over which diffusion takes place, the concentration difference of the gases between the air in the alveoli and the blood, and the thickness of the membrane they diffuse across. The structure of the alveoli has evolved to ensure that conditions in the lung are favourable for the fastest possible rate of diffusion.

Gaseous exchange takes place in the alveoli. The air in the alveoli does not have the same composition as the atmospheric air which is breathed in. In fact, the levels of oxygen and carbon dioxide in atmospheric air would be toxic to most body cells with prolonged exposure.

There is always a substantial volume of air in the respiratory tract. The incoming air mixes with this, changing the relative proportions of the gases to levels which suit the cells much better. In normal quiet breathing, about $500 \, cm^3$ of air are drawn in with each breath. Of this, about $350 \, cm^3$ reach the alveoli and mix with the air that is already there – usually about $2500 \, cm^3$ ($2.5 \, dm^3$). This mixture or **alveolar gas** is involved in gaseous exchange with the blood. Table 2.4.1 shows the relative proportions of the main respiratory gases at various points of the respiratory tract.

Gas	Inspired air	Alveolar air	Expired air
Oxygen	20.8	13.1	15.3
Carbon dioxide	0.04	5.2	4.2

Table 2.4.1 The percentages of the main respiratory gases found in inspired air, alveolar air and expired air

The alveoli provide the enormous surface area needed for the exchange of gases in the human body. They fulfil the requirements for gaseous exchange – a large surface area, thin walls (single flattened cuboidal epithelial cells), moist surfaces and close proximity to the blood. The number of alveoli increases tenfold from birth to adulthood, giving an increased surface area to supply the increased body size. Within an adult human lung there are around 300 million alveoli, supplied by 280 million capillaries. The two lungs together give a surface area of between 60 and $80 \, m^2$ for gaseous exchange – equivalent to the surface area of a tennis court.

Partial pressures of gases

The relative proportions of the respiratory gases in table 2.4.1 have been shown as their percentages of the total constituents of the air. A more scientific way of comparing the gases is to consider their **partial pressures**.

The partial pressure of a gas in a mixture of gases in a fixed volume is the pressure that the individual gas would exert if it alone occupied the container. Kinetic theory says that gas molecules exert a pressure by colliding with the sides of the container. The partial pressure of a gas in a mixture is related to the number of molecules of that gas present in the mixture – in other words, the mole fraction of the gas.

Partial pressures are measured in kilopascals (kPa). In the case of the respiratory gases in the air, the percentages and the partial pressures give very similar proportions. The percentage of oxygen in the inspired air is 20.8%, while the partial pressure of oxygen is $21.1 \, kPa$. The percentage of carbon dioxide in inspired air is 0.04% and the partial pressure is $0.04 \, kPa$.

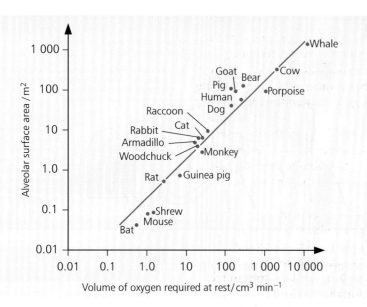

Figure 2.4.7 The alveoli of the lungs are well adapted to supply the oxygen demands of a wide range of mammals, as this graph shows. (*After S.M. Tenney and J.E. Remmes, Comparative quantitative morphology of the mammalian lung: diffusing area. Nature 197: 54, 1963.*)

Keeping the enormous surface for gaseous exchange folded into the controlled environment of the lungs is vitally important in the control of water loss. The alveolar air is saturated with water vapour, so evaporation from the moist alveolar epithelium is reduced. If this area of moist respiratory surface was on the outside of the body, death by desiccation would occur very rapidly due to an enormous water loss by evaporation.

Gaseous exchange occurs by a process of simple diffusion between the alveolar air and the deoxygenated blood in the capillaries. This blood has a relatively low oxygen content and a relatively high carbon dioxide content. The gases are exchanged between the blood and the air so that the blood leaving the alveolus has similar proportions of oxygen and carbon dioxide as the expired air, as figure 2.4.8 illustrates.

The alveoli of our lungs are basically minute bubbles of gas. They naturally have a tendency to collapse when you breathe out, because as the bubble gets smaller the surface tension inside it rises, and this pulls the alveolus in more and more. However, our alveoli don't collapse – we carry on breathing with no trouble at all. How do we manage it? The secret lies in a special chemical secreted by the lungs known as **lung surfactant**. This is a phospholipid, and it forms a layer over the surfaces of the alveoli which is only one or two molecules thick. This thin layer of surfactant reduces the effects of surface tension in our alveoli and allows our lungs to inflate and deflate with ease.

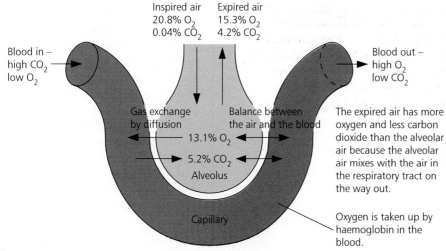

Inspired air 20.8% O_2 0.04% CO_2

Expired air 15.3% O_2 4.2% CO_2

Blood in – high CO_2 low O_2

Blood out – high O_2 low CO_2

Gas exchange by diffusion

Balance between the air and the blood

13.1% O_2

5.2% CO_2

Alveolus

Capillary

The expired air has more oxygen and less carbon dioxide than the alveolar air because the alveolar air mixes with the air in the respiratory tract on the way out.

Oxygen is taken up by haemoglobin in the blood.

Figure 2.4.8 Diffusion across the alveolar surface provides a very successful means of obtaining oxygen and getting rid of carbon dioxide.

(3) Control and regulation of breathing

The respiratory system must be tightly controlled. If too little oxygen is taken in the tissues work less efficiently – and eventually death results. Too little carbon dioxide in the blood results in the pH of the body fluids rising which causes, surprisingly, lack of oxygen. Too much oxygen means the body is doing unnecessary work and wasting energy, whilst too much carbon dioxide can lead to death.

The oxygen needs of the body can change very rapidly from the relatively low levels at rest to the high levels during strenuous exercise, and the amount of carbon dioxide to be removed changes similarly. The ventilation rate must be able to adjust, by increasing both the tidal volume and the frequency of inspiration. How is this control brought about?

The basic stimulus to inhale and exhale is given by an area of the hindbrain (medulla) known as the **respiratory centre**. This gives a basic deep, slow breathing rhythm. Impulses from the respiratory centre travel along the **phrenic nerve** and the **thoracic nerve** and stimulate the intercostal muscles and the diaphragm to contract, so we inhale. As the lungs inflate, the stretch receptors they contain send nerve impulses increasingly rapidly to the respiratory centre until it stops stimulating the breathing muscles, which relax and we exhale.

Inputs from other receptors interact with this basic rhythm to give a finely tuned respiratory response to most situations, including stress, exercise and oxygen deprivation. There are stretch receptors in the bronchi, and we also have a number of receptors which are sensitive to the level of carbon dioxide in the blood, its pH and to some extent its oxygen level. These **chemoreceptors** include the **central receptors** of the **medulla oblongata** (in the hindbrain itself), the **carotid bodies** found in the carotid arteries and the **aortic bodies** which are in the aortic arch as the aorta leaves the heart. By monitoring the chemical make-up of the blood in these areas, and feeding back information to the main respiratory control system, we make sure that our respiratory rate matches our oxygen needs. In addition, the higher centres of the brain can override the respiratory centres while we are conscious. We are capable of choosing to hold our breath, or take a deep breath, or breathe faster – but as soon as we become unconscious, our breathing returns to purely automatic control.

The human respiratory system has evolved to cope with the problems of gaseous exchange for a large, land-dwelling animal. All mammals and most land vertebrates have developed a somewhat similar system. But internal lungs are not the only way to solve these problems, as a look at the respiratory systems of insects shows.

The insect respiratory system

Many insects are very active during parts of their life cycles. They are therefore in a similar position to the mammals, being complex and largely land-dwelling animals with relatively high oxygen requirements and an external surface through which little or no gaseous exchange can take place.

Most animals have an internal respiratory system linked to a transport system, with oxygen diffusing into the blood or a similar fluid and being carried around the body to the individual cells in this way. Figure 2.4.9 shows an example of the respiratory system of insects, which has evolved to deliver oxygen directly to the cells and to remove carbon dioxide in the same way.

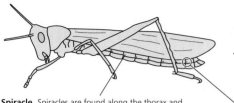

Spiracle Spiracles are found along the thorax and abdomen of most insects. They are the site of the entry and exit of the respiratory gases. In many insects they can be opened or closed by sphincters, which is of great value in the control of water loss.

Trachea Tracheae are the largest tubes of the insect respiratory system, carrying the air into the body. They may be up to 1 mm in diameter. They run both into and along the body of the insect. The tubes are lined by spirals of chitin which keep them open if they are bent or pressed. Chitin is the material which makes up the cuticle. The tracheae are therefore relatively impermeable to gases and little gaseous exchange takes place there. The tracheae branch to form narrower and narrower tubes until they break up into the tracheoles.

Watery fluid in the tracheoles. Water can be withdrawn from the tracheoles by osmosis when extra oxygen is needed, giving a form of control over the level of respiration.

Tracheoles Tracheoles are minute tubes of diameter 0.6–0.8 μm. Each is a single greatly elongated cell, with no chitin lining, so they are freely permeable to gases. Because of their very small size they spread throughout the tissues of the insect, running between individual cells. Most of the gaseous exchange takes place between the air and the respiring cells in the tracheoles.

Figure 2.4.9 The respiratory system of an insect has to fulfil the same requirements as the human respiratory system. In spite of its very different design, there are many similar features.

How the insect respiratory system works

Air enters the system through the spiracles. To minimise the amount of water lost the spiracle sphincters are kept closed as much as possible. For example, an adult flea which has sphincters is much more resistant to desiccation than a larval flea which has no sphincters. Figure 2.4.10 shows the effect of opening the spiracles on water loss in an insect.

When an insect is inactive and its oxygen demands are very low, the spiracles will all be closed. The occasional opening of just one or two pairs brings in enough air for gaseous exchange. When the oxygen demand is higher or the carbon dioxide levels build up, more spiracles open.

Air moves along the tracheae and tracheoles and reaches all the tissues by diffusion alone. The vast numbers of tiny tracheoles, even penetrating into the cells themselves, give a very large surface area for gaseous exchange. The tracheoles contain a watery fluid towards the end of their length. This limits the penetration of the gases for diffusion. However, when oxygen demands build up – when the insect is flying, for example – lactic acid in the tissues causes water to be withdrawn from the tracheoles by osmosis and exposes additional surface area for gaseous exchange.

All the oxygen needed by the insect's cells is supplied to them by the respiratory system. However, up to 25% of the carbon dioxide produced by the cells is lost directly through the cuticle.

The extent of respiration in most insects is controlled by the opening and closing of the spiracles. There are respiratory centres in both the ganglia of the nerve cord and the brain. They are stimulated by increasing carbon dioxide levels and by the lactic acid which builds up in active tissues when there is a lack of oxygen. It seems that a combination of lack of oxygen and carbon dioxide build-up work together to provide the insect with a flexible and responsive respiratory system.

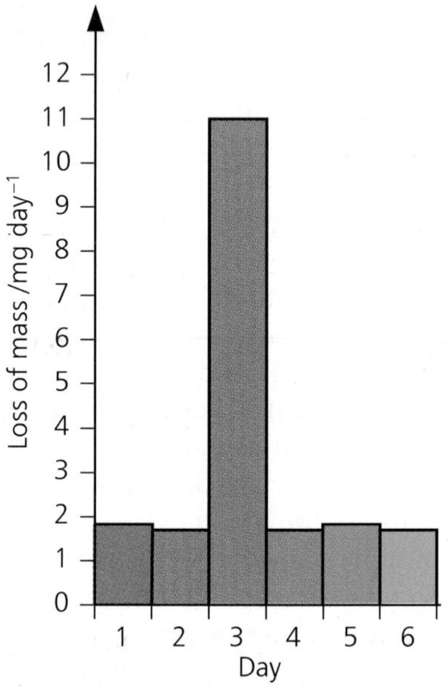

Figure 2.4.10 The effect of opening the spiracles on water loss can be seen clearly from this graph. An adult *Rhodnius* (a blood-sucking bug) was kept in dry air for 6 days. It was not fed, to keep it relatively inactive throughout. On day 3 the bug was exposed to a raised level of carbon dioxide in the air which made the spiracles open. The air was returned to normal on day 4.

Very active insects

The type of respiratory system described so far works well for small insects and for large but slow ones. Those insects which have more active lifestyles, for example larger beetles, locusts and grasshoppers, bees, wasps and flies, have much higher energy demands. To supply the extra oxygen needed, alternative methods of increasing the level of gaseous exchange are used.

(1) Some form of mechanical ventilation of the tracheal system may be introduced – in other words, air is actively pumped into the system. This is usually brought about by increased opening of the spiracles along with muscular pumping movements of the thorax and/or abdomen.

(2) Some active insects have collapsible tracheae or **air sacs** which act as air reservoirs and are used to increase the amount of air moved through the respiratory system. They are usually inflated and deflated by the ventilating movements of the thorax and abdomen. In some insects they can be ventilated by the general body movements, for example, when a locust is in flight the air sacs within the muscles are automatically inflated.

Respiratory systems in fish

As we have seen, animals living on the land have to overcome the problems of water loss from their respiratory surfaces. For animals which live in, and obtain oxygen from, water this is not a problem – but there are other difficulties to overcome.

Water is 1000 times denser than air. It is 100 times more viscous and has a much lower oxygen content. To cope with the viscosity of water and the slow rate of oxygen diffusion, aquatic animals such as fish have evolved very specialised respiratory systems. Moving water in and out of lung-like respiratory organs under water would use up an enormous amount of energy. Moving water in one direction only is much simpler and more economical in energy terms.

How the fish respiratory system works

The bony fish, such as cod, salmon and sticklebacks, cannot undergo gaseous exchange through their scaly external covering, but they have evolved a respiratory system which works very well in the water. **Gills** incorporate the large surface area, large blood supply and thin walls needed for efficient gaseous exchange. In the bony fish they are contained in a gill cavity covered by a protective **operculum** which is also active in maintaining a flow of water over the gills. Figure 2.4.11 shows the respiratory system of a bony fish.

When looking at the respiratory system of the fish, there are two main questions we shall consider:

Figure 2.4.11 The gills make up the respiratory surface of the fish. They have many features in common with both mammalian and insect respiratory surfaces, but are particularly adapted to their environment.

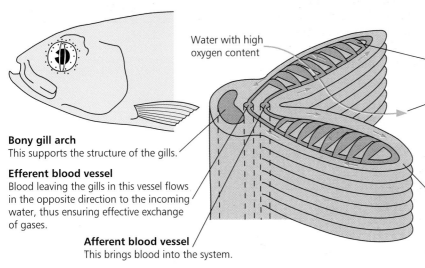

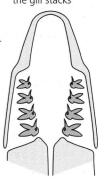

Water with high oxygen content

Gill lamellae
These are the main site of gaseous exchange in the fish. They have a very rich blood supply and give the gill filaments their large surface area.

Water with low oxygen content

Arrangement of the gill stacks

Gill filaments
The fragile gill filaments occur in large stacks. They need water to keep them apart and so to expose the large surface area needed for gaseous exchange. A fish does not last long out of water because these stacks of filaments collapse onto each other and insufficient surface area is exposed to supply the respiratory needs.

Bony gill arch
This supports the structure of the gills.

Efferent blood vessel
Blood leaving the gills in this vessel flows in the opposite direction to the incoming water, thus ensuring effective exchange of gases.

Afferent blood vessel
This brings blood into the system.

1 How is a flow of water maintained over the gills to allow continuous gaseous exchange?

2 How is gaseous exchange carried out as effectively as possible in a medium where diffusion tends to be slow?

(1) Water flow over the gills

While fish are swimming it is easy to see that they could keep a flow of water over their gills simply by opening the mouth and operculum. Problems arise when the fish stops moving. The more primitive cartilaginous fish such as the sharks often rely on continual movement to ventilate the gills. But the majority of the bony fish have evolved a more sophisticated system involving the operculum, shown in figure 2.4.12.

(2) Effective gaseous exchange

Gills, like other respiratory surfaces, have a large surface area, a rich blood supply and thin walls. There are two other aspects of the gills which help to ensure that effective gaseous exchange occurs.

The tips of adjacent gill filaments overlap. This increases the resistance to the flow of water, slowing down the movement of water over the gill surfaces. The result is more time for the exchange of gases to take place.

The blood in the gill filaments and the water moving over the gills flow in different directions. Diffusion occurs down a concentration gradient, and the steeper the concentration gradient, the more effective is diffusion. By having this **countercurrent exchange system**, steeper concentration gradients are maintained and so more gaseous exchange can take place than if the blood and water flowed in the same direction (in a **parallel system**). Figure 2.4.13 illustrates this. The cartilaginous fish – the sharks and rays – have parallel systems and extract only about 50% of the oxygen from the water. The bony fish, with their countercurrent systems, remove about 80%.

From these examples it can be seen that respiratory systems are very highly developed to enable larger organisms to carry out gaseous exchange. Mammalian lungs, insect tracheal systems and the gills of fish are not the only ways of carrying out gaseous exchange. However, they demonstrate the type of features which enable an animal with an unfavourable surface area:volume ratio to obtain the oxygen it needs for life.

The buccal cavity (mouth) is first expanded as the floor is lowered. This causes the pressure to drop in the mouth and water moves in through the mouth opening. The operculum is shut and the opercular cavity containing the gills expands. This lowers the pressure in the opercular cavity containing the gills. The floor of the buccal cavity moves up, increasing the pressure there and so water moves from the buccal cavity over the gills.

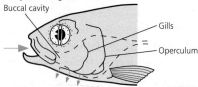

The mouth is then closed, the operculum opens and the sides of the opercular cavity move inwards, increasing the pressure and forcing water out of the operculum. The floor of the buccal cavity continues to be raised, maintaining a flow of water over the gills.

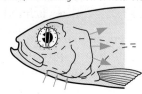

Figure 2.4.12 This continuous process ensures that water is flowing over the gills at all times.

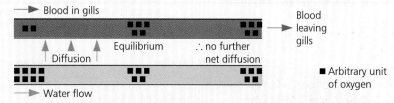

If the blood in the gills travelled in the same direction as the water flowing over the gills there would be a steep concentration gradient between the two at the beginning. Diffusion would take place until the blood and water were in equilibrium, after which no net movement of oxygen into the blood or carbon dioxide out of the blood would occur.

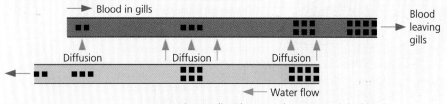

In a countercurrent system a concentration gradient between the water and the blood is maintained along the gill. As a result, a far higher saturation of the blood with oxygen is possible, and larger amounts of carbon dioxide can be removed.

Figure 2.4.13 The advantages of a countercurrent exchange system. These systems occur in a variety of different roles throughout the animal kingdom.

SUMMARY

- **Respiratory systems** are a means of effecting gaseous exchange in multicellular organisms, necessitated by the process of cellular respiration which uses oxygen and produces carbon dioxide.

- Gaseous exchange takes place at **respiratory surfaces**, which have a large surface area and are permeable, thin, moist and in many animals have a rich blood supply.

- In plants the gaseous exchange needed for both photosynthesis and cellular respiration takes place through the stomata.

- The land vertebrates have **lungs** to provide a respiratory surface while limiting water loss.

- The **human respiratory system** consists of the **trachea** (windpipe) connected to the nose and mouth and covered by the **epiglottis** during swallowing. The trachea is lined with **columnar epithelial** cells with **cilia** which move mucus and trapped microorganisms and dust away from the lungs. The **mucus-secreting** cells are below the epithelium. The trachea splits to form two **bronchi** which like the trachea are lined with C-shaped **cartilage rings**.

- The bronchi are further divided to form **bronchioles**. The larger ones are lined with columnar epithelium and supported with cartilage rings, while the smaller ones are lined with **flattened cuboidal epithelium**. Some gaseous exchange takes place in these bronchioles.

- **Alveoli** are sacs at the ends of the smallest bronchioles, lined with **squamous epithelium**. Capillaries with walls one cell thick run alongside the alveoli and gaseous exchange occurs between the alveolar air and the blood in the capillaries.

- Two **pleural membranes** surround the lungs, between which is the **pleural cavity**.

- The **ribs** protect the lungs and their movement is brought about by the **intercostal muscles**. The **diaphragm** forms the floor of the chest cavity.

- **Inhalation** is brought about by contraction of the **external** intercostal muscles pulling the rib cage up and out, and the contraction of the diaphragm which moves it down. This increase in volume decreases the pressure in the lungs so air moves in.

- During **exhalation**, the **internal** intercostal muscles contract, pulling the rib cage down and in, while the diaphragm relaxes and moves up, so forcing air out of the lungs.

- The rate of breathing is expressed as the **ventilation rate**, which is the **tidal volume** (the volume breathed in) × the **frequency of inspiration**.

- The ventilation rate is controlled by signals from the respiratory centre in the brain, from stretch receptors in the bronchi and from receptors sensitive to carbon dioxide levels in the blood.

- The **insect respiratory system** consists of **spiracles** which can open and close, leading to tubes called **tracheae**, lined with chitin for support and so impermeable. These lead to **tracheoles**, single elongated cells permeable to gaseous exchange, which run between the insect body cells. Watery fluid can be withdrawn from the tracheoles when necessary to increase the surface area for gaseous exchange.

- The **respiratory system of a bony fish** consists of **gills** within a protective **operculum**. A bony **gill arch** supports stacks of **gill filaments** which contain **gill lamellae**, the site of gaseous exchange, which are well supplied with blood.

- Water is constantly forced over the gills by the combined action of the buccal cavity and the operculum. The overlapping gill filaments slow down the flow of water, and the blood runs in the opposite direction to the water, so **countercurrent exchange** takes place.

QUESTIONS

1 a Why are respiratory systems necessary?
b What are the main features of successful respiratory systems?
c Why are active respiratory systems not found in plants?
d Sketch the human respiratory system and annotate the main regions.

2 a How is the rate of breathing in human beings determined experimentally?
b What factors are most likely to affect the breathing rate?
c Describe how the rate of breathing is controlled.

3 Draw up a table to compare the respiratory systems of a mammal, an insect and a fish.

Developing Key Skills

The maternity unit at your local hospital wants to produce a simple leaflet which can be given to all expectant parents at the antenatal clinics. It wants to explain to parents the importance of breathing and of their baby's first breath. The unit also wants to explain the breathing problems that can be experienced if babies are born too early and the ways in which these problems can be solved. It is important that the leaflet can be read and understood by as many people as possible.

Your brief is to produce a suitable leaflet for the maternity unit, with clear illustrations and appropriate language.

FOCUS A HEALTHIER HEART

From the heart?

In reality the heart is not even heart shaped. It is a bag of powerful red-brown muscle divided into four chambers. It begins to beat long before we are born, and continues to beat day and night throughout our lives. The heart contracts or beats to force blood around the body, and the blood carries oxygen and food for the cells and removes the waste products of metabolism. We rarely think about our hearts until something goes wrong – and then it may be too late.

Heart disease – what can we do?

Heart disease can affect anyone at any age, but it is a particular threat to men over 30 and women after the menopause. Heart problems in young children are usually the result of a problem with the development of the heart. Sometimes not all the chambers of the heart develop properly, whilst in other cases the valves do not work as they should. Babies with problems like these can often be helped by surgery, but sadly some babies with very serious heart defects die.

A common heart problem in babies is known as a 'hole in the heart'. In the fetus there is a gap in the central wall of the heart so the blood on the two sides can mix. Once the baby is born, it is important that this mixing no longer happens so the hole closes up (see page 145). Sometimes this does not happen properly, and the baby's blood is not properly oxygenated as a result. The problem can be so mild that no action is taken, or it can be so severe that immediate surgery is needed, but almost all 'holes in the heart' can be successfully treated.

Heart disease in adults is more likely to be the result of their genetic inheritance and their lifestyle. Eating a diet high in saturated fats, smoking and lack of exercise all increase our risk of suffering from heart disease.

Whilst we cannot yet change our genetic tendency towards heart disease, we can certainly influence the other factors that increase our risk. Regular exercise makes the heart muscle stronger and more efficient, and the resting heart rate drops. The coronary arteries get bigger and more extensive as a result of the increased blood flow during exercise, and exercise has also been shown to reduce the levels of dangerous high-density lipoproteins in the blood whatever sort of diet we eat. So by exercising regularly, watching our diet and not smoking we all have it in our power to load the dice in our favour when it comes to heart disease (see section 7.3).

Figure 1 The human heart is endowed with many attributes in popular culture. We love with all our hearts, our hearts are broken, we make a heart-felt plea. From childhood we assume that the seat of life is in the heart, and yet in spite of this most people are very careless about their hearts.

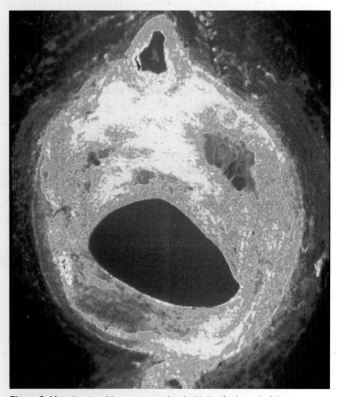

Figure 2 Many heart problems are associated with the 'furring up' of the coronary arteries – the arteries that supply the heart itself with oxygenated blood – by a fatty substance called cholesterol. This leads to an increasingly inefficient heart and can result in angina or a heart attack, which may well be fatal.

2.5 Transport systems in animals

The features of transport systems were discussed in section 2.3. Most of the larger animal groups possess a specific system for the transport and distribution of materials around the organism. This usually takes the form of a **cardiovascular system**.

The cardiovascular system

A cardiovascular system is made up of a series of vessels with a pump (the heart) to move blood through the vessels. The heart and blood vessels form a transport system with the blood as the transport medium. The system delivers the materials needed by the cells of the body, and carries away the waste products of their metabolism. The cardiovascular system often carries out other functions as well, such as carrying hormones (chemical messages) from one part of the body to another, transporting the defence system of the body and distributing heat. Transport systems of this type are found in a wide range of animals, but we shall concentrate on the human cardiovascular system. This has been widely researched and is a good representative of systems of this type.

The human cardiovascular system

The human cardiovascular system includes various structures with different functions – the heart, the arteries, the arterioles, the capillaries, the venules and the veins. Mammals and birds possess the most complex type of transport system, known as a **double circulation** which involves two systems, shown in figure 2.5.1. One, the **systemic circulation**, carries oxygen-rich blood from the heart to the cells of the body and deoxygenated blood back to the heart. The other, the **pulmonary circulation**, carries deoxygenated blood to the lungs and oxygenated blood back to the heart.

The blood is contained within the closed circulation system, making a continuous journey out to the most distant parts of the body and back to the heart. The ancient Chinese had a good understanding of the circulation of the blood around 100 BC, but it was not until William Harvey, in his writings of 1628, showed how the circulation worked that the idea was accepted in Europe.

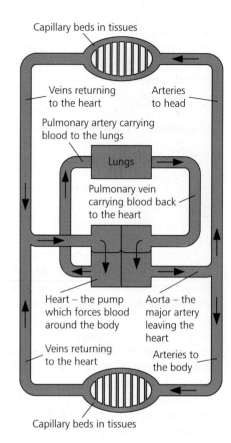

Capillary beds in tissues

Veins returning to the heart — Arteries to head

Pulmonary artery carrying blood to the lungs

Lungs

Pulmonary vein carrying blood back to the heart

Heart – the pump which forces blood around the body

Aorta – the major artery leaving the heart

Veins returning to the heart

Arteries to the body

Capillary beds in tissues

Figure 2.5.1 A double circulation of this type ensures that the blood sent to the active cells of the body is carrying as much oxygen as possible.

The blood vessels

Transport routes

The various types of blood vessels which make up the circulatory system show differences in their structures which are closely related to their functions. The largest vessels are the major named arteries and veins, such as the pulmonary vein coming away from the lungs or the mesenteric artery supplying the small intestine. The blood flows quickly through these vessels, which then divide into smaller and smaller vessels until they are linked by the vast, branching and spreading capillary network. As the diameter of the vessels decreases, so their resistance to the flow of blood increases. It is interesting to look at the approximate numbers of some of these linked vessels shown in table 2.5.1 and figure 2.5.2.

Type of blood vessel	Total number
Mesenteric artery	1
Main branches of mesenteric artery	15
Short and long branches to intestine	1 899
Branches to villi	328 500
Arteries of villi	1 051 000
Capillaries of villi	47 300 000
Veins at base of villi	2 102 400
Branches from villi	131 400
Long and short branches from intestine	1 899
Branches of mesenteric vein	15
Mesenteric vein	1

Table 2.5.1

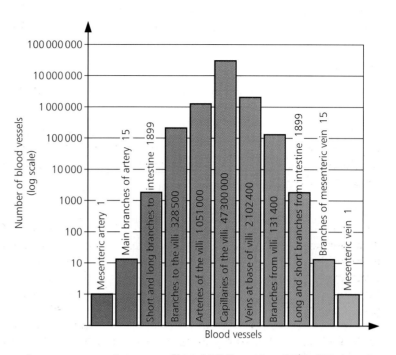

Figure 2.5.2 The numbers of different blood vessels within the mesenteric system of a dog. The mesenteric system carries blood to and from the very active intestinal region.

When considering the blood vessels we shall look at each type separately, considering the relationship between structure and the function. It must be remembered, however, that the vessels do not exist as separate structures – they are interlinked within the complexities of the whole circulatory system.

Arteries

The **arteries** carry blood *away from* the heart. The structure of an artery is shown in figure 2.5.3. Arteries almost all carry **oxygenated** or oxygen-rich blood towards the cells of the body. The only exceptions are the pulmonary artery, which carries deoxygenated blood from the heart to the lungs, and the umbilical artery, which carries deoxygenated blood from the fetus to the placenta. As arteries get further from the heart they branch, and the diameter of the lumen gets smaller. The very smallest branches of the arterial system are referred to as **arterioles**.

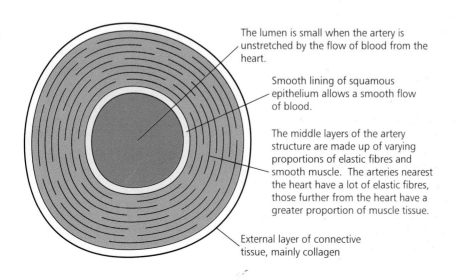

The lumen is small when the artery is unstretched by the flow of blood from the heart.

Smooth lining of squamous epithelium allows a smooth flow of blood.

The middle layers of the artery structure are made up of varying proportions of elastic fibres and smooth muscle. The arteries nearest the heart have a lot of elastic fibres, those further from the heart have a greater proportion of muscle tissue.

External layer of connective tissue, mainly collagen

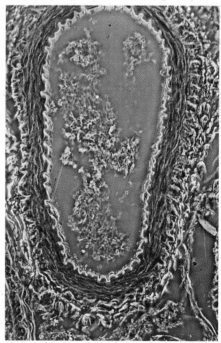

Figure 2.5.3 The structure of an artery enables it to cope with the surging of the blood as the heart pumps.

Blood is pumped out from the heart in a regular rhythm, about 70 times a minute. The major arteries close to the heart have to be able to withstand the pressure of these spurts of blood, and stretch to accommodate the increased volume. They also 'even out' the blood pumped from the heart to give a continuous, if pulsing, flow. The large proportion of elastic fibres in artery walls helps them fulfil these functions, allowing them to stretch without being damaged when blood is pumped out from the heart. Then, when the heart relaxes and no further blood is being forced into the arteries, the elastic fibres return to their original length, squeezing the blood and so moving it along in a continuous flow. The pulse which can be felt in an artery is the effect of the surge each time the heart beats, which the arteries do not completely eliminate.

In the more peripheral arteries, contracting or relaxing the muscle fibres in the artery walls can be used to change the size of the lumen. The smaller the lumen, the harder it is for blood to flow through the vessel. Thus the muscular walls of the arteries supplying blood to the various organs of the body can control the amount of blood that flows into these organs, and so affect the level of their activity.

The blood pressure in all arteries is relatively high, but drops with distance away from the heart. Figure 2.5.4 compares the structures of different sized arterial vessels.

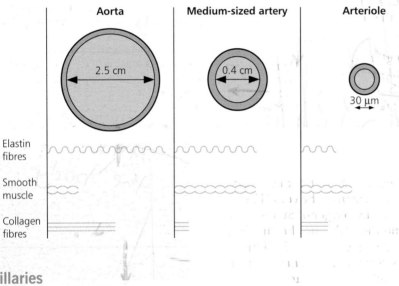

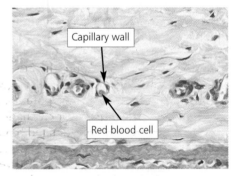

Figure 2.5.4 The differences in function of these three different types of artery are reflected in the proportions of the tissues making up their walls.

Capillaries

Linking the arterial and venous system is the network of **capillaries**. These minute vessels spread throughout the tissues of the entire body. They are found between cells, and no cell is far from a capillary to supply its needs. The capillary system provides an enormous surface area for the diffusion of substances into and out of the blood. Also, because the diameter of each individual capillary is very thin, the blood travels relatively slowly through them, again giving more opportunity for diffusion.

Capillaries have a very simple structure well suited to their function. Their walls contain no elastic fibres, smooth muscle or collagen as this would interfere both with the ability of the capillaries to penetrate between individual cells and with efficient diffusion. The walls consist of **squamous epithelium**, which is extremely thin in cross-section. Oxygen is removed from the blood as it travels through the capillaries, and carbon dioxide is loaded into it, so the capillaries are said to carry mixed blood – oxygenated when it enters the capillary network but deoxygenated by the time it leaves.

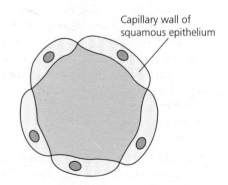

Figure 2.5.5 Capillary walls are extremely thin to allow for diffusion of oxygen, carbon dioxide and food molecules.

The lymphatic system

Capillary walls are permeable to everything in the blood apart from the erythrocytes (red blood cells) and the plasma proteins. As blood flows through the capillaries under pressure from the arterial system, fluid is squeezed out of the vessels. This fluid fills the spaces between the cells and is known as **intercellular fluid** or **tissue fluid**. It is through this fluid that diffusion between the blood and the cells takes place.

Much intercellular fluid is eventually returned to the blood. Some of it returns by osmosis and diffusion at the venous end of the capillaries. Most of it drains into a system of blind-ended tubes called **lymph capillaries** and once in these vessels the fluid is called **lymph**. The lymph capillaries join up to form larger and larger vessels. The fluid is transported through them by the squeezing effect of muscular movements and backflow is prevented by a system of valves. The lymph is returned to the blood in the neck area, into the left and right subclavian veins (underneath the collar bone or clavicle).

Situated along the lymph vessels are **lymph glands**. Lymphocytes accumulate in these glands and produce antibodies which are then emptied into the blood. The glands also filter out bacteria and other foreign particles from the lymph to be ingested by phagocytes. Thus the lymphatic system, shown in figure 2.5.6, plays a major role in the defence mechanisms of the body.

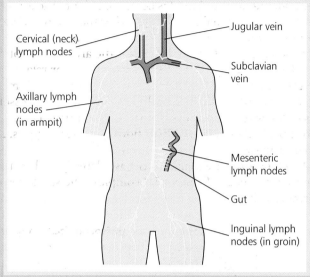

Figure 2.5.6 Enlarged lymph glands are a sign that the body is fighting off an invading pathogen. You can see why doctors often examine the neck, armpits, stomach and groin of patients – these are the main sites of the lymph glands.

Veins

The **veins** carry blood *towards* the heart. This means that most of them carry blood which is **deoxygenated** – it has given up its oxygen to the cells. There are two exceptions to this. The pulmonary vein carries oxygen-rich blood from the lungs back to the heart for circulation around the body, and the umbilical vein of the fetus carries oxygenated blood from the placenta into the fetus.

From the capillary network in the tissues, blood enters tiny **venules** which merge into larger and larger vessels. Eventually only two veins carry the returning blood to the heart – the inferior vena cava from the lower parts of the body and the superior vena cava from the upper parts of the body.

Veins can hold a large volume of blood – in fact, more than half of the total body volume of blood is in the venous system at any one time. The veins act as a blood reservoir. The blood pressure in the veins is relatively low – the pressure surges from the heart have been eliminated as the blood passes through the capillary beds. Figure 2.5.7 shows how the structure of veins differs from that of arteries.

The venous system has two main methods of ensuring that blood is returned to the heart:

1 There are one-way valves at frequent intervals throughout the venous system called **semilunar valves**. These are formed from infoldings of the inner wall of the vein, shown in figure 2.5.8. Blood can pass through in the direction of the heart, but if it tends to flow backwards the valves close, preventing this.

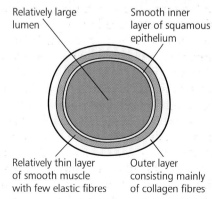

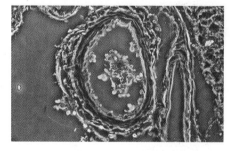

Figure 2.5.7 Veins do not have to withstand the high pressures of the arterial system and this is reflected in their structure.

2 Many of the larger veins are situated between the large muscle blocks of the body, particularly in the arms and legs. When the muscles contract during physical activity they squeeze these veins. As the valves make sure that the blood can only travel towards the heart, this squeezing helps to force the returning blood on its way.

The heart

The heart is the organ that moves blood around the body. In some animal groups it is no more than a simple muscular tube. In mammals the heart is a complex, four-chambered muscular bag. It is found in the chest, protected by the ribs and sternum. An effectively beating heart is vital to the successful functioning of the human transport system and to the overall health of the body.

The structure of the human heart

The heart is one of the first organs to be completed as the embryo develops. It consists of two pumps joined together and working synchronously. The right-hand side of the heart receives blood from the body and pumps it to the lungs. The left-hand side of the heart receives blood from the lungs and pumps it to the body. The blood from the two sides of the heart does not mix. The whole heart is surrounded by the inelastic **pericardial membranes**, one attached to the heart itself. Fluid is secreted between these membranes which allows them to move easily over each other. They help prevent the heart from over-distending with blood. The structure of the heart is shown in figure 2.5.10.

How the heart works

Relating the structures of the heart to their functions as in figure 2.5.10 gives a good picture of how the heart works. In order to do this a particular volume of blood is followed on its journey round the heart. However, it is important to remember that the heart works as a unit, with both sides contracting at the same time.

Months before birth the heart has begun its regular contraction and relaxation which will continue throughout life. The contraction of the heart is called **systole**. First the atria contract, closely followed by the ventricles. Systole forces blood out of the heart to the lungs and general body circulation. Between contractions the heart relaxes and fills with blood. This relaxation stage is called **diastole**. Diastole and systole together make up a single heartbeat, which lasts about 0.8 s in humans and is known as the **cardiac cycle**. This cycle is made up of the following sequence of events:

1 Blood enters the right atrium from the body and the left atrium from the lungs. The atria fill and then the atrioventricular valves open under pressure so allowing the ventricles to fill as well. This is **diastole**.

2 The two atria contract together, forcing more blood into the ventricles which in turn both contract at the same time. During this **systole** blood is forced out of the heart into the pulmonary artery and the aorta, as figure 2.5.9 shows.

The heartbeat

The beating of the heart produces sounds known as the **heartbeat**. The heartbeat can be heard by putting an ear to the chest wall, but an instrument called a **stethoscope** makes the heartbeat clearer. The sounds of the heartbeat are made not by the contracting of the heart muscle, but by blood hitting the

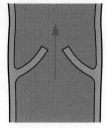
Blood moving in the direction of the heart forces the valve open, allowing the blood to flow through.

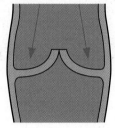
A backflow of blood will close the valve, ensuring that blood cannot flow away from the heart.

Figure 2.5.8 An extensive system of valves in the venous system makes sure that the blood only flows towards the heart.

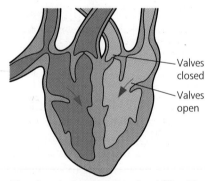
Valves closed

Valves open

Diastole – the heart is relaxed and fills with blood.

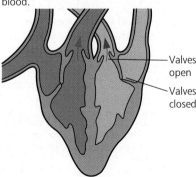
Valves open

Valves closed

Systole – the heart (atria followed by ventricles) contracts and forces blood out to the lungs and round the body.

Figure 2.5.9 The sequence of events in the cardiac cycle

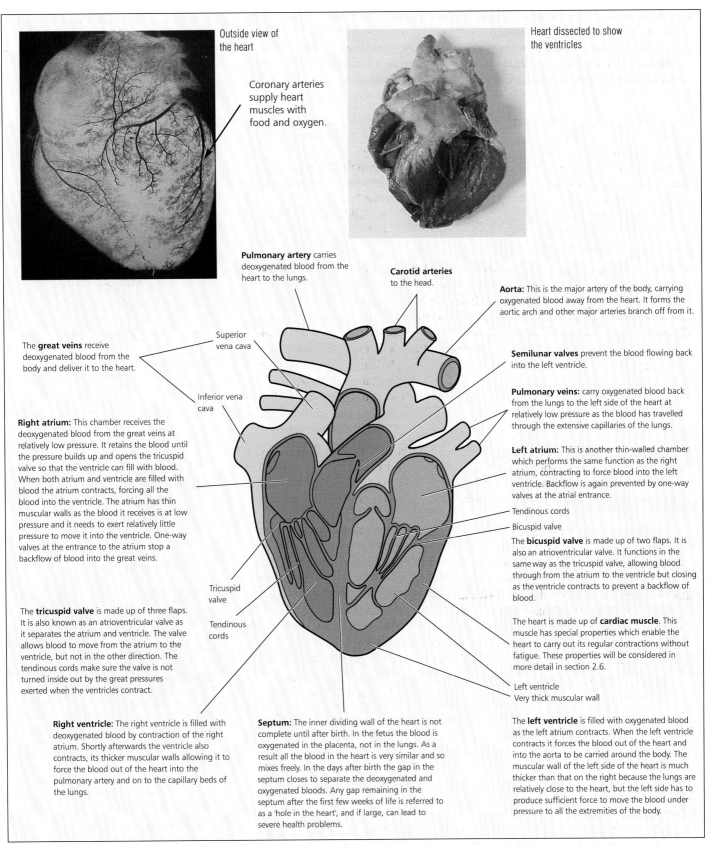

Outside view of the heart

Heart dissected to show the ventricles

Coronary arteries supply heart muscles with food and oxygen.

Pulmonary artery carries deoxygenated blood from the heart to the lungs.

Carotid arteries to the head.

Aorta: This is the major artery of the body, carrying oxygenated blood away from the heart. It forms the aortic arch and other major arteries branch off from it.

The **great veins** receive deoxygenated blood from the body and deliver it to the heart.

Superior vena cava

Inferior vena cava

Semilunar valves prevent the blood flowing back into the left ventricle.

Pulmonary veins: carry oxygenated blood back from the lungs to the left side of the heart at relatively low pressure as the blood has travelled through the extensive capillaries of the lungs.

Right atrium: This chamber receives the deoxygenated blood from the great veins at relatively low pressure. It retains the blood until the pressure builds up and opens the tricuspid valve so that the ventricle can fill with blood. When both atrium and ventricle are filled with blood the atrium contracts, forcing all the blood into the ventricle. The atrium has thin muscular walls as the blood it receives is at low pressure and it needs to exert relatively little pressure to move it into the ventricle. One-way valves at the entrance to the atrium stop a backflow of blood into the great veins.

Left atrium: This is another thin-walled chamber which performs the same function as the right atrium, contracting to force blood into the left ventricle. Backflow is again prevented by one-way valves at the atrial entrance.

Tendinous cords

Bicuspid valve

The **bicuspid valve** is made up of two flaps. It is also an atrioventricular valve. It functions in the same way as the tricuspid valve, allowing blood through from the atrium to the ventricle but closing as the ventricle contracts to prevent a backflow of blood.

Tricuspid valve

Tendinous cords

The **tricuspid valve** is made up of three flaps. It is also known as an atrioventricular valve as it separates the atrium and ventricle. The valve allows blood to move from the atrium to the ventricle, but not in the other direction. The tendinous cords make sure the valve is not turned inside out by the great pressures exerted when the ventricles contract.

The heart is made up of **cardiac muscle**. This muscle has special properties which enable the heart to carry out its regular contractions without fatigue. These properties will be considered in more detail in section 2.6.

Left ventricle

Very thick muscular wall

Right ventricle: The right ventricle is filled with deoxygenated blood by contraction of the right atrium. Shortly afterwards the ventricle also contracts, its thicker muscular walls allowing it to force the blood out of the heart into the pulmonary artery and on to the capillary beds of the lungs.

Septum: The inner dividing wall of the heart is not complete until after birth. In the fetus the blood is oxygenated in the placenta, not in the lungs. As a result all the blood in the heart is very similar and so mixes freely. In the days after birth the gap in the septum closes to separate the deoxygenated and oxygenated bloods. Any gap remaining in the septum after the first few weeks of life is referred to as a 'hole in the heart', and if large, can lead to severe health problems.

The **left ventricle** is filled with oxygenated blood as the left atrium contracts. When the left ventricle contracts it forces the blood out of the heart and into the aorta to be carried around the body. The muscular wall of the left side of the heart is much thicker than that on the right because the lungs are relatively close to the heart, but the left side has to produce sufficient force to move the blood under pressure to all the extremities of the body.

Figure 2.5.10 The structure of the heart is closely related to its function. In an average lifetime it will beat more than 2.5×10^9 times, and each ventricle will pump over 150 million litres of blood.

heart valves. The two sounds of a heartbeat are described as 'lub-dub'. The first sound is made when blood is forced back against the atrioventricular valves as the ventricles contract, and the second when a backflow of blood hits the semilunar valves in the aorta and pulmonary artery as the ventricles relax. Some of the changes in the heart which cause the heartbeat are shown in figure 2.5.11.

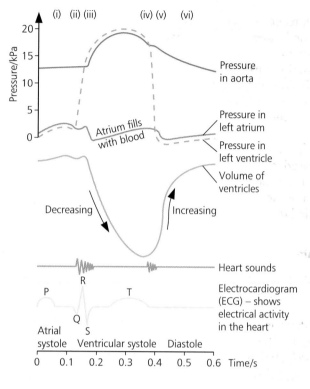

(i) Atrium contracts, blood flows into ventricle.

(ii) Ventricle starts to contract, atrioventricular valve closes.

(iii) Aortic valve forced open, blood flows from ventricle into aorta, and volume of ventricle falls.

(iv) Aortic valve closes, volume of ventricle starts to rise.

(v) Blood flows from atrium to ventricle, volume of ventricle rises rapidly.

(vi) Atrium fills with blood from pulmonary vein, blood flows from atrium to ventricle.

Figure 2.5.11 The cardiac cycle and causes of the heartbeat. The first and second heart sounds are due to the closure of the atrioventricular and aortic valves. Look at how the differences in pressure cause these closures – the atrioventricular valve closes when the ventricular pressure rises above the atrial pressure (ii), and the aortic valve closes when the ventricular pressure falls below the aortic pressure (iv). (*After Winton and Bayliss*, Human Physiology, *Churchill*)

Control of the heart

The heart beats continually throughout life, with an average of about 70 beats per minute, although in small children the heart rate is much higher. The heart can respond to the varying needs of the body – during physical exercise when the tissues need more oxygen, it beats faster to supply more oxygenated, glucose-carrying blood to the tissues and to remove the increased waste products. Stress can raise the heart rate, whilst rest and relaxation can lower it.

How is the heart controlled? In the very early embryo, cells which are destined to become the heart begin contracting rhythmically long before the organ forms. They have **intrinsic rhythmicity**. An adult heart removed from the body will continue to contract as long as it is bathed in a suitable oxygen-rich fluid. The intrinsic rhythm of the heart, that is, the rate at which it beats when isolated from the nervous and hormonal control of the body, is around 60 beats per minute. This rhythm is maintained by a wave of electrical excitation similar to a nerve impulse which spreads through special tissue in the heart muscle. Figure 2.5.12 shows the spread of excitation through the heart.

The intrinsic rhythm of the heart does not explain how the heart is able to respond to changes in the body's requirements. This sensitivity is supplied by nervous control of the heart. A nerve from the sympathetic nervous system speeds up the heart rate and the vagus nerve from the parasympathetic system slows it down. More details about the nervous system will be found in section 4. Other factors such as hormones, pH changes caused by carbon dioxide levels and temperature all have an effect on heart rate.

The **sinoatrial node (SAN)** or **pacemaker** sets up a wave of electrical excitation which causes the atria to start contracting and also spreads to an adjacent area of similar tissue. This is the P wave in the ECG in figure 2.5.11.

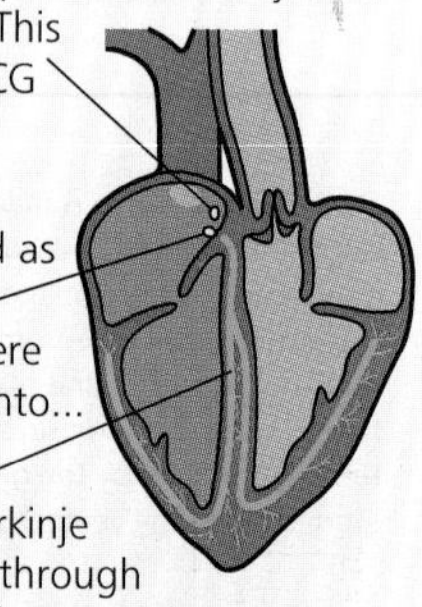

The **atrioventricular node (AVN)** is excited as a result of the SAN's excitation and from here the excitation passes into...

the **Purkyne tissue**. Formerly called the Purkinje tissue, this penetrates through the septum between the ventricles. As the excitation travels through the tissue it sets off the contraction of the ventricles, starting at the bottom and so squeezing blood out. This is the Q,R,S and T waves of the ECG. The speed at which the excitation spreads makes sure that the atria have stopped contracting before the ventricles start.

Figure 2.5.12 The area of the heart with the fastest intrinsic rhythm is a group of cells in the right atrium known as the **sinoatrial node**, and this acts as the heart's own natural pacemaker.

The blood pressure in our circulatory system has an effect on the heart rate. Special **baroreceptors** (receptors that are sensitive to pressure) are found in the carotid sinuses of the carotid arteries in the neck. If the blood pressure in these arteries gets too high, the baroreceptors are stretched and send nerve impulses to the cardiovascular centre in the medulla of the brain. In turn, the medulla sends out signals which decrease the heart rate and cause vasodilation. These two actions lower the blood pressure.

Another element of control over the heart rate comes from stretch receptors in the walls of the chambers of the heart itself. As the atria are stretched when the heart is filling, these receptors send impulses which help bring about contraction. If more blood than usual returns to the heart, perhaps at the start of exercise as the big muscle blocks squeeze blood along the veins, then these receptors are stretched more than usual and they stimulate an increase in heart rate. This link between an increase in heart volume and an increase in the heart rate is sometimes known as the **Bainbridge reflex**.

The heart can respond to an increased demand for glucose and oxygen by the body in two ways. The rate at which the heart beats can be increased, as mentioned above. Also, the volume of blood pumped at each heartbeat, called the **cardiac volume**, can be increased by a more efficient contraction of the ventricles. The combination of these two factors gives a measure called the **cardiac output**:

$$\textbf{Cardiac output (dm}^3\textbf{ min}^{-1}\textbf{) = cardiac volume} \times \textbf{heart rate}$$

At rest in a normal individual the heart beats about 70 times and pumps between 4 and 6 litres of blood each minute. In a trained athlete this blood flow can be increased to around 30 litres a minute during exercise. The increased blood flow is brought about both by an increase in the rate of the heartbeat and by an increase in the amount of blood pumped each time the heart contracts. The response of the heart to exercise is very rapid, and when exercise is anticipated in a fit individual the heart rate will begin to increase before the exercise begins, as shown in figure 2.5.13. At the end of exercise in a fit individual, the heartbeat drops back to normal very rapidly. In those of us who are less fit, the pounding continues for several minutes!

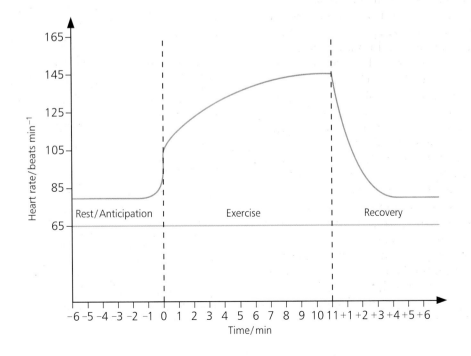

Figure 2.5.13 The heart rate response before, during and after moderate exercise.

Blood pressure

The blood travels through the arterial system at pressures which vary as the heart beats. The blood pressure is also affected by the diameter of the blood vessels themselves. Narrowing the arteries is one way in which the body affects and controls local blood pressure, but permanent changes in the artery can cause severe health problems.

Most people have their blood pressure taken at some point in their lives. The blood pressure reading is expressed as two figures, the first higher than the second. The most common way to take the blood pressure uses a **sphygmomanometer**. A cuff is connected to a mercury manometer (an instrument which measures pressure using the height of a column of mercury). The cuff is placed around the upper arm and inflated until the blood supply to the lower arm is completely cut off.

A stethoscope is positioned over the blood vessels at the elbow. Air is slowly let out of the cuff. The pressure in the cuff at which blood sounds first reappear is recorded. The first blood to get through the vessels under the cuff is that under the highest pressure – in other words, when the heart is contracting strongly. The height of the mercury at this point gives the **systolic blood pressure**. The blood sounds return to normal when blood at the lowest pressure during diastole can get through the vessels under the cuff. The pressure in the cuff at this point gives the **diastolic blood pressure**. A systolic reading of 120 mm Hg and a diastolic reading of 80 mm Hg is regarded as 'normal'. The blood pressure is expressed as '120 over 80' or '120/80'.

Blood pressure is used as an indicator of the health of both the heart and the blood vessels. A weakened heart may produce a low blood pressure, whereas damaged blood vessels which are closing up or becoming less elastic will give a raised blood pressure. For more information on hypertension, see section 7.

Figure 2.5.14 Most people have their blood pressure taken at some point during their lives, often with a sphygmomanometer but increasingly with a smaller machine that gives a digital reading from a finger or wrist cuff.

The blood

The components of blood

Blood is the transport medium of the body. It is an extremely complex substance carrying a wide variety of cells and substances to all areas of the body. Figure 2.5.15 shows the components of blood.

Functions of the blood

The blood carries out a wide variety of functions, summarised as follows:

1 transport of digested food products from the villi of the small intestine to all the areas of the body where they are needed for either immediate use or storage.

2 transport of food molecules from storage areas to the cells which need them.

3 transport of excretory products from the cells where they have been formed to the areas where they will be excreted.

4 transport of chemical messages (hormones) from the glands where they are made around the body.

5 helping to maintain a steady body temperature by distributing heat from deep-seated or very active tissues around the system.

6 transport of oxygen from the lungs to all cells for respiration.

Blood component	Main features
Plasma	This straw-coloured liquid is the main component of blood, and consists largely of water. Plasma contains **fibrinogen**, a protein vital for the clotting of the blood. The removal of fibrinogen from plasma results in **serum,** which contains a wide range of dissolved substances to be transported.
Erythrocytes (red blood cells)	Erythrocytes are biconcave discs. There are approximately 5 million erythrocytes per mm^3 of blood. The cells contain **haemoglobin**, the red oxygen-carrying pigment which gives them their colour.
	Erythrocytes are formed in the red bone marrow of the short bones. Mature erythrocytes do not contain a nucleus and have a limited life of about 120 days.
Leucocytes (white blood cells) Granulocytes — Neutrophils (engulf bacteria), Eosinophils (antihistamine properties), Basophils (produce histamine and heparin) — Agranulocytes — Monocytes (engulf bacteria), Lymphocytes (produce antibodies)	Leucocytes are much larger than erythrocytes, but can squeeze through narrow gaps by changing their shape. There are approximately 7000 leucocytes per mm^3 of blood. They all contain a nucleus and have colourless cytoplasm. Most are formed in the white bone marrow of the long bones, although some lymphocytes are formed in the lymph glands and spleen. Their main function is in defence against pathogens (see section 1.6).
Platelets	Platelets are tiny fragments of large cells called **megakaryocytes** which occur in the bone marrow. There are about 0.25 million platelets per mm^3 of blood. They are involved in the clotting of the blood.

Figure 2.5.15 The main components of the blood. The plasma and the erythrocytes are involved in transport of oxygen and food molecules while the leucocytes defend the body against pathogens and the platelets, along with blood proteins, enable the blood to clot in case of damage to the circulatory systems.

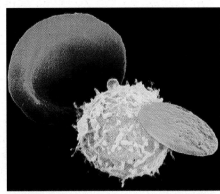

False-colour scanning electron micrograph showing an erythrocyte (left), a leucocyte (centre) and a platelet (right)

7 transport of carbon dioxide from respiring cells to the lungs.

8 clotting of the blood, to prevent excessive blood loss and the entry of pathogens.

9 providing immunity through the lymphocytes.

10 engulfing and digesting pathogens by the phagocytotic action of the granulocytes.

11 acting as a buffer to pH changes.

The first six of these functions are carried out by the plasma. Substances move into and out of the plasma by diffusion or active transport, and are carried around the body in a mass flow system as the blood is pumped by the heart.

The defence functions of the blood discussed in section 1.6 are separate from its role as a transport system, though they take advantage of the rapid transport the blood offers to all areas of the body.

The erythrocytes are specialised transport cells used only for carrying oxygen and carbon dioxide.

The carriage of oxygen

The erythrocytes are ideally adapted for the carriage of oxygen. They contain the red pigment haemoglobin, which is largely responsible for oxygen transport. The shape of the cells means that they have a large surface area:volume ratio for

The blood as a damage limitation system

In theory a minor cut or scrape, or even a hard bang on the body surface, could endanger life due to loss of blood as the torn blood vessels bleed. In normal circumstances this does not happen because the body has a highly efficient damage limitation system in the **clotting mechanism** of the blood.

When a blood vessel is damaged a semi-solid mass called a **clot** forms and seals the wound as the result of a complex sequence of events:

- Blood plasma, blood cells and platelets flow from a cut vessel.
- Contact between the platelets and some of the tissue components (for example collagen fibres) causes the platelets to break open in large numbers. They release several substances, two of which are particularly important. **Serotonin** causes the smooth muscle of the arterioles to contract and so narrows the vessels, cutting off the blood flow to the damaged area. **Thromboplastin** is an enzyme which sets in progress a cascade of events that lead to the formation of a clot.
- In the presence of sufficient levels of calcium ions, thromboplastin catalyses a large-scale conversion of the globular plasma protein **prothrombin** into the enzyme **thrombin**.
- Thrombin acts on another plasma protein called **fibrinogen**, converting it to **fibrin**. Fibrin consists of fibrous strands.
- Further platelets and blood cells pouring from the wound get trapped and tangled within the fibrin meshwork, forming a clot.
- Contractile proteins in the cytoskeleton of the platelets contract, pulling the clot into a tighter and tougher configuration.

These events are an example of a cascade system where a relatively small event is **amplified** through a series of steps, as shown in figure 2.5.16. The speed and efficiency of clotting is effective in preventing blood loss. The difficulties of life without it are seen in the genetic condition of **haemophilia**, where normal life is impossible without regular injections of clotting factors.

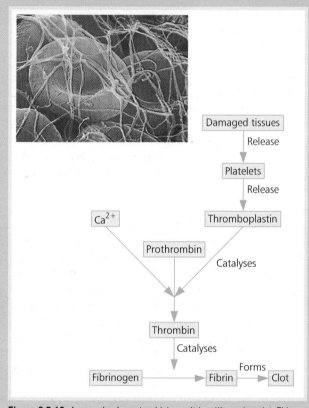

Figure 2.5.16 A cascade of events which result in a life-saving clot. This seals the blood vessels and prevents excessive blood loss, and also protects the delicate new skin growing underneath.

the diffusion of gases, and the lack of a nucleus means that the maximum amount of space is available to pack in haemoglobin molecules. In fact, each red blood cell contains around 250 million molecules of haemoglobin, giving it the capacity to carry 1000 million molecules of oxygen.

Haemoglobin

Haemoglobin is the key to oxygen uptake. It is a very large globular protein molecule made up of four globin polypeptide chains. Each chain has a prosthetic haem group which contains iron and gives the molecule its red colour. Haemoglobin (Hb) has a high affinity for oxygen. The oxygen is bound quite loosely to the haem groups to form **oxyhaemoglobin** (HbO_8):

$$\textbf{Hb} + \textbf{4O}_2 \rightarrow \textbf{HbO}_8$$

The first oxygen molecule to be bound to haemoglobin alters the shape of the molecule in such a way that it is easier for the next oxygen to be taken on.

This in turn alters the shape and makes it easier for the next oxygen to be taken up, until the fourth and final oxygen molecule combines with the haemoglobin several hundred times more rapidly than the first. The same process happens in reverse when oxygen dissociates from haemoglobin – it gets progressively harder to remove the oxygen.

This has very important implications for the way in which oxygen is taken up in the lungs and released in the respiring cells. Figure 2.5.17 shows that a very small change in the proportion of oxygen in the air (represented by the partial pressure) makes a big difference to the saturation of the blood with oxygen. This means that as the blood enters the lungs it is rapidly loaded with oxygen. Equally, a relatively small drop in the oxygen levels of respiring tissues will initiate the release of oxygen from the blood.

An additional factor is the effect of carbon dioxide. The way in which haemoglobin takes up and releases oxygen is affected by the proportion of carbon dioxide in the tissues, as figure 2.5.18 demonstrates.

The effect of the Bohr shift seen in figure 2.5.18 is that in higher partial pressures of carbon dioxide, haemoglobin needs higher levels of oxygen to become saturated. More importantly, it gives up oxygen more easily. Thus in active tissues with high carbon dioxide levels, haemoglobin releases the oxygen needed very readily. On the other hand, carbon dioxide levels in the lung capillaries are relatively low, and so it is easier for oxygen to bind to the haem groups.

Other respiratory pigments

Two respiratory pigments other than haemoglobin are found in mammals. One is another form of haemoglobin known as **fetal haemoglobin**. The fetus in the uterus is dependent on the mother to supply it with oxygen. Oxygenated blood from the mother runs through the placenta close to the deoxygenated fetal blood. If the blood of the fetus had the same affinity for oxygen as the blood of the mother, transfer of oxygen would occur with difficulty. Fetal haemoglobin has a higher affinity for oxygen than the mother's haemoglobin, and so can take up oxygen from the maternal blood.

Myoglobin is structurally like a single haemoglobin chain. It is found mainly in the skeletal muscle, and has a much higher affinity for oxygen than haemoglobin, thus readily becoming saturated with oxygen. It does not give up oxygen easily, however, and so acts as an oxygen store. When the oxygen levels in very active muscle tissue get extremely low, and the carbon dioxide levels are correspondingly high, then myoglobin releases its store of oxygen.

Figure 2.5.19 compares the oxygen dissociation curves for haemoglobin, fetal haemoglobin and myoglobin.

The carriage of carbon dioxide

Carbon dioxide can be carried in the blood in three different ways. A small amount – about 5% – is carried in solution in the plasma. A further 10–20% combines with amino groups in the polypeptide chains of haemoglobin molecules to form **carbaminohaemoglobin**. But the bulk of the carbon dioxide is transported in the blood as **hydrogencarbonate ions**. This is explained in figure 2.5.20.

The reactions shown in figure 2.5.20 take place in the tissues, where there is a relatively high concentration of carbon dioxide and a low concentration of oxygen. In the lungs there are high oxygen concentrations and low carbon dioxide concentrations. The reactions go in reverse, releasing carbon dioxide into the lungs and freeing the haemoglobin to pick up more oxygen.

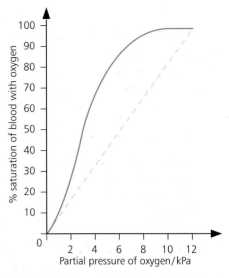

Figure 2.5.17 Oxygen dissociation curve for human haemoglobin. The dotted line shows what the curve would look like without haemoglobin's particular affinity for oxygen.

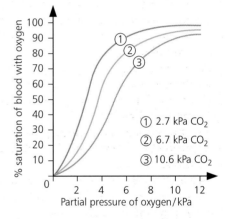

Figure 2.5.18 As the proportion of carbon dioxide increases, the haemoglobin curves move downwards and to the right. This is known as the **Bohr shift**.

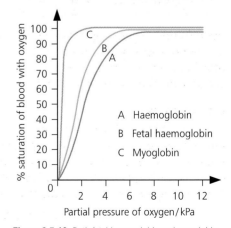

Figure 2.5.19 Both fetal haemoglobin and myoglobin have higher affinities for oxygen than does haemoglobin, so they can take up oxygen from haemoglobin.

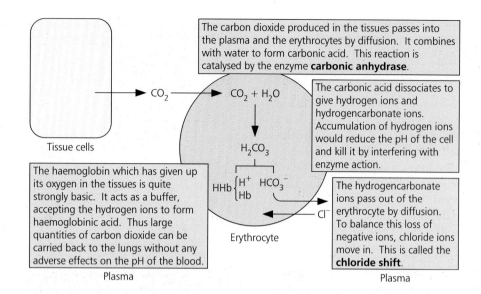

The carbon dioxide produced in the tissues passes into the plasma and the erythrocytes by diffusion. It combines with water to form carbonic acid. This reaction is catalysed by the enzyme **carbonic anhydrase**.

The carbonic acid dissociates to give hydrogen ions and hydrogencarbonate ions. Accumulation of hydrogen ions would reduce the pH of the cell and kill it by interfering with enzyme action.

The haemoglobin which has given up its oxygen in the tissues is quite strongly basic. It acts as a buffer, accepting the hydrogen ions to form haemoglobinic acid. Thus large quantities of carbon dioxide can be carried back to the lungs without any adverse effects on the pH of the blood.

The hydrogencarbonate ions pass out of the erythrocyte by diffusion. To balance this loss of negative ions, chloride ions move in. This is called the **chloride shift**.

Tissue cells

Plasma

Erythrocyte

Plasma

CO_2

$CO_2 + H_2O$

H_2CO_3

$HHb \begin{cases} H^+ \\ Hb \end{cases} \quad HCO_3^-$

Cl^-

Figure 2.5.20 The carriage of carbon dioxide by the blood.

Adaptations of transport systems

The transport vessels, the pumping heart and the blood of a mammal are all highly specialised and adapted for their functions. They have evolved to suit the way of life of the majority of mammals – land-dwellers at or around sea-level. But some species live in the oceans, and others at high altitudes. Humans attempt to survive in almost all the available environments. How do the cardiovascular and respiratory systems cope with some of these adverse conditions?

The diving mammals

The seals and the whales are two of the best-known groups of water-living mammals. They are very successful aquatic animals, in spite of their need to return to the surface at regular intervals to breathe air into the lungs. Land-dwellers of comparable size need to breathe many times in a minute. If the diving mammals had to breathe as often as this they would not be able to stay underwater long enough to catch any food.

There are several major adaptations of the respiratory and cardiovascular systems of the diving mammals. The lungs are large, so that extra air can be taken in to oxygenate the blood as fully as possible before diving. There is an increased blood volume, so that large amounts of oxygen can be loaded into the blood. Once a dive begins, the capillary beds in many of the non-vital organs are shut off, so that blood flows mainly to the brain and the swimming muscles. This minimises the oxygen consumption of the tissues. Also, the heart rate slows dramatically to only a few beats per minute. This is known as **bradycardia**. Again this greatly reduces the oxygen consumption of the tissues. There is increased tolerance of oxygen debt, which means that the tissues can cope with relatively high levels of lactic acid without damage. These features enable diving mammals to dive for considerable periods of time, as figure 2.5.21 shows.

Interestingly, humans who make a habit of prolonged diving without additional air, such as pearl divers, begin to develop some of these adaptations. The lung volume increases and a degree of bradycardia occurs, with the heart rate slowing noticeably. Although these adaptations are not to the same extent as in true diving mammals, they make possible dives of much longer duration than would normally be expected.

Figure 2.5.21 Dives of up to 20 minutes are not uncommon in some seals and the great whales.

Living at altitude

With increased height above sea level, both the atmospheric pressure and the partial pressure of oxygen in the air are reduced. At heights of more than about 3650 m above sea level there is a noticeable oxygen lack, and the highest permanent human habitations are at about 5500 m above sea level. That is well below the summit of Everest at 8848 m above sea level.

For most people, moving to a high altitude area is an unpleasant experience. Symptoms resulting from lack of oxygen include headaches, dizziness, breathlessness even at rest, sweating, dim vision and reduced hearing, even loss of consciousness on physical exertion. These symptoms are known as **mountain sickness**. Much of the problem is the result of the fact that lack of oxygen causes an increased breathing rate, but this removes too much carbon dioxide. Thus the normal stimulus to breathe is lost, resulting in very abnormal breathing patterns.

After some time, people experience **acclimatisation**. This includes a sustained increase in the ventilation of the alveoli, an increase in the oxygen-carrying capacity of the blood with the formation of extra erythrocytes, and an increase in cardiac output. However, someone who has moved to a high altitude after years at sea level can never truly acclimatise and may suffer severe mountain sickness at any time. Those who are born at high altitude show a very different level of acclimatisation, although even they may be struck with mountain sickness at times.

Figure 2.5.22 People who live high in the mountains of the Andes and the Himalayas are born and live at high altitudes. They develop an increased lung volume by increasing the numbers of both alveoli and capillaries. The number of red blood cells rises to a level where the blood becomes measurably thicker. The acid/base balance in the system is altered to affect the control of breathing. With these adaptations the people of the mountains can carry out tasks which would daunt most of us even at sea level, as they maintain an existence in a most inhospitable environment.

SUMMARY

- Transport systems in larger animals take the form of **cardiovascular systems** consisting of vessels carrying blood, the transport medium, pumped around the animal by the heart.

- The **human cardiovascular system** is a **double circulation** consisting of the **systemic circulation** to the body and the **pulmonary circulation** to the lungs.

- **Arteries** are vessels which carry blood away from the heart. They are lined with **squamous epithelium** and have elastic walls to allow them to stretch and absorb the pulsing flow of the blood pumped from the heart. There is an external layer of connective tissue, mainly collagen, to prevent overstretching.

- Arteries divide to form smaller branches called **arterioles** which have a lower proportion of elastin in their walls than larger arteries. Arterioles subdivide further to form the **capillaries**.

- Capillary walls consist of a layer of squamous epithelium thus allowing diffusion to take place. As blood in the capillaries passes through the tissues, oxygen is removed and carbon dioxide loaded in.

- Fluid is forced out of the capillary vessels, forming the **intercellular** or **tissue fluid**. Diffusion takes place between the tissue fluid and the cells of the tissues. Tissue fluid is collected into **lymph capillaries**, vessels with valves to prevent backflow, and this forms the **lymph**. **Lymph glands** produce antibodies and filter out foreign particles from the lymph, which is returned to the blood into the subclavian veins.

- Capillaries join to form **venules** which lead to **veins** – vessels which carry blood back to the heart. Veins have a large lumen, are lined with squamous epithelium and have thin walls with few elastic fibres. Their outer layer is made up mainly of collagen.

- Veins have one-way **semilunar valves** which prevent the backflow of blood. Many larger veins are between big muscle blocks, contraction of which forces blood along the veins.

- The **heart** is a four-chambered organ surrounded by the **pericardial membranes**. The left-hand side pumps blood from the lungs to the body, while the right-hand side pumps blood from the body to the lungs.

- The **right atrium** receives deoxygenated blood from the great veins. Blood fills the atrium and flows into the **right ventricle** until both atrium and ventricle are full. The right atrium then contracts, forcing all the blood into the right ventricle, which then also contracts to force the blood into the pulmonary artery. The **tricuspid atrioventricular valve** prevents flow from the ventricle back into the atrium, while similar one-way valves prevent backflow from the right atrium to the great veins.

- The **left atrium** receives oxygenated blood from the pulmonary veins, which passes down into the **left ventricle**. Contraction of the left atrium is followed by contraction of the left ventricle, forcing blood into the aorta. Again, valves in the aorta and the **bicuspid atrioventricular valve** prevent backflow. The left ventricle is more muscular than the right ventricle as it has to force blood to the capillary beds of the extremities of the body.

- The **cardiac cycle** describes the chain of events that makes up a heartbeat: the relaxed atria fill and then the ventricles (**diastole**), then both atria contract forcing the blood into the ventricles which then also contract (**systole**), forcing the blood into the pulmonary artery and aorta. The sounds of the **heartbeat** are caused by the closing of the aortic and atrioventricular valves.

- **Cardiac muscle** cells have an intrinsic rhythm of contraction maintained by a wave of electrical excitation spreading from the **sinoatrial node** or **pacemaker** to the **atrioventricular node** and then down into the **Purkyne tissue**. The heart rate is also under the control of the sympathetic and parasympathetic nervous systems, hormones, pH changes and temperature changes.

- **Cardiac output** is given by the **cardiac volume** (the volume of blood pumped per heartbeat) multiplied by the **heart rate**.

- **Blood** consists of liquid **plasma**, **erythrocytes** (red blood cells), **leucocytes** (white blood cells) and **platelets**. Plasma contains **fibrinogen**, a protein involved in blood clotting, and **serum** is plasma with fibrinogen removed. Erythrocytes are biconcave discs with no nuclei, containing **haemoglobin**. They are formed in the red bone marrow. Leucocytes include **lymphocytes** and **monocytes** (the **agranulocytes**) and **neutrophils**, **eosinophils** and **basophils** (the **granulocytes**) mainly formed in the white bone marrow. They are involved in defence against pathogens. Platelets are involved in the clotting of blood.

- The blood transports oxygen, carbon dioxide, food molecules, excretory products and hormones. It distributes heat around the body and provides immunity, engulfs pathogens and buffers pH changes.

- Erythrocytes have a large surface area:volume ratio and carry large amounts of haemoglobin, a globular protein made up of four polypeptide chains each with a prosthetic iron-containing **haem group**. Oxygen can bind to each haem group forming **oxyhaemoglobin**.

- The binding of one oxygen molecule to a haem group causes successive haem groups to bind more easily, and vice versa, giving a characteristic **oxygen uptake curve** for haemoglobin. This curve is shifted by higher carbon dioxide concentrations so that oxygen is given up more easily (the **Bohr shift**).

- **Fetal haemoglobin** and **myoglobin** both have higher affinities for oxygen than does haemoglobin, to enable them to take up oxygen from the blood.

- Carbon dioxide is carried in the blood in solution, as carbaminohaemoglobin, and (mainly) as hydrogencarbonate ions. **Carbonic anhydrase** catalyses the formation of carbonic acid, and the hydrogen ions from this acid are accepted by haemoglobin to form **haemoglobinic acid**. The hydrogencarbonate ions pass out of the erythrocyte and are replaced by chloride ions. These reaction are reversed in the lungs to give up carbon dioxide.

- The diving mammals have large lungs and an increased blood volume. The blood supply to capillary beds in non-vital organs is shut off during a dive, and the heart rate slows (**bradycardia**).

- People at high altitudes can suffer **mountain sickness**, where lack of oxygen brings about an increased breathing rate, while too much carbon dioxide is removed so interfering with the normal breathing stimulus. **Acclimatisation** takes place as the ventilation rate of the alveoli is increased, more erythrocytes are formed so more oxygen can be carried in the blood, and cardiac output is increased.

QUESTIONS

1 a What is the role of diffusion in the distribution of gases and nutrients to the individual cells of:
   i   single-celled animals
   ii large multicellular animals?
  b What is the function of a circulatory system?

2 a Visualise the journey of a red blood cell from the extremity of a toe around the body and back to the toe. Describe the route taken by the red blood cell.
  b Produce a table to summarise the structure and functions of the main types of blood vessels – arteries, capillaries and veins.
  c Blood is moved around the circulatory system by the heart. How is the heart rate controlled?

3 Summarise the main functions of mammalian blood. Select two of these functions and explain them fully.

Developing Key Skills

A large health and fitness centre is opening in your local area. It is to be used both by members of the public and by local GPs who will be able to prescribe 'fitness training' for patients who are at risk of developing heart disease and/or blood pressure problems.

You have been asked to produce a short feature on the new centre for the local television network, explaining why it is important for everyone to undertake physical exercise and maintain a good level of fitness. The report should give special emphasis to the effects of exercise on the health of the heart and blood vessels.

FOCUS A CRUMBLING OLD AGE?

Measurable changes take place in our bones and joints as we age, some simply the result of wear and tear and others due to age-related cellular changes. Within the major ball and socket joints the cartilage may become worn away, or get thin as it is replaced less effectively. This predisposes an individual to arthritis. In **osteoarthritis**, the bones no longer slide smoothly over each other and bony knobs develop on the bone surface. In **rheumatoid arthritis**, bone cells begin to appear in cartilage. Both conditions make the joints considerably less mobile, and can lead to great pain.

The bones themselves are also prone to ageing problems. In young, healthy individuals bone is a relatively fluid material, with old bone being removed and new bone being laid down constantly in response to the needs of the body. However, as people get older bone is destroyed faster than it is replaced. This happens in all individuals, although the age at which it begins and the speed at which it progresses is very variable. If the loss of calcium from the bones becomes too marked, the individual will suffer from **osteoporosis**.

Osteoporosis appears from middle age onwards, and is a major problem in the well-being of older people, particularly women. There seems to be some imbalance in the hormones involved in normal bone formation which results from the marked drop in the female hormone oestrogen after the menopause. Another major factor in the development of osteoporosis in both men and women seems to be age-related changes in the cells lining the gut, reducing their ability to absorb calcium and vitamin D from the diet. Vitamin D is important for promoting the absorption of calcium across the wall of the gut, as well as in promoting the uptake of calcium by the bone itself. To have a metabolic effect, the vitamin D must be converted to an active form in the cells of the liver and the kidneys but these too show degeneration with age.

Once substantial bone thinning has taken place it is very difficult to repair the damage. However, if evidence of osteoporosis is found early, women in particular can be offered treatment with the female hormone oestrogen. This has been shown to have a beneficial effect on calcium balance, and also slows the rate at which bone density is lost.

The best protection against osteoporosis is to develop high bone density when young by eating a diet rich in calcium and vitamin D, and also to take plenty of weight-bearing, bone-building exercise such as walking and jogging. If this type of diet and exercise is then continued into later life, the risks of serious osteoporosis developing are substantially reduced. There also seems to be a genetic factor – the tendency to develop osteoporosis runs in families. However, it certainly appears that an active lifestyle along with a healthy diet reduces the likelihood of major musculoskeletal problems in later life.

Figure 1 Although we tend to think of arthritis as a disease of old age, children and people of all ages can be affected by it.

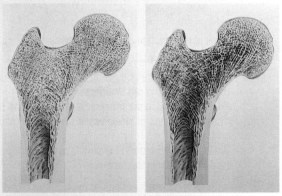

Figure 2 In these photos we can see the difference between the dense normal bone and the fragile network of the bone affected by osteoporosis.

2.6 Support systems and movement in animals

Almost all animals and plants have some kind of support system. In general, as organisms get larger, they need increasingly complex systems of support. We have already considered in section 2.2 how the cellulose walls, the turgor of the cells, the vascular xylem and phloem tissues and lignification in woody plants support even the giant redwood trees of America, the largest living organisms on Earth today. We are now concerned with support systems in animals, which usually take the form of a skeleton of some type.

Functions of support systems

Support systems provide a framework for the body of the organism and often help to determine its shape. Land animals in particular need skeletons to support their weight against gravity. Many organs are attached to the skeleton for support and stability.

Another major function of many support systems is protection. Whether inside or outside the body, a hard skeleton can protect particularly important or delicate organs.

Strong, relatively rigid skeletons would fulfil these functions of support and protection. Indeed, in large plants the rigid wooden trunks of trees support the great mass of photosynthesising leaves and growing fruits. But almost all animals need to locomote – that is, move their whole bodies around in order to feed, escape, find a mate, etc. Most animals have evolved to use their support systems to enable locomotion to occur, with muscles acting against and often joining to the skeleton via tendons.

Types of support systems

Three main types of support system have evolved in animals. In each case there is a close relationship between the skeleton which forms the support system and the muscles which act upon it to bring about locomotion.

- **Hydrostatic skeletons** are found in soft-bodied creatures such as sea anemones, flatworms and annelids (segmented worms). These animals have a fluid-filled body cavity surrounded by tubes of muscles.

- **Exoskeletons** are found exclusively in the arthropods. This group includes the insects (for example bees, water boatmen and ladybirds) and the crustaceans (such as crabs, lobsters and woodlice). As the name suggests, an exoskeleton is on the outside of the body. To allow movement an external skeleton is made of many jointed pieces, similar to a suit of armour, with strong solid sections protecting delicate organs.

- **Endoskeletons** are most typically found in vertebrates, although they do occur in other groups such as sponges and some molluscs. An endoskeleton is an internal skeleton, encased within the body tissues. Vertebrate skeletons are made of living material, either cartilage or bone, which can grow as needed with the organism. A variety of different types of joints make a whole range of movements possible. The functioning of an endoskeleton will be considered by looking in detail at the skeleton of a mammal.

Figure 2.6.1 Over 100 million years ago bony skeletons were already performing their prime functions of support, protection and movement, as this fossil triceratops shows.

Figure 2.6.2 In an animal like an earthworm, the contraction or relaxation of circular and longitudinal muscles can have a localised effect on small groups of segments. In unsegmented animals the fluid is moved around the whole tube.

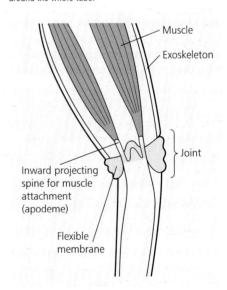

Figure 2.6.3 Joints and the contraction of the internal muscles within an insect exoskeleton allows a rigid protective box made of chitin to move about.

The mammalian skeleton

Structure of the mammalian skeleton

Mammalian skeletons are typical of vertebrate endoskeletons. They are composed largely of **bone**, with varying amounts of **cartilage**. **Ligaments** hold bones together at joints and **tendons** join muscles to bones to allow movement. The precise arrangements of the different bones vary from species to species depending on their adaptations for a particular way of life. However, the overall pattern of mammalian skeletons is similar to that of humans, in spite of our unusual habit of walking on two legs. The human skeleton and its associated ligaments and tendons are described in figure 2.6.6, pages 160–61.

The endoskeleton and movement

The way in which the internal skeleton of mammals is used to give support and protection is explained by looking at the arrangement and properties of the tissues, particularly in the strong bones and protective cages. However, the use of the internal skeleton to bring about locomotion is not so immediately obvious. It involves the structure of the joints within the skeleton, and also the interaction with the muscles.

The structure of the joints

The **joints** are points of weakness in the support system of the skeleton, though they are vital to allow movement and locomotion. As you can see in figure 2.6.4, bones are held in position in the joints by ligament capsules which allow movement of the bones over, but not away from, each other. Anyone who has experienced the pain of a dislocated joint will know that keeping the bones lined up correctly is necessary to the working of a joint.

The ends of the bones at a joint are shaped to move smoothly over each other, and the way in which the two bones meet varies according to the type of movement required. The **ball and socket joints** found at the hip and shoulder give very free movement, whereas the **hinge joints** of the fingers and knees are much more restrictive.

Two solid masses moving over each other whilst subjected to quite severe compressive forces would soon wear each other away. To prevent the bones from being eroded in this way the joint is lined with a replaceable layer of rubbery cartilage which allows the joint to articulate smoothly. The most mobile joints produce a liquid lubricant known as **synovial fluid** which fills the joint cavity and ensures easy, friction-free movement, as shown in figure 2.6.4.

Endoskeletons and size limits

The size of the arthropods is limited to a large extent by the resources needed to repeatedly replace the entire body surface. But what limits the size of animals possessing an internal skeleton capable of growing with them? It is the properties of bone which put a brake on the growth of vertebrates.

The strength of a bone under compression is mainly affected by its cross-sectional area. As an animal doubles in size, the length and width of the leg bones will double too. This increases the cross-sectional area by a factor of 4 (2^2). The volume of the animal, and so its mass, will increase by a factor of 8 (2^3). A point is reached where the limb bones can no longer withstand the compressive forces in an enormous animal, and would snap or crumble as soon as the weight is shifted as the creature moves.

Organisms can get bigger under various circumstances, such as living in water to gain extra support or evolving areas of relatively light tissue or air-filled cavities. However, eventually limits of support by the endoskeleton are reached.

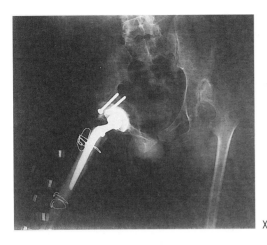

X-ray showing replacement hip joint

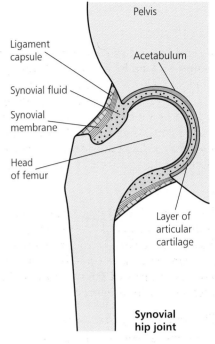

Figure 2.6.4 The adaptations of the skeleton normally allow smooth, easy, pain-free movement. But bones can become damaged and replacements do not come cheap – £1500 to buy and fit an artificial hip.

How is movement brought about?

Movement is brought about by the action of muscles on bones. Each of the skeletal muscles of a vertebrate is attached by tendons to at least two different bones, spanning at least one joint. The attachment nearest to the heart is known as the **origin** of the muscle and this bone moves very little when the muscle contracts. The attachment furthest away from the heart is called the **insertion** and this is the bone which moves when the muscle contracts.

When muscles contract they exert a pull on a bone and so it moves relative to another bone. However, when muscles relax they do not exert a corresponding push – they simply stop contracting, and become capable of being pulled back to their original shape. Thus the muscles of the skeleton are usually found in pairs. One pulls the bone in one direction, the other pulls it back to its original position. Because they work in direct opposition to each other these muscle pairs are known as **antagonistic pairs**. A clearer picture of how movement is brought about can be gained from figure 2.6.5.

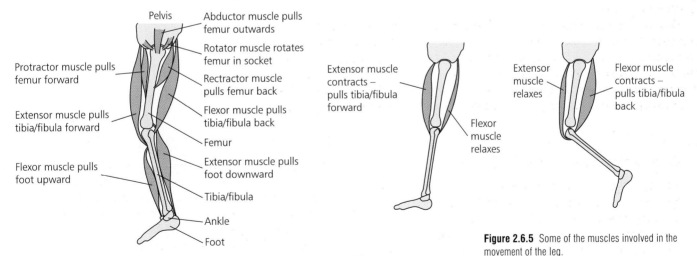

Figure 2.6.5 Some of the muscles involved in the movement of the leg.

Stability

When an object is stationary it will remain standing upright as long as all the forces acting on it are balanced. For four-legged animals, the four legs act like the legs of a table with the centre of gravity somewhere in the middle, so quadrupeds are very unlikely to fall over. Once only three legs are in contact with the ground, during locomotion, the animal must shift its weight so its

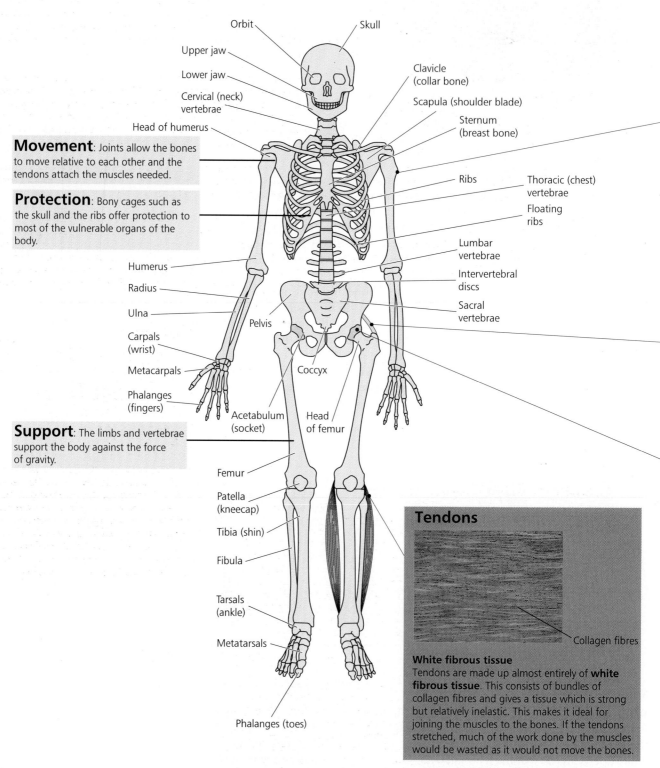

Orbit

Skull

Upper jaw

Lower jaw

Cervical (neck) vertebrae

Head of humerus

Clavicle (collar bone)

Scapula (shoulder blade)

Sternum (breast bone)

Ribs

Thoracic (chest) vertebrae

Floating ribs

Lumbar vertebrae

Intervertebral discs

Sacral vertebrae

Movement: Joints allow the bones to move relative to each other and the tendons attach the muscles needed.

Protection: Bony cages such as the skull and the ribs offer protection to most of the vulnerable organs of the body.

Humerus

Radius

Ulna

Pelvis

Carpals (wrist)

Metacarpals

Coccyx

Phalanges (fingers)

Acetabulum (socket)

Head of femur

Support: The limbs and vertebrae support the body against the force of gravity.

Femur

Patella (kneecap)

Tibia (shin)

Fibula

Tarsals (ankle)

Metatarsals

Phalanges (toes)

Tendons

Collagen fibres

White fibrous tissue
Tendons are made up almost entirely of **white fibrous tissue**. This consists of bundles of collagen fibres and gives a tissue which is strong but relatively inelastic. This makes it ideal for joining the muscles to the bones. If the tendons stretched, much of the work done by the muscles would be wasted as it would not move the bones.

Figure 2.6.6 The human endoskeleton shows specialist adaptations for support, protection and movement.

Bone

Compact bone

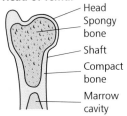

Head of femur

- Head
- Spongy bone
- Shaft
- Compact bone
- Marrow cavity

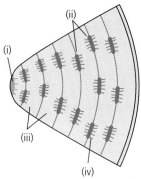

(i) **Haversian canal** containing an artery and a vein. Capillaries run from these to the lacunae and so to the bone cells. Haversian canals also contain a lymph vessel and nerve fibres

(ii) **Lacuna** containing the inactive bone cells or **osteocytes**

(iii) Bony lamellae or layers

(iv) **Canaliculi,** thin links of cytoplasm ramifying through the structure maintaining a communicating network

Bone is strong and hard. It is a composite material, which means it is made up of more than one substance. The bone cells or **osteocytes** are embedded in a **matrix** which consists of about 30% organic **collagen fibrils** impregnated with **calcium salts** which make up the remaining 70% of the matrix. Bone is particularly strong under compressive (squashing) forces, which means it stands up well to the stresses of supporting and moving an animal. It is relatively weak under tensile or pulling forces, but is exposed to these far less frequently.

Bone needs to be strong and hard, and as light as possible to reduce the weight an animal must move about. There are two types of bone. **Compact bone** is very dense and heavy, but very strong. It is found in areas such as the shafts of the long bones of the body. **Spongy bone** has a much more open structure and is lighter. It is found in growing regions and in large masses of bone such as the head of the femur.

Bones contain **marrow**. The long bones contain white bone marrow where the white blood cells are made. The short bones such as the ribs contain red bone marrow where the red blood cells are made.

We tend to think of bones as rigid stable structures. In fact bone is constantly laid down or removed in response to the different stresses imposed upon it. New activities can cause the bones to be altered slightly. This change is brought about by the bone cells. The **osteocytes** are inactive bone cells. If more bone is needed, they are rapidly stimulated and form **osteoblasts** which lay down new matrix. If bone needs to be removed, **osteoclasts** result which reabsorb the matrix.

Ligaments

Collagen fibres

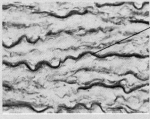

The **ligaments** form capsules around the joints, holding the bones in place. However, they also need to be elastic to allow the bones of the joint to move when necessary. **Yellow elastic tissue** gives a combination of strength with elasticity. By varying the amounts of collagen and incorporating some white fibrous tissue if needed, the ligament capsules can be relatively loose or very tight as required by the body at different joints.

Cartilage

Hyaline matrix

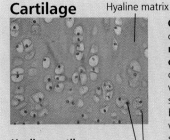

Hyaline cartilage

Chondrocytes

Cartilage is a hard but flexible tissue made up of cells called **chondrocytes** within an organic **matrix** which consists of varying amounts of **collagen fibrils**. The matrix is produced by the chondrocytes. Cartilage is elastic and able to withstand compressive forces. It is a very good shock absorber and is frequently found between bones such as the vertebrae and in the joints. A few vertebrates, mainly the cartilaginous fishes, have skeletons made up entirely of cartilage.
There are three main types of cartilage:
(1) **Hyaline cartilage** found at the ends of bones and in the nose, air passageways and parts of the ear.
(2) **Yellow elastic cartilage** which has a high proportion of elastic fibres so that the tissue quickly recovers its shape after distortion. It is not usually part of the skeleton.
(3) **White fibrous cartilage** has bundles of densely packed collagen in the matrix. It has great tensile strength but is less flexible than the other forms of cartilage. It forms the intervertebral discs and is found between the bones in joints.

centre of gravity falls within the tripod of legs left in contact with the ground. By judicious shifting of the weight animals can remain upright with two, one or even no legs on the ground.

The complexity of this becomes apparent when watching a newborn animal such as a calf or a foal trying out different gaits in the first few days of life – and not always getting the centre of gravity in the right place. Remaining stable with only two legs is even more difficult. For example, if a human being takes in too much alcohol the brain cannot correctly interpret the information it receives, and remaining upright becomes a major problem.

Locomotion on land

Locomotion on land involves the animal moving through air, which offers relatively little resistance to movement. Contraction of the muscles causes the limbs to act as levers, pressing downwards and backwards into the ground. As a result of this a force acts upwards and forwards on the animal. This force brings about locomotion. By altering the angle at which the limb presses into the ground, the balance between the forward force and the upward force can be altered, allowing for leaps into the air and low, fast running.

How muscles work

Types of muscle

Throughout this section we have referred to the interaction of muscles with skeletal systems to bring about movement and locomotion. But what *is* muscle? It is a very specialised tissue which is remarkably similar throughout the animal kingdom, so we will concentrate mainly on mammalian muscle. Muscles are largely made up of protein and they consist of large numbers of very long cells known as **muscle fibres** bound together by connective tissue. They can contract (shorten) and relax, and have a good blood supply to provide them with the glucose and oxygen they need when they are working and remove the waste products which result.

In mammals the muscle tissues can make up as much as 40% of the body weight. There are three main types of muscle, each specialised to perform a particular function.

- **Skeletal muscle** is also known as striated muscle or voluntary muscle. This is the muscle which is attached to the skeleton and so is involved in locomotion. It is under the control of the voluntary nervous system, and its appearance under the microscope is striated or stripy. It contracts rapidly but also fatigues or tires relatively quickly.

- **Smooth muscle** is also known as involuntary muscle. It does not appear striated under the microscope and is under the control of the involuntary nervous system. It is found in the gut where it is involved in moving the food along, and in the blood vessels. It both contracts and fatigues slowly.

- **Cardiac muscle** is found exclusively in the heart. It is striated and the fibres are joined by cross-connections. It contracts spontaneously and does not fatigue.

Skeletal muscle

There are two types of skeletal muscle in mammals. **Slow-twitch muscles** are adapted for steady action over a period of time. They can stay in tetanus and are used for the maintenance of posture and long periods of activity. Slow-twitch muscles have a rich blood supply, lots of mitochondria and plenty of myoglobin so that they can maintain their activity without developing an

Properties of skeletal muscle

If an isolated calf muscle (gastrocnemius) from a frog is given a variety of different electrical stimuli the effects on the length of the muscle can be recorded on a revolving drum (kymograph). The results tell us several things about the way in which muscles work. Experiments from a single muscle fibre give the clearest results – in a whole muscle, different fibres work together to give more confusing results.

A single stimulus causes a single contraction or twitch of the muscle fibre. It is an 'all-or-nothing' response. If the stimulus is below a certain level, nothing happens. If it is above the **threshold** level, the muscle fibre twitches. However big the stimulus above the threshold level, the size of the twitch is always the same. Single twitches are relatively rare.

If two stimuli are given quite close together, the muscle fibre will contract again before it is fully relaxed and so it gets shorter than with a single twitch.

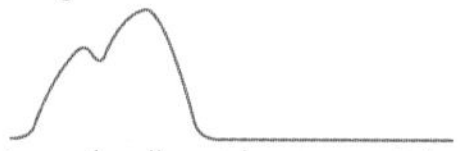

If the two stimuli are close enough together the two contractions are so close that there is no relaxing and lengthening of the muscle fibre between them. This gives the appearance of a single large contraction and is called **summation**.

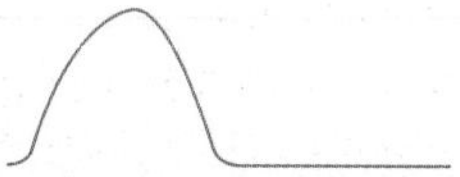

When a series of rapid stimuli are given the muscle fibre becomes fully contracted (as short as possible), and stays like this. This is known as **tetanus** and is the normal situation in a muscle when you are lifting an object or standing up and maintaining your posture against gravity.

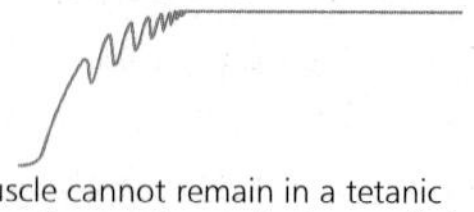

A muscle cannot remain in a tetanic contraction continuously. Eventually it **fatigues** and cannot contract any longer.

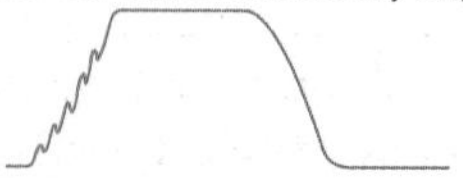

Figure 2.6.7 Kymographic traces from experiments on a muscle fibre taken from a frog gastrocnemius.

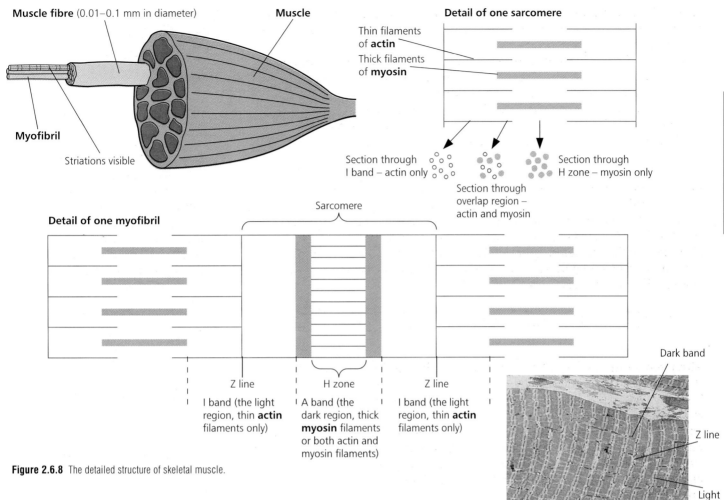

Figure 2.6.8 The detailed structure of skeletal muscle.

Labels in figure:
- Muscle fibre (0.01–0.1 mm in diameter)
- Muscle
- Myofibril
- Striations visible
- Detail of one sarcomere
- Thin filaments of **actin**
- Thick filaments of **myosin**
- Section through I band – actin only
- Section through overlap region – actin and myosin
- Section through H zone – myosin only
- Detail of one myofibril
- Sarcomere
- Z line
- H zone
- Z line
- I band (the light region, thin **actin** filaments only)
- A band (the dark region, thick **myosin** filaments or both actin and myosin filaments)
- I band (the light region, thin **actin** filaments only)

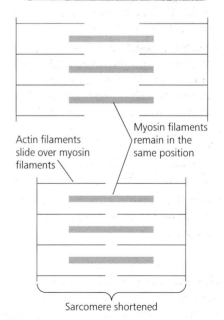

Dark band
Z line
Light band

Actin filaments slide over myosin filaments
Myosin filaments remain in the same position
Sarcomere shortened

Figure 2.6.9 The sliding of the actin filaments over the myosin filaments explains the changes seen in the myofibrils when they contract.

'oxygen debt' (this is explained in section 3.4). **Fast-twitch muscles** contract very rapidly, making them well suited for sudden, rapid bursts of activity. They often have to function anaerobically (without oxygen – this is explained further in section 3.4) and partly because of this they fatigue quite quickly. Most people have roughly equal amounts of slow- and fast-twitch muscles, but the proportions may vary in people who have trained in a particular sport. People who have a naturally high proportion of fast-twitch fibres will be good sprinters, whilst people with lots of slow-twitch muscle will tend to be good at marathon running! Training builds up more of the desired muscle fibres.

Structure of skeletal muscle

To begin to understand how skeletal muscle contracts, we need to look at its microscopic structure. The light microscope shows stripes in the tissue of muscle fibres. The details of the structure of muscle fibres have become clear since the development of the electron microscope, as shown in figure 2.6.8.

Muscle fibres are made up of many **myofibrils** lying parallel to each other. The myofibrils are made up of **sarcomeres**, the individual units of the muscle structure. The proteins actin and myosin make up a large part of the structure of a sarcomere. The cytoplasm of the myofibrils is called the **sarcoplasm**, and there are many associated mitochondria. A network of membranes running through the system is called the **sarcoplasmic reticulum** and there is also a system of tubules running between the fibrils known as the **T tubules**. These store and release calcium ions.

What happens when a muscle contracts?

Within a myofibril, filaments of actin and myosin form an interlocking structure, as shown in figure 2.6.8. When the myofibril contracts, bridges are formed between the actin and myosin filaments. The bridges pull the filaments across each other to increase the interlocking region. The combined effect of this happening in each sarcomere along the length of the myofibril is a shortening of the myofibril, and the shortening of many myofibrils together brings about the contraction of a muscle. How do we know about this mechanism?

In the 1950s a theory to explain the contraction of muscle was developed by Hugh Huxley and Jean Hanson. Known as the **sliding filament theory**, it is still the basis of our understanding of muscle contraction. Observations of micrographs show that whether a muscle fibre is contracted or relaxed, the dark A bands remain the same length. However, the light I bands and the H zone get shorter when the muscle contracts, and return to normal length when it relaxes again. This gave rise to the idea that the two types of filaments slide over each other and overlap more when the muscle contracts, as figure 2.6.9 illustrates.

This raises another question – *how* do the filaments slide across one another? If actin and myosin are mixed together in the laboratory, nothing happens. If they are mixed and ATP is added, they form actomyosin (a blob of protein) and contract, so the process must be an active one. (ATP transfers energy to the process by releasing a phosphate group and forming ADP. This is explained in section 3.1.) Increasingly clear electron micrographs showed the presence of 'bridges' between the actin and myosin strands, and it seems that these are formed and broken down during contraction.

A sort of ratchet mechanism has been proposed. The heads of the myosin attach to the actin to form cross-bridges of actomyosin. This changes shape and in doing so pulls the actin filament further across the myosin. This process is repeated between 50 and 100 times per second. For the ratchet mechanism to work, both calcium ions and ATP must be present. More details of the way in which the sliding filaments work can be seen in figure 2.6.10.

All the systems described in this section, from the movement of organic substances around plants to the beating of the heart, from the breathing movements which draw air into the lungs to the muscle contractions which bring about locomotion, require energy to function. Energy is a fundamental requirement of all living things. In the next section we shall go on to see how this energy is obtained and utilised.

(1) When the muscle is relaxed, the binding sites on the actin are covered by a chemical called tropomyosin.

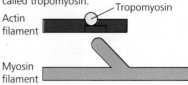

(2) When a muscle is stimulated to contract, calcium ions are released from the T tubules and join to another chemical called troponin. This in turn affects the tropomyosin and reveals the binding site.

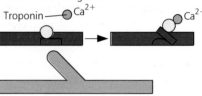

(3) The myosin head binds to the actin, forming an actomyosin bridge.

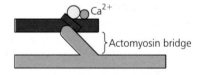

(4) This activates the enzyme ATPase, which also needs the calcium ions from the T tubules to work. The bridge changes shape and moves the actin filament along.

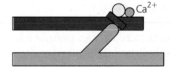

(5) Using the energy from the ATP, the bridge is broken. Calcium is actively pumped back into the T tubules and the myosin binding site is covered once more, ready for the cycle to be repeated.

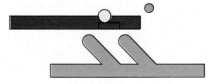

Figure 2.6.10 A complex but elegant series of events which seems to be the basis of skeletal muscle contraction

SUMMARY

- Support systems in animals are adapted for support, protection and locomotion. They may take the form of **hydrostatic** skeletons consisting of muscles contracting against fluid, **exoskeletons** of hardened chitin with joints moved by internal muscles, or **endoskeletons**.

- The mammalian endoskeleton consists of **bone** and **cartilage** with **ligaments** holding bones together at joints and **tendons** attaching muscles to bones.

- Bone consists of bone cells or **osteocytes** in a matrix of collagen fibrils and calcium salts. **Compact bone** is dense and strong, **spongy bone** has a more open, lighter structure. In the matrix, the **Haversian canal** contains an artery and vein with capillaries running to the osteocytes within spaces called **lacunae**. Osteocytes may form **osteoblasts** to lay down new bone, or **osteoclasts** to reabsorb the matrix.

- Cartilage is made up of cells called **chondrocytes** in a matrix of collagen fibrils. It is elastic but hard. The three types are **hyaline cartilage** found at the ends of bones, **yellow elastic cartilage** and **white fibrous cartilage** with densely packed collagen in the matrix which forms the intervertebral discs.

- Tendons are made up of **white fibrous tissue** – bundles of collagen fibrils with cells called **fibrocytes**. They are strong but inelastic. Ligaments are made up of **yellow elastic tissue** containing collagen fibres for strength and elasticity.

- Bones are held in position at joints by ligaments. **Ball and socket** joints allow free movement in most directions while **hinge** joints are more restrictive. A **synovial joint** such as the hip joint consists of a ligament capsule enclosing the head of a bone in a socket, both of which are lined with cartilage. **Synovial fluid** lubricates the joint.

- Muscles act on bones to bring about movement. The **origin** is the point of attachment on a bone nearest the heart and the **insertion** that on another bone further from the heart. Contraction of a muscle brings about movement of the bone at the insertion. Muscles act as **antagonistic pairs**, one moving a bone one way and the other reversing this movement.

- Locomotion on land depends on the reaction of the ground to a force exerted by the animal.

- Muscles may be **skeletal** (striated or voluntary, involved in locomotion), **smooth** (involuntary) or **cardiac** (heart muscle).

- Skeletal muscle includes **slow-twitch muscles** for steady prolonged action and **fast-twitch muscles** for rapid activity.

- Skeletal muscle fibres are made up of **myofibrils**, themselves consisting of units called **sarcomeres**. **Sarcoplasm** makes up the cytoplasm, which contains many mitochondria and a network of membranes called the **sarcoplasmic reticulum**. **T tubules** which store and release calcium ions run between the myofibrils.

- **Actin** (thin) and **myosin** (thick) filaments interlock in the sarcomere. The **I band** contains actin filaments only and the **H zone** contains myosin filaments only. The overlap or **A band** contains both actin and myosin filaments.

- When a myofibril contracts, the actin filaments slide over the myosin filaments, increasing the overlap or A band. **Actomyosin bridges** form between the filaments to move the actin filaments along. The formation and breaking of the bridges depends on calcium ions and ATP.

1 **a** What are the main functions of a skeletal system?
   b What are the differences between an endoskeleton and an exoskeleton?

2 **a** Name and compare the major tissues which make up the mammalian skeletal system.
   b Using a named joint, illustrate how these tissues interact to allow movement to occur.

3 **a** Describe the structure of striated muscle.
   b How does a muscle fibre contract? (Include reference to ATP, calcium, troponin, actin, myosin and tropomyosin in your answer.)

Developing Key Skills

As the Internet becomes ever more accessible, increasing numbers of older people are making use of the facilities it offers – indeed 'silver surfers', as they are known, are one of the fastest growing user groups. This same age group is the one most likely to be affected by age-related skeletal disorders such as osteoporosis and arthritis. Design a website giving information about skeletal health and problems, remembering that the target audience will tend to be over fifty – although young people can also be affected. Give careful thought to navigation about the site and to the level of material that is appropriate for your target audience.

1 a Name **two** cell types which are found in xylem tissue. **(2 marks)**

b One of the functions of xylem tissue is to provide support. Explain how this function is achieved. **(2 marks)**

c Name **one** other tissue which provides support in a plant and explain how the cells in this tissue are adapted for this function. **(2 marks)**

(Edexcel, June 1999)

2 The diagram shows two cells from the root of a plant.

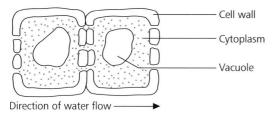

Direction of water flow ⟶

a Copy the diagram roughly and add arrows to show the apoplast pathway of water movement. **(1 mark)**

b Explain how the rate of water movement through th apoplast pathway is affected by increased humidity of air around the leaves. **(2 marks)**

c Weeds can be killed by watering the soil around the weed with a concentrated salt solution. Explain in terms of water potential how the weed is killed. **(2 marks)**

d Leaves from four different plants, **A**, **B**, **C** and **D** were detached and weighed. The mean number of stomata per mm^2 was estimated. The leaves were hung from a line and left in the same environment. After 24 hours the leaves were reweighed. The table shows the results of this investigation.

	Plant A	Plant B	Plant C	Plant D
Percentage loss of mass	28	42	50	32
Mean number of stomata per mm^2	8	10	9	9

i Which **two** plants are likely to show adaptations to a dry environment? What evidence in the table supports your answer? **(1 mark)**

ii The four species had similar numbers of stomata per mm^2 per leaf surface. Explain **two** adaptations of leaf structure which could account for the differences in the amount of water lost by these plants. **(2 marks)**

(AQA, June 1999)

3 a Explain what is meant by the term **transpiration**. **(2 marks)**

The figure shows a potometer which can be used to measure the rate of water uptake in a leafy shoot. The rate of movement of a bubble through the potometer is measured as water is taken up by the shoot. This may be used as a measure of the rate of transpiration by the shoot.

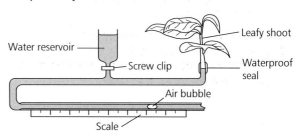

b i List **three** practical precautions which should be taken when using a potometer. **(3 marks)**

ii Suggest an assumption that has to made if the potometer is used to measure the rate of transpiration. **(1 mark)**

A lack of water in herbaceous plants results in wilting. Plant cells are no longer turgid and mechanical strength is lost. The graph shows the results of an investigation to compare the rates of transpiration and water absorption in a plant during a hot day in summer. There was adequate soil moisture available to the plant throughout the investigation, which began at midnight.

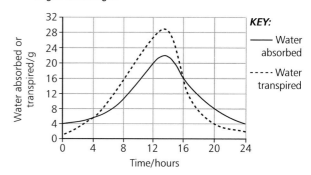

c With reference to the graph

i describe how the rate of transpiration varied during the investigation, and compare this with the rate of water absorption *(In this question, 1 mark is available for the quality of written communication.)* **(8 marks)**

ii suggest, **in terms of transpiration and absorption**, when wilting would be most likely to occur in this investigation **(1 mark)**

iii explain, **in terms of water potential**, when plant cells will no longer be turgid and wilting may occur. **(2 marks)**

(OCR, specimen 2000)

4 The diagram shows a model used to demonstrate mass flow.

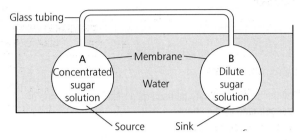

a Explain the processes which lead to mass flow from **A** to **B**. **(3 marks)**

b It has been suggested that mass flow in plants occurs in the same way as in the model. Cooling the stem of an actively photosynthesising plant slows the rate of transport of carbohydrates. Explain whether the observation supports the suggestion. **(2 marks)**

(AQA, specimen 2000)

5 The figure shows the structure of the mammalian heart.

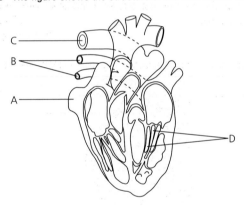

a Name structures **A** to **D** and, for each structure, state its function. **(8 marks)**

Each atrium is separated from the ventricle by a valve.

b State at which point in the cardiac cycle these valves would be closed, and explain why they would be closed. **(2 marks)**

c Name the part of the heart that initiates the heart beat. **(1 mark)**

(OCR, specimen 2000)

6 a Describe how the heart beat is maintained when a person is at rest. **(5 marks)**

b When a person undergoes exercise, the heart responds by beating faster. Describe how this increase in heart rate is brought about. **(4 marks)**

(AQA, specimen 2000)

7 Read the following extract.

Human proteins are boosting performance: the evidence
Genetic engineers have found a way to produce erythroporietin (EPO), which is a hormone and is a front-line drug for treating anaemia. Use of EPO boosts red blood cell production and consequently blood haemoglobin levels. The increase in haemoglobin is a powerful lure for athletes in endurance events. Evidence for the use of EPO has come from comparing two cross-

country skiing events at Lahti and Thunder Bay. EPO is detectable in the body for only six to eight hours, but its effect lasts as long as a red blood cell – around 120 days.

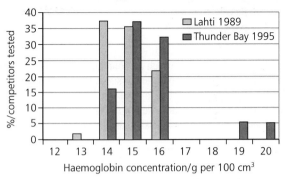

(Reproduced with permission from an article in The Daily Telegraph)

a Explain how the graph provides evidence that EPO has been used by some cross-country skiers. **(2 marks)**

b Explain how increased haemoglobin concentration might lead to increased performance in endurance events. **(4 marks)**

c The graph shows the oxygen-dissociation curve for haemoglobin as blood passes through capillaries in the lungs and in the skeletal muscles of an athlete. Explain how features of the oxygen–haemoglobin curves for haemoglobin in the lungs and in the skeletal muscles benefit an athlete. **(5 marks)**

(AQA, specimen 2000)

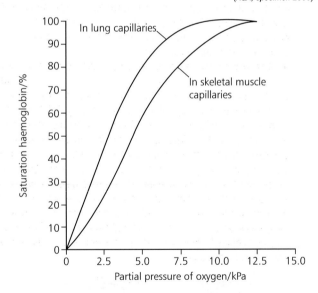

8 The diagram shows some of the process involved in the loading of carbon dioxide by the blood.

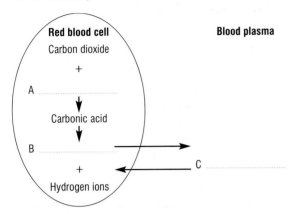

a Name substances **A**, **B** and **C**. **(3 marks)**
b What is the role of carbonic anhydrase in these processes? **(1 mark)**
c Although hydrogen ions are produced the pH of the red blood cell changes very little. Explain how a change in pH is prevented. **(2 marks)**
d The higher the concentration of carbon dioxide in a tissue the higher the percentage of oxygen unloaded by haemoglobin. Suggest why this is an advantage in muscle tissue. **(2 marks)**

9 Stem cells in the bone marrow divide to form reticulocytes, which are immature red blood cells. They have no nucleus, but retain the remains of some RNA in their cytoplasm. Some of these reticulocytes leave the bone marrow before becoming fully developed red blood cells.
a State **two** consequences of red blood cells lacking a nucleus. **(2 marks)**

Samples of blood were taken from two Peruvians, one living at sea level and the other at high altitude (approximately 5000 metres). The number of all red blood cells, including reticulocytes, was counted in each sample of blood. The number of reticulocytes was also counted. The concentration of haemoglobin in the blood samples was measured in mg per 100 mm³ whole blood. The release of new red blood cells from the bone marrow of each person was estimated. A small quantity of each blood sample was placed into a capillary tube and spun in a centrifuge to measure the percentage of the total blood volume occupied by red blood cells and reticulocytes. This percentage is known as the haematocrit. The results of this test are shown in the diagram.

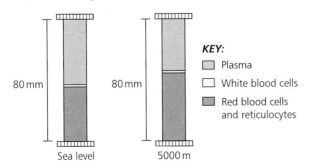

KEY:
- Plasma
- White blood cells
- Red blood cells and reticulocytes

The table compares the results for the blood samples from the two Peruvians.

| | Peruvian at | |
	sea level	5000 metres
red cell count/cells mm^{-3}	5.0 x 10^6	6.4 x 10^6
reticulocytes/cells mm^{-3}	1.8 x 10^4	4.5 x 10^4
red cell production/ no. cells produced per day	2.0 x 10^{11}	2.6 x 10^{11}
concentration of haemoglobin/ mg 100 mm^{-3} whole blood	15.0	20.0
haemocrit/%	45.0	

b Calculate the haematocrit of the blood sample for the Peruvian living at 5000 metres. **(1 mark)**
c i With reference to the information given about the two blood samples, explain how the haemoglobin concentration is raised in people living at high altitude. **(4 marks)**
ii Explain why this high concentration is necessary when living at high altitude. **(3 marks)**

(OCR, specimen 2000)

10 The diagram below shows a section through a human synovial joint.

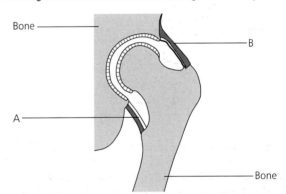

a i Name the type of synovial joint shown in the diagram. **(1 mark)**
ii State **one** location of this type of joint in the human skeleton. **(1 mark)**
iii Describe the range of movement permitted at this type of joint. **(1 mark)**
b Describe **one** function for each of the structures labelled **A** and **B**. **(2 marks)**
c One form of arthritis, which is common in elderly people, causes the joints to become painful so that movement is difficult. Suggest how the joints of a person affected by arthritis would differ in appearance from that shown in the diagram. **(2 marks)**

(Edexcel, June 1999)

ENERGY SYSTEMS

Introduction

Energy is the currency of life. If the supply of energy to the cells of a living organism fails for any reason, the organism will die.

Plants are the energy providers for almost all other living organisms on Earth, using sunlight as their own energy source. Plants have the ability to use light energy from the Sun for photosynthesis, to build up carbohydrates such as glucose and starch. These molecules are used to make other organic compounds such as proteins and fats, and become part of the body of the plant. Animals, fungi and most protoctista cannot trap and use light energy in this way. They need to take in energy in the form of food – namely some other living organism that they break down (**digest**) and which then supplies their energy needs and provides building blocks for their own body tissues.

All living organisms break down the food molecules they have made or taken in in a process known as **cellular respiration**. In a complex series of reactions, the food molecules are converted to water and carbon dioxide (or another waste product such as lactate), producing ATP, an energy store which is available for direct use to drive the biochemistry of the cells.

Within cells, specialised organelles have evolved in which the reactions of photosynthesis and respiration are carried out. The chloroplasts are the site of photosynthesis in plants, whilst the mitochondria present in all eukaryotic cells contain the enzymes needed for cellular respiration. Plants have evolved special pigments which make photosynthesis possible, and on a larger scale their organs, particularly their leaves, are adapted to maximise photosynthesis in a wide range of conditions. Animals and other heterotrophs have developed many different methods of digesting their food, including quite complicated digestive systems in larger animals. Heterotrophs also have specific dietary requirements to provide all the biochemicals they need for healthy growth and reproduction.

The biochemistry of both photosynthesis and respiration can appear daunting at first glance. However, a more careful consideration will reveal that both processes proceed by a series of simple and remarkably elegant steps within the cell. An understanding of how cells work as chemical factories gives new insight into our view of the world around us.

Figure 1 Plants are the energy producers for most of the food chains on Earth, using light energy to make organic compounds which we use to fuel our respiration and thus all the activities that make up life.

AN ENERGY CRISIS

Energy needs of the developed world ...

Throughout the twentieth century, the world has faced an escalating crisis in the supplies of energy to fuel industry, transport and domestic life. Eighty per cent of the world's energy resources are consumed by 25% of the world population – those people living in the developed world. Cheap oil has been used to finance rapid industrial development in North America, the countries that made up the old USSR, Europe, Australia, Japan and South Africa. As we begin the twenty-first century, the supplies of fossil fuels such as coal, oil and natural gas are dwindling rapidly. Nuclear energy is an available alternative, but public confidence in this source of energy is low following several serious accidents and near accidents along with media scare stories. New and renewable energy sources are needed, and soon.

... and of the developing world

The 75% of the world who cannot afford coal, oil or gas, or the electricity produced from them, also need cheap, renewable and readily available sources of energy for cooking and warmth. For example, at present most of the energy needs of the African countries are met by firewood. The increasing demands of a growing population mean that wood is becoming a scarce resource, and women in some places spend most of their time looking for wood. There is as yet no sustainable replanting programme, and what is more the removal of the trees that are left exposes the soil to erosion.

Sustainable energy supplies

The challenge that faces the human race in the coming years is to develop sustainable energy sources which will supply the needs of everyone in the world for the foreseeable future. Autotrophic organisms such as plants have the unique ability to capture the energy of the Sun and transfer it into energy that can be used to build plant and animal bodies (**biomass**). If we can exploit this biomass to fulfil our energy needs, then we will be tapping into a virtually everlasting energy supply streaming daily from the Sun. Already the technology exists to use digested dung – solid waste from animals or people – producing methane gas. This can be used for heating, cooking or – on a large enough scale – generating electricity. Alcohol produced from plants is already used as an alternative to petrol in some countries, and it could find wider uses in the future.

No one can gaze into a crystal ball and tell us what will happen to world energy production in the future, but we do know that we will be forced to use different energy sources as the stocks of fossil fuels become more and more depleted. One thing is certain – when it comes to energy, biological systems already have most of the answers. We simply need to ask the right questions!

Figure 1 In the developed world, fuel is often squandered without a thought for our ever-dwindling energy supplies.

Figure 2 Fuel is a basic necessity of life around the world, but the wood used by so many people is becoming a scarce resource.

Energy flow in the biosphere

Where does energy come from?

Living organisms need energy to grow, to move, to reproduce – energy is needed for life. Energy is needed for **anabolic reactions**, the building up of new molecules within a cell. It is needed in the process of active transport, moving substances against either a concentration gradient or an electrochemical gradient. Whenever an organism moves either part or all of its body, energy is needed to bring that movement about. And in animals that are able to control their own body temperature, a great deal of energy is needed to keep the body temperature lower or higher than that of their surroundings.

There is a massive flow of energy in the biosphere. Organisms can be classed according to their different energy sources. **Autotrophic** organisms make organic compounds from carbon dioxide. Most autotrophic organisms do this by **photosynthesis** – they trap solar energy, which is transferred to chemical energy within the bonds of glucose and other organic products. There are a few autotrophic organisms, the **chemosynthetic** bacteria, which synthesise organic compounds from carbon dioxide using chemical, rather than solar, energy. **Heterotrophic** organisms take in organic compounds by feeding on autotrophs or other heterotrophs. They use the chemical energy in the products of photosynthesis to make the structural molecules they need, and as fuels to supply energy for a wide variety of activities. The Sun is thus the ultimate source of energy for almost all organisms (the exceptions being the chemotrophs).

Where does energy go?

Energy is not cycled in the biosphere – there is a one-way flow, with all energy eventually being dissipated. Solar energy is captured by photosynthetic cells and transferred to chemical energy in the products of photosynthesis. It is then used by both heterotrophs and autotrophs to carry out cell work – synthesis of new materials for growth and reproduction, contraction of muscles for movement, etc. In the course of these reactions much of the energy is transferred to relatively useless forms from a biological point of view. For example, much is transferred into heat energy, which may warm the animal on a temporary basis but is then simply dissipated in the environment. (It is important to remember that energy is not destroyed – all the energy that is captured by photosynthesis still exists, but is eventually converted to a less useful form.)

The flow of energy in the biosphere, shown in figure 3.1.1, is of enormous proportions. Around 10^{19} kJ of solar energy is used each year to convert carbon dioxide into biological material (**biomass**) in photosynthetic organisms. This biological energy flow is some 20 times greater than the flow of energy through all the machines that people have created in the world.

Identifying energy sources

In everyday life we often refer to energy, for example in terms of how energetic we feel, or of saving electrical energy. Much of the energy we know about comes

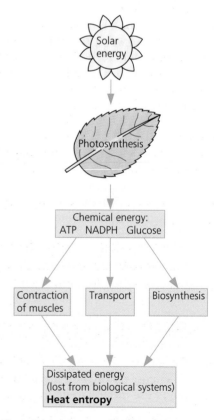

Figure 3.1.1 A summary of the flow of energy in the biosphere.

from particular sources. The electrical energy we use is produced either from the release of heat energy when fossil fuels are burned or during a controlled nuclear reaction, or from the conversion of potential to kinetic energy as water moves downhill, or from the kinetic energy as wind turbines are turned. The chemical energy stored in the molecules of gas, coal or other fuels may be transferred to heat energy for heating, cooking or electricity production. The chemical energy present in the molecules of petrol may be transferred to kinetic energy to move a car.

In the same way, the energy used by living organisms for their daily functioning has very specific sources. As we have already mentioned, the source of energy for almost all living things is ultimately the Sun. The Sun is the direct source of energy for those organisms that are capable of trapping it. (The process of photosynthesis by which the energy of the Sun is captured and transferred to chemical energy in organic molecules within the plant is considered later.) For heterotrophs, such as animals, the direct source of energy is the food they eat. This food may be plants for **herbivores**, other animals for **carnivores** or both plants and animals for **omnivores**. The chemical energy stored in the bonds of the food molecules, particularly the carbohydrates and fats, is used for all the biochemical reactions of life.

Energy supplies for lifestyles

Concern about energy supplies has led to much research into energy sources for the future. Wind power, tidal power and solar power are all well known possibilities. Perhaps less well known is the concept of using biomass. **Biomass** is all organic material produced by living organisms. Not only is biomass readily available, but the source of the energy in living organisms is (directly or indirectly) the Sun. The Sun's energy is free to everyone, and as an added bonus it is not due to run out for some considerable time!

At the moment about 15% of the world's energy is provided from biomass. Most of it – wood, straw and animal dung – is used as a simple fuel, being burned in rural areas of the developing world. This simple combustion is an inefficient and dirty use of biomass. Much of the energy is wasted and the process is smoky and often smelly. The task for scientists and biotechnologists is to develop ways of using biomass which are more efficient but not too expensive for the developing world. Similar technology may be useful in the developed world as fossil fuels are increasingly depleted.

1	How abundant is the energy source, and is it readily available?
2	Can it be stored easily?
3	Can it be used easily for a variety of purposes?
4	Is it a constantly renewable source of energy?
5	How much pollution does it cause?
6	Is it safe?
7	What is the relationship between the energy put into the system to make it work and the energy gained from it (the output:input ratio)?
8	How expensive is it compared with other forms of energy?
9	Is technology sufficiently advanced to allow its use on a large scale?
10	Can the members of the community afford the energy?
11	Does the energy source place conflicting demands on a scarce resource, such as land?

Table 3.1.1 Some of the questions that need to be asked before a new energy source is introduced into a community

Figure 3.1.2 At the moment our electricity is generated using fossil fuels, nuclear power or water (hydroelectric power stations). In years to come we may use body wastes, rubbish or specially grown plants.

Where does biomass come from?

Energy radiates from the Sun at an enormous rate – around 10^{31} kJ each year. The energy results from multiple collisions of protons in the central core of the Sun at temperatures of around 20 million degrees Celsius. However, only a small proportion of the radiation from the Sun reaches the Earth – about 3×10^{21} kJ – and on arriving at the Earth's atmosphere much more is absorbed or otherwise prevented from reaching the surface of the Earth. Light is absorbed by the ozone layer, scattered by dust and water particles or reflected back into space by the clouds and water at the surface of the Earth. Even when the light does reach the surface, not all is available to living organisms as much falls on relatively barren areas such as oceans, mountains and deserts. However, in the region of 10^{19} kJ of the Sun's energy is captured each year by plants – around 0.33% of the total energy that reaches the Earth.

The energy from the Sun is captured by plants using the green pigment chlorophyll. Solar energy is then transferred into chemical energy in the process of photosynthesis. It is stored in the chemical bonds of the glucose molecules made from carbon dioxide and water. This energy is then transferred into other organisms – animals, fungi and microbes – by processes of digestion and assimilation which are not efficient. For example, only about 10% of the biomass eaten by a cow is converted into new cow, and only about 10% of the cow eaten by a person gets turned into new person. All along the process, biomass and therefore potential energy is lost.

Using biomass as a fuel

Part of the energy within a plant or animal is in the form of ATP, which is used to supply energy for all the cells' metabolic reactions. Metabolism results in heat production, and the energy transferred to heat is effectively lost for further use. However, considerable energy remains in the tissues of a plant, and animals pass out large quantities of energy-containing material in their faeces. Using biomass as a fuel takes advantage of these sources of energy which would otherwise be wasted.

As we have already seen, both plant material (wood and straw) and animal dung are already used as fuel, but generally for inefficient combustion – only about 10% of the energy in the biomass is used. However, cleaner and more efficient ways of using biomass are being developed. Some, such as a process known as gasification, are complex and require expensive technology. Other more simple techniques rely on the actions of microorganisms to produce either methane gas (biogas) or ethanol. The anaerobic digestion by bacteria of waste from cattle to biogas is 60% efficient. An added advantage of producing biogas from dung is that the slurry left at the end is a valuable fertiliser for fields as all the nitrates, phosphates and other minerals remain intact. This is another advantage over burning the dung, when the resource disappears in flames and a much-needed fertiliser is lost completely.

Dung digestion and biogas production

Cattle dung is a potentially enormous energy resource. It can be added to by the dung of pigs, sheep and poultry and, of course, human excrement. The only difficulty with using human waste is that in some cultures there are religious and social taboos against it. The successful conversion of manure into biogas depends on manipulating the digestive and respiratory processes of microorganisms. By the process of respiration, the energy in molecules produced by photosynthesis or digested by animals is transferred into molecules of ATP, the energy currency of the cell. When respiration takes place

Figure 3.1.3 You may not realise that if you eat beef, all the energy you are taking in is derived originally from the Sun. What is more, the waste biomass from the cow and from your body could be used to cook more beef.

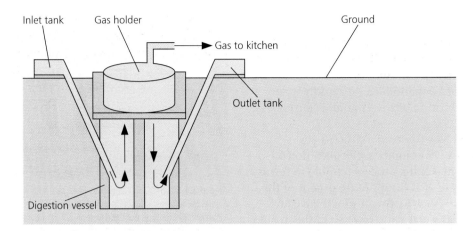

Inlet tank   Gas holder   Ground

→ Gas to kitchen

Outlet tank

Digestion vessel

Figure 3.1.4 A regular supply of dung from animals or people can supply a clean and efficient energy source for cooking and heating when processed in a biomass digester.

in the presence of oxygen, carbon dioxide and water are the waste products of the process. But in some bacteria, when respiration occurs in the absence of air or oxygen (that is, anaerobically), the gas produced is a mixture of methane and carbon dioxide in the ratio of about 2 volumes of methane for every 1 volume of carbon dioxide. After the carbon dioxide is removed, the methane provides a clean and efficient fuel and the residual sludge is a good fertiliser.

A mixed population of bacteria is needed to digest the dung, and the process is similar to that which occurs in the guts of ruminants like the cow. Small family biogas producers are currently used in both China and India. In China waste vegetables, animal dung and human waste is used and the digesters produce excellent fertiliser but relatively low quality gas. In India only cattle and buffalo dung is used and the generators are used to produce high quality gas but less fertiliser.

Although the main use of biogas generators has so far been in the developing world, more and more countries are experimenting with them on a larger scale to deal with the problems of municipal sewage and rubbish tips, and with a view to reducing dependence on fossil and nuclear fuels. The efficiency of biogas generators is increased when the fuel is readily available. In India, for example, many people do not own cows and therefore cannot use a generator, as religious beliefs prevent the use of human excrement. Even those people who do own cows often only manage to find and collect 30–40% of the dung produced. In intensive rearing units in the developed world, almost 100% of the dung produced can be collected and used, making the production of biogas more efficient.

Advantages of anaerobic biogas generators	Disadvantages of anaerobic biogas generators
Relatively cheap	Best adapted for warm climates, although underground tanks and the exothermic nature of the reactions do make it feasible elsewhere
Versatile – a whole range of waste and raw materials can be used	The chemical processes are slow and it may take up to four weeks to produce the gas from a load of dung
The process can be carried out on either a small or a large scale	Carbon dioxide has to be removed from the gas mixture
Works at relatively low temperatures of 30–35 °C so energy input is not high	
pH is not critical – works within a fairly wide pH range	
Can be run continuously or in batches when fuel is available	

Table 3.1.2 Anaerobic biogas generators convert the energy of the Sun into energy for cooking and heating through a complicated pathway which includes plants, photosynthesis, animals, digestion and egestion, microorganisms and respiration. This table sums up some of the pros and cons of biogas as a fuel of the future

Alcohol – another fuel of the future?

As well as the production of biogas from dung, energy may be obtained from biomass by the fermentation of carbohydrate-rich crops such as sugar cane, sweet potato and maize into ethanol. This alcohol can then be used as a fuel for cars instead of petrol. Not only does this avoid dependence on rapidly disappearing oil resources, but also the combustion of the ethanol is far less polluting to the atmosphere.

To produce alcohol from the biomass involves yeasts in a process of anaerobic respiration known as **fermentation**. The sugars are broken down incompletely to form ethanol and water. To make this process feasible in terms of output:input ratios it is important that there is as little pre-treatment of the biomass as possible. As a result, only countries such as Brazil which have an enormous capability for growing crops such as sugar cane have so far been able to make much use of this process. However, in Brazil oil imports have been reduced by about 20% and car engines have been converted to run on a mixture of petrol and ethanol. Most new cars in Brazil will run on ethanol alone. The disadvantage of this development is that land valuable for growing food crops has been taken over to produce the enormous quantities of sugar cane needed to replace oil.

The major stumbling block in the conversion of biomass to ethanol as a major world-wide proposition is that we need to be able to utilise the cellulose element of the biomass which makes up much of agricultural waste (straw) and dung. At the moment it can be used only after expensive shredding, chemical or enzyme treatments. For ethanol to become the motor fuel of the future a major breakthrough is required in the development of a low-cost technology for preparing cellulose for fermentation. It may be that genetic engineering will produce enzymes capable of doing this cheaply and easily, so that waste biomass can be used to produce fuel instead of specific crops being cultivated specially.

Biodiesel is another exciting fuel possibility. Made from the oils produced by soya beans and other similar plants, biodiesel is biodegradable, less toxic than normal diesel and can be used in ordinary diesel engines. It looks to be a promising energy source for the future.

Figure 3.1.5 So far, only countries like Brazil with vast natural resources can produce useful amounts of ethanol from biomass, but the development of new cellulose-digesting processes could see alcohol-powered cars for everyone in the future.

Energy stores in living organisms

Most living things need to store energy. Plants cannot photosynthesise at night and animals do not spend all their time feeding, yet the demands of the cells for energy are continual. Thus energy must be stored, and then produced when needed in a readily usable form. In plants, some products of photosynthesis are immediately used to create new plant tissue or to provide energy for their synthesis. However, any products not used in this way are converted into starch (in dicotyledons) or sucrose (in monocotyledons). These carbohydrate molecules are stored in the cells until needed, when they are broken down into glucose.

In animals, some digested food which is not immediately required may be converted into a carbohydrate store of glycogen in the liver, muscles and brain. The larger part is converted into fat and stored in special fat cells. The way these stores may be used by an animal is shown in figure 3.1.6.

For the individual cells of any living organism, energy has to be available in a much more accessible form than fat or starch, ready for use in any one of a multitude of different reactions immediately it is needed. One molecule is believed to be the universal energy supplier in cells. It is found in all living organisms in exactly the same form. Anything which interferes with its production or breakdown is fatal to the cell and, ultimately, the organism. This remarkable compound is called **adenosine triphosphate**, more commonly referred to as **ATP**.

Figure 3.1.6 Animals that hibernate eat copious quantities of food before the winter. This is converted into large fat stores. During the time of hibernation this fat is slowly used up to supply energy to the cells, with an amount saved for the final surge of energy needed to bring the creature out of hibernation at the end of the winter. The weight loss can be quite dramatic.

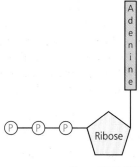

Figure 3.1.7 ATP is a nucleotide with three phosphate groups attached. Hydrolysis of the phosphate group liberates energy which is made available to cells.

Adenosine triphosphate (ATP)

A chemical energy store

Figure 3.1.7 shows the structure of ATP. When energy is needed, the third phosphate bond can be broken by a hydrolysis reaction catalysed by the enzyme **ATPase**. The result of this hydrolysis is **adenosine diphosphate** or **ADP**, and a free inorganic phosphate group (P_i). About 34 kJ of energy are released per mole of ATP hydrolysed. Some of this energy is lost as heat and wasted, but some is used for any energy-requiring biological activity.

The breakdown of ATP into ADP and phosphate is a reversible reaction. Catabolic reactions, for example the breakdown of glucose in respiration in both plants and animals, can be coupled to the synthesis of molecules of ATP from ADP and phosphate groups. This reaction is also catalysed by ATPase. Energy is thus stored in the ATP molecule, ready for use when required. Figure 3.1.8 shows the cycle between ADP and ATP, and figure 3.1.9 illustrates how the cycle is used in living organisms.

ATP is the single energy-providing and energy-storing molecule for all processes in all cells.

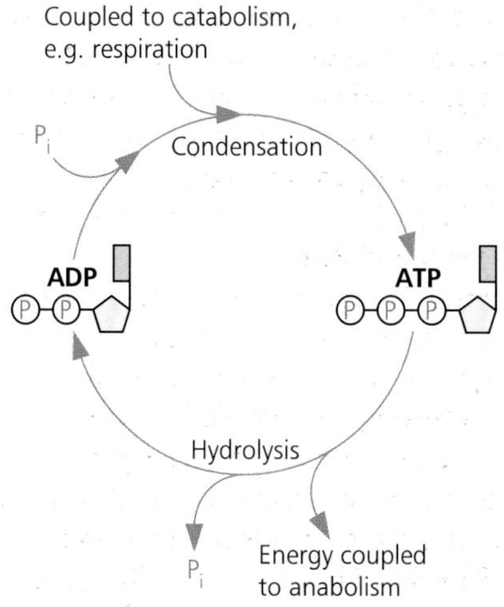

Figure 3.1.8 The storing and release of energy in ATP.

Sources of energy for ATP synthesis

We have already stated that ATP is made as a result of catabolic or breakdown reactions. Most of the ATP synthesised in a cell is produced as a result of the breakdown of food molecules in the process known as cellular respiration, which takes place in the mitochondria. Much of the detail of this process will be considered later. However, ATP synthesis also takes place in chloroplasts and in chemosynthetic bacteria. We shall consider the way ATP is produced during respiration as a basic model, and look at this in isolation. We can then later insert this model of ATP synthesis into large biochemical pathways when needed.

When sugars are broken down in respiration, energy for the production of ATP from ADP and inorganic phosphate is made available in two ways:

1 Catabolic reactions are exothermic – they release energy. This energy may be sufficient to drive the production of a molecule of ATP. Relatively little ATP is actually formed this way.

2 The other main source of energy for ATP synthesis results from the removal of hydrogen atoms from several intermediates in a metabolic pathway. This removal of hydrogen atoms brings about a series of **redox reactions** in a chain of compounds called the **electron transfer chain**. The term 'redox' is explained in the box overleaf. The redox reactions in the electron transfer chain each release a small amount of energy, which is incorporated into an ATP molecule.

Redox reactions

Reduction and **oxidation** are two important chemical concepts which help us to understand the terminology of the electron transfer chain.

Reduction is the addition of electrons to a substance. In biological systems this addition of electrons is usually brought about by the addition of hydrogen or the removal of oxygen. Any compound which has oxygen removed, or hydrogen or electrons added, is said to be **reduced**.

Oxidation is the removal of electrons from a substance. In biological systems this removal of electrons is usually brought about by the addition of oxygen or the removal of hydrogen. Any compound which has oxygen added, or hydrogen or electrons removed, is said to be **oxidised**.

In the electron transfer chain, electrons are passed from one member of the chain to the next. The components of the chain are therefore reduced when they receive the electrons, and oxidised again when they pass them on.

In a **redox reaction**, one compound will be oxidised while another is simultaneously reduced.

The electron transfer chain

Figure 3.1.11 shows the electron transfer chain. The various elements of the chain are described below. As you can see, two hydrogens are removed from a compound (which is therefore oxidised) and are picked up by NAD, the first

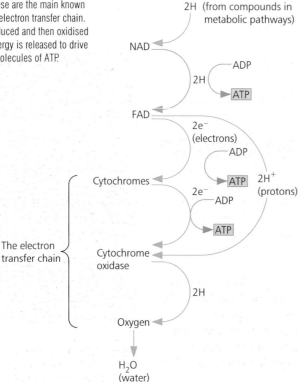

Figure 3.1.10 These are the main known components of the electron transfer chain. As they become reduced and then oxidised again, sufficient energy is released to drive the production of molecules of ATP.

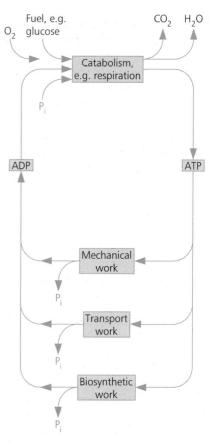

Figure 3.1.9 Catabolic (breakdown) reactions are used to drive the production of ATP. The ATP acts as a store of energy which is released as needed for cell functions, producing ADP and inorganic phosphate for resynthesis into ATP.

Chemical death

Cyanide is a well known chemical in murder stories. It smells faintly of bitter almonds. This deadly poison acts on one of the enzymes of the electron transfer chain, stopping the production of ATP. Deprived of their supply of energy, the cells of the body cease to function – the most obvious effect is that the muscles spasm and convulse, so the victim of the poison cannot breathe.

hydrogen carrier or **acceptor**. The acceptor is therefore reduced. The hydrogens are then passed to the next acceptor and then along the molecules of the electron transfer chain, so a series of redox reactions takes place.

Although it is hydrogen atoms which are removed from the compounds of the metabolic pathways, and hydrogen atoms which eventually join up with oxygen atoms at the end of the chain to form water, it is in fact electrons which are passed along the carrier system. Hydrogen atoms split into protons and electrons and it is the electrons that are passed from one carrier to the next. This is why the system is most accurately known as the electron transfer chain rather than the hydrogen carrier chain. The various elements of the chain are at different energy levels, the first member of the chain being at the highest level with subsequent steps down. Thus the electron is passed down from one energy level to another, powering the production of ATP.

Hydrogen acceptors

The hydrogen acceptors include:

1 **NAD** or **nicotinamide adenine dinucleotide**. When this accepts hydrogen atoms from a metabolic pathway it becomes reduced to **NADH$_2$**.

2 **FAD** or **flavine adenine dinucleotide**. This is synthesised from vitamin B2, riboflavin. It accepts hydrogens from NADH$_2$, which is therefore oxidised again to NAD. The FAD is reduced to **FADH$_2$** at the same time. A molecule of ATP is produced at this stage.

The electron transfer chain

1 **Cytochromes** are protein pigments with an iron group rather like haemoglobin. Cytochromes are reduced by electrons from FADH$_2$ which is oxidised again to FAD. A molecule of ATP is produced at this stage.

2 **Cytochrome oxidase** is an enzyme which receives the electrons from the cytochromes and is reduced as they are oxidised. A molecule of ATP is produced at this stage.

3 **Oxygen** is the final electron acceptor in the chain. The reduction of oxygen forms water at the end of the chain.

As a result of the electrons from each molecule of hydrogen passing along the electron transfer chain, sufficient energy is released to make three molecules of ATP. The process is also known as **oxidative phosphorylation** – ADP is phosphorylated in a process which depends on the presence of oxygen.

The site of ATP synthesis

The main site of ATP synthesis in the cell is the mitochondria. The main reactions of respiration appear to take place in the matrix, while the reactions of the electron transfer chain and so the production of ATP seem to take place on the inner membrane of the mitochondria. This is folded up to form cristae, which in turn are covered with closely packed stalked particles, shown in figure 3.1.11.

The chemiosmotic theory of ATP production

In the 1960s Peter Mitchell put forward a mechanism for the production of ATP in the mitochondria. Other scientists were sceptical at first but by 1978 Mitchell's **chemiosmotic theory** was widely accepted, and he won the Nobel prize.

The theory is very elegant. The members of the electron transfer chain are found within the inner mitochondrial membrane, and electrons are passed along them as we have seen. What happens to the hydrogen ions (protons) that are left?

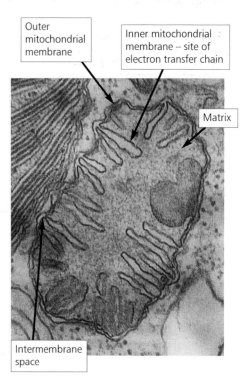

Figure 3.1.11 The site of most ATP production in cells appears to be the inner membrane of the mitochondria, with the ATPase sited in the stalked particles.

Figure 3.1.12 shows the mechanism. The protons are actively transported into the space between the inner and outer mitochondrial membranes. The inner mitochondrial membrane is impermeable to protons. This means that as a result of the active transport of the protons there are different hydrogen ion concentrations on the two sides of the inner membrane. The intermembrane space has a higher concentration of hydrogen ions than the matrix, so there is a concentration gradient across the membrane. As a result of the different hydrogen ion concentrations there is also a pH gradient. Because positive hydrogen ions are concentrated in the membrane space, there is also an electrochemical gradient.

All this means that there is a tendency for the hydrogen ions to move back into the matrix. However, the membrane is generally impermeable to hydrogen ions. The only way they can move back into the matrix is through special pores involving the stalked particles where the electron transfer chain is situated. The movement of the hydrogen ions along their electrical, concentration and pH gradients is thereby linked to an ATPase enzyme. The energy from the gradients is used to drive the synthesis of ATP. Thus the universal energy carrier is produced in a universal process, found in all living things.

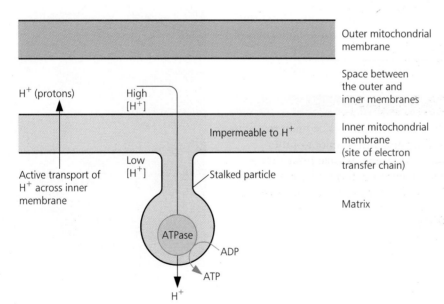

H$^+$ (protons) leave the space between the membranes along the only route available to them – through the stalked particles. They move along concentration, pH and electrochemical gradients, driving the production of ATP.

Figure 3.1.12 Peter Mitchell, seen here receiving a Nobel prize for his work, developed the chemiosmotic theory which explains the formation of ATP not just in the mitochondria but also in chloroplasts and elsewhere. The hydrogen ion gradient explains all the current observations about the process.

SUMMARY

- Organisms may be classed according to their energy sources. **Autotrophs** make organic compounds from carbon dioxide, mainly by photosynthesis using solar energy. The exceptions are **chemotrophs** which synthesise organic compounds using chemical energy. **Heterotrophs** take in organic compounds by feeding on autotrophs or other heterotrophs.

- Energy is transferred within organisms to different forms and is eventually dissipated.

- **Biomass** is all organic material produced by living organisms. We can use biomass as a renewable source of energy, for example, by burning wood, digesting dung to produce methane (biogas) or using ethanol or biodiesel to fuel vehicles.

- Energy is stored in chemicals within organisms – in plants as starch or sucrose and in animals as glycogen or fat.

- At a cellular level energy is made available for biochemical reactions in the form of **adenosine triphosphate** or **ATP**. The terminal phosphate group can be hydrolysed from this molecule forming **adenosine diphosphate** or **ADP**, and energy is released which can be used to drive other reactions. The reaction is reversible and so ATP can act as an energy store. The reaction is catalysed by **ATPase**.

- ATP may be produced as a result of exothermic catabolic reactions, though this is not very common.

- Most ATP is produced as electrons pass down the **electron transfer chain** during the process of **oxidative phosphorylation**. The process results in the reduction of oxygen and the oxidation of hydrogen (from metabolic intermediates) to form water. As electrons move down the different energy levels in the chain, energy is made available to synthesise ATP.

- **Hydrogen acceptors** that take the hydrogen from other molecules and pass it on to the electron transfer chain include **nicotinamide adenine dinucleotide** or **NAD**, which is reduced to **$NADH_2$**, and **flavine adenine dinucleotide** or **FAD**, which is reduced to **$FADH_2$**. This reaction results in the production of a molecule of ATP.

- Hydrogens split into protons and electrons and the electrons pass from $FADH_2$ to the **cytochromes** and then to **cytochrome oxidase**, both of which reduction reactions result in a molecule of ATP. The electrons finally reduce oxygen, and water is formed at the end of the chain.

- The **chemiosmotic theory** says that the protons, once separated from the electrons, are actively transported to the space between the inner and outer mitochondrial membranes. The concentration of protons in the intermembrane space is higher than that in the matrix, resulting in a chemical, electrochemical and pH gradient. Protons can only move back into the matrix at the stalked particles, where their movement is linked to an ATPase enzyme and drives the synthesis of ATP.

1 **a** What are the main energy sources in the biosphere?

    b Where is energy stored within the biosphere?

    c Describe the flow of energy through the biosphere.

2 **a** What is the main function of ATP within a cell?

    b Describe the structure of an ATP molecule and explain how its structure is related to its function.

    c Explain where ATP production takes place and describe the evidence which supports the hypothesis.

3 With reference to the structure of the mitochondrion, describe how Mitchell's chemiosmotic pump works and how ATP is produced.

Developing Key Skills

For many years now it has been predicted that the world supplies of fossil fuels would eventually run out. However, over the same timescale more and more reserves have been discovered under the Earth and methods of extraction have been improved so that more oil, gas or coal can be obtained from any given site.

Nevertheless, if world energy consumption were to remain constant at current levels, our known reserves would supply world petroleum needs for about 40 years, natural gas needs for 60 years and coal needs for well over 200 years. This means that these vital fuels could run out during your lifetime. As the developing world races to 'catch up' with countries such as the USA, use of fossil fuels can only increase, which will mean that the reserves are used up even more rapidly.

Alternative energy sources include a number of renewable biological resources such as wood, alcohol from plants as a fuel (gasohol), biodiesel, dung and methane gas from dung and rubbish digesters.

Chose one of these biological alternative fuels. Find out as much about it as you can using a variety of sources. Produce a presentation to a World Commission investigating the potential energy crisis. You need to explain the advantages of the type of renewable energy resource you are suggesting and any disadvantages. Remember that you will need numbers as well as words to be convincing in your arguments and that clear graphs and diagrams can carry as much information as many written words.

Your presentation can be produced using IT and if desired could be in the form of a 'powerpoint' presentation.

SUGAR-SENSING PLANTS

Sugar is vital to living organisms as the raw material of cellular respiration. Plants not only use sugar to provide energy for growth, reproduction and all the other functions of their cells, they also make sugar in the process of photosynthesis – around 160 billion tonnes of carbohydrate are produced on the Earth in this way every year! Scientists have recently begun to realise that plants can sense the presence of sugar, and can use this information to regulate their biochemical pathways in order to strike a balance between the manufacture of sugar by photosynthesis and its use in cellular respiration.

Switched on by a famine ... or switched on by a feast

It seems that plants are sensitive to sugar levels at the initial part of cellular respiration, the first stage of glycolysis. Once the presence of sugar has been sensed, it has an effect in a number of ways which include switching on and off the genes that code for particular enzymes. The genes can be described as having either 'feast' or 'famine' functions. For example, the genes that ensure the right proteins are present for photosynthesis are famine genes. They are switched on when sugar levels are low, when the plant needs to photosynthesise as fast as it can, and switched off when sugar levels climb.

On the other hand, genes that control the conversion of sugar to storage chemicals such as starch are feast genes. They are switched on when the plant has made lots of sugar, and off again if the rate of photosynthesis drops.

Applications: bigger potatoes?

Scientists hope to use this new knowledge to manipulate plant responses to sugar levels to our advantage. For example, if potato plants can be encouraged to carry on photosynthesising even when the levels of sugar are high by preventing the feast genes from switching off, the plants will store extra starch in the tubers, making bigger and better potatoes. We might also be able to change the growth rate of the plant as a whole, or even change the way parts of the plant respond to attack.

These possible future developments depend on a more detailed understanding of the sugar sensitivity of plants than we have at present. Before we can use this newly discovered plant sense to benefit us, we need more research to help us understand how it benefits the plants themselves.

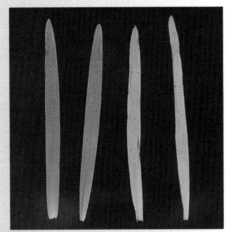

Figure 1 Two of these leaves have been floated on water for five days ,whilst the other two were floated on sugar solution. The yellow colour shows that in the presence of sugar, the photosynthetic mechanism is switched off and the levels of chlorophyll have fallen.

Figure 2 Once we understand the way plants use their sensitivity to sugar levels to switch genes on and off, who knows what size of vegetable we might be able to produce?

What is photosynthesis?

Photosynthesis is the process by which living organisms, particularly plants, capture solar energy and use it to convert carbon dioxide and water into simple sugars. The process is dependent on pigments, particularly chlorophyll, present in the chloroplasts of the plant cells. These pigments absorb light energy and transfer it to chemical energy. Photosynthesis is summarised by the equation:

$$\text{Carbon dioxide} + \text{water} \xrightarrow[\text{chlorophyll}]{\text{light energy}} \text{glucose} + \text{oxygen}$$

$$6CO_2 + 6H_2O \xrightarrow[\text{chlorophyll}]{\text{light energy}} C_6H_{12}O_6 + 6O_2$$

The whole structure of the plant body has evolved around the process of photosynthesis. As we have seen in section 2 the stems, roots and leaves of plants are adapted both for obtaining the raw materials carbon dioxide and water, and for trapping the energy of the Sun.

As already mentioned, organisms capable of synthesising their own food are known as **autotrophs**, which can be roughly translated as 'self-feeding'. Of the autotrophs, the **phototrophs** or 'light feeders' rely on the Sun as their source of energy, and the **chemotrophs** rely on energy from breaking chemical bonds to synthesise their food. The most important autotrophs are the plants, which are one of the most successful groups on Earth. Their ability to synthesise new biological material (roughly 3.5×10^{16} kg of carbon dioxide are fixed into sugars each year), along with the resulting waste product oxygen, means that phototrophs are of vital importance to the survival of all species on Earth.

Figure 3.2.1 Plants all around us are continually carrying out the photosynthesis that underpins all life on Earth.

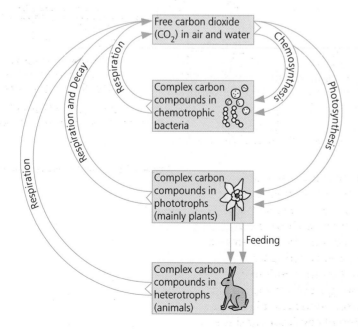

Figure 3.2.2 The carbon cycle shows the way in which carbon is cycled in nature, and also demonstrates the interdependence of animals and plants.

Factors affecting photosynthesis

As shown in the equation for photosynthesis, carbon dioxide and water are needed for the process, along with a supply of light energy and the means to capture that energy. In order to show that certain factors are needed for photosynthesis, or have an effect on its rate, we need a way of demonstrating that photosynthesis has in fact taken place. The simplest way to do this is to look at the end products of the process.

Demonstrating the products of photosynthesis

The immediate products of photosynthesis are glucose and oxygen. As glucose is osmotically very active, it is rapidly converted to the large polysaccharide molecule starch, which has little effect on the movement of water in cells. Thus we have two simple ways of demonstrating that photosynthesis is taking or has taken place – the production of oxygen gas and the formation of starch.

The production of oxygen by a photosynthesising plant can be shown very simply by collecting the gas over water. But as is shown in figure 3.2.3 this basic technique can be relatively easily adapted into a much more sophisticated experimental device. By measuring the amount of oxygen gas given off in a period of time a measure of the rate of photosynthesis can be found. By changing the conditions such as light intensity or temperature the influence of these factors on the rate of photosynthesis can be seen.

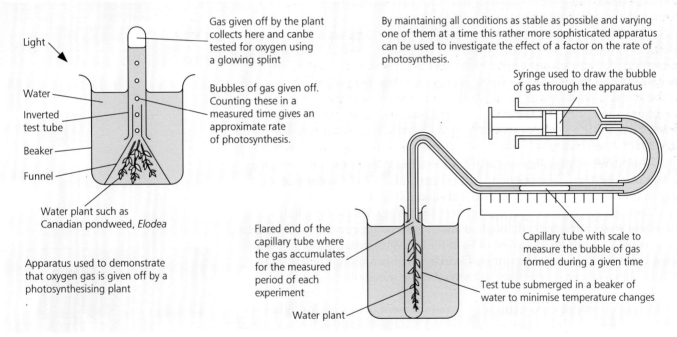

Light

Gas given off by the plant collects here and canbe tested for oxygen using a glowing splint

Water

Bubbles of gas given off. Counting these in a measured time gives an approximate rate of photosynthesis.

Inverted test tube

Beaker

Funnel

Water plant such as Canadian pondweed, *Elodea*

Apparatus used to demonstrate that oxygen gas is given off by a photosynthesising plant

By maintaining all conditions as stable as possible and varying one of them at a time this rather more sophisticated apparatus can be used to investigate the effect of a factor on the rate of photosynthesis.

Syringe used to draw the bubble of gas through the apparatus

Flared end of the capillary tube where the gas accumulates for the measured period of each experiment

Capillary tube with scale to measure the bubble of gas formed during a given time

Test tube submerged in a beaker of water to minimise temperature changes

Water plant

Figure 3.2.3 Investigating the rate of photosynthesis.

The production of oxygen gas as a waste product by a photosynthesising plant is relatively easy to demonstrate in water plants, as shown in figure 3.2.3, but considerably less so in land plants. Thus for land plants the most useful indicator of the occurrence of photosynthesis is whether starch has been produced. If a plant is deprived of light for about 48 hours, then the stores of starch in the leaves are substantially depleted. The plant is said to be **destarched**. Any subsequent production of starch is then the result of new photosynthesis occurring since the destarching. Testing a leaf for the presence of starch using iodine solution is a familiar procedure, summarised in the box overleaf. Destarched plants can be subjected to different conditions and the effects of various factors on photosynthesis in land plants thus investigated.

Testing a leaf for starch

A common way of demonstrating whether a plant has carried out photosynthesis is to test a leaf for the presence of starch. The test reagent used is iodine in potassium iodide solution, which turns from yellowish-red to blue-black in the presence of starch.

Simply applying the iodine solution to the surface of a leaf is not effective as the leaf is covered by a waterproof layer – the waxy cuticle. In order for the test to show clearly whether starch has been produced, a series of experimental steps must be followed:

(1) Remove a leaf from the plant, plunge it into boiling water and continue to boil briefly. This serves two main purposes – it stops all the biochemical processes by killing the leaf, and it breaks open the cells making them more accessible to the removal of chlorophyll and to the iodine solution.
(2) Boil the leaf again in methanol for several minutes until all the colour is removed. This must be carried out in a water bath and great care taken as methanol is very flammable. The removal of the green pigment from the leaf enables any colour changes in the test reagent to be more clearly seen.
(3) Wash the leaf once more in hot water. Methanol makes the leaf brittle, and this softens it.
(4) Spread the leaf out on a white tile, again to make colour changes more obvious, and apply the iodine solution.

Figure 3.2.4 The striking colour change in iodine solution when starch is present demonstrates photosynthesis very clearly.

Requirements for photosynthesis

Light

Light is needed for some, but not all, of the reactions of photosynthesis. There is a **light-dependent stage** of photosynthesis, and also a **light-independent stage** in which the reactions occur in the absence of light.

For most plants the source of light energy for the reactions of the light-dependent stage is the Sun, although artificial light of appropriate wavelengths can be used. If plants are deprived of light for any substantial amount of time they will die, because once the stores of starch have been used up they are not replaced and so there is no energy available for the metabolic reactions of the cells.

The simplest way of demonstrating the requirement of a plant for light is to cover either a whole leaf or part of a leaf of a destarched plant with black paper or foil. This prevents light from reaching the covered area. The plant is left in the light for several hours and the covered leaf tested for the presence of starch and compared with an uncovered leaf. The difference is plainly visible, as figure 3.2.5 demonstrates.

Carbon dioxide

A source of carbon is needed for the synthesis of sugars. There are numerous carbon-containing chemicals in existence, but carbon dioxide from the air, or in solution or as hydrogencarbonate ions (HCO_3^-) in water, is the only form which plants can use in photosynthesis. Carbon dioxide is found more or less everywhere and is produced by plants as a result of their metabolic processes.

Figure 3.2.5 Only the 'L' on the lower leaf was exposed to light, and the resulting absence of starch is clear to see.

However, although there is always sufficient carbon dioxide available for some photosynthesis to take place, there are circumstances when the levels are too low for plants to take full advantage of the light available.

Demonstrating the absolute requirement of a plant for carbon dioxide is not easy. Carbon dioxide can readily be removed from the air surrounding a leaf or a plant using potassium hydroxide solution, which absorbs carbon dioxide, as figure 3.2.6 shows. However, the cells produce carbon dioxide as they respire and so it is almost impossible to entirely deprive a plant of the gas. A more valid approach is to change the levels of carbon dioxide in the air surrounding a plant in high-intensity light, and measure the changes in the rate of photosynthesis. As the carbon dioxide level increases, the rate of photosynthesis rises.

Water

Carbon dioxide alone is not sufficient to produce carbohydrates. Hydrogen ions are needed too, and water is the only source of hydrogen ions that plants can make use of. As a result of metabolic processes and the transpiration stream, there is always an adequate supply of water for photosynthesis.

Water is vital to all the functions of a plant. We cannot demonstrate that water is required for photosynthesis just by depriving the plant of it – the plant would die long before any effect of water lack on photosynthesis could be seen. To show that water is needed for photosynthesis, the plant can be supplied with water containing the 'heavy' isotope oxygen-18. This experiment shows that water is needed for photosynthesis, and also makes clear its role. We shall look at this role in more detail later, on pages 189–91.

Chlorophyll

The final requirement for photosynthesis is a means of capturing the energy from the Sun. The photosynthetic pigment **chlorophyll** fulfils this role, although it has been estimated that of all the light which reaches the Earth from the Sun, only about 0.33% is used in photosynthesis.

The simplest way to demonstrate that chlorophyll is required for photosynthesis is to consider the leaves of a variegated plant. Variegated leaves have areas which contain chlorophyll and areas which do not. The chlorophyll-free regions are usually yellow or creamy-white in colour. If a destarched variegated plant is exposed to light for several hours and one of the leaves tested for the presence of starch, the iodine solution changes colour only in those regions of the leaf which were green. This shows that without chlorophyll, photosynthesis does not take place.

Photosynthetic pigments

The green colouring in plants that we have so far loosely referred to as chlorophyll is not produced by a single pigment, but by a group of five closely related ones. These are **chlorophyll *a*** (blue-green), **chlorophyll *b*** (yellow-green), **carotene** (orange) and **xanthophyll** (yellow) along with a grey pigment **phaeophytin**. Phaeophytin has been considered for many years to be a breakdown product of the other photosynthetic pigments. Recent reports suggest that it may after all play a part in the process of photosynthesis.

Chlorophyll *a* is found in all photosynthesing plants and is the most abundant of the five. The other pigments are found in varying proportions, and it is these differences which give the leaves of plants their variety of shades of green.

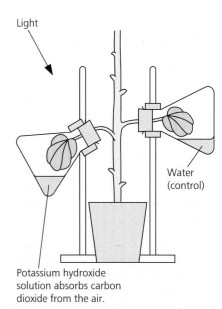

Light

Water (control)

Potassium hydroxide solution absorbs carbon dioxide from the air.

Figure 3.2.6 Although rather crude and not entirely successful, this experiment can be used to show that when carbon dioxide levels are very low, photosynthesis is substantially reduced.

3

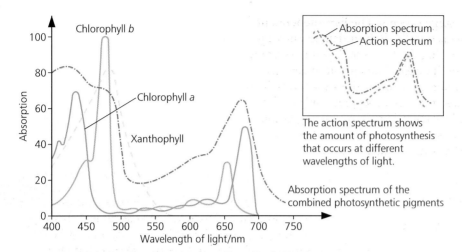

The action spectrum shows the amount of photosynthesis that occurs at different wavelengths of light.

Absorption spectrum of the combined photosynthetic pigments

Figure 3.2.7 The different photosynthetic pigments absorb light at a variety of different wavelengths, making more of the light available for use by the plant.

Why is there this variety of photosynthetic pigments? Figure 3.2.7 shows that each of the pigments absorbs light well from particular areas of the spectrum. As a result, far more of the light falling on the plant can be absorbed than if only one pigment was present. It is also interesting to note that none of the pigments absorb well in the green/yellow areas of the spectrum, around 500–550 nm. This light, not being absorbed, is reflected, which is why plants appear green.

Explaining the absorption spectrum of the photosynthetic pigments

Figure 3.2.7 shows that the photosynthetic pigments tend to absorb light most readily at the blue or shorter wavelength end of the spectrum. Is this just coincidence, or is there a good reason for it?

There are two models of light. One is the **wave model**, which we use to look at the light absorbed by photosynthetic pigments. Light of different wavelengths is shone into solutions of the photosynthetic pigments and the amount of absorption measured.

The other model of light is **particulate**. In this model light behaves as a series of particles called **photons**. Each photon of light contains a fixed amount of energy called a **quantum**. The size of the quantum varies with the wavelength of the light – the shorter the wavelength, the larger the quantum. This is the model of light we use when we are explaining the events in photosynthesis.

By absorbing strongly in the blue end of the spectrum, plants are using photons of light with larger quanta and are therefore obtaining more energy.

Evidence for photosynthetic pigments

Plants look green. We can extract the pigments from a plant by grinding leaves with acetone and filtering. The resulting filtrate looks green. So how do we know that there are five different pigments? The answer is paper chromatography. With a suitable solvent the pigments travel up the paper at different speeds and are readily separated.

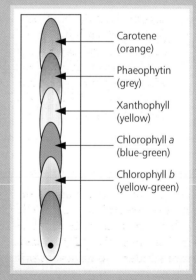

- Carotene (orange)
- Phaeophytin (grey)
- Xanthophyll (yellow)
- Chlorophyll *a* (blue-green)
- Chlorophyll *b* (yellow-green)

Figure 3.2.8 Chromatograph showing the five photosynthetic pigments.

The biochemistry of photosynthesis

The equation for photosynthesis shown earlier gives the impression that photosynthesis is a simple, one-step process by which carbon dioxide and water are converted into simple sugars and oxygen. In fact, photosynthesis is a complex series of reactions making up a biochemical pathway fundamental to the existence of all life on Earth.

As we have seen, photosynthesis is a two-stage process. The light-dependent reactions produce materials which are then used in the light-independent stages. The whole process takes place all the time during the hours of daylight, but only the light-independent reactions can occur in the dark. The light-independent reactions of photosynthesis are sometimes referred to as the **dark reactions**. This phrase can be misleading, implying that these reactions take place only in the dark, whereas in fact they occur continuously. We shall begin by looking at the events of the light-dependent stage of photosynthesis, and then see how the products of these reactions are used in the light-independent stage.

Evidence for two stages of photosynthesis

There are several strands of evidence for the two stages of photosynthesis.

(1) A chemical reaction or series of reactions which are dependent on light should be completely independent of the temperature of the surroundings. However, as figure 3.2.9 shows, the rate of photosynthesis is not independent of temperature. Temperature has a very distinct effect on the rate of photosynthesis, particularly at higher light intensities.

(2) A plant which is exposed to rapidly alternating periods of dark and light will form more carbohydrate than a plant which is exposed to continuous light. This suggests that the light-dependent reactions result in a product which is then fed into the light-independent stage. Continuous light would cause a build-up of this product which might then inhibit further reactions, whereas a period of darkness would ensure that all the product of the light stage was converted into the end product thus making the system more efficient.

(3) More recent techniques have allowed areas of the chloroplast to be isolated. The reactions occurring on the grana have been shown to depend on the presence of light, but those of the stroma do not.

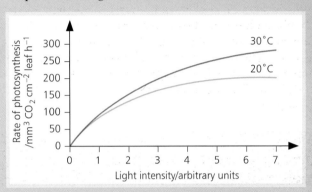

Figure 3.2.9 Graph to show the effect of temperature on the rate of photosynthesis in cucumber plants with increasing light intensity at fixed carbon dioxide concentration. To begin with, the amount of light is not sufficient for photosynthesis to progress rapidly. Photochemical or light-dependent reactions are limiting the rate of the overall process and so temperature has no effect. But once there is plenty of light available, another set of reactions begins to limit the overall rate and these are temperature sensitive.

The light-dependent stage

The light-dependent stage of photosynthesis has two main functions. Water molecules are split in a photochemical reaction. This provides hydrogen ions which can then be used to reduce fixed carbon dioxide and so produce carbohydrates. Also ATP is made, which supplies the energy for the synthesis of carbohydrates. How does it work?

An understanding of the light stage of photosynthesis depends on the following idea. When a photon of light hits a chlorophyll molecule, the quantum of energy is transferred to the electrons of that molecule. The electrons are **excited** – they are raised to higher energy levels. One may be raised to a sufficiently high energy level to leave the chlorophyll completely. If this happens the excited electron will be picked up by a carrier molecule, and this can result in the synthesis of ATP by one of two processes – **cyclic** or **non-cyclic photophosphorylation**.

Cyclic photophosphorylation

The light-excited electron may be passed along an electron transfer chain (see section 3.1), with each member of the chain at a lower energy level, until it is returned to the chlorophyll molecule that it left. As the electron moves along the chain, down the energy levels, ATP is produced by the phosphorylation of ADP. The electron leaves the chlorophyll and returns to it, so may then be excited in exactly the same way again. This is known as **cyclic photophosphorylation** (the phosphorylation of ADP in a cyclical process which depends on light). The process is illustrated in figure 3.2.10.

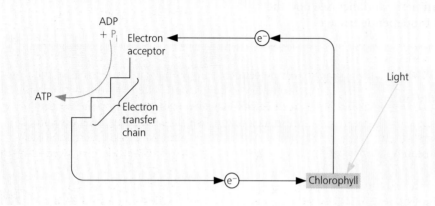

Figure 3.2.10 Cyclic photophosphorylation – the electron passes down the electron transfer chain back to the chlorophyll molecule.

Non-cyclic photophosphorylation

The excited electron may instead be used to provide the reducing power needed in the second, light-independent stage of the photosynthetic process. Water dissociates spontaneously into hydrogen (H^+) ions and hydroxide (OH^-) ions. As a result there are always plenty of these ions present in the cell, including in the interior of the chloroplasts. Interactions between these ions and chlorophyll molecules bring about the process of **non-cyclic photophosphorylation**, described below and illustrated in figure 3.2.11.

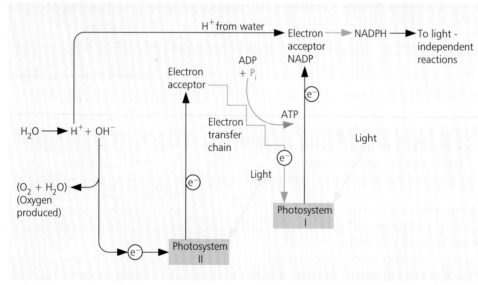

Figure 3.2.11 Non-cyclic photophosphorylation. NADPH and ATP are produced, which power the light-independent reactions. The biochemistry of the two photosystems was worked out by R.Hill and R.Bendall at Cambridge and is often referred to as the Z scheme because of its shape.

There are two distinct complexes or forms of chlorophyll known as **photosystem I** and **photosystem II**. An excited electron from photosystem II passes to an electron acceptor and down an electron transfer chain to photosystem I, which is at a lower energy level than photosystem II. This loss of energy allows the synthesis of a molecule of ATP. Light energy can then excite an electron from photosystem I, and this excited electron passes to another electron acceptor – **nicotinamide adenine dinucleotide phosphate** (**NADP**).

NADP also takes up a hydrogen ion from water and is thus reduced, forming NADPH. The NADPH is a source of reducing power for the light-independent reactions.

So photosystem I receives electrons via the electron transfer chain from photosystem II. This leaves photosystem II electron deficient. The electron from photosystem II is replaced by an electron from a hydroxide ion:

$$4OH^- - 4e^- \rightarrow O_2 + 2H_2O$$

The hydroxide ions are 'left behind' from the hydrogen ions taken up in the reduction of NADP to NADPH. The removal of the electrons from hydroxide ions by the photosystem II results in the by-product oxygen.

Thus the reactions of the light-dependent stage of photosynthesis provide a source of reducing power (NADPH) and the universal energy-supplying molecule ATP, with oxygen gas given off as a waste product. To find out how the NADPH and ATP are used to make carbohydrates we must move on and consider the reactions of the light-independent stage.

The light-independent stage

The light-independent reactions are known as the **Calvin cycle**. This is a cyclic reaction consisting of a series of small steps resulting in the reduction of carbon dioxide to bring about the synthesis of carbohydrates. NADPH and ATP from the light-dependent reactions provide the reducing power and the energy needed for the various steps. The stages of the cycle are controlled by enzymes and are independent of light. Figure 3.2.12 shows the reactions of the Calvin cycle.

Carbon dioxide from the air combines with ribulose bisphosphate (RuBP), a 5-carbon compound which **fixes** the carbon dioxide by accepting it and making it part of the photosynthetic reactions. The enzyme ribulose bisphosphate carboxylase is necessary for this step. The result is a theoretical highly unstable 6-carbon compound which immediately splits to give two molecules of glycerate 3-phosphate (GP), a 3-carbon compound. This is reduced to give a 3-carbon sugar, glyceraldehyde 3-phosphate (GALP). The hydrogen for the reduction comes from NADPH and the energy required from ATP, both produced in the light-dependent stage. Some of the 3-carbon sugar is synthesised into the 6-carbon sugar glucose, which is supplied to the cells or

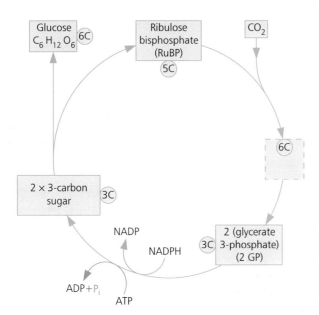

Compensation point

In the dark, a plant takes in oxygen and releases carbon dioxide due to respiration. Under dark conditions only the light-independent reactions of photosynthesis can occur. As the light intensity increases, so the amount of oxygen taken in and carbon dioxide given out by the plant becomes less. With the increase in light the rate of photosynthesis increases, thus more oxygen is produced as a waste product of photosynthesis which can be used for respiration. The carbon dioxide produced in cellular respiration is used up in photosynthesis.

As the light intensity continues to increase, a point is reached at which there is no net exchange of gases. All the oxygen produced by photosynthesis is used up in respiration, and all the carbon dioxide produced in respiration is used for photosynthesis. This is known as the **compensation point**.

With any further increase in light intensity, oxygen is produced by the plant and carbon dioxide taken in. More oxygen is produced by photosynthesis than can be used up in respiration, and insufficient carbon dioxide is produced in respiration to supply the rapid photosynthesis taking place.

Figure 3.2.12 The Calvin cycle – here the products of the light-dependent stage are used in a continuous cycle, the end result being new carbohydrates.

converted to starch for storage. However, much of it is passed through a series of steps to replace the ribulose bisphosphate, without which further carbon dioxide cannot enter the cycle.

The products of photosynthesis, although initially carbohydrates, are rapidly fed into other biochemical pathways to produce amino acids and lipids for the requirements of the cells of the plant.

Melvin Calvin and the Calvin cycle

Melvin Calvin worked at the University of California. He came up with a novel, simple method of investigating the reactions which occur in photosynthesis. He produced a thin, transparent vessel known as a 'lollipop' because of its shape. Into this was placed a suspension of photosynthetic protoctists called *Chlorella* which were supplied with radioactively labelled carbon dioxide containing carbon-14. Light was shone through the suspension of organisms and they were allowed to photosynthesise.

The experiment was repeated time after time, with the *Chlorella* being killed at intervals ranging from a few seconds to a few minutes after the start of photosynthesis. They were killed in boiling ethanol, which stopped all enzyme-controlled reactions immediately. The radioactive compounds formed were then extracted, separated by paper chromatography and identified. In this way the biochemical pathway which we now call the Calvin cycle was built up.

Summary of photosynthesis

Figure 3.2.13 shows how the light-dependent stages of cyclic and non-cyclic photophosphorylation and the light-independent Calvin cycle interact.

Figure 3.2.13 The process of photosynthesis, which occurs continuously in plants that are exposed to light.

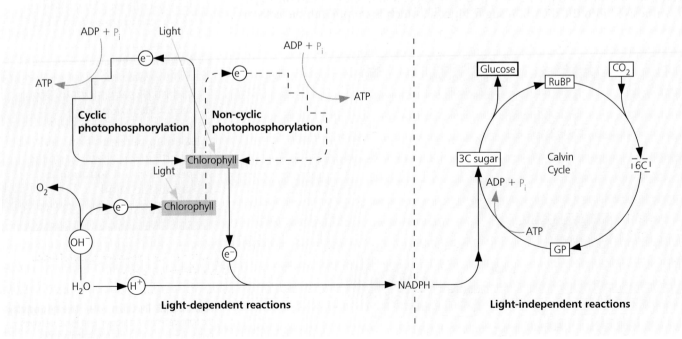

C₃ and C₄ plants

The Calvin cycle is the pathway by which carbohydrates are made in all plants. But not all plants fix carbon dioxide directly into the Calvin cycle using ribulose bisphosphate. The ones that do – and they are the majority of the plant kingdom – are known as **C₃ plants** because the product of the carbon fixation is the three-carbon (C_3) compound glycerate 3-phosphate.

We already know that in order to obtain carbon dioxide for photosynthesis, plants must open their stomata. This in turn increases their water loss. In hot dry conditions C_3 plants are at extreme risk from desiccation with open stomata and so the stomata are closed. This prevents gaseous exchange taking place, and so levels of oxygen build up and carbon dioxide is depleted. As a result of the raised oxygen levels, the enzyme ribulose bisphosphate carboxylase joins oxygen to ribulose bisphosphate instead of to carbon dioxide as the two compete for the active site. Phosphoglycerate is metabolised and carbon dioxide is lost. This wasteful process, whereby no carbohydrate is formed and energy is used, is known as **photorespiration**.

Some plants in these areas, for example sugar cane and maize (sweetcorn), have overcome the problems of photorespiration by evolving a different pathway for fixing carbon dioxide, shown in figure 3.2.14. The ribulose bisphosphate carboxylase is concentrated deep in bundle sheath cells, insulated from fluctuations in oxygen levels, and the fixed carbon dioxide is transported to the bundle sheaths. The product of the carbon fixation is a four-carbon (C_4) compound, oxaloacetic acid, and so these plants are known as **C₄ plants**.

The carbon dioxide acceptor in C_4 plants is phosphoenolpyruvate (PEP) and the reaction is catalysed by the enzyme PEP carboxylase. The importance of this is that the carbon dioxide is fixed extremely rapidly, even at very low concentrations. As a result, sufficient carbon dioxide can be fixed to supply the plant for a day by having the stomata open for a very short time. The oxaloacetate is converted into malate, and this donates carbon dioxide to ribulose bisphosphate in the Calvin cycle. The result of the removal of carbon dioxide from malate is pyruvate, which is recycled into PEP using energy from ATP. The pathway was worked out by Hal Hatch and Roger Slack and is known as the **Hatch-Slack pathway**. In C_4 plants, carbohydrate is synthesised in the Calvin cycle as usual.

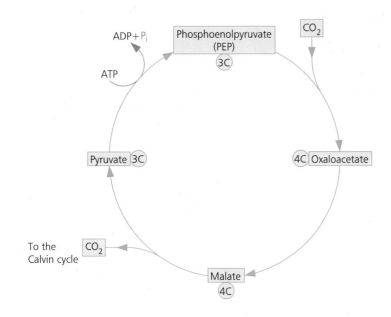

Figure 3.2.14 The Hatch-Slack pathway of carbon dioxide fixation in C_4 plants.

The site of photosynthesis

Any part of a plant that is green contains chlorophyll and so is capable, at least in theory, of carrying out photosynthesis. In practice, most photosynthesis takes place in the leaves. As we have seen earlier, the leaves are the organs of the plant which are specially adapted for photosynthesis. Carbon dioxide and water are readily available to the cells. The palisade mesophyll cells in particular contain a vast number of chloroplasts which can be moved around the cells depending on the light intensity, enabling the plant to trap the maximum amount of solar energy. Further chloroplasts in the spongy mesophyll layer enable extra photosynthesis to take place.

The chloroplasts are the site of photosynthesis. Chloroplasts are large organelles containing the chlorophyll and other pigment molecules and the enzymes associated with photosynthesis. Their internal structure, shown in figure 3.2.15, consists of **thylakoids**, discs made up of pairs of membranes with a small gap between. Stacks of thylakoids make up the grana, and elongated thylakoids the intergrana. Arranged on these membranes are the molecules of chlorophyll, held in the best possible position for trapping light energy. Electron micrographs have shown that the membranes of the grana are covered with particles which seem to be involved in ATP synthesis. Isolated fragments of the granal membranes will split water and release oxygen. The picture which results from all these threads of evidence is that the grana are the site of both the chlorophyll and the enzymes involved in the light-dependent stage of photosynthesis. The enzymes associated with the Calvin cycle are found in the stroma of the chloroplasts.

Grana – stacks of membranes or thylakoids. The chlorophyll molecules and the enzymes of the light-dependent reactions are sited here. On average a chloroplast contains about 60 grana, and each granum is made up of about 50 thylakoids, so the resultant surface area available for the light-dependent reactions of photosynthesis is substantial.

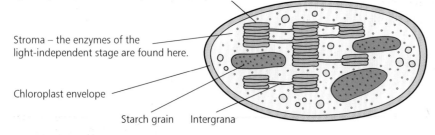

Stroma – the enzymes of the light-independent stage are found here.

Chloroplast envelope

Starch grain   Intergrana

Figure 3.2.15 A chloroplast – site of photosynthesis.

Understanding limiting factors in photosynthesis

Light

With an understanding of the process of photosynthesis, it is easy to see how certain factors might affect the ability of a plant to photosynthesise. In a biochemical process which depends on or is affected by a number of factors, it is a matter of common sense that the process will be limited by the factor which is nearest to its minimum value. For example, the amount of light available affects the amount of chlorophyll which has excited electrons and therefore the amount of NADPH and ADP produced in the light-dependent stage. If there is a low level of light then insufficient NADPH and ATP will be produced to allow the reactions of the light-independent stage to progress at their maximum rate. In this situation light is said to be the **limiting factor** for the process.

Carbon dioxide

Carbon dioxide levels are very important in photosynthesis – insufficient carbon dioxide available for fixing in the Calvin cycle means that the reactions cannot proceed at the maximum rate. When this is the case, carbon dioxide is the limiting factor. In the natural situation of plants it is most often carbon dioxide which is the limiting factor. Changes in the level of carbon dioxide have a clear effect on the rate of photosynthesis, as figure 3.2.16 shows. Commercial growers of some fruits and vegetables make use of this effect to increase their production – tomatoes, for example, may be grown in greenhouses with a carbon dioxide-enriched atmosphere.

Temperature

The other main factor which limits the rate of photosynthesis is temperature. All the Calvin cycle reactions and many of the light-dependent reactions of photosynthesis are controlled by enzymes and are therefore sensitive to temperature. This means that even when the light and carbon dioxide levels are suitable for a very high rate of photosynthesis, unless the temperature is also satisfactory the plant will be unable to take advantage of the conditions.

The rate of photosynthesis in a wild plant is often determined by a combination of factors, some or all of them limiting the process to an extent.

Limiting factors in action

Photosynthesis and its limiting factors are relatively easy to investigate in the laboratory – but what about the real world? The way in which plants grow, and the ecosystems which develop, are basically governed by competition between plants for those factors which can limit photosynthesis and growth.

Carbon dioxide levels do not generally vary very much, but plants compete for situations with suitable conditions of light and warmth, as well as for soil nutrients which enable the carbohydrate produced by photosynthesis to be converted to proteins and fats. Growth in height, spreading of leaves into a mosaic pattern, climbing and developing large leaves are all ways in which plants endeavour to obtain as much light as possible so that photosynthesis is not limited. Methods of seed dispersal have also evolved to reduce competition as much as possible by ensuring that seedlings do not develop in the shade of their parents. Figure 3.2.17 shows the effect of light as a limiting factor in a laboratory investigation – limiting factors also play their part in the real world outside.

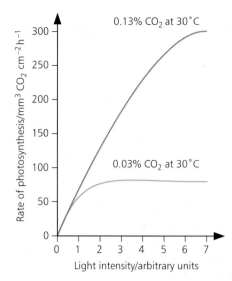

Figure 3.2.16 The effect of carbon dioxide as a limiting factor in photosynthesis.

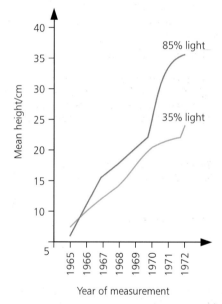

Figure 3.2.17 Growth of oak tree seedlings grown in 85% light and 35% light. The effect of growing in an environment where light is a continually limiting factor can be seen clearly.

SUMMARY

- **Photosynthesis** is the process by which **phototrophs** convert carbon dioxide and water into simple carbohydrates and oxygen in the presence of chlorophyll, using sunlight energy.
- The effects of various factors on the rate of photosynthesis can be followed by collecting oxygen gas from an aquatic plant or using iodine solution to detect the presence of starch in a previously destarched plant. Such experiments can help demonstrate that light, carbon dioxide, water and chlorophyll are needed for photosynthesis.
- Photosynthetic pigments include **chlorophyll *a*** (blue-green), **chlorophyll *b*** (yellow-green), **carotene** (orange), **xanthophyll** (yellow) and **phaeophytin** (grey). None of these pigments absorbs light well in the green area of the spectrum, so plants look green.

- Photosynthesis has a **light-dependent stage** which provides ATP and NADPH for the **light-independent stage** which uses carbon dioxide to produce glucose.

- The light-dependent stage involves the excitation by light energy of an electron in chlorophyll, which is picked up by an electron acceptor and passed to the electron transfer chain, and brings about the synthesis of ATP by either **cyclic** or **non-cyclic photophosphorylation**.

- In **cyclic photophosphorylation** the excited electron is passed along the electron transfer chain, moving down the energy levels. This is coupled to the production of ATP. The electron returns to the chlorophyll.

- In **non-cyclic photophosphorylation**, an excited electron from **photosystem II** passes down an electron transfer chain, again coupled to the production of ATP, to **photosystem I**, which is at a lower energy level than photosystem II. An excited electron from photosystem I then teams up with a hydrogen ion from the splitting of a water molecule to reduce NADP to NADPH. The hydroxide ion remaining from the splitting of the water molecule provides an electron to photosystem II, and produces oxygen gas as a by-product.

- The ATP and NADPH produced by the light-dependent reactions are used to drive the light-independent reaction of the **Calvin cycle**. Carbon dioxide is fixed by combination with ribulose bisphosphate to form an unstable 6-carbon intermediate which splits to form two molecules of **glycerate 3-phosphate** (**GP**). These are reduced to **glyceraldehyde 3-phosphate** (**GALP**) using NADPH and ATP. The GALP molecules are then either used to form glucose, or allow the cycle to continue by reforming ribulose bisphosphate.

- C_3 **plants** fix carbon dioxide to form the 3-carbon molecule GP. C_4 **plants** in hot dry areas have a more efficient method of fixing carbon dioxide prior to the Calvin cycle which involves stomata being open for a shorter time. In the **Hatch-Slack pathway** carbon dioxide is accepted by the 4-carbon compound **phosphoenolpyruvate**, which is converted to **oxaloacetate** and then **malate**. Malate supplies carbon dioxide to the Calvin cycle and is converted to **pyruvate**, which can be used to regenerate phosphoenolpyruvate using ATP.

- The site of photosynthesis in plants is the chloroplasts. Stacks of membranes called **thylakoids** make up the grana, and these membranes hold the chlorophyll molecules. The light-dependent reactions take place here, while the light-independent reactions take place in the **stroma**.

- **Limiting factors** for photosynthesis include light levels, carbon dioxide levels and temperature. Plants have evolved to compete for these limiting factors.

QUESTIONS

1 Photosynthesis involves two sets of reactions – those which are light-dependent and those which are independent of light.
  a Where do the two stages of photosynthesis take place?
  b Describe the light-dependent events, explaining clearly the difference between cyclic and non-cyclic photophosphorylation.

2 Describe the structure of chlorophyll and relate this to the role of the molecule in the process of photosynthesis.

3 What is meant by the term 'limiting factors' in photosynthesis? Give a brief explanation of how limiting factors might be investigated experimentally. Summarise the effects of limiting factors on the growth of plants in their natural habitats.

DEADLY DISTORTION

In developing countries across the world, people are dying because they don't have enough to eat. In the developed world, self-imposed dietary deprivation is commonplace as people try to lose weight. Such deprivation can lead to severe effects in people suffering from food-related disorders such as **anorexia nervosa** and **bulimia**. In these conditions the normal appetite and feeding controls are disrupted, the causes of which involve a strong psychological component.

Anorexia

Anorexia sufferers severely restrict their food intake. They reduce the number of calories taken in to an absolute minimum, losing weight rapidly. They become secretive and manipulative, lying about when and where they have eaten in order to avoid having meals, secreting food off their plates to throw away later and vomiting food up again. They have a distorted body image – even if they are skeletally thin, anorexics still perceive themselves as overweight. Many anorexics are girls and young women, although increasing numbers of boys are presenting with the disease.

Treatment of anorexia involves hospitalisation to try and restore a more normal body weight, and counselling and support to overcome the psychological problems that led to the anorexia in the first place. Sadly anorexia remains potentially fatal – a number of people die from the disease every year in the UK and in many other countries. Anorexia may begin as normal dieting in response to social and peer group pressures to be 'slim', but it is thought to be psychologically much more deep rooted. For many sufferers anorexia seems to be a way of exerting some control over their lives – perhaps of rebelling against over-dominant parents, or of denying the body changes that come with puberty, or a cry for help in coping with all the pressures placed on young people in their adolescent and early adult years.

Figure 1 Fairground mirrors can be fun but the distorted perception of anorexics that their wasted bodies appear fat is no joke – the disease can kill.

Bulimia

Bulimia is another similar disease, although it does not always lead to life-threatening weight loss. Bulimics 'comfort' themselves by bingeing, gorging on large amounts of food, often sweet food like chocolate and cakes or junk food like burgers and chips. Following the binge the bulimic will make themself vomit violently to get rid of all the excess food. For some this binge–vomit cycle occurs only rarely when they are under pressure; for others it can occur several times a day. This behaviour puts severe stresses on the physiology of the body. Like anorexia, bulimia is associated with low self-esteem and a need for psychological help. One of the most famous sufferers from bulimia was Diana, Princess of Wales.

Figure 2 Anorexics starve the body over a long period of time, resulting in devastating weight loss.

Heterotrophic nutrition

Heterotrophs

As we saw in section 3.1, all living organisms which cannot provide their own energy supply by either photosynthesis or chemosynthesis are known as **heterotrophs**. 'Heterotrophic' means 'feeding on others'. The carbohydrates, proteins and fats originally made by autotrophs are broken down and reassembled by heterotrophs in a wide variety of ways.

The most obvious heterotrophic organisms are animals, but many bacteria, some protoctists (unicells), a few flowering plants and all fungi also use this method of nutrition. In this section we shall consider mainly mammals, particularly humans, although other groups with interesting specialisations will be mentioned as appropriate.

Types of heterotrophic nutrition

There are three main types of heterotrophic nutrition:

1 **Holozoic nutrition** means feeding on solid organic material from the bodies – living or dead – of other organisms, which may be either plant or animal. This method of nutrition is usually seen in animals, and carnivorous plants and some protoctists also feed in this way.

2 **Parasitic nutrition** is found in most groups of organisms – animals, plants, protoctists, fungi and bacteria. A **parasite** feeds on organic material, often but not always soluble, from the body of another living organism known as the **host**.

3 **Saprotrophic nutrition** means feeding on soluble organic material from dead animals or plants. It occurs mainly in protoctists, bacteria and fungi, although there are a few saprotrophic animals. Saprotrophic nutrition is of great importance because it plays a significant role in decomposing biological material and returning nutrients to the soil and the atmosphere.

So what does heterotrophic nutrition involve? A heterotrophic organism has to be able to obtain, digest and absorb food.

Obtaining food

Adaptations designed to make obtaining food easier or more effective appear to have been the driving force behind much evolutionary development.

Those heterotrophs which rely on eating plants, the **herbivores**, do not have to catch their food. However, because of the cellulose walls of plant cells, digesting the food efficiently is not a straightforward process. The enzymes needed to digest cellulose are present in very few organisms. Also, plants are constantly evolving defences against being eaten, via either digestibility reducers (celluloses, tannins, silicates) or specific toxins. Herbivorous mammals can *only* digest plant material with the help of microbes. Herbivores frequently need to eat very large quantities of plant material to get enough energy to survive. As a result much of their time is taken up with eating, leaving them open to attack as they graze. They also have less time for other activities such as sleeping and searching for a mate. Great demands are put on the teeth of herbivores too, with special adaptations needed to cope with the enormous amounts of chewing, as figure 3.3.2 illustrates.

Figure 3.3.1 There are many ways in which heterotrophs can obtain their nutrition – herbivores eat plants, carnivores eat other animals and omnivores such as ourselves eat either. Parasites get their nutrition from a living host whilst saprotrophs live on dead and decaying tissues. Whatever their food source, all heterotrophs ultimately depend on energy from the Sun via autotrophs.

Heterotrophs which kill and eat other animals, the **carnivores**, have food that is easier to digest as it contains more accessible protein, but it is frequently much harder to obtain. Carnivores have a variety of adaptations which allow them to successfully capture their prey. These range from the burst of speed of a hunting cheetah to the paralysing poison of a spider, from the worm-like snapping turtles' tongue to the communication system between the members of a wolf pack, allowing them to hunt as a team. They include sonar systems in bats and whales along with stings and many kinds of complex traps. The teeth of carnivorous mammals are specialised for killing prey and for tearing flesh, and the jaws are frequently very strong, as figure 3.3.3 shows.

Parasites, heterotrophs which feed off a living host, need adaptations which will enable them to survive either within or on their host without being attacked or rejected. Saprotrophs which gain their food from decaying animal or plant material have a food supply that is finite, and they need to be able to find more decaying material when one rotting organism has been used up.

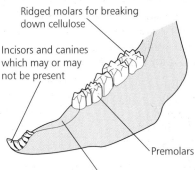

Ridged molars for breaking down cellulose

Incisors and canines which may or may not be present

Premolars

Diastema - gap to manipulate the food onto the molars and keep chewed and unchewed material separate

Figure 3.3.2 Many herbivores live in groups or herds to minimise the risk of attack whilst feeding and also to make finding a mate a less time-consuming activity. They have a variety of front teeth which may be adapted to nibbling, gnawing, tearing or biting. The back teeth or molars almost always show ridges of alternating dentine and enamel which help to break open the cellulose cell walls of plants. Another common adaptation of herbivores is to have many sets of teeth or continuous growth of the teeth to cope with the almost continuous wear.

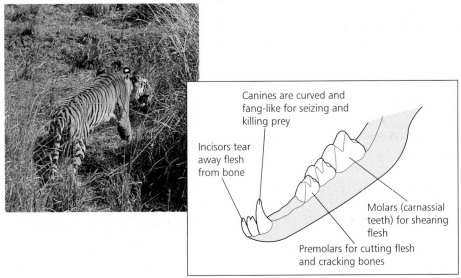

Canines are curved and fang-like for seizing and killing prey

Incisors tear away flesh from bone

Molars (carnassial teeth) for shearing flesh

Premolars for cutting flesh and cracking bones

Figure 3.3.3 Carnivores sometimes live and hunt in groups, but are more likely than herbivores to lead quite solitary lives. They eat relatively infrequently, often gorging at a meal and then sleeping for long periods of time to digest it. They have more 'spare time' to search for a mate. Their teeth are specialised for holding and killing animals and removing flesh from the bone.

Digestion of food

All heterotrophs have to digest food to a greater or lesser extent, but particularly those which, like the mammals, feed holozoically. The food is usually taken into the body in relatively large pieces. The molecules present in these food pieces, be they plant or animal, are large, complex and frequently insoluble. Thus the majority of heterotrophs must break down these large complex molecules into simple, soluble ones that can later be absorbed. We call this process of breaking down large molecules **digestion**. The food of parasites and saprotrophs is often partially digested, but some form of digestion is frequently still needed.

Digestion is catalysed by the digestive enzymes. Digestion may be intracellular, occurring within the cell, as in the protoctists (see figure 3.3.4) and other small organisms which survive by heterotrophic nutrition. However, in the larger heterotrophic organisms, including the mammals, digestion is mainly extracellular, with the digestive enzymes working in a specialised environment known as the **alimentary canal** or **gut**.

How do heterotrophs take in food?

Most heterotrophic organisms – herbivores, carnivores, parasites and saprotrophs – deal with their food in similar ways once it is inside the system. However, there are three main forms in which the food may be taken into the body. These are as big chunks, small chunks and liquids.

Mammals and most larger animals take in their food in relatively large chunks – they use teeth, mandibles, tentacles or other specialised organs to bite or tear portions off their food which then enter the gut. This is known as **macrophagous feeding**.

Other heterotrophs take in their food in the form of much smaller particles relative to their body sizes. Examples include filter feeders such as many of the shellfish, and protoctists – organisms such as *Amoeba* which use a pseudopodium (see figure 3.3.4) and *Paramecium* which relies on cilia. These are known as **microphagous feeders**.

Some heterotrophic organisms are capable of taking in only liquid food, for example the aphids met in section 2.3. They are known as **fluid feeders**.

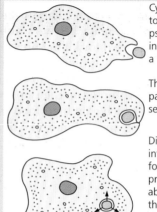

Cytoplasmic streaming leads to the formation of a pseudopodium. If this comes into contact with a food particle a 'food cup' is formed.

The cup flows round the food particle until it forms a complete sealed **food vacuole**.

Digestive enzymes are secreted into the food vacuole and the food particle is digested. The products of digestion are absorbed into the cytoplasm through the membrane of the food vacuole. The whole process takes place intracellularly (within the single cell).

Figure 3.3.4 Intracellular digestion is demonstrated within the cell of a protoctist such as *Amoeba*.

Absorption of food

The products of digestion have to be absorbed into the body of the organism and distributed around its cells before they can be used to provide the energy needed by the cells for contraction, transport and biosynthesis. Thus heterotrophs have many specialised features to enable the products of digestion to be absorbed into the body quickly and effectively.

Heterotrophic nutrition in humans

We shall develop an understanding of heterotrophic nutrition by looking in detail at a fairly representative animal – the human. We can then consider some of the different specialisations found elsewhere in the living world.

People are holozoic, omnivorous, macrophagous feeders – that is to say, we take in large chunks of organic material from plants and other animals which are then broken down into simple soluble molecules to be absorbed and used by our cells. The same is true of all mammals, except that not all are omnivorous – the majority are either carnivores or herbivores.

Holozoic nutrition can be considered as a series of steps. These are:

1 **Ingestion** – the taking in of complex organic food by the organism.

2 **Digestion** – the breakdown of large, complex molecules into simpler, soluble ones by enzyme action.

3 **Absorption** – the uptake of the soluble products of digestion into the main system of the organism, either directly into the cells, or into the bloodstream and then into the cells.

4 **Assimilation** – the ultimate use of the products of digestion, either as an energy source or to be incorporated into new biological material.

5 **Egestion** – the removal from the organism of any undigested food materials.

In the human being, these processes are closely associated with the alimentary canal or gut. The gut is a continuous muscular tube which runs from the mouth to the anus. It is an integral part of the body and yet in a way is not 'inside' the body at all. The cavity of the gut is a contained part of the outside world, although the structures relating to it and supplying it are part of the body proper.

The human digestive system

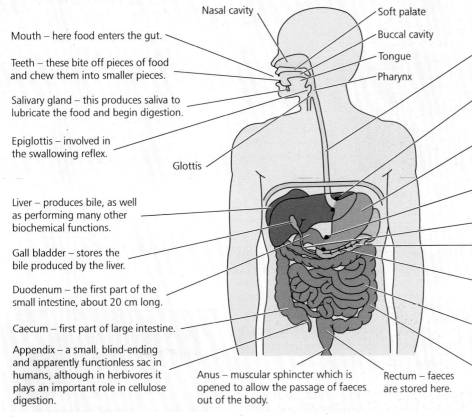

Nasal cavity
Soft palate
Buccal cavity
Tongue
Pharynx
Glottis

Mouth – here food enters the gut.

Teeth – these bite off pieces of food and chew them into smaller pieces.

Salivary gland – this produces saliva to lubricate the food and begin digestion.

Epiglottis – involved in the swallowing reflex.

Liver – produces bile, as well as performing many other biochemical functions.

Gall bladder – stores the bile produced by the liver.

Duodenum – the first part of the small intestine, about 20 cm long.

Caecum – first part of large intestine.

Appendix – a small, blind-ending and apparently functionless sac in humans, although in herbivores it plays an important role in cellulose digestion.

Anus – muscular sphincter which is opened to allow the passage of faeces out of the body.

Rectum – faeces are stored here.

Oesophagus – a tube about 25 cm long, which carries food from the pharynx to the stomach.

Cardiac sphincter – a thickened ring of circular muscle which opens to allow food into the stomach.

Stomach – a muscular bag which churns food up and produces enzymes, hydrochloric acid and mucus.

Pyloric sphincter – a thickened ring of circular muscle which opens to allow food out of the stomach.

Bile duct – carries the bile into the gut.

Pancreas – produces digestive enzymes (and hormones).

Pancreatic duct – carries the digestive enzymes produced by the pancreas into the gut.

Ileum – the main part of the small intestine, about 5 m long and the major site of digestion and absorption in the gut.

Colon – main part of the large intestine in which much reabsorption of water into the blood takes place.

The human digestive system shown in figure 3.3.5 is a long tube with a series of areas and compartments specialised for particular functions. The bulk of the food we eat, whether from a plant or an animal source, consists largely of complex proteins, carbohydrates and fats, along with indigestible material known as fibre or roughage. There are also minute amounts of various minerals and vitamins which are vital to our health but need no processing as they are already in a form which is soluble and can be absorbed into the body. How does the gut bring about the breakdown of the food? If we consider each area of the alimentary canal in turn we can see how it works as a coordinated whole to carry out both physical and chemical digestion.

The mouth or buccal cavity

The process of digestion begins in the mouth. Food is taken in and subjected to both physical and chemical breakdown before it is passed on.

Physical digestion – the teeth

Physical digestion begins as pieces of food are bitten off by the teeth and then chewed. The main reason for chewing is to break down the food into smaller pieces, making it easier for them to be swallowed, and also increasing the surface area available for enzymes to act on.

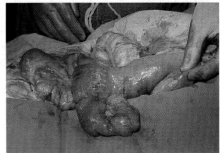

Figure 3.3.5 Up to 9 m of gut can look relatively simple when drawn, but a glance at the real state of affairs seen during abdominal surgery shows the complexity of the gut. Each part of the alimentary canal is basically a muscular tube, adapted to carry out a specific function.

Teeth have evolved to be very strong and are important to mammals in the obtaining and initial digestion of their food. The structure of human teeth is shown in figure 3.3.6. In the wild, it is frequently the loss of effective teeth in older animals which heralds the end of their lives, as they can no longer feed properly. This is not true for humans as we can prepare and cook food to soften it, and can even replace worn out, damaged or decayed teeth with artificial ones.

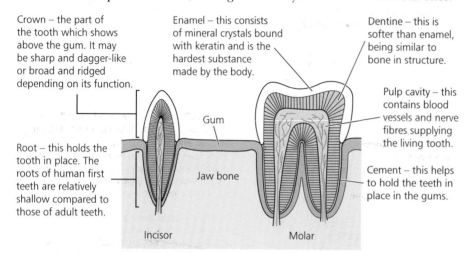

Crown – the part of the tooth which shows above the gum. It may be sharp and dagger-like or broad and ridged depending on its function.

Enamel – this consists of mineral crystals bound with keratin and is the hardest substance made by the body.

Dentine – this is softer than enamel, being similar to bone in structure.

Pulp cavity – this contains blood vessels and nerve fibres supplying the living tooth.

Root – this holds the tooth in place. The roots of human first teeth are relatively shallow compared to those of adult teeth.

Cement – this helps to hold the teeth in place in the gums.

Gum

Jaw bone

Incisor

Molar

Figure 3.3.6 The structure of teeth makes them well suited to their function. Problems arise when the protective and relatively impenetrable layer of enamel on the surface of the tooth is damaged. This is commonly due to a build-up of **plaque** – sugary food residues along with the bacteria which feed on them. The bacterial waste products are acidic and eat into the enamel and destroy it, leaving an entry hole for the bacteria to attack the inside structure of the tooth.

Saliva

As food is chewed in the mouth, it is coated with **saliva** secreted by the **salivary glands**. Saliva production and secretion increases in response to the taste, smell or thought of food as a result of nervous stimulation by the parasympathetic nervous system (see section 4.2). Saliva performs a variety of functions, although digestion can occur without it.

Saliva moistens and lubricates the food, making swallowing easier. Eating several dry crackers in succession will help you to see these effects of saliva. Saliva also dissolves some of the food, allowing it to be tasted. This in turn stimulates enzyme production in other parts of the gut. The food begins to be diluted, reducing the osmotic disruption which could result from the ingestion of, for example, large amounts of sweet or salty food.

Saliva is often very slightly alkaline. This makes it effective in helping to prevent dental caries – it neutralises the effects of acidic foods or acids produced by mouth bacteria. Saliva also contains an enzyme, **salivary amylase**. This begins the process of carbohydrate digestion by hydrolysing the polysaccharide starch into disaccharide units of maltose. Once the food has been chewed and coated in saliva it is swallowed (see figure 3.3.7) and so moved into the next part of the gut, the oesophagus.

The oesophagus

The oesophagus is a tube about 25 cm long which links the buccal cavity with the stomach. The inner lining is folded, which allows it to stretch and accommodate the bolus of food as it is swallowed. Waves of muscular activity known as **peristalsis** move the food down the oesophagus. This peristaltic activity occurs throughout the gut. We are usually unaware of this gut movement apart from during vomiting, when the squeezing actions of the gut muscles become obvious. The structure of the oesophagus, as seen in figure 3.3.8, exemplifies the basic structure of the entire gut.

Pavlov's dogs and the control of digestive juices

In the late nineteenth and early twentieth centuries Ivan Pavlov performed a series of classic experiments on the control of the secretion of digestive juices. He was awarded a Nobel prize for his work. He implanted tubes in dogs in order to allow the secretions of various regions of the digestive tract to be collected and measured. Pavlov demonstrated clearly the important role of the nervous system, including the sight and smell of food, in the stimulation of the secretions of the gut, particularly the saliva and the gastric juices.

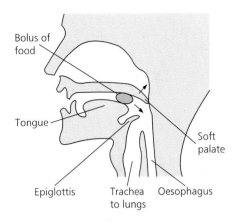

Bolus of food

Tongue

Epiglottis   Trachea   Oesophagus
             to lungs

Soft palate

At the back of the mouth food is shaped into a bolus or ball by the tongue. The pressure of this against the soft palate triggers the swallowing reflex. The upward movement of the soft palate closes off the nasal cavity so that food does not return down the nose.

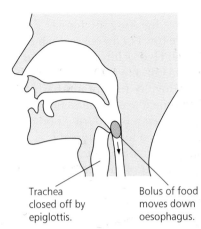

Trachea closed off by epiglottis.

Bolus of food moves down oesophagus.

The opening to the lungs is closed off by the epiglottis, so the food has a clear route down into the oesophagus. For the brief moment of the reflex breathing is inhibited, so that in theory at least it is impossible to swallow and breathe at the same time.

Figure 3.3.7 It is important that food does not enter the respiratory system during swallowing, as the risk of blocked airways or infection would be high. The swallowing reflex ensures the smooth passage of the food to the gut, and the violent choking response ensures that any food entering the trachea is returned to its rightful route.

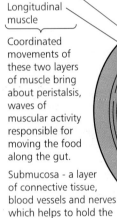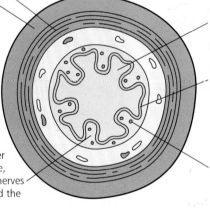

Circular muscle
Longitudinal muscle

Coordinated movements of these two layers of muscle bring about peristalsis, waves of muscular activity responsible for moving the food along the gut.

Submucosa - a layer of connective tissue, blood vessels and nerves which helps to hold the structure together.

Lumen - the space through which the food travels

Mucosa made up of **stratified squamous epithelium**. These simple epithelial cells are regularly replaced. They are interspersed with mucus-producing cells.

Mucus glands - The function of the mucus is to lubricate the food as it moves through the oesophagus and protect the oesophageal lining from damage.

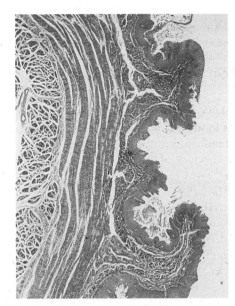

Figure 3.3.8 The structure of the oesophagus is typical of that of the digestive system, with specific modifications in different regions.

The stomach

At the end of the oesophagus, the entrance to the stomach is marked by a greatly thickened ring of circular muscle known as the **cardiac sphincter**. Most of the time this sphincter is closed, keeping the food in the stomach. It is relaxed and opened only to allow food into the stomach from the oesophagus, and during vomiting.

The stomach is a muscular bag, which can hold about 5 dm³ of food when fully distended. It is rarely stretched to this limit – imagine the discomfort of the equivalent of about eight pints of milk in your stomach at any one time! Both physical and chemical digestion is brought about by the stomach. Physical digestion is caused by the continual churning movements of the muscular walls which mix the food and gastric juice thoroughly and also help reduce the food to a uniform creamy paste known as **chyme**. Chemical digestion is brought about by the enzymes and acid secreted by the cells of the gastric glands, shown in figure 3.3.9.

The liquid in the stomach is a powerful protein-digesting mixture. **Pepsinogen** is an **enzyme precursor** – an inactive form of an enzyme which must be activated before it can catalyse a reaction. Hydrochloric acid brings about the conversion of pepsinogen to **pepsin**, an enzyme which catalyses the hydrolysis of proteins into polypeptides. It also provides the optimum pH (around pH2) for the enzyme pepsin to work. The acidic environment also helps destroy any microorganisms which might be taken in with the food.

Both acid and pepsinogen are released largely when food enters the stomach. This is partly as a result of the nervous stimulation which results from the sight, smell and taste of food, and partly as a result of the physical distending of the stomach. The presence of food in the stomach also causes the release of the hormone **gastrin**. This is a polypeptide molecule released by the lining of the pyloric (lower) region of the stomach into the blood. It travels back to the stomach in the blood and stimulates the production of acidic gastric juice for about 4 hours.

Rennin is of much less general importance, but in young mammals it is needed to coagulate the soluble protein in milk which is known as casein. This coagulation curdles the milk, forming solid curds and liquid whey. The curds stay in the stomach much longer than the liquid milk, making digestion more effective.

Food stays in the stomach on average for about 4 hours, although this depends on the type of food taken in. Liquid is retained for a much shorter time, while a large, protein-rich meal might be held for longer. Once the stomach has turned all the food to chyme, it releases the paste a little at a time into the duodenum by the opening and closing of the **pyloric sphincter**.

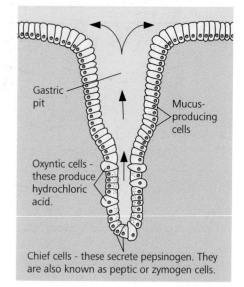

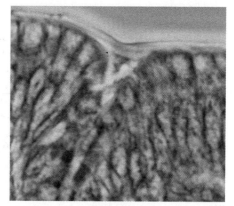

Figure 3.3.9 The digestive juices of the stomach are produced by the cells of the gastric glands. The main secretions are pepsinogen and hydrochloric acid, whilst in babies rennin is also formed.

Protecting the gut from autodigestion

A brief consideration of the human gut shows that it is a potentially dangerous system, capable of causing self-destruction by autodigestion. Protein- and lipid-digesting enzymes along with areas of high hydrochloric acid concentration are far from ideal conditions for cells. Autodigestion is prevented by several strategies.

(1) The lining of the gut is often thicker than that of other systems and is constantly and rapidly replaced.

(2) Large quantities of mucus are produced by many areas of the gut. This has a double function. Physical damage to the cells of the gut by the passage of food is greatly reduced as the mucus acts as a lubricant. Chemical damage is reduced as the mucus forms a protective barrier. Mucus can eventually be digested, reabsorbed and used again.

(3) Enzymes are only produced or released once food arrives in a particular area of the gut. This coordination is brought about by nervous control and by the production of hormones by some regions of the gut, for example gastrin in the stomach.

(4) Several of the protein-digesting enzymes which are most likely to inflict damage on the cells of the gut are produced as inactive precursors, for example pepsinogen and trypsinogen, which are then converted into the active, protein-digesting form only when the food is present.

If some of these protective mechanisms go wrong, then autodigestion can occur. Both gastric (stomach) ulcers and duodenal ulcers result from the very acidic stomach contents breaking down the wall of the digestive tract. These complaints cause great pain, and the gut wall can be completely digested so that the contents of the gut are released into the body cavity, with potentially fatal results. The most used pharmaceutical drug worldwide is for the treatment of stomach ulcers.

Villi – found throughout the small intestine, these finger-like extensions are frequently covered with microvilli only clearly visible with the electron microscope.

Capillary plexus
Arteriole

Rich blood supply to villi – arterioles bring the blood and venules carry it away to the hepatic portal vein.

Venule

Circular muscle
Longitudinal muscle

The muscles contract and relax to move the villi within the food, mixing the enzymes and moving the food along.

Lacteal

Longitudinal muscle in the villus – contraction and relaxation moves the villus ensuring that there is a constant contact with food for absorption, particularly in the ileum.

Crypt of Lieberkuhn, found throughout the small intestine – the cells at the base produce many digestive enzymes, particularly in the ileum.

Thin layer of muscle

Brunner's glands, found only in the duodenum – these produce alkaline secretions and mucus.

Lymph vessel into which the lacteals drain

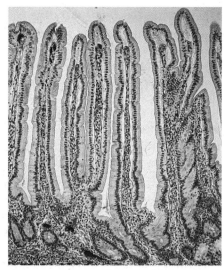

Figure 3.3.10 The duodenum and the ileum are very similar in structure, with differences due to the different emphasis of their functions.

3

The small intestine

The small intestine is a long, coiled tube about 5–6 m long with a rich supply of blood and lymph vessels. It performs two major functions. Firstly it brings about most of the chemical breakdown of large food molecules into simpler and more soluble ones. Much of this function is carried out in the first few centimetres of the small intestine known as the **duodenum**. Secondly, the small intestine brings about the absorption of digested food into the blood supply so that it can be transported to the active cells of the body. This takes place along the length of the **ileum**. The structure of the small intestine is very closely related to its function, as can be seen in figure 3.3.10.

The structure of the small intestine

The lining of the small intestine forms millions of finger-like projections known as **villi**. These increase the surface area available both for enzyme action and, more importantly, for the absorption of digested foodstuffs. The outer layer of cells of the villi are columnar epithelial cells, shown in figure 3.3.11, which have a brush border of slender, closely packed finger-shaped projections or microvilli, about 1700 per cell. It has been estimated that this brush border increases the surface area of the lining of the small intestine 15–40 times. Add to this the 600-fold increase in surface area given by the villi themselves, and the total surface area of the small intestine available for action is in the region of 200 m² – about the area of a tennis court.

The villi are well supplied with both blood and lymph vessels. These ensure that good diffusion gradients are maintained and also carry away the dissolved food molecules. A normal meal consisting of a mixture of protein, carbohydrate and fat is absorbed to a large extent within the first metre or so of the small intestine – the remainder acts as a reserve.

Between the villi are the **crypts of Lieberkuhn**. New columnar epithelial cells are made here, but their most important role is in the production of digestive enzymes. Some of these enzymes such as **amylase**, **maltase** and **lactase** work in association with the membrane of the villus. Others are released into the lumen of the intestine.

In the duodenum, **Brunner's glands** secrete into the crypts and so into the lumen. They produce mucus and an alkaline fluid. These secretions both protect the lining of the duodenum from damage by the acidic chyme which leaves the stomach and also, by neutralising the acid, provide the optimum pH (around 8) for the duodenal enzymes to work in.

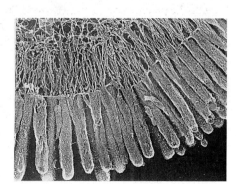

Figure 3.3.11 The brush border of the intestinal columnar epithelial cells increases the surface area available for the absorption of digested food, as well as being the site of much enzyme activity. The mitochondria present in these cells are indicative of the level of activity in the cytoplasm, both in producing enzymes and in active transport.

Digestion in the small intestine

Physical digestion plays a relatively small part in the functioning of the small intestine, though peristalsis moves the food along. Chemical digestion is brought about by a variety of enzymes, some produced by the small intestine, some by the pancreas. Other chemicals are also produced which affect digestion.

Bile from the gall bladder is released into the ileum. This contains sodium hydrogencarbonate which helps to neutralise the stomach acid and maintain the correct pH for the intestinal enzymes to function effectively. It also contains the **bile salts**, sodium taurocholate and sodium glycocholate. These have a physical effect on large fat droplets, emulsifying them into many smaller droplets and so greatly increasing the surface area available for digestion by enzymes. Alkaline juice from the pancreas is also of value in the maintenance of an optimum pH.

The activity of the various components of the intestinal juices is summarised in table 3.3.1.

The table shows the wide variety of chemicals, mainly enzymes, which are produced by the small intestine and the closely associated pancreas and gall bladder. The chemical breakdown of the larger food molecules, particularly the carbohydrates and proteins, often occurs in two stages. One enzyme breaks up the large molecule into smaller pieces (polysaccharides to disaccharides, proteins to polypeptides and peptides). Another enzyme then acts to complete the process (disaccharides to monosaccharides, peptides to amino acids). As a result of the action of the enzymes of the small intestine, a watery fluid known as **chyle** is produced. This contains all the products of digestion which are then absorbed into the blood.

Secretion	Source	Function
Bile – contains no enzymes	Made in liver, stored in gall bladder, released into duodenum	Neutralises gut contents, emulsifies fats
Amylase	Made in pancreas, released into duodenum. Also made in crypts of Lieberkuhn and associated with brush border of villi in ileum	Breaks down *starch* to *maltose*
Trypsin - secreted as trypsinogen	Trypsinogen is made in the pancreas and secreted into the duodenum. Activated by enterokinase	Breaks down *proteins* to *polypeptides*
Lipase	Made in the pancreas and secreted into the duodenum	Breaks down *fats* to *fatty acids* and *glycerol*
Endopeptidase, e.g. chymotrypsin, trypsin	Made in the pancreas and secreted into the duodenum	Break down *proteins* to *polypeptides* and *polypeptides* to short *peptides*
Exopeptidases, e.g. aminopeptidase, carboxypeptidase	Made in the pancreas and secreted into the duodenum	Break down *peptides* to *amino acids*
Nuclease	Made in the pancreas and secreted into the duodenum	Breaks down *nucleic acids* (DNA, RNA) into *nucleotides*
Enterokinase	Secreted by the lining of the small intestine	Converts inactive *trypsinogen* to active *trypsin*
Maltase	Secreted by the lining of the small intestine	Breaks down *maltose* to *glucose*
Sucrase	Secreted by the lining of the small intestine	Breaks down *sucrose* to *glucose* and *fructose*
Lactase	Secreted by the lining of the small intestine	Breaks down *lactose* (milk sugar) to *glucose* and *galactose*
Nucleotidases	Secreted by the lining of the small intestine	Breaks down *nucleotides* to *pentose sugars* + *phosphate* + *organic base*

Table 3.3.1 The main secretions associated with the small intestine

Endopeptidases and exopeptidases

As can be seen in table 3.3.1, the breakdown of proteins is brought about by two different groups of enzymes known as **endopeptidases** and **exopeptidases**. What are they, and what is their purpose?

To put it simply, endopeptidases break bonds within the polypeptide chains producing shorter peptides, whilst exopeptidases act only on the bonds at the very end of the peptide chain, thus releasing individual amino acids. Figure 3.3.12 shows this.

The value to the organism of having these two different types of protein-digesting enzymes is simple. Exopeptidases on their own would take a relatively long time to break down proteins, working on one amino acid at a time from the two ends of the polypeptide chain. Endopeptidases speed up the process enormously, because the result of their action is to provide many short peptide chains with terminal amino and carboxyl ends for exopeptidases to attack, effectively increasing the substrate concentration and so the rate of reaction.

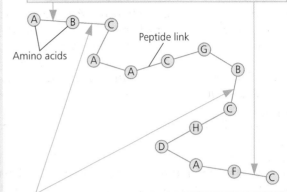

Exopeptidases act only on the terminal peptide links in a peptide chain – for example, aminopeptidase will only hydrolyse the final link at the amino end of the molecule and carboxypeptidase will only hydrolyse the link at the carboxyl end. As a result the amino acids are released from the chains one at a time.

Amino acids

Peptide link

Endopeptidases are often very specific, hydrolysing the peptide links only between particular amino acids. They break these particular bonds wherever they occur in the polypeptide molecule. As a result, endopeptidases such as trypsin produce many short peptide chains.

Figure 3.3.12 The action of endopeptidases and exopeptidases.

Control of secretions in the small intestine

Table 3.3.1 shows the large number of secretions which are produced by the small intestine and its associated organs. For the digestive functions to work properly it is important that the right substances are present only at the appropriate time. How is this control brought about?

As with other areas of the gut, the sight, smell and taste of food cause increases in the secretions of both bile from the liver and pancreatic juices. This is the result of nervous reflexes. In addition, the acidic chyme entering the duodenum from the stomach has a direct effect on the cells lining the small intestine. It stimulates them to produce enzymes, and also to produce hormones. These hormones are carried in the blood and in turn stimulate the liver, gall bladder and pancreas. The main hormones are **secretin** and **cholecystokinin** (also known as cholecystokinin-pancreozymin or CCK-PZ). The action of these hormones is described in figure 3.3.13.

Absorption in the small intestine

One of the major roles of the small intestine is the chemical digestion of food. However, the products of digestion must be taken into the bloodstream for distribution to the cells of the body, and this is the other major role of the small intestine.

We have already discussed the enormous surface area of the small intestine available for the absorption of digested food which results from the villi and the brush border cells. The villi also have an excellent blood supply which ensures a good diffusion gradient. The products of the digestion of carbohydrates and proteins – that is, monosaccharides, disaccharides and

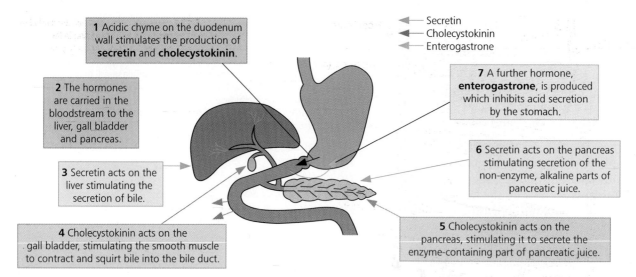

1 Acidic chyme on the duodenum wall stimulates the production of **secretin** and **cholecystokinin**.

2 The hormones are carried in the bloodstream to the liver, gall bladder and pancreas.

3 Secretin acts on the liver stimulating the secretion of bile.

4 Cholecystokinin acts on the gall bladder, stimulating the smooth muscle to contract and squirt bile into the bile duct.

Secretin
Cholecystokinin
Enterogastrone

7 A further hormone, **enterogastrone**, is produced which inhibits acid secretion by the stomach.

6 Secretin acts on the pancreas stimulating secretion of the non-enzyme, alkaline parts of pancreatic juice.

5 Cholecystokinin acts on the pancreas, stimulating it to secrete the enzyme-containing part of pancreatic juice.

Figure 3.3.13 A complex control system by hormones in addition to nervous control means that the digestive functions of the small intestine work only as and when they are needed.

amino acids – pass through the epithelial cells to the blood capillaries of the villi. They are moved mainly by simple diffusion and active transport, although facilitated diffusion may play some part.

The results of fat digestion (fatty acids and glycerol) may also be taken directly into the blood. However, there is an alternative route. Many years ago it was observed that after a fatty meal the fluid in the lymph vessels appeared milky-white. In fact, this is why the tiny lymph vessels of the villi are known as 'lacteals' – the word means 'milky'. The milky appearance is due to tiny lipoprotein droplets appearing in the lymph.

The fatty acids and glycerol, once absorbed, can be recombined in the lining cells of the villi forming minute droplets of fat. These pass into the lacteals and are coated in protein to stop them forming much larger droplets. These lipoproteins are known as **chylomicrons** and they travel in the lymphatic system until they reach the thoracic duct where they are returned to the blood system. They are then converted back into fatty acids and glycerol before being taken up by the cells.

Blood is brought to the small intestine by the **mesenteric artery**, but it is not then returned in the veins directly to the heart in the usual way. The blood which leaves the ileum is rich in digested food products. It is carried in the **hepatic portal vein** to the liver, which is a site of major biochemical activity in the body. Here some of the digested products are stored or converted into other forms, whilst others continue to the heart via the **hepatic vein** to be distributed to the cells. Figure 3.3.14 shows the blood supply to and from the ileum.

The large intestine

By the end of the small intestine, all the digested food products and the minerals and vitamins that are useful to the body should have been removed from the watery contents. The remaining fluid consists of indigestible or undigested food, bacteria, dead cells sloughed off from the digestive tract, mucus, bile and a large amount of water, much of which has been secreted into the gut by the body in the form of digestive juices. The function of the large intestine is to reabsorb as much of this as is useful and to remove the remainder from the body in the process of egestion.

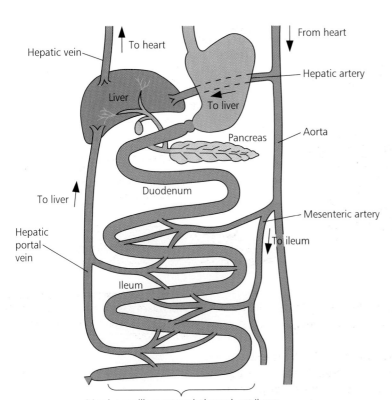

To heart
Hepatic vein
From heart
Hepatic artery
Liver
To liver
Aorta
Pancreas
To liver
Duodenum
Mesenteric artery
Hepatic portal vein
To ileum
Ileum

Massive capillary network throughout ileum

Figure 3.3.14 The products of digestion are carried to the liver for processing before continuing in the bloodstream to be supplied to all the body cells.

The large intestine is thin-walled and wider in lumen than the small intestine, but much shorter in length. The main function of the large intestine is to reabsorb water into the blood. The remaining waste material is known as **faeces**. It accumulates in the colon and the rectum until that area of the digestive tract is stretched sufficiently to trigger the opening of the muscular sphincter known as the anus.

The length of time spent by the indigestible food in the large intestine determines the amount of water which will be reabsorbed and so the state of the faecal material. For example, when the lining of the colon is irritated by a viral or bacterial infection, the food is passed through very quickly and little reabsorption of water takes place. This results in diarrhoea, which can in turn cause rapid dehydration of the system if the water lost is not replaced. This sequence of events – infection of the gut, water loss through diarrhoea and subsequent death from dehydration – kills more children worldwide than anything else, clearly demonstrating the importance of this final stage of the alimentary canal.

The human diet

Any heterotrophic organism must take in sufficient raw materials of the right type for the synthesis of new biological material, and enough energy-providing foods. To maintain the human body a balance of foods is needed, which must include carbohydrates, proteins and fats along with mineral salts, vitamins, water and fibre. We shall consider each in turn.

Carbohydrates

Carbohydrates provide energy – they are used largely in cellular respiration in the production of ATP. Some carbohydrate is stored as glycogen, a storage carbohydrate found in the liver, muscles and brain. Any excess carbohydrate is converted to fat for storage.

Fats

Fats are also used to provide energy, and they are stored in readiness for times of food shortage.

Proteins

Proteins are used for body building. They are broken down in digestion to their constituent amino acids and these are then rebuilt by the process of protein synthesis to form the appropriate proteins for that particular individual. Certain amino acids are vital in the diet because they cannot be synthesised. Mainly found in animal protein, these are called the **essential amino acids**.

Essential ingredients

There are certain **essential fatty acids** which cannot be synthesised in the body, so they must be taken in as part of the diet if an individual is to remain healthy. **Linoleic acid** and **gamma-linolenic acid** are needed as precursors (starting molecules) in the synthesis of other fatty acids, such as arachidonic acid, not found in the diet. They are also needed as precursors in the formation of prostaglandins, hormone-like compounds which are very important in many physiological systems including the reproductive system.

Certain amino acids cannot be synthesised in the body and so are also vital in a balanced diet. These are called the **essential amino acids**, mainly found in animal protein. They include **isoleucine**, **leucine**, **phenylalanine**, **methionine**, **threonine** and **valine**. Once they have been ingested, they are no more important than any other amino acids in the body.

Figure 3.3.15 The rich content of essential fatty acids in oil of evening primrose helps overcome dietary deficiencies.

Mineral salts

Mineral salts are in general needed in minute amounts, but lack of them in the diet can lead to a variety of adverse conditions, as table 3.3.2 shows.

Mineral	Functions	Deficiency symptoms	Source
Calcium (Ca^{2+})	Activates some enzymes. Needed for skeleton and teeth formation, muscular contraction and blood clotting	Poor bone growth, rickets (soft bones), muscle spasms, delayed blood clotting	Milk, cheese, fish
Iron (Fe^{2+})	Part of cytochromes. Activates the enzyme catalase. Needed for haemoglobin and myoglobin	Anaemia	Liver, red meat, eggs, apricots, cocoa powder
Iodine (I^-)	Constituent of thyroxine	Goitre (swollen thyroid gland)	Sea-fish, shellfish, drinking water, added to salt
Nitrogen (N)	Constituent of proteins	Kwashiorkor – swelling, stunted growth and weakness	Protein foods – milk, eggs, meat, pulses
Phosphorus (P)	In phospholipids, proteins, ATP, nucleic acids. Also needed for skeletal growth	—	Most foods

Table 3.3.2 Some of the main minerals needed in the diet and the deficiency diseases associated with a lack of them

Vitamins

Vitamins are similarly required in very small amounts. They are usually complex organic substances which can nevertheless be absorbed directly into the bloodstream from the gut. If any particular vitamin is lacking from the diet in the long term, it will result in a deficiency disease, shown in table 3.3.3. These deficiency diseases can be avoided or remedied using vitamin supplements if the dietary intake remains inadequate.

Table 3.3.3 The main vitamins needed in the human diet and their associated deficiency diseases

Vitamin letter	Name	Function	Principal sources	Deficiency diseases
Fat-soluble vitamins				
A	Retinol	Involved in photochemical reaction in rods in retina of eye	Liver, carotenoid pigments in vegetables, particularly carrots	Poor dark adaptation, xerophthalmia (drying and degeneration of cornea)
D	Calciferol	Calcification and hardening of bone and teeth	Fish liver oil	Softening of bones – rickets in children, osteomalacia in adults
K	Phylloquinone	Required for synthesis of certain blood-clotting factors	Cabbage, spinach, pig's liver	Prolonged blood clotting time
Water-soluble vitamins				
B1	Thiamine	Coenzyme for decarboxylation of pyruvic acid to acetyl CoA in respiratory pathway	Yeast, cereals	Beri-beri – wasting of muscles, gastric upsets, circulatory failure and paralysis
B2	Riboflavine	Forms flavine coenzymes (FAD etc.) – electron carriers in cell respiration	Leafy vegetables, fish, eggs	Sore mouth, ulcerations
PP	Nicotinic acid	Forms coenzymes NAD and NADP – hydrogen acceptors in cell respiration	Meat, fish, wheat	Pellagra – diarrhoea, dermatitis and mental disorder; pigmentation of neck (Casal's necklace)
M or Bc	Folic acid	Required for formation of erythrocytes	Leafy vegetables, liver, kidney	Anaemia
C	Ascorbic acid	Required for formation of intercellular material	Citrus fruits and green vegetables	Scurvy

Evidence for the importance of vitamins

Over the years an enormous amount of evidence for the importance of vitamins in the diet has been built up. Modern techniques can show the positions in biochemical pathways where vitamins are used. Work done at Cambridge in the early years of this century by Sir Frederick Gowland Hopkins remains a classic piece of evidence. He took two sets of eight young rats and fed both sets a diet consisting of purified casein, starch, sucrose, mineral salts, lard and water. In addition, one set only was given 3 cm³ of milk every day for the first 18 days of the experiment. At this point the milk supplement was stopped and given to the other set of young rats until the end of the experiment.

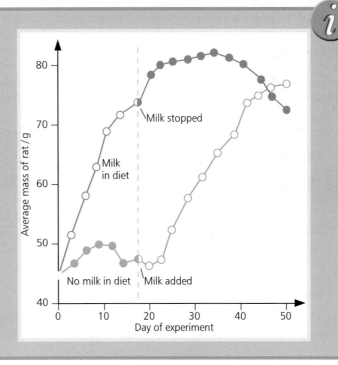

Figure 3.3.16 These results show that a diet consisting of carbohydrate, protein, fat, minerals and water is not enough for the long-term health and growth of young rats. The vitamins present in the milk were also needed.

Water

The importance of water in biological systems has already been considered. Suffice it to say that, whereas the average person can survive with little or no food for days if not weeks, complete lack of water will bring about death in two to four days, depending on other conditions such as temperature.

Fibre

Roughage or fibre cannot be digested in the human gut, yet it is an essential part of the diet because it provides bulk for the intestinal muscles to work on and also holds water. In a diet low in roughage peristalsis is sluggish and the food moves through the gut relatively slowly. This can lead to minor ailments such as constipation and haemorrhoids, and is implicated in more serious conditions such as cancer of the bowel.

A balanced diet

The balance of food required by different types of animals will obviously vary, but for any species the right balance of food is of enormous importance to the overall health and well-being of the animal. If too little food is eaten (undernutrition) then the organism will suffer from **malnutrition**. Too much food may also be eaten (overnutrition). This is well illustrated by the human animal.

One of the most important factors of a balanced diet is that enough food is eaten to supply the energy needs of the organism. For vast areas of the world, particularly the developing world, this is a major problem. There is simply not enough food available to supply the energy needs of the people. As a result much of the population is seriously underweight, with shortened lifespans and reduced resistance to disease. Hand in hand with insufficient food go insufficiencies of essential amino acids, minerals and vitamins and so the deficiency diseases seen in tables 3.3.2 and 3.3.3 are also found.

However, it is also important that too much food is not consumed. The energy requirements of each individual vary depending on age, sex and levels of activity. If more energy is taken in than is required, the excess is stored as fat and obesity may result. Frequently a problem in the developed world, up to a third of the population of the USA is thought to be seriously overweight, mainly due to eating a diet rich in high-energy fat. This causes coronary heart disease, high blood pressure and other disorders which reduce life expectancy. A high proportion of sugar in the diet leads to the formation of dental caries, as bacteria digest the sugar in the mouth, producing acid which in turn attacks the enamel of the teeth. Many people have lost their teeth as a result of their diet and poor dental hygiene.

Control of body fat

The most obvious effect of overeating is an increase in body fat, eventually resulting in obesity. The long-term effects of overeating are a shortened lifespan and poor health in old age. Longer, fitter lives result from eating just sufficient to supply the needs of the body. However, it is more the fashion-driven desire to look younger and sexier that has resulted in a large proportion of the adult populations in countries such as Britain, France and the USA spending at least part of their life on a weight-loss diet.

Sadly for these well-meaning efforts, recent evidence suggests that the weight of an organism is strongly governed by factors other than the amount of food eaten. There appears to be a **set point** rather like a thermostat, a genetically determined level for each individual's body weight and in particular the amount of fat stored. In most people tested and many other mammals, a large increase in calories results in little weight gain over the set point – the excess calories are burned off and lost as body heat. Similarly, a lowering of the food intake did not result in a large weight loss below the set point – the metabolism simply functioned more efficiently. The only way of adjusting the set point thermostat seems to be to change the level of physical activity.

Figure 3.3.17 Reducing food intake and increasing the levels of exercise can result in quite dramatic weight loss, but for most adults with fairly stable eating and exercise habits their genetic set point will largely determine their levels of body fat.

The Western diet also contains many added chemicals. Strangely, the diet of the average inhabitant of the developed world, whilst full of fat and refined carbohydrate, may be low in vitamins as relatively little fresh fruit and vegetables are consumed. Roughage is also frequently missing in any quantity, causing not only constipation but also many diseases of the gut and bowel, including, it would seem, some bowel cancers. The saying 'You are what you eat' may be truer than many of us would like to think.

Figure 3.3.18 Whether you are forced by circumstances to eat too little or choose to eat too much, the wrong type of nutrition can seriously damage your health.

Different types of foods contain different amounts of energy stored within their chemical bonds. The amount of energy contained in any individual food can be revealed using a process known as **calorimetry**, shown in figure 3.3.19.

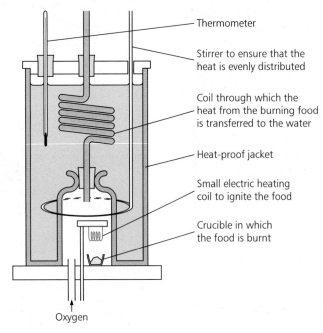

- Thermometer
- Stirrer to ensure that the heat is evenly distributed
- Coil through which the heat from the burning food is transferred to the water
- Heat-proof jacket
- Small electric heating coil to ignite the food
- Crucible in which the food is burnt

Oxygen

Figure 3.3.19 Food is burnt in pure oxygen, so that it is completely oxidised. The energy released as the chemical bonds are rearranged is transferred to the surrounding water as heat. The resulting rise in the temperature of the water can be measured and used to calculate the energy value of the food, based on the fact that 4.2 J of heat energy raise the temperature of 1 g of water by 1 °C.

Calories

When measuring the energy in food using a calorimeter, the units of energy previously used were calories and kilocalories. Indeed, most confusingly, what many non-scientists referred to as a Calorie was in fact a kilocalorie! Old habits die hard, and the 'Calorie' is still a common term in everyday language, particularly when people are talking about weight-reducing diets. Biologists no longer refer to calories at all, but most food packaging indicates the energy value of food in both kilocalories and kilojoules. The relationship between the two is very simple:
4.2 joules = 1 calorie.

Calorimetry measures the amount of energy released when a known quantity of food is completely oxidised by burning it in pure oxygen. Carbohydrates have an energy value of 17.2 kJ g^{-1}, fats 38.5 kJ g^{-1} and proteins 22.2 kJ g^{-1}. Food tables exist which show the energy values of an enormous range of foods.

Changing times, changing needs

One of the main purposes of the food in the diet is to provide an individual with sufficient energy to maintain basic body functions and also to carry out all the activities of daily life. The amount of energy needed varies from person to person, and also varies throughout life. The energy you need on a daily basis will depend on your **basal metabolic rate** (**BMR**) and how active you are. The BMR is measured when an individual is at complete rest, calculated from temperature changes that result from heat production in the human body over a period of hours or days in a heat-proof room (another type of calorimeter). The BMR is proportionately higher in babies and young children than in adults as they use a great deal of energy in growth. The BMR is also related to the total body mass and the lean body mass. People with a high proportion of muscle will have a higher BMR as muscle tissue requires more energy for maintenance than fat does. This is one of the main reasons why men usually have higher BMRs than women, because they tend to have a higher proportion of muscle to fat. As people age, not only is their tissue replaced less often but they also tend to lose muscle and so the BMR tends to drop with age. The BMR makes up, on average, about 75% of the metabolic needs of the body.

It has been worked out that an 'average' man needs to take in about 7500 kJ per day to maintain his BMR, and an 'average' woman needs about 5850 kJ per day, but this assumes that the person lies on a bed all day and night and expends no extra energy above that needed to breathe and excrete. The BMR is therefore of relatively little use on its own in assessing the energy intake needed in a healthy diet. To make the measure more useful, the physical activity level must also be taken into account. By multiplying the BMR by a factor which reflects the **physical activity level** (**PAL**), we can obtain the **estimated average requirements** (**EAR**) for energy. A PAL of 1.4 is used for adults in the UK, reflecting the rather sedentary way of life most of us have. The energy EARs of people throughout life are shown in table 3.3.4. If we do not match our energy intakes to the requirements of our body then we will either gain weight (if we eat too much) or lose weight (if we eat too little).

Age	EAR /kJ day^{-1} (males)	EAR /kJ day^{-1} (females)	Age	EAR /kJ day^{-1} (males)	EAR /kJ day^{-1} (females)
0–3 months	2280	2160	11–14 years	9270	7720
4–6 months	2890	2690	15–18 years	11 510	8830
7–9 months	3440	3200	19–50 years	10 600	8100
10–12 months	3850	3610	51–59 years	10 600	8000
1–3 years	5150	4860	60–64 years	9930	7990
4–6 years	7160	6460	65–74 years	9710	7960
7–10 years	8240	7280	75+ years	8770	7610

Table 3.3.4 The estimated average requirements (EARs) for energy at different ages in the UK – the levels change quite dramatically with age

In the developed world, food is produced in abundance and the majority of people eat more than is necessary to supply the metabolic needs of the body. In the process of evolution many animals, ourselves included, have developed the ability to convert excess food energy into a store of fat ready for times of food shortage. Thus people in the affluent and developed areas of the world can become overweight. Tables of energy values of foods are often used by overweight people trying to lower their total intake of energy and lose weight. In stark contrast, around two-thirds of the world's population do not get enough food to provide them with the recommended minimum daily intake, and for many their food barely yields sufficient energy to cover the BMR.

Recommended nutritional guidelines

Although taking in sufficient energy is an important aspect of the diet, there are many other important factors. The major nutrients need to be taken in both in appropriate quantities and in the right balance with other aspects of the diet. To try and clarify which nutrients people need and in what quantities, **nutritional requirements** have been worked out and built up into recommended national guidelines for nutrition. Obviously these will vary from individual to individual depending on age and lifestyle, but estimates for groups of the population are based on advice given by the Committee on Medical Aspects of Food Policy (COMA). This committee reviews scientific evidence from research into diet and disease, and then uses this to advise the Government on policy. In 1991, the committee published a detailed report of the estimated nutritional requirements of different groups in the population. It included **dietary reference values** (**DRVs**) which indicate the range of requirements and appropriate intakes for the population, as illustrated in figure 3.3.21.

- The **estimated average requirement** (**EAR**) is an estimate of the average requirement for a particular nutrient. This means about 50% of the population will need less than this in their diet, and 50% will need more. If people are taking in adequate amounts, the intake will vary around the EAR.

Figure 3.3.20 During the last three months of pregnancy the daily energy requirements of women increase by about 200 kJ. They also need extra energy during breast feeding, but this depends on how much fat they have stored, the amount of milk they produce and for how long they breast feed – it takes a great deal more energy to produce enough milk to fully satisfy a five-month-old baby than it does for a five-week-old baby.

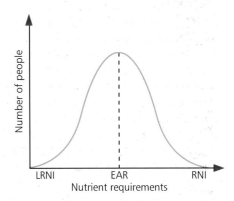

Figure 3.3.21 The distribution of nutrient requirements within a population.

- The **reference nutrient intake** (**RNI**) is the intake of a particular nutrient which will make sure that the needs of almost everyone in the population will be met. This used to be known as the RDA (recommended daily amount).
- The **lower reference nutrient intake** (**LRNI**) is enough for only a very small proportion of the population who have naturally low requirements.
- The **safe intake** is a DRV used when there is no precise scientific evidence to provide an RNI. The safe level is judged to be probably sufficient for everyone, and with no evidence that levels above this are beneficial.

The COMA report includes RNIs for protein, nine vitamins and eleven minerals, EARs for energy, safe intakes for four further vitamins and minerals and desired population intakes for fat and carbohydrates. Table 3.3.5 shows some of these data.

Table A Reference nutrient intakes for protein

Age	Reference nutrient intake /g day^{-1}	Age	Reference nutrient intake /g day^{-1}	
			Males	Females
0–3 months	12.5	11–14 years	42.1	41.2
4–6 months	12.7	15–18 years	55.2	45.0
7–9 months	13.7	19–50 years	55.5	45.0
10–12 months	14.9	50+ years	53.3	46.5
1–3 years	11.5			
4–6 years	19.7	Pregnancy[a]		+6
7–10 years	28.3	Lactation[a]		
		0–4 months		+11
		4+ months		+8

[a] To be added to adult requirement through all stages of pregnancy and lactation

Table B Reference nutrient intakes for vitamins

Age	Thiamin / mg day^{-1}	Riboflavin / mg day^{-1}	Niacin / mg day^{-1}	Vitamin B6 / mg day^{-1}	Vitamin B12 / mg day^{-1}	Folate / µg day^{-1}	Vitamin C / mg day^{-1}	Vitamin A / µg day^{-1}	Vitamin D / µg day^{-1}
0–3 months	0.2	0.4	3	0.2	0.3	50	25	350	8.5
4–6 months									
7–9 months			4	0.3	0.4				7
10–12 months	0.3		5	0.4					
1–3 years	0.5	0.6	8	0.7	0.5	70	30	400	
4–6 years	0.7	0.8	11	0.9	0.8	100		500	–
7–10 years		1.0	12	1.0	1.0	150			
Males									
11–14 years	0.9	1.2	15	1.2	1.2		35	600	–
15–18 years	1.1		18	1.5		200			
19–50 years	1.0	1.3	17		1.5		40	700	
51–64 years	0.9		16	1.4					10
65+ years									
Females									
11–14 years	0.7	1.1	12	1.0	1.2	200	35	600	–
15–18 years			14						
19–50 years	0.8		13	1.2	1.5		40		
50–64 years			12						10
65+ years									
Pregnancy	+0.1	+0.3	No increase	No increase	No increase	+100	+10	+100	+10
Lactation	+0.2	+0.5	+2	No increase	+0.5	+60	+30	+350	+10

Table 3.3.5 Tables like these are valuable in assessing whether the diet of a group within the population is adequate or not for any particular nutrient. They can also be used to show how the requirements for a particular nutrient change throughout the lifetime.

Table C Reference nutrient intakes for selected minerals

Table 3.3.5 Continued

Age	Calcium /mg day^{-1}	Iron /mg day^{-1}	Zinc /mg day^{-1}
4–6 months	525	4.3	4.0
7–10 years	550	8.7	7.0
Males			
11–14 years	1000	11.3	9.0
19–50 years	700	8.7	9.5
50+ years	700	8.7	9.5
Females			
11–14 years	800	14.8**	9.0
19–50 years	700	14.8**	7.0
50+ years	700	8.7	7.0
Pregnancy	*	*	*
Lactation			
0–4 months	+500	*	+6.0

*No increment required   **Insufficient for women with high menstrual losses where the most practical way of meeting iron requirements is to take iron supplements

DRVs are useful in assessing the diet of a group of people. For example, if the average intake of a mineral of a group of people is close to the RNI it is unlikely that anyone will be deficient in that mineral. On the other hand, if the average intake of a group approaches the LRNI, then it is very likely that some people in the group are not getting adequate amounts of the mineral in their diet.

The requirements for different nutrients change throughout life, and this is clearly reflected in the DRVs. However, in some cases unusual output takes place and needs to be taken into account. For example, girls and women who have particularly heavy or frequent menstrual periods lose more iron than normal, and so they may need iron supplements to prevent themselves suffering from anaemia even if their dietary intake of iron is around the RNI.

The three nutrients that provide the energy in the diet are carbohydrates, proteins and fats, along with any alcohol which is also taken in. There is evidence that the proportion of energy-giving foods in the diet can increase or decrease the likelihood of problems such as heart disease developing. Thus a balance of the energy-giving nutrients is suggested as part of the DRV. By comparing this with the average British diet (see figure 3.3.22) we can see that a number of changes need to be made if we are to become a healthier nation.

Figure 3.3.22 The recommended dietary make-up for the UK population differed from the actual energy gained from various nutrients in British households in several ways (1993 data). Most obviously, more fat and less carbohydrate were eaten than is recommended.

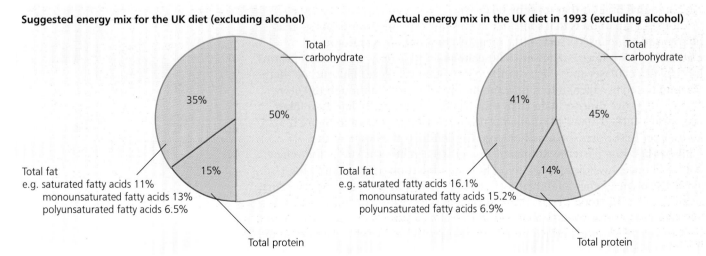

Suggested energy mix for the UK diet (excluding alcohol)

Total carbohydrate 50%
35%
15%
Total fat e.g. saturated fatty acids 11% monounsaturated fatty acids 13% polyunsaturated fatty acids 6.5%
Total protein

Actual energy mix in the UK diet in 1993 (excluding alcohol)

Total carbohydrate 45%
41%
14%
Total fat e.g. saturated fatty acids 16.1% monounsaturated fatty acids 15.2% polyunsaturated fatty acids 6.9%
Total protein

Carnivores and herbivores

The human digestive system gives us a good picture of the major adaptations and mechanisms necessary for heterotrophic nutrition. Other mammalian groups add to the picture showing specialisations that apply to different types of organisms as well.

Carnivores eat a diet which is largely made up of protein – the largest component of the skin, muscle and many of the internal organ systems of their prey. Protein is relatively easy to digest. The breakdown begins in the stomach and is completed by the endo- and exopeptidases of the small intestine. Therefore the guts of carnivores tend to be shorter than those of omnivorous or herbivorous animals of the same size, as figure 3.3.23 shows. Also, relatively little undigested material is egested by carnivores.

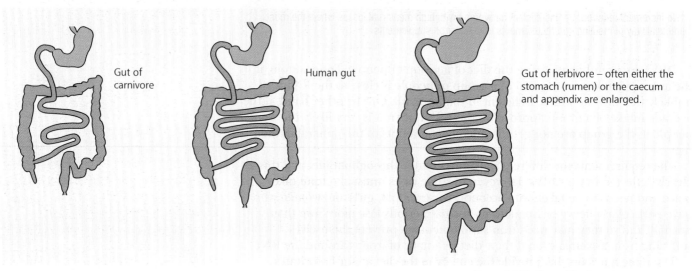

Gut of carnivore

Human gut

Gut of herbivore – often either the stomach (rumen) or the caecum and appendix are enlarged.

Figure 3.3.23 The modifications observed in the guts of different animals reflect the varying digestive demands of their diet.

In the case of herbivores, most animals cannot digest cellulose, so there is no food value in the cellulose cell walls of the plants they eat. The nutrition, in the cytoplasm, is trapped inside an indigestible box. We have already considered the adaptation of herbivore teeth for the chewing needed to break open the cell walls. Alongside this, most herbivores have extremely long guts to maximise the opportunities for nutrients to be extracted, and also to hold the large amounts of food that must be taken in.

Another adaptation is that some herbivores (for example ruminants such as the cow and some insects such as the termites) have set up **symbiotic** relationships with microorganisms. These are mainly bacteria which manufacture the enzyme cellulase, and which can therefore digest cellulose. This means that less food has to be taken in to supply the herbivore's needs, although the more effective digestive process often takes some time. The cellulose digestion takes place in specialised areas. In ruminants this is the **rumen**, shown in figure 3.3.23, but in other herbivores the much-enlarged appendix is the home of the cellulose-digesting bacteria. Ruminants in particular 'chew the cud' – they chew their food once, swallow it for some preliminary digestion, regurgitate it for another prolonged chew and then carry on digesting it again. Other species such as rabbits allow the food to pass through the gut once, eat the faeces produced and then redigest the food to obtain as much value as possible from it. In spite of measures such as these, herbivores in general egest large quantities of undigested plant material as faeces.

Other feeding relationships

There are many other variations on the theme of digestion. Parasites have particular adaptations. Internal parasites, particularly those found in the gut such as many roundworms and the tapeworms, have little digestion to perform. They absorb the ready-digested material present in the gut of their host. However, they must protect themselves from being digested in turn. Even if they do not live within the gut, they still have to avoid destruction by the host's immune system. External parasites too have many difficulties to overcome before they begin digestion. Hosts must be found and attacked without damage to the parasite. As a result of these obstacles many parasitic feeders have evolved extremely complex ways of life and immune systems which in turn make them a major problem for the human race.

Internal parasites

- Like other parasites, tapeworms have lost organ systems they do not need. They live surrounded by digested food, so have no need for a gut – they simply absorb the nutrients they need through their outer epidermis.
- Parasites need to be protected against attack by the host. The outer epidermis of the tapeworm is resistant to attack by the host's digestive enzymes.
- Parasites need to be firmly attached to their host. The tapeworm has an effective array of hooks and suckers (the scolex) to keep it fixed to the gut of the host.

Figure 3.3.24 Internal parasites such as the tapeworm *Taenia* have many adaptations to their strange lifestyle.

- Parasites need to reproduce quickly and in large numbers. Surrounded by digested food, the tapeworm grows rapidly, producing many segments or **proglottids** all capable of sexual reproduction. Ripe proglottids break off and pass out in the faeces where they can infect another intermediate host.
- It is vital to the success of the parasite that it has a way of passing from one host to another. The tapeworm's system of reproduction is adapted for this, as described in figure 3.3.24.

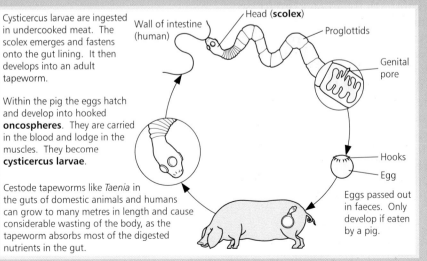

Cysticercus larvae are ingested in undercooked meat. The scolex emerges and fastens onto the gut lining. It then develops into an adult tapeworm.

Within the pig the eggs hatch and develop into hooked **oncospheres**. They are carried in the blood and lodge in the muscles. They become **cysticercus larvae**.

Cestode tapeworms like *Taenia* in the guts of domestic animals and humans can grow to many metres in length and cause considerable wasting of the body, as the tapeworm absorbs most of the digested nutrients in the gut.

Head (**scolex**)
Wall of intestine (human)
Proglottids
Genital pore
Hooks
Egg
Eggs passed out in faeces. Only develop if eaten by a pig.

3

Mutualism

In a mutualistic relationship, both partners benefit. One of the most important mutualistic relationships in nature is that between *Rhizobium* bacteria and the leguminous plants such as peas, beans, clover and alfalfa.

The *Rhizobium* infect the roots of leguminous plants and live in swollen root nodules. They make use of some of the carbohydrates stored in the roots as a food supply. In return they provide the plants with a continuous supply of fixed nitrogen that can be used to build plant proteins. This benefits the individual plants, and also means that the nitrates in the soil are not used up. When the legume dies or is ploughed in, it will actually increase the nitrate levels in the soil, thus improving fertility.

Figure 3.3.25 The mutualism between *Rhizobium* and the leguminous plants helps maintain soil fertility.

Saprotrophs

Saprotrophic nutrition (also known as **saprobiotic nutrition**) is another very important form of heterotrophic nutrition. Saprotrophs feed on dead and decaying material, breaking down dead bodies and piles of dung. Land-living saprotrophs are known as **decomposers** and most of them are either bacteria or fungi. They digest their food externally by making and secreting digestive enzymes including proteases, amylases, lipases, cellulases and even lignases. Decomposers absorb their digested food back through their outer surface, so they tend to have permeable walls and structures which give a large surface area to aid diffusion. Decomposers usually grow and reproduce very quickly to colonise an area, and also to spread further onto new sources of food. There are many common saprotrophs, including those that break down wood (such as dry rot), those that break down sewage, and the moulds and fungi that appear on bread, fruit and other foods if we keep them too long. (For more detail about the life cycle of these moulds see section 6.)

Saprotrophs that live in water are known as **detritivores**. Again, they include many bacteria, but fungi do not grow underwater. Some molluscs, crustaceans and worms feed saprotrophically in water, breaking down the dead and decaying matter produced when all the aquatic and marine organisms excrete and die.

SUMMARY

- **Heterotrophs** obtain their food by eating autotrophs or other heterotrophs. **Holozoans** feed on the bodies of other organisms. **Parasites** feed on organic material from a host. **Saprotrophs** feed on soluble organic material from dead animals and plants.

- Heterotrophs have to obtain, digest and absorb their food. **Herbivores** expend little energy obtaining food but cannot digest cellulose so have to eat large quantities to obtain enough energy. They have ridged molars adapted to break down cellulose cell walls. **Carnivores** expend more energy obtaining their food and have teeth adapted for trapping and tearing flesh, but they can digest their food more easily. **Parasites** are adapted to prevent rejection by the host and **saprotrophs** to find new food sources.

- **Digestion** of food is the breakdown of large complex food molecules into simple soluble molecules that can be absorbed into the body and distributed. Digestion is catalysed by enzymes and takes place in the **alimentary canal** or **gut**.

- Humans are holozoic feeders. Holozoic nutrition consists of **ingestion** (taking food in), **digestion**, **absorption** of the digested products into the cells, **assimilation** (use of the products of digestion by the cells) and **egestion** (removal of undigested food material).

- Food is ingested in the mouth and chewed to break it down (mechanical digestion). Chemical digestion starts in the mouth by the action of **saliva**, which also moistens and lubricates the food. A **bolus** of food is swallowed and passes into the oesophagus.

- The **oesophagus** has a folded inner lining typical of the alimentary canal. The **mucosa** is made up of **stratified squamous epithelium** interspersed with **mucus-producing cells**. Mucus protects the oesophageal lining and lubricates the food. The **submucosa** is a layer of connective tissue, nerves and blood vessels. **Peristalsis** is brought about by the coordinated movement of the **circular** and **longitudinal muscles**.

- The food passes from the oesophagus through the **cardiac sphincter** to the **stomach**, a muscular organ which churns the food and continues chemical digestion. The stomach lining contains **gastric pits** which have **mucus-producing cells**, **oxyntic cells** which produce hydrochloric acid and **chief cells** which secrete pepsinogen. The **chyme** which results from the action of the stomach passes through the **pyloric sphincter** to the duodenum.

- The **duodenum** is the first part of the small intestine where digestion is more or less completed by secretions from the duodenum wall, the pancreas and the liver. The later part of the small intestine is the **ileum** where absorption of digested food takes place. The small intestine has finger-like **villi** which are frequently covered with a **brush border** of **microvilli** to increase the surface area for absorption. Villi contain a **lacteal** (lymph vessel) and a capillary. **Crypts of Lieberkuhn** in the duodenum wall produce digestive enzymes while **Brunner's glands** produce alkaline secretions and mucus. Circular and longitudinal muscles in the wall of the small intestine move the villi.

Food molecule	Converted to	By (enzyme)	Secreted by	Acts in (organ)
Polysaccharides e.g. starch	Disaccharides e.g. maltose	Salivary amylase	Salivary glands	Mouth
		Amylase	Pancreas and crypts of Lieberkuhn in duodenum	Duodenum
Maltose	Glucose	Maltase	Lining of small intestine	Small intestine
Sucrose	Glucose + fructose	Sucrase	Lining of small intestine	Small intestine
Lactose	Glucose + galactose	Lactase	Lining of small intestine	Small intestine
Protein	Polypeptides	Pepsin	Stomach as pepsinogen, activated by hydrochloric acid	Stomach
		Trypsin	Pancreas as trypsinogen, activated by enterokinase which is secreted by the lining of the small intestine	Small intestine
	Polypeptides and short peptides	Endopeptidases e.g. chymotrypsin	Pancreas	Duodenum
Peptides	Amino acids	Exopeptidases e.g. aminopeptidase	Pancreas	Duodenum
Casein (soluble milk protein)	Coagulated protein	Rennin	Stomach of young mammals	Stomach
Fats	Fatty acids and glycerol	Lipase	Pancreas	Duodenum
Nucleic acids	Nucleotides	Nuclease	Pancreas	Duodenum

Table 3.3.6 Chemical digestion in the human alimentary canal

- Chemical digestion is summarised in table 3.3.6.
- **Nervous stimulation** and **gastrin** stimulate the production of acidic gastric juices. Gastrin is produced in response to food in the stomach. **Secretin** and **cholecystokinin** are secreted in response to acidic chyme in the duodenum and stimulate the liver and pancreas to secrete digestive juices. **Enterogastrin** then inhibits acidic secretion in the stomach.
- Amino acids, disaccharides and monosaccharides are absorbed into the blood capillaries of the villi by diffusion, active transport and possibly facilitated diffusion. Fatty acids and glycerol can pass directly into the blood or may recombine in the lining of the villi to form **chylomicrons** – droplets of lipoprotein. These pass in the lymphatic system to the blood where they are again converted into fatty acids and glycerol for uptake by the cells.
- Blood comes to the small intestine from the **mesenteric artery** and blood carrying the products of digestion is then taken to the liver via the **hepatic portal vein**. Digested food is stored in the liver or converted to other molecules which leave the liver by the **hepatic vein** to be distributed to the body cells.
- The **large intestine** is thin walled and larger in lumen but shorter than the small intestine. Water is reabsorbed into the blood from the large intestine and the remaining **faeces** are stored in the **rectum** until **egestion** through the **anus**.
- A balanced human diet consists of carbohydrates, fats, proteins including essential amino acids, mineral salts, vitamins, water and fibre. Lack of essential amino acids, certain minerals or vitamins can result in **deficiency diseases**.
- The energy values of different foods can be determined by **calorimetry**.

- The minimum amount of energy taken in in food that will keep the body alive is the **basal metabolic rate** (**BMR**).

- The balance of nutrients in the diet plays an important role in maintaining health. Too much or too little fat, protein or other nutrient can cause disease. The energy content of the food taken in also affects health. The recommended guidelines for nutrition highlight the nutritional requirements of the population.

- **Malnutrition** can result from eating too little and deficiency diseases are a common result. **Overnutrition** causes obesity which can lead to coronary heart disease, high blood pressure and other disorders.

- The structure of the alimentary canal is adapted to suit different diets. Carnivores have shorter alimentary canals than omnivores since most of their food is protein, and easy to digest, and they egest small quantities. Herbivores have long guts to maximise the absorption area and some are specially adapted to digest cellulose. Symbiotic bacteria living in their guts, in the **rumen** or enlarged **appendix**, secrete the enzyme cellulase. Ruminants chew their food several times during the digestive process while rabbits eat their faeces and redigest the food.

QUESTIONS

1 **a** Explain the terms heterotroph, ingestion, digestion and egestion.
  b Produce an annotated sketch of the organs of the human alimentary canal and describe the role played by each in the process of digestion.
  c Describe some of the ways in which the functioning of the different areas of the gut are coordinated.

2 All heterotrophs obtain their food from other organisms. Describe some of the adaptations of heterotrophic organisms which enable them to obtain their food.

3 Many diseases have now been linked to the type of food we eat, or do not eat. Summarise the main ways in which diet and disease are linked.

Developing Key Skills

The information in the table provided is from the side of a so-called 'healthy' cereal.

Ingredients Wheatflakes (wheat, sugar, salt, malt); raisins; cornflakes (maize, sugar, salt, malt); dates; honey-dipped banana; dried apple

Nutrition

	Average value	
	Per 100 g	Per 40 g serving
Energy	1358kJ	571 kJ
	325 kcal	135 kcal
Protein	5.9 g	2.4 g
Carbohydrate	72.1 g	28.8 g
of which sugars	30.4 g	12.2 g
Fat	2.8 g	1.1 g
of which saturates	1.6 g	0.6 g
Fibre	6.2 g	2.5 g
Sodium	0.4 g	0.2 g

As part of a 'Food Awareness Week' you will be speaking to a group of parents with overweight children to help them plan a healthier diet for their offspring. As part of this you will include the importance of looking to see what is actually in ready made foods. Prepare your talk, using the following ideas to help you:

- Why is it useful to be given information about the sodium and fibre content of food such as this cereal?

- What extra information would have been useful on this cereal packet?

- What percentage of the carbohydrate in a 100 g portion of this cereal comes from sugar? What are the adverse effects of sugar on the health?

- Is this cereal a healthy balanced food?

- What suggestions can you make about ideas for healthy breakfasts and about the diet in general?

MITOCHONDRIAL EXECUTIONERS

Mitochondria act as the 'powerhouses of the cell', producing ATP in cellular respiration, the reaction that is central to all life. New research suggests that mitochondria are also closely involved in the mechanism of cell death – they not only act as executioner, but also determine the way in which the cell dies.

Cell death

Cell death can occur in one of two different ways. The regular turnover of cells within our bodies, and the loss of tissue such as a tadpole's tail during metamorphosis, involve a carefully controlled form of cell death known as **apoptosis**. A cascade of reactions is set in place which results in the death of the cell, but without the cell bursting or triggering an inflammatory response in the body. Apoptosis is sometimes referred to as programmed cell death. However, if cells are seriously damaged or traumatised, a different type of cell death results called **necrosis**. In necrosis, organelles swell, many enzymes are released and the cell bursts, releasing its contents to trigger a violent inflammatory response. Necrosis or accidental cell death takes place after an event such as a heart attack, or in the cells of the liver after an overdose of paracetamol. The mitochondria are involved in both apoptosis and necrosis.

Mitochondrial madness

In apoptosis, it seems likely that mitochondria release cytochrome c, one of the components of the electron transfer chain usually bound safely to the membranes. Cytochrome c triggers apoptosis, starting up the cascade of enzymes that bring about controlled cell death. As this mechanism becomes better understood, it may be possible to use it to treat cancer, triggering apoptosis in tumour cells but not in healthy ones.

Necrotic cell death involves more disruption. The inner mitochondrial membrane contains special pores which open when the mitochondria are exposed to high levels of calcium ions. This occurs at times of great stress, such as a heart attack. Once these pores open, they reverse the normal reactions of the mitochondrion, so it starts breaking down ATP instead of making it. The mitochondria swell and release cytochrome c, which triggers rampant apoptosis. The functioning of the cell is completely disrupted, leading to the breakdown and death of the whole cell.

During a heart attack the pH falls, and this protects the heart to some extent from necrotic changes while the heart attack is going on. The problems start as blood returns to the heart, so scientists and doctors are working on ways of preventing the mitochondrial pores opening at this stage. Understanding how the damage occurs is the key to preventing it, and the mitochondria are central players in this process.

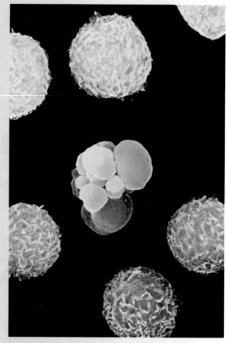

Figure 1 Cell death can take place by apoptosis, shown here, or by necrosis. We are just beginning to understand the role of mitochondria in both of these processes.

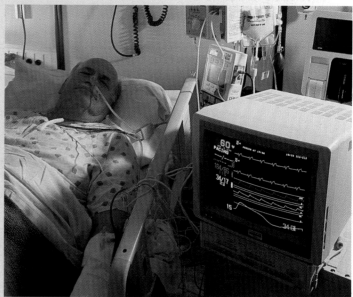

Figure 2 Knowledge of how the damage occurs following a heart attack or stroke may lead to the development of a treatment at mitochondrial level.

3.4 | Energy from food – cellular respiration

All living things need energy, which they get from food. Autotrophic organisms make their own food, frequently using the energy of the Sun to do so. Heterotrophic organisms eat and digest other organisms to get their food. However it is obtained, food is used to provide energy for all the metabolic reactions which occur in a cell or organism. The energy source which is used by the cells is ATP. In this section we shall look at the ways in which the energy in the food molecules is transferred to the molecules of ATP needed by the cell.

Cellular respiration

The energy in food is of no value until it is transferred from the chemical bonds in the food to the phosphate bond in ATP. **Cellular respiration** is the process by which organisms use oxygen to release energy from their food and transfer it into molecules of ATP. The energy in the bonds of the ATP formed can then be used to drive all the other biochemical reactions of life. Carbon dioxide and water are formed as waste products. Cellular respiration, like the calorimeter, oxidises the food as completely as possible.

Respiratory quotients

The amounts of oxygen used and carbon dioxide produced during cellular respiration change depending on the level of activity of the organism, the type of food being respired and other factors. By measuring the amounts of carbon dioxide produced and oxygen used up by an organism in a given time period, we can produce what is known as the **respiratory quotient**:

$$\text{Respiratory quotient (RQ)} = \frac{\text{carbon dioxide produced}}{\text{oxygen used}}$$

The respiratory quotient helps us to develop a picture of the type of foods which are being oxidised in the body at a particular time. In theory at least, carbohydrates give an RQ of 1, fats of 0.7 and protein of 0.9. Under normal conditions protein is not much used to provide energy, so an RQ of around 1 suggests that a large proportion of carbohydrate is being used in cellular respiration, and an RQ of less indicates that a combination of carbohydrate and fat is being respired. If the RQ of an organism is greater than 1 then anaerobic respiration may well be taking place, with relatively little oxygen being used compared with the carbon dioxide produced. Very low RQs tend to be found in photosynthetic organisms, when much of the carbon dioxide produced is used up in making new sugars and so cannot be measured.

The process of cellular respiration

Cellular respiration takes place in both autotrophic and heterotrophic organisms. The process involves a complex series of reactions, many of them involving oxidation or reduction. Hydrogen is removed from the food molecules and, in the same way as we have seen earlier, split into protons and electrons which are passed along an electron transfer chain to result in the formation of ATP. As in all biochemical pathways, the reactions are controlled by enzymes. A sequence of reactions is controlled, often by various types of enzyme inhibition, so that one reaction does not occur unless a preceding one has taken place. The process of gaseous exchange, carried out at the respiratory systems considered in section 2.4, provides the oxygen needed and removes the carbon dioxide produced, enabling the chemical reactions to proceed.

The complex process of cellular respiration can be summed up in the following simple equations. It is interesting to note that the equation for respiration is basically the equation for photosynthesis in reverse:

Glucose + oxygen → ATP (energy) + water + carbon dioxide

$$C_6H_{12}O_6 + 6O_2 \rightarrow ATP + 6H_2O + 6CO_2$$

Requirements for cellular respiration

The description used so far for cellular respiration is a simplification. The process takes place in two distinct phases. The first part of the process, called **glycolysis**, does *not* require oxygen. It produces a little ATP, but more importantly it primes the food molecules ready for entry into the second stage of the process which produces more ATP. This second stage is called the **Krebs cycle**, and for this set of reactions to proceed oxygen *is* needed. Thus the most important requirement for respiration is food, as some energy at least can be obtained from glycolysis without oxygen. This food is usually glucose, although as we shall see later, other substances can be used when there is a glucose shortage. In autotrophs the glucose is usually the product of photosynthesis, in heterotrophs it comes from digested food material. Oxygen is required for the Krebs cycle and so oxygen is needed for cellular respiration to proceed completely, producing the maximum amount of ATP from the breakdown of the food molecules.

Aerobic and anaerobic respiration

Most organisms depend on **aerobic respiration**, which means that they use oxygen for the Krebs cycle in order to provide them with sufficient energy to survive. They may be able to cope with a temporary lack of oxygen, but only in the very short term.

Some organisms can survive without oxygen – they rely on **anaerobic respiration**. **Facultative anaerobes** only respire without oxygen when it is strictly necessary. However, there are a few groups which cannot use oxygen at all and may in fact be killed by it. They are known as **obligate anaerobes**. Figure 3.4.1 gives examples of an aerobic and an anaerobic organism.

Demonstrating cellular respiration

It is not easy to demonstrate the requirements for cellular respiration practically without sophisticated biochemical techniques. Depriving aerobic organisms or cells of oxygen simply kills them. Apparatus such as spirometers or the respirometer in figure 3.4.2 can give some valuable information but has limitations. Depriving an organism of its food is also not informative – most organisms will self-digest for some time before dying. It is easier to observe cellular respiration by considering the waste products of the reactions.

The products of cellular respiration

ATP is the desired end product of cellular respiration. But along with this, carbon dioxide and water are also produced. These waste products, particularly the potentially toxic carbon dioxide, are then removed from the cell or organism. The production of carbon dioxide by an actively respiring organism is the most readily observed feature of cellular respiration, by the use of

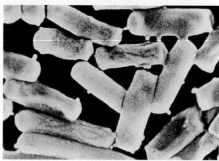

Figure 3.4.1 Deprive the kestrel of oxygen and it will survive for only a very short time – the cells simply cannot obtain enough ATP. Supply *Clostridium perfringens* (the bacterium responsible for gas gangrene in wounds) with oxygen and it will die. Aerobic organisms must have oxygen, obligate anaerobes are poisoned by it.

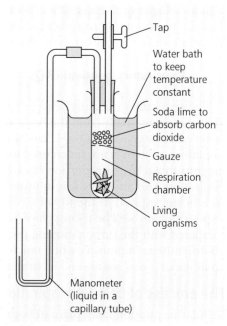

Figure 3.4.2 Any movement of the liquid in the tube indicates an uptake of oxygen by the organism. This type of respirometer can be useful for comparing the effect of, for example, temperature on the uptake of oxygen. However, a little thought will show that there are many limitations to apparatus of this type.

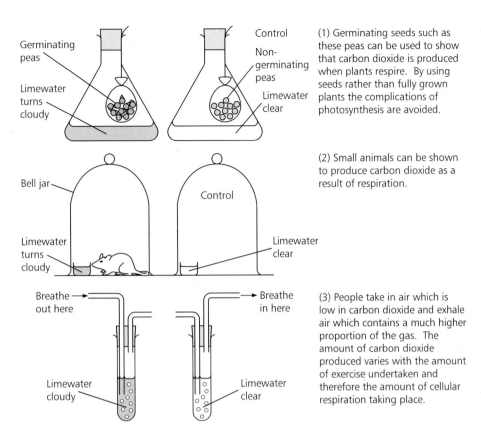

(1) Germinating seeds such as these peas can be used to show that carbon dioxide is produced when plants respire. By using seeds rather than fully grown plants the complications of photosynthesis are avoided.

(2) Small animals can be shown to produce carbon dioxide as a result of respiration.

(3) People take in air which is low in carbon dioxide and exhale air which contains a much higher proportion of the gas. The amount of carbon dioxide produced varies with the amount of exercise undertaken and therefore the amount of cellular respiration taking place.

Figure 3.4.3 Simple laboratory experiments such as these demonstrate respiration by the production of the waste gas carbon dioxide. They depend on the reaction between the carbon dioxide in the air and the calcium hydroxide solution known as limewater. Insoluble calcium carbonate is formed and this precipitate turns the limewater cloudy when carbon dioxide passes through it.

limewater (see figure 3.4.3), although again making precise measurements can be difficult.

The site of cellular respiration

As we have seen, glycolysis is the first part of the respiratory pathway and does not require oxygen. Glycolysis provides comparatively little ATP but it occurs in all cells. It is not associated with any particular cellular organelle – the enzymes controlling glycolysis are found in the cytoplasm.

The second part of respiration, the Krebs cycle, involves oxygen and yields considerably more ATP than glycolysis. The biochemical events of the Krebs cycle and the electron transfer chain involved in producing ATP are found in the mitochondria. The structure of these organelles was discussed in section 1 and their role as the site of ATP production in section 3.1. The partially permeable outer membrane allows the products of glycolysis to enter the mitochondria. The matrix seems to contain the enzymes of the Krebs cycle. Those cells with very low energy requirements, for example fat storage cells, tend to contain very few mitochondria. On the other hand, cells which are very active such as those of the muscles and the liver have very large numbers of mitochondria packed into the cytoplasm.

The biochemistry of respiration

As with photosynthesis, the equation summarising the process of respiration is a vast oversimplification. We have seen that it consists of two stages, glycolysis occurring in the cytoplasm and the Krebs cycle in the mitochondria. The two pathways of glycolysis and the Krebs cycle are part of a coordinated sequence of reactions bringing about the oxidation of glucose and the production of ATP, but for ease of understanding we shall consider them separately and then look at the overall process.

Glycolysis

Glycolysis literally means 'sugar-splitting' and in this initial part of the respiratory pathway glucose, a 6-carbon sugar, is split by a series of reactions into two molecules of the 3-carbon compound pyruvate. It is this pyruvate which is then taken into the mitochondria to supply the enzymes of the Krebs cycle. The main stages of glycolysis are shown in figure 3.4.4.

The first steps in glycolysis actually use up some ATP, phosphorylating the glucose molecule by the addition of two phosphate groups. This makes the glucose more reactive, and also ensures that it can no longer be transported readily across the cell membrane. The phosphorylated sugar is then split to give two 3-carbon (triose) sugar molecules. One is **glyceraldehyde 3-phosphate** (**GALP**) which continues on along the glycolytic pathway. The other triose sugar is dihydroxyacetone phosphate, which is readily converted to GALP.

In the next stage each molecule of GALP is converted by several steps into a molecule of **pyruvate**. Two hydrogen atoms are removed from the GALP and taken up by NAD. Because this is occurring in the cytoplasm, the other members of the electron transfer chain are not immediately available, but the reduced $NADH_2$ can be shunted through the outer mitochondrial membrane

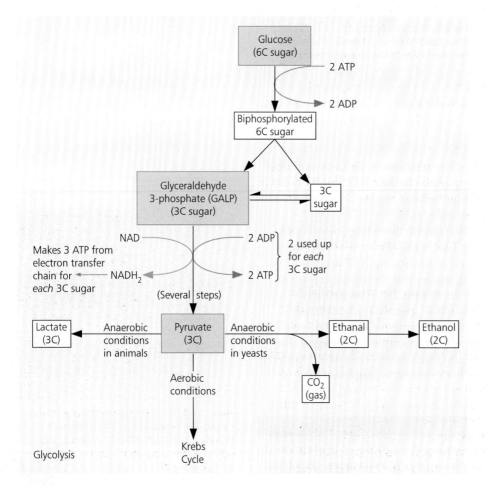

Glycolysis

Figure 3.4.4 With oxygen in plentiful supply pyruvate continues on into the mitochondria and the Krebs cycle. But when oxygen is not available, yeasts and animals have alternative strategies which will allow them, on a temporary basis at least, to respire by anaerobic means.

into the electron transfer chain of the inner mitochondrial membrane and so has the potential to produce ATP. Three molecules of ATP could result from the $NADH_2$ from each triose sugar in this way, as figure 3.1.10 (page 178) shows. We shall return again to the electron transfer chain when considering the Krebs cycle.

There is also some direct ATP formation from an energy transfer when the GALP is converted to pyruvate. For each GALP molecule converted (via several intermediates), 2 ATP molecules are made. So for each glucose molecule glycolysed, 2 ATP molecules are used and 4 produced (2 from *each* triose sugar). There is a net gain of 2 molecules of ATP per molecule of glucose and the potential to make 6 more via the electron transfer chain (3 from *each* triose sugar).

Pyruvate marks the end point of the reactions of glycolysis. In the presence of oxygen the pyruvate enters the mitochondria and is used in the aerobic reactions of the Krebs cycle. If there is insufficient oxygen for this, the pathway continues to form the end products of anaerobic respiration with no further ATP production.

Glycolytic products of anaerobic respiration in animals and fungi

Animals

We are all familiar with the pain which develops in our muscles if we overdo exercise. This is the result of insufficient oxygen reaching the muscles to supply the demand – we are using more ATP than we can produce by aerobic respiration, so the muscles are forced to respire anaerobically. The body is said to be in a state of **oxygen debt**. At the end of the glycolytic pathway pyruvate, instead of entering the Krebs cycle which depends on oxygen, is converted to **lactate**. Lactate is toxic and causes pain in the muscles as it builds up, until eventually we give in and stop exercising. As the body returns to normal this lactate has to be converted back to pyruvic acid and broken down to carbon dioxide with the use of oxygen, or otherwise metabolised, so paying off the oxygen debt.

Fungi

In fungi and plants too anaerobic respiration may occur. It is then known as **fermentation**. Here the result is not lactate but ethanol – an end product which people have been exploiting for many hundreds of years to make intoxicating drinks. The pyruvate is converted first to the intermediate product ethanal, by the removal of carbon dioxide which is given off as a gas. It is this carbon dioxide which is used to make bread rise and which gives beer its 'head', as figure 3.4.5 illustrates. The ethanal is then further reduced to ethanol.

Controlling the rate of glycolysis

Although ATP is often regarded as an energy store for the reactions of the body, it is perhaps better to regard it as a means of transferring energy from the food molecules to the molecules of the organism itself. ATP is not stored as such – it is made as and when it is needed. This means that it is important for the rate of glycolysis (and therefore the Krebs cycle which produces more ATP) to be tightly controlled. When energy demands are high, glycolysis needs to occur rapidly to supply plenty of pyruvic acid for the Krebs cycle. When the energy demands are low, less oxygen needs to be taken in and glycolysis must slow down so the Krebs cycle reactions proceed more slowly too.

Each individual step in the process of glycolysis is controlled by an enzyme, and these enzymes are sensitive to various substrates and products of the pathway, giving a greater or lesser degree of control. One enzyme is worth

Figure 3.4.5 The anaerobic respiration of yeast, with the glycolytic pathway ending in the production of ethanol along with carbon dioxide, is utilised by the brewing industry to produce millions of gallons of beer and lager each year.

Evidence for glycolysis

It took many years for the pathways of glycolysis and the closely associated process of alcoholic fermentation to be worked out. There are several landmarks along the way.

(1) In 1897 Eduard Buchner discovered that an extract of yeast without any cells in it could still convert glucose to ethanol. This showed that the enzymes of glycolysis and fermentation are not associated closely with the cell structure.
(2) In the early 1900s Arthur Harden and W. J. Young showed that phosphate was needed for the pathway to proceed, and also that two particular elements of the yeast extracts were needed before

fermentation could go ahead. One of these was inactivated by heat – it contained the enzymes. The other was not affected by heat in the same way and contained NAD, ADP and ATP.
(3) After work with inhibitors had allowed some of the pathway intermediates to be studied, the German biochemists Gustav Embden and Otto Meyerhof worked out much of the rest of the sequence.
(4) By the 1940s, Embden and Meyerhof, along with important contributions from others, had worked out the individual steps of the glycolysis pathway.

particular mention. **Phosphofructokinase** is an allosteric enzyme which catalyses one of the early reactions in the conversion of glucose to GALP:

$$\text{Fructose-6-phosphate} \xrightarrow{\text{PFK}} \text{fructose-1,6-diphosphate}$$

Phosphofructokinase is activated by high concentrations of ADP, and of its own substrate. It is also inhibited by high levels of ATP and citrate, an intermediate in the Krebs cycle. So when there is plenty of ATP or the components of the Krebs cycle begin to build up, the whole process of glycolysis is slowed down. Conversely, when the cell needs energy and the components of the Krebs cycle are low, glycolysis is speeded up to remedy the situation. In changing the rate of glycolysis the rate of the whole process of cellular respiration is controlled. Most biochemical pathways have particular enzymes which, like this one, play a vital role in controlling the rate of the entire pathway. They are called **regulatory enzymes**.

The Krebs cycle

The reactions of the Krebs cycle were worked out by Sir Hans Krebs. They have had an enormous impact, not just on our understanding of cellular respiration but also on our understanding of biochemical pathways in general. The cycle is also known as the **tricarboxylic acid cycle** (from the types of chemicals involved) or the **citric acid cycle** (from one of the main components of the pathway). The reactions occur in the matrix of the mitochondrion in the presence of oxygen, and are shown in figure 3.4.6.

The 3-carbon molecule pyruvate produced by the glycolysis pathway crosses the mitochondrial membrane and is immediately converted to a 2-carbon acetyl group which is linked to a coenzyme to form **acetylcoenzyme A (acetylco A)**. A molecule of carbon dioxide is removed in this reaction, along with a molecule of hydrogen which reduces NAD to $NADH_2$ and is split and passed into the electron transfer system resulting in the formation of ATP. The enzymes in this step which remove carbon dioxide are known as **decarboxylases** and those which remove hydrogen are **dehydrogenases**.

Acetylco A enters the Krebs cycle by combining with a 4-carbon compound forming the 6-carbon compound **citrate**. The Krebs cycle is a cyclical series of reactions during which the 6-carbon citrate is broken down to give the original 4-carbon compound. This then combines with more acetylco A and the cycle

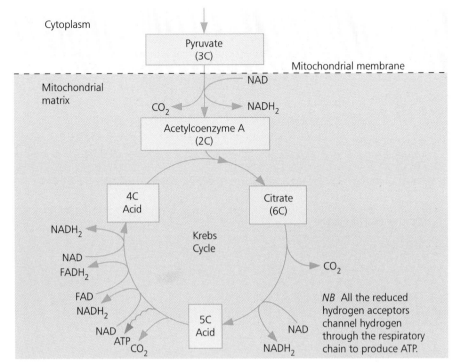

Figure 3.4.6 The Krebs cycle turns continuously to provide the cells with energy, and the rate of its turning is carefully controlled to ensure that the right amount of ATP is produced to meet the demands of the body.

turns again. As the cycle progresses two further molecules of carbon dioxide are removed, to be given off as a waste product. Also, four of the steps involve the removal of hydrogen atoms and thus the reduction of a carrier molecule. These can then be split and the electrons passed along the electron transfer chain and used to produce ATP, as described in the box opposite. The final hydrogen acceptor of the electron transfer chain is oxygen. This explains the need for oxygen by the Krebs cycle, and also the production of water as a waste product of respiration.

Depending on which carrier accepts the hydrogen atoms (for four of the reactions it is NAD but for one it is FAD), either 3 or 2 molecules of ATP will result. The repeated oxidation and reduction sequence beginning with NADH$_2$ yields 3 molecules of ATP each time. It must be remembered that for each molecule of glucose which enters the glycolytic pathway, the Krebs cycle turns twice (6-carbon glucose giving 2 molecules of 3-carbon pyruvate). The reactions of the cycle itself take place in the matrix of the mitochondrion, but the ATP is produced from the electron transfer system in the stalked particles on the inner mitochondrial membranes.

How much ATP is gained from cellular respiration?

The whole process of cellular respiration, from the beginning of glycolysis to the release of carbon dioxide and water as the Krebs cycle turns, has evolved to produce energy in the form of ATP for use in the cells. The fact that the process is the same in almost all living organisms suggests that it is a very effective method of doing just that. But exactly how much ATP is gained during the oxidation of one molecule of glucose in its journey along the respiratory pathways? The easiest way to look at this is to consider where ATP results in the whole process, and figure 3.4.8 does this. The average amount is 38 molecules of ATP assuming that glucose enters the cycle and that oxidation is complete. If this is compared with the meagre 2 molecules of ATP which

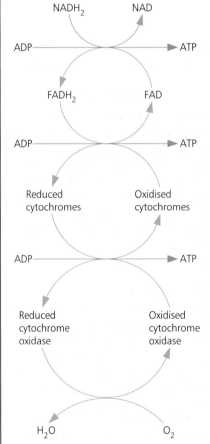

The electron transfer chain revisited

How does the electron transfer chain produce ATP? The carrier molecules sited on the inner mitochondrial membranes are alternately reduced and oxidised and these reactions are used to drive the synthesis of ATP. Oxygen is required in aerobic respiration as the final hydrogen acceptor with the production of water.

Figure 3.4.7 Another look at the electron transfer chain.

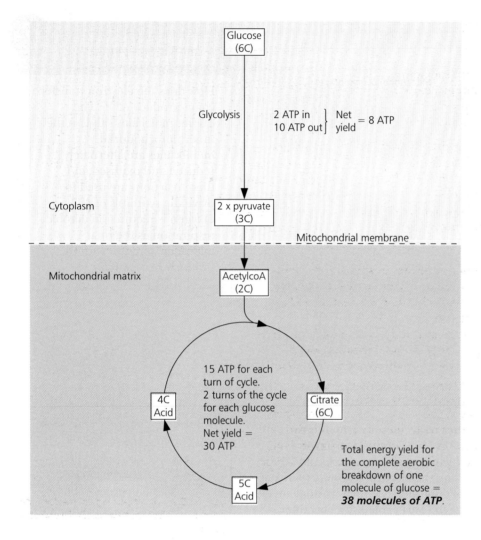

Glucose
(6C)

Glycolysis   2 ATP in ⎱ Net = 8 ATP
              10 ATP out ⎰ yield

Cytoplasm

2 x pyruvate
(3C)

Mitochondrial membrane

Mitochondrial matrix

AcetylcoA
(2C)

15 ATP for each
turn of cycle.
2 turns of the cycle
for each glucose
molecule.
Net yield =
30 ATP

4C
Acid

Citrate
(6C)

5C
Acid

Total energy yield for
the complete aerobic
breakdown of one
molecule of glucose =
38 molecules of ATP.

Figure 3.4.8 The ATP gained by the complete oxidation of a molecule of glucose in cellular respiration.

result when the breakdown of glucose is purely anaerobic, the importance of the oxygen-using process becomes clear.

Respiration of other substrates

There is not always sufficient glucose to provide all the ATP needed in a cell. When this is the case, other substances can be respired, in particular other carbohydrates and fats. It is easy to see that, for example, disaccharide sugars could be broken down and enter the pathway, but where do the other substances fit in?

Fats are an excellent source of energy. They are split by lipases into their constituent fatty acids and glycerol. The glycerol is phosphorylated and feeds into the glycolytic pathway as GALP. The fatty acids are passed through a series of reactions which split off 2-carbon sections of acetylco A. Hydrogen atoms are removed in the process and are passed through the electron transfer system to form ATP even before the acetylco A enters the Krebs cycle. The fatty acid then goes through the reaction series again to remove the next 2-carbon fragment. A single fatty acid can yield a large amount of ATP – stearic acid gives about 180 molecules. As you can see, the complete oxidation of fat gives a great deal of energy and this is why fat is a very important energy source, particularly for active tissues such as heart muscle, liver and kidneys.

Evidence for the Krebs cycle

Hans Krebs first put forward his ideas for the now famous cycle in 1937. It was the result of brilliant reasoning and experimentation in the preceding years, both by Krebs and by others.

(1) In the period 1910–20 several biochemists showed that dehydrogenases are active in minced animal tissues, transferring hydrogen atoms from certain organic acid ions known to occur in cells.
(2) In 1935 A. Szent-Györgyi produced a sequence of enzymic reactions showing the oxidation of the organic ion succinate, and it was then shown that citrate is converted to succinate in cells.
(3) At this stage Krebs stepped in to show that only certain organic acid ions are oxidised by cells, and that certain inhibitors could bring the oxidations to a halt. After much work he came up with the sequence we now know as the Krebs cycle. He also showed that all his suggested reactions could take place at a fast enough rate to account for the known use of pyruvate and oxygen by the tissue, implying that his pathway was the main if not the only pathway for the oxidation of foodstuffs.

Protein is not usually used as a respiratory substrate. It is broken down only when supplies of both carbohydrate and fat are very low – basically when the body perceives itself to be starving. The amino acids must be deaminated before the residues can be used as a substrate for respiration.

Figure 3.4.9 shows that the respiratory pathway is not only the route by which carbohydrates are broken down to provide energy. It also provides a sort of biochemical crossroads for interconversions from storage compounds such as fats, starch and glycogen to glucose, and also from carbohydrates to fats.

Even a relatively brief look at the biochemistry of photosynthesis and respiration such as we have taken in this section shows us both the complexity of the processes and the importance of controls over the rate at which the various reactions occur. This need for control is present in all aspects of living organisms, and in the next section we shall consider in more detail the ways in which this control can be brought about.

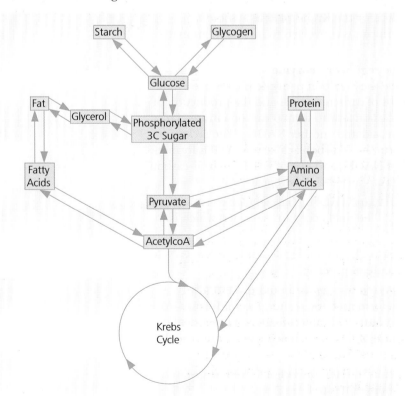

Figure 3.4.9 A biochemical 'Spaghetti Junction' – the respiratory pathways bring many strands of metabolism together.

SUMMARY

- The energy in food molecules is transferred to energy in ATP for use by cells by the process of **cellular respiration**, which uses oxygen and produces carbon dioxide and water.

- The **respiratory quotient (RQ)** is the carbon dioxide produced divided by the oxygen used by a person in a given time period. RQ values can help show which food types are being respired predominantly at a given time.

- Cellular respiration is a complex series of reactions involving two stages – **glycolysis** which can take place without oxygen and produces a little ATP, and the **Krebs cycle** which uses oxygen and the product of glycolysis to produce much more ATP.

- **Aerobic organisms** respire by the reactions of the Krebs cycle so need oxygen, though they may be able to respire anaerobically for short periods. **Anaerobic organisms** rely on glycolysis only to produce their ATP. **Facultative anaerobes** respire anaerobically only when oxygen is not available, while **obligate anaerobes** can only respire anaerobically.

- Glycolysis takes place in the cytoplasm of the cell, while the reactions of the Krebs cycle take place in the matrix of the mitochondria. ATP production involves the electron transfer chain, which is sited on the stalked particles of the cristae in the mitochondria.

- In glycolysis, a molecule of glucose is biphosphorylated using two molecules of ATP and then splits to form two 3-carbon molecules which are **GALP** and another intermediate which can be converted into GALP. GALP is converted into **pyruvate**, a process which produces 2 molecules of ATP and one of $NADH_2$ for each GALP molecule. $NADH_2$ has the potential to generate 3 molecules of ATP via the electron transfer chain, if oxygen is available as the final hydrogen acceptor.

- Pyruvate may pass into the mitochondria for the Krebs cycle in aerobic conditions. In anaerobic conditions pyruvate is converted to **lactate** in animals. In plants it is fermented to **ethanol**.

- The rate of glycolysis is controlled by the **regulatory enzyme phosphofructokinase**. In the Krebs cycle the 3-carbon pyruvate is converted into 2-carbon **acetylcoenzyme A** with the loss of carbon dioxide and the production of $NADH_2$. Acetylco A combines with a 4-carbon acid to form 6-carbon **citrate**. This loses carbon dioxide to form a 5-carbon acid and another $NADH_2$. The 5-carbon acid loses another carbon dioxide to form the 4-carbon acid again. ATP is formed at this stage along with two molecules of $NADH_2$ and one of $FADH_2$. The 4-carbon acid can then combine with more acetylco A and the cycle repeats.

- The reduced hydrogen acceptors $NADH_2$ and $FADH_2$ channel electrons through the electron transfer chain to form ATP. The final acceptor is oxygen which is reduced to form water.

- Glycolysis yields 8 ATP molecules for each glucose molecule, and the Krebs cycle 30, giving a total of **38 ATPs per molecule of glucose**.

- In the absence of glucose, fats are converted to fatty acids and glycerol. Fatty acids are split into 2-carbon sections to form acetylco A and glycerol forms GALP, so both can feed into the Krebs cycle. A fatty acid molecule gives a great deal of energy in the form of ATP. In the absence of fats or carbohydrates, amino acids may be deaminated and respired.

- The respiratory pathway provides a means of interconversions from fats, starch and glycogen to glucose, and from carbohydrates to fats.

1 a What is cellular respiration?
 b Where does cellular respiration take place?
 c What is the function of each of the following in the metabolism of a cell?
   i NAD
   ii cytochromes
   iii oxygen

2 Describe the events in the breakdown of a molecule of glucose in the muscles of an athlete:
 a in the absence of oxygen
 b in the presence of oxygen.

3 a Where are the enzymes involved in glycolysis found?
 b Where are the enzymes of the electron transport system found?
 c What is the evidence for the stated positions of both sets of enzymes?

Developing Key Skills

Write an examination question designed to enable students to show clearly their understanding of mitochondria and their role in the cell. The question should be as interesting and original as possible. It carries a total of 20 marks and must be broken down into a series of parts. The marks awarded for answering each part of the question must be clearly shown.

3

1 The drawing below shows part of the respiratory pathway. The broken arrows represent intermediate stages.

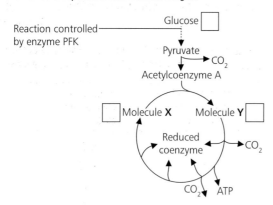

a Write in **each** of the three boxes on the diagram the number of carbon atoms in the molecules indicated. **(1 mark)**

b Give **two** different chemical processes which are involved in the conversion of Molecule **Y** to Molecule **X** in the Krebs cycle. **(2 marks)**

c ATP regulates its own production in respiration by affecting the activity of the enzyme PFK. Suggest how this regulation may be achieved through negative feedback. **(2 marks)**

(AQA, specimen 2000)

2 The diagram below summarises the biochemical pathways involved in photosynthesis.

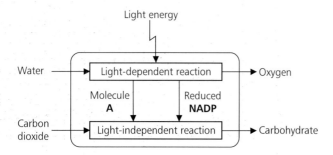

a Name Molecule **A** **(1 mark)**

b i Describe how NADP is reduced in the light-dependent reaction. **(2 marks)**

ii Describe the part played by reduced NADP in the light-dependent reaction. **(2 marks)**

(AQA, specimen 2000)

3 An indicator which turns from red to yellow in the presence of carbon dioxide was used in a class experiment designed to compare the rates of respiration of a range of different living organisms. The time it took to change colour with the same mass of each organism was recorded.

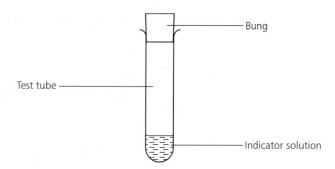

a i Show on the diagram the modification you would make to the apparatus to obtain results with blowfly larvae (maggots).

ii Before this apparatus was used to measure the rate of respiration of carrot root, the root was cut into small pieces. How might this have made the results more comparable with those obtained using maggots? **(3 marks)**

b Before the students introduced organisms into any tube, they were told to take a separate tube containing indicator and blow into it using a straw. This tube was bunged and kept on one side for the duration of the experiment. One student incorrectly described this tube as a 'control'. What was its actual purpose? **(1 mark)**

c The pooled class results are shown in the table below.

Tube	Organisms	Mean time taken for indicator to turn yellow / minutes	Relative rate of respiration
A	Blowfly larvae	15.0	
B	Carrot root	50.0	
C	Mushroom	35.0	
D	Yeast	10.0	
E	Cabbage leaves	no change	

Using the information in the table, calculate values for the relative rates of respiration of organisms A to D, taking the rate of the organism with the slowest rate to be 1.0. Enter these rates in the appropriate spaces in the table above. **(2 marks)**

d Students in the class differed in their interpretation of the results obtained with cabbage leaves. Some thought they were caused because the leaves were photosynthesising (Hypothesis 1) but others thought that the rate of respiration was too slow to be detected by this experiment (Hypothesis 2). Suggest a way in which you might modify the experiment to test each hypothesis. In **each** case use a different modification, and explain your reasoning in full.

  i Hypothesis 1
  ii Hypothesis 2   **(4 marks)**
(AQA specimen 2000)

4 The figure shows the flow of energy through the trees in a forest ecosystem. The numbers represent inputs and outputs of energy in kilojoules per m² per year.

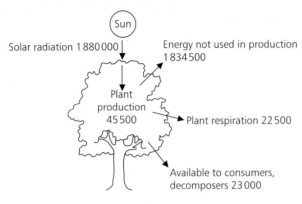

  a **i** On the figure, draw a ring around the number which indicates the energy entering the system via photosynthesis. **(1 mark)**
      ii The total energy available to the plants in the ecosystem is 1 880 000 kJ per m² per year. Calculate the efficiency of photosynthesis. Show your working. **(2 marks)**
  b Suggest **four** reasons why so much solar energy is **not** used in production in the forest ecosystem. **(4 marks)**
  c In what form will energy from plant respiration escape from the ecosystem? **(1 mark)**
(OCR specimen 2000)

5 The figure shows a diagram of a longitudinal section of a villus, from the small intestine, highly magnified.

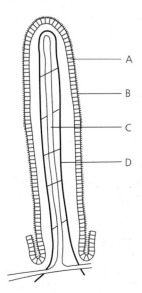

  a **i** On the figure, label structures A to D. **(4 marks)**
      ii Put a ring around the figure below which is the most appropriate for the actual length of the villus.
        2.5 mm   15 mm   2.5 μm   0.75 mm   250 μm
(1 mark)

  b **i** State in which tissue you would expect to find goblet cells.
(1 mark)

      ii Explain their function. **(1 mark)**
  c Explain how the products of digestion pass across the outer membrane of the cells labelled A in the figure. **(9 marks)**
(OCR specimen 2000)

6 The table shows the rate of phosphate absorption by barley roots in a solution aerated with different mixtures of nitrogen and oxygen,

Percentage of oxygen in aeration mixture	Phosphate absorption/ μmol g⁻¹ h⁻¹
0.1	0.07
0.3	0.15
0.9	0.27
2.1	0.32
21.0	0.33

  a State the conclusions that can be drawn about phosphate absorption from the data in the table. **(3 marks)**

The figure shows the rate of phosphate absorption by barley roots placed in solutions containing different concentrations of DNP (2,4-dinitrophenol). DNP is an uncoupler of the electron transport chain. Each solution was aerated with 21% oxygen.

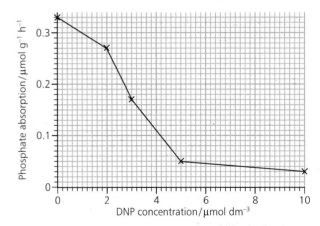

  b With reference to the figure, describe and explain the effect on phosphate absorption of adding DNP to barley roots. **(4 marks)**

Malonate is an inhibitor of the Krebs cycle.

  c **i** Predict the effect of adding malonate instead of DNP, on the uptake of phosphate by the barley roots. **(1 mark)**
      ii Explain your answer to **i**. **(3 marks)**
  d Discuss the significance of phosphate for living organisms.
(6 marks)
(OCR specimen 2000)

7 Living organisms exchange materials with their environment. These exchanges occur across surfaces which have special features. With reference to **named** examples, discuss how these surfaces are adapted for efficient exchange. (*In this question, 1 mark is available for the quality of written communication*.) **(10 marks)**

(OCR specimen 2000)

8 The flow chart represents the breakdown of starch in the human gut.

starch $\xrightarrow{\text{amylase}}$ maltose $\xrightarrow{\text{maltase}}$ glucose

a Name **two** organs which produce amylase in humans. **(1 mark)**

b Describe how the release of amylase from each of these organs is controlled. **(3 marks)**

c Describe the precise location of maltase in the human gut. **(2 marks)**

(AQA June 1999)

9 Cockroaches are insects. The table shows the rates of oxygen consumption and carbon dioxide production of cockroaches kept under different conditions.

Time after last fed/hours	Temperature/°C	Rate of oxygen consumption/ $cm^3\ g^{-1}\ hour^{-1}$	Rate of carbon dioxide/production $cm^3\ g^{-1}\ hour^{-1}$
1	20	2.82	2.82
72	20	2.82	1.97
1	30	5.12	5.12
72	30	5.12	3.57

a When the temperature is raised from 20 °C to 30 °C, the cockroach becomes more active and its respiration rate and oxygen consumption increase. What causes the increase in respiration rate? **(1 mark)**

b i Calculate the Respiratory Quotient (RQ) of a cockroach kept at a temperature of 20 °C, 72 hours after it had last been fed. Show your working. **(2 marks)**

ii The rate of carbon dioxide production by cockroaches is less 72 hours after they were last fed than it is 1 hour after they were last fed. Explain why. **(2 marks)**

(AQA, January 1999)

10 The diagram shows the main steps in the biochemical pathways involved in respiration.

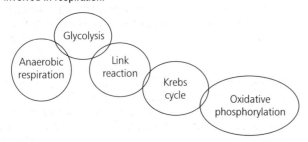

a i Which step or steps take place on the cristae of the mitochondria? **(1 mark)**

ii In which step or steps is carbon dioxide produced in an animal cell? **(1 mark)**

b If a pond freezes over during the winter, goldfish can remain alive in the water under the ice. Explain why they use the carbohydrate stores in their bodies much faster in these conditions. **(2 marks)**

c What is the main difference between the way in which ATP is produced by oxidative phosphorylation and the way in which it is produced in photosynthesis? **(1 mark)**

(AQA January 1999)

11 Photosynthesis takes place in the chloroplasts. These are disc-shaped organelles surrounded by an outer envelope consisting of two layers of membrane. Inside, there are further membranes which are arranged in stacks called grana. Surrounding these is the stroma. Chlorophyll and other light-capturing pigments are found on the membranes of the grana and it is here that the light-dependent reaction takes place. This generates the ATP and reduced NADP which are used in the light-independent reaction in the stroma.

a Suggest how you could use chromatography to separate and identify the different light-capturing pigments present in leaf tissue. **(5 marks)**

b i Describe the way in which ATP and reduced NADP are produced in the light-dependent reaction of photosynthesis.

ii Explain how ATP and reduced NADP are used in the light-independent reaction of photosynthesis. **(4 marks)**

c Using the information in the passage, describe how the structure of a chloroplast is adapted to its function in photosynthesis. **(3 marks)**

(Quality of language 3 marks)

(AQA June 1999)

12 The graph shows the total amount of gastric juice secreted over a four hour period following a meal. The curves **A** and **B** show the individual contributions made to the total secretion of gastric juice by nervous and hormonal stimulation.

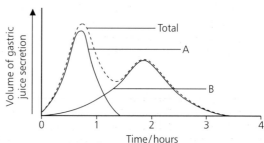

a Which of the curves, **A** or **B**, represents gastric juice secretion resulting from nervous stimulation? Give a reason for your answer. **(1 mark)**

b Name the hormone which stimulates the secretion of gastric juice. **(1 mark)**

c Suggest the advantage in having the secretion of gastric juice controlled by both nervous and hormonal systems. **(2 marks)**

d Some people produce excessive amounts of gastric juice which can aggravate stomach ulcers. One treatment for stomach ulcers is cutting the connections of the parasympathetic nerve to the stomach. Suggest how this treatment is effective. **(2 marks)**

(AQA March 1999)

13 a The process of photosynthesis can be subdivided into two stages, one dependent on light, the other independent of light.

  i Complete the table to show the substances used in and the end products of each of these stages. (Do not include solar energy.)

	Light dependent stage	Light independent stage
Substances used	1. Water	1. Reduced NADP
	2. Inorganic phosphate	2. ATP
	3. ADP	3. ....
	4. NADP	4. ....
End products	1. ATP	1. NADP
	2.	2. ADP
	3.	3. Inorganic phosphate
		4. Carbohydrate

(**2 marks**)

  ii What are the functions of reduced NADP and ATP in the light dependent stage of photosynthesis? (**2 marks**)

b The graph shows the effect of temperature on the rate of photosynthesis.

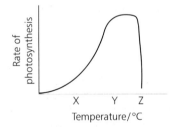

  i Explain why increasing the temperature from **X** °C to **Y** °C increases the rate of photosynthesis. (**2 marks**)

  ii Explain why increasing the temperature from **Y** °C to **Z** °C decreases the rate of photosynthesis. (**2 marks**)

(AQA June 1999)

14 In an investigation of digestion in fungi, three Petri dishes with agar medium containing equal concentrations of starch were used. Equal sized samples of three different saprophytic fungi were placed in the centre of the agar in each dish. After incubating for 48 hours, each dish was flooded with iodine solution and the diameter of the clear area was measured. The diagrams show the appearance of the dishes after 48 hours.

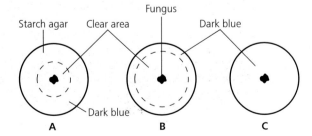

a Explain the appearance of the agar in Petri dishes **A** and **B** after flooding with iodine solution. (**4 marks**)

b What do the results of the investigation suggest about fungus **C**? (**1 mark**)

(AQA, March 1999)

15 The diagram shows chemical pathways involved in respiration and photosynthesis.

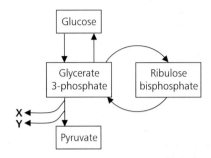

a Name the process that produces pyruvate from glucose. (**1 mark**)

b Name the compounds labelled **X** and **Y**. (**2 marks**)

c i In which part of a chloroplast is glycerate 3-phosphate converted into ribulose bisphosphate? (**1 mark**)

  ii Describe the role of ribulose bisphosphate in photosynthesis. (**1 mark**)

(AQA June 1999)

16 a i A living organism is respiring aerobically and the respiratory substrate is glucose. Explain, with the aid of a suitable equation, how the respiratory quotient (RQ) is calculated. (**3 marks**)

  ii The RQ of a hibernating animal, such as a dormouse, living entirely on its reserve store of fat, would differ from the above RQ. Suppose the fat is represented by 'triolein', $C_{57}H_{104}O_6$, and each molecule of this requires 80 molecules of oxygen for complete oxidation to CO_2 and H_2O (there being no other products). Give the representative equation and calculate the RQ for the hibernating dormouse. (Show your working.) (**2 marks**)

b i The RQ for an adult human being at rest is normally about 0.85. What does this suggest about the body's source of energy? (**1 mark**)

  ii Patients with lung disease and breathing difficulties are sometimes given diets which include fat but are deliberately low in carbohydrate. Suggest how this might benefit the patient. (**2 marks**)

(OCR, June 1998)

17 Explain what is understood by the term *vitamin*. Using appropriate examples, describe some of the ways in which vitamins are important in the metabolism of living organisms. In your answer, point out what may happen if the vitamins you mention are in short supply. (**14 marks**)

(OCR June 1998)

4 CONTROL SYSTEMS

Introduction

Coordination and control are key issues for success in larger animals and plants. These multicellular organisms need a system of communication between the cells of the body to enable, for example, plants to open leaves and flowers in response to light and animals to move around to hunt other animals or change their behaviour as a female becomes fertile.

Control in an organism can be brought about in two basic ways – nervous control and chemical control. Nervous control systems occur in animals, and provide the fastest possible forms of communication in the body. The biochemistry of these electrical messages is both complex and fascinating. The sensory regions of a nervous system detect changes in both the internal and external environment. These sensory areas may be relatively simple, or highly developed organs such as the human eye. Nerves carry messages from the sense organs to the central nervous system, which processes the incoming information and sends out suitable commands to bring about a response in other organs such as muscles. In some animals the nervous system also provides the seat of conscious thought, with its associated aspirations and emotions.

Chemical control systems generally, though not always, work more slowly than nervous ones, but they are no less important. Chemical control ensures that growth and reproduction take place, that the blood sugar is regulated, that caterpillars turn into butterflies and that plants move their leaves to face the Sun. The chemical messages are often produced in special glands, and they bring about their effects by binding to specific receptor molecules in the membranes of their target cells.

Control systems work together to coordinate the different parts of the body, and to bring about that most important state for a living organism – homeostasis. This means that the internal environment of an animal or plant is kept the same regardless of fluctuations in the conditions around it. Successful homeostasis is the key to life in a complex organism, allowing all its cells to function and work together in an environment that suits them.

Figure 1 Communication both within and between organisms is vital – the peacock provides a dramatic example.

FOCUS THE TALKING APES

In the animal world, coordination does not take place just within the body – communication between individual animals and between groups of animals plays an important part in life too. In human beings, communication between people is a vital facet of our way of life. The most striking thing about human communication is our use of language, and for many years this ability to talk to each other, to express abstract ideas in language, has been considered unique to people.

Aping humans?

Biologically, our closest relatives are the great apes, highly intelligent animals with complex social interactions. But are they capable of anything approaching human language? The vocal cords of apes are simply not capable of human speech, so researchers have tried alternative languages to allow apes to communicate with them. The first breakthrough came in the 1960s, when Beatrix and R. Allen Gardner taught American sign language for the deaf to a chimpanzee called Washoe. Washoe appeared to be able to use the language to express his own wants. This work has been continued, first with sign language and more recently using computers and specific symbols linked to words. Another husband and wife team, Duane Rumbaugh and Sue Savage-Rumbaugh, have developed a portable keyboard which apes, including chimpanzees, bonobos and gorillas, can use to communicate with them.

Figure 1 People do not always need language to communicate. Non-verbal communication – body language, gestures and expressions also allows us to make our feelings known.

Kanzi and friends

One of the apes being studied using this keyboard is a young male called Kanzi. He has a vocabulary of about 149 words, and has been shown through rigorous testing to understand spoken English at the same level as a $2\frac{1}{2}$-year-old child. He can carry out commands, such as 'take the peas and beans to Kelly,' and instructions, such as 'Stab the ball with the stick.' Kanzi followed his instructions correctly 74% of the time, while a $2\frac{1}{2}$-year-old child tested at the same time in the same way had a 66% success rate!

Apes have used this new language inventively to try and explain unfamiliar situations, and have been shown to have some awareness of other people's thoughts and feelings. Direct communication like this between two species is fascinating and exciting, but it also raises some serious questions. If we can use language to open a window into the minds of our closest relatives, to begin to find out their thoughts and feelings, then surely we will need to reassess the way we treat them both in the wild and, more importantly, in our medical and scientific research laboratories.

Figure 2 Research programmes that provide non-human primates like these with language allow us surprisingly intimate communication. When Panbanisha, a bonobo, was travelling quietly in the car with a researcher she was asked what she was thinking about. 'Kanzi,' (another ape) she replied.

4.1 Nervous control

All living organisms have a basic need for control systems. The complex biochemistry of all cells needs to be controlled to ensure that the right products are available at the right time. Processes such as digestion in animals need to be controlled to make sure that food is digested and body tissues are not. Growth must occur at the appropriate time and place, food and mates must be found and danger avoided. One of the most important requirements for controlling all of these factors is a system of rapid internal communication.

Chemical and nervous communication

Messages may be transmitted in two main ways within a living organism to provide a communication system. Specific chemical messengers may be released by cells. Within single-celled organisms these can carry information by diffusion very rapidly over the small distances involved. Chemical messages are used for communication between the different parts within a plant, and some aspects of control in animals are carried out in this way too. We shall be looking at chemical control in more detail in sections 4.4 and 4.5. But for many animals a relatively large size, combined with the need to move around and react rapidly to the external as well as the internal environment, means that chemical communications alone are not adequate. Such organisms have evolved a **nervous system** which uses electrical rather than chemical signals. Even simple, sedentary animals such as sea anemones have systems of specialised cells known as **nerves**, whose function is to carry electrical messages around the organism in a faster and more targeted way than would be possible with a chemical message.

What is a nervous system?

A nervous system is made up of interconnected **nerve cells** specialised for the rapid transmission of messages throughout the organism. The nerve cells carry messages from special **receptor cells**, giving information to the organism about both the internal and the external environment. Nerve cells also carry messages to specialised **effector cells** – often muscles – which then bring about the appropriate response.

The organisation of nervous systems

At its most simple, a nervous system consists of receptor cells and effector cells connected by nerve cells, as shown in figure 4.1.1. However, in many organisms the nervous system is much more complex than this. Groups of receptors have evolved to work together in **sensory organs** such as the eye and the ear. Simple diffuse nerve nets are replaced by complex nerve pathways. Some nerves carry information in one direction only, from the internal or external environment into the central processing areas of the nervous system. These are known as **sensory nerves**. **Motor nerves** carry messages only to the effector organs. More specialised concentrations of nerve cells develop in some animals to give rise to a **central nervous system** (**CNS**), an area where incoming information is processed and coordinated and from where messages are sent out into the

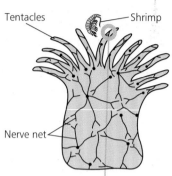

The tentacle of a sea anemone detects the presence of prey. Messages are sent through the nerve net to control the other tentacles, causing them to bend over and help to capture the shrimp.

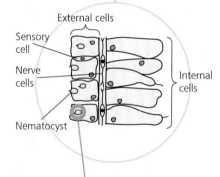

Messages travelling through the nerve net also stimulate the firing of the 'attack or defence' system of the sea anemone. Cells called nematoblasts may release a poisoned dart from their nematocyst to paralyse the prey or sticky threads to help hold it tight.

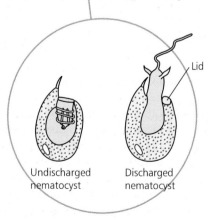

Figure 4.1.1 The nerve net of the sea anemone allows coordinated action by the whole animal.

motor nerves. In vertebrates the central nervous system consists of the **brain** and **spinal cord**.

Nerve cells

Nerve cells or **neurones** are the basic unit of a nervous system – millions of neurones work together as an integrated whole in mammals such as ourselves. Neurones are cells specialised for the transmission of electrical signals (**impulses**). They have a cell body which contains the cell nucleus, mitochondria and other organelles along with **Nissl's granules**, prominent groups of ribosomes for protein synthesis. The cell body has slender finger-like processes called **dendrites** which connect with neighbouring nerve cells. The most distinctive feature of all nerve cells is the **nerve fibre**. This is called the **axon** if it transmits impulses away from the cell body, and the **dendron** if it transmits impulses towards the cell body. The nerve fibre is extremely long and thin, as shown in figure 4.1.2, and carries the nerve impulse.

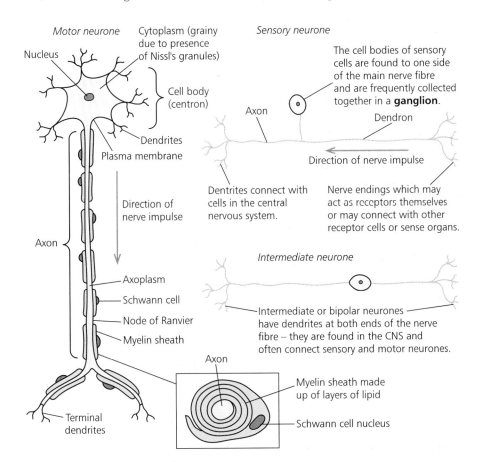

Motor neurone

Nucleus
Cytoplasm (grainy due to presence of Nissl's granules)
Cell body (centron)
Dendrites
Plasma membrane
Direction of nerve impulse
Axon
Axoplasm
Schwann cell
Node of Ranvier
Myelin sheath
Terminal dendrites

Sensory neurone

The cell bodies of sensory cells are found to one side of the main nerve fibre and are frequently collected together in a **ganglion**.

Axon
Dendron
Direction of nerve impulse
Dentrites connect with cells in the central nervous system.
Nerve endings which may act as receptors themselves or may connect with other receptor cells or sense organs.

Intermediate neurone

Intermediate or bipolar neurones have dendrites at both ends of the nerve fibre – they are found in the CNS and often connect sensory and motor neurones.

Axon
Myelin sheath made up of layers of lipid
Schwann cell nucleus

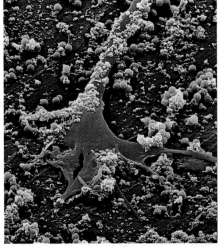

A motor neurone

Figure 4.1.2 All nerve cells have the same basic structure of a cell body, dendrites and a nerve fibre. The detailed arrangements vary in motor, sensory and intermediate neurones.

Some vertebrate neurones are associated with another specialised type of cell, the **Schwann cell**. The Schwann cell membrane is wrapped repeatedly around the neurone, forming a fatty layer known as the **myelin sheath**. This sheath has gaps in it known as the **nodes of Ranvier**. The myelin sheath is important for two reasons – it protects the nerves from damage, and speeds up the transmission of the nerve impulse, as we shall see later.

Nerve fibres are bundled together to form **nerves**. Some carry only motor fibres and are known as **motor nerves**, some carry only sensory fibres and are known as **sensory nerves**, whilst others carry a mixture of motor and sensory fibres and are called **mixed nerves**.

Speed of transmission in neurones

The role of neurones is the passage of electrical messages from one area of an organism to another as fast as possible. The speed at which the messages can be carried depends largely on two things. The first is the diameter of the nerve fibre. In general, the larger the fibre, the more rapidly impulses travel along it. The second is the presence or absence of a myelin sheath. Myelinated nerve fibres can carry impulses much faster than unmyelinated ones.

Invertebrates do not have myelin sheaths on any of their nerve fibres, and many of their fibres are less than 0.1 mm in diameter, so in general invertebrate nerve impulses travel quite slowly, at around 0.5 m s^{-1}. But there are times when even a relatively slow-moving invertebrate needs to react quickly to avoid danger, and to allow for a more rapid passage of impulses many groups have evolved **giant axons**. These are nerve fibres with diameters of around 1 mm which allow impulses to travel at around 100 m s^{-1}, fast enough for most escape strategies to have a chance of success.

Vertebrates have both myelinated and unmyelinated nerves. The voluntary motor nerves that transmit impulses to voluntary muscles, for example to control movement, are myelinated while the autonomic nerves that control involuntary muscles such as those in the digestive system have some unmyelinated fibres. There is more about the voluntary and autonomic nervous systems in section 4.2. The effect of the myelin sheath is to speed up the transmission of a nerve impulse without the need for giant axons. A more versatile network of relatively small nerve fibres can carry messages extremely rapidly, at speeds of up to 120 m s^{-1}.

Figure 4.1.3 Invertebrates like this squid have giant axons to give them rapid responses when they need to escape from danger.

Nerve impulses

What is a nerve impulse?

The nervous system carries nerve impulses very rapidly from one part of the body to another. But what is a nerve impulse? The attempt to discover the answer to this question began many years ago. Long before Georg Ohm and Michael Faraday made their contributions to the understanding and measurement of electricity at the beginning of the nineteenth century, two other famous scientists had a dispute over the electrical activity of the body. In 1791 Luigi Galvani discovered that the muscles in severed frogs' legs twitched when touched by brass and iron simultaneously. He thought this was the result of what he called 'animal electricity'. A few years later Alessandro Volta showed that the effect was in fact due to the difference in electrical potential between the two metals, and nothing to do with animal electricity in the muscles at all. This dispute at the end of the eighteenth century was the starting point for a huge range of experiments in physiology, physics and physical chemistry which has led to our present day understanding of the nature of the nerve impulse.

The nerve impulse is a minute electrical event which is the result of charge differences across the membrane of the nerve fibre. It is based on ion movements through specialised protein pores and by an active transport mechanism. To look at the events of a nerve impulse we shall consider a 'typical' axon – ignoring for the moment size, myelination or type.

The resting neurone

The membrane of an axon, like any other cell surface membrane, is partially permeable. It is the difference in permeability of this membrane to sodium and potassium ions which sets neurones apart from other cells and gives them their special conducting properties. The axon membrane is relatively impermeable to sodium ions, but quite freely permeable to potassium ions. It also contains a very active sodium/potassium pump which uses ATP to move sodium ions out of the axon and potassium ions in. The effect of this is to reduce the concentration of sodium ions inside the axon – they are pumped out and cannot diffuse back in. At the same time, potassium ions are moved in – but then diffuse out again along a concentration gradient. As a result, the inside of the cell is left slightly negatively charged relative to the outside – it is **polarised**, as shown in figure 4.1.4. There is a potential difference across the membrane of –70 mV which is known as the **resting potential**.

Potassium ions diffuse out of the axon along a concentration gradient, leaving the axoplasm negative with respect to the surrounding medium.

The sodium pump actively moves sodium ions out of the axon and potassium ions in. This uses ATP.

The membrane is impermeable to sodium ions so they cannot move back in by diffusion, and the concentration of positive ions builds up outside the axon.

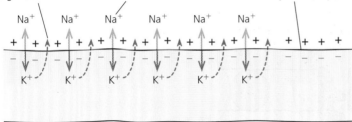

Figure 4.1.4 The resting potential of the axon is maintained by the sodium pump, the relative permeability of the membrane and the movement of potassium ions.

The active neurone

The resting potential represents the normal situation in the nervous system. What happens when an impulse travels along an axon? The key event in an active nerve fibre is a change in the permeability of the cell surface membrane to sodium ions. This change occurs in response to a **stimulus** which in a living organism could be one of a variety of things – light, sound, touch, taste or smell, for example. In the experimental laboratory situation the stimulus is usually a minute and precisely controlled electrical impulse.

When a neurone is stimulated the axon membrane shows a sudden and dramatic increase in its permeability to sodium ions. Specific **sodium channels** or **sodium gates** open up, allowing sodium ions to rush in along both concentration and electrochemical gradients. As a result the potential difference across the membrane is briefly reversed, the cell becoming positive on the inside with respect to the outside. This **depolarisation** lasts about 1 millisecond. The potential difference across the membrane at this point is about +40 mV. This is known as the **action potential**.

At the end of this brief depolarisation, the sodium channels close again and the excess sodium ions are rapidly pumped out by the sodium pump. Also, the permeability of the membrane to potassium ions is temporarily increased so that potassium ions diffuse out along an electrochemical gradient. It takes a few milliseconds before the resting potential is restored and the nerve fibre is ready to carry another impulse, as figure 4.1.5 shows. It is this **refractory period** which ensures that the nerve impulse only travels in one direction. Until the resting potential is restored, the part of the nerve fibre that the impulse has just left cannot conduct another impulse, so the impulse can only continue travelling in the same direction.

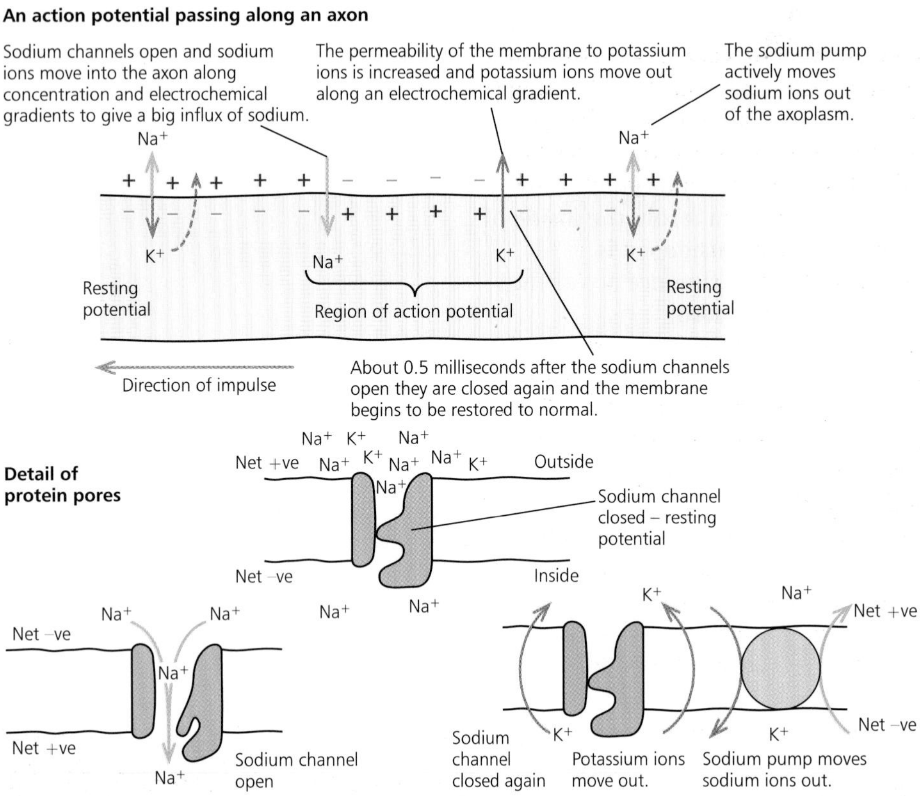

An action potential passing along an axon

Sodium channels open and sodium ions move into the axon along concentration and electrochemical gradients to give a big influx of sodium.

The permeability of the membrane to potassium ions is increased and potassium ions move out along an electrochemical gradient.

The sodium pump actively moves sodium ions out of the axoplasm.

Na$^+$

Na$^+$

+ + + + + − − − − + + + + +
− − − − + + + + − − − − −

K$^+$ Na$^+$ K$^+$ K$^+$

Resting potential   Region of action potential   Resting potential

Direction of impulse

About 0.5 milliseconds after the sodium channels open they are closed again and the membrane begins to be restored to normal.

Figure 4.1.5 The action potential is brought about by the movement of sodium ions through the opened sodium channels. The resting situation is restored by the closing of the channels, the action of the sodium pump removing excess sodium ions and the movement of potassium ions out along an electrochemical gradient.

Detail of protein pores

Na$^+$ K$^+$ Na$^+$
Net +ve Na$^+$ K$^+$ Na$^+$ Na$^+$ K$^+$ Outside
Na$^+$

Sodium channel closed – resting potential

Net −ve   Inside

Na$^+$ Na$^+$ Na$^+$ Na$^+$ K$^+$ Na$^+$

Net −ve   Net +ve
Na$^+$

Net +ve   Net −ve
Na$^+$ K$^+$ K$^+$

Sodium channel open   Sodium channel closed again   Potassium ions move out.   Sodium pump moves sodium ions out.

Evidence for the nerve impulse mechanism

Some of the most convincing evidence for this model of the nerve impulse comes from work done using poisons. A metabolic poison such as dinitrophenol prevents the production of ATP. It also prevents the nerve fibre from functioning properly. But how does this confirm the active pumping out of sodium ions and the movement of potassium ions due to differential permeability?

(1) When an axon is treated with a metabolic poison the sodium pump runs down and the resting potential is lost at the same rate as ATP is used up by the poison. This suggests that ATP is being used to power the pump – when it runs out, the pump no longer works.

(2) If the poison is washed away, the metabolism returns to normal and ATP production begins again. The resting potential is restored, suggesting that the sodium pump started up again with the return of ATP (see figure 4.1.6).

(3) If a poisoned axon is supplied with ATP by experimenters, the resting potential will be at least partly restored. This again confirms our model, suggesting that the poison is acting by depriving

the sodium pump of energy rather than by interfering with the membrane structure and its permeability. If the latter were the case, then supplying ATP to the pump would have no effect because ions would move freely across the membrane and a potential difference could not be maintained.

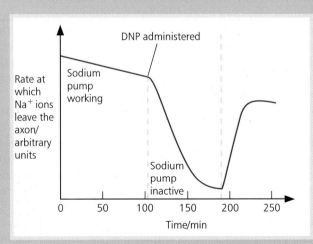

Figure 4.1.6 This graph, based on work by Hodgkin and Keynes in 1955, illustrates clearly the effect of dinitrophenol on the removal of sodium ions from the axon of a cuttlefish.

Investigating nerve impulses

Because the nerve impulse is an electrical event, albeit a very small one, an effective way of investigating it is to record and measure the electrical changes in a nerve. This is done using apparatus sensitive to small electrical changes, usually a **cathode ray oscilloscope**. A pair of recording electrodes is placed on a nerve which is then given a controlled stimulus. The impulses which result are detected by the electrodes and passed into an amplifier which magnifies them. They are then passed to the oscilloscope and displayed on a screen.

Much of the earliest work on nerves and nerve impulses was carried out using this method. The recordings of nerve impulses were taken from the outsides of entire nerves, made up of large numbers of different nerve fibres. These fibres are of varying diameter and sensitivity, and so the results of the recordings can be difficult to interpret. As most nerve fibres are around $20\ \mu m$ in diameter, making a recording from inside is not an easy procedure. The breakthrough came around 40 years ago when Alan Hodgkin and Andrew Huxley began work on the giant axons of the squid. These unmyelinated nerve fibres are around 1 mm in diameter. They supply the mantle muscles of the squid and allow for very rapid nerve transmission in situations when the squid needs to move quickly, either when hunting or when escaping. The development of electrodes which could be inserted inside these giant axons allowed a far greater understanding of the events of the action potential.

Action potentials – the inside story

For work on the squid giant axons, very fine glass microelectrodes were made which could be inserted into the giant axon. Another electrode recorded the electrical potential from the outside. This combination of an internal and an external electrode allowed the electrical changes during the passage of an individual nerve impulse to be accurately recorded for the first time, as figure 4.1.7 shows. Since the early revolutionary work by Hodgkin and Huxley, they and others have refined the techniques so that now internal electrodes can be used with almost any nerve fibre.

Figure 4.1.7 Comparing the traces for the internal electrode with that made with external electrodes from a whole nerve shows the impact of internal electrodes on our understanding of nerve impulses.

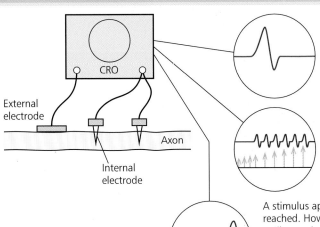

The events of a single action potential (also known as the 'spike' due to the shape of the oscilloscope trace). The trace shows clearly the change in the potential difference with the inrush of sodium ions followed by a return to the resting potential as the permeability of the membrane changes again.

A stimulus applied to a single axon gets no response until it reaches a certain threshold level. Beyond that threshold, the size of the response is always the same. However much the stimulus increases in size, the impulse in the nerve fibre is identical. This is the 'all-or-nothing law' – a nerve fibre either carries an impulse or it does not.

A stimulus applied to a whole nerve also gets no response until a threshold is reached. However, as the strength of the stimulus increases, so does the response until a maximum is reached. Without further knowledge, it looks as if the strength of the nerve impulse increases in response to the strength of the stimulus. But from work on individual axons we know that different nerve fibres have different thresholds. Once the threshold is reached they obey the 'all-or-nothing law'. Thus in a whole nerve, as the stimulus is increased, the threshold of more and more nerve fibres is reached until all the fibres in the nerve are responding.

A closer look at the nerve impulse

Work using techniques such as those just described has allowed us to build up the detailed picture of the events of the action potential shown in figure 4.1.8, including the timing and the cause of the refractory period. It has also led to an understanding of many other observed aspects of nervous transmission.

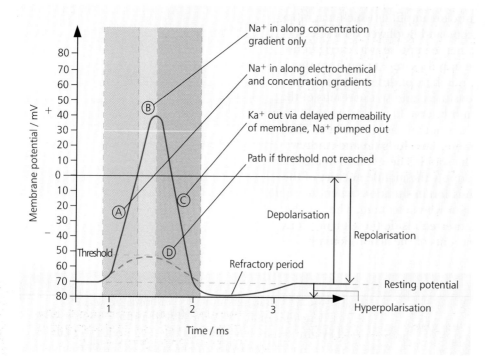

Figure 4.1.8 A representation of an action potential combining information from recordings made using an internal electrode and the movements of ions which cause the observed electrical changes.

The threshold

The **threshold** for any nerve fibre is the point at which sufficient sodium channels open such that the rush of sodium ions into the axon is greater than the outflow of potassium ions. Once the threshold has been reached, the action potential occurs. The size of this action potential is always the same – it is an **all-or-nothing** response.

The refractory period

The **refractory period** is the time it takes for an area of the axon membrane to recover after an action potential, that is, the time it takes for ionic movements to repolarise the membrane and restore the resting potential. As we have seen, this is brought about by the sodium pump and the membrane permeability to potassium ions. For the first millisecond or so after the action potential it is impossible to restimulate the nerve fibre – the sodium channels are completely blocked and the resting potential has not yet been restored. This is known as the **absolute refractory period**. After this there is a period of several milliseconds during which the nerve fibre may be restimulated, but it will only respond to a much stronger stimulus than before – the threshold has effectively been raised. This is known as the **relative refractory period**.

The refractory period is important in the functioning of the nervous system as a whole. It limits the frequency with which impulses may flow along a nerve fibre to 500–1000 each second. It also ensures that impulses flow in only one direction along nerves, making it possible to have motor and sensory systems with no internal confusion.

The propagation of the nerve impulse

So far we have considered the action potential as an isolated event in one area of a nerve fibre. In fact, once an action potential has been set up in response to a stimulus, it will travel the entire length of that fibre, which may be many centimetres or even metres long. How is the impulse **propagated** (spread)?

The movement of the nerve impulse along the axon is the result of local currents set up by the ion movements at the action potential itself. They occur both in front of and behind the action potential, and depolarise the membrane sufficiently to cause the sodium channels to open in front of the action potential, as shown in figure 4.1.9. (The refractory period prevents the sodium channels opening behind the spike.) In this way the impulse is continually propagated in the required direction.

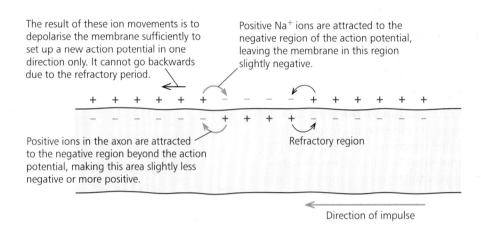

The result of these ion movements is to depolarise the membrane sufficiently to set up a new action potential in one direction only. It cannot go backwards due to the refractory period.

Positive Na$^+$ ions are attracted to the negative region of the action potential, leaving the membrane in this region slightly negative.

Positive ions in the axon are attracted to the negative region beyond the action potential, making this area slightly less negative or more positive.

Refractory region

Direction of impulse

Figure 4.1.9 Tiny local currents propagate the action potential along a nerve fibre. The refractory period ensures that it moves in only one direction.

Saltatory conduction

In myelinated vertebrate nerves, the mechanism of propagation is slightly more complex. Ions can only pass freely into and out of the axon at the nodes of Ranvier, which are about 1 mm apart. This means that action potentials can only occur at the nodes, and so they appear to jump from one node to the next, as figure 4.1.10 shows. The effect of this is to speed up transmission, as the ionic movements associated with the action potential occur much less frequently, taking less time. This conduction is known as **saltatory conduction** from the Latin verb *saltare*, which means 'to jump'.

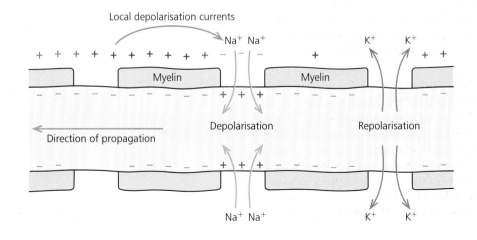

Local depolarisation currents

Na$^+$ Na$^+$ K$^+$ K$^+$

Myelin   Myelin

Depolarisation   Repolarisation

Direction of propagation

Na$^+$ Na$^+$ K$^+$ K$^+$

Figure 4.1.10 By 'jumping' from node to node along a myelinated nerve fibre, the nerve impulses can travel very rapidly along very narrow axons – allowing the development of complex but compact nervous systems.

The nerves are the basic units of the nervous system, adapted for the rapid passage of electrical impulses from one region to another. But nerves must be able to intercommunicate. Receptors must pass their information into the sensory nerves, which in turn must relay the information to the central nervous system. Information needs to pass freely around the central nervous system and the messages sent along the motor nerves must be communicated to the effector organs so that action can be taken. How is this intercommunication brought about?

Synapses

Wherever two nerve cells meet they are linked by a **synapse**, as shown in figure 4.1.11. Every cell in the central nervous system is covered with synaptic knobs from other cells – several hundred in some cases. Neurones never actually touch their target cell, so a synapse is a gap between two nerve cells which the nerve messages must somehow cross.

The electrical nature of the nerve impulse was deduced long before it could be accurately recorded and measured. Similarly, it was suspected that transmission at the synapses was not electrical but chemical long before the electron microscope and other techniques could demonstrate this clearly. Once the structure of the synapse had been seen using the electron microscope the synaptic gap could be measured. This settled the argument – the gap is simply too wide for an impulse the size of an action potential to jump across. Synaptic transmission had to be chemical – and all the available evidence confirms this.

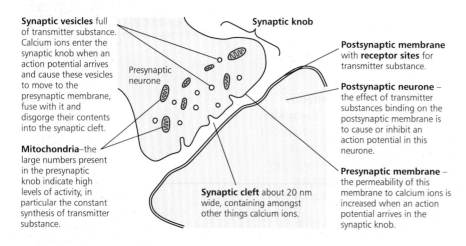

Synaptic vesicles full of transmitter substance. Calcium ions enter the synaptic knob when an action potential arrives and cause these vesicles to move to the presynaptic membrane, fuse with it and disgorge their contents into the synaptic cleft.

Mitochondria–the large numbers present in the presynaptic knob indicate high levels of activity, in particular the constant synthesis of transmitter substance.

Presynaptic neurone

Synaptic knob

Synaptic cleft about 20 nm wide, containing amongst other things calcium ions.

Postsynaptic membrane with **receptor sites** for transmitter substance.

Postsynaptic neurone – the effect of transmitter substances binding on the postsynaptic membrane is to cause or inhibit an action potential in this neurone.

Presynaptic membrane – the permeability of this membrane to calcium ions is increased when an action potential arrives in the synaptic knob.

Figure 4.1.11 The structure of the synapse as revealed by the electron microscope. Once these details were revealed, the way in which the system functions could be worked out in detail.

The synapse at work

The arrival of an impulse at the synaptic knob increases the permeability of the presynaptic membrane to calcium ions. Calcium ions therefore move into the synaptic knob along a concentration gradient. The effect of these calcium ions is to cause the synaptic vesicles containing transmitter substance to move to the presynaptic membrane. Each vesicle contains about 3000 molecules of transmitter. Some of the vesicles fuse with the membrane and release the transmitter substance into the synaptic cleft. The transmitter diffuses across the gap and becomes attached to specific protein receptor sites on the postsynaptic membrane. As a result, ion channels are opened and there is usually a local depolarisation and influx of sodium ions, causing an **excitatory postsynaptic potential (EPSP)** to be set up. If there are sufficient of these potentials the positive charge in the postsynaptic cell builds up to the threshold level and an action potential is set up which then travels on along the postsynaptic neurone.

In some cases the transmitter has the opposite effect. Channels allowing the inward movement of negative ions are opened in the postsynaptic membrane, which makes the inside more negative than the normal resting potential. An **inhibitory postsynaptic potential** results, which makes it less likely that an action potential will occur in the postsynaptic fibre.

Once the transmitter has had its effect it is destroyed by enzymes. This is very important because unless the transmitter is removed from the synaptic cleft, subsequent impulses would have no effect, as the receptors on the postsynaptic membrane would all be bound.

The transmitter substances

The most common transmitter substance, found at the majority of synapses, is **acetylcholine** (**ACh**). It is synthesised in the synaptic knob using ATP produced in the many mitochondria present. Nerves using acetylcholine as their transmitter are known as **cholinergic nerves**. Once the acetylcholine has done its job it is very rapidly hydrolysed by the enzyme **cholinesterase**. This ensures that it no longer affects the postsynaptic membrane, and it also releases the components to be recycled – they pass back into the synaptic knob and are resynthesised into more acetylcholine.

Some vertebrate nerves, particularly those of the sympathetic nervous system (see section 4.2), produce **noradrenaline** in their synaptic vesicles and are known as **adrenergic nerves**.

Neuromuscular junctions

Nerves have to communicate not only with each other, but with receptors and effectors as well. Motor nerves need to communicate with muscles. Where a motor nerve and muscle fibre meet, a special kind of synapse is found known as a **neuromuscular junction**. The membrane of the muscle fibre (the sarcolemma) is very folded in this region and forms a structure known as an **end plate**, to which the end of the motor nerve joins. Electron microscopy shows us that the structure of the neuromuscular junction is remarkably similar to that of any other synapse, as figure 4.1.12 shows. The end of the motor neurone is full of mitochondria and synaptic vesicles which contain acetylcholine. It appears that when an impulse arrives at the end of the motor neurone acetylcholine is discharged into the synaptic cleft. As a result of its effect on the postsynaptic membrane an **end plate potential** is set up which can be recorded. If sufficient end plate potentials are set up an action potential is fired off in the muscle fibre, spreading through the **T tubules** and leading to a contraction of the muscle as described in section 2.6.

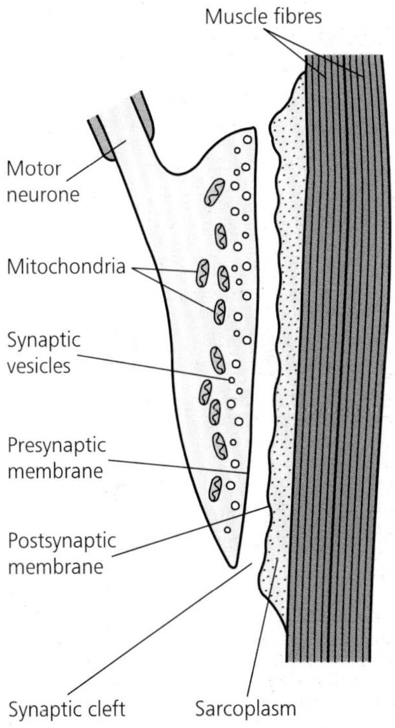

Figure 4.1.12 The neuromuscular junction is very similar to any other synapse. The end result is not an action potential propagated along the postsynaptic fibre, but the contraction of the muscle.

Evidence for the functioning of synapses

There are several convincing strands of evidence supporting the current model of the working of the synapse.

(1) Apart from the basic structural details revealed by the electron microscope, micrographs taken after a nerve has been strongly stimulated for some time show a lack of synaptic vesicles. This reflects the observed fact that after a period of stimulation a

nerve can no longer respond (it becomes accommodated, see opposite) and suggests that the reason for this is that all the transmitter substance has been used up. Thus it is reasonable to deduce that normal transmission across the synapse results from the release of transmitter from a small number of vesicles.

(2) A variety of drugs and poisons interfere with the working of synapses or neuromuscular junctions. A look at the effect of some of these substances throws light onto the normal working of the system (see table 4.1.1). Any substance which interferes with the formation of acetylcholine, stops it being released, prevents it interacting with the postsynaptic receptors or reduces the rate at which it is broken down will in turn have a major effect on the nervous communication system of the body.

Substance	Where does it act?	What does it do?
Botulinus toxin	Affects the presynaptic membrane and stops the release of acetylcholine	Prevents transmission of impulses across synapses and so prevents the nervous system working
Nicotine	Mimics the action of acetylcholine on post-synaptic membranes	Stimulates the nervous system
Strychnine, eserine, organophosphorus compounds used as weedkillers and insecticides, some nerve gases	Inactivate cholinesterase at the postsynaptic membrane and so prevent the breakdown of acetylcholine	Enhance and prolong the effects of acetylcholine as it is no longer destroyed. This means that nerves fire continuously, or at the slightest stimulus, and muscles are sent into tetanus
Curare (used on arrow tips by South American Indians)	Interferes with the action of acetylcholine and stops the depolarisation of the postsynaptic membrane	Causes paralysis as the muscles can no longer be stimulated by the nerves

Table 4.1.1

Coordination and control of neurones

Summation and facilitation

Neurones interact in a variety of complex ways. Sometimes a single nerve fibre will carry an action potential to a synapse with another cell, and transmission across that synapse will set up the next action potential. But in many cases the situation is much more complex than this. Often a single synaptic knob does not release enough transmitter substance to set up an action potential in the postsynaptic fibre. However, if two or more synaptic knobs are stimulated and release transmitter at the same time onto the same postsynaptic membrane the effects add together and a postsynaptic action potential results. This is known as **spatial summation**, illustrated in figure 4.1.13.

In other cases, a single knob does not release enough transmitter substance to stimulate the postsynaptic nerve fibre, but if a second impulse is received from the same knob in quick succession an action potential results. This effect is known as **temporal summation** (adding over time). It involves **facilitation** – in other words, the first impulse does not trigger off a response but it has an effect which makes easier (facilitates) the passage of the next impulse.

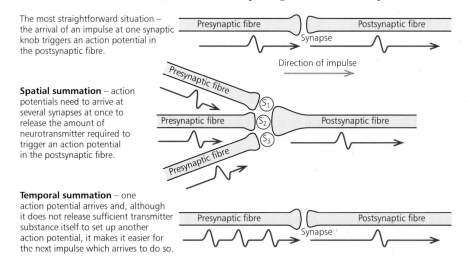

The most straightforward situation – the arrival of an impulse at one synaptic knob triggers an action potential in the postsynaptic fibre.

Spatial summation – action potentials need to arrive at several synapses at once to release the amount of neurotransmitter required to trigger an action potential in the postsynaptic fibre.

Temporal summation – one action potential arrives and, although it does not release sufficient transmitter substance itself to set up another action potential, it makes it easier for the next impulse which arrives to do so.

Figure 4.1.13 Different types of synaptic transmission.

Accommodation

On first applying perfume or aftershave we tend to be very aware of the smell ourselves. After a short time we lose that awareness, and it is other people who notice how pleasant we smell! If we reapply our scent another day, we can smell it again. This reaction is the same as that of a sea anemone which, when poked with a pointer, will withdraw its tentacles. If the sea anemone is poked repeatedly, the response is lost. If left alone for a while, the sea anemone reacts to the pointer again. Both of these examples are the result of a process known as **accommodation**.

If a nerve is repeatedly stimulated it eventually loses the ability to respond. Each time an impulse arrives at a synapse, vesicles full of transmitter discharge their contents into the synaptic cleft. The transmitter can only be synthesised at a certain rate. If the synapse is used too often, all of the vesicles are discharged into the synaptic cleft and the rate of synthesis simply cannot keep up. At this point the nerves can no longer respond to the stimulus – they are said to have **accommodated** or **fatigued**. A short rest restores the response as new vesicles and transmitter molecules are made. Some synapses never fatigue – they have an extremely rapid resynthesis rate – whilst others accommodate very quickly.

The implications of the organisation of the nervous system

The nerve fibres and synapses which we have been considering in isolation make up enormously complicated systems. Bundles of nerve fibres form nerves capable of carrying vast numbers of messages in different directions to gather all the available information and control all the actions of the body. Neurones and synapses in the central nervous system collate information and send out instructions. Synapses, whilst susceptible to both fatigue and drugs, allow for great flexibility, intercommunication between cells, facilitation and inhibition. They also play a vital and incompletely understood role in the brain, closely linked with both learning and memory.

Nerves give rapid communication. They also give the ability, in people at least, for long and involved nervous activity to take place in the brain before a particular action is undertaken. But for most simpler organisms most nervous activity and behaviour involves reflex actions which have a minimum of input from the central nervous system. Even human beings are ruled by reflexes to a remarkable extent. In section 4.2 we shall look in more detail at what happens in a reflex, and how other specialised parts of the nervous system such as the sense organs work.

SUMMARY

- Control and coordination may be achieved in an organism by **chemical messages** or by **electrical impulses**. Electrical or **nerve** impulses are carried within a **nervous system** and allow quicker and more specific communication.

- **Neurones**, cells specialised to transmit electrical impulses, interconnect to form a nervous system. Messages from the internal or external environment are received at **receptor cells** and carried in **sensory neurones**. **Motor neurones** carry impulses to **effector cells** which bring about a **response**. In larger animals a **central nervous system** coordinates and processes information.

- Neurone cell bodies contain **Nissl's granules** for protein synthesis and have projections called **dendrites**. There is one long **nerve fibre**, the **axon** in motor neurones and the **dendron** in sensory neurones. This carries the impulses. **Myelinated** nerve fibres have a fatty **myelin sheath** formed by a series of **Schwann cells** wrapped around the neurone. The sheath is interrupted at the **nodes of Ranvier**.

- Invertebrates have only unmyelinated fibres which transmit impulses more slowly than myelinated fibres of the same diameter. **Giant axons** are unmyelinated nerve fibres about 1 mm in diameter found in some invertebrates. They transmit vital impulses relatively quickly.

- The membrane of a nerve fibre is impermeable to sodium ions but more permeable to potassium ions. Sodium ions are actively pumped out of the fibre and potassium ions pumped in. Potassium ions then diffuse out again along a concentration gradient. The inside of the fibre is negatively charged relative to the outside – it has a **resting potential** of –70 mV.

- When an impulse or **action potential** is set up, sodium channels open allowing sodium ions to move in. The fibre becomes **depolarised** – it is more positive on the inside than the outside by about +40 mV. The sodium channels then close and sodium ions are pumped out as usual. The permeability to potassium ions is temporarily increased so that they diffuse out more quickly. The resting potential is thus restored after a **refractory period**.

- An action potential is an **all-or-nothing** response – it either happens or not, and is always the same size. It is only activated once the **threshold** has been reached – the point at which sufficient sodium channels are open for there to be more sodium ions entering the cell than potassium ions leaving by diffusion.

- During the **absolute refractory period** the sodium channels are blocked and the resting potential has not yet been restored. The neurone cannot be restimulated. During the **relative refractory period** restimulation is possible but the threshold is raised. The refractory period limits the frequency at which impulses can travel along a neurone, and also ensures that impulses travel in one direction only. This speeds up conduction.

- An action potential is **propagated** by local currents caused by ion movements around the action potential. These cause the sodium channels to open in front of the action potential (but not behind it because of the refractory period).

- In myelinated fibres **saltatory conduction** occurs – the impulse jumps from node to node, where ions can pass freely in and out of the fibre.

- Nerve fibres are linked by **synapses**, gaps between neurones across which chemical messages called **neurotransmitters** pass. When an impulse arrives at the **synaptic knob**, the **presynaptic membrane** becomes permeable to calcium ions which move into the synaptic knob. **Synaptic vesicles** then fuse with the presynaptic membrane and release neurotransmitter into the **synaptic cleft**. The transmitter diffuses across the cleft and binds to receptor sites on the **postsynaptic membrane**. This causes channels to open, local depolarisation and an influx of sodium ions causing an **excitatory postsynaptic potential**. These EPSPs build up to a threshold level and an action potential is set up in the postsynaptic neurone. The effect of the neurotransmitter binding to the postsynaptic membrane is sometimes to allow negative ions to enter resulting in an **inhibitory postsynaptic potential**.

- Neurotransmitters include **acetylcholine** (ACh) in **cholinergic nerves** and **noradrenaline** in **adrenergic nerves**. Acetylcholine is hydrolysed by **cholinesterase**.

- Neurones meet muscle fibres at a **neuromuscular junction** which contains **motor end plates** similar to synapses. Acetylcholine is discharged into the cleft and causes an **end plate potential** in the muscle fibre. These potentials summate to fire an action potential in the muscle fibre.

- In **spatial summation**, several synaptic knobs release neurotransmitter on the same postsynaptic membrane, and their effects add to produce a postsynaptic action potential.

- **Temporal summation** involves the same synaptic knob producing bursts of transmitter in succession. The first burst **facilitates** (makes easier) the passage of the next impulse across the cleft.

- **Accommodation** happens when a nerve is repeatedly stimulated and loses its ability to respond. This is due to depletion of the neurotransmitter which takes time to be resynthesised.

QUESTIONS

1 a Why are communication systems necessary?
  b Describe the structure of a typical motor nerve cell and explain how its structure is related to its function.
  c Explain what is meant by the terms:
   i   central nervous system
   ii peripheral nerves.

2 a What is the resting potential of a nerve cell and how is it maintained?
  b Describe an action potential and explain how it is propagated along a nerve cell.
  c Explain briefly how nerve impulses are investigated.

3 a What is a synapse?
  b How is the structure of a synapse related to its function?
  c What is the role of:
   i   myelin sheath
   ii   ATP
   iii refractory period
   in the transmission of nerve impulses?

FOCUS HEAR THIS!

Hearing is one of the major senses by which we learn about the world around us. It is also important in the lives of a wide range of species including most vertebrates and also arthropods (particularly the insects).

The advantages of detecting sound

A sense of hearing provides an awareness of danger. For modern humans this is likely to warn us of an approaching car, for example, but other species have different requirements. Hunting animals rely on their sense of hearing to help find their prey, while the prey listen out for the sound of an approaching predator. Hearing is often central to communication between individuals, to identify members of the same species or find a mate or offspring, or to mark out territory or warn of danger. The sounds heard may be relatively quiet during close-range encounters, or can be very loud to provide communication over a distance too long for sight to be useful. Human beings have probably taken aural communication further than any other species, with our complex language, music, poetry and drama.

Figure 1 Howler monkeys make sure that any animal in the area with a sense of hearing knows they are there.

Different but the same

Although different species of animal may have very different-looking ears – think of a donkey, a grasshopper and a person, for example – biologists have found that most ears have a surprising amount in common. Mammalian ears are generally very like human ears, except that they often have a large, mobile flap which can be used for 'capturing' sounds. Even invertebrate ears often have certain key elements in common with our own. These include drum-like membranes which help magnify the sound, and hair cells which act as transducers, converting the vibrations of the sound energy into nerve impulses.

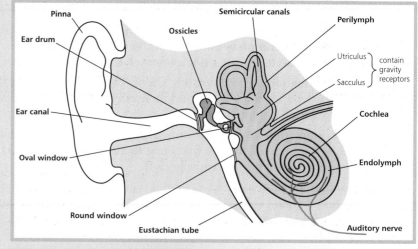

Figure 2 The human ear is a sense organ of remarkable sensitivity, capable of detecting sounds over a wide range of pitch, volume and direction.

Figure 3 Dr Andrew King and some of his team at Oxford University working to unveil some of the deeper secrets of our hearing.

Listening to the future …

Biologists already know quite a lot about how the ear works and how the messages are carried to and interpreted in the brain, but there is still much to find out. The more we understand about how we hear, the greater the potential for solving the problems that cause deafness in people of all ages. For example, some recent work has shown that the blood flow to certain brain areas increases when we are listening to speech. Other research teams are analysing the hearing mechanisms in animals with ears very similar to our own, in the hope that what they learn can be applied to human hearing. Our ears are truly remarkable sense organs – we can hear sounds that move our eardrums little more than the diameter of a hydrogen atom – and we can look forward to more revelations about how they work.

4.2 The mammalian nervous system

At the most basic level, the nervous systems of animals are made up of receptor cells and interconnected nerve cells which eventually stimulate effector cells. In mammals nervous systems are complex, involving highly specialised sensory organs containing many receptors, nerves made up of large numbers of nerve fibres bringing in information or carrying out instructions, and highly developed central nervous systems containing millions of interconnecting nerve cells capable of extremely sophisticated thought processes.

In simpler organisms, almost all actions take place without conscious thought – they are simply **reflex responses** to particular stimuli. Surprisingly, a large number of the actions of more complex animals are also the results of unconscious reflex actions – and this is true for ourselves as well as for any other mammal. Thus before considering the details of the nervous system such as the workings of sensory organs or the major nerve types, it is important to understand this most basic type of nervous response.

Reflexes

Unconditioned reflexes

Unconditioned reflexes are responses that are not learned, but inborn. The contracting of the tentacles of a sea anemone or the writhing of a worm when touched are examples of these reflexes in invertebrates. Well known examples in humans include moving a hand or foot away rapidly from a hot or sharp object, swallowing as food moves down towards the back of the throat, blinking if an object approaches the eyes and the contracting and dilating of the pupil of the eye in response to light levels.

An unconditioned reflex involves a fixed response (an **unconditioned response**) to a particular stimulus (an **unconditioned stimulus**). Such reflexes are controlled by the simplest type of nerve pathway in the body, known as a **reflex arc**. In vertebrates, including the mammals, this involves at its simplest a receptor, a sensory neurone and a motor neurone connected to an effector cell. Part of the pathway takes place in the central nervous system, often the spinal cord. The reflex arc may involve simply a motor neurone and a sensory neurone with a synapse between them, or there may be a third small **relay** or **intermediate neurone**, situated in the central nervous system, as shown in figure 4.2.2.

However the reflex arc is organised physically, its function is to bring about an appropriate response to a particular stimulus as rapidly as possible without the time delay which occurs when the conscious centres become involved.

Figure 4.2.2 shows clearly the structure of a vertebrate reflex arc. When a stimulus is detected by the receptor cell an impulse is set up in the sensory nerve fibre and an action potential travels along the spinal nerve to the dorsal root of the spinal nerve. The impulse enters the grey matter of the spinal cord. Synaptic transmission then takes place which results in another action potential being set up. This may be directly in a motor neurone, or first in a relay neurone and then, via another synapse, in the motor neurone. The impulse then travels out through the ventral root along the spinal nerve to the effector organ, causing the unconditioned response to occur.

Figure 4.2.1 Reflex responses to very specific stimuli shown by newborn infants are quickly lost as conscious control grows, but they illustrate how the nervous systems of even highly developed mammals are based around the unconditioned reflex. The **Moro reflex** is a response to a startling stimulus such as a sudden loud noise or movement, or the loss of a feeling of support. The infant throws up his arms and legs, and brings them together in a grasping movement. It is thought that this reflex is useful to the infants of monkeys and apes, allowing them to grasp the fur of the mother. In humans it has obviously lost its usefulness and fades over the first couple of months.

4

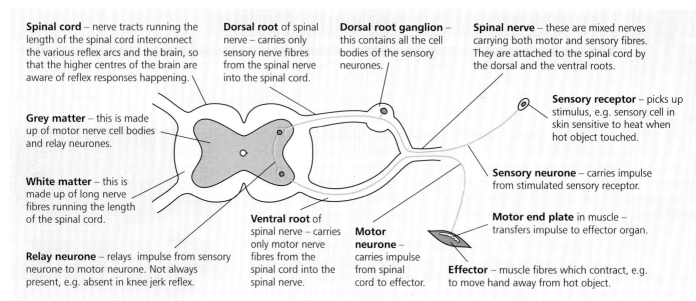

Spinal cord – nerve tracts running the length of the spinal cord interconnect the various reflex arcs and the brain, so that the higher centres of the brain are aware of reflex responses happening.

Dorsal root of spinal nerve – carries only sensory nerve fibres from the spinal nerve into the spinal cord.

Dorsal root ganglion – this contains all the cell bodies of the sensory neurones.

Spinal nerve – these are mixed nerves carrying both motor and sensory fibres. They are attached to the spinal cord by the dorsal and the ventral roots.

Grey matter – this is made up of motor nerve cell bodies and relay neurones.

Sensory receptor – picks up stimulus, e.g. sensory cell in skin sensitive to heat when hot object touched.

White matter – this is made up of long nerve fibres running the length of the spinal cord.

Sensory neurone – carries impulse from stimulated sensory receptor.

Relay neurone – relays impulse from sensory neurone to motor neurone. Not always present, e.g. absent in knee jerk reflex.

Ventral root of spinal nerve – carries only motor nerve fibres from the spinal cord into the spinal nerve.

Motor neurone – carries impulse from spinal cord to effector.

Motor end plate in muscle – transfers impulse to effector organ.

Effector – muscle fibres which contract, e.g. to move hand away from hot object.

Figure 4.2.2 This simplified description of a reflex arc shows how the information can be carried rapidly from the sensory system into the central nervous system and back out through the motor system, resulting in an almost immediate response by the appropriate effector organ.

The importance of reflexes

Reflexes are the single most common form of nervous control throughout the animal kingdom. However, there are two other reasons for their importance in animals such as mammals. One has already been mentioned. By avoiding the areas of the nervous system involved in conscious thought, reflex actions can occur very rapidly. This means that they are of great importance when it comes to potentially dangerous situations. Evasive or avoiding action can be taken as quickly as possible, thus minimising the risk of damage to an animal.

The second major role of reflexes in mammals is in the control of everyday bodily functions. Under normal conditions there is no conscious thought involved in vital processes such as breathing, controlling the heart rate, swallowing food or secreting digestive enzymes. This is because all these processes and many others besides are controlled by simple unconditioned reflexes. There are two major advantages to this. The brain is freed from tasks which, whilst far from trivial, are continuous and repetitive and would occupy a great deal of concentration if they had to be thought about all the time. Reflexes release the brain to deal with other things and therefore, in our own case, make complex and abstract thought possible. Secondly, the use of reflexes means you cannot forget to breathe or digest food when something more interesting to think about crops up. Without reflexes, watching a Cup Final or sitting an exam might be a rather hazardous occupation!

Conditioned reflexes

Unconditioned reflexes are not learned – they are present from birth and do not at any point involve the conscious areas of the brain, other than the knowledge that a reflex action has taken place. **Conditioned reflexes** on the other hand are learned, although often without us realising it. If an unconditioned stimulus, such as the sight of food which produces the unconditioned salivation reflex, is associated with a second unrelated stimulus such as the ringing of a bell, an animal can unconsciously learn to react to the second stimulus alone – it salivates at the ringing of a bell when no food is present. Some of the best-known experimental work on this was done by Pavlov on the salivation reflex in dogs (see section 3.3, page 202).

Conditioned reflexes are important as they allow us to develop control of our bladder and bowel sphincters amongst other things, and at a more basic level they are an important part of the learning process throughout the animal kingdom. (Learning is dealt with in more detail in section 4.3.)

Sensory systems

The coordinated activity of any organism depends on a continuous input of information from both the outside world and the internal environment. It is important to know that a predator is creeping up on you, but it also matters when the level of carbon dioxide in your blood increases. Either situation could be fatal if undetected. Thus sensory receptors play a vital role in providing an animal with information about both its internal and external environments.

Sensory receptors

In its simplest form a sensory receptor is a neurone with a dendrite which is sensitive to one particular stimulus. When the dendrite receives such a stimulus, chemical events occur which result in an action potential being transmitted in the fibre of the neurone to the central nervous system. This type of cell is known as a **primary receptor**. A **secondary receptor** is slightly more complicated, consisting of a modified epithelial cell which is sensitive to a particular type of stimulus. This then synapses with a sensory nerve fibre which in turn carries the impulse into the central nervous system. Figure 4.2.4 shows a primary and a secondary receptor.

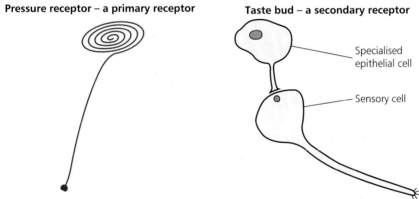

Figure 4.2.4 The two main types of sensory receptors found in vertebrates.

Whilst many sensory receptors are always found as isolated entities, in vertebrate animals sensory receptors are increasingly found associated together in systems known as **sense organs**.

Receptors at work

Just like the rest of the nervous system, receptor cells have a resting potential which is dependent on the maintenance of an electrically negative interior as a result of the activity of the membrane sodium pumps. When a receptor cell receives a stimulus to which it is sensitive, its membrane is affected and the sodium pump mechanism interfered with. It seems that ions move rapidly across the cell membrane along concentration and electrochemical gradients. This influx of sodium ions is known as a **generator current** and it results in the setting up of a **generator potential**. A small stimulus results in a small generator potential and a large stimulus results in a large generator potential – generator potentials do not obey the all-or-nothing law. However, if the generator potential produced is large enough, an action potential will result in the receptor neurone. If it is not, there will be no action potential – the action potential does obey the all-or-nothing law.

This process:

$$\text{Stimulus} \rightarrow \begin{array}{c}\text{local change in}\\ \text{permeability}\end{array} \rightarrow \begin{array}{c}\text{generator}\\ \text{current}\end{array} \rightarrow \begin{array}{c}\text{generator}\\ \text{potential}\end{array} \rightarrow \begin{array}{c}\text{action}\\ \text{potential}\end{array}$$

is common in one form or another to most sensory receptors.

Muscle spindles

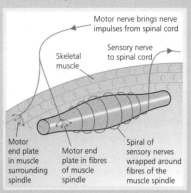

Figure 4.2.3 Muscle spindles allow us to stand or sit upright without thinking about it.

Deep-set in the middle of human muscles are some very special receptors called **muscle spindles** (also known as **stretch receptors**). These proprioceptors play a vital role in maintaining body posture – their input allows us to maintain muscle tone and hold ourselves upright against gravity.

Each muscle spindle consists of a small bundle of muscle fibres deep within a major muscle block. Around these fibres spirals a sensory nerve with sensory endings within the bundle of fibres itself. When the muscle is stretched – in other words, when the antagonistic muscle contracts – the muscle spindle is also stretched, and it sends impulses in the sensory nerve leading to the spinal cord. The more the muscle is stretched the more frequently the impulses are sent. Impulses are sent back in a reflex arc from the spinal cord to a motor nerve, stimulating the muscle to contract. The muscle is no longer stretched, and the muscle spindle stops sending nerve impulses. This keeps a constant level of tension in the muscle, unless it is overridden by the conscious brain during a deliberate action.

Types of sensory receptors

Sensory receptors transfer the energy of a particular stimulus – light, heat, sound or movement – into the electrochemical energy of an action potential in a sensory nerve fibre. There are various different types of receptors and a variety of ways of categorising them. The major receptor groupings are given here.

By complexity of receptor structure

1 **Primary receptors**
2 **Secondary receptors**
3 **Sense organs**

This classification refers to the structure of the receptor and tell us whether a single cell, two cells or a large collection of receptor cells are involved.

By source of stimulus

1 **Exteroceptors** – respond to stimuli outside the body
2 **Interoceptors** – respond to stimuli inside the body
3 **Proprioceptors** – specifically sensitive to the relative positions of the skeleton and degrees of muscle contraction

This classification refers to the source of the stimuli to which the receptors are sensitive.

By function of receptor

1 **Chemoreceptors** – sensitive to chemical stimuli such as smell, taste and pH level of the blood
2 **Mechanoreceptors** – sensitive to mechanical stimuli such as pressure, tension, movement and gravity
3 **Photoreceptors** – sensitive to electromagnetic stimuli, particularly visible light and in insects ultraviolet light
4 **Thermoreceptors** – sensitive to heat stimuli, and particularly effective at detecting temperature differences

This classification refers to the type of receptor by function and is the most useful way of classifying receptors.

Convergence

In secondary receptors, several receptor cells will often synapse with a single receptor neurone as shown in figure 4.2.5. This means that while the generator potential from an individual receptor cell may be insufficient to set up an action potential across the synapse, the generator potentials from several receptor cells may add together or summate and trigger an action potential. This is known as **convergence** and is a useful adaptation for increasing the sensitivity of a sensory system to low level stimuli. As we will see later, this is an important feature of the light-sensitive cells of the eye.

When the stimulus received is weak, a low frequency of action potentials results along the receptor neurone. But if the stimulus is strong, then a rapid stream of action potentials is fired along the receptor nerve fibre. The importance of this is that, although the nerve fibre obeys the all-or-nothing law in terms of the size of each individual action potential, a graded response is still possible giving information about the strength of the stimulus, as illustrated in figure 4.2.6. What this means in practice is that, for example, we are aware not only of the difference between light and dark, but of all the varying degrees of light and shade.

Adaptation

The most important information carried by the sensory system is about changes in the environment, which are potential problems to be dealt with by an organism. Thus if a sensory receptor is exposed to a steady stimulus that continues unchanged for a period of time, the information becomes of decreasing importance to the animal until it does change. The nervous system is adapted to cope with this situation. Instead of simply responding constantly to a steady stimulus, most receptors show a gradual decline in the generator potentials produced and so the action potentials in the receptor neurone become less frequent and may eventually stop. This is known as **adaptation**. The mechanism by which it is brought about is not fully understood, but seems

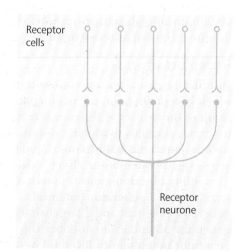

Figure 4.2.5 Weak stimuli result in small generator potentials – too small to trigger an action potential. But if several receptor cells synapse onto a single receptor neurone, then the weak generator potentials add together and an action potential can result, ensuring that information about the stimulus reaches the central nervous system.

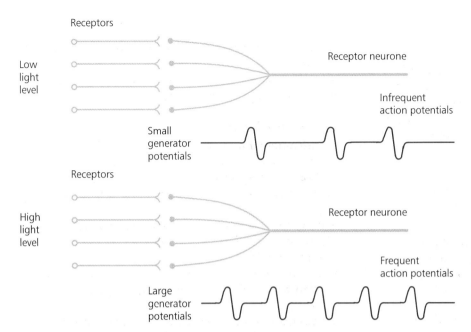

Receptors

Low light level

Receptor neurone

Infrequent action potentials

Small generator potentials

Receptors

High light level

Receptor neurone

Frequent action potentials

Large generator potentials

Figure 4.2.6 The ability to differentiate between varying levels of light is given by the number of action potentials travelling along the sensory neurones. Each action potential in the receptor neurone obeys the all-or-nothing law – they are all the same size and show no variation with the size of the stimulus. But the small generator potentials from a low level of light cause few action potentials to travel along the receptor neurone fibre. Increasing the level of light results in larger generator potentials and as a result increased numbers of action potentials being fired off along the neurone. This gives information to the brain about the level of light intensity acting as the stimulus.

to involve changes at the membrane. It may well also be linked to the accommodation of the synapses in the pathway. Some receptors adapt very rapidly, others only slowly or not at all. But in general, adaptation serves to prevent the system from carrying too many unnecessary messages and frees the central nervous system from irrelevant information. Thus an unpleasant smell rapidly becomes tolerable, a hot bath feels comfortable and an irritating label in a jumper is forgotten – unless the stimulus changes, when we become sensitised again (see section 4.1, page 253).

Pacinian corpuscles

Within the structure of the human skin sit some sensory receptors called **Pacinian corpuscles**, which in section look rather like an onion. They are **mechanoreceptors**, which means that when they are physically distorted they respond and send off a nerve impulse. Pacinian corpuscles are particularly sensitive to firm pressure applied to the skin, for example from holding an object like a tennis racket firmly, or hitting yourself accidentally with a hammer! Pacinian corpuscles do not respond to light pressure, or to any other type of touch to the skin.

When there is firm pressure on the skin, the connective tissue and collagen which make up part of the Pacinian corpuscle are stretched, and this deforms the shape of the corpuscle. This deformation changes the shape of stretch-mediated sodium channels in the membrane, setting up a generator potential and leading to an action potential in the sensory nerve leading from the corpuscle to the brain.

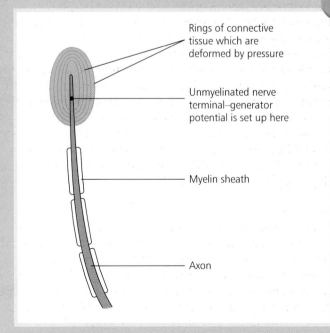

Rings of connective tissue which are deformed by pressure

Unmyelinated nerve terminal–generator potential is set up here

Myelin sheath

Axon

Figure 4.2.7 Pacinian corpuscles are receptors in the skin that are sensitive to firm pressure.

The sense organs

Single sensory receptor cells are very useful and can carry vital information. But groups of receptor cells all specialised for picking up a particular stimulus can be even more useful. Relatively early in the development of the animal groups collections of receptors evolved together to form specialised regions which we know as **sense organs**. Throughout the animal kingdom, the most common sense organs are those which respond to light and to sound or vibration. For this reason we shall consider in some detail the human eye and ear, with reference to some of the alternative structures which are found in other groups.

The human eye

Sensitivity to light is found in some of the most basic living organisms. In the human animal it has developed far beyond a simple sensitivity to the absence or presence of light into a remarkably sophisticated optical system, allowing clear and focused vision in a wide variety of circumstances. Our eyes are sensitive to electromagnetic radiation with a wavelength between 400 and 700 nm, although the ranges detected by other species may vary from this.

The structure of the human eye

The structure of the eye is very closely related to its function, as can be seen in figure 4.2.8. The muscles attached to the tough outer coat of the eyeball allow it to be swivelled in the bony socket or **orbit** to point in many different directions. The shape, size and contents of the eyeball allow for the focusing of light on the sensitive receptor cells which make up the **retina**. The **iris** and **pupil** control the amount of light entering the eye. The **lens**, with its associated muscles and ligaments, allows for fine focusing of objects. The **choroid** prevents internal reflection of light. The **sclera** forms a tough outer coat and along with the eyelids and orbit helps to reduce the likelihood of physical damage.

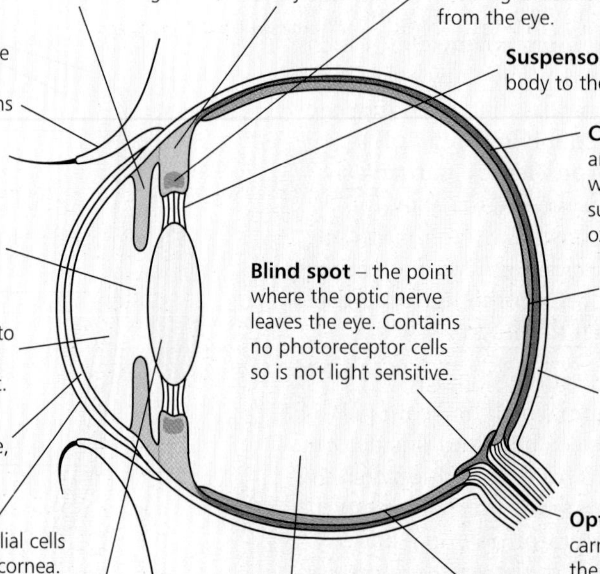

Figure 4.2.8 The main structures of the human eye along with their functions.

Iris – a circular sheet of muscle dividing the eye into two chambers. The pigment it contains gives the eye its colour. The reflex contraction and relaxation of the muscles of the iris control the amount of light entering the eye.

Eyelid and **eyelashes** – help to protect the eye from physical damage by closing in a reflex action when an object approaches. Eyelid cleans and moistens the surface of the eye by spreading tears over the surface in another reflex action – blinking.

Pupil – circular hole in the iris through which light enters the eye. The size of the aperture is controlled by the muscles of the iris.

Anterior chamber – filled with **aqueous humour**, a clear solution of salts which helps to maintain the shape of the front part of the eye and continues the process of focusing the light.

Cornea – transparent area at front of the eyeball. Part of the tough outer layer of the eye, it plays a major role in focusing the light as it enters the eye.

Conjunctiva – thin layer of transparent epithelial cells over the surface of the eye which protects the cornea.

Lens – a transparent, biconvex structure which is elastic and can change shape. It separates the two regions of the eyeball and is important for the fine focusing of light onto the retina.

Ciliary body – contains the ciliary muscles.

Blind spot – the point where the optic nerve leaves the eye. Contains no photoreceptor cells so is not light sensitive.

Vitreous humour – clear, jelly-like substance giving the eyeball its shape.

Ciliary muscles – bundles of smooth muscle which act to change the shape of the lens to enable it to focus light from objects both close to and far away from the eye.

Suspensory ligament – attaches the ciliary body to the lens.

Choroid – pigment cells prevent any internal reflection of light within the eye and blood vessels supply the retina with nutrients and oxygen.

Fovea – area of the retina containing only cones, region of highest visual acuity.

Sclera – tough outer covering of the eye which maintains the shape of the eyeball and protects it from physical damage.

Optic nerve – bundle of nerve fibres carrying impulses from the retina to the brain.

Retina – layer of light-sensitive cells (the **rods** and **cones**) and the neurones leading from these photoreceptors to the optic nerve.

The eye at work

The role of the iris

When we look at something our eyeballs are moved in their sockets by muscles so that the pupil at the centre of the iris is pointing at the object of our interest. Light from the object enters the eye through the pupil, and the amount of light entering is controlled by the size of the opening. This in turn is controlled by the iris muscles, as shown in figure 4.2.9.

The role of the lens

As the light enters the eye the process of focusing it onto the retina begins. The rays of light have to be bent (**refracted**) sufficiently first to pass through the pupil and also to arrive focused on the retina. Most of this focusing is in fact carried out by the cornea and the fluid through which the light passes, but the degree of refraction is the same for light from every object. When considering the working of the eye most attention is given to the working of the lens. Although the lens is not responsible for much of the bending of the light, it plays a very important role in giving fine, accurate focusing of light seen from objects both distant and close at hand.

The lens is a transparent elastic disc. Its shape can be changed by the action of the **ciliary muscles**, as described in the box below.

Light rays from an object spread out in all directions – they are said to **diverge**. When we look at an object which is close to us a cone of diverging light enters our eyes. When we look at objects from further away the light rays are spreading less – in fact they appear almost parallel, as shown in figure 4.2.11. The light entering the eye is refracted by its passage through the conjunctiva, cornea, aqueous humour and vitreous humour in exactly the same way regardless of whether it is from a near or a distant object. But by changing the shape of the lens the degree of bending of the light can be altered. Light from distant objects needs relatively little bending to bring it into focus on the retina and so the lens has to be thin. To bring light from near objects into focus on the retina more refraction is needed and so the lens must be short and fat. This ability to focus light from objects at various distances is known as **accommodation** and the way it is brought about is shown in figure 4.2.10.

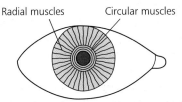

In bright light the circular muscle is contracted and the radial muscles are relaxed so that the pupil is reduced to a narrow aperture to prevent damage to the light-sensitive cells by strong light.

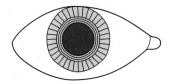

In dim light the circular muscles relax and the radial muscles contract, opening the pupil aperture as wide as possible to allow in the maximum amount of light to ensure the best possible vision.

Figure 4.2.9 The size of the pupil is determined by the state of the iris muscles. These respond in a reflex action to the levels of light entering the eye through the pupil, so the system is constantly being modified with changes in light intensity.

4

Changing the shape of the lens

The **ciliary muscles** are arranged circularly around the ciliary body. The effects of their contractions and relaxations are relayed to the lens by the **suspensory ligaments**. The lens itself is elastic and its unstretched shape is relatively short and fat.

Figure 4.2.10 A newborn baby can only see clearly at a certain distance from his or her eyes – roughly where the mother's face will be when the baby is feeding. With age, the ability to focus on objects at a great variety of distances develops. The shape of the lens is changed by the action of the ciliary muscles. To allow light from objects at different distances to be brought into focus, the thickness of the lens can be varied between the two extremes shown here. As the ability to do this develops, so does our visual understanding of the world around us.

The usual section through the eye makes it difficult to visualise what is happening to the lens. By looking at the lens and ciliary body from the front it is easier to see how the changes are brought about.

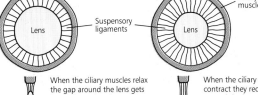

When the ciliary muscles relax the gap around the lens gets larger, increasing the tension in the suspensory ligaments. These in turn pull on the lens making it long and thin. Its ability to bend light is now at a minimum and it is said to be **unaccommodated**.

When the ciliary muscles contract they reduce the gap around the lens. This reduces the tension in the suspensory ligaments allowing the lens to become short and fat. In this state it is **fully accommodated** and its ability to bend the light is at a maximum.

The role of the retina

As we have seen, light from an object is focused onto the retina. The retina must then perceive that light and inform the brain of its presence. In order to do this the retina contains about a hundred million light-sensitive cells (**photoreceptors**), along with the neurones with which they synapse. There are two main types of photoreceptors in the retina, known as the **rods** and the **cones**, shown in figure 4.2.12. Both types are secondary exteroceptors.

Rods are spread evenly across the retina except at the fovea where there are none. They provide black and white vision only and are used mainly for seeing in low light intensities or at night. The total number of rods is estimated as about 1.2×10^8. Rods are very sensitive to light, even of relatively low intensity. They contain a single **visual pigment** called **rhodopsin** (visual purple). Rods are not very tightly packed together and several of them synapse with the same sensory neurone. This means that they do not give a particularly clear picture, but makes them extremely sensitive both to low light levels and to movements in the visual field, because several small generator potentials can trigger an action potential to the central nervous system.

Cones, on the other hand, are found tightly packed together in the region known as the fovea. There are only around 6×10^6 of them. They are used principally for vision in bright daylight and may have one of three visual pigments, so provide colour vision. As a result of their tight packing in the fovea, and the fact that each cone usually has its own sensory neurone, cones provide a picture of great visual acuity. In fact, it is only when light falls directly on the fovea that it can be clearly in focus.

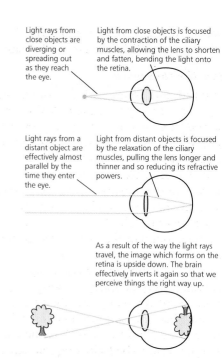

Figure 4.2.11 The ability to accommodate – focus on objects which are different distances away – develops gradually after birth and is important for giving us a clear and accurate view of the world.

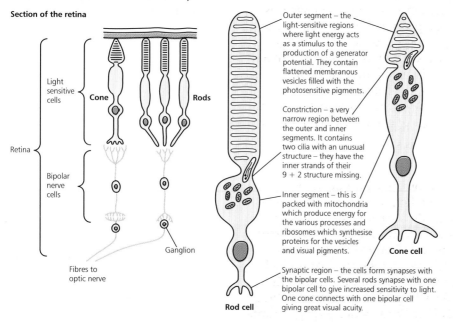

Figure 4.2.12 The two types of receptor cells along with their different arrangements of synapses in the retina give a visual system which combines great sensitivity to low levels of light with high visual acuity and clarity of vision.

An interesting point to note about the arrangement of the retina is that it is 'back to front'. The outer segments are actually next to the choroid, and the neurones are at the interior edge of the eyeball. This is why there is a blind spot where all the neurones pass through the layers of the eye to go into the brain. The light has to pass through the synapses and the inner segments before reaching the outer segments containing the visual pigments. The reason for this somewhat unexpected arrangement is the origin of the retinal cells in the embryo and the way in which the eye is formed during embryonic development. To add to the confusion, the optic nerves carrying the visual information cross over on their way to the visual cortex in the brain so that the information seen with the right eye is taken to the left side of the brain for processing!

How the rods work

Both rods and cones work in a similar way, based on the reactions of the visual pigments with light. In the rods this visual pigment is rhodopsin, which is formed from two components. These are **opsin** and **retinene**. Opsin is a lipoprotein, and retinene is a light-absorbing derivative of vitamin A. Retinene exists in two isomeric forms, *cis* retinene and *trans* retinene. In the dark, it is all in the *cis* form. When a photon of light hits a molecule of rhodopsin, it converts the *cis* retinene into *trans* retinene and the rhodopsin then breaks up into opsin and retinene. This breaking up of the molecule is referred to as **bleaching**. The bleaching of the rhodopsin sets up a generator potential in the rod, and if this is large enough or if several rods are stimulated at once an action potential is set up in the receptor neurone.

Once bleaching of the visual pigment has occurred, the rod cannot be stimulated again until the rhodopsin is resynthesised. It takes energy from ATP produced by the many mitochondria in the inner segment to convert the retinene back to the *cis* isomer and rejoin it to the opsin. In normal daylight the rods are almost entirely bleached and can no longer respond to dim light – the eye is said to be **light adapted**. After about 30 minutes in complete darkness the rhodopsin will be almost fully reformed. The eye is now sensitive to dim light and is said to be **dark adapted**.

Cones and colour vision

Cones work in a very similar way to rods, except that their visual pigment is known as **iodopsin**. There appear to be three types of iodopsin, each sensitive to one of the primary colours of light. Iodopsin needs to receive more light energy than rhodopsin in order to break down, and so it is not sensitive to low light intensities. But the cones provide colour vision, because the brain interprets the numbers of different types of cones stimulated as different colours, as shown in table 4.2.1. This model of how cones sensitive to the three primary colours of light can provide a wide range of colour vision is known as the **trichromatic theory** of colour vision.

Vision in other animals

Mammals as a group generally have eyes based on the same pattern as humans, although many of them do not possess the cones necessary for colour vision. For some mammals, the ability to judge distance is of great importance. The apes and monkeys need to do this very accurately in order to climb trees and swing from branch to branch. Also, along with their close relatives the humans, these animals use tools and need delicate manipulative skills which are greatly enhanced by good judgement of distances. Many carnivores also need to judge distance in order to leap on their prey without missing. In all of these animals the eyes are sited at the front of the head, both looking forward. This gives an overlapping area of vision where sufficient information is fed into the brain to result in a three-dimensional picture, giving excellent distance judgement.

Many other animals have the opposite problem – they are vulnerable to attack by predators. For these animals the important factor is not distance judgement but all-round vision and sensitivity to movement, increasing the chances of spotting a predator before it is close enough to attack. Because of this most herbivores have eyes on the sides of their heads, often giving a 360° field of vision.

Light stimulates			Colour perceived
red cones	green cones	blue cones	
✓	✗	✗	Red ●
✗	✓	✗	Green ●
✗	✗	✓	Blue ●
✓	✓	✗	Orange/yellow ●
✗	✓	✓	Cyan ●
✓	✗	✓	Magenta ●
✓	✓	✓	White ○

Table 4.2.1 The perception of different colours by the brain, as explained by the trichromatic theory of colour vision

Most arthropods including the insects have **compound eyes**. These are made up of hundreds or thousands of tiny units called **ommatidia**, each providing part of the whole picture. Thus the field of vision of an insect is made up of thousands of overlapping images. The visual acuity this gives is poor, but there is great sensitivity to movement – hence the difficulties in swatting a fly!

The ageing eye

As we get older our eyes can change in a number of ways, some subtle and others all too obvious. The lens gradually loses its ability to change focal length. Throughout life the lens grows by adding protein fibres known as crystallins. By the age of 50–60 the lens is usually so large and thick that it cannot change shape. This usually results in distant objects being in focus, but near objects appearing blurred. People tend to hold books and papers further and further away to try and bring them into focus, until eventually their arms are not long enough and so they have to resort to wearing glasses, for close work at least. In addition, the pigment lipofuscin begins building up in the rods and cones from the age of about 10 years old. By 24 years old up to 8% of the volume of the rods and cones is lipofuscin, and this rises to over 20% by the time we reach 80 years old. As a result of this gradual accumulation of lipofuscin, the ability of the rods and cones to respond to light is reduced. This is turn slows the manufacture and recycling of the visual pigments of the eye, contributing to the gradual loss of visual powers which is almost inevitable with increasing age.

Another common change in the eye as people grow older is the development of cataracts. The lens of the eye is made largely of water and the protein crystallin. Molecules of crystallin are arranged to let light pass through them and focus on the retina. But sometimes, and increasingly with age, some of the protein clumps together. This clouds small areas of the lens, preventing some light reaching the retina and making vision increasingly blurred. This is a cataract.

In the early stages a cataract does not cause problems, but as the lens becomes more and more cloudy vision becomes duller and more blurred until eventually blindness results. People often get cataracts in both eyes, so if nothing is done they become completely blind. No one is entirely sure what causes cataracts. Some are congenital – sometimes babies are born with cataracts – and sometimes they develop after an eye injury. The likelihood of cataracts developing is increased by diseases such as diabetes and kidney disease, glaucoma, high blood pressure and also by lifestyle choices such as smoking and excessive exposure to bright sunlight, but the most common cause is simply changes in the body chemistry with ageing.

The treatment for cataracts is surgery, in which the clouded lens is removed and replaced with an artificial lens. This operation restores clear full colour vision for the vast majority of people.

Figure 4.2.13 Untreated cataracts lead to complete loss of vision not only in people but also in other animals.

The human ear

Sensitivity to vibrations is another basic sense. For many higher animals sensitivity to vibrations in the air is interpreted in the brain as hearing sounds. Hearing is often of vital importance for survival, and many species have far more acute hearing than we do ourselves. But while our ears may not be the most sensitive in the animal kingdom, we rely heavily on speech in our everyday communications so that to be without hearing is perceived as a disadvantage in society.

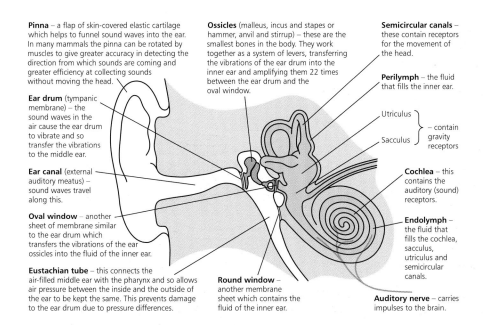

Pinna – a flap of skin-covered elastic cartilage which helps to funnel sound waves into the ear. In many mammals the pinna can be rotated by muscles to give greater accuracy in detecting the direction from which sounds are coming and greater efficiency at collecting sounds without moving the head.

Ear drum (tympanic membrane) – the sound waves in the air cause the ear drum to vibrate and so transfer the vibrations to the middle ear.

Ear canal (external auditory meatus) – sound waves travel along this.

Oval window – another sheet of membrane similar to the ear drum which transfers the vibrations of the ear ossicles into the fluid of the inner ear.

Eustachian tube – this connects the air-filled middle ear with the pharynx and so allows air pressure between the inside and the outside of the ear to be kept the same. This prevents damage to the ear drum due to pressure differences.

Ossicles (malleus, incus and stapes or hammer, anvil and stirrup) – these are the smallest bones in the body. They work together as a system of levers, transferring the vibrations of the ear drum into the inner ear and amplifying them 22 times between the ear drum and the oval window.

Round window – another membrane sheet which contains the fluid of the inner ear.

Semicircular canals – these contain receptors for the movement of the head.

Perilymph – the fluid that fills the inner ear.

Utriculus

Sacculus

– contain gravity receptors

Cochlea – this contains the auditory (sound) receptors.

Endolymph – the fluid that fills the cochlea, sacculus, utriculus and semicircular canals.

Auditory nerve – carries impulses to the brain.

Figure 4.2.14 The human ear – an organ sensitive not only to sound but also to movement and gravity.

The structure of the human ear

The ear is the human organ of hearing. Because it detects a mechanical wave in the air, the ear contains mechanoreceptors. However, the ear is not simply sensitive to sound. It also detects both gravity and movement, again using specially adapted mechanoreceptors. As in the case of the eye, the structure of the ear is closely related to its functions, as shown by figure 4.2.14.

How do we hear?

For us to hear, the ear has to collect sound waves from the air and funnel them into the region containing the sound receptors – that is, the inner ear. The **pinna** helps to do this and the sound waves are funnelled along the **ear canal** and set up vibrations in the **ear drum**. These vibrations in turn set the ear **ossicles** rocking against each other, with the smallest bone, the stapes, rocking against the **oval window** and setting up vibrations there which are transferred to the **perilymph**, the fluid of the inner ear. The area of the ear drum is relatively large compared with that of the oval window, and so vibrations transferred across the middle ear are amplified by a factor of 22. The movements set up in the perilymph are picked up by sensory receptors in the **cochlea** and the information sent to the brain as impulses in the **auditory nerve**. The brain interprets these messages as sounds.

The role of the cochlea

The cochlea is the organ which is sensitive to sound within the ear. It is coiled rather like the shell of a snail, but to understand how it works it is easier to consider the structure uncoiled. Figure 4.2.15 shows a simplified diagram of the cochlea. The oval window and the round window are the two ends of a narrow perilymph-filled canal around the cochlea. The upper part is called the **vestibular canal** and the lower part is the **tympanic canal**. Vibrations run through the perilymph from the oval to the round window. The cavity within the cochlea, called the **median canal**, is filled with endolymph.

The **Reissner's membrane** separates the endolymph from the vestibular canal and the **basilar membrane** separates it from the tympanic canal. Running through the centre of the whole cochlea is a third, rather rigid membrane known as the **tectorial membrane**. The basilar membrane has a bulge running

What we perceive as sound is usually the result of vibrations (mechanical waves) travelling through air. These sound waves can also travel through liquids such as water or solids such as the laboratory bench or the wall of a house. Sound is difficult to define because sounds do not exist until a mechanical wave in the air is picked up by the ear and interpreted by the brain – the term 'sound' describes the sensation that we hear.

The frequency of vibration of an object determines the frequency of the vibrations travelling through the air. The human ear is sensitive to frequencies of between 40 and 20 000 Hz (cycles per second). Low-frequency sound waves are perceived as deep sounds and high-frequency sound waves as high-pitched sounds.

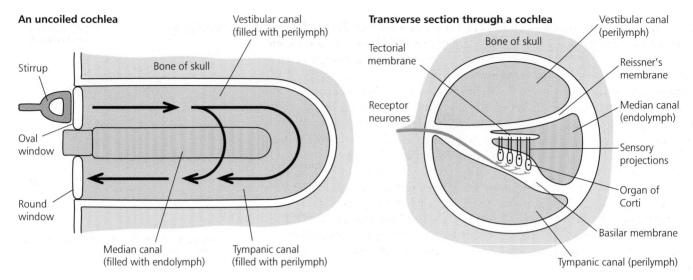

An uncoiled cochlea

Stirrup
Oval window
Round window
Bone of skull
Vestibular canal (filled with perilymph)
Median canal (filled with endolymph)
Tympanic canal (filled with perilymph)

Transverse section through a cochlea

Tectorial membrane
Receptor neurones
Bone of skull
Vestibular canal (perilymph)
Reissner's membrane
Median canal (endolymph)
Sensory projections
Organ of Corti
Basilar membrane
Tympanic canal (perilymph)

Figure 4.2.15 The cochlea is a remarkably complex and delicate hearing apparatus.

along its entire length, and this bulge contains receptor cells. The bulge is called the **organ of Corti**. The receptor cells of the organ of Corti have sensory projections which are embedded in the tectorial membrane (see figure 4.2.15).

When a sound wave causes the oval window to vibrate, the vibrations of the membrane result in pressure waves passing along the perilymph in the vestibular canal. At some point along the cochlea, depending on the frequency of the vibration, these waves cause the Reissner's membrane to vibrate. This causes vibrations in the endolymph which in turn causes vibration in the basilar membrane. The tectorial membrane is too rigid to vibrate. This means that as the basilar membrane vibrates it moves relative to the tectorial membrane. This stretches the sensory projections between them which causes a generator potential to be set up in the receptor cells in the organ of Corti. The generator potential is transmitted across synapses to receptor neurones where action potentials are set up which carry information to the brain.

The basilar membrane is thinnest and so vibrates most easily near the oval window. This is where high-frequency, high-pitched sounds are picked up. Deeper sounds are detected further along the cochlea towards the round window, where the basilar membrane is thicker. Information about the pitch of a sound is given to the brain by the position along the cochlea of the receptor cells stimulated. Information about the loudness comes from how many receptor cells are stimulated at a particular site. Quiet sounds stimulate only a few receptor cells whereas loud sounds stimulate many. Spatial summation occurs to give the brain detailed information about the sounds heard. The information is passed to the brain along the auditory nerve.

The other senses of the ear

The ear contains many receptors sensitive to sound in the cochlea, but it also contains receptors sensitive to movement and gravity in other areas of the inner ear. These senses are vital to both our sense of balance and our coordination. Anyone who has experienced disorientation after a rapidly rotating fairground ride will recognise the problems of staying upright and walking straight which can result from only a minor disturbance of these systems. So how are our senses of gravity and movement achieved? We shall look at the two systems separately.

The perception of gravitational fields

The **sacculus** and **utriculus** (shown on figure 4.2.14) are the organs involved in the perception of gravitational fields. We do not have a direct awareness of

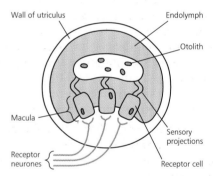

Wall of utriculus
Endolymph
Otolith
Macula
Sensory projections
Receptor neurones
Receptor cell

When the head is upright there is no pull on the sensory projections in the utriculus.

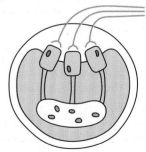

When the head is tilted or, in the extreme example shown here, upside down, the otoliths fall away from the macula. As a result some or, as seen here, all of the sensory projections are stretched. This causes generator potentials to be set up in the receptor cells and messages to be sent to the brain giving information about the orientation of the head.

Figure 4.2.16 A simplified section of a utriculus shows how the organ works.

this sense – we might comment on the brightness of a light or the loudness of a sound but we do not usually discuss the state of gravity! However, we do know which way up we are, or whether our heads are on one side or upright, and this is the result of our gravitational sense.

Figure 4.2.16 shows the internal structure of the utriculus, and the sacculus works on the same plan. Both organs are filled with endolymph, like the cochlea. There is a bulge or mound called the **macula** containing receptor cells. These receptor cells have sensory projections which are embedded in the **otoliths**, chalky crystals in a mass of jelly-like material. When the head is upright there is no pull on the sensory projections, but as the head tilts in one direction the otoliths on that side move away from the macula under the influence of gravity. This causes a strain on the sensory projections and generator potentials are set up in the receptor cells of the macula. Varying numbers of generator potentials and differing strengths give information which the brain can interpret to produce a picture of the amount and direction of the tilting of the head.

The awareness of movement

Movements of the head in any direction can be detected by the **semicircular canals**. These sense organs are arranged so that each one is at right angles to the other two, making comprehensive detection of movement possible. Each semicircular canal is filled with endolymph and has a swelling called the **ampulla**. Inside the ampulla is a mound of receptor cells known as the **crista**, and these have sensory projections embedded in a jelly-like structure, the **cupula**, as shown in figure 4.2.17. When we turn our heads, the semicircular canals move with us. The movement of the cupula is opposed by the inertia of the endolymph, which tends to stay still. This results in a distortion of the cupula and consequently a strain on the sensory projections. This pull sets up generator potentials in the receptor cells on one side of the ampulla, followed by action potentials in the sensory nerves, giving the brain information as to in which direction the head is turning.

Processing sensory information

The eyes and ears, although major and very important sense organs, supply only a part of the huge amount of sensory information constantly gathered by the body. This is carried by sensory nerve fibres to the central nervous system. In many cases these fibres are part of reflex arcs and the body responds in an immediate, preprogrammed way. But in many other cases the sensory information is sent to the higher centres of the brain and the information from many sources is put together and processed. As a result of all this information, messages need to be sent to effector cells and organs. These messages are sent out along motor nerves in the peripheral nervous system, which we shall now go on to consider in more detail.

The peripheral nervous system

The mammalian nervous system is made up of the **central nervous system** (brain and spinal cord, discussed in section 4.3) and the **peripheral nervous system** extending from and coordinated by the central nervous system. The peripheral nervous system is made up of the sensory or afferent nerves carrying messages from the receptors into the central nervous system, and the motor or efferent nerves carrying messages out to the effectors. All the sensory nerves function in much the same way, but the motor nerves can be divided into two main types.

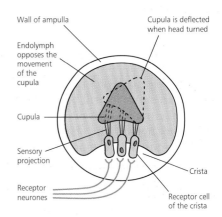

Figure 4.2.17 A simplified section through a cupula in one of the semicircular canals.

Dizziness

The endolymph in the movement-detecting organs resists movement in normal circumstances. But if we spin round rapidly for a prolonged time – as on a fairground ride – the endolymph eventually begins to move. Just as it takes time to start moving, it also takes time to stop moving again. For some moments after the spinning has stopped, the cupula is distorted by the moving endolymph, although now the pressure is on the other side. Our brains receive false information, implying that we are still spinning, although in the opposite direction. The information from our eyes denies this and the conflict of inputs results in a sensation of disorientation and failure of our usual balance control.

The motor system

The **voluntary** motor nerves, as the name suggests, are under voluntary or conscious control. The higher areas of the brain are involved and they function as a result of conscious thought. When we consider an action, such as picking up a cup of tea or switching on a CD player, the instructions which need to be issued to the muscles will be carried along voluntary nerve fibres.

The other major division of the motor nervous system is the **autonomic** or **involuntary** nerves. The nerves of the autonomic nervous system are involved with the control of involuntary activities – bodily functions such as the movements and secretions of the gut, sweating, breathing and dilating or constricting blood vessels, which are normally not dealt with by the conscious area of the brain.

The autonomic nervous system can itself be subdivided into the **sympathetic nervous system** and the **parasympathetic nervous system**. The differences between these two groups are both anatomical and functional. The structural differences can be seen in figure 4.2.18. The main functional differences relate to the neurotransmitters at the synapses. The sympathetic system produces noradrenaline, whilst the parasympathetic system produces acetylcholine.

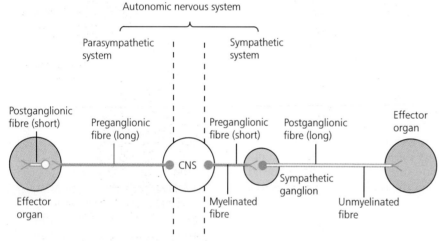

Figure 4.2.18 In both the parasympathetic and the sympathetic systems, myelinated preganglionic fibres leave the central nervous system and synapse within a ganglion with unmyelinated postganglionic fibres. In the sympathetic system the ganglia are very close to the CNS, so the preganglionic fibres are short and the postganglionic fibres are long. In the parasympathetic system the situation is reversed. The ganglia are near to or in the effector organ, so the preganglionic fibres are very long and the postganglionic ones very short.

Most of the body organ systems are supplied by both the sympathetic and the parasympathetic systems. So what are the functional effects of the differences between them? Put simply, the sympathetic nervous system usually has an **excitatory effect**, whilst the parasympathetic system has an **inhibitory effect**. What this means in terms of individual organs can be seen in figure 4.2.19.

Several bodily functions which we might consider to be under voluntary control – opening the bowel and bladder sphincters, for example – are shown on the figure as under the control of the autonomic system. The nervous system is of enormous sophistication and complexity and many areas of the body are supplied with voluntary as well as involuntary nerves. Most of us have control over our bladder and bowels, and can control our breathing rate if we wish to. It is relatively easy to control the heart rate to some degree, and mystics the world over have shown control over many other normally involuntary activities. The nervous system still has many elements of mystery about it, and the central nervous system which we go on to consider next is the least understood of all.

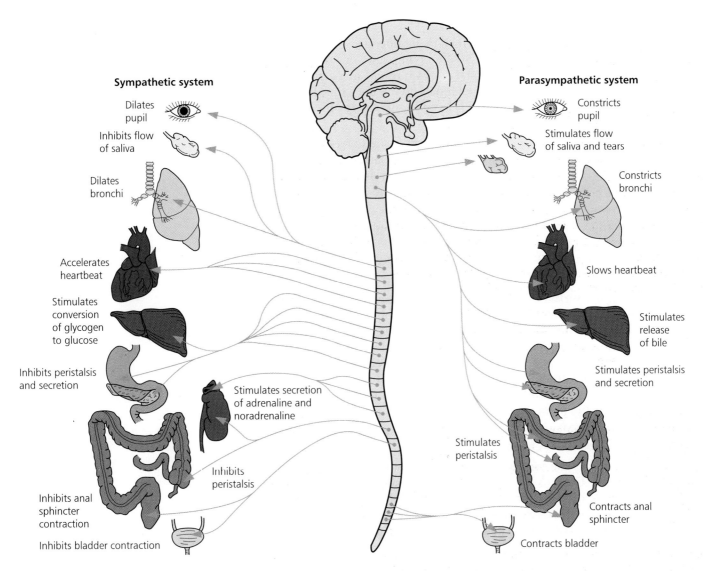

Sympathetic system

Dilates pupil

Inhibits flow of saliva

Dilates bronchi

Accelerates heartbeat

Stimulates conversion of glycogen to glucose

Inhibits peristalsis and secretion

Stimulates secretion of adrenaline and noradrenaline

Inhibits peristalsis

Inhibits anal sphincter contraction

Inhibits bladder contraction

Parasympathetic system

Constricts pupil

Stimulates flow of saliva and tears

Constricts bronchi

Slows heartbeat

Stimulates release of bile

Stimulates peristalsis and secretion

Stimulates peristalsis

Contracts anal sphincter

Contracts bladder

Figure 4.2.19 The opposing effects of the sympathetic and parasympathetic nerves on body systems.

SUMMARY

- An **unconditioned reflex** is a fixed or **unconditioned response** to a particular or **unconditioned stimulus**. Such responses are controlled by a nerve pathway called a **reflex arc**.

- In a vertebrate reflex arc a stimulus in the receptor sets up an impulse in the sensory neurone which travels along the spinal nerve to the spinal cord. Synaptic transmission sets up another impulse in a motor neurone, either directly or via a **relay neurone**. The impulse leaves the spinal cord and passes along the spinal nerve to the effector organ.

- Reflex actions happen quickly and so are useful to evade danger. They also control bodily functions and free the central nervous system to deal with non-routine activities.

- A **primary receptor** is a neurone with a specialised dendrite which detects a stimulus and sets up an action potential in its fibre. A **secondary receptor** is a modified epithelial cell which synapses with a sensory neurone.

- Receptors have a negative resting potential maintained by sodium pumps. A stimulus interferes with the sodium pump and ions move into the neurone setting up a generator current which results in a generator potential of varying size – generator potentials do not obey the all-or-nothing law. If the generator potential is large enough it sets up an action potential in the neurone.

- Several secondary receptor cells may synapse with a single receptor neurone. In **convergence**, generator potentials summate to trigger an action potential. A graded response is achieved by varying the rate at which action potentials pass along the sensory neurone.

- A receptor exposed to an unchanging stimulus **adapts** – the generator potentials produced gradually die away until the stimulus changes, when they build up again.

- **Sense organs** such as the eye and the ear are specialised regions where receptors sensitive to a particular stimulus are collected together.

- The human eye is surrounded and protected by the **sclera**, inside which is the **choroid** which prevents internal reflection of light. The **conjunctiva** is an epithelium covering the **cornea**, a transparent area at the front of the eyeball enclosing the **aqueous humour**. The coloured **iris** surrounds the **pupil**, an aperture through which light passes to the **lens**. Light then passes through the **vitreous humour** to the light-sensitive **retina** at the back of the eyeball. The **fovea** is the most sensitive part of the retina while the **blind spot** is the point where the **optic nerve** leaves the eye.

- The **radial** and **circular** muscles of the iris control the size of the pupil and thus the amount of light entering the eye.

- Light is refracted by the cornea, the aqueous humour, the lens and the vitreous humour. The lens carries out the fine focusing necessary to ensure that the image is formed on the retina. The shape of the lens is adjusted by the action of the **ciliary muscles** in the **ciliary body** surrounding the lens, which is supported in the ciliary body by the **suspensory ligaments**. This adjustment or **accommodation** allows light from objects at different distances to be focused.

- The retina contains **photoreceptors** called **rods** and **cones**. Rods provide black and white vision. They contain a visual pigment called **rhodopsin**. Several rods synapse with the same sensory neurone giving sensitivity to low levels of light. Rhodopsin is formed from **opsin** and **retinene**. Retinene exists in the *cis* form in the dark and the *trans* form in the light. When retinene is converted to the *trans* form in the light, the rhodopsin breaks up or **bleaches**, setting up a generator potential. In the light the rods are bleached and the eye is **light adapted**. In the dark rhodopsin is reformed and the eye becomes **dark adapted**.

- Cones are concentrated at the fovea and produce colour vision in bright light. Each cone has its own sensory neurone and contains one of three visual pigments.

- The human ear consists of the external **pinna** which funnels the sound waves through the **ear canal** to the **ear drum**. This transmits the vibration to the **ossicles**, small bones which amplify the vibrations and transmit them to the **oval window** of the **cochlea**. Vibrations run through the **perilymph** in the cochlea to the **round window**. Three membranes run the length of the cochlea and between two of them are the sensory projections of the

organ of Corti. These vibrate when the sound wave matches their own particular frequency and set up a generator potential in the receptor cell.

- The ear perceives gravitational fields by the action of the **sacculus** and **utriculus**. The **macula** of both these organs contains receptor cells and sensory projections embedded in the **otoliths**, crystals which move under the influence of gravity.

- Movement of the head is perceived by three **semicircular canals** arranged at right angles. The **ampulla** contains a mound of receptor cells called the **crista** with sensory projections embedded in the **cupula** which exerts a strain on the sensory projections when the head is moved.

- The **peripheral nervous system** consists of sensory and motor nerves carrying impulses between the central nervous system and the rest of the body. The motor nerves are divided into the **voluntary system**, under conscious control, and the **autonomic** (involuntary) **system**.

- The autonomic system is further subdivided into the **sympathetic** and **parasympathetic** systems. The sympathetic system has adrenergic nerves while the parasympathetic has cholinergic nerves. In both systems myelinated preganglionic fibres leave the central nervous system and synapse in a ganglion with unmyelinated postganglionic fibres. The ganglia are close to the central nervous system in the sympathetic system and close to the effector in the parasympathetic system. The two systems coordinate to control body systems, the sympathetic system generally having an excitatory effect and the parasympathetic an inhibitory effect.

QUESTIONS

1 Describe a typical mammalian reflex response. Discuss the role of reflexes in the survival of different groups of animals.

2 Sketch a diagram of the structure of the human eye. Annotate the diagram to indicate the main features and how their structure is related to their function.

3 a Glue ear is a condition found in young children. It is the result of sticky secretions produced in the middle ear being unable to drain away through the Eustachian tube, due to blockage or to the angle of the tube in the immature skull. Explain why this may result in temporary deafness.

 b Why may ear infections be associated with sensations of giddiness and loss of balance?

Developing Key Skills

When people begin to have problems with their vision they may not want to acknowledge what is happening. However, sight problems can be dangerous. An individual can burn themselves or cut themselves in their own homes if they cannot see properly. And on the roads sight problems can be fatal – a misjudgement of the speed of an oncoming car when crossing the road or driving can lead to death. The National Association of Over-60s Clubs has decided to take action to try and make their members aware of possible problems and also the solutions which are now available. You have been asked to design a leaflet for the members explaining the sorts of changes which can take place in the eye as it ages and what can be done to solve the problems these changes bring.

Young people often have visual problems too – how would your design for a leaflet targeted at teenagers differ from the leaflet you have designed for older people?

Throughout our lives, human beings learn. From the moment of birth we learn how to behave as a human, about the world around us, about school subjects, to do our adult jobs, to be partners, parents and grandparents. How do we learn all this? Much of what we know about learning has come from the study of the way other animals behave, and many different researchers have contributed to our present knowledge.

Pavlov's dogs

Ivan Pavlov was a Russian physiologist who did a great deal of work on the digestive responses of dogs at the turn of the twentieth century. He collected saliva and gastric juices from dogs at different times of day, and found that the level of secretion rose when the dogs saw and smelled their food. He then set up a training pattern, ringing a bell before the dogs were fed. He found that in a relatively short time the dogs would produce digestive juices when the bell was rung, regardless of whether it was a normal feed time or not. This type of learned behaviour is known as **classical conditioning**. It produces a **conditioned reflex**, and it can be seen in a wide range of animals.

Skinner's pigeons

A few years later Burrhus Frederic Skinner showed that animals, including people, learn by another process known as **operant conditioning**. Skinner worked with pigeons, and built special experimental containers for them which have become known as Skinner boxes. Inside these boxes were levers which the pigeons would press accidentally as they moved around. When they pressed a lever, a portion of food was delivered to them. Skinner showed that pigeons realised quite quickly that they could press the lever by choice and get an unlimited supply of food.

Kohler's chimps

Other animals might show certain forms of learning, but it was believed for a long time that only humans could solve problems by reasoning and using tools. In the 1920s Wolfgang Kohler challenged that idea with his four chimpanzees Chica, Grande, Konsul and Sultan. In Kohler's basic experiment he put one of his chimpanzees in an enclosed play area in which he had placed a bunch of bananas well out of reach. Boxes and sticks were scattered around in the play area. The chimpanzees soon began to build towers out of the boxes to reach the bananas, and used the sticks to bring them within reach.

Kohler believed that the chimpanzees were using insight and reasoning to solve the problems he set them. Some scientists have disagreed with his conclusions, but the work done by Kohler and others has opened the way for many more experiments done in the same field, throwing light on the way we and our fellow species learn.

Figure 1 We think our pets are clever to know when it is dinner time. Pavlov showed that they have learned to pick up the clues that precede feeding, and respond to them.

Figure 2 Pigeons are more intelligent than they might appear.

A nervous system made up of receptors, nerves and effectors provides sufficient sensitivity to an animal's surroundings for it to capture food and avoid at least some predators. But complex animals need a 'sorting station' where information can be processed and from where instructions can be issued to give fully coordinated responses to a wide range of situations. Evolution has provided the **central nervous system** (**CNS**), and in particular the **brain**.

The brain

The development of complex nervous systems

As nervous systems became increasingly complex, one of the first developments was **ganglia** – collections of cell bodies and synapses in one enclosed area. These gave increased coordination and efficiency, enabling larger numbers of nerve fibres to exchange information. The development of a central nerve cord (the **spinal cord** in vertebrates) was another major step in the evolution of nervous systems. A central major nerve pathway facilitates whole-body communications and gives a specific route for incoming and outgoing messages. Ganglia and a central nerve cord made it possible for animals to respond in a much greater variety of ways to their environment. As an example, the brains of insects may seem relatively rudimentary, yet in combination with a central nerve cord and ganglia in every body segment they enable some extremely sophisticated patterns of behaviour to be developed in the insect world.

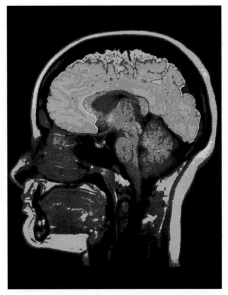

A CAT scanner allows us to see sections of the living brain.

Figure 4.3.1 The brain is a remarkable organ of enormous complexity. So far our knowledge of it is somewhat primitive and rudimentary.

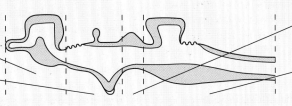

The **forebrain**. The **endbrain** at the end contains the olfactory lobes, and in higher vertebrates forms the cerebral hemispheres.

The **'tweenbrain** forms the pineal gland and the pituitary gland.

The **midbrain** contains the optic lobes.

The **hindbrain** forms the cerebellum and the medulla.

Cerebral hemispheres (cerebrum) – the seat of intelligence, this area controls the voluntary behaviour of the body along with learning, memory, personality and the ability to reason.

Thalamus – this processes all the sensory impulses before directing them to the appropriate area of the brain. It is also involved in the perception of pain and pleasure.

Hypothalamus – this coordinates the autonomic nervous system. It monitors the chemistry of the blood and controls the hormone secretions of the pituitary gland. It also controls thirst, hunger, aggression and reproductive behaviour.

Pituitary gland

Pons – literally 'bridge' – relays impulses to the cerebellum.

Medulla – the most primitive part of the brain, containing reflex centres which control functions such as the heart rate, blood pressure, breathing rate, coughing, sneezing, swallowing, saliva production and peristalsis.

Meninges – protective membranes which cover the brain. Between them is the **cerebrospinal fluid** which surrounds the central nervous system and fills any available spaces.

Corpus callosum – this area connects the left and right cerebral hemispheres, giving communication between the two.

Corpora quadrigemina – this controls the reflexes associated with sight and hearing. Its origin is the midbrain.

Cerebellum – the 'tree of life', so called because of the patterns of white and grey matter within it. It coordinates smooth movements and uses information from the muscles and ears to maintain posture and balance.

However, it is the development of increasingly large and complex brains that has led to the success of some groups of vertebrates. In the vertebrates the central nervous system develops as a hollow tube of nervous tissue which forms the **spinal cord**, containing the **grey matter** made up of the neurone cell bodies and the **white matter** consisting of the tracts of nerve fibres. At the front or **anterior** end of a vertebrate embryo, this tube swells and to some extent folds back on itself to form a **brain**. In some vertebrates this brain remains fairly simple, with areas very specific to particular functions such as sight or smell. The brain has three distinct areas – the **forebrain**, **midbrain** and **hindbrain**.

The human brain

In other vertebrates such as humans the brain becomes a remarkably complex structure. The original simple arrangement into three areas is very difficult to see because a part called the **cerebral cortex** is folded back over the entire brain. There are areas of the human brain with very specific functions concerned with the major senses and control of basic bodily functions. Equally there are many regions of the brain where the precise functions and interrelationships with other areas are not clearly understood. The basic pattern of a vertebrate brain along with a simplified representation of the human brain are given in figure 4.3.1.

Investigating the brain

Our understanding of the human brain has been developed using evidence from two different sources – the brains of other animals, and the human brain itself.

The brains of other animals

Over the years many investigations have been carried out on the brains of other animals from insects to monkeys. Some results have been related directly to the human brain, although this is not always possible. Examples include the effect of removing the cerebral hemispheres from animals such as dogs and monkeys, and also implanting electrodes to see the effect on behaviour of artificially stimulating a region of the brain. Many people find the idea of this type of research distasteful, and there are moves to minimise the experiments that are permitted. On the other hand, much information has been gained which has been put to good use in human medicine.

The brains of humans

Experiments such as those described above are obviously not carried out on humans. However, volunteers have allowed areas of their brains to be artificially stimulated during brain surgery under local anaesthetic. The volunteers have described the resulting sensations to the experimenters. As a result we have a fairly clear picture of how certain areas of the brain are associated with very particular functions (**localisation of function**).

Most of our information about the functions of the human brain has come from situations where parts of the brain are damaged or missing either at birth or as the result of illness or injury.

The brain at work

The way in which the brain works is still not fully understood. We know that it contains several hundred million cells working together. We also know that the great nerve tracts from the spinal cord cross over as they enter and leave the brain, so that the left-hand side of the brain receives information from and controls the right-hand side of the body, and vice versa. We are aware that the cerebral cortex is only about 3 mm thick, and yet controls most of those functions which make us what we are. Damage to the cortex affects our memory, intelligence, learning ability and decision-making skills. Sensory awareness and speech may be affected too. **Centres** or **nuclei** in the brain are made up of cell bodies which may have hundreds of synapses, making intercommunication between thousands and indeed millions of cells possible.

The cerebral hemispheres

The cerebral hemispheres are the part of the brain where much of the activity takes place that we can regard as making us human. The outer thin (3 mm) folded layer of grey matter (nerve cells) makes up the cerebral cortex, and this is arranged over a mass of white matter (the nerve fibre tracts). The cerebral hemispheres have a number of very important functions, often localised in very specific areas. Within the thin grey covering over the top of our brain lies much of what makes us not only human, but also uniquely ourselves.

The **sensory** areas receive information from sensory nerves all over the body. Information from different sense organs arrives at different areas of the cerebral cortex. The big optic tracts cross over, so information about what is seen by the right eye is received on the left-hand side of the brain, whilst information from the left eye travels to the right-hand side of the brain. The areas of the brain that receive the different sensory information vary in size depending on the number of nerves feeding information in. So, for example, the olfactory lobes of the brain are particularly large in an animal like a dog or a rat which relies heavily on the sense of smell, whereas in humans the olfactory region is relatively small – but the visual areas are larger.

The **motor** areas of the brain are output regions, sending impulses to the voluntary muscles and other effectors around the body, initiating and controlling our actions. As with the sensory regions of the brain, the size of each motor area is related to the complexity of the activity it is controlling.

As well as sensory and motor areas, the cerebral cortex has **association areas**. These are involved in the processing of the information that comes into the brain. They compare the signals coming in with previous experience, by accessing memories. They also link together the information coming in from various sources, so that if a scary sound is accompanied by a terrifying image, this is combined and perceived as a situation to escape from as fast as possible! However, that is not the whole story because the association areas also relate the information they are receiving to other messages to put them in context. If the scary sound and images are accompanied by information about safe surroundings such as a cinema or the sitting room, your fright response will be considerably more subdued than by contextual information about being on your own in a dark alley in the middle of the night. The association areas are involved in memory, reasoning and learning – at least in part they are the seat of what we call intelligence.

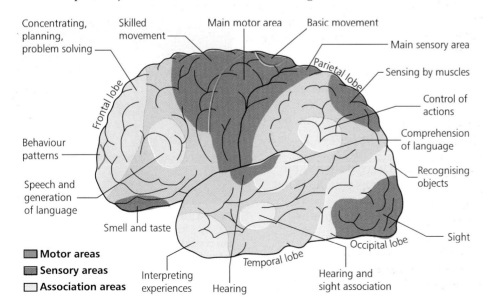

Figure 4.3.2 The main recognised areas of the cerebral hemispheres on the surface of the brain.

Intriguingly, what we know about the specific functions of parts of the cerebral cortex is far outweighed by what we do not know. There are large areas, particularly at the front of the cerebral hemispheres, which are known as the **silent areas**. They do not seem to respond to electrical stimulation, but if they are damaged this can cause personality disorders. These silent areas of the brain appear to hold the secrets of our personality, the unique things about us which make each of us quite unlike anybody else.

The split brain

The human brain is not split physically in two, but there are two clear sides to the brain which carry out quite distinct roles. Each side of the body is controlled by the opposite side of the brain – as we have already seen, information from the right eye comes to the left brain and vice versa. Some functions are controlled almost exclusively on one side of the brain. There are a number of brain areas associated with speech, for example, but in most people they are all found on the left-hand side of the brain. There are specific sites associated with the comprehension of language, where the form and meaning of speech are generated and understood, and with speech production, from where the appropriate facial, throat and tongue muscles are stimulated to contract to produce the right sound.

The left-hand side of the brain is good at processing information analytically, whereas the right-hand side is better at spatial recognition – it tends to process information as a whole. Another important function of the right brain is in the recognition of faces – if it is damaged we may be unable to recognise even our nearest and dearest.

The brain in crisis – Alzheimer's disease

Much of what we know about the location of specific functions in the brain comes from the study of people who through birth defect, injury or disease have damage to that particular area of the brain. But there are some diseases that attack large areas of the brain, with devastating effect. **Alzheimer's disease** can affect people in their earlier years, but is most common in old age. Research indicates that it is a multifactorial condition (it has many causes) with age as one of the major factors – the chances of developing the disease increase dramatically after the age of 65. There is also a genetic factor – if several family members suffer from the disease, then other members of that family are at increased risk.

In Alzheimer's disease the brain cells shrivel and disintegrate, leaving sticky clumps of damaged cells and tangled fibres as the only remains of once healthy, functioning central nervous tissue. Protein plaques are formed in the tissue and levels of the neurotransmitter acetylcholine fall sharply. The cerebral cortex is particularly badly affected by the disease.

As this disintegration of the brain tissue progresses, normal brain function is progressively lost. Although the disease progresses differently in each individual, there is a common overall pattern to the deterioration.

The initial deterioration of the cells of the brain, which seems to include increased apoptosis, obviously precedes the behavioural symptoms but is not usually detected unless the brain is investigated for other reasons, such as a suspected brain tumour. So for the vast majority of sufferers, the onset is completely unexpected. The first symptoms are relatively minor, and easily ignored as the sort of memory lapses and mistakes we all make from time to time, particularly as we get older and our memories have more information to store and sift. The memory lapses tend to develop into more serious problems, such as disorientation over time, and an increasing tiredness and lethargy can

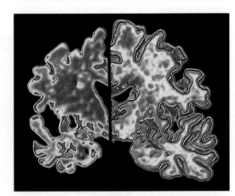

Figure 4.3.3 The slow reduction of active brain tissue to sticky clumps of damaged cells is mirrored in the loss of memory and control and the changes in behaviour as an individual progresses through the stages of Alzheimer's disease. The affected brain (left) is shrunken compared with the normal brain (right) due to degeneration and death of the nerve cells.

become obvious. Sufferers may feel persecuted, convinced that people are stealing from them or falsely accusing them of blunders. They may hoard things and hide them for years. As the disease progresses individuals often begin to wander, leaving their homes at all hours of the day and night. They also lose control of both their bladder and bowels, yet may remain aware enough to be enormously embarrassed about this initially and try to pass the blame onto others. It is a great relief in some ways when the awareness, although not the continence problem itself, is lost in the disintegrating brain. The memory of how to perform simple everyday tasks such as laying the table or cleaning the teeth disappears. Control of the emotions becomes much reduced, returning to the tantrums and unreasonable demands of toddler years, along with a similar need for comfort, reassurance and the presence of only very familiar faces.

Gradually the power of speech is lost, so that Alzheimer's victims can no longer care for themselves, control their bodily functions, feed themselves or speak. By this stage they have lost their ability to recognise their loved ones, so that before speech is completely lost husbands, wives and children may hear their partner or parent asking who they are.

Eventually Alzheimer's disease leads to death. The distress this disease can cause within a family is immeasurable, because whilst the family has to cope with all the problems of managing an individual suffering from Alzheimer's disease and the sadness of losing the person they knew and loved, they still have an emaciated human shell of the same name and appearance and so can neither grieve properly nor enjoy the existence of that person. The only blessing is that for the person who is affected by Alzheimer's disease, the progression of the disease ensures that their awareness of the situation and their own tragedy is continually and slowly eroded as their brain tissue dies.

Apart from age and genetics, what else increases our risk of developing this disease – and is there anything we can do to avoid it? Aluminium, zinc and food-borne poisons have all been implicated by some research. Most scientists feel they are relatively unimportant, although new research on zinc shows interesting results. Head injuries seem to increase the risk slightly, as does gender: women are more likely to develop Alzheimer's disease than men, though this may simply be a reflection of the fact that they live longer. Finally, it appears that education may have an effect. The longer you stay in formal education, the less likely you are to develop Alzheimer's disease – yet another good reason for studying hard at school and college!

The role of the brain

Brains perform a vital role in coordinating the activities of many multicellular organisms. They give unconscious control over many vital bodily functions. They receive information from a vast array of sensory inputs, correlate it all and send out instructions for an appropriate response. But perhaps one of the most important functions of a brain is to allow the development of increasingly complex forms of behaviour and communication.

Animal behaviour

Intelligence and behaviour

Some invertebrates have very simple behaviour patterns which are almost entirely predictable. Take the sea anemone which we saw in figure 4.1.1, page 242. If you poke the sea anemone its tentacles withdraw. It will repeat this behaviour until it adapts to the stimulus and stops responding. If it is then left for a while its neurotransmitters will be replenished and the same pattern of behaviour will be repeated. In animals with bigger and more complicated brains, this type of simple, repetitive behaviour is seen less frequently. The elaboration of original behaviour patterns enables animals to become more efficient hunters, to avoid attack, to develop successful foraging strategies and to attract mates – they become generally more successful. Communication skills are also developed, making cooperative behaviour possible and improving group survival chances.

What do we mean by behaviour?

We continually observe animal behaviour in the lives of those species which coexist with us such as cats and dogs, hamsters and goldfish, birds and insects, but most particularly in the members of our own species. Not only do we observe the behaviour of others, we also behave ourselves. **Behaviour** can be defined as an action in response to a stimulus which modifies the relationship between the organism and the environment.

This sounds rather daunting – it means that animals respond to any change in their environment which might affect them, and attempt to make sure that their situation either remains the same or improves. A simple example is to imagine a fly buzzing around your head. You might brush it away, or swat it, or fetch the fly spray – you would act in some way to get rid of the irritating stimulus and return the situation to normal. Animal behaviour is not always as clear cut as this, but the principle behind it is the same.

Studying behaviour

Our knowledge of animal behaviour is based largely on observations of the way animals behave, either in their natural environment or in the laboratory. Both these approaches have advantages and disadvantages. Whilst animals are most likely to behave normally in their natural environment, they might travel great distances in a day, or live somewhere inaccessible to people, or be almost impossible to see. It is also impossible to control all the variables in a natural environment. In the laboratory all the surrounding conditions can be carefully controlled and observation is easy, but the animals are in an artificial setting and may not behave in a normal way. In vertebrates, more of these factors have to be considered when evaluating any observations made. Flatworms behave no differently whether the water they are in is part of a pond or in a Petri dish. Monkeys that are used to a natural environment behave quite differently in a cage or in a forest.

Much animal behaviour is either very rapid or very slow, and it is also frequently repetitive. Thus as well as direct human observations, time-lapse photography and video recordings are often used to analyse the sequence of events in a piece of behaviour. Because animal behaviour is more open to subjective interpretation and anthropomorphism than most other areas of biology, it is important to realise that observations and conclusions in this area of biology are still very much open to discussion.

In observing how animals progress from the reception of a stimulus to a behavioural response, two major categories of behaviour have emerged. The first is **innate** or **species-characteristic behaviour**. The second is **learned** or **individual-characteristic behaviour**. We shall consider the two types separately, but this distinction is largely for our convenience, as there is considerable overlap between the categories.

Figure 4.3.4 A problem in studying animal behaviour is our tendency to put ourselves in the place of others, and to interpret animal actions in the light of human responses (anthropomorphism). Cats used to a caged existence, or rats which frequently explore mazes in the interests of science, may well be healthy, well-fed individuals displaying normal behaviour for their species. But our natural response tends to be to feel sorry for them, perhaps even deciding that they look 'unhappy' – because we are mentally putting ourselves in their place and endowing them with our reactions to the situation. To draw any worthwhile conclusions about animal behaviour, we must be objective and dispassionate in our observations.

Innate behaviour

What is innate behaviour?

Innate behaviour is a large collection of responses which are usually seen in every member of a particular species, hence the term species-characteristic behaviour. This type of behaviour is not learned but is a genetically determined response to a particular stimulus. It occurs as a result of very specific nerve pathways laid down in the embryo from the instructions in the DNA of the organism. Innate behaviour covers an enormous range of types of response, from the simplest avoidance reflexes to highly complex courtship and territorial displays. The stimulus for a piece of innate behaviour will always elicit the same response, which has been selected over generations for its survival value. Some examples are shown in figure 4.3.5. In animals with relatively highly developed brains, innate behaviour frees the conscious areas of the brain for dealing with situations which present new problems for solution.

The courtship display of the bowerbird is a complex sequence of behaviour. Yet it is completely unlearned, an example of a piece of behaviour where it is vital that all members of the species respond in the same way to the stimulus. If only some birds knew the ritual, or not all completed the sequence, successful pair-bonding and mating would not occur.

Figure 4.3.5 Innate behaviour is not learned, and is usually important to the survival of the individual. Inborn responses vary from simple reflexes to complex sequences of behaviour.

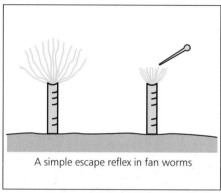

A simple escape reflex in fan worms

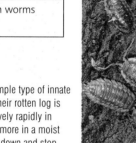

Woodlice demonstrate kinesis, a very simple type of innate response, when the protective cover of their rotten log is removed. They all move and rotate relatively rapidly in random directions until they arrive once more in a moist environment, when the movements slow down and stop.

Types of innate behaviour

Innate behaviour can be divided into categories which again are not rigid divisions, but consider the levels of complexity involved.

1 **Taxes** involve the whole organism moving in response to an external, directional stimulus – in other words, it moves towards or away from the stimulus. Taxic responses can be seen to a wide variety of stimuli in the animal kingdom. Examples of **phototaxis** (responses to light), **geotaxis** (to gravity), **chemotaxis** (to chemicals) and **rheotaxis** (resistance to movement) amongst others can easily be demonstrated. When the organism moves towards the stimulus it is a positive (+) taxis, and when it moves away it is a negative (–) taxis. Examples include earthworms and woodlice moving away from light (negative phototaxis) and moths flying into the wind (positive rheotaxis).

2 **Kineses** involve the whole organism moving in response to a stimulus, but not in a directional way. The rate of movement is related to the *intensity* of the stimulus, not to the direction from which it comes. For example, when woodlice are placed in a dry environment their rate of random movement

and turning increases until they find themselves back in a more humid, damp area when the rate of movement decreases again.

3 **Simple reflexes** have been discussed in section 4.2. A very rapid response is made to a stimulus such as a potentially damaging situation or the presence of food. In some cases several simple reflexes are linked together to form behaviour that looks more complex and directed. A good example of this is the feeding responses of a newly born human infant, in which there are several distinct reflex responses. If a newborn baby is touched on the cheek, there is a reflex response and the head turns towards the touch. This touch may be by a nipple, a finger or a toy – the same reflex response results. Similarly, a touch on the lips causes a reflex opening of the mouth, and anything placed inside the mouth, particularly touching the roof of the mouth, is sucked on hard. The benefits of these reflexes to the infant are obvious – in response to the touch of a nipple on the face he or she turns to face the food, opens the mouth when the nipple touches it and sucks to feed. The parents generally see this behaviour not as simple reflexes but as the baby choosing to seek the comfort of the breast. This view that their child is actively looking for them elicits more caring behaviour from the parents.

4 **Modified reflexes** result when some reflex actions with no conscious control become modified until they are largely conscious operations. A good example is the opening of the bladder and bowel. A small baby urinates as a reflex response whenever the wall of the bladder is stretched. Similarly, the bowel is emptied in a reflex response to the stretching of the rectum by the presence of faeces. But as the baby grows into a toddler it becomes aware of the sensations associated with a full bladder or a full bowel and sooner or later develops some conscious control. In time the bladder and bowel come almost completely under the control of our conscious mind. Rewards such as praise from parents hasten the process. However, the bladder is not completely under control of the conscious mind – the reflex actions can return following a sudden shock or a bad fright, a drift into unconsciousness or excessive laughter. In old age and illness the conscious control may once again fade – many very elderly people have to wear incontinence pants because their bladders no longer respond to the conscious pathways but once more rely on reflex responses to tell them when to empty.

5 **Instinct** is the most complex form of innate behaviour. Konrad Lorenz, one of the great researchers in animal behaviour, defined instinct as 'unlearned, species-specific motor patterns'. Instinctive actions may be inborn, but they can be very sophisticated. However, they show a high degree of stereotyping – the same behaviour is seen in all members of a species with little or no individual differences, and the same pattern of behaviour is always produced in response to a particular stimulus known as a **sign stimulus**. For example, the tick *Ixodes* begins to bite when it finds itself on a surface at a temperature of about 37 °C which also smells of butyric acid. This unlikely sounding combination actually describes conditions on mammalian skin, the usual hosts of ticks. A sign stimulus sets in motion an **innate releasing mechanism** that results in a particular behaviour. These sign stimuli/releasers are vital in controlling many instinctive patterns of behaviours with direct survival value to the animals, such as feeding, courtship, parenting and territorial behaviour.

Some classic work on sign stimuli and the innate releasing mechanism was done by Niko Tinbergen using herring gulls. Herring gull chicks peep in a particular way which stimulates their parents to go and find food. When the parent returns to the nest it points its bill downwards and waves it from side to side in front of the chicks. The chicks peck at the tip of the parent's beak, which has a species-specific red spot on it, and the parent bird then regurgitates the food. Tinbergen and his colleagues made a wide variety of wood and cardboard herring gull heads with different colours and arrangements of spots to find out what makes the chicks peck at the bill. They found that the downward orientation of the bill, the side-to-side movement and, most importantly, the red spot acted as sign stimuli. The best pecking response of all was given to a vertical pencil with three red dots on it moving from side to side. It looked nothing like a parent herring gull, but it had all the right sign stimuli to trigger the instinctive pecking behaviour in the chicks. Similar work has been done on robins, aggressive birds that will defend their territory to the death. The red breast of any robin coming into the territory is the sign stimulus that releases the innate aggression – robins have fought for hours with a stuffed sock with a daub of red paint on the front!

Invertebrates are frequently very short lived. They do not have time to rely on trial-and-error learning for their basic responses if they are to complete their life cycles successfully. Instinctive behaviour patterns equip them to cope with most of the situations they will meet. Vertebrates tend to live longer, and certainly some of them have plenty of time for learning. But innate behaviour is still important. Infants and young animals need instincts to enable them to survive until learning and experience take over. And even in adults, innate behaviour is an economy measure, a ready-made set of responses to a given situation leaving the higher areas of the brain free for other less basic functions.

Learned behaviour

What is learned behaviour?

Learned behaviour is an adaptive change in the behaviour of an individual which occurs as the result of experience. This is why it is also known as individual-characteristic behaviour. Individuals learn as a result of their own experience, and modify their behaviour accordingly. No two members of a group or species will have identical experiences, and so learned behaviour is specific to each individual. An example of learned behaviour is the reaction of a child to touching a hot oven door. The hand will be withdrawn rapidly as a result of a piece of reflex, innate behaviour. But the child will learn from the experience not to touch the door again deliberately. This learning will vary from child to child. Some will need only one experience of the heat to modify their behaviour. Others will try the experiment several times before the change in behaviour is made. Some individuals may not even need to touch the hot door themselves – seeing another child's reaction or being warned by an adult may be enough.

Memory

For learning to occur, there must be an ability to **memorise** or store information. There appear to be two types of memory – **short-term memory**, which lasts only a few minutes, and **long-term memory**, which is much more stable and can last for many years. The mechanism by which memory is laid down is not yet fully understood. It appears to involve synaptic changes and the synthesis of proteins. RNA is involved, demonstrated by experiments of the type shown in figure 4.3.7. By injecting different fractions from previously trained flatworms, it was shown that only RNA-containing fractions had an

Figure 4.3.6 The permanence of any learned behaviour depends on the memory, and not everything that is learned remains in the memory very long. Facts swotted up for an examination may well be forgotten soon afterwards – but the knowledge of how to ride a bicycle, once learned, is usually with you for life.

effect on the learning ability of the recipients. But for an experience to bring about a long- term change in the behaviour of an organism, a memory of either the experience, the modified behaviour pattern or both is necessary.

Types of learned behaviour

We tend to assume that learning and learned behaviour happen only in vertebrates, and particularly in the mammals. In fact learned behaviour occurs in the vast majority of animal groups, as we shall see in considering some of the types of learned behaviour.

1 **Habituation** occurs when a stimulus is repeated many times and nothing happens – there is neither 'punishment' nor 'reward'. The stimulus is then ignored. This is not a simple adaptation of the sensory system like accommodation because once a response is habituated or lost it does not return. Examples include birds learning to ignore a scarecrow and babies learning not to 'startle' at every sudden noise. Habituation is particularly important in the development of young animals, as they have to learn not to react to the neutral elements in the world around them. For instance, the movement and noise of the wind must be ignored by a large number of animals or their nervous systems would be constantly firing off 'false alarms'.

2 **Conditioned reflexes** are the result of animals learning to associate new stimuli with an existing unconditioned reflex, as in the case of Pavlov's dogs mentioned in section 4.2.

3 **Trial-and-error (operant) learning** occurs when a piece of trial behaviour on the part of the animal is either rewarded (for example, food is found) or punished (for example, the animal is hurt). If the animal associates the outcome of a piece of behaviour with a reward, that behaviour is likely to be repeated. If the behaviour is associated with punishment, it is less likely to be tried again. The American psychologist B. F. Skinner did extensive studies on this type of learning using pigeons.

4 **Imprinting** is a simple and specialised sort of learning which only occurs in very young animals. At one receptive stage the young animal identifies with another organism, which is usually the parent, or if no parent is available on another large object. It will then follow this object and relate to other similar objects throughout its life.

5 **Exploratory (latent) learning** takes place when an animal explores new surroundings and learns them, without any immediate reward or punishment. The information may then be useful at another time.

6 **Insight learning** is based on thought and reasoning. It is mainly seen in the mammals, particularly the primates. It is regarded as the highest sort of learning. Once a problem has been solved, the solution is then remembered.

Some examples of these types of learned behaviour are illustrated in figure 4.3.8.

How behaviour is modified

Think about your own behaviour – do you always react in the same way to the same situation? The answer is almost certainly no. The behaviour of any animal is modified by the circumstances of the moment. The **motivational state** of an animal depends on a range of factors. The length of time since the last meal, the reproductive state, the presence of other individuals who may be dominant

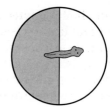

Flatworms move from a light area to a dark one. By giving a mild electric shock each time the dark area is entered, this tendency can be reversed so that the 'trained' worms move from dark to light.

Different fragments of a 'trained' flatworm are injected into an untrained worm.

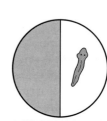

When RNA fragments are injected, the flatworm learns dark avoidance more rapidly than the original worm did. Other fragments had no effect on learning, so it appears some 'memory' may have been passed on in the RNA of the 'trained' worm.

Figure 4.3.7 Can memory be passed on? Experiments with flatworms suggest it might be.

The importance of rewards and punishments in operant learning was demonstrated using pigeons and Skinner boxes. The use of these boxes has been extended to studies of other birds.

When young animals imprint on an adult of the wrong species, all kinds of problems can result!

Figure 4.3.8 Learning takes place in a great variety of ways throughout the animal kingdom. Humans use most of the available methods to increase our knowledge and understanding of the world around us.

or lower in status and whether or not the animal is on its own territory will all affect both the innate and learned behaviour of an individual. An animal will not indulge in exploratory learning if it is very hungry. Sexual desire, aggression and fear may interfere with foraging or hunting. It is almost impossible to predict how an animal will behave unless all the factors of its mental and physiological state are known.

If an animal is torn between fighting and running away, or feeding and displaying to a potential mate, or any situation where two strong drives are involved, it will often show **displacement behaviour**. This involves an activity such as grooming or exploring, to take the pressure off until the situation resolves itself one way or the other and a course of action becomes clear.

The study of behaviour is fascinating and in a book such as this we can only scratch the surface. But the behaviour of animals is the end result of all that we have looked at in terms of nervous coordination and control – the importance of the sensory inputs, the computations of the brain and the messages to the effector organs are seen in the way that living organisms behave.

SUMMARY

- The **central nervous system** processes information and coordinates responses. Vertebrate central nervous systems consist of a well-developed **brain** and the **spinal cord**. The insect central nervous system comprises a **central nerve cord** and **ganglia**, collections of cell bodies and synapses.

- The vertebrate spinal cord has **grey matter** made up of neurone cell bodies and **white matter** containing nerve fibres.

- The vertebrate brain has specialised areas – the **forebrain** contains olfactory lobes and forms the cerebral hemispheres, the **'tweenbrain** forms the pineal gland and pituitary gland, the **midbrain** contains the optic lobes and the **hindbrain** forms the cerebellum and medulla.

- In the human brain the **cerebrum** controls voluntary behaviour and conscious thought. The **thalamus** coordinates the autonomic nervous system. The **cerebellum** coordinates smooth movements, posture and balance. The **medulla** contains reflex centres that control bodily functions.

- The **cerebral hemispheres** of the cerebrum consist of the surface layer of the **cerebral cortex** (grey matter containing nerve cells) and the inner white matter (nerve cell bodies). Their functions are localised in specific areas, within the overall sensory, motor and association areas.

- **Alzheimer's disease** is a disintegration of the brain cells, leading to behavioural changes, disorientation, loss of memory, loss of control of bodily functions and eventually death.

- **Behaviour** is an action in response to a stimulus which modifies the relationship between the organism and the environment – it is the action of an organism to try to maintain or improve its situation. The study of behaviour is called **ethology**.

- In **innate (species-characteristic) behaviour**, an organism has a genetically determined (unlearned) response to a particular stimulus. **Taxes** are movements of the whole organism in response to an external directional stimulus. **Kineses** are non-directional movements of the whole organism to a stimulus. **Simple reflexes** involve a rapid response for example to a potentially damaging stimulus, and some simple reflexes may become **modified reflexes** under largely conscious control. **Instinctive behaviour** consists of sophisticated inborn actions specific to a species, made in response to a **sign stimulus**.

- **Learned** or **individual-characteristic behaviour** is an adaptive change in the behaviour of an individual as a result of experience, and depends on **memory**. **Habituation** is the ignoring of a stimulus which has been repeated with neither punishment nor reward. A **conditioned reflex** is the association of a new stimulus with an unconditioned reflex response. **Operant learning** is the result of trial and error, when an organism is either punished or rewarded. **Imprinting** occurs in young animals when they identify with a parent. **Latent learning** takes place when the organism explores and learns its environment. **Insight learning** is based on thought and reasoning.

- Behaviour is modified by circumstances (the **motivational state**). **Displacement behaviour** occurs when the most appropriate behaviour is unclear due to conflicting circumstances.

QUESTIONS

1 Identify and briefly describe the main areas of a mammalian brain.

2 Compare and contrast species-characteristic behaviour with individual-characteristic behaviour.

3 Discuss the following types of learning, giving examples of each:
   a trial-and-error learning
   b imprinting
   c insight learning.

Developing Key Skills

Select an animal (e.g. dog, hamster, woodlouse) and choose a behaviour or task which you want to teach it. Then devise a training programme by which you would teach the animal to perform the task. Prepare a report to present to your fellow students explaining:

- the animal and task or behaviour you have chosen and why you have chosen it

- how you would set out to train the animal and what natural behaviour you are modifying

- your criteria for success.

BIOLOGICAL CLOCKWORK

Human beings, along with almost every other type of living organism, show rhythms both in their behaviour and in the events taking place within their bodies. For example, more people die in the early hours of the morning than at any other time. At this time their body temperature dips to its lowest, which can put a strain on an already failing system. On the other hand, athletic records are most likely to be broken later in the afternoon, when body temperature is at its highest and the body performance peaks.

The 24-hour clock

In normal life, these rhythms are tied in to the 24-hour day/night cycle. If we are allowed to 'free-run' (in an environment where we receive no cues as to the actual time of day) our cycles still run at between 23 and 25 hours. For this reason these rhythms are known as **circadian rhythms** (*circa* = about, *dian* = day).

Circadian rhythms are reset and tied in to 24 hours by the presence of day and night, but the fact that they free-run shows they are deeply embedded in our biology. The mechanisms of the biological clock have puzzled scientists for many years, but there does now seem to be some agreement about elements of the control. Structures called **suprachiasmatic nuclei** lie very close to the optic nerve, and seem to have a very important role in setting the basic rhythm. Also very important is the **pineal gland**. This tiny gland positioned in the roof of the forebrain is an endocrine gland producing the hormone melatonin, which has enormous influence on the working of the body. The pineal gland produces melatonin in the dark, so as the nights lengthen and winter approaches, the levels of melatonin in the body increase. Bright light inhibits the production of the hormone. We know that melatonin is important in triggering hibernation in many animals, but it now seems that it affects human habits in the winter as well.

Are you SAD?

Many people enjoy the changing seasons of the year and relish the varying conditions around them. But for a surprising number of people the beginning of autumn brings on real feelings of depression and panic. Throughout the autumn and winter months, with their short dark days and long nights, they feel tired, lethargic, depressed and often gain body mass – almost as if they ought to hibernate.

This has been recognised as a specific complaint called **seasonal affective disorder (SAD)**, sometimes referred to as the 'winter blues'. It is not yet known whether affected people make more melatonin than the rest of us, or whether they are simply more sensitive to the level of the hormone in the body. Whichever it is, spending some time each day under a bright daylight-mimicking light seems to help. Melatonin production is reduced in the light, and the symptoms of depression are lifted.

As our understanding of the mechanisms of our circadian rhythms increase, we will find many benefits, such as the optimum time for people to take therapeutic drugs and ways of coping with shift work and jet lag. Perhaps eventually we will all be able to enjoy the winter!

Figure 1 Anyone who has kept a hamster in their bedroom will know that their sleep and activity cycles run at very different times of the day from ours!

4

Figure 2 The extra melatonin that comes with long nights means that some people can't appreciate the countryside in winter.

4.4 Chemical control systems

Chemical control was mentioned in section 4.1 as an alternative to the nervous system. The nervous system is extremely effective at carrying messages rapidly from one specific place to another. However, in order to carry these messages relatively large amounts of energy need to be expended in the production of transmitter substances. The messages are carried along distinct pathways, and to give a maintained stimulus over a long period of time a constant stream of nerve impulses has to be sent.

Some of the functions of the body require long-term stimulation of tissues, for example growth and sexual development, and in other cases it is necessary to send messages which have an effect on many different areas of the body simultaneously. Plants rarely need rapid responses but they have to coordinate and control their cells just as animals do. In these situations chemical messages are economical for the system to produce as they can have an effect over a long period of time. They can also reach the entire body as they are carried to their target organs in the transport system of the animal or plant. In plants, chemical control is the main system of coordination. In animals it interacts with and complements the nervous system.

Chemical control in animals

Hormones

Chemical control is brought about in animals by the action of **hormones**. These are organic chemicals produced by the body which are released into the blood or body fluid and bring about widespread changes. The changes your body undergoes during puberty and the sensations you experience before an interview or an examination are the result of hormone action.

Hormones are usually either proteins, parts of proteins such as polypeptides, or steroids. They are secreted by glands. The glands which produce the secretions of the gut release their juices along small tubes or **ducts**, and are known as **exocrine glands**. The glands which produce hormones do not have these ducts – they release the hormones directly into the bloodstream and are known as **endocrine** or **ductless glands**. Once a hormone enters the bloodstream it is carried around the system and will reach the target organ or organs, as figure 4.4.1 shows. The cells of the target organs have specific receptor molecules on the surface of their membranes which bind to the hormone molecules. This brings about a change in the membrane and elicits a response.

Most of the hormones described in this section will be mammalian hormones, although we shall also consider the role of hormones in the moulting of insects.

The positions of the endocrine glands

The endocrine glands are found around the body, often in association with other organ systems. Several of the glands have more than one function – for example, the ovaries produce ova as well as hormones, and the pancreas is both an exocrine gland producing digestive enzymes and an endocrine gland

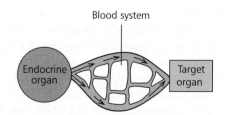

Figure 4.4.1 The pathway followed by a hormone from the endocrine gland where it is produced to the cells of the target organ. There are similarities to the pathway taken by a nerve impulse from the sensory neurone to the effector cell, but the chemical pathway is much less specific.

producing the hormone insulin. The glands all have rich blood supplies, with plenty of capillaries within the glandular tissue itself so that the hormones can pass directly into the blood when needed. The sites of the main glands in humans and the hormones they secrete are shown in figure 4.4.2.

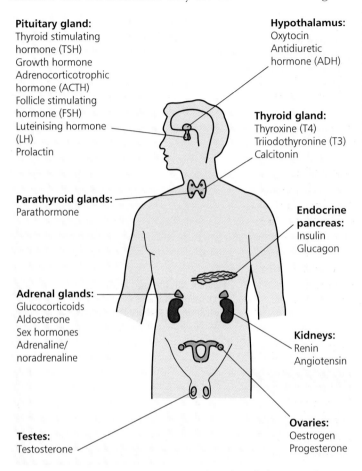

Pituitary gland:
Thyroid stimulating hormone (TSH)
Growth hormone
Adrenocorticotrophic hormone (ACTH)
Follicle stimulating hormone (FSH)
Luteinising hormone (LH)
Prolactin

Hypothalamus:
Oxytocin
Antidiuretic hormone (ADH)

Thyroid gland:
Thyroxine (T4)
Triiodothyronine (T3)
Calcitonin

Parathyroid glands:
Parathormone

Endocrine pancreas:
Insulin
Glucagon

Adrenal glands:
Glucocorticoids
Aldosterone
Sex hormones
Adrenaline/noradrenaline

Kidneys:
Renin
Angiotensin

Ovaries:
Oestrogen
Progesterone

Testes:
Testosterone

Figure 4.4.2 The endocrine organs of the body. Although small, these organs have a profound effect on the processes of life.

Differences between nervous and endocrine control

Table 4.4.1 summarises how nervous and endocrine control differ.

Nervous system	Endocrine system
Messages travel fast – generally have a rapid effect	Messages transported less rapidly – generally take longer to have an effect
Usually a short-lived response	Often a long-lasting response
Very localised effects as the impulse is transmitted to individual effector cells	Effects often widespread as the hormone is carried throughout the body in the bloodstream. A very specific response can be achieved by the siting of receptors
Relatively few neurotransmitters – acetylcholine and noradrenaline most commonly used	Variety of hormones produced by the different organs, each hormone producing a very specific effect

Table 4.4.1

Release of hormones

Hormones are released from the endocrine glands into the bloodstream in response to specific stimuli. The endocrine system interacts very closely with the nervous system. Some glands release their secretions as a result of direct stimulation by nerves. For example, the adrenal medulla of the adrenal glands releases adrenaline when it is stimulated by the sympathetic nervous system. The tissue of the adrenal medulla is so similar to the cells of the nervous system that it seems likely that they both form from the same origins in the embryo.

Many hormones are released from the endocrine glands in response to another hormone in the blood. As we shall see in more detail later, the pituitary gland in the brain secretes several hormones which directly stimulate other endocrine glands. Raised levels of certain chemicals such as glucose and salt in the blood can also stimulate the release of hormones, which in turn act to regulate the levels of the chemicals.

When hormones are released in response to nervous stimulation, the control of the release is simple. If the gland is stimulated, hormone is released. If it is not stimulated, no hormone is released. The level of stimulation determines the level of response. The situation is slightly more complex when hormones are released in response to a chemical stimulus such as another hormone or glucose. In this instance secretion is controlled by a **negative feedback loop**. The presence of the appropriate chemical in the blood stimulates the release of the hormone. As the hormone levels rise, the amount of stimulating chemical in the blood drops, as shown in figure 4.4.3. As a result of this, the endocrine gland receives less stimulation and so the hormone levels drop. This kind of feedback loop is very common, and it gives a sensitive level of control which can be constantly adjusted to the needs of the body. Negative feedback loops are also a common control feature in mechanical systems – for example, the thermostat of a central heating system works in this way.

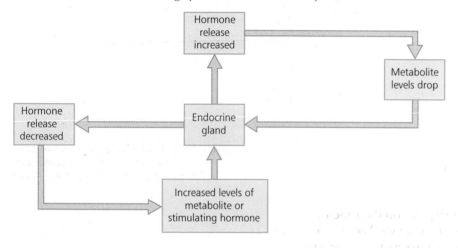

Figure 4.4.3 The basic principle of negative feedback. More specific examples will be seen when we consider the hormones insulin and thyroxine, and how their levels are controlled.

Human hormones in action

The hormones of the pancreas

The level of glucose in the blood, often referred to as the blood sugar level, is of great importance to the cells of the body because they use glucose for respiration. If the level of glucose falls too low, the body cells are starved of energy. The cells of the brain are particularly vulnerable and a coma quickly results. Too much sugar in the blood affects the osmotic balance and water is lost from the body cells. Ideally a level of around 80–100 mg of glucose per 100 cm³ of blood needs to be maintained for the optimum working of the body systems. This is achieved by the interactions of several hormones with the glycogen stores in the liver. Two of the most important of these hormones are produced by the pancreas.

The pancreas plays an important role in digestion by producing a mixture of enzymes which are released into the small intestine, as we saw in section 3.3. This is the function of the **exocrine pancreas**. But the pancreas is also a vital endocrine organ. Scattered within the enzyme-producing cells are groups of endocrine cells known as the **islets of Langerhans**, shown in figure 4.4.4. The islets contain two different types of cells and produce two different hormones. The large α (alpha) cells produce the hormone **glucagon**. The smaller β (beta) cells produce **insulin**. Both these hormones are relatively short-chain polypeptides. Insulin is well known for its role in the control of blood sugar levels, and the less well-known hormone glucagon is also involved in the regulation of the blood sugar level. Glucagon has the opposite effect to insulin. The control of the blood sugar level is a good example of **homeostasis** – maintaining a constant internal environment in spite of changing conditions. Homeostasis is discussed in more detail in sections 4.6 and 4.7.

Figure 4.4.4 The islets of Langerhans in the pancreas contain the cells involved in the control of sugar level in the body. The darker stained β cells make insulin, and the paler α cells produce glucagon. The islets are surrounded by the pancreatic cells which make digestive enzymes.

Insulin and the β cells

The β cells of the islets of Langerhans are sensitive to a rise in blood sugar levels such as occurs after a meal has been digested. Raised blood sugar levels are known as **hyperglycaemia**. The effect of this is to stimulate the secretion and release of insulin by the β cells. When the blood sugar levels fall (**hypoglycaemia**) the secretion of insulin also falls. This interaction between glucose levels and insulin secretion is an example of a negative feedback loop – see figure 4.4.5.

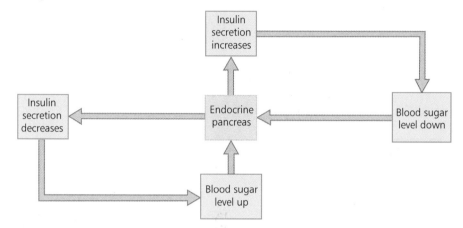

Figure 4.4.5 Negative feedback systems such as this allow the body to make constant small adjustments to the blood sugar level and so maintain it at the optimum level.

The majority of body cells have insulin receptors on their membranes, although there are a few exceptions such as the red blood cells. Once insulin is bound to the receptor sites on the membrane it lowers the blood sugar in one or more of four different ways, depending on the type of cell:

1 The rate of cellular respiration goes up, increasing the use of glucose.
2 The rate of conversion of glucose into the carbohydrate store glycogen is increased in cells such as the liver and the muscles.
3 The rate of conversion of glucose to fat goes up in adipose (fat storage) tissue.
4 The rate of glucose absorption goes up in muscle cells in particular.

The overall effect of all these strategies is to remove glucose from the blood and so reduce the level of hyperglycaemia. Insulin is the only hormone in the body which lowers the blood glucose level.

Diabetes and its effects

In some people the pancreas does not function properly and insulin is not produced in sufficient quantity to control the level of glucose in the blood. In others, the cells of the body do not appear to have insulin receptors on their membranes. Whatever the cause, the effect is the same – the body cannot control the blood glucose level. After a meal high in carbohydrates the glucose level rises to a point at which the kidneys cannot cope (section 4.6 gives more details on the functioning of the kidney) and glucose appears in the urine. This, along with copious amounts of urine, is one of the classic symptoms of **diabetes mellitus** (literally, 'sweet fountain').

Obviously, diabetics need treatment of some sort as their cells cannot function properly without glucose as a fuel for cellular respiration.

When diabetes is caused by a failure of the β cells to produce sufficient hormone, the treatment is regular injections of insulin, originally extracted from pigs. More recently human insulin has been produced by bacteria as a result of genetic engineering. Diabetics need to monitor their diets carefully to avoid an overload of carbohydrates. They also need to inject insulin at an appropriate time to avoid going into a coma due to lack of glucose (hypoglycaemic coma) when the hormone is given without an intake of food. Insulin cannot usually be taken orally as, being a

Glucagon and the α cells

The α cells are also sensitive to blood glucose levels, but they respond to a drop in blood glucose by secreting increased amounts of glucagon. Only the cells of the liver have receptors for this hormone. When the molecules of glucagon bind to the membranes of the liver cells the level of glucose in the blood is increased in two ways:

1 Glucagon increases the rate of conversion of glycogen stores in the liver into glucose.

2 Glucagon also increases the rate at which new glucose is formed from amino acids.

Figure 4.4.6 shows how glucagon and insulin interact to maintain a steady blood glucose level. Other hormones, particularly adrenaline, also increase the levels of glucose in the blood.

polypeptide chain, it is digested by the body, hence the need for injections.

Once diabetics become used to managing their own insulin and blood glucose levels they can lead perfectly normal and active lives, though they may suffer from long-term effects which are as yet unavoidable.

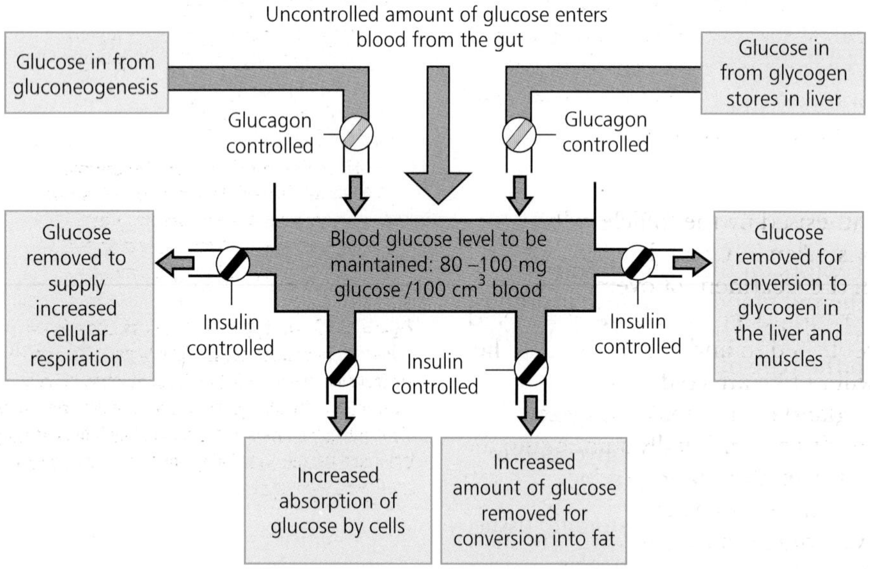

Figure 4.4.6 The interaction of the two hormones insulin and glucagon gives a very sensitive control system of the blood glucose level, allowing the body to respond continually to the changing demands of the cells for glucose.

Human insulin

In 1922 there was a breakthrough in the treatment of diabetes. Insulin extracted from the pancreases of pigs and beef cattle was injected into human diabetics to replace the insulin they did not make for themselves. Insulin injections have been a life saver ever since, but the treatment has not been without some problems. The molecules of cow and pig insulin are not exactly identical with those of human insulin, and some people developed antibodies to this insulin and could not use it. Another problem was that the amount of insulin that could be made depended on the numbers of animals killed for meat, not the numbers of people needing insulin, so sometimes supplies ran short.

In the 1980s a new breakthrough was made. Bacteria were genetically engineered to produce human insulin, and so the source of the hormone moved from the

abattoir to the fermenter full of bacteria. It seemed the perfect answer – human insulin would surely be far better for people than cow or pig insulin. In most cases this was certainly true, and the majority of diabetics easily made the swap to the new form of insulin. But the human hormone did cause some problems. Human insulin is absorbed more easily and acts more rapidly than cow or pig insulin, and some diabetics found they developed very low blood sugar levels. Others lost the warning symptoms which usually let them know that they were becoming hypoglycaemic.

For the majority of insulin users the genetically engineered insulin has been a great improvement, but against all expectations the British Diabetic Association had to fight to keep cow and pig insulin in production for those diabetics whom the human form did not suit.

The hormones of the thyroid gland

The rate of cellular metabolism affects many aspects of life. Growth and development are closely linked to the metabolic rate and if this is too low, severe abnormalities can result. In adult life body weight and both physical activity and mental attitudes can be affected by the rate of the metabolism. The metabolic rate is controlled by the hormones of the **thyroid gland**.

The thyroid gland is shaped rather like a bow-tie and found in the neck in roughly the position where a bow-tie would be worn (see figure 4.4.2). It produces three hormones – **thyroxine** (T4), **triiodothyronine** (T3) and **calcitonin**. The first two of these are closely involved in the control of metabolism. Their secretion is controlled by a special releasing factor produced by the hypothalamus of the brain, and thyroid stimulating hormone produced by the anterior pituitary gland. This is a complex negative feedback system which is shown in more detail in figure 4.4.7.

Calcitonin plays an important role in calcium metabolism, lowering the blood levels of calcium ions by speeding up the absorption of calcium ions by the bones. Yet again a negative feedback loop is in operation – raised blood calcium levels stimulate the release of calcitonin, which in turn lowers the blood calcium levels and so reduces the amount of hormone secreted.

Iodine and the thyroid gland

Thyroxine and triiodothyronine are both synthesised by the follicle cells of the thyroid gland using iodine. All the iodide ions taken in by the body in the diet end up in the thyroid gland. This is useful in the treatment of overactive thyroid glands. Radioactive iodine-containing compounds can be administered in the sure knowledge that they will be concentrated in and destroy part of the thyroid gland, and other parts of the body will not be affected.

If the diet is lacking in iodine, the thyroid gland cannot make sufficient thyroxine. The feedback system goes into overdrive, continually stimulating the thyroid gland which gets larger and larger in a vain attempt to produce enough thyroxine. A swollen neck resulting from the enlarged gland is typical of this condition, known as **simple goitre**. Nowadays iodide is added to table salt in the developed world to prevent this condition, but it was so common during European history that it was regarded in some countries as normal. There are even paintings of the Madonna and child where Mary, presumably modelled on a local beauty of the time, shows a distinctly goitrous neck.

The hormones of the hypothalamus and pituitary

The **pituitary gland** in the brain has been described as 'the conductor of the endocrine orchestra' because of the role it plays in controlling the secretions of the other endocrine glands. The pituitary gland has an **anterior lobe** and a **posterior lobe**. It produces and releases secretions which affect the activity of most of the other endocrine glands in the body. However, whilst the pituitary is most frequently referred to as the 'master gland', control of the pituitary itself falls largely to the **hypothalamus**.

Control of the pituitary by the hypothalamus

The hypothalamus is a small area of brain directly above the pituitary gland. It carries out a variety of functions, one of which is to monitor the blood levels of a number of metabolites and hormones. In response to the levels of these chemicals the hypothalamus controls the activity of the pituitary gland.

Figure 4.4.8 shows the anatomical relationship between the hypothalamus and the pituitary. As the embryo forms, the posterior lobe develops as an

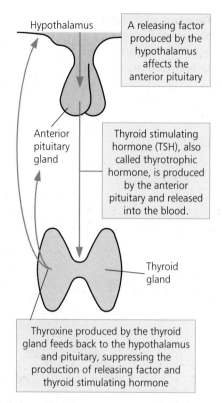

Figure 4.4.7 The hypothalamus is sensitive to the requirements of many areas of the body. Its secretions are involved in the control of the production of both thyroxine and triiodothyronine. Levels of thyroxine in the blood affect the levels of secretion of both the releasing factor and thyroid stimulating hormone, giving a very sensitive control system.

outgrowth of the hypothalamus itself, whilst the anterior lobe grows out from the roof of the mouth. Then the two parts fuse and the connection with the roof of the mouth is lost. But the two different origins of the parts of the gland are reflected in their different functions.

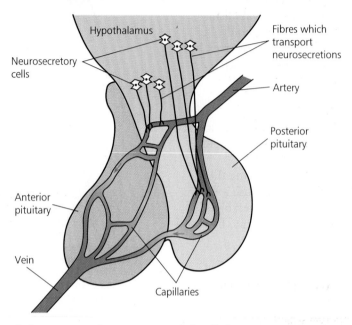

Figure 4.4.8 The close structural relationship of the hypothalamus and pituitary is reflected in their functions, the hypothalamus producing neurosecretions which control both lobes of the pituitary.

The hypothalamus contains some unusual cells known as **neurosecretory cells**. These are nerve cells which produce secretions from the ends of their fibres. One group of these cells (neurosecretory cells 1) produces substances which stimulate or inhibit the release of hormones from the anterior pituitary. They are known as **releasing factors** or **release-inhibiting factors**, depending on their function (see figure 4.4.7 for the role of a releasing factor on the control of thyroxine secretion). The other group of neurosecretory cells (neurosecretory cells 2) produce secretions which are stored in the posterior pituitary and then later released as hormones.

Secretions of the pituitary

The pituitary gland, under the control of the hypothalamus, produces six hormones from the anterior lobe and two from the posterior lobe. These range in function from controlling the secretions of the thyroid gland to the control of growth, from sexual development to the control of urine volume. The hormones produced and the roles they play are described in figure 4.4.9.

There are many other hormones which play important roles in communication and control in the body. We shall meet some of these later when we consider in more detail how the internal environment of the body is kept as constant as possible.

How do hormones have their effects?

Hormones act by binding to specific receptor sites on the membranes of their target cells. The hormone then affects the target cell in some way to bring about the desired change in activity. There appear to be three main ways in which hormones may have their effect:

1   The binding of the hormone molecule to a receptor site may result in the formation of a second chemical messenger inside the cell. This second messenger then takes effect by activating enzymes within the cell and so altering its metabolism. The most common second messenger is a

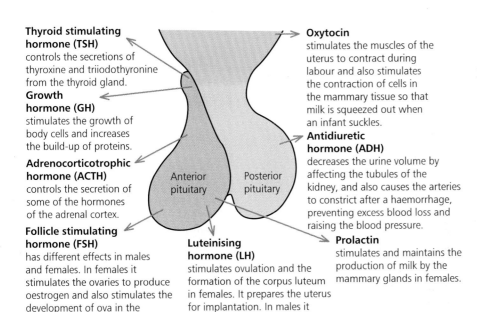

Thyroid stimulating hormone (TSH) controls the secretions of thyroxine and triiodothyronine from the thyroid gland.

Growth hormone (GH) stimulates the growth of body cells and increases the build-up of proteins.

Adrenocorticotrophic hormone (ACTH) controls the secretion of some of the hormones of the adrenal cortex.

Follicle stimulating hormone (FSH) has different effects in males and females. In females it stimulates the ovaries to produce oestrogen and also stimulates the development of ova in the menstrual cycle. In males it stimulates the testes to produce sperm.

Anterior pituitary

Posterior pituitary

Luteinising hormone (LH) stimulates ovulation and the formation of the corpus luteum in females. It prepares the uterus for implantation. In males it stimulates the testes to produce testosterone.

Oxytocin stimulates the muscles of the uterus to contract during labour and also stimulates the contraction of cells in the mammary tissue so that milk is squeezed out when an infant suckles.

Antidiuretic hormone (ADH) decreases the urine volume by affecting the tubules of the kidney, and also causes the arteries to constrict after a haemorrhage, preventing excess blood loss and raising the blood pressure.

Prolactin stimulates and maintains the production of milk by the mammary glands in females.

Figure 4.4.9 The hormones of the pituitary gland, particularly those from the anterior lobe, have their effect by stimulating another endocrine organ elsewhere in the body.

substance called **cyclic AMP**, which is formed from ATP. Adrenaline is thought to have an effect in this way.

2 The hormone may have a more direct effect, for example, it may change the permeability of the cell membrane to particular substances. Insulin works in this way, increasing the activity of glucose carriers across the membrane.

3 The hormone linked to its receptor may pass through the membrane and act as the internal messenger itself. In this case the hormone usually reaches the nucleus of the cell and turns on or off sections of the DNA. The lipid-soluble steroid hormones such as oestrogen and testosterone can pass through the membrane and act in this way.

Hormones in insects

The control of moulting

Hormones and their mechanisms of action in most mammals are relatively similar to those in humans. But some of the most interesting light thrown on the action of hormones has come from considering the control of moulting (**ecdysis**) in insects. The hard exoskeleton of insects imposes limits on growth, so the development of many insects such as butterflies, fruit flies and bees occurs as a series of transformations from an egg through a variety of larval stages to the adult insect (**imago**). Each time an insect sheds its exoskeleton (moults) and 'grows' it becomes more mature. The moulting is controlled by two hormones:

1 **Ecdysone**, the 'moulting and metamorphosis' hormone, controls the events of the moult itself. It is a steroid hormone which was first extracted from the pupae of silkworms – it took 3 tons of silkworms to extract 100 mg of hormone!

2 **Juvenile hormone** determines the kind of moult that occurs. When juvenile hormone is present, another larval form results, and as juvenile hormone levels get lower more adult characteristics occur. When there is no juvenile hormone the pupa becomes an adult, as shown in figure 4.4.10.

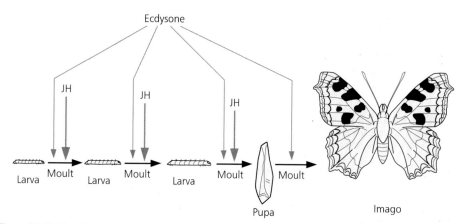

Figure 4.4.10 The effects of ecdysone and juvenile hormone (JH) on the life cycle of an insect.

The way in which ecdysone has its effect has been studied using the larvae of *Drosophila* (fruit flies) and *Chironomus* (midge). In the cells of the salivary glands of these insects there are **giant chromosomes**, 100 times thicker and 10 times longer than normal chromosomes and easily visible with the light microscope. Bands visible on these chromosomes are thought to represent genes or small groups of genes. When insects are undergoing a moult, or when ecdysone is injected artificially into an insect, 'puffs' result on the chromosomes, as shown in figure 4.4.11. These chromosome puffs appear to be areas of genetic material made available for transcription, and they are very rich in RNA. Presumably they carry information about new proteins to be formed in a more adult stage of the life cycle. This supports the theory that some hormones such as steroids can have a direct effect on the DNA of a cell.

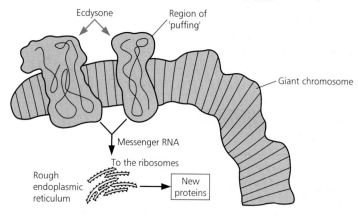

Figure 4.4.11 Chromosome puffs appear as a result of the hormone ecdysone. The puffing of the chromosome is followed by much RNA synthesis, and this in turn moves to the ribosomes and gives rise to the formation of new proteins. It is thought that many steroid hormones have their effect in this way. Unfortunately, not many organisms possess giant chromosomes for us to observe.

The role of hormones in animals

We have seen the basic roles played by hormones in animals, the feedback loops which control the secretion of the hormones and the ways in which they bring about their effects. There are many more hormones than those which we have studied here. Many others will be highlighted in later sections, particularly those on homeostasis and reproduction, where they will be considered more as part of an integrated whole. As we have seen, for animals hormones are but a part of a complex system of intercellular communication and control. For the plants which we go on to consider next, hormones give the only means of control.

Changing lifestyle, changing diet

Insects such as the Lepidoptera (butterflies and moths) have very different forms during their life cycle. The larval stage, when they are caterpillars, grows rapidly. It needs a huge input of food containing both carbohydrate and protein to build new body tissues. The larvae are plant-eaters – caterpillars can reduce a leaf to a network of veins in a remarkably short time. They have mouthparts which include large chewing mandibles to cut through the plant material. Part of the gut, the proventriculus, has hard, rough areas to help break open the plant cells. A range of digestive enzymes is present to deal with the contents of the cells, including proteases, lipase, amylase, maltase and invertase. However, Lepidoptera cannot digest cellulose, and so the cell walls and any unbroken plant cells pass through the body undigested.

After metamorphosis, the adult insect eats only nectar. Its nutritional requirements are completely different – now it simply needs energy to fly, find a mate and reproduce. The mouthparts take the form of a long, coiled proboscis which can be inserted into flowers to suck up nectar. The proventriculus has become a simple valve leading into the mid-gut, and only one digestive enzyme is present, invertase, which converts one form of sugar to another. The changes in the systems of these insects as they metamorphose from larval form to adult ensure that at each stage of the life cycle the insect is perfectly adapted for its lifestyle.

SUMMARY

- Chemical control often has a long-term general effect on an organism, and in animals it is brought about by **hormones**. These are secreted by **endocrine** (ductless) glands in response to specific stimuli, which may be nervous or chemical.

- The release of hormones is often controlled by a **negative feedback loop**. The presence of a chemical in the blood stimulates the release of a hormone which reduces the level of the stimulating chemical. This reduced level then results in reduced stimulation of the gland and so less hormone is produced.

- The hormones of the **pancreas** play a major role in the control of the blood glucose level. The β cells of the **islets of Langerhans** secrete **insulin** when the blood glucose levels rise (**hyperglycaemia**). Insulin brings about a reduction in blood glucose. The α cells respond to a drop in blood glucose levels (**hypoglycaemia**) by secreting **glucagon**. This brings about a rise in the blood glucose levels. Insulin and glucagon interact to maintain a steady blood glucose level.

- The hormones of the **thyroid gland** control the rate of metabolism. The secretion of **thyroxine** (T4) and **triiodothyronine** (T3) is controlled by the **hypothalamus** in a complex negative feedback loop. **Calcitonin** lowers the calcium concentration in the blood and is controlled by a negative feedback loop. T4 and T3 are both synthesised using **iodine** and iodine is concentrated in the thyroid gland. Goitre is a swelling of the thyroid gland which may result from a lack of iodine in the diet.

- The **pituitary gland** controls the secretions of many of the endocrine glands. The pituitary is itself controlled by the **neurosecretions** (releasing factors and release-inhibiting factors) of the **hypothalamus**. The pituitary gland has an **anterior** and a **posterior lobe** and many of its secretions stimulate other endocrine glands in the body.

- Hormones bind to receptor sites on the membranes of their receptor cells. This may result in the formation of another messenger chemical inside the cell such as **cyclic AMP**. The hormone may have an effect on the cell such as changing its membrane permeability to a particular substance. The hormone–receptor complex may pass through the cell membrane and act as an internal messenger by acting on a part of the DNA.

- In insects hormones control **ecdysis** (moulting). **Ecdysone** controls the moulting, and **juvenile hormone** results in another larval form. Absence of juvenile hormone results in adult characteristics.

QUESTIONS

1 a What is a hormone?
  b What are the functional and chemical similarities and differences between the nervous system and the endocrine system?

2 Describe the role played by the pancreatic hormones in glucose metabolism. What other glands and hormones affect the metabolism of glucose?

3 The pituitary gland is often referred to as the 'middleman' in endocrine functions. Explain why it is described in this way.

CELL, HORMONE, CLONE

The discovery that plants as well as animals have a chemical coordination system has had an enormous impact on agriculture and food production in recent years, as scientists learn to use both naturally occurring plant hormones and synthetic versions of them to control the plants for our benefit.

Ripeners and weedkillers

It is very useful to be able to control when fruit ripens. We imagine our bananas, oranges and lemons growing and ripening on the tree in the sunshine, but in reality most fruit is picked and transported unripe and then exposed to the plant hormone ethene to ripen it ready for sale. The hormone auxin is vital for plant growth, but synthetic auxins have been developed for use as weedkillers. Most weeds are broad-leaved dicotyledonous plants, which absorb a large amount of auxin weedkiller. This causes rapid uncontrolled growth which the plant cannot sustain, and it soon dies. The narrower leaves of many monocotyledonous crops are relatively unaffected, and the crop grows on.

Clones

Plants clone themselves frequently in asexual reproduction. In recent years we have taken the art of cloning way beyond the natural capabilities of the plants. Whilst there has been enormous publicity surrounding the cloning of mammals like Dolly the sheep, most people are unaware of the massive plant-cloning programme going on all around us.

The forestry and agricultural industries have invested a great deal of time and money in plant-cloning technology, removing the lottery element of sexual reproduction. If a particular tree or other crop plant has proved itself to have all the characteristics the grower wants, then thousands or even millions of copies can be made, each repeating those desirable properties. If the plant produced seeds, some would be useful, but others might be quite different from the parent plant. Cloning has the advantage of certainty.

It is now commonplace to grow a whole new plant from a single meristem cell by culturing it in a particular way. Cytokinins and auxins are plant hormones involved in stimulating cell division and tissue growth. If they are applied in the right concentrations at the right stages of development, a complete new plant will result. A large clump of unspecialised callus cells can first be prepared and kept alive in culture almost indefinitely. When plants are wanted, individual cells are taken and treated with hormones to grow plants to order.

Cloning is also valuable following the development of a new plant by the expensive process of genetic engineering. By cloning the engineered cells, thousands more engineered plants can be produced cheaply. Scientists are now working on small amounts of engineered callus and carefully manipulating the hormone mixture to induce them to form minute embryo plants. Encasing these in an organic medium with a biodegradable skin would make synthetic seeds. This has already been achieved with some types of plant such as alfalfa. In plant technology, with the help of hormones, it seems the sky is the limit.

Figure 1 All plants contain auxins, but an artificial overdose can be lethal.

Step 1
A small piece of tissue is taken from a leaf in sterile conditions and placed on a sterile medium impregnated with plant hormones – the balance and type of hormones vary from plant to plant.

Step 2
A mass of undifferentiated plant cells (known as a **callus**) develops.

Step 3
A small amount of callus is placed on a different sterile medium impregnated with a a mixture of auxins (to stimulate root growth) and cytokinins (to stimulate shoot formation).

Step 4
A small plantlet forms.

Step 5
The plantlet is transferred to soil and a normal plant develops. In this way thousands of genetically identical plants can be grown from one parent.

Figure 2 Careful use of plant hormones allows us to grow a whole plant with predictable features from a single cell produced by cloning.

4.5 Control systems in plants

Control systems in plants

In animals the nervous and endocrine systems interact to ensure a high degree of coordination and control. The body of an animal can respond rapidly to the smallest change in either the internal or the external environment whilst long-term growth and development patterns are also maintained. For plants the situation is somewhat different. They do not, in general, need fast responses to small changes in their immediate environment. But plants do need to respond to factors such as light levels and direction, gravity and seasonal changes in conditions. They also need to coordinate growth of the cells in different areas. Plants do not appear to have nervous systems – their sensitivity and coordination is the result of chemical control alone.

Plant responses

Chemical messages affecting growth

Plants respond to a variety of stimuli by producing or moving chemical messages. Many of these messages are similar to animal hormones – they are produced in one area of the plant, transported around the body of the plant and have their effect on cells elsewhere. Animals can respond to nervous and chemical messages in a variety of ways which include the release of further chemicals, the contraction of muscle cells and growth. The main way in which plants respond to their chemical messages is by growth. In some cases growth is stimulated while in others it is inhibited to bring about an appropriate response to the original stimulus. Sometimes one side of a plant grows more than the other, resulting in the bending of shoots or roots in response to a particular stimulus.

How plants grow

Growth is a permanent increase in the size of an organism or of some part of it. It is brought about by **cell division**, the **assimilation** of new material into the cells which result from the division and the **cell expansion** which follows. This is shown in figure 4.5.2, and there is more about growth in section 5.1. Cell expansion is particularly noticeable in plants, where rapid enlargement can occur as a result of water taken up by osmosis before the cell wall becomes rigid.

The main areas of cell division in plants are known as the **meristems**. These are areas which occur just behind the tip of a root or shoot. Not only are the meristems the main areas of growth, they are also particularly sensitive to the chemical messages produced. These chemical messages seem to make it easier for the cellulose walls to be stretched.

Stimuli affecting plants

Plants are a major part of our environment. Because their movements are usually invisible to the naked eye, we tend to look upon plants as being living but inert.

In fact plants respond to a variety of stimuli. They are sensitive to light, and not simply its presence or absence. Plants respond to the direction from which light comes, the intensity of the light and the length of daily exposures to it.

Figure 4.5.1 Chemical control allows plants to maximise their opportunities for photosynthesis and coordinate their reproductive cycles with the most opportune times of the year.

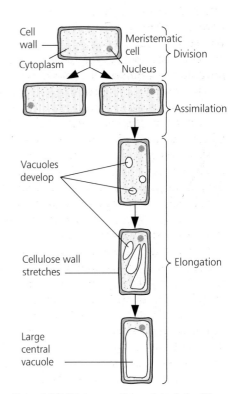

Figure 4.5.2 Plants respond to a variety of stimuli by differential growth. The growth regulating chemicals generally seem to affect cell elongation, making it easier for the cellulose cell wall to be stretched, although they also affect the cell division stage, increasing the number of divisions that occur.

They are also sensitive to gravity, to water, to temperature and in some cases to chemicals. Different parts of the same plant may react differently to the same stimulus (for example, shoots grow towards light but roots grow away from it). Not all plant responses involve growth – stomatal opening and flowering are both affected by light stimuli, for example. As well as these responses to external stimuli plants also respond to internal chemical signals. Most of the responses of plants are concerned either directly or indirectly with maximising the opportunities for photosynthesis and reproduction.

Chemical control in plants

Tropic responses in plants

Once a seed begins to germinate in the soil, the shoot and root must keep growing if the developing plant is to survive. But growth must take place in the right direction. The shoot must grow up towards the light source which will provide the energy for its cells via photosynthesis. The roots must grow downwards into the soil which will provide support, minerals and water for the plant. The movements of these parts of the plant take place in direct response to external stimuli. The direction of the response is related to the direction from which the stimulus comes. Responses such as these are known as **tropisms**. Simple observations tell us that shoots bend towards the light, and even when developing seedlings are deprived of light they still grow upwards, away from the pull of gravity.

Evidence for tropisms

Much of the evidence for and work on tropisms has been carried out using germinating seeds and very young seedlings. This is because they are easy to work with and manipulate. As they are growing rapidly any changes in their growth show up quickly and tend to affect the whole organism rather than a small part as might be the case with a mature plant. The most widely used seedlings are those of monocotyledonous plants, usually cereals such as oats and wheat. This is because the shoot, when it emerges, is a single spike with no leaves apparent. This makes manipulation and observations easier than in dicotyledonous shoots. The newly emerged oat shoot is known as a **coleoptile**, although the more general term 'shoot' will be used. It must be remembered that these early shoots are relatively simple plant systems and that the control of the responses to light in an intact adult plant may well be more complex than our basic model allows. Figure 4.5.3 shows some simple experiments that demonstrate **geotropism** – the response to gravity.

Regardless of the orientation of a seed, the shoot will grow upwards and the root will grow downwards. This could be a response to light, or gravity, or both.

If the stimulus of light is removed, the shoot still grows upwards and the root downwards. This is a response to gravity and is called **geotropism**. Roots are said to be **positively geotropic** – they grow towards the force of gravity. Shoots are said to be **negatively geotropic** – they grow away from the force of gravity.

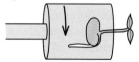

The stimulus of gravity is removed by placing a developing seedling on a klinostat. By rotating the drum at a constant speed the effects of gravity are applied evenly to the whole seedling – and the response of the root and shoot is lost.

Figure 4.5.3 As seeds generally germinate underground away from the stimulus of light, it seems likely that they should orientate as a result of gravity. This is in fact the stimulus involved, as these simple experiments show.

Phototropism

If plants are grown in bright, all-round light they thrive and grow more or less straight upwards. If plants are grown in even but low light, they also grow straight upwards, and in fact grow faster and taller than those in bright light.

But if the light is brighter on one side of the plant than another or only shines from one side (**unilateral light**) then the shoots of the plant will bend towards that light and the roots, if they are at all exposed, will grow away from it. Shoots are said to be **positively phototropic** and roots are **negatively phototropic**. This response has an obvious survival value for a plant. It helps to ensure that the shoots receive as much all-round light as possible, allowing the maximum amount of photosynthesis to take place. Also, if the roots should emerge from the soil – as they might do after particularly heavy rain, for example – they will rapidly return to the soil. But how are phototropisms brought about?

To answer this satisfactorily we need a picture of how growth is controlled in a shoot under conditions of all-round light. The control of growth was shown to be by chemical messages early in this century, by the Dutch plant scientist Went. He had the simple idea of attempting to block or collect any message that passed from the tip to the growing region behind it, and thus to show the nature of the message. He hypothesised that a chemical carrier could be collected in small blocks of agar and the effects then demonstrated on other shoots. Figure 4.5.4 gives a brief résumé of some of the work done on the mechanisms of phototropisms.

Figure 4.5.4 Experiments such as these gave rise to our understanding of the control of growth in plants. Substances referred to as growth hormones are produced at the tip of a shoot and move back to the dividing and elongating regions of the apical meristems, where they have their effect.

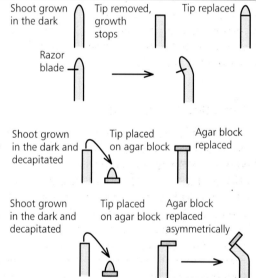

A shoot germinated in the dark grows straight upwards. When the tip is removed, the upward growth stops. If the tip is then replaced, growth begins again. This simple experiment shows that the tip of the shoot exerts an influence on the region of growing cells behind it.

A razor blade inserted into one side of the shoot just behind the tip stops the growth of the shoot on that side. As a result the shoot bends over. This shows that whatever normally stimulates growth is blocked by the razor blade, and therefore the message must be a chemical one, as an electrical signal would pass through the metal blade.

The tip of a shoot growing in the dark is removed, placed on an agar block and left for several hours. The decapitated shoot does not grow. The agar block is then placed on the cut end of the shoot, and normal growth is resumed. This again shows that a chemical message is produced in the shoot tip. It has diffused into the agar block and then diffuses from there into the rest of the shoot, stimulating normal growth. Subsequent experiments with blocks of cocoa butter showed no response in the decapitated shoot, demonstrating that the chemical message is water soluble and not fat soluble.

The tip of a shoot grown in the dark is removed and placed on an agar block. After several hours the block is placed asymmetrically on the decapitated shoot. The side with the agar block on it grows more than the other side, so that the shoot bends away from the stimulated side. Went showed that the amount of bending of the shoot is directly related to the amount of chemical messenger in the block. The biological activity of the messenger chemical can be measured or **assayed** in terms of the amount of bending observed in the shoot. This is known as the Went bioassay.

The people behind the theories

Work on the tropic movements of plants began a long time ago, and a succession of people developed experiments, each of which made the picture clearer. The following list mentions a few of these scientists and the contributions they have made to our understanding of how tropisms work.

● Nineteenth century: Charles Darwin and his son Francis carried out some experiments on oat coleoptiles and showed that the phototropic response of plants to light was due to some sort of message being passed from the root tip to the growing region.

● 1913: Boysen-Jensen, a Danish plant biologist, inserted a thin, impermeable mica plate into coleoptiles which appeared to act as a barrier to the message from the tip. This suggested that the message was chemical, but as mica does not conduct electricity these experiments could not rule out the possibility of electrical, nerve-like impulses.

● 1928: the Dutch plant physiologist Went proved the presence of a chemical transmitter substance in experiments such as those described in figure 4.5.4.

Unilateral illumination

So far we have considered shoots kept entirely in the dark or in full illumination. However, plants are usually in a situation where the light from one side is stronger than from the other. Experiments done on shoots illuminated from one side only (unilateral light) confirm the results from earlier experiments and add more detailed information of their own, as figure 4.5.5 shows.

The shoot kept in the dark and the shoot kept exposed to all-round light grow straight up, with the shoot in the dark growing faster.

The shoot exposed to light from one side bends towards it. A foil cap covers the tip of the shoot and the response to unilateral light is lost, confirming that it is the very tip of the shoot that is sensitive to light.

The tip is removed from a shoot kept in unilateral light. It is placed on an agar block for several hours, and the block is then cut in half. Each half is placed on one side of a decapitated shoot. The agar block from the unilluminated side of the shoot causes greater growth and therefore curvature in the decapitated shoot than the block from the illuminated side, showing how the plant would be caused to bend towards the source of the light.

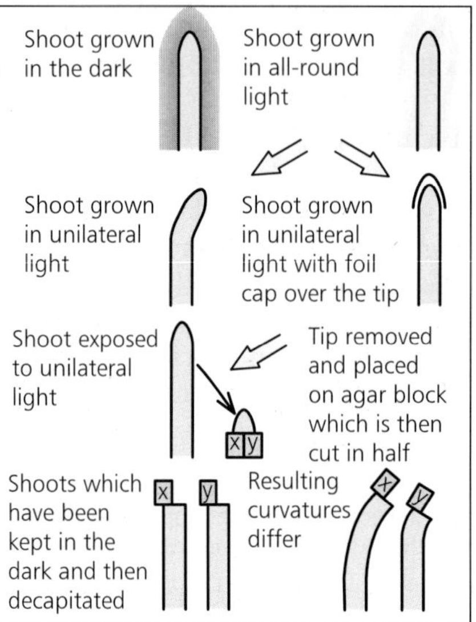

Shoot grown in the dark

Shoot grown in all-round light

Shoot grown in unilateral light

Shoot grown in unilateral light with foil cap over the tip

Shoot exposed to unilateral light

Tip removed and placed on agar block which is then cut in half

Shoots which have been kept in the dark and then decapitated

x y

Resulting curvatures differ

Figure 4.5.5 As a result of experiments such as these a more detailed hypothesis for the mechanism of phototropisms can be built up.

Auxins

The responses which we know as phototropisms are the results of chemical messages made in the tip of the shoot and transported to the growing region where they have an effect. The messages are known as **plant hormones** or **growth regulators**. The growth substances involved in phototropisms are called **auxins**. Auxins are powerful growth stimulants and are effective in extremely low concentrations. The first auxin discovered was IAA (indoleacetic acid). The term 'auxins' covers a group of substances similar to IAA which have the same effect.

Auxins are now produced commercially. They can be bought in garden centres to help cuttings to root and are proving important in agriculture for improving the yields of crops.

How does light bring about its effects?

In any garden or woodland, plants can be seen responding to unilateral light. Where plants are partially shaded the shoots bend towards the light and then grow on straight towards it. This response seems to be the result of the way auxin moves within the plant under the influence of light.

Figure 4.5.6 shows a model in which the side of a shoot exposed to light contains less auxin than the side which is not illuminated. It appears that light causes the auxin to move laterally across the shoot, so there is a greater concentration on the unilluminated side. This in turn stimulates cell elongation and so growth on the dark side, resulting in the observed bending towards the light. Once the shoot is growing directly towards the light, the unilateral stimulus is removed. The transport of auxin stops and the shoot then grows straight towards the light. The original theory was that light destroyed the auxin, but this has been disproved by experiments along the lines of those in figure 4.5.6, which show that the levels of auxin in shoots are much the same regardless of whether they have been kept in the dark or under unilateral illumination.

How do plants grow more rapidly in the dark than in the light?

The mechanism of this response is not well understood. The old theory that auxin was destroyed by light gave a good model of how plants in the dark might grow more rapidly, as their auxin was not being destroyed. In contrast, plants in all-round illumination would be losing a lot of auxin and so growing less rapidly. However, the current theory based on evidence such as that shown in figure 4.5.6 does not provide such a clear explanation of the phenomenon and work on this continues.

1 The current model for the effect of unilateral illumination assumes that the auxin moves away from the light source. This gives a greater concentration of auxin on the shaded side of the shoot, which in turn causes increased cell elongation and thus bending of the shoot.

2 This experiment involved maize coleoptiles, some of which were kept intact and some divided. They were either exposed to unilateral light or kept in the dark. The tips were then removed and placed on agar blocks for several hours, before the agar blocks were placed on decapitated coleoptiles to assay the auxin levels.

When the shoots were kept in the dark it made no difference whether the shoot was split or not – the amount of auxin produced was virtually the same.

When the shoot was illuminated unilaterally the total amount of auxin was much the same whether or not the shoot was divided, and was also very similar to the level when the shoot was kept in the dark.

When the shoot was illuminated unilaterally but *not* divided, auxin accumulated on the dark side. In the divided shoot the auxin levels on both sides were the same. This evidence suggests that the normal situation in a shoot exposed to unilateral light is for auxin to be transported laterally (sideways) across from the lit side to the shaded side.

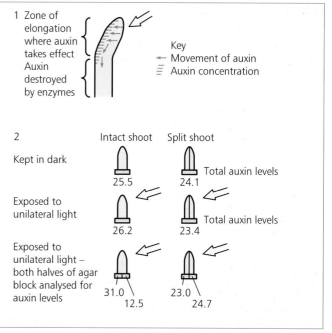

1 Zone of elongation where auxin takes effect
Auxin destroyed by enzymes

Key
← Movement of auxin
≡ Auxin concentration

2   Intact shoot   Split shoot
Kept in dark
                      25.5   24.1   Total auxin levels

Exposed to unilateral light
                      26.2   23.4   Total auxin levels

Exposed to unilateral light – both halves of agar block analysed for auxin levels
                  31.0 \   23.0 \
                      12.5   24.7

Figure 4.5.6 It appears that, whilst light may alter the distribution of auxin within the plant, it does not destroy it.

Etiolation

The fact that plants grow more rapidly in the dark than when they are illuminated can at first seem to be illogical. However, careful consideration shows that this is in fact useful to the plant. If a plant is in the dark it needs to grow upwards as rapidly as possible to reach the light and so be able to photosynthesise. Once it is in the light, a slowing of upward growth is valuable as it allows resources to be used for synthesising leaves, strengthening stems and generally consolidating the position.

This aspect of the response of plants to light is utilised by gardeners to 'force' plants. In order to give plants a good start or to develop a crop such as rhubarb particularly early, gardeners cover the plants so that they demonstrate this rapid upward growth known as etiolation, as shown in figure 4.5.7.

Geotropisms

The response of plants to gravity can be seen in the laboratory when seedlings placed on their sides are grown either in all-round light or in the dark (to eliminate the response to directional light). Figure 4.5.3 showed how geotropic responses can be demonstrated. Under normal conditions shoots are **negatively geotropic** and roots are **positively geotropic**. This makes good sense, as roots need to grow down into the soil and shoots need to grow up.

Figure 4.5.7 Rhubarb grown under a cover such as an upturned dustbin undergoes rapid growth (etiolation). These young rhubarb stems are pale because they have been deprived of light. The end result of forcing in this way is advantageous to the gardener as it allows the crop to be brought forward and so better prices obtained.

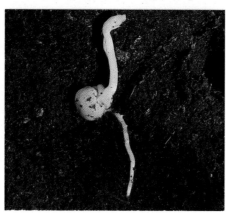

Figure 4.5.8 Both in 'real life' and in the laboratory plants can be seen to respond to gravity – shoots grow away from it and roots down towards it.

As we saw in the box 'Evidence for tropisms' on page 300, the response can be removed using a rotating drum known as a klinostat. Instead of receiving an effectively unilateral gravitational stimulus, by growing the plants on a klinostat rotating at about 4 revolutions per hour, the stimulus is applied evenly to all sides of the plant, and the root and shoot grow straight.

How does gravity bring about its effects?

The classic theory for the mechanism of geotropisms follows closely the pattern for phototropisms. It is thought that gravity causes auxin to build up on the lower side of the root and shoot, and that the cells of the two areas respond differently to the hormone. The cells on the lower side of the shoot are stimulated by the auxin to elongate and grow faster than the cells on the upper surface. This causes the shoot to bend upwards. In the root, on the other hand, the cells are inhibited by the raised auxin levels and so the growth and bending is downwards, as shown in figure 4.5.9.

This description of geotropism is very neat and fits in with what we know about phototropisms, but it begins to appear that auxin may not be the whole story. In fact, auxin may play only a minor part in the geotropic response, particularly in shoots. Many experimenters have been unable to find auxins in the root tips of oat coleoptiles, one of the most commonly used plants for work on tropisms. Two other plant growth regulators have been found and appear to be involved. **Abscisic acid** is a growth inhibitor. It has been shown to occur in the areas where differential growth takes place to give a response to gravity. Also in these regions, and particularly in the rapidly growing sides of roots and shoots, **gibberellins** (growth promoters) are found. (These growth inhibitors and promoters are discussed in more detail on pages 306–308.) Thus the response of plants to gravity may well be more complex than was at first thought and research into this continues.

Plant sensitivity to gravity

The way in which plants appear to sense gravity is not dissimilar from the method used by mammals (see section 4.2, pages 268–269). It depends on particles being affected by gravity and that effect in turn causing a response in the organism. In some plants the particles which move in response to gravity appear to be very large starch grains which occur in certain root and shoot cells. They are known as **starch statoliths** and are contained within organelles called **amyloplasts**. The cells containing these starch grains are the **statocytes** – the gravity receptors. The starch grains fall to the lower sides of the cells under the influence of gravity. This aggregation of amyloplasts shown in figure 4.5.10 affects the distribution of growth substances in the region and results in a geotropism. The way in which this is brought about is not yet clearly understood. Also, there are plants without observable statoliths which nevertheless respond to gravity.

Does auxin have the same effect on all cells?

The effect that auxin has on the cells of the shoot and the root depends on its concentration:

- Relatively high levels of auxins stimulate growth in the shoot. Levels of auxins that would stimulate root growth are too low to have an effect on the cells of the stem.
- Relatively low levels of auxins stimulate growth in the roots. The higher levels of auxins that stimulate growth in the shoot actually inhibit growth in the root.

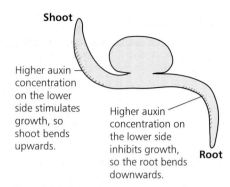

Figure 4.5.9 Geotropism has been assumed until recently to be due to the auxin response shown here – but recent research suggests there may be more to it than this.

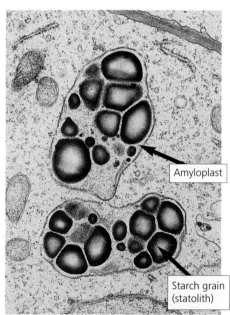

Figure 4.5.10 Raising the temperature of a seedling increases the rate at which the starch grains fall to the lower surface of the cells, and also increases the speed at which the seedling responds to gravity. This and other evidence confirms that these statoliths are the sensory mechanism for gravity in plants, but exactly how their movement is converted into a geotropic response is still not fully understood.

How are auxins used?

So far we have looked at auxins involved in the tropic responses of plants to both light and gravity. Their involvement in plant responses to their environment is far greater than this, however. They are needed for a wide variety of processes to occur successfully. Biologists have studied the natural role of these remarkable chemicals and then produced both naturally occurring and artificial versions in order to manipulate the 'auxin effect' in a variety of areas of plant life. The following list shows just some of these.

1   Auxin from the main apical bud inhibits the growth of side branches from lateral buds on stems. This is known as **apical dominance**. If the apical bud is removed the inhibition on the growth of side buds is lifted and lateral buds develop. If auxin is placed experimentally on the cut apical stem, the inhibition is continued. Gardeners prune plants regularly to remove the apical buds, which results in lateral growth (bushiness). They may not all understand the underlying plant physiology, but they know that it works.

2   Auxin stimulates the growth of adventitious roots from a cut stem. This is used commercially and by gardeners when taking plant cuttings. Dipping the end of a stem cutting in auxin-containing powder dramatically increases the chances of the cutting developing roots and 'taking'. However, excess rooting hormone may inhibit lateral root growth.

3   Auxin helps fruit to set – spraying with auxin greatly increases the natural success rate for pollination and fertilisation. It can also bring about fruit formation even in the absence of fertilisation, which has the added bonus of producing seedless fruits.

4   Auxin helps to prevent the fruit of a plant falling before it is ripe, which is important for successful reproduction.

5   Some synthetic auxins have a greatly exaggerated and abnormal effect on the growth of plant cells. They also affect the metabolism of the cells, making them respire excessively. These effects cause the death of the plant. As a result, synthetic auxins can be used as very effective weedkillers. They are absorbed much more effectively by broad-leaved (dicotyledonous) plants than by monocotyledons and are therefore particularly useful for removing broad-leaved weeds from monocotyledonous cultures such as lawns and wheat fields.

Other plant responses

Nasties

Although many plant responses are tropisms to light, gravity, chemicals or touch, plants also exhibit another type of response known as a **nasty** or **nastic response**. Nastic responses are to rather general stimuli, and involve differential growth in one part of a plant which results in a localised response. Nastic movements are often observed using techniques such as time-lapse photography. Although thermonasties and photonasties are well described, the mechanism by which they are brought about is not yet known.

Thigmotropisms

Some of the most interesting and least understood plant responses are in response to touch. Plants such as vines and sweet peas have tendrils which coil round other plants or sticks in response to one-sided contact or touch. These **thigmotropisms** seem to involve similar mechanisms of auxins and differential growth as the other tropic responses we have seen. But some plants react to touch in a much more unexpected way. Some of the carnivorous plants such as the Venus flytrap in figure 4.5.11 respond very rapidly, snapping shut to capture their prey insect. *Mimosa pudica*, better known as the 'sensitive plant', also reacts very rapidly to touch. The leaflets fold up immediately and, if the touch is really rough, the stems collapse too. The mechanisms of these rapid responses are not understood, although some workers have recorded electrical activity in the cells. Recently, proteins with contractile properties closely related to the muscle proteins actin and myosin have been found. Some plants may have a response system which is closer to animal nerves and muscles than had previously been considered possible.

Plant growth regulators

As well as giving relatively immediate responses to stimuli such as unilateral light, gravity and touch, plants respond to changes on a much longer time scale. The growth of plants follows a seasonal pattern, with growth occurring in the spring, and fruit developing and then ripening at the appropriate time. Deciduous trees lose their leaves before the adverse conditions of winter, when the light levels are so low that photosynthesis would not produce sufficient food to support a large plant structure. Seeds exhibit dormancy, a period of inactivity before they germinate and begin to grow. These are all responses to the seasonal changes in light levels, length of daylight and temperature. They are brought about by a variety of plant growth regulators and chemical messages. Substances which regulate growth in plants may be naturally occurring plant hormones such as IAA, gibberellic acid and abscisic acid, or they may be synthetic compounds which, although not naturally occurring within the plant, nevertheless affect its growth.

Gibberellins

Gibberellins are involved in the growth of stems in particular. The effect of these growth promoters is best demonstrated by their absence. Dwarf plants are bred so that they do not produce gibberellins. Auxins have no effect on the growth of dwarf plants but if gibberellins are applied to them, they will grow to normal height.

Gibberellins were discovered in the 1920s as a result of work done in Japan on a fungus which attacked the rice crop. Affected rice seedlings grew very tall and spindly, then either died or produced a very low yield. Chemicals extracted from culture solutions on which the fungus *Gibberella* had grown were found to give this effect and were named 'gibberellins'. They have subsequently been found to be naturally occurring in many plants.

Gibberellins have their effect on plant stems in the same way as auxins, by stimulating cell elongation in particular. They also seem to have an effect on the dormancy of seeds, with gibberellin levels rising towards the end of dormancy. Gibberellins are also produced in the germinating seeds of some cereal seeds, where they in turn stimulate the production of enzymes which break down the food stores in the seed so that the embryonic plant can develop.

Cytokinins

Cytokinins are a group of plant growth regulators which are found particularly in regions of very active cell division. They occur in very small quantities and are most readily extracted from fruits and seeds where they seem to be involved in the growth of the embryo. Cytokinins are involved in many plant responses

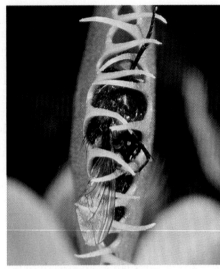

Figure 4.5.11 The Venus flytrap needs a series of three touches to the sensitive hairs inside its jaws before it snaps shut, trapping the fly or other insect attracted by its sweet sticky secretions. Anyone who has tried to swat a fly will know how rapid this movement must be to be successful. The requirement for three touches is a defence against unnecessary responses to touches by a leaf or by an insect which immediately flies away.

because of their effect on plant growth. They stimulate cell division, but only if auxin is present too. As auxin equally cannot stimulate cell division without cytokinins, it appears that the two substances interact. They work together to affect the dividing cells. This is an important difference between plant and animal hormones. Animal hormones work quite independently of each other. They may be complementary or antagonistic to each other, but they are produced and have an effect without other hormones necessarily being present. In plants, the hormones bring about their effects as a result of interactions with each other. A single hormone is usually ineffective.

Abscisic acid

The growth regulating substances we have considered so far are all growth promoters – they stimulate the growth of the plants in one way or another. **Abscisic acid** (**ABA**) is a growth inhibitor. It was discovered in the 1960s during investigations into the loss of fruits from the cotton plant. It has an inhibitory effect on auxins, gibberellins and cytokinins, and seems to be involved in the production of a weakened area of cells at the base of a fruit or leaf which finally breaks as the fruit or leaf falls. Abscisic acid also seems to be involved in dormancy in seeds and the prevention of germination. Recent research indicates that abscisic acid may play a role in geotropisms, and also that its role in leaf fall may be considerably less than was originally thought.

Ethene

The chemicals which we have so far considered as plant growth regulators are all fairly complex (see box 'The chemicals that control plants' overleaf) and are carried around the body of the plant in solution. But there is another substance produced by plants which does not fit into this general pattern – the gas **ethene**. This is produced by plants in small amounts and seems to be involved in several responses. The effect of ethene on the plant is to raise the respiration rate, and this causes the ripening of fruit. Ethane can also cause leaf fall, and the release of buds and seeds from dormancy.

Traces of ethene are produced by oil-fired central heating boilers, which can have unfortunate effects on both house plants and bowls of fruit. The plants lose their leaves and the fruit gets over-ripe very quickly.

Synergism and antagonism

Many of the growth substances just described do not work on their own but by interaction with other substances. By this means, very fine control over the responses of the plant can be achieved. The growth regulators interact in one of two ways. If they work together, complementing each other and giving a greater response than each regulator alone, the interaction is known as **synergism**, for example the effect of auxin on growth is much more dramatic if gibberellin is present as well. If the substances have opposite effects, for example one promoting growth and one inhibiting it, the balance between them will determine the response of the plant. This is known as **antagonism**.

Our knowledge of plant growth regulators is still far from complete. The mechanisms by which they have an effect are far from understood, and there may yet be more regulators to be discovered.

ABA and stomata

It is now generally accepted that the movement of potassium ions is important in the opening and closing of stomata, but the control mechanisms of the potassium pump are not yet well understood. Recent evidence suggests that another level of control may involve the plant hormone abscisic acid (ABA), particularly in conditions of water shortage. When plants are deprived of water, the levels of ABA around the stomata increase considerably. This seems to stimulate the potassium pump to reverse, actively moving potassium ions out of the guard cells. Water follows by osmosis, the turgor level drops and the stomata close, conserving water. Whether or not this mechanism has any role to play in the normal opening and closing of stomata remains to be seen.

4

The chemicals that control plants

Table 4.5.1 summarises the main plant growth regulators and their structures.

Regulator	Chemical structure	Main functions
Auxins		Promote stem growth by cell elongation. Stimulate root growth at very low concentrations. Involved in apical dominance and tropisms.
Gibberellins		Promote stem growth of the internodes by cell elongation. Promote fruit growth. Break seed dormancy and involved in germination.
Cytokinins		Promote cell division in the apical meristems and the cambium. Interact with auxins in these areas, but promote lateral bud growth, helping overcome apical dominance.
Abscisic acid		Inhibits cell division and growth in stem and root. Promotes dormancy in both buds and seeds.
Ethene		Inhibits growth of stem and root. Promotes fruit ripening and fruit and leaf fall.

Table 4.5.1

The effects of light on plants

The importance of light

As we have already seen, light is fundamental to the existence of plants in a wide variety of ways. Light-dependent photosynthesis is the ultimate source of food not only for plants but for animals as well. Chlorophyll formation depends on light and the phototropic responses already discussed are made in response to light. Day length is the cue which determines changes such as bud development, flowering, fruit ripening and leaf fall in many plants. Without light the metabolism of a plant is severely disrupted and prolonged light deprivation causes death.

'Sensory' systems in plants – phytochrome

There must be a mechanism for sensing the presence of light in order for a plant to respond to it. Plants do not have a nervous system. But just as the pigments in the rods and cones in the human eye undergo chemical changes in the presence of light, so plants seem to have evolved a chemical photoreceptor system. The details of the way in which plants sense and respond to light have not yet been fully worked out, but it appears to involve a photoreceptor known as **phytochrome**.

For many years it has been known that the seeds of many plants will only germinate if they are exposed, even very briefly, to light. Much of the research on this was done using some varieties of lettuce seeds which need only a very short flash of light to trigger germination. Researchers in the US Department of Agriculture did some classic work in the 1950s which showed that red light (wavelength 580–660 nm) is most effective at stimulating germination whilst far red light (wavelength 700–730 nm) actually inhibits germination.

If the lettuce seeds are exposed to a flash of red light, they will germinate. If they are exposed to a flash of red light followed by a flash of far red light, they will not germinate. If experimenters expose the seeds to a series of flashes of light, it is the colour of the final flash which determines whether or not the seeds will germinate (see figure 4.5.13). As a result of this and other work it was hypothesised that plants contain a pigment which reacts with the different types of light, and then in turn affects the responses of the plant. In 1960, the American group carrying out the research isolated this theoretical pigment from plants and called it **phytochrome**.

The phytochrome light receptor system

Phytochrome is a blue-green pigment which exists in two interconvertible forms. P_R or P_{660} absorbs red light and P_{FR} or P_{730} absorbs far red light as shown in figure 4.5.12. When one form of the pigment absorbs light it is converted reversibly into the other form. The length of time it takes for one form of the pigment to be converted into the other depends on the light intensity. In low light intensity it takes minutes, in high light intensity it takes seconds.

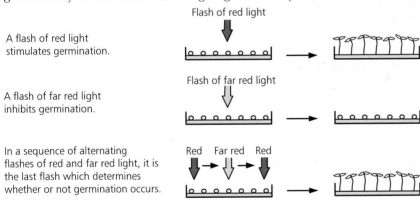

A flash of red light stimulates germination.

Flash of red light

A flash of far red light inhibits germination.

Flash of far red light

In a sequence of alternating flashes of red and far red light, it is the last flash which determines whether or not germination occurs.

Red   Far red   Red

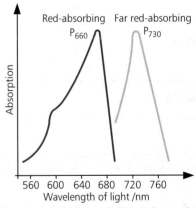

The absorption spectra of the two forms of phytochrome – the peaks of absorption give the two forms their symbols, P_{660} and P_{730} (after Hendricks).

Figure 4.5.12 The idea of a phytochrome light receptor system in plants developed from a theory to a fact once the theoretical light-sensitive chemical was extracted and analysed in 1960.

When P_R absorbs red light it is converted rapidly into P_{FR}. When P_{FR} absorbs far red light it is converted rapidly into P_R, and this conversion also takes place very slowly in the dark. P_R is the more stable form of the pigment, but it is P_{FR} which is biologically active.

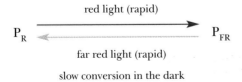

red light (rapid)

P_R P_{FR}

far red light (rapid)

slow conversion in the dark

As normal sunlight contains more red light than far red light, the usual situation in a plant during daylight hours is for most of the phytochrome to be in the far red form. During the night it is all converted back into the red form. The control of the germination of lettuce seedlings by flashes of red and far red light seen in figure 4.5.13 is due to a flash of red light producing P_{FR}, the biologically active form of the phytochrome which then initiates germination, but a flash of far red light converting P_{FR} back to the inactive form.

In some cases phytochromes have a stimulating effect on growth in plants while in others they have an inhibitory effect, as table 4.5.2 shows. How the phytochromes influence the responses of plants is not fully understood. It appears that the presence of phytochromes may stimulate the production of other growth regulators and plant hormones, and thus the response to light is brought about.

Part of plant affected	Effect of red and far red light
Seed	Red light stimulates germination, far red light inhibits germination.
Stem	Stem elongation is stimulated by far red light and inhibited by red light. Exposure to far red light gives the same effect as etiolation.
Leaf	Leaf expansion is stimulated by red light and inhibited by far red light.
Lateral roots	Growth of lateral roots is stimulated by far red light and inhibited by red light.
Flowering	The stimulus to flower depends on alternating periods of light and dark and involves the phytochrome system.

Table 4.5.2 The main effects of red and far red light on various areas of a plant give an indication of the importance of the phytochromes

Photoperiodism

One of the best known plant responses involving phytochromes is the control of flowering in some plants, known as **photoperiodism**. At the equator the days and nights are always of approximately the same length, around 12 hours each. In temperate areas of the world, at some distance from the equator, the lengths of the days and nights change throughout the year so that the period of daylight can vary between around 9 and 15 hours out of 24. In these temperate areas the lengths of the days and nights give important physiological cues to both animals and plants, directing their growth, development and behaviour. In plants one of the most clearly affected activities is flowering.

The day length affects the flowering of many plants. Some plants only flower when the days are short and the nights are long. They are known as **short-day plants** (**SDPs**) and examples include strawberries, chrysanthemums, cockleburs and the tobacco plant. Others flower when the days are relatively long and the nights short. These are the **long-day plants** (**LDPs**) which include snapdragons, cabbages and henbane. Short-day plants will not flower with more than a critical amount of daylight, and long-day plants will not flower with less than a critical amount of daylight. It can be very difficult to decide whether a plant is a short- or long-day plant, as the two groups merge. Yet other plants are unaffected by the length of the day. Plants such as cucumbers, tomatoes and pea plants which flower regardless of the photoperiod are known as **day-neutral plants**.

The value of these different flowering patterns to plants seems to be to take advantage of different circumstances. In temperate regions woodland short-day plants tend to flower in spring and autumn, taking advantage of the Sun at times when the full canopy of leaves either has not developed or has fallen off. Short-day plants are also found near the equator, where the days are never longer than about 12 hours. On the other hand, long-day plants flower in the summer in temperate regions, and are found further from the equator where there are very long days for part of the year.

In spite of the naming of these different types of flowering plants as 'long-day' or 'short-day', it has subsequently been discovered that it is the length of the period of darkness rather than the length of daylight which affects flowering. For example, if short-day plants have their long night interrupted by flashes of light, they do not flower. Some experiments demonstrating this are summarised in figure 4.5.13.

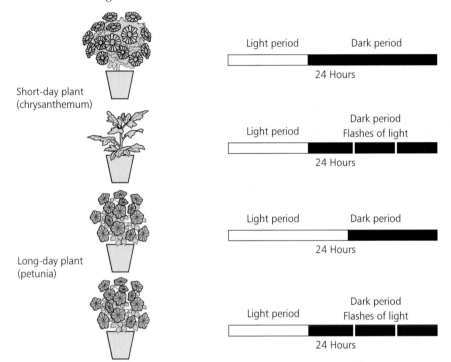

This discovery has led to a number of commercial ventures based on changing the time at which a plant flowers by manipulating the periods of darkness to which it is exposed. As a result, breeders have crossed varieties of plants which would otherwise not have flowered simultaneously, and at Christmas time we are awash with poinsettias and chrysanthemums which would not naturally be flowering.

How is the day length signal received?

All the research points to the involvement of the phytochromes in the sensitivity of plants to the photoperiod. The changes in flowering patterns which can be brought about by disturbing the dark periods can also be affected by red or far red light alone. It has been found that red light inhibits the flowering of short-day plants. If the red light is followed by far red light, the inhibition is lifted. What is the implication of this?

Red light leads to the formation of P_{FR}. Far red light converts this back to P_R. The current hypothesis is that P_{FR} inhibits flowering in short-day plants, and the lack of P_{FR} when it is exposed to far red light allows flowering to occur. It is thought that it is the lack of P_{FR} rather than the build-up of P_R which allows the flowering to go ahead. As the two forms of phytochrome are almost always present to some degree in a plant, it is the balance between them which is affected by varying periods of light and dark, and which in turn affects flowering. In long-day plants the situation is reversed. It appears that a build-up of P_{FR} during the daylight hours stimulates flowering.

The detection of the photoperiod seems to take place in the leaves of the plant. Experiments have been carried out where the whole plant has been kept in the dark apart from one leaf which is exposed to the appropriate periods of light and dark. Flowering has occurred as normal, whereas a plant kept in total darkness does not flower. How the message received in the leaves by the phytochromes is carried to the flower buds is not yet understood. The presence of a plant hormone known as **florigen** has been hypothesised, as illustrated in figure 4.5.14. This would be made in response to the levels of phytochromes and be carried in the plant transport system to the flower buds. However, no one so far has been able to demonstrate or isolate this hormone successfully, and so the mechanism for the control of flowering remains to be fully clarified.

Thus we can see that plants which may seem unresponsive in fact have complex systems of coordination and control. These systems appear to be almost entirely chemical in nature, and some are very similar in their mechanisms to the hormones used in animal responses. By interactions between their various growth regulators, plants are well adapted to respond to small changes in their environment, maximising their opportunities for survival and successful reproduction.

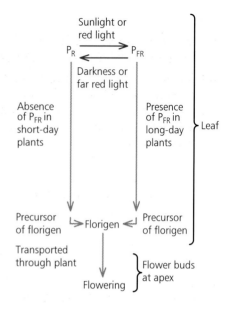

Figure 4.5.14 Until further research either confirms or disproves the theory, this is the best picture we have for the effect of the photoperiod on the flowering of long- and short-day plants.

SUMMARY

- Plants are controlled by chemical messages which bring about their actions by controlling growth. Growth is brought about by **cell divisions**, the **assimilation** of new material into the cells and then **cell expansion**. The **meristems** are the main areas of growth and are most sensitive to chemical control.

- Directional responses in plants to directional stimuli are called **tropisms**.

- Shoots are **positively phototropic** (they bend in unidirectional light towards the light source) and roots are **negatively phototropic** (if exposed to light they grow away from it).

- Experiments have shown that tropisms are controlled by **plant hormones** (growth regulators) produced at the tip of a shoot which are transported to the meristems where they have an effect.

- **Auxins** are growth substances that bring about phototropism. It is thought that light causes auxin to move across a shoot to the dark side and promote growth there, causing the shoot to bend towards the light.

- Plants grow more rapidly in the dark (**etiolation**) than in the light so that they can have more chance of reaching the light.

- Shoots are **negatively geotropic** (they grow away from gravity) and roots are **positively geotropic.** It is thought that this is brought about by the action of auxin along with **abscisic acid**, a growth inhibitor, and **gibberellins**, growth promoters. Plants appear to sense gravity by large starch grains called **statoliths** which fall under the influence of gravity inside organelles called **amyloplasts** in cells called **statocytes**.

- Pruning of apical buds promotes side branches to grow, normally inhibited by auxin produced at the apical bud. Auxin stimulates growth of adventitious roots from stems so is used in plant rooting preparations. Auxin helps fruits to set, and prevents them falling prematurely. Some auxins are used as weedkillers, as they cause abnormal exaggerated growth.

- **Nastic responses** are localised responses to general stimuli, such as flowers opening in response to rising temperature.

- **Thigmotropisms** are responses to touch, such as tendrils coiling around supports or the Venus flytrap snapping shut.

- **Gibberellins** are plant growth regulators which affect stems particularly. **Cytokinins** stimulate cell division in the presence of auxin. **Abscisic acid** has an inhibitory effect on auxin, gibberellins and cytokinins and is thought to be involved in the weakening of fruit and leaf stems before they fall. **Ethene** raises the respiratory rate and causes ripening of fruit, leaf fall and the release of buds and seeds from dormancy.

- The complementary action of growth regulators is called **synergism**, while the inhibition of one regulator by another is **antagonism**.

- Plants respond to light by the action of a photoreceptor called **phytochrome**. P_R absorbs red light and is converted to P_{FR}, which absorbs far red light and is reconverted to P_R. P_{FR} also converts slowly in the dark to P_R. P_R and P_{FR} have opposing biological activities.

- Phytochromes control **photoperiodism**, the flowering of plants in response to the day length. **Short-day plants** flower when the nights are long and **long-day plants** flower when the nights are short. **Day-neutral plants** flower regardless of the photoperiod. It is thought that P_{FR} inhibits flowering in short-day plants, and lack of P_{FR} allows flowering to happen. In long-day plants a build-up of P_{FR} stimulates flowering. The detection of the photoperiod takes place in the leaves and may be transmitted to the flower buds by a hypothetical hormone called **florigen**.

QUESTIONS

1 a How does growth occur in plants?
   b To what stimuli do plants respond?
   c Explain how plants respond to unilateral light.

2 a List *five* plant growth regulators and briefly describe their role in plants.
   b Plant growth substances are frequently synergistic or antagonistic to each other. What does this mean?
   c The response of plants to gravity is known as geotropism. How are plants sensitive to gravity?

3 a How are plants sensitive to light?
   b Produce a leaflet for sale in a garden centre explaining how people might bring on or delay the flowering of particular plants. You will need to explain how flowering is initiated in plants and what is meant by photoperiodism.

Developing Key Skills

There is an uproar in your community because it has been discovered that a well known local farmer has been using cloned plants in his fields for the last three years. Prepare a 'Science Snippet' for the local paper explaining exactly what plant cloning means, the benefits it brings and why it is unlikely to be a threat to the environment or to the surrounding fields.

FOCUS LIVING ON THE EDGE

All living organisms need water to survive, and in the deserts that cover almost one-fifth of the Earth's surface, water is in very short supply. Temperatures soar during the day and then plummet at night – the desert is an inhospitable place to live and those animals and plants that make it their home are specially adapted to survive there.

Losing water ...

Land animals lose water in three different ways: by evaporation from the body surface, by exhaling moisture during respiration and by expelling liquid during excretion. Desert dwellers have devised ways of reducing water loss in all these ways to a minimum.

Because mammals control their own body temperature, their metabolisms are far more demanding than those of 'cold-blooded' animals such as the reptiles. Mammals have to eat much more to supply their energy needs, and finding this food increases the risk of water loss. Small desert mammals have a relatively large surface area:volume ratio, which also increases their heat loss and moisture loss. Yet small rodents are amongst the most successful desert dwellers.

Figure 1 The desert – arid, awe inspiring and one of the most inhospitable environments on Earth.

... and saving it

Many small desert mammals such as the kangaroo rat and the jerboa never drink once they are weaned. They eat dry plant material and seeds, and get enough water for their body needs from the metabolic water released as these food substances are broken down in their cells. Water conservation is obviously a priority, and excretory loss is kept to an absolute minimum. Almost all the water is reabsorbed from the faeces in the large intestine before they are passed out of the body. The kidneys have enormously long loops of Henle to maximise water absorption, and they produce only tiny amounts of highly concentrated urine. The rodents have no sweat glands so water is not lost through the skin. Some water is lost in respiration, but many small mammals have a special cooling exchange system in their noses. This cools the air before it leaves the nostrils, so the moisture condenses and is not lost from the body.

As well as all these physiological adaptations, most small desert mammals also behave in certain ways which reduce their water loss. They dig burrows and stay underground where it is relatively dark and cool during the heat of the day, and their exhaled breath increases the humidity of the burrow and reduces water loss. Emerging only in the morning and evening to hunt for food, they avoid the worst of the heat. Kangaroo rats and jerboas have long back legs and a kangaroo-like gait which gives them speed and agility, but also reduces the area of their body in contact with the hot sand. Finally, many desert mammals are tolerant of temperature fluctuations which would cause cell damage in most other mammals. The way these small animals manage their water resources is a vivid illustration of the way living organisms can adapt to survive almost anywhere.

Figure 2 Small animals like this Hairy-footed pygmy gerbil found in the deserts of Namibia thrive against all the odds because of a series of adaptations common to all small desert mammals.

4.6 Homeostasis: Control of water balance

Sections 4.1–4.5 have considered the nervous and hormonal communication systems in animals and plants which allow them to respond to changes in both their internal and their external environments. But why are these systems of coordination and control so important?

Homeostasis

Cells are extremely sensitive to changes in their environment. They only function properly within relatively narrow limits of temperature and pH, they require particular concentrations of nutrients such as glucose and they can tolerate very little build-up in the levels of waste products. To minimise any changes in the cellular environment, there are several systems which work to keep the internal conditions of the body as stable as possible.

The maintenance of a steady internal state is known as **homeostasis** (from the Greek *homoios* meaning 'like' and *stasis* meaning 'state'), and it is vital to the successful functioning of any organism as it provides independence from fluctuating external conditions. Homeostasis in animals involves a high level of coordination and control. Any changes in the composition of the blood are detected by a sensor or receptor. This causes an effector to work to reverse the change. Feedback systems provide a very sensitive way of maintaining the concentration of a substance within a very narrow range. In some cases there are separate mechanisms controlling changes in different directions – for example in the control of blood sugar level – and this gives a particularly sensitive response and a greater degree of control. The nervous and hormonal systems interact to maintain a steady state in the body. There are four main homeostatic systems in mammals, controlling:

1 the water balance of the body (**osmoregulation**), brought about largely by the kidney
2 the levels of nitrogenous waste products and other solutes, brought about by the kidney and the liver
3 the blood sugar level by the pancreas and the liver (see section 4.4)
4 temperature, brought about largely by the skin (**thermoregulation**).

In this section we shall look at osmoregulation in animals, and the role of the mammalian kidney in osmoregulation and in the excretion of nitrogenous waste products. We shall also consider osmoregulation in plants. Section 4.7 looks at the control of other waste products by the liver, and thermoregulation.

Osmoregulation

The need for osmoregulation in animals

As we saw in section 1.4, water moves into and out of cells by the process of osmosis. If the balance of water and solutes inside and outside a cell is not correct, water may enter, causing the cell to swell and burst. On the other hand, water may leave so that the cytoplasm becomes shrunken and unable to function.

The problem of osmoregulation affects animals living in the sea rather differently from those in fresh water or on the land. The water potential of the sea is similar to that of cells, although the sodium chloride concentration is higher. Many marine invertebrates cannot osmoregulate, and have no need to do so. For many marine vertebrates the problem is getting rid of excess salt taken in when the salt water is drunk. In fresh water, there is a great tendency for water to move into cells by osmosis, whilst on land the conservation of water becomes a priority. Animals have evolved to overcome the challenges of their particular environment, but species which can move freely between the different environments are relatively few and need sophisticated osmoregulatory systems.

Figure 4.6.1 The contractile vacuole is an effective way of controlling the composition of the cytoplasm for a protoctist such as *Amoeba*. It removes the excess water which enters by osmosis in an energy-dependent process, and so prevents osmotic damage. If the protoctist is given a metabolic poison which interferes with the utilisation of ATP the contractile vacuole no longer fills, the water entering by osmosis is not removed and the cell bursts.

1. Water moves into the cell by osmosis. It is collected by the contractile vacuole in a process which involves energy, produced by the numerous mitochondria which surround the vacuole.

2. The contractile vacuole fills up with water.

3. The contractile vacuole gets rid of its contents through a small pore, discharging the water back into the external medium.

4. The process is repeated.

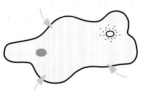

In fresh water the contractile vacuole fills and empties relatively rapidly to prevent the cell swelling up and bursting. As the amount of salt dissolved in the water increases and the water potential of the medium moves closer to that of the cytoplasm, the rate at which the vacuole fills and empties falls. Marine protoctists do not have contractile vacuoles.

Unicellular organisms living in fresh water have a specialised **contractile vacuole** for osmoregulation, as shown in figure 4.6.1. Because the whole cell is immersed in water and the surface area:volume ratio is high, a great deal of water enters the cell. In contrast, many larger animals have relatively few cells in contact with water and a reduced surface area:volume ratio. Water still enters the cells but this can be overcome by **kidneys** producing large quantities of very dilute urine.

Osmoregulation in fish

Fish demonstrate clearly the different problems which face organisms living in fresh and salt water, as figure 4.6.2 describes.

Figure 4.6.2 The osmotic problems facing fish in fresh and salt water, and the ways in which the difficulties are overcome.

Water balance in a salt-water teleost fish

The body fluids of salt-water teleost fish are hypotonic to their surroundings. As a result water tends to move out of the fish by osmosis, a process which would quickly lead to dehydration of the tissues.

Sea water is swallowed to make up fluid and the filtration rate of the kidney is slow, so relatively little urine is produced. The urine is isotonic with the sea water.

Nitrogenous waste is excreted as **trimethylamine oxide** which is very soluble but non-toxic. This means it can be excreted in a concentrated solution without harming the fish or upsetting the water balance.

Salt is actively removed by the **chloride secretory cells** in the gills, moving chloride ions against a concentration gradient in the opposite direction to that in freshwater fish.

Water balance in a freshwater teleost (bony fish)

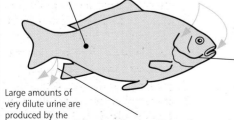

Salts are reabsorbed in the kidney tubules to prevent excess loss in the copious urine. The urine is very hypotonic to the blood.

The body fluids of freshwater teleost fish are hypertonic to their environment. As a result water moves into the fish by osmosis across the gills and through the lining of the mouth and pharynx.

Chloride secretory cells in the gills actively take up salts from the external medium to make up for those lost in the copious urine. Chloride ions are 800 times more concentrated in the blood of the fish than in their watery environment as a result.

Large amounts of very dilute urine are produced by the kidneys to remove excess water.

Nitrogenous waste is excreted as **ammonia**, highly toxic but very dilute in the large volumes of water excreted.

Osmoregulation in mammals

Land-dwellers need to conserve water as they must drink all that they need. In these organisms osmoregulation involves the internal environment rather than the interface between the cell and the outside world. The cells of a land-living mammal are surrounded by tissue fluid which comes from the blood capillaries running close to them. By controlling the water potential of the blood (its water content and solute concentration), the body can control the water potential of the tissue fluid and so protect the cells from osmotic damage. Osmoregulation in mammals is largely brought about by the kidneys.

Structure of the mammalian kidney

The kidneys of mammals are capable of producing waste fluid which is more concentrated than (hypertonic to) the body fluids, and this allows mammals to conserve water and inhabit relatively inhospitable environments.

In humans, as in other mammals, the kidneys are a dark reddish brown in colour and are attached to the back of the abdominal cavity. They are surrounded by a thick layer of fat which helps to protect them from mechanical damage. They control the water potential of the blood that passes through them, removing substances which would affect the water balance as well as getting rid of **urea**, the nitrogenous waste product of protein breakdown. (The production of urea by the liver is discussed in section 4.7, page 331.) The kidneys produce a fluid called **urine**, which is collected and stored in the **urinary bladder**. This is emptied at intervals when full. The position of the kidneys in the body and the overall structure of the organs is shown in figure 4.6.3.

The kidney at work

Functions of the kidney

The kidney carries out three main functions in its osmoregulatory role:

1 **ultrafiltration**
2 **selective reabsorption**
3 **tubular secretion.**

In humans, blood passes through the kidneys at a rate of 1200 cm³ per minute, which means that all the blood in the body travels through the kidneys and is filtered and balanced approximately once every 5 minutes. The functions of the kidney are carried out by the individual nephrons. Each nephron is about 12–14 mm long, and there are about 1.5 million of them in each kidney. This means that there are many kilometres of tubules in the kidneys, all engaged in filtering and balancing the blood. The three major functions occur in different areas of the kidney. The first stage is ultrafiltration, and this takes place in the Malpighian bodies.

Ultrafiltration

Ultrafiltration occurs due to a combination of very high blood pressure in the glomerular capillaries, and the structure of the Bowman's capsule and glomerulus. The high blood pressure develops in the capillaries because the diameter of the afferent vessel is greater than that of the efferent vessel. The high pressure squeezes the blood plasma out through the pores in the capillary wall. All the contents of the plasma can pass out of the capillary – its wall retains only the blood cells. The basement membrane between the capillary and the Bowman's capsule acts as the filter, preventing platelets and the large

---

Excretion

Excretion is the removal of metabolic waste from the body, including the waste products of the chemical processes of the body. Metabolic waste in human beings is mainly **carbon dioxide** from respiration and **urea** from the breakdown of excess proteins. Both of these chemicals are poisons and would eventually cause death if they were allowed to build up. Carbon dioxide is removed as we exhale. A small amount of protein waste is lost in our sweat once we have gone through puberty, but the main organ involved in the removal of urea from the body is the kidney.

Figure 4.6.3 The kidney is a complex organ carrying out a vital role in homeostasis. It is involved in osmoregulation, in the removal of nitrogenous waste products, in the pH balance of the blood and in the removal of certain drugs from the system.

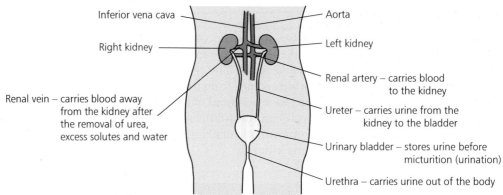

Inferior vena cava

Aorta

Right kidney

Left kidney

Renal artery – carries blood to the kidney

Renal vein – carries blood away from the kidney after the removal of urea, excess solutes and water

Ureter – carries urine from the kidney to the bladder

Urinary bladder – stores urine before micturition (urination)

Urethra – carries urine out of the body

The human urinary system. Blood from the body is passed through the kidneys where urea, excess salts and water are removed and form urine. The urine is stored in the bladder and released from the body at intervals.

The internal structure of the kidney. The relationships between structure and function become clearer when the details of the nephron are revealed.

Cortical nephron – the loop only just enters the medulla.

Fibrous capsule

Cortex – this has a particularly rich capillary network and so is a very dark red colour. It contains the Malpighian bodies of all the nephrons.

Medulla – this contains the loops of Henle from the nephrons.

Pelvis – central chamber where urine arrives from the collecting ducts.

Ureter – carries urine down to the bladder.

Juxtamedullary (next to the medulla) **nephron** – the long loop penetrates right through the medulla.

Pyramid – a collection of tubules, collecting ducts and blood vessels.

The nephron of the kidney – a highly complex structure which removes waste products from the blood and conserves water for the body.

Glomerulus – a tangled knot of capillaries in the Bowman's capsule. The pressure of blood in the glomerulus is high as the efferent vessel carrying blood away from the Malpighian body is narrower than the afferent vessel which brings the blood into it. Fluid is forced out of the capillaries under this pressure, passed through the basement membrane which retains the plasma proteins and then the remaining ultrafiltrate passes into the Bowman's capsule and so into the rest of the nephron.

Proximal or **first convoluted tubule** – active reabsorption of the glucose and of about 67% of the sodium ions which have left the blood occurs here, which also causes passive reabsorption of water and chloride ions. Microvilli on the lining epithelial cells give a greatly increased surface area for reabsorption to occur. The filtrate is considerably reduced in volume before it reaches the loop of Henle.

Bowman's capsule – the site of ultrafiltration of the blood. The ultrafiltrate from the glomerulus passes into the Bowman's capsule through specialised cells known as **podocytes**.

Malpighian body – found in the cortex, made up of the Bowman's capsule and the glomerulus. About 200 μm in diameter, it can just be seen with the naked eye.

Distal or **second convoluted tubule** – water is lost from the urine in this part of the tubule under the influence of the hormone ADH, and certain ions and drugs are actively secreted into it from the blood. It is involved in the concentration of the urine, the removal of unwanted substances from the blood and also in the control of the blood pH.

Afferent vessel bringing blood into the glomerulus

Efferent vessel taking blood away from the glomerulus – the blood has been reduced in volume by 15–20% by ultrafiltration.

Loop of Henle – this is where the urine is concentrated and water is conserved.

Collecting duct – water is reabsorbed from this region by osmosis. The amount of water lost depends in part on the permeability of the tubule to water, which in turn is affected by the hormone ADH.

Capillary networks into which substances are reabsorbed.

Vasa recta – the capillaries of the medulla which run closely with the loops of Henle.

In the body the kidney is surrounded by a thick, protective cushion of fat.

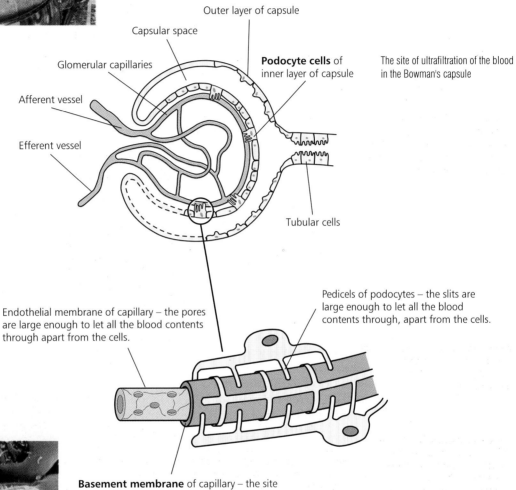

Outer layer of capsule

Capsular space

Glomerular capillaries

Afferent vessel

Efferent vessel

Podocyte cells of inner layer of capsule

The site of ultrafiltration of the blood in the Bowman's capsule

Tubular cells

Endothelial membrane of capillary – the pores are large enough to let all the blood contents through apart from the cells.

Pedicels of podocytes – the slits are large enough to let all the blood contents through, apart from the cells.

Basement membrane of capillary – the site of ultrafiltration as plasma proteins cannot pass through this membrane.

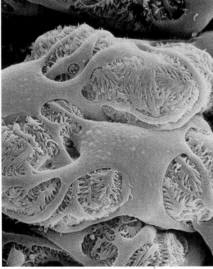
The complexity of the cellular structures in the Malpighian bodies can be seen on this electron micrograph. About 100 litres of blood are filtered through the pedicels every hour.

4

plasma proteins from passing through. The structure of the wall of the Bowman's capsule ensures that any cells which may have left the capillary do not get through into the tubule itself. The filtrate which enters the capsule contains glucose, salts, urea and many other substances in the same concentrations as in the blood plasma, as table 4.6.1 shows.

Substance	Approximate concentration/g dm^{-3}	
	In plasma	*In filtrate*
Water	900.0	900.0
Protein	80.0	0.0
Inorganic ions	7.2	7.2
Glucose	1.0	1.0
Amino acids	0.5	0.5
Urea	0.3	0.3

Table 4.6.1 The compositions of human plasma and glomerular filtrate

The process of ultrafiltration is very efficient, with up to 20% of the water and solutes from the plasma entering the nephron. If all of this filtrate was then passed out of the body, we would produce around 200 dm^3 of urine a day – the equivalent of about 350 milk bottles! Obviously then, ultrafiltration is only the first step in the process, and the kidney has more work to do before the urine finally leaves the organ.

Selective reabsorption

Ultrafiltration removes urea, the waste product of protein breakdown, from the blood. However, it also removes a lot of water and all the glucose, salt and other substances which are present in the plasma. Much of the water and salt may be needed by the body. Glucose is a vital energy supply for the body and is never, under normal circumstances, excreted.

The ultrafiltrate is hypotonic to (less concentrated than) the blood plasma. Therefore, after the ultrafiltrate has entered the nephron, the main function of the kidney tubule is to return to the blood most of what has been removed.

The first convoluted tubule

The cells of the first or proximal convoluted tubule are covered with microvilli which greatly increase the surface area through which substances can be absorbed. Figure 4.6.4 shows that the cells also have large numbers of mitochondria, indicating that they are involved in active processes.

In this first part of the nephron over 80% of the glomerular filtrate is reabsorbed into the blood. All of the glucose, amino acids, vitamins and hormones are taken back into the blood by active transport. About 85% of the sodium chloride and water are reabsorbed as well. The sodium ions are actively transported, and the chloride ions and water follow passively along diffusion gradients. Once the substances are removed from the tubule they pass by diffusion into the extensive capillary network which surrounds the tubules. The blood is then removed so there is a constant concentration gradient along which this diffusion occurs. By the time the filtrate reaches the loop of Henle it is isotonic with the tissue fluid which surrounds the tubule. The amount of reabsorption that occurs in the first convoluted tubule is always the same – the fine tuning of the water balance takes place further along the nephron.

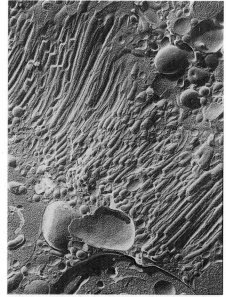

Figure 4.6.4 The cells of the first convoluted tubule show a high level of adaptation to their function. The brush border of microvilli provides a large surface area and the mitochondria a source of energy (ATP).

The loop of Henle

The loop of Henle is found in the medulla of the kidney, in close contact with the network of capillaries known as the vasa recta. The loop of Henle is the region of the kidney tubule which enables mammals to produce hypertonic urine, an important adaptation to the mammals as a group. The way in which this is brought about is complicated and not fully understood, but the current understanding is as follows.

The loop of Henle is shown in figure 4.6.5. It has a **descending limb** which leads from the first convoluted tubule. This limb is permeable to water and runs down into the medulla. A hairpin bend at the bottom of the loop leads into the **ascending limb**. This passes back up through the medulla until it joins the second convoluted tubule. The ascending limb of the loop is effectively impermeable to water. The second convoluted tubule leads into the collecting duct which then travels through the medulla to the pelvis of the kidney.

The concentrated urine is formed because the loop of Henle creates a diffusion gradient in the tissue of the medulla, which means that when water is in short supply it leaves the collecting duct by diffusion as it passes through the medulla and enters the blood vessels of the vasa recta. How does it work?

The simplest way to consider what happens in the loop of Henle is to begin with the filtrate entering the descending limb. This is isotonic with the blood. As the filtrate travels down the limb, the external concentration of sodium and chloride ions in the tissue fluid of the medulla increases. As a result, water diffuses out of the loop into the tissue fluid and then back into the blood of the vasa recta. Sodium and chloride ions also move into the limb by diffusion along concentration gradients. By the time the filtrate reaches the hairpin bend at the bottom of the loop it is very concentrated – hypertonic to the arterial blood.

As the filtrate moves up the ascending limb of the loop, chloride ions are actively secreted out of the tubule into the tissue fluid of the medulla, and sodium ions follow passively along an electrochemical gradient. It is this which causes the tissues of the medulla to have such high salt concentrations. However, because the ascending limb is impermeable to water, water cannot follow the ions and so the filtrate left in the ascending limb becomes increasingly dilute again, although the volume is not substantially changed. These processes are summarised in figure 4.6.6.

Once the dilute filtrate reaches the top of the ascending limb it is hypotonic to the blood again, and it then enters the second convoluted tubule and collecting duct, discussed below.

The second convoluted tubule

The second convoluted tubule is permeable to water, but the permeability varies with the levels of the hormone ADH. It is here and in the collecting duct that the balancing of the water needs of the body takes place. If there is too little salt in the body, sodium ions may be pumped out of the tubule with chloride ions following. Water also leaves by diffusion if the walls of the tubule are permeable.

The collecting duct

The permeability of the collecting duct is strongly affected by the hormone ADH. Water moves out of the collecting duct as it passes through the medulla, with the urine becoming steadily more concentrated. Because the level of sodium ions increases through the medulla, so water may be removed from the collecting duct all the way along, leading to very hypertonic urine when it is necessary to conserve water.

The loop of Henle

The loop of Henle is the specialised part of the nephron that enables mammals to produce urine that is more concentrated than their own blood. The length of the loops of Henle present in a mammal is a good indication of the water stress under which it lives. Animals with free access to water, such as otters, tend to have very short loops of Henle as water conservation is not a problem. Desert animals such as jerboas have very long loops of Henle to maximise water retention, while animals like ourselves have loops of intermediate length.

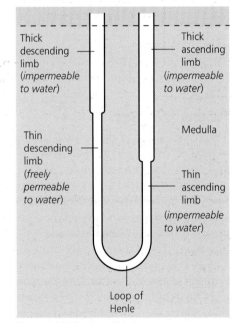

Figure 4.6.5 The loop of Henle.

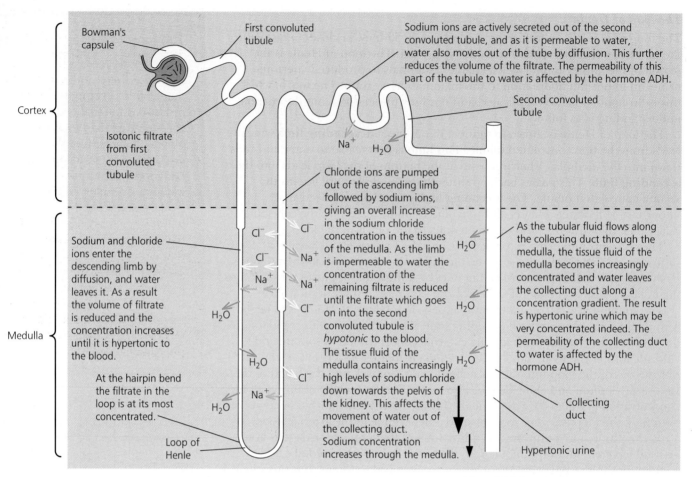

In the figure (labelled areas):

Cortex

Bowman's capsule

First convoluted tubule

Sodium ions are actively secreted out of the second convoluted tubule, and as it is permeable to water, water also moves out of the tube by diffusion. This further reduces the volume of the filtrate. The permeability of this part of the tubule to water is affected by the hormone ADH.

Isotonic filtrate from first convoluted tubule

Second convoluted tubule

Na^+ H_2O

Medulla

Sodium and chloride ions enter the descending limb by diffusion, and water leaves it. As a result the volume of filtrate is reduced and the concentration increases until it is hypertonic to the blood.

Chloride ions are pumped out of the ascending limb followed by sodium ions, giving an overall increase in the sodium chloride concentration in the tissues of the medulla. As the limb is impermeable to water the concentration of the remaining filtrate is reduced until the filtrate which goes on into the second convoluted tubule is *hypotonic* to the blood. The tissue fluid of the medulla contains increasingly high levels of sodium chloride down towards the pelvis of the kidney. This affects the movement of water out of the collecting duct. Sodium concentration increases through the medulla.

At the hairpin bend the filtrate in the loop is at its most concentrated.

Cl^- Cl^- Na^+ Na^+ Na^+ Cl^- H_2O H_2O Cl^- Na^+ H_2O

As the tubular fluid flows along the collecting duct through the medulla, the tissue fluid of the medulla becomes increasingly concentrated and water leaves the collecting duct along a concentration gradient. The result is hypertonic urine which may be very concentrated indeed. The permeability of the collecting duct to water is affected by the hormone ADH.

H_2O H_2O H_2O

Loop of Henle

Collecting duct

Hypertonic urine

Figure 4.6.6 The role of the loop of Henle in the reabsorption of water is still not fully understood. However, this complex system known as a **countercurrent multiplier** is very effective at producing concentrated urine.

Tubular secretion

The composition of the urine is also affected by substances actively secreted into it. This secretion occurs mainly in the second convoluted tubule. Potassium ions and creatinine (a nitrogenous excretory product) may be secreted from the blood into the tubule, and certain drugs such as penicillin are also removed from the body in this way. But perhaps the most important aspect of active secretion in the second convoluted tubule is its role in balancing the pH of the blood. If the pH of the blood starts to fall (if it becomes more acidic) hydrogen ions are secreted from the second convoluted tubule into the filtrate. Also, the kidney cells make and secrete ammonium ions which combine with the anions brought to the kidney and are excreted as ammonium salts. Equally, if the pH rises the tubule secretes hydrogencarbonate ions into the filtrate. As a result of this tubular secretion the pH of the urine may vary from 4.5 to 8.5, whilst the pH of the blood is maintained within a very narrow band.

The urine

The fluid produced by the kidney tubules is collected first in the pelvis of the organ. It then passes along the ureters to the bladder, where it is stored until the bladder is sufficiently stretched to stimulate micturition.

The urine contains variable amounts of water and salts, and large quantities of urea. Substances such as glucose or protein appearing in the urine indicate either that there are problems elsewhere in the body – in the pancreas, for example – or that the kidneys themselves are not working properly.

Control of the kidney and homeostasis

The kidney is of vital importance in the balance of both water and solutes in the body. The removal of the waste product urea is a continuous and important part of this role as urea is produced all the time by metabolic processes. However, levels of other important substances vary according to the situation of the individual. The functioning of the kidney must be adjusted to cope with changes in circumstances. A night out at the pub, a long walk on a hot summer's day or a very salty meal all threaten the steady state of the body. How is the functioning of the kidney controlled to bring about homeostasis?

Osmoregulation

The water potential of the blood is maintained at a more or less steady level by balancing the fluid taken in by eating and drinking with the fluid lost by sweating, defaecation and in the urine. It is the concentration of the urine which is most important in this balancing act, and this is controlled by **antidiuretic hormone** (**ADH**). As we saw in section 4.4, ADH is produced by the hypothalamus and secreted into the posterior lobe of the pituitary where it is stored. ADH increases the permeability of the second convoluted tubule and the collecting duct to water.

When water is in short supply, or a lot of sweating takes place, or very salty food is eaten, the blood concentration rises – its water potential becomes more negative. If this was allowed to continue the osmotic balance of the tissue fluids would be disturbed and cell damage would occur. However, the change in blood concentration is detected in the hypothalamus by receptors called **osmoreceptors**. These send impulses to the posterior pituitary which in turn releases stored ADH. The ADH increases the permeability of the second convoluted tubule and the collecting duct to water. As a result water leaves the tubules by diffusion into the concentrated tissues of the medulla and then moves into the blood vessels of the vasa recta. This means that more water is returned from the filtrate to the blood, and only small amounts of concentrated urine are produced.

When large amounts of liquid are taken in the blood becomes more dilute – its water potential becomes less negative. Again the change is detected by the osmoreceptors of the hypothalamus, and in this case the release of ADH by the pituitary is inhibited. The walls of the second convoluted tubule and the collecting duct remain impermeable to water and so little or no reabsorption takes place. Thus the concentration of the blood is maintained and large amounts of very dilute urine are produced. This control of water excretion is shown in figure 4.6.7.

If ADH is not produced at all then a clinical condition known as **diabetes insipidus** occurs. The diabetes mellitus ('sweet fountain') described in section 4.4 is caused by insufficient insulin being produced, resulting in large amounts of urine containing sugar. In diabetes insipidus ('dilute fountain') large amounts of very dilute urine are formed continuously as the tubules are permanently impermeable to water. There is no sugar in the urine, however. The patient feels extremely thirsty and has to drink large quantities of liquid to avoid severe dehydration.

Regulation of salt concentrations

The other major homeostatic system involving the kidney is in the control of the salt concentrations of the body. This is brought about by the hormone **aldosterone** produced by the cortex of the adrenal glands. It causes the active uptake of sodium ions in the second convoluted tubule from the filtrate into

Evidence for the way the kidney functions

How do we know what happens in the kidney tubules, and that the concentration of the filtrate changes as just described? Electron microscopy has allowed a detailed picture of the cells in the different parts of the nephron to be built up. Our knowledge of the changes in the filtrate as it passes along the tubule comes from work done by a number of investigators using a micropipette to withdraw fluid from various points along the nephron in a living organism.

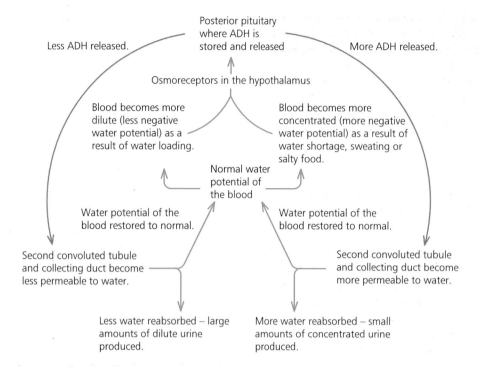

the plasma, and water follows by osmosis, increasing the blood volume and consequently the blood pressure.

If sodium ions are lost from the blood, for example after copious sweating, then the blood water potential becomes less negative and water tends to be lost from the blood into the tissue fluid and cells. This causes a slight drop in blood pressure, which is detected by a group of cells in the kidney found between the second convoluted tubule and the afferent arteriole. These cells are called the **juxtaglomerular complex**, and when the blood pressure drops they produce an enzyme called **renin**. This acts on a protein in the blood to produce **angiotensin**, a hormone which in turn stimulates the release of aldosterone from the adrenal glands. Once aldosterone is being produced the adrenal glands are stimulated by adrenocorticotrophic hormone (ACTH) from the pituitary gland as well. This is a complex system which helps to fine tune the concentration of sodium ions and the volume of the blood, as illustrated by figure 4.6.8.

Osmoregulation in plants

The maintenance of a steady internal environment is important to plants as well as to animals. For example, the enzymes controlling the biochemistry of plant cells are just as sensitive to temperature as are those in animal cells, though they have much lower optimum temperatures. Water balance is of great importance for the maintenance of turgor and the transport of substances within the plant. However, plant cells are, by their nature, less vulnerable than animal cells to osmotic damage because of the cellulose cell wall. Osmoregulation in plants tends to involve strategies for preventing water loss rather than a specific controlling organ such as the mammalian kidney.

Plant osmotic habitats

Plants live in a wide range of habitats, and these affect the water balance of the organism. Plants which live in fresh water are known as **hydrophytes** and they obviously have no shortage of water. Plants living in a normal terrestrial

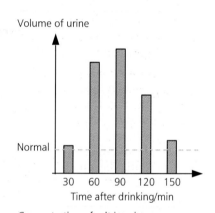

Figure 4.6.8 These graphs show the effect of drinking a given volume of distilled water on both the volume and salt concentration of the urine. Urine was collected at 30-minute intervals after drinking the water. This shows the sensitivity of the response to an imposed change – the water load is removed but without an unwanted loss of salt.

environment are known as **mesophytes**. They have to balance water loss by transpiration with water uptake from the soil, but conditions are usually such that this can be achieved without major specialised adaptations. **Xerophytes** live in conditions of great water shortage such as desert regions, and so they require drastic measures to avoid water loss. And finally there are plants living where there is plenty of water, but water which is unsuitable for them to use – the **halophytes** live on seashores and salt marshes, surrounded by salty water with a more negative water potential than their tissue fluids. As a result they exist in a state of physiological drought.

Methods of conserving water

There are a variety of ways in which plants conserve water, some common to most species, others very specific. Some of the main strategies for maintaining water balance in plants are given below.

1 The **waxy cuticle** reduces water loss from the surfaces of leaves and is very important in the conservation of water by plants.

2 **Stomata** are common to all plants, except those submerged in water. As we have seen in sections 2.2 and 2.3, these pores are opened and closed to allow gaseous exchange to take place for photosynthesis. A side effect of stomatal opening is that water is lost by evaporation. Plants which are under particular water stress have evolved ways of reducing water loss by evaporation from stomata. These include:

    a most stomata being sited on the underside of the leaves, minimising their exposure to the Sun

    b hairy leaves – the hairs trap a layer of still air which reduces water loss (see figure 2.2.4, page 107)

    c stomata sunk in pits, creating a microenvironment of still air

    d reduced leaves such as the very narrow 'needles' of conifers. Plants which live in extremely dry conditions may have leaves reduced to almost nothing and use the stem as the main photosynthetic organ, for example cacti with leaves reduced to spines (see figure 2.2.4, page 107)

    e curled leaves, such as those of the marram grass found colonising sand dunes, creating a microenvironment and so reducing water loss. Some of these strategies are shown in figure 4.6.9.

3 **Succulents** store water in specialised parenchyma tissues in their stems and roots. Water is stored when it is in plentiful supply and then used in times of drought.

4 **Root adaptations** for coping with water stress include very deep roots which can absorb water from deep down in the soil, and superficial roots close to the surface, spread out a long way from the plant. These provide a large surface area to absorb water when it penetrates the top layers of the soil.

5 Avoiding the problem entirely is an alternative solution to the problem of water balance. In winter time frosts may make it impossible to obtain water from the soil. Deciduous trees lose their leaves in the winter and drop their metabolism to a very low level. Many other plants survive dry periods by forming seeds, spores or underground perennating organs capable of withstanding long periods of desiccation.

Thus we can see that osmoregulation is a major homeostatic function in both plants and animals. Section 4.7 looks at other homeostatic mechanisms and how they are controlled.

Sunken stomata are in a microenvironment of moist air.

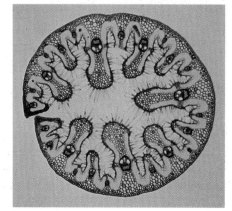
A curled or rolled leaf provides a protected microenvironment.

Figure 4.6.9 Some of the strategies plants have evolved to reduce water loss by evaporation

SUMMARY

- **Homeostasis** is the maintenance of a steady internal state, and is necessary for cells to function properly. Homeostasis involves **osmoregulation** (control of water balance), control of nitrogenous and other waste products, control of blood glucose levels and **thermoregulation** (control of body temperature).

- Unicells such as *Amoeba* have a **contractile vacuole** for osmoregulation which collects and expels excess water.

- In mammals the **kidneys** are the main osmoregulatory organs. They can produce urine hypertonic to the body fluids in order to conserve water. The kidney has three main areas – the **cortex**, **medulla** and **pelvis**. The cortex contains the **Malpighian bodies** of the **nephrons**, and the **loops of Henle** extend down into the medulla.

- Blood from the **renal vein** enters the Malpighian body of the nephron. It passes at high pressure into a knot of capillaries called the **glomerulus** inside the **Bowman's capsule**. **Ultrafiltration** takes place here – the fluid is forced out of the capillaries and into the Bowman's capsule through cells called **podocytes**. Blood cells are retained by the capillary wall and plasma proteins and platelets by the **basement membrane**.

- The ultrafiltrate (hypotonic to blood) is passed into the first convoluted tubule where **selective reabsorption** occurs. Glucose, amino acids, hormones, vitamins and sodium ions are reabsorbed into the blood and chloride ions follow by passive diffusion.

- The filtrate is concentrated in the loop of Henle. The **descending limb** is permeable to water. As it passes down into the medulla there is a high concentration of sodium chloride in the surrounding tissue and water passes out of the tubule and into the blood vessels of the **vasa recta**, and sodium and chloride ions pass into the tubule – the filtrate becomes hypertonic. As the filtrate moves up the **ascending limb**, which is impermeable to water, chloride ions are secreted out of it but water cannot leave it – it becomes hypotonic again.

- In the **second convoluted tubule** and **collecting duct**, sodium ions may be pumped out or water may leave the filtrate – the permeability of the tubule and duct is controlled by the hormone ADH. Active secretion of potassium ions, creatinine and drugs takes place in the second convoluted tubule. The pH balance of the blood is also controlled here – hydrogen ions and ammonium ions are secreted into the tubule to increase blood pH, and hydrogencarbonate ions secreted to reduce blood pH.

- As the filtrate passes into the collecting duct and again through the medulla, water again passes out under the control of ADH and the urine may become very concentrated (hypertonic).

- Changes in blood concentration are detected by **osmoreceptors** in the hypothalamus which send impulses to the posterior pituitary so that it releases ADH. This increases the permeability of the second convoluted tubule and collecting duct to water, which therefore passes out into the vasa recta, and the urine is concentrated. If the blood becomes too dilute, the osmoreceptors inhibit the release of ADH from the pituitary and the tubule walls are impermeable to water, which remains in the urine and is excreted.

- **Aldosterone** produced by the cortex of the adrenal glands causes the active uptake of sodium ions (and also water by osmosis) from the filtrate. If sodium ions are lost from the blood there is a drop in blood pressure which is detected by the **juxtaglomerular apparatus**. This in turn produces the enzyme **renin** which acts on a protein in the blood to produce **angiotensin**. This stimulates the adrenals to produce aldosterone, and ACTH then also stimulates the adrenals.

- Plants may be classified according to their osmotic habitat. **Hydrophytes** live in water and **mesophytes** on land. **Xerophytes** live in arid conditions and **halophytes** in salty water.

- Plants have various measures to prevent excessive water loss. A waxy cuticle prevents water loss from the leaf surface. Plants under water stress may have stomata on the undersides of leaves or sunken into pits. Hairy leaves trap a layer of still air and reduced or curled leaves also cut down transpiration. Succulents store water in specialised tissues. Roots may be very deep, or shallow and spreading. Dropping leaves and producing spores or seeds allow plants to survive prolonged dry periods.

QUESTIONS

1 a What is meant by the term *homeostasis*?
  b What is meant by the term *osmoregulation*?
  c Describe how the following osmoregulate:
   i freshwater amoebae
   ii salt-water fish.

2 Teenagers newly diagnosed as suffering from severe kidney disease face diet restrictions, dialysis and possible transplants. Produce a leaflet explaining clearly and concisely the role of the kidney in the body and how it works. Make clear the reasons for dietary and drinking restrictions, and for the artificial filtering of the blood they may have to undergo.

3 a Explain how the kidneys of desert animals are adapted to cope with a lack of water available for drinking.
  b Explain how plants living in deserts are adapted to dry conditions.

Developing Key Skills

Kidney failure can happen to anyone without any warning. Infections, accidents, inherited problems can all strike children, teenagers and adults and leave them needing dialysis or kidney transplants. Kidney donors are always in short supply, because the kidneys come from people killed in accidents or who have died after sudden illnesses that do not affect the kidneys. Many people who die in these ways do not carry kidney donor cards. In an attempt to encourage more people to carry donor cards, so that if they are killed in an accident their organs can be used to give life to others, a new web site is to be launched called **Kidney Crisis**.

Within this site the idea is for people to be able to find out what the kidney does, why it is so vital and how carrying donor cards can help.

Carry out some research and produce a minimum of three web pages for this site.

FOCUS THE COLD KILLER

People, like other endothermic or 'warm-blooded' animals, maintain a constant body temperature regardless of the temperature of their surroundings. At the beginning of our lives and as we become elderly, we can find this very difficult.

The ageing trap

As we get older, our thermoregulatory systems become less efficient. Older people tend to be less physically active, perhaps because of health problems or simply the choice of a more sedentary lifestyle, so they generate less body heat. Following bereavement or because money is short, older people may not cook and eat the proper meals which would help keep them warm. Some older people cannot afford to heat their homes adequately. All of these factors combine to increase the risk of older people developing hypothermia.

Hypothermia

Hypothermia is diagnosed as a lowering of the normal core temperature of the human body from 37 °C to below 35 °C, but the body will begin to malfunction even before this point. In hypothermia the skin turns greyish blue and pale, with a puffy face and blue lips. The skin is cold to the touch, even in places where it is almost always warm such as the armpits. The sufferer becomes drowsy and confused, with very slow reflexes and slurred speech, but is very unlikely to complain of feeling cold – that sensation is long past. The breathing is slow and shallow, the heart rate falls and the blood pressure drops. If the temperature continues to fall the person will become unconscious and eventually die. People can recover completely from hypothermia as long as they are warmed up gently – sudden heating can cause a severe fall in blood pressure which can result in death.

Figure 1 Each year several hundred old people die of hypothermia, and thousands more will die in the cold winter months of illnesses which they might well have shrugged off in the summer.

Not just the old

Although hypothermia is a particular problem for the elderly, it can affect anyone. In severe frosty or snowy weather, hypothermia kills people stranded in cars, particularly if they try to walk to get help. The blood is diverted from the body core to the muscles as they move, and is cooled in the cold body tissues. This makes the temperature drop faster and often brings unconsciousness if not death before help is found. Drinking alcohol speeds up hypothermia, as the drug causes vasodilation of blood vessels in the skin and increases heat loss further. The best way to survive if stranded in the cold is to put on all the clothing you have with you – most importantly cover your head, from where 20% of your body heat is lost – stay in the car or find a small enclosed space, curl up so that you have the minimum surface area exposed to the cold, and if there is more than one of you huddle together. Cold kills the old – and the young, and those in between …

Figure 2 Young people die every winter on the mountains. The confusion that sets in with the start of hypothermia makes sensible route planning or thinking of survival strategies impossible.

4.7 Homeostasis: Control of waste products and temperature

In section 4.6 we saw the importance of maintaining a steady internal state for the successful functioning of a living organism. The balance of water and solutes is particularly important because of the dramatic effect osmotic changes can have on cells. However, the concentrations of various waste products and the temperature of the organism also have a major effect on the functioning of cells. In mammals the main organ involved in water balance is the kidney. The liver plays a major role in other aspects of homeostasis.

Structure of the mammalian liver

The liver is one of the major body systems concerned with homeostasis. It is the largest individual organ contained within the body, a reddish-brown organ which makes up about 5% of the total body mass. It lies just below the diaphragm and is made up of several lobes. The cells of the liver are surprisingly simple and uniform in appearance, considering the variety and complexity of the functions of the organ. Liver cells are called **hepatocytes**, shown in figure 4.7.1. The appearance of the hepatocytes shows that they are metabolically active cells – they have large nuclei, prominent Golgi apparatus and many mitochondria.

The liver has a unique blood supply within the body. Oxygenated blood is supplied to the liver by the **hepatic artery** and removed from the liver and returned to the heart in the **hepatic vein**. However, the liver is also supplied with blood by a second vessel, the **hepatic portal vein** which carries blood from the intestines straight to the liver (see figure 4.7.1). Blood from the hepatic artery and the hepatic portal vein is mixed in spaces called **sinusoids** which are surrounded by hepatocytes. This mixing increases the oxygen content of the blood from the hepatic portal vein, supplying the hepatocytes with sufficient oxygen for their needs. The hepatocytes secrete bile from the breakdown of the blood into spaces called **canaliculi**, and from these the bile drains into the bile ductiles which take it to the gall bladder.

The liver at work

The liver carries out about 500 different tasks, which can be considered under a manageable number of major roles. Some of these we have met before and so will only discuss briefly here. Others are of major homeostatic importance and so will be considered more fully.

Carbohydrate control

All the hexose sugars which are absorbed from the gut are converted into glucose by the hepatocytes. Also, the hepatocytes are closely involved in the homeostatic control of glucose levels in the blood under the control of insulin and glucagon. When blood glucose levels rise, hepatocytes convert glucose to the storage carbohydrate glycogen under the influence of insulin. Similarly, when blood sugar levels start to fall, the hepatocytes convert the glycogen back to glucose under the influence of the hormone glucagon. The action of these hormones was discussed in section 4.4.

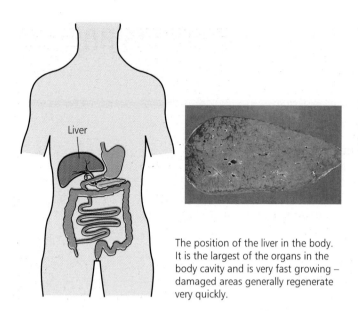

Liver

The position of the liver in the body. It is the largest of the organs in the body cavity and is very fast growing – damaged areas generally regenerate very quickly.

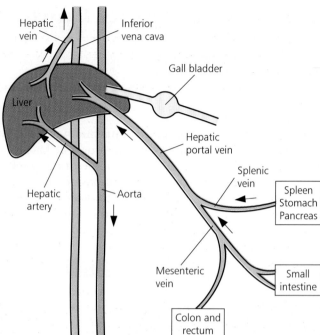

Hepatic vein

Inferior vena cava

Gall bladder

Liver

Hepatic portal vein

Splenic vein

Spleen
Stomach
Pancreas

Hepatic artery

Aorta

Mesenteric vein

Small intestine

Colon and rectum

The liver has a very rich blood supply – about 1 dm³ of blood flows through it every minute. Up to three-quarters of this blood comes from the gut via the hepatic portal vein and is loaded with the products of digestion and absorption. These are the raw materials for the many metabolic activities of the liver.

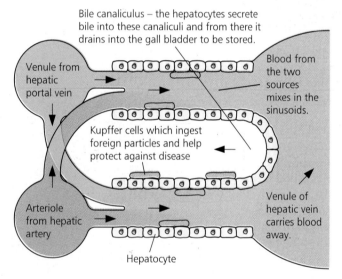

Bile canaliculus – the hepatocytes secrete bile into these canaliculi and from there it drains into the gall bladder to be stored.

Venule from hepatic portal vein

Blood from the two sources mixes in the sinusoids.

Kupffer cells which ingest foreign particles and help protect against disease

Arteriole from hepatic artery

Venule of hepatic vein carries blood away.

Hepatocyte

The arrangement of the tissues in the liver, giving all the hepatocytes close contact with the blood for both removing and adding materials

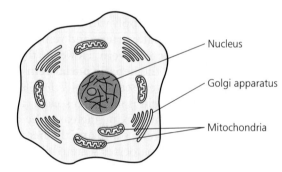

Nucleus

Golgi apparatus

Mitochondria

One of the unspecialised hepatocytes which carries out the metabolic and homeostatic functions of the liver

Figure 4.7.1 The microscopic structure of the liver is relatively simple and surprisingly uniform considering its roles in the metabolism of carbohydrates, proteins and fats and its major part in the maintenance of a steady state within the body.

Lipid control

Some carbohydrate (about 100 g) can be stored as glycogen by the liver, and some glycogen is stored in the muscles. Any excess carbohydrate eaten over and above this amount is converted to lipids by the hepatocytes for storage elsewhere in the body. The hepatocytes are also involved in removing **cholesterol** and various other lipids from the blood and breaking them down or modifying them for use elsewhere. Cholesterol is needed by the body for the formation of cell membranes, particularly in the nerve cells, and for the production of hormones. Excess cholesterol is excreted in the bile and may precipitate to form gall stones in the gall bladder or bile duct. A raised blood cholesterol level can cause problems as cholesterol may be deposited in the blood vessels and cause angina or heart attacks. The homeostatic function of the liver in removing excess cholesterol from the blood is therefore most important to the health of the organism as a whole, as illustrated by figure 4.7.2.

Protein control

The liver plays a vital role in protein metabolism. It produces certain plasma proteins. The hepatocytes also carry out **transamination**, the conversion of one amino acid into another. The diet does not always contain the required balance of amino acids, but transamination can overcome many potential problems this might cause.

The most important role of the liver in protein metabolism is in **deamination**. The body cannot store either protein or amino acids. Any excess protein eaten would be excreted and therefore wasted were it not for the action of the hepatocytes. They deaminate the amino acids, removing the amino group and converting it first into the very toxic **ammonia** and then to **urea**. Urea is less poisonous and can be excreted by the kidneys, as we have seen in section 4.6. The remainder of the amino acid can then be fed into cellular respiration or converted into lipids for storage.

The ammonia produced in the deamination of proteins is converted into urea in a set of enzyme-controlled reactions known as the **ornithine cycle** (see box below).

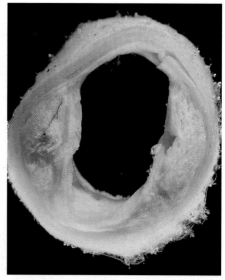

The biochemistry of deamination

Removing the amino group from amino acids and converting the resulting highly poisonous ammonia into the less toxic and more manageable compound urea involves some complex biochemistry.
This can be simplified and summarised as in figure 4.7.3.

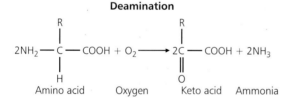

Deamination

$$2NH_2 - \underset{\underset{H}{|}}{\overset{\overset{R}{|}}{C}} - COOH + O_2 \longrightarrow 2\underset{\underset{O}{\|}}{\overset{\overset{R}{|}}{C}} - COOH + 2NH_3$$

Amino acid   Oxygen   Keto acid   Ammonia

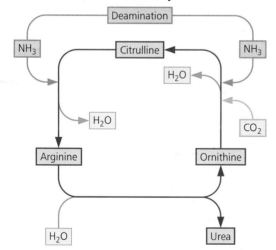

The ornithine cycle

Deamination
NH₃ → Citrulline ← NH₃
H₂O
H₂O   CO₂
Arginine   Ornithine
H₂O   Urea

Figure 4.7.3 Excess amino acids in the body cannot be stored for later use. They have to be broken down, so that as little of the molecule as possible is wasted. This is carried out by the cells of the liver in the process known as deamination, with the waste products being converted into urea by the reactions of the ornithine cycle.

Figure 4.7.2 An excess of cholesterol in the blood can lead to circulatory problems as the lipid is deposited on the walls of blood vessels. The liver works to prevent such problems by regulating the levels of cholesterol in the blood and excreting excess into the bile. However, this can cause its own problems, as these gall stones show.

Excretion of nitrogenous wastes

Animals produce nitrogenous waste as a by-product of protein metabolism. Most animals need to conserve water, yet they also need to get rid of their poisonous nitrogenous wastes. How do they do this? Mammals produce the soluble substance **urea** as their nitrogenous waste, and this is then excreted in the urine by the kidney. But different types of animals living in different environments have evolved a variety of different strategies. A few of them are described below.

- **Fish** – freshwater fish excrete **ammonia** as their nitrogenous waste. It takes less energy to form ammonia than urea, but ammonia is the most poisonous of the nitrogenous waste products. However, because water is constantly moving into the bodies of freshwater fish by osmosis, they produce enormous quantities of urine. The ammonia is so dilute that it does not harm them. Marine fish, on the other hand, do need to conserve water. They produce ammonia and then convert it to **trimethylamine oxide**, which is very soluble but not toxic. This allows them to produce very concentrated urine, conserving water but getting rid of their nitrogenous waste (see page 316).

- **Insects** – water conservation is a major issue for insects, and they have evolved an excretory system which produces **uric acid** as the main nitrogenous waste, sometimes alongside urea. Uric acid is high in nitrogen content but not very soluble (so it can be excreted without carrying water with it) and not very toxic. The **Malpighian tubules** present in many insects produce small amounts of urine containing uric acid crystals. In times of water shortage the urine will be almost a paste, usually mixed with the faeces before passing out of the body.

- **Birds** – like insects, birds produce **uric acid** as their nitrogenous waste product, in urine which is hypertonic to the body fluids. This concentrated urine is passed into the cloaca, where more water is removed and the faeces are added to produce the familiar semi-solid bird droppings.

Red blood cell control

The red blood cells of a developing fetus are made by the fetal liver, although by the time the baby is born this function has been taken over by the bone marrow. The Kupffer cells in the sinusoids (see figure 4.7.1) break down red blood cells that are at the end of their 120-day life. The haemoglobin is broken down to form the bile pigments **biliverdin** (green) and **bilirubin** (brown) which are excreted in the bile and are responsible for its colour, and so indirectly for the colour of the faeces.

Bile production

The production of bile by the hepatocytes is important in homeostasis for several reasons. Bile contains:

- bile salts which have a valuable role in the digestion of fats

- bile pigments which excrete the breakdown products of haemoglobin

- cholesterol, the removal of which helps to control the blood level within narrow boundaries.

Storage

The liver stores a variety of substances, releasing them as necessary to maintain a steady concentration in the blood. Substances stored include glycogen, with its important role in sugar metabolism, the lipid-soluble vitamins A, D, E and K and the water-soluble vitamins of group B and vitamin C. Along with these the liver is also a store for iron, copper, zinc and cobalt ions. Polar bear liver contains so much vitamin A that it is actually toxic for humans to eat!

Hormone control

It is important that hormones are broken down once they have carried their message to the appropriate areas of the body. The liver is the site where hormones, particularly steroids such as the sex hormones, are broken down. Some are sent for excretion by the kidney whilst others are excreted in the bile.

Control of toxins

Toxins are constantly produced in the body. Apart from urea which we have already considered, many other metabolic pathways produce potentially poisonous substances. We also take in a wide variety of poisons on a voluntary basis, such as alcohol and drugs like paracetamol. The liver is the site where all these substances are absorbed and detoxified.

A classic example is the way the liver deals with **hydrogen peroxide**, a by-product of various metabolic pathways. Hepatocytes contain the enzyme catalase, one of the most active of all known enzymes, which splits the hydrogen peroxide into oxygen and water.

Temperature control

The liver has a very high metabolic rate. For many years it has been assumed that as a result of the number of biochemical reactions which occur in the liver and its large size, much heat was generated there and distributed round the body by the extensive blood supply. More recently this view has been questioned and it is now thought that under normal circumstances endothermic and exothermic reactions cancel each other out and the liver produces little excess heat.

The liver has many important homeostatic functions – it is involved in the control of the blood levels of a wide range of substances and in preventing the build-up of a wide range of toxic substances. But even the actions of the liver and the kidney combined do not complete the homeostatic picture, even at this relatively simple level. The third major element of homeostasis, particularly in mammals, is the control of temperature.

Thermoregulation

The need for thermoregulation

The chemical reactions which occur in cells only take place within a relatively narrow range of temperatures. As we have seen in section 1.5, this is largely due to the sensitivity of the enzymes which control the reactions. For example, most enzymes have an optimum temperature and once temperatures rise above 40 °C most enzymes are denatured as their tertiary and quarternary structure is destroyed. Because of this sensitivity to temperature, many organisms control their internal body temperature – **thermoregulation** is important to their survival and is a major aspect of their homeostasis.

Losing and gaining heat

When we discuss the 'temperature' of an organism, we are considering the core temperature of the body. The surface temperature of an animal or plant fluctuates rapidly, but it is the internal temperature which is relevant to enzyme activity. Living organisms are continually losing heat. They are also continually gaining heat. The balance between the gains and losses determines whether

Trapping a layer of air in the feathers helps small birds to avoid heat loss by convection.

Basking in the Sun on a warm rock allows the lizard to gain heat by both radiation and conduction.

Figure 4.7.4 Organisms use a variety of methods to allow them to gain or lose heat as needed.

the core temperature of the organism rises, falls or stays the same. This is illustrated in figure 4.7.5.

Most of the ways in which animals exchange heat with their surroundings are affected by the additional factor of the size of the animal. Small animals have a large surface area:volume ratio and this means that they lose and gain heat more rapidly than a larger organism.

There are several ways in which organisms gain and lose heat.

- Heat is gained as a by-product of *metabolism*. Heat produced by exothermic reactions warms the core of the organism.

- Heat is lost by the *evaporation* of water from the body surfaces. A certain amount of heat is always lost in this way from the mouth and respiratory surfaces of land-dwelling animals, and this cannot generally be controlled. Sweating and behavioural patterns such as wallowing can increase this heat loss.

- Heat may be lost to or gained from the environment by *radiation*. This is the transfer of energy in the form of electromagnetic waves. Infra-red radiation is the most important form of heat energy absorbed and radiated by animals.

- Heat may be lost to or gained from the environment by *convection*. This is the transfer of heat by currents in air or water. Convection currents are set up around objects that are warmer than their surroundings (warm air or water rises, cold air or water sinks), and so adaptations to prevent heat loss by these currents are common in animals.

- Heat may be lost to or gained from the environment by *conduction*. This is the transfer of heat by the collisions of molecules. Conduction is particularly important between organisms and the ground or water, as air does not conduct heat well. Neither does fat, so fat deposits in adipose tissue are therefore a valuable insulator preventing heat exchange with the environment.

How do animals control their body temperatures?

Not all animals need to control their body temperatures. Protoctists and small animals living in water have no means of temperature regulation. For those organisms living in large water masses such as the sea this raises no difficulties, because the temperature of their environment is very stable. Similar organisms living in small ponds either develop tolerance of temperature fluctuations, or have survival strategies to cope with adverse conditions, such as forming cysts and emerging when the temperature is suitable again.

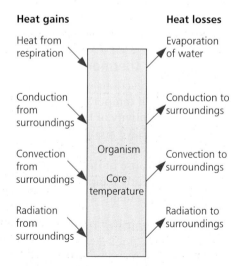

Figure 4.7.5 The heat gains and losses experienced by an organism. It is the balance of these which determines the core temperature.

However, larger animals in a wide variety of habitats need to regulate their temperatures, either to avoid damage to cells or to enable them to have an active way of life. Animals may be classified by their thermoregulation mechanisms in two different ways.

One approach, which has been used for many years, is to consider the stability of the body temperature of an animal.

- **Homoiothermic animals** – mainly the mammals and birds – regulate their body temperatures within a very narrow range (mammals 37–8 °C, birds 40 °C).

- **Poikilothermic animals** – such as the fish and reptiles – allow their body temperature to fluctuate much more widely, approximately following the external environment.

However, more recently there has been dissatisfaction with this way of looking at thermoregulation in animals. Many so-called homoiothermic animals in fact have body temperatures which fluctuate quite widely. Equally, many poikilothermic animals regulate their temperatures within a fairly narrow band. The number of species which have large fluctuations in their core temperature following the environment is relatively small. As a result, animals are often now classified according to the major source of their body heat.

- **Endothermic animals** rely on their own metabolic reactions to provide at least some of their body heat.

- **Ectothermic animals** depend largely on the environment for their body heat.

Endotherms

Endotherms produce at least some of their own body heat and usually have a body temperature higher than the ambient temperature. They are adapted to conserve their body heat when necessary, and also to take advantage of warmth from the environment when possible. This means that there are few environments where they cannot remain active, and the main groups of endotherms, the mammals and birds, are found in an extremely wide variety of environmental niches. They can cope with high external temperatures and can also live in areas with very low ambient temperatures where ectotherms would not be able to remain active. In order to maintain the body temperature against adverse environmental conditions, the metabolic rate has to be high – endotherms on average have a metabolic rate five times higher than an ectotherm of comparable size – and this means they have to eat considerably more food to supply their metabolic needs.

Ectotherms

Ectotherms may produce a significant part of their own body heat, but rely on behavioural and structural modifications that take advantage of the environment in order to maintain a reasonably steady temperature. When cold they may bask in the Sun, press themselves to warm surfaces or have special areas of skin which they erect in order to maximise their absorption of radiation from the Sun. To cool down they may move into the shade, or into water or mud. (Endotherms also modify their behaviour to aid thermoregulation. There is more about this on pages 338–342.) By a variety of strategies such as these, many ectotherms maintain a body temperature which is almost as stable as that of an endotherm, although they are always more vulnerable to fluctuations. Because their metabolic rate is much lower, ectotherms need less food, an advantage in many environments where food may be in short supply.

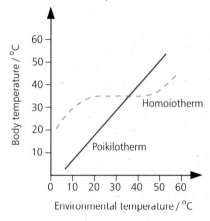

Relationship between body temperature and environmental temperature for homoiotherms and poikilotherms

Figure 4.7.6 Endothermic control of the body temperature allows large animals such as the polar bear to lead an active life where ectotherms of similar size would have difficulty, while both groups can exploit the warmer regions of the world. The graph shows why the majority of organisms have evolved to show at least some degree of homoiothermy – the fluctuations in temperature shown by a true poikilotherm make survival in anything but a very stable environment difficult in the extreme.

The mechanisms of temperature control

Mammals and birds are endothermic animals. Temperature control in humans is a good example of homeostasis in mammals as we are not only endotherms but also homoiotherms – we regulate our body temperature within a very narrow range. How is this control brought about? The main source of heat is from our metabolism, but humans survive in almost every area of the world and have effective ways of both losing and conserving heat.

The skin

The major homeostatic organ involved in thermoregulation is the skin. Heat loss through the gut and the respiratory surfaces occurs and cannot be prevented, but the skin has evolved to provide an enormous surface area which can be modified either to conserve or to lose heat, as figure 4.7.7 shows.

The skin is the largest single organ. It covers the entire surface of the body in a waterproof layer, providing protection both against mechanical damage and from the ultraviolet radiation of the Sun. The skin can be regarded as a sense organ, containing thousands of sensory nerve endings providing the brain with information about many aspects of the outside world, including temperature, touch and pain. It is also an excretory organ, with urea, salt and water being lost in the sweat. But the major homeostatic function of the skin is in thermoregulation and this is summarised in table 4.7.1.

Figure 4.7.7 The human skin and its functions. The same major structures are present in the skin of all other mammals.

Sweat pore – sweat reaches the surface of the skin from the sweat gland through the pore.

Hair – these are erected to trap a layer of still air and so prevent heat loss by convection.

Hair follicle – the cells which produce the hair.

Sebaceous gland – this produces an oily secretion called **sebum** which helps keep the hair flexible and waterproofs the surface of the skin.

Epidermis – made up of many layers of cells produced by the Malpighian layer. They contain varying amounts of pigment to protect the lower cells from damage by ultraviolet radiation from the Sun. The cells gain keratin which makes them waterproof but also kills them. These layers of dead and dying cells form an outer layer preventing the entry of pathogens, protecting against radiation damage and also reducing friction damage to the underlying tissues.

Cornified layer

Granular layer

Malpighian layer

Sweat gland – produces sweat by absorbing water and solutes from the capillaries. The evaporation of sweat from the surface of the skin causes cooling and the sweat contains excess water, urea and salts so is also a method of excretion.

Hair erector muscle (erector pili) – contracts to erect the hair. In humans the muscles are seen as 'goose-pimples'.

Connective tissue – holds the components of the skin together.

Arteriovenous shunt vessel

Temperature receptor

Pacinian corpuscle

A micrograph of a section through the human skin

Pain receptor

Subcutaneous fat layer made up of adipose cells – this layer helps to protect the body from mechanical damage and acts as an insulating layer against heat loss.

Capillary network – the blood flow through these capillaries determines the amount of heat lost from the surface of the skin by convection and radiation. The blood flow is determined by the arteriovenous shunt vessel.

Measures to encourage heat loss when the external temperature rises	**Measures to conserve heat when the external temperature falls**
The arteriovenous shunt closes to increase the blood flow through the capillaries and so increase heat loss by conduction and radiation.	The arteriovenous shunt opens, reducing the blood flow through the capillaries and so reducing the heat lost from the surface of the skin by conduction and radiation.
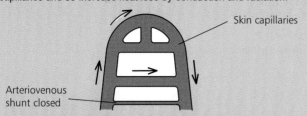	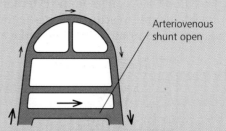
The rate of sweat production by the sweat glands increases. As more sweat is released onto the skin surface, heat is lost as the water evaporates. Almost 1 dm³ of sweat is usually produced and lost in a day, but this can rise to 12 dm³ in very hot conditions.	Sweat production is reduced and so heat loss by evaporation is also reduced.
The erector pili muscles are relaxed and the hairs lie flat against the body. In humans this has little effect, but in hairy mammals the insulating layer of air trapped by the hair is reduced and so more heat can be lost by convection.	The erector pili muscles are contracted, pulling the hairs upright. In humans this is visible as 'goose-pimples' and has little effect on temperature regulation, but in hairy mammals it traps an insulating layer of air which reduces heat loss by convection.
The metabolic rate drops so that less heat is produced by the body – animals tend to be less active in hot weather.	The metabolic rate of the body rises, producing extra heat. This takes place particularly in the liver and the muscles. Shivering – involuntary contractions of the skeletal muscles – also helps to generate metabolic heat. Special **brown fat** may also be metabolised. Raising the body temperature by increased metabolism in this way is particularly important in emergence of animals from hibernation and for temperature control in very young human babies.

Table 4.7.1 Some major homeostatic activities of the skin

Temperature limits

Experiments carried out on human subjects in calorimeters, along with observations on seriously ill patients and people who have been exposed to extreme cold, have allowed us to build up a picture of the temperature tolerance of the human body. The subject must be naked so that any responses to changes in temperature are purely physiological and do not involve the physical properties of clothes or coverings. The environmental temperature is changed, and the internal core temperature of the subject is recorded.

As the external temperature drops a range of thermoregulatory mechanisms is used to conserve heat. Below a certain point simple measures such as controlling the blood supply to the skin surface and raising the body hairs are no longer sufficient, and the metabolic rate starts to go up. This point is known as the **low critical temperature**. If the temperature keeps on falling the metabolic rate will rise to produce sufficient heat to maintain the core temperature.

Eventually the chemical reactions can no longer take place and the subject dies – this is the **low lethal temperature**.

As the external temperature rises, thermoregulating mechanisms such as sweating can keep the core temperature stable until the **high critical temperature** is reached. This is very variable as it also depends on the level of humidity – sweating is more efficient in dry air. If the external temperature continues to increase, the metabolic rate starts to go up as the body's reactions double their rate for every 10 °C rise in temperature. Once this happens, positive feedback occurs, because the faster the metabolic rate, the more heat is produced. Death usually occurs when the core temperature reaches about 42 °C – the **high critical temperature** – when the enzymes controlling cell reactions fail.

Control of blood temperature

In any homeostatic system there are receptors sensitive to changes in the system. In the case of temperature regulation there are two types of receptors. Receptors in the brain directly monitor the temperature of the blood, whilst receptors in the skin detect changes in the external temperature. This allows for great sensitivity not only to actual changes in the core temperature but to potential changes too as a result of changes in the environmental temperature.

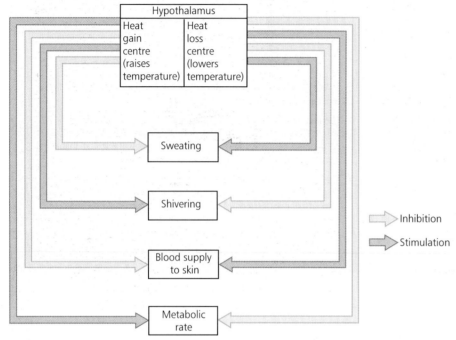

Figure 4.7.8 The hypothalamus acts as the 'thermostat' of the body. As a result of sensitive feedback mechanisms, the temperature of the body is controlled to within 1 °C of its normal temperature.

The temperature receptors in the brain are sited in the hypothalamus. If the temperature of the blood flowing through the hypothalamus drops, the **heat gain centre** reacts by sending nerve impulses to the skin. These cause a reduction in the blood flow through the capillaries in the skin, along with a reduction in the production of sweat and contraction of the erector pili muscles to erect the hairs. Messages from the heat gain centre also stimulate involuntary muscle contractions (shivering) and raise the rate of metabolism.

When the temperature of the blood flowing through the hypothalamus rises, the **heat loss centre** is activated and sends out impulses which increase the blood flow through the skin and increase sweating. The erector pili muscles are relaxed so that the hairs lie flat and shivering stops. The metabolic rate is reduced to generate less heat in the body. Thus the core temperature is usually maintained within very narrow limits, as figure 4.7.8 shows.

Responses to the thermoreceptors (temperature receptors) in the skin are also important in the homeostatic control of temperature. Messages from skin receptors inform the brain if the environment is hot or cold, and the behaviour of the animal is modified accordingly. For example, as the skin heats up an animal will seek shade, whilst cooling of the skin surface might give rise to increased activity to raise the amount of metabolic heat produced.

Adaptations of endotherms

Heat loss and its control are important elements in homeostatic temperature regulation. The rate of heat loss is related to the surface area:volume ratio of an animal, and this affects the type of endotherms found in particular environments.

Temperature control in premature infants

The mammalian fetus does not have to control its own body temperature – a stable temperature is maintained for it in the uterus by the maternal control systems. Therefore when a baby is born very prematurely it is poorly prepared for the regulation of its body temperature. There is a minimal amount of insulating subcutaneous fat. The shivering response is poorly developed and brown fat has not been laid down in any quantity. The skin is very thin and so the blood flows close to the surface. The skin is also extremely porous so water evaporates freely from it, causing cooling of the blood. Because of the small size of such infants, the surface area:volume ratio means that all types of heat loss occur very readily.

How are these problems overcome? One of the main priorities in the care of premature infants is to allow as much of the energy intake as possible to be used for the growth and maturation of the body systems. Thus it is vital to minimise heat loss and prevent the expenditure of energy on attempting to keep warm. Incubators are designed to maintain a constant temperature for the air surrounding the baby. The air may also be humidified to reduce cooling by the evaporation of water from the skin, and thin plastic and aluminium sheeting wrapped around the baby for the first few weeks will reduce this effect still further.

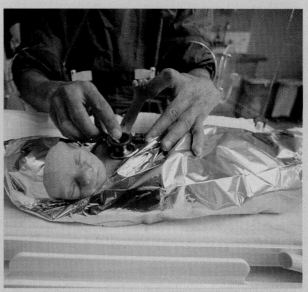

Figure 4.7.9 The temperature control mechanisms which adults take for granted are simply not ready to function in a premature baby.

Cold environments

In a cold environment mammals and birds are usually larger than their equivalent in a warmer climate. This reduces their surface area:volume ratio and so reduces their heat loss. Animals develop thick layers of subcutaneous fat which insulates against heat loss. They also tend to have small extremities such as ears. Parts that stick out are particularly vulnerable to heat loss, and so the smaller they are the better, in terms of heat conservation. Finally, some mammals and birds living in cold external conditions have developed **countercurrent heat exchange systems** in their limbs which allow body heat to be conserved, as shown in figure 4.7.10.

Hibernation

Some endotherms cannot generate enough heat for them to survive in cold conditions, generally small animals living in Arctic or temperate regions, where the winter temperatures are considerably lower than the summer ones. This problem can be overcome by **hibernating**. In hibernation the animal goes into a very deep sleep. Its metabolic rate slows down greatly and the core body temperature is substantially lowered. Many hibernating animals, for example dormice and hamsters, allow their body temperature to fall just so far and then maintain it at this lower level, making substantial energy savings. A few such as bats allow their body temperature to follow that of the external environment. This saves even more energy, but if the temperature drops too low the tissues might freeze, killing the animal.

Animals usually go into hibernation as a result of both low ambient temperatures and a shortening of the day length. Warm temperatures and lengthening days bring them out of hibernation again. The restoration of the metabolic rate needs to occur quickly to allow the animal to feed and to make sure that it does not become easy prey for predators. Stores of **brown fat** (fat stored in tissues with a particularly rich blood supply) are conserved during hibernation and used up rapidly to produce metabolic heat at the end of hibernation.

Hot environments

A hot environment poses different problems. As losing heat is not a problem, animals do not need to be particularly large in order to conserve heat. Indeed, one of the problems for animals in very hot areas is to lose sufficient heat to prevent themselves from overheating. This is why the extremities of many such animals are large and thin with a rich blood supply, for example an elephant's ears. Heat can be lost to the environment relatively easily through adaptations such as these. There is very little insulating fat, so increasing the amount of heat that can be lost.

Some endotherms simply cannot lose enough heat to maintain a steady internal temperature, and they have evolved the ability to tolerate much larger fluctuations in body temperature than most organisms. The camel is a classic example.

Living in the desert, their major priority is to conserve water. Camels do this most effectively, largely because they do not sweat. This saves water but also removes a major cooling mechanism. As a result the body temperature of a camel climbs to around 40 °C during the day. This is high but not lethal, and the cells can continue to function at this temperature. Desert nights are very cold and the camel then loses heat so that the body temperature falls to a low of 34 °C – cooler than most mammals but still within a range where the cells can function. The low night temperature ensures that the temperature does not climb too high during the day as the temperature rise starts from a low base. By tolerating these fluctuations in temperature the camel conserves water, achieving osmoregulation. At the same time, by maintaining the temperature fluctuations within the limits of normal functioning, temperature damage to its cells is avoided.

Control of body temperature by behaviour

As well as physiological controls, modification of behaviour can help avoid major changes in core temperature. Endotherms use behaviour to control their body temperature to some extent (wallowing in mud or water, panting to increase heat loss by evaporation, etc.). In ectotherms the major thermoregulatory mechanism is the modification of behaviour to control body temperature.

Behavioural modifications which help maintain animal body temperatures within manageable limits include:

● **Basking** – desert lizards are among many groups of animals which bask in the Sun when their body temperature is tending to fall. By orientating the body differently to the Sun, or by erecting special areas of tissue which have evolved to absorb heat from the Sun, the body temperature may be raised.

● **Sheltering** – when the core temperature is rising too high many animals shelter from the direct heat of the Sun in burrows, holes or crevices in rocks. They may also attempt to lose extra heat by conduction, pressing the body against the cool earth.

● **Evaporation** – by panting and so exposing the moist tissues of the mouth, by licking the body surface or by wallowing in mud or water an animal can increase evaporation and so heat loss from the body.

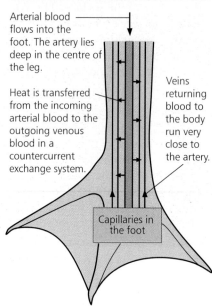

Figure 4.7.10 In a countercurrent heat exchange system such as those found in ducks' legs and dolphins' flippers, the arterial blood cools as it flows to the extremity and the venous blood is warmed as it returns to the body. This minimises the heat loss to the environment and so conserves energy.

Arterial blood flows into the foot. The artery lies deep in the centre of the leg.

Heat is transferred from the incoming arterial blood to the outgoing venous blood in a countercurrent exchange system.

Veins returning blood to the body run very close to the artery.

Capillaries in the foot

By absorbing as much heat from the Sun as possible, an ectotherm such as this locust can warm up its body sufficiently to allow for early morning flight. Depending on the temperature of the body and the heat from the Sun the insect will climb higher or lower, and turn its body in different directions, to gain just the amount of heat needed.

Increasing the level of evaporation from the body allows for increased cooling.

Figure 4.7.11 Behavioural modifications such as these allow both ectotherms and endotherms to thermoregulate.

4

Cooling the brain

The brain is the part of most mammals which is particularly susceptible to damage as a result of overheating. A modification of a countercurrent exchange system helps to prevent this heat damage, as shown in figure 4.7.12. This system is valuable in many mammals, but is of particular importance and is extremely well developed in animals such as the camel which live in conditions of heat stress.

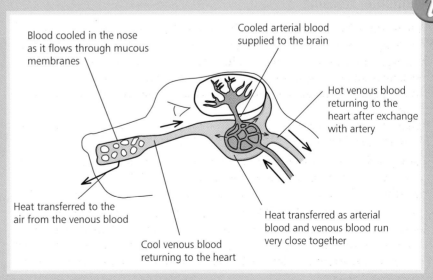

Blood cooled in the nose as it flows through mucous membranes

Cooled arterial blood supplied to the brain

Hot venous blood returning to the heart after exchange with artery

Heat transferred to the air from the venous blood

Heat transferred as arterial blood and venous blood run very close together

Cool venous blood returning to the heart

Figure 4.7.12 A heat exchange system like this involving the nasal passages can prevent brain damage due to overheating and so make more environments available as habitats.

Moving into or out of the Sun is one of the most common behavioural means of regulating body temperature. It is used by both endotherms and ectotherms as part of their homeostatic control system. However, such simple methods of modifying the internal temperature are only available to animals. Plants cannot move around and so rely on physical and physiological adaptations to help them avoid heat damage.

Temperature control in plants

As we saw in section 4.6, it is just as important for plants to maintain a reasonably stable internal environment as it is for animals. Plants lose and gain heat by the same physical processes as animals – radiation, evaporation, conduction and convection. They have adapted to live in a variety of habitats and can cope with a wide range of temperatures. In general plant tissues are rather like those of the camel – they can tolerate relatively large fluctuations in temperature. However, plant enzymes, like any others, denature if the temperature gets too high, and most plants have optimum temperatures. How do plants thermoregulate?

Prevention of overheating

Transpiration is an inevitable result of stomatal opening for photosynthesis. But as plants lose water by evaporation from their leaves there is a valuable side-effect – the plant is cooled down. This is very effective in helping to maintain the internal temperature of the plant within working limits until water becomes limiting. If there has been insufficient rain and drought conditions exist, the plant cannot take up enough water through its roots to maintain transpiration at the high level needed to cool the plant. In this situation the plant will **wilt**, with the unspecialised parenchyma cells losing turgidity and the leaves and stems drooping. This has the effect of reducing the surface area of the leaves exposed to the Sun, and so the plant avoids overheating to damaging levels. In very hot regions many plants have evolved shiny cuticles which reflect up to 50% of the Sun's radiation and so help to keep the plant cool. Small needle-like leaves are also useful for preventing too much heat gain.

Prevention of freezing

Heat loss is less frequently a problem to plants. The leaves are orientated to take maximum advantage of the light at any one time. Most plants living where the temperature is sometimes low have evolved ways of coping with the problem of excess heat loss – usually by avoiding it, as shown in figure 4.7.13. By losing the easily damaged leaves or by producing seeds or spores which are very temperature resistant, plants survive long periods of very low temperatures without suffering tissue damage.

Thus in this section we have seen something of the range and complexity of the control systems that are found in both animals and plants. The sensory systems and nerves of the animals combined with hormonal systems give fine control over the internal environment of the organism. This interaction is clearly demonstrated when we look at homeostasis. And in plants, chemical messages allow coordination, control and the maintenance of a relatively steady state in the organism.

Figure 4.7.13 By taking avoiding action plants can prevent the tissue damage which can be caused by very low temperatures. Only if we plant them in unsuitable areas, where the temperature fluctuations are greater than they can cope with, do plants suffer the type of damage shown here on the right.

SUMMARY

- The liver is a large organ made of several lobes. **Hepatocytes** (liver cells) have large nuclei, prominent Golgi apparatus and many mitochondria.

- The liver is supplied with blood by the hepatic artery and the hepatic portal vein, which carries the products of digestion and absorption. The blood leaves the liver in the hepatic vein. Blood from the hepatic artery and the hepatic portal vein is mixed in **sinusoids** surrounded by hepatocytes which detoxify it and regulate the levels of various substances. **Kupffer cells** ingest foreign particles. Hepatocytes secrete bile into **canaliculi** and it drains into the gall bladder via the **bile ductiles**.

- The hepatocytes convert all hexose sugars to glucose. They convert glucose to glycogen under the control of insulin, and glycogen to glucose under the control of glucagon. Excess carbohydrate is converted to lipid. The hepatocytes remove cholesterol and other lipids from the blood.

- Hepatocytes produce certain plasma proteins and also interconvert amino acids (**transamination**). They **deaminate** excess amino acids, removing the amino group and converting it first to **ammonia** and then to **urea** via the **ornithine cycle** for excretion by the kidneys. The remainder of the amino acid molecule is used for cellular respiration or stored as fat.

- The fetal liver cells made red blood cells. In the adult the Kupffer cells break down worn-out red blood cells. Haemoglobin is broken down to form the bile pigments **biliverdin** and **bilirubin** for excretion. Bile also contains **bile salts** for the digestion of fats and **cholesterol** for excretion.

- The liver stores glycogen, vitamins and mineral ions. It breaks down hormones and absorbs and detoxifies toxins.

- **Thermoregulation** is necessary as most enzymes only function within a narrow range of temperature. The **core temperature** of an organism is determined by heat exchange with its environment and the heat it produces by exothermic metabolic reactions.

- Heat is transferred between the environment and an organism by evaporation (which produces cooling), radiation, convection and conduction.

- Animals may be classified as **homoiotherms**, which regulate their body temperature within a narrow range, and **poikilotherms**, which allow their body temperature to fluctuate more widely. An alternative classification is as **endotherms** which produce their own body heat and **ectotherms** which depend largely on the environment for their body heat.

- Endotherms can survive in wide extremes of temperature. They have a relatively high metabolic rate and so need to eat a large amount of food. Ectotherms rely largely on behavioural modifications to maintain their body temperature, their metabolic rate is lower and they eat less food than endotherms.

- Humans are endotherms and homoiotherms. The main thermoregulatory organ is the skin, which is also a protective, sensory and excretory organ. When the temperature rises, the **arterioventricular shunt** closes to increase blood flow to the surface capillaries. Sweat is produced from the sweat glands. The **erector pili** muscles relax so hairs lie flat. The metabolic rate drops, producing less heat.

- In cold conditions the arterioventricular shunt opens, reducing blood flow to the surface capillaries. Sweat production is reduced and the erector pili muscles contract, pulling hairs upright (goose pimples in humans). The metabolic rate rises and shivering generates heat.

- There are blood temperature receptors in the hypothalamus. Messages are sent to the skin if the blood is too cold or too warm. Messages about the environmental temperature are sent to the brain from the skin so behavioural modifications can be made.

- Endotherms adapted to cold environments are generally larger than equivalent organisms in warm environments (small surface area:volume ratio) and have thick layers of subcutaneous fat. They have small extremities such as ears, and some have developed a **countercurrent heat exchange** system in their limbs.

- Some endotherms **hibernate** through the winter – their metabolic rate slows and their core temperature is reduced. **Brown fat** is conserved and used up rapidly at the end of hibernation to quickly raise the metabolic rate.

- Endotherms adapted to hot environments have large extremities with a good blood supply, and relatively little subcutaneous fat. Some endotherms such as the camel living in environments with widely fluctuating temperatures do not maintain a steady internal temperature.

- Behavioural adaptations to aid thermoregulation include basking in the Sun to warm up, sheltering from the Sun to cool down and panting or wallowing to increase cooling by evaporation.

- Plant tissues can generally tolerate wider fluctuations in temperature than most animals, but need to thermoregulate to avoid enzymes denaturing and tissues freezing. Plants **wilt** in drought conditions – parenchyma cells lose turgidity and leaves and stems droop. This reduces the surface area exposed to the Sun. Plants may have shiny cuticles which reflect heat, and small leaves prevent excessive heat gain.

- To gain heat in cold conditions, leaves are orientated so that they do not shade each other. Plants avoid excessive heat loss by overwintering as spores or seeds or by losing leaves in the winter.

QUESTIONS

1 Draw up a table to summarise the functions of the liver, with particular reference to those involved in homeostasis.

2 **a** What is:
   i an endotherm
   ii an ectotherm?
 b Sketch a diagram to show the main structures of mammalian skin, with annotations relating structures to functions.
 c Explain how a mammal regulates its body temperature when:
   i the external temperature drops
   ii the external temperature rises.

3 Both endothermic and ectothermic animals and plants are found in a wide range of habitats, both hot and cold. Describe some of the ways in which living organisms have adapted to cope with extremes of temperature.

Developing Key Skills

You have a slot on a national radio station with a brief to warn young people about the risks of hypothermia both on mountain and hill expeditions and getting home from pubs, parties and broken down cars in bad weather. You have to capture and keep the interest of your audience and at the same time get across some serious science. Prepare your slot and record it with any music/special effects you choose.

1 a Outline the functions of the *cerebrum, cerebellum* and *medulla oblongata* in the brain. **(7 marks)**
The figure shows neurones from the brain of a healthy 75 year old (**A**), and from the brain of a 75 year old suffering from Alzheimer's disease (**B**).

 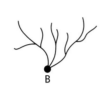

b State **two** differences between the neurones from **A** and **B**. **(2 marks)**
c Name the region of the brain from which the neurones in **B** might have come. **(1 mark)**
d Suggest **three** symptoms of Alzheimer's disease likely to arise from the appearance of the neurones in individual **B**. **(3 marks)**
e Describe what other changes might occur in the brain of a patient suffering from Alzheimer's disease. **(3 marks)**
(OCR specimen 2000)

2 The liver is unusual in having a double blood supply, from the hepatic portal vein and the hepatic artery. The liver receives over 1 dm³ of blood every minute when the body is at rest.
a Suggest why the liver has a double blood supply. **(2 marks)**
b Outline the role of the liver in the control of blood glucose. (*In this question, 1 mark is available for the quality of written communication.*) **(8 marks)**
c i Explain why it is important that the liver regulates blood cholesterol. **(4 marks)**
ii State **two** possible consequences of having a high blood cholesterol concentration. **(2 marks)**
d Suggest why a person suffering from liver damage is often prescribed smaller doses of any medication required for other complaints. **(2 marks)**
Jaundice is frequently an indication of liver damage. In this condition, the skin takes on abnormal yellow coloration because bile pigments are circulating in the blood.
e Explain why the bile pigments are circulating in the blood of a person suffering from jaundice. **(2 marks)**
(OCR specimen 2000)

3 The figure represents a section through the back of the eye to show details of the nervous connections in the mammalian retina.

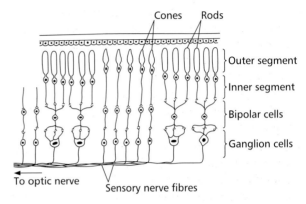

a Draw an arrow beside the figure to show the direction that light takes through the retina. **(1 mark)**
b Name the light sensitive pigment present in the rod cells, and describe the effect that light has on this pigment. **(2 marks)**
c Explain how the different neural connections of the rods and the cones, shown in the figure, account for the following.
i cones can transmit information to form a more accurate image than rods **(2 marks)**
ii rods can transmit information in dimmer light conditions than cones. **(2 marks)**
The figure shows a graph of the numbers of rods and cones at different distances across the retinal of the eye, passing through the fovea and the optic nerve.

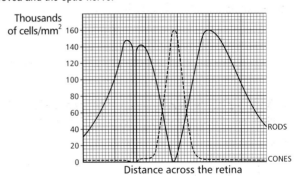

d i Use the information in the figure to calculate the density of cones at the fovea. **(1 mark)**
ii On the figure, mark with an arrow labelled **B**, the point representing the position of the blind spot. **(1 mark)**
Looking out of the 'side' of the eye at a very dim object improves the chances of seeing it.
e On the figure, mark with an arrow labelled **X**, the best place on the retina for the image to fall to make it most likely to be seen. **(1 mark)**
(OCR specimen 2000)

4 The figure shows a reflex arc which results in the lower leg being kicked forwards.

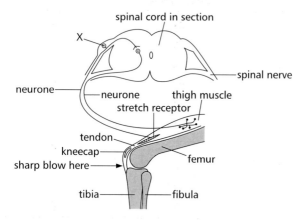

spinal cord in section

X

spinal nerve

neurone — neurone — thigh muscle
stretch receptor
tendon
kneecap
sharp blow here
femur
tibia — fibula

a i State the common name for the reflex action shown in the figure. **(1 mark)**

ii Draw **two** arrows on the figure to show the direction of nerve conduction.

iii Describe the role of neurone **X** in this reflex arc. **(1 mark)**

Simple human reflex actions, such as the one shown in the figure, are examples of innate behaviour.

b Explain the meaning of the term *innate*. **(2 marks)**

(OCR specimen 2000)

5 a Explain how the eye is able to detect an object that is purple. **(1 mark)**

b When we look directly at an object, its image is focused on part of the retina known as the fovea. Explain how the fovea provides more information to the brain than do other parts of the retina. **(2 marks)**

c The eyes of short-sighted people focus light rays from a distant object in front of the retaina instead of on it, producing a blurred image on the retina. Laser surgery can be used to correct this defect. The diagram shows the results of one treatment in which part of the cornea is removed by laser surgery. After the surgery, the surface of the cornea heals to give a new, smooth surface, with a smaller curvature.

Transverse section of cornea

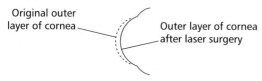

Original outer layer of cornea

Outer layer of cornea after laser surgery

Explain how the surgery corrects the patient's short-sightedness. **(2 marks)**

d Blindness can be caused by a cataract, a condition in which the lens of the eye becomes cloudy. If the lens is removed, the patient can see again, but vision is not as good as before the cataract developed. Explain why this is so. **(2 marks)**

(AQA specimen 2000)

6 a What is the function of **each** of the following parts of the cerebral hemispheres?

i Sensory areas

ii Association areas

iii Motor areas **(3 marks)**

b In 1861 a man called Leborgne suffered a stroke. As a result of this he was unable to speak and was paralysed on his right side. The drawing shows the location of the damage found in Leborgne's brain.

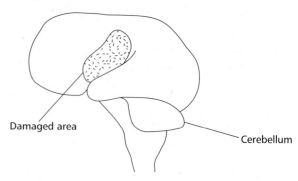

Damaged area

Cerebellum

Suggest an explanation for:

i Leborgne being unable to speak

ii Leborgne being paralysed on his right side. **(2 marks)**

(AQA questions)

7 Read the following passage.

Arrow poisons were widely used for hunting in South America where most of the powerful poisons such as curare originated. Charles Waterton carried out experiments on curare in the 1920s. He gave curare to a donkey which appeared to die ten minutes later. The animal was then revived by artificial ventilation of its lungs with a pair of bellows and went on to make a full recovery. The experiment showed that injection of arrow poison into the blood stream causes death by respiratory failure. It is now known that curare competes with acetylcholine molecules for receptors at neuromuscular junctions.

Since Waterton's work, many other chemicals have been discovered which also affect the nervous system, two of which are anatoxin and saxotoxin. Anatoxin also affects synapses. Its molecules are very similar to those of acetylcholine but they are not broken down by the enzyme, acetylcholinesterase. Saxotoxin is quite different and blocks the sodium channel proteins in nerve axons.

a During synaptic transmission, acetylcholine is released from the presynaptic neurone into the synaptic cleft.

i Describe how an action potential brings about the release of acetylcholine into the synaptic cleft. **(2 marks)**

ii Describe how this acetylcholine may cause a new action potential to develop in the postsynaptic nerve cell. **(3 marks)**

b Explain how injection of arrow poison into the blood stream causes death by respiratory failure. **(3 marks)**

c i Explain how acetylcholinesterase is important in the functioning of a synapse. **(2 marks)**

ii Suggest an explanation for the fact that one of the symptoms of anatoxin poisoning is the excessive production of tears. **(3 marks)**

d Explain how saxtoxin may cause paralysis. **(2 marks)**

(AQA questions 2000)

8 Read the following passage.

A few deaths have been due to drinking too much water. This occurred either because people thought that water was an antidote to *Ecstasy* (it is only an antidote to dehydration) or because the drug induced repetitive behaviour. Under the influence of *Ecstasy* people have been known to drink 20 litres of fluid and smoke 100 cigarettes within three hours. Drinking pure water to replace the fluid lost in sweating is dangerous because it does not put back the sodium ions and so dilutes the blood. This makes the cells of the body swell up, which is particularly lethal in the brain which can expand and be crushed against the skull. The centres in the brain that regulate breathing and the heart can be irreversibly damaged, and the person dies. *Ecstasy* increases the risk of brain damage by triggering the release of antidiuretic hormone (ADH).

(Reproduced by permission of *The Guardian*)

a Describe the mechanisms which lead to copious sweating by a person dancing in a night club. **(5 marks)**

b Explain in terms of water potential why the drinking of large amounts of pure water after copious sweating may lead to swelling of cells in the brain. **(5 marks)**

c Explain how '*Ecstasy* increases the risk of brain damage by triggering the release of antidiuretic hormone (ADH)'. **(4 marks)**

(AQA specimen 2000)

9 The diagram shows the results of an investigation into the water balance of a small mammal. The animal was given only dry seeds to eat and nothing to drink.

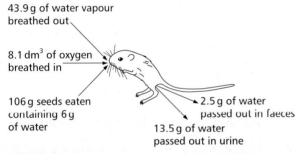

43.9 g of water vapour breathed out

8.1 dm³ of oxygen breathed in

106 g seeds eaten containing 6 g of water

2.5 g of water passed out in faeces

13.5 g of water passed out in urine

The animal obtained only 6 g of water directly from its food. It obtained the rest from the oxidation of carbohydrates present in the seeds.

a Assuming that water intake and output were balanced, calculate the mass of water obtained by oxidation of carbohydrate during the investigation. Show your working. **(2 marks)**

b Further investigation showed that a small mammal's kidneys had large medullas with long loops of Henle and that its blood contained high amounts of the hormone ADH.

i Explain the role of the medulla of the kidney in the reabsorption of water from fluid in the kidney tubule. **(5 marks)**

ii Explain the advantages to the animal of a high level of ADH secretion. **(3 marks)**

(AQA specimen 2000)

10 In an investigation into learned behaviour, a person was asked to draw a line around a metal five-pointed star as quickly as possible. This was done while only looking at the star in a mirror. The number of times contact with the edge of the star was lost was recorded, together with the total time taken to complete the trace around the star. This was repeated ten times, using the same hand each time, with a 10 second rest between attempts.

Attempt	Time taken to complete trace/seconds	Number of errors
1	42	8
2	33	5
3	35	5
4	29	7
5	29	2
6	14	1
7	10	2
8	13	0
9	10	1
10	11	0

a What conclusions can be drawn from these data? **(2 marks)**

b A student was asked to design and carry out an experiment to determine if the ability to draw the star is transferred to the hand not used to learn the task. The following account was produced. The class was divided into two groups, each consisting of five students. All the individuals in one group drew the star once with their right hand, followed by practice with their left hand, before drawing the star again with their right hand. The other group of five students all drew the star twice in succession with their right hand. The average time taken to complete the second star drawn with the right hand was calculated for the two groups, and a statistical test was carried out to see if the difference between the times was significant.

Give **three** criticisms of this experimental design. **(3 marks)**

(AQA specimen 2000)

11 a Describe how urea is produced in the liver. **(4 marks)**

b Describe how each of the following processes is involved in the formation of urine by the kidney: active transport, osmosis and selective reabsorption. **(9 marks)**

4

5 REPRODUCTION AND GENETICS

Introduction

Reproduction is a central feature of all living organisms. If the individuals that make up a species are not capable of making more copies of themselves, that species will rapidly become extinct. Throughout the living world a huge variety of strategies for reproduction have evolved, including the remarkable 'dance' seen under the microscope when cells divide, the endless array of flowering plants and the incredible colours, plumage and behavioural displays seen in some parts of the animal kingdom.

All cells (except for special sex cells) reproduce in a very similar manner – they simply split in two. This is **asexual reproduction** and it has many advantages. In some animals and many plants, highly advanced methods of asexual reproduction produce identical fully formed multicellular offspring.

Asexual reproduction has its limitations. It provides no variety between the new individuals, making them vulnerable to changes in environmental conditions. A wide range of living organisms have adopted a much more risky way of making more of themselves – **sexual reproduction**. This involves the joining together of two special sex cells to form a new, genetically unique individual. Vertebrate animals can only reproduce sexually by mating with another member of the same species, but millions of other animals and plants can reproduce both asexually and sexually, often depending on conditions at the time. Any organism that reproduces sexually has a system of specialised organs. In animals these are usually a permanent part of the anatomy, but in flowering plants they only appear when needed.

Driving all reproduction is the continuation of the genetic material of the individuals concerned, and of the species. In the last 100 years our understanding of what this genetic material is and the way it is passed on has developed enormously. The science of genetics has shown us how particular features, including certain inherited diseases, are passed from one generation to another. Scientists even have the ability to change the genetic information within the cells, and in future we may be able to cure genetic diseases before they occur. In this section we shall be considering some of the ways in which living organisms reproduce, and looking at the genetics that make us what we are.

Figure 1 Reproduction – the miracle that sustains life.

NEW ORGANS FOR OLD?

Making new cells in the body ...

As we go through life, some tissues or organs may become damaged or diseased, and they cannot always replace themselves by making new cells. If nervous tissue is crushed or damaged in a spinal injury it cannot regrow and the person will remain paralysed for the rest of their life. In a heart attack, heart muscle is damaged and destroyed. It is replaced by useless scar tissue. Scientists have long been looking for a way to replace such damaged tissues.

... and in the laboratory

Scientists can culture tissue cells in the laboratory by providing them with a specialised nutrient medium and the right conditions of oxygen, temperature and pH. For a number of years skin cells have been taken from patients and large sheets of new skin grown from them to replace tissue affected by burns. The technique has so far been relatively limited, but at the end of 1998 two groups of American scientists announced a breakthrough. Both teams, one led by Dr James Thomson at Wisconsin and the other by John Gearhart in Baltimore, developed a technique for culturing embryonic stem cells. Embryonic stem cells have the potential to become any of the specialised cells the body needs. These cells are called **totipotent** (or **pluripotent**). The scientists took embryonic cells and reproduced them successfully in cultures in the laboratory, without mutating or changing, for up to eight months – and this time will almost certainly be extended. Then, by changing the conditions, they persuaded the embryonic cells to differentiate into different types of adult cells, forming clusters of cartilage, bone, nerve and intestinal cells. So far the scientists have not learned how to control exactly which adult cells develop – but that will surely come.

Medical applications

It is hoped that developments of this technique will allow scientists to grow nerve cells, heart cells, brain cells, islet cells – the possibilities are almost endless. Because embryonic cells do not trigger the normal immune response in the mother, transplants of tissues from embryonic stem cells may not cause rejection that has previously beset tissue and organ transplants. In the future it may be possible to collect stem cells for each person during embryonic development or from the umbilical cord at birth, and then store and save the cells until needed in later life.

Right or wrong?

This work does raise some ethical questions. Where does the embryonic tissue used to begin the cultures come from? Thomson's team used spare embryos from couples having fertility treatment, with the positive consent of the people concerned. Gearhart used primordial germ cells from fetuses that had been medically aborted. Whilst many people have heralded their work as a major breakthrough with the same potential to change health care as the discovery of antibiotics, there are others who feel that the use of embryonic tissue is wrong and an abuse of human rights. The work is still going ahead, but in America the strength of this debate is holding up public funding, delaying the potential benefits of this tissue culture technique. Is it right or is it wrong – who is to decide?

Figure 1 Christopher Reeve was a well known actor famous as Superman when he broke his neck in a riding accident. He is determined to try any treatment available to help him to walk again, but the problem is that nerve cells do not reproduce and repair themselves in the body.

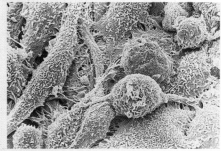

Figure 2 The ability to keep these embryonic stem cells dividing asexually for long periods of time promises hope of a cure to patients with a wide range of problems.

5.1 Reproductive strategies and asexual reproduction

The need to reproduce is fundamental to all living things. Animals and plants grow, feed, respire and excrete for a certain length of time, and then become increasingly less efficient until eventually they die. For life to continue an organism must reproduce itself before it dies. Parent organisms age and die so they do not compete with their offspring for resources. The ability of individuals to reproduce successfully is also the main factor which decides whether a whole group of organisms survives.

Each group of animals and plants has very distinct and specific genetic material. Reproduction passes this genetic material to a new generation. Reproduction uses up many resources and may often be the cause, either directly or indirectly, of the death of the parent organism. In spite of this, it can be considered that all other life processes (respiration, feeding, etc.) exist simply to provide the resources for reproduction. Indeed, the success of an organism (its **biological fitness**) is measured in terms of the production of fertile offspring which survive to reproductive maturity, thus replacing their parents.

One parent or two?

There are two main methods of reproduction. **Asexual reproduction** involves only one parent individual, be it plant or animal. Asexual reproduction has many advantages. It is safe, certain (there are no problems of finding a receptive mate) and can give rise to large numbers of offspring very rapidly. The offspring produced are almost all genetically identical to the parent organism, and so a successful genetic combination can be passed on without change. This is an important advantage of asexual reproduction until living conditions change in some way. However, the introduction of a new disease to an environment, a change in the temperature or human intervention can cause the total destruction of a group of genetically identical organisms, because if one cannot cope with the new environment, neither can all the others.

Sexual reproduction carries considerably more risk. It involves the combining of genetic information from two individuals. The meeting of the special sex cells (**gametes**) which carry this information is by no means certain and arranging for them to meet often carries an element of risk, for animals at least. But the great advantage of sexual reproduction is that it introduces **variety**, which is of great value when conditions are not stable. Variety increases the chance of survival because it provides the opportunity to evolve and take advantage of new conditions and surroundings.

Reproductive strategies

Whether organisms employ asexual reproduction, sexual reproduction or a combination of the two, the most important factor is their reproductive strategy. In the plant world many species undergo both sexual and asexual reproduction as a matter of course. They reproduce sexually by flowering, but they also produce bulbs, corms, tubers, rhizomes, runners or suckers as asexual methods.

Most plants are hampered in terms of sexual reproduction by being rooted to the spot, but they have evolved a wide variety of methods to ensure that the

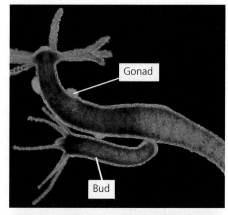

Gonad

Bud

Figure 5.1.1 These organisms take full advantage of all the reproductive opportunities, both sexual and asexual, presented to them. The daffodil's flower is a means of sexual reproduction, while its bulb reproduces by asexual means. The hydra too has both sexual organs (gonads) and asexual reproductive buds.

male gametes (carried in the pollen) reach the female parts of the flower. A range of **vectors** is used to transfer the pollen to the female parts of the plant. These include the use of insects (attracted by colours, patterns, scents and food rewards such as nectar), the wind, small mammals and water.

Animals too have evolved a wide variety of strategies to bring about successful reproduction. Many simple organisms, such as *Amoeba*, reproduce in the simplest way possible and split in two. *Hydra* and other pond-water species may be seen with small, identical individuals forming as buds, but they also form gonads producing eggs and sperm for sexual reproduction.

Strategies for asexual reproduction

There are a variety of strategies for asexual reproduction which are outlined below.

Fission

Fission involves the splitting of an individual. It is a method of reproduction found in many invertebrate organisms. As two new individuals are usually formed it is also known as **binary fission**. Bacteria and protoctists such as amoebae undergo this form of asexual reproduction. Bacteria are capable of enormous and rapid increases in numbers, since under ideal conditions they may divide every 20 minutes. Bacteria also undergo a form of sexual reproduction or **conjugation** whereby some or all of the genetic material is exchanged (there is more about this in section 5.2). This introduces variety.

Amoebae do not rely solely on straightforward fission either. Under normal conditions the organisms divide when they have reached a certain size, but in adverse conditions an amoeba will form a cyst and then undergo a series of fissions so that a number of very small, identical organisms are released when conditions improve.

Although fission has its limits as a reproductive strategy, a similar process is used in cell reproduction for growth and repair in all living things.

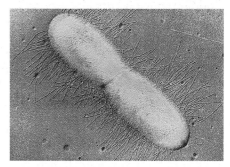

Figure 5.1.2 Fission is an effective reproductive strategy.

Sporulation

Sporulation involves the production of asexual **spores** which are capable of growing into new individuals. Spores can usually survive adverse conditions, and are dispersed very readily. They are produced most commonly in very large numbers by fungi and plants, in organs known as **sporangia**. The spores produced by bracken are **carcinogenic** (cancer causing) and the levels of spores in the air of bracken-covered hillsides can be so high that hill farmers and walkers are advised to wear masks to filter the air, thus removing the spores and so the risk of disease. Some protoctists also produce spores and these are called **zoospores**.

Fragmentation and regeneration

Some organisms can replace parts of the body which have been lost. Many lizards shed their tails when attacked and then grow another. This is known as **regeneration**. Some organisms manage an even more spectacular form of regeneration – they can reproduce themselves asexually from fragments of their original body. Starfish can not only survive being chopped into pieces, but if conditions are suitable each piece will regenerate to form an entire new starfish. Some members of groups as diverse as fungi, flatworms, filamentous algae and sponges fragment and then regenerate as a preferred method of reproducing.

Budding

Budding in a reproductive sense does not in general include the production of buds by flowers. In reproductive budding, there is an outgrowth from the parent organism which produces a smaller but identical individual. This 'bud' eventually becomes detached from the parent and has an independent existence. Yeast cells reproduce by budding. In single-celled organisms like these the only recognisable difference between budding and binary fission is that in budding the parent cell is larger than the bud. Budding is relatively rare in the animal kingdom, occurring, for example, in *Hydra* which reproduce sexually as well.

Vegetative propagation

In some ways, **vegetative propagation** is a more sophisticated version of budding which occurs in flowering plants. A structure forms which develops into a fully differentiated new plant, identical with the parent. The new plant may be propagated from the stem, leaf, bud or root of the parent, depending on the type of plant. Vegetative propagation often involves **perennating organs**. These contain stored food made by photosynthesis and can remain dormant in the soil to survive adverse conditions. They are often not only a means of asexual reproduction, but also a way of surviving from one growing season to the next. Examples are shown in figure 5.1.4.

Vegetative propagation is exploited by gardeners to produce new plants. Splitting off new daffodil bulbs, removing strawberry plants from their runners and cutting up rhizomes all increase plant numbers cheaply, and the new plants have exactly the same characteristics as their parents.

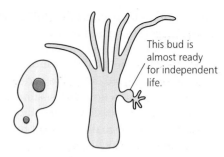

Figure 5.1.3 Budding in yeast cells and in *Hydra*. Notice the asymmetry of the yeast cell and the bud which distinguish this process from binary fission in single-celled organisms.

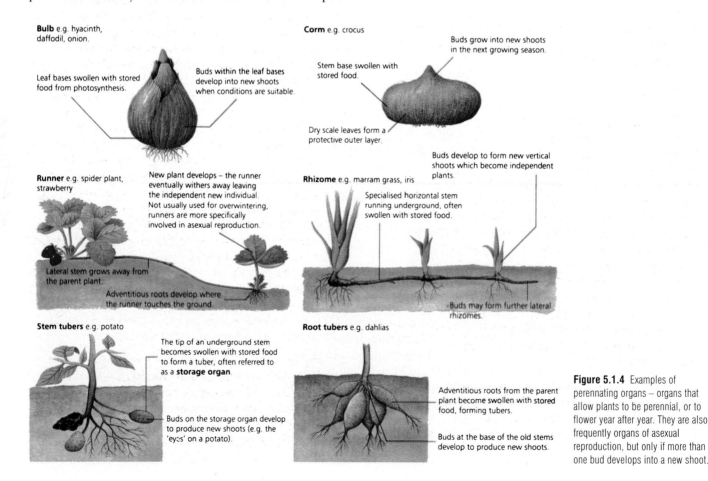

Bulb e.g. hyacinth, daffodil, onion.

Leaf bases swollen with stored food from photosynthesis.

Buds within the leaf bases develop into new shoots when conditions are suitable.

Corm e.g. crocus

Buds grow into new shoots in the next growing season.

Stem base swollen with stored food.

Dry scale leaves form a protective outer layer.

Runner e.g. spider plant, strawberry

New plant develops – the runner eventually withers away leaving the independent new individual. Not usually used for overwintering, runners are more specifically involved in asexual reproduction.

Lateral stem grows away from the parent plant.

Adventitious roots develop where the runner touches the ground.

Rhizome e.g. marram grass, iris

Buds develop to form new vertical shoots which become independent plants.

Specialised horizontal stem running underground, often swollen with stored food.

Buds may form further lateral rhizomes.

Stem tubers e.g. potato

The tip of an underground stem becomes swollen with stored food to form a tuber, often referred to as a **storage organ**.

Buds on the storage organ develop to produce new shoots (e.g. the 'eyes' on a potato).

Root tubers e.g. dahlias

Adventitious roots from the parent plant become swollen with stored food, forming tubers.

Buds at the base of the old stems develop to produce new shoots.

Figure 5.1.4 Examples of perennating organs – organs that allow plants to be perennial, or to flower year after year. They are also frequently organs of asexual reproduction, but only if more than one bud develops into a new shoot.

Cloning

What is a clone?

A **clone** is a group of cells or organisms which are genetically identical and have all been produced from the same original cell. In the 1950s a carrot was produced by Frederick Steward from a single carrot phloem cell which was grown in a rich nutritive medium. For this to happen the original cell needs to have retained the capacity, present in the cells of an embryo, to go through all the stages of development. Since it produced a normal adult, none of the genes in the phloem cell must have been permanently switched off. A cell which is capable of being used in this way is known as **totipotent** (**pluripotent**).

Cloning has two major uses. In horticulture, plants such as orchids are now almost always produced commercially by cloning. In research, it is of great value to have plants and animals to work on which are known to be genetically identical. Any differences in their development or behaviour can then reasonably be put down to the experimental variable.

Cloning of plants is now commonplace and relatively easy (see page 298). The cloning of animals is less straightforward, but huge steps have been made with the cloning of Dolly the sheep.

Dolly

One of the main problems with cloning animals including mammals is that the differentiated cells making up the tissues and organs are no longer totipotent. However, in 1997 a team from Edinburgh managed to clone a sheep. Dolly was produced when the nucleus of a mammary tissue cell from one ewe was incorporated into the ovum of another ewe (from which the nucleus had been removed). This new cell was then transferred to the uterus of yet another ewe where it developed successfully, resulting 5 months later in the safe arrival of Dolly. This piece of scientific research had an enormous impact on the media and the public imagination. Cloning plants, or even frogs, was one thing, but cloning a mammal like Dolly suddenly opened everyone's eyes to the possibility of cloning human beings.

The team had carried out the same procedure hundreds of times to achieve only one success, and three different females were involved in the process. If the process could be made more reliable it would open the way for cloning animals that have been genetically modified to make human proteins and medicines in their milk. This would dramatically increase the biological production levels of scarce and expensive treatments, improving the quality of life for many people.

With the technology available at present human cloning is not as close as it might seem but inevitably it must, in the not too distant future, become possible. Exaggerated media stories paint pictures of evil dictators cloning themselves to rule forever, but it must not be forgotten that each of us is much more than simply the sum of our genes. Our environment before and after birth has a major effect on us too, so no one could ever have an exact duplicate of themselves in every character trait. Even if society decides that human cloning should not be done, it will surely happen somewhere – but whether it will give people what they want is another matter entirely.

Cloning embryos

Another type of animal cloning which is much easier to carry out is now in regular use. This involves cloning embryos. In the early stages of embryonic development every cell is totipotent and has the potential to form a complete new animal. Early embryos are created using gametes from the best stock animals, particularly in cattle. These individual embryos are then cloned to produce large numbers of genetically identical embryos. Each of these is replaced in the uterus of an ordinary cow which then carries the calf to term and delivers a calf which is not biologically hers at all. This technique makes it possible to transport prize stock around the world very cheaply. Cloned early cattle embryos are placed in the uterus of a rabbit 'surrogate mother' where they begin to develop. The rabbits are flown cheaply to another country, where the embryos are removed and again implanted into cows to continue their development. The value of this over simply transporting frozen sperm for artificial insemination is that the parentage of both animals can be carefully selected for the best, disease-free features.

Cloning animals or plants has the great advantage of certainty. We know exactly what characteristics are going to result. The major disadvantage is that it reduces variety. If we have entire orchards, forests or fields full of genetically identical organisms, it only takes one change in conditions or one new virus to

wipe out all the plants or animals. With ordinary plants and animals, some will be genetically equipped to cope with the change, and will survive to breed again, but a clone population cannot adapt.

Figure 5.1.5 Dolly, the first cloned large mammal, has gone on to prove how normal she is by producing a lamb of her own (using the conventional method of reproduction). However, scientists are watching her closely to see if she ages like a normal sheep, or at the rate of the nucleus of her original cell.

Strategies for sexual reproduction

Relatively few organisms rely solely on asexual reproduction. In almost every case there is at the very least a back-up system of sexual reproduction, often used in adverse conditions. In many organisms – most flowering plants, most arthropods and the vertebrates in particular – sexual reproduction is the main or only method. Some flowering plants and arthropods reproduce asexually as well.

Plants

Reproductive strategies developed to ensure the success of sexual reproduction are many and varied. Some plants have evolved complex combinations of colours, scents and rewards to attract appropriate pollinators. Others have a floral anatomy particularly suited to releasing their pollen into the wind. There are also a vast number of strategies for making sure that the seeds which result are dispersed as widely as possible from the parent plant, as figure 5.1.6 shows.

Figure 5.1.6 Some of the sexual reproductive strategies of plants.

Colours, scent and nectar are used by plants to attract pollinators to the flowers.

Some adaptions of plants for dispersing seeds.

Where wind carries the pollen the anatomy of the flower is modified to allow the sexual organs to be exposed.

Animals

In animals reproductive strategies include linking sexual receptiveness to times of high fertility, regular sexual cycles in the female animal and lifestyles which range from constant coexistence of the male and female to the sexes living completely separately except when mating needs to occur. Fertilisation may occur outside the body (**external fertilisation**) or inside the body (**internal fertilisation**). Once fertilisation has taken place there are varying levels of parental care of the offspring. Many organisms just release eggs and sperm into the water and provide no care to the offspring at all. Amphibians, reptiles and birds lay eggs. On the whole, amphibians provide less parental care than reptiles, whilst birds are well known for the effort they expend raising their young. In mammals, the young develop within the body of the mother. Once they are born the female provides all the nutrition required by her offspring in the early stages of independent life in the form of milk from her own body. Examples of reproductive strategies in both animals and plants will be considered in more detail in sections 5.2–5.5.

Some organisms such as this starfish release their sex cells into the water and provide no care of the resulting offspring.

Anatomical specialisation and complex mating rituals and manoeuvres have enabled land-living animals to ensure that eggs and sperm meet. Eggs provide the developing offspring with both food and protection.

Many amphibians ensure that eggs and sperm are deposited together by close association between the male and female. The young, however, generally receive little care. The midwife toad which carries the fertilised eggs in special 'pockets' in the skin of its back as they develop, and the spitting toad shown here, are striking exceptions.

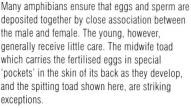

Mammals mate to ensure egg and sperm meet. The offspring develop in the uterus of the mother and are provided with a food supply after birth.

Figure 5.1.7 Some reproductive strategies of animals.

The mechanism of asexual reproduction – mitosis

How cells divide

During reproductive processes, both at the level of the whole organism and at a cellular level, like begets like. Buttercups produce new buttercups, amoebae produce more amoebae and liver cells generate more liver cells. Most of this new biological material comes about as a result of the process of nuclear division known as **mitosis**. This is usually followed by an equal division of the cytoplasm, resulting in two identical cells. The entire process is known as **cell division**. Asexual reproduction and growth are the result of mitotic cell division. The production of offspring by sexual reproduction is also largely dependent on mitosis to produce the new cells which form after the gametes have fused. It is only the formation of the sex cells themselves which involves a different type of nuclear division, **meiosis**, which we shall look at in section 5.2. In meiosis the chromosome numbers are halved and four non-identical daughter cells result. Cell replication involving mitosis can be regarded as normal cell division.

Chromosomes

As we have seen in section 1.3, the chromosomes are found in the nucleus of the cell. They are made up of DNA and carry the blueprint for the proteins which determine the make-up of the cell and indeed the entire organism. The information is carried in the genes and is translated into living cellular material by the process of protein synthesis. A chromosome is made up of a mass of coiled threads of DNA and proteins. In a cell which is not actively dividing the chromosomes have relatively little structure and cannot easily be identified as individual entities. When the cell enters an active dividing stage the chromosomes 'condense' – they become much shorter and denser. They then take up stains very readily (this is the basis of the name 'chromosome' or 'coloured body') and individual chromosome pairs can be identified.

If a chromosome was as long as five consecutive letters on this page, the DNA molecule it contains would stretch the length of a football pitch or more. When the molecules condense prior to cell division, they have to be packaged very efficiently. This is done with the help of positively charged proteins called **histones**. The DNA winds round the histones to form dense clusters known as **nucleosomes**. These nucleosomes then interact to give more coiling and even supercoiling to end up with the dense chromosome structure we can see through the microscope in the nucleus of a dividing cell.

The cells of each species possess a characteristic number of chromosomes – in our own case there are 46. These chromosomes occur in matching pairs, one of which originates from each parent. Humans have 23 pairs of chromosomes in their cells, whilst turkeys have 41 pairs. In mitosis the cells resulting from the division will both receive the same number of chromosomes. Thus before a cell divides it must duplicate its original set of chromosomes. Then during mitosis these chromosomes are divided equally between the two new cells so that each has a complete and identical set of genetic information. A normal cell which contains the full set of chromosome pairs is known as **diploid**. Cells exist which have only one of each pair of chromosomes, as we shall see in section 5.2. Such cells are **haploid**.

When the chromosomes become very coiled and condensed during the active phases of cell division, they are relatively easy to photograph and a special display or **karyotype** can be made, as shown on page 455.

Not all cells are haploid or diploid. In a surprising number of organisms the cells have three (triploid), four or more copies of each chromosome. They are known as **polyploid**. For organisms such as the cultivated strawberry where polyploidy is the normal situation, it causes no problems. But if polyploidy of one or all of the chromosomes occurs unexpectedly then the consequences for the organism are usually devastating, causing major abnormalities or death.

The cell cycle

Cells divide on a regular basis to bring about growth and asexual reproduction. They divide in a sequence of events known as the **cell cycle** which involves several different phases. There is a period of active division by mitosis, and a period of non-division called **interphase** which is when growth, replication of the DNA and normal cellular activities occur. The cell cycle can be very rapid, taking 24 hours or less to be completed, though it may only occur once every few years. In multicellular organisms it is repeated very frequently in almost all cells during development. However, once the organism is mature the cell cycle may be slowed down or stopped completely in some tissues. Figure 5.1.9 shows the main stages of the cell cycle.

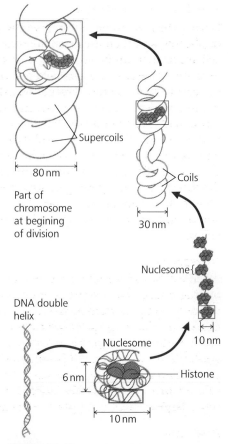

Figure 5.1.8 Histones play a vital role in the organisation of the DNA into orderly chromosomes which can be replicated.

The stages of mitosis

During the process of cell division the chromosomes are duplicated and then they and the remaining contents of the cell are divided up in such a way that two identical daughter cells are formed. Walther Fleming, a German cytologist, was the first to describe the 'dance of the chromosomes'. This is the description sometimes given to the complex series of movements which occur as the chromosomes jostle for space in the middle of the nucleus and then pull apart to opposite ends of the cell. The events of mitosis are continuous, but as in the case of so many biological processes it is easier to describe what is happening by breaking events down into phases. These are known as **prophase**, **metaphase**, **anaphase** and **telophase**, shown in figures 5.1.10–11 and described below.

Interphase

A cell will be in interphase for much of its life. This used to be called the **resting phase**, but nothing could be further from the truth. During interphase not only do the normal metabolic processes of the cell continue, but also new DNA is produced as the chromosomes replicate, as we have seen in figure 5.1.9. Sufficient new proteins, cytoplasm and cell organelles are also synthesised so that the cell is prepared for the production of two new cells. ATP production is also raised at times to provide the extra energy needed by the cells for division by mitosis. Once all that is needed is present and the parent cell is large enough, interphase ends and mitosis begins.

Prophase

Before mitosis begins the genetic material has been replicated to produce exact copies of the original chromosomes. By the beginning of prophase both the originals and the copies are referred to as chromatids. In prophase the chromosomes coil up, take up stain and become visible. Each chromosome at this point consists of two daughter chromatids which are attached to each other in a region known as the **centromere**. The nuclear membrane breaks down and the nucleolus disappears. In animal cells the centrioles begin to pull apart to form the **spindle** of microtubules. In plant cells there are no centrioles, but spindles form at this stage in a very similar way.

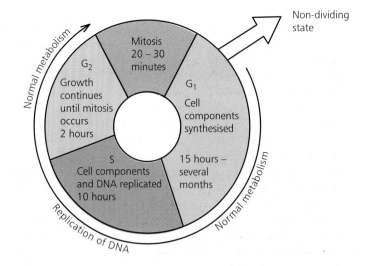

Figure 5.1.9 Phases of the cell cycle. In very actively dividing tissue the cycle is repeated often, whilst in other regions the gaps between successive divisions may be years.

Evidence for mitosis

Mitosis can be seen relatively easily in the cells of rapidly dividing tissues such as a growing root tip. Using an appropriate dye (such as acetic orcein) which stains the chromosomes, tissue squashes can be produced which show the stages of mitosis quite clearly, as shown in figure 5.1.10.

Stained tissue squashes are obviously dead, but living tissue can also be observed, and time-lapse photography has enabled dramatic recordings of the activity of chromosomes to be made. Such a view of the movements of the cell contents during mitosis shows why it is called the 'dance of the chromosomes'.

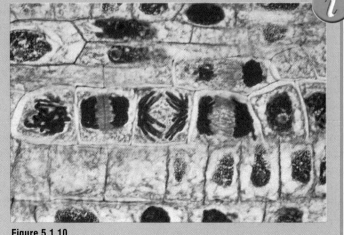

Figure 5.1.10

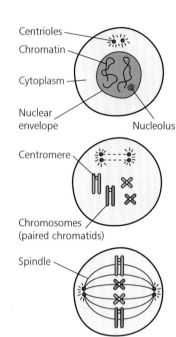

Centrioles
Chromatin
Cytoplasm
Nuclear envelope
Nucleolus

Interphase – Before mitosis, the tangled, uncoiled mass of chromosomes fills the nucleus. DNA is replicated during this stage.

Centromere

Chromosomes (paired chromatids)

Prophase – The chromosomes begin to condense. They replicate to form two **chromatids**. The nuclear membrane and the nucleolus disappear, and the centrioles begin to separate to form the **spindle**.

Spindle

Metaphase – Spindles made of microtubules are formed by the centrioles. The chromatids line up on the metaphase plate.

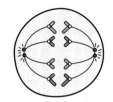
⟞ Chromosome inherited from mother
⟞ Chromosome inherited from father

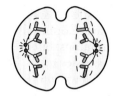

Anaphase – The centromeres separate and each pulls its chromatid along a spindle tubule towards one of the poles.

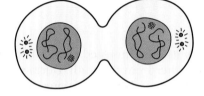

Early telophase – The chromatids reach the poles of the cell and become chromosomes. The nuclear membrane begins to reform and the cytoplasm begins to divide.

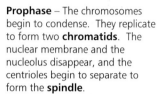

Late telophase – The chromosomes begin to unravel or 'decondense'. The nuclear membranes and nucleoli are fully reformed and centrioles are present again. The division of the cytoplasm continues until two new identical cells are formed which once more enter interphase.

Figure 5.1.11 These diagrams show the main phases of mitosis in a simplified animal cell which has only two pairs of chromosomes.

Metaphase

The formation of a spindle made of microtubules is completed. The chromosomes appear to jostle about for position on the **metaphase plate** or **equator** of the spindle during metaphase. They eventually line up along this plate, with each centromere associated with a microtubule of the spindle.

Anaphase

The centromeres linking the two identical chromatids divide, and from then on the chromatids act as separate entities and effectively become new chromosomes. One chromatid from each pair is drawn towards opposite poles of the cell, the centromeres moving first. This separation occurs quickly, taking only a matter of minutes. At the end of anaphase the two sets of chromatids are at opposite ends of the cell.

Telophase

During telophase the spindle fibres disappear and nuclear membranes form around the two sets of chromosomes. Nucleoli and centrioles also reform. The chromosomes begin to unravel and become less dense and harder to see. The final step is the division of the cytoplasm, sometimes referred to as **cytokinesis**.

In animal cells a ring of contractile fibres tightens around the centre of the cell, rather like a belt tightening around a sack of flour. These fibres appear to be actin and myosin, the proteins found in animal muscles (see section 2.6). They continue to contract until the two cells have been separated. In plant cells the division of the cell occurs rather differently, with a cellulose cell wall building up from the inside of the cell outwards, as shown in figure 5.1.12. In both cases the end result is the same – two identical daughter cells which will then enter interphase and begin to grow and prepare for the next cycle of division.

Mitosis is the method by which organisms undergo asexual reproduction. It is also the source of all the new cells needed for organisms to grow and to replace worn-out cells. We shall take time here to consider what growth entails and how it is measured before moving on to look at sexual reproduction in more detail, in sections 5.2–5.5.

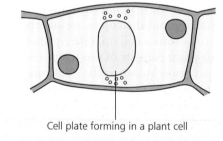

Cell plate forming in a plant cell

Animal cells dividing

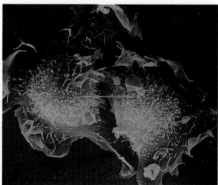

Figure 5.1.12 To complete the process of mitosis the two new sets of chromosomes need two new cells to house them. The cytoplasm of animal and plant cells is divided in different ways to bring this about.

How the spindle moves the chromosomes

Chromosomes cannot move on their own. They rely on the microtubules of the spindle to allow them to move. The spindle was for many years envisaged as a structure running from one end of the cell to the other. It is now known to be made up of overlapping microtubules containing contractile fibres not dissimilar to the actin and myosin of animal muscles. It is by the contraction of these overlapping fibres that movement of the chromosomes is brought about. This is an energy-using process, and is one of the main reasons why energy is made and stored in interphase.

Growth

What is growth?

Growth is a permanent increase in the mass or size of an organism. There are three distinct aspects of growth, **cell division**, **assimilation** and **cell expansion**, already considered in section 4.5. Cell division or mitosis is the basis of growth. New plant cells are supplied with fresh material which is the product of photosynthesis in other, mature cells. Similarly new animal cells are provided with new material from the products of digestion. This is what is meant by assimilation, and the result is cell expansion. However, cells can expand in other ways, for example by taking in water. The increase in size which results from this may only be temporary and so we define growth as involving a *permanent* increase in size or mass.

How is growth measured?

The measurement of growth is important in many ways, both scientifically and medically. Growth may be affected by factors such as the availability of food, temperature and light intensity as well as the genetic make-up of the organism. The measurement of growth is not at all easy. A linear dimension such as height or circumference can be very deceptive – cake mixture will increase in

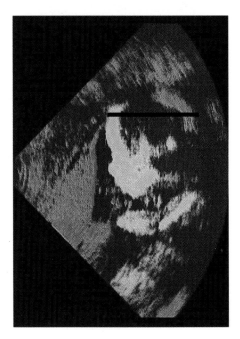

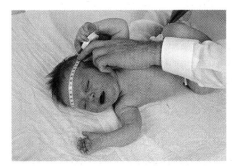

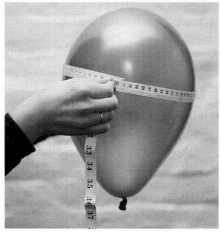

Figure 5.1.13 Starting long before birth, head circumference is measured at intervals as a child grows, to make sure all is well. Scientific as this may seem, an increase in circumference does not always indicate biological growth, as the example of the balloon shows.

both height and circumference as it cooks, but it has not grown! Measuring mass also has its problems – the water content of the cells may vary greatly, particularly in plants, and animals may have varying quantities of faecal material and urine held in their bodies.

As growth involves an increase in the cytoplasmic content of an organism, mass is the best and most commonly used measure. To avoid the difficulties mentioned above of varying water content, the **dry mass** can be measured. This gives an accurate picture of the amount of biological material present but has a major drawback in that removing all the water from an organism kills it, so that further growth cannot be measured. For dry mass to give useful results, large samples of genetically identical organisms need to be grown under similar conditions. Random samples are then taken for drying to a constant mass. This method is very useful for plants but has obvious limitations for animals. It is neither easily possible nor ethical to maintain large colonies of genetically identical animals and then kill and dry them. Because of the limitations of using dry mass other, less reliable methods of measuring growth are often used. These include measuring height or measuring wet mass. Large samples are usually measured, in order to average out some of the possible inaccuracies – for example, some animals may just have drunk, which will increase their apparent mass, but others will just have urinated, reducing their mass.

Working with microorganisms presents further problems, as they are far too small for any individual measurements to be made. Again dry mass can be used, but to avoid destroying the culture two alternatives are often used. If the microbes are being cultured on agar plates or similar media, the diameter of the colonies of microorganisms or the area they cover can be measured. If the culture is in a liquid, passing light through the culture and measuring how much light is absorbed by the liquid (its turbidity) gives an indication of the concentration of microorganisms. Both of these methods give a fairly accurate picture of the growth of a colony of microorganisms.

Growth patterns

In spite of the difficulties in the measuring of growth, we do have a good picture of the patterns of growth of many organisms. **Growth curves** made up from measurements of growth throughout the life of an organism show when most growth takes place. Growth curves are very similar for most organisms, whether animals or plants, as figure 5.1.14 shows. After an initial relatively slow start there is a rapid period of growth until maturity is reached, when growth slows down and stops. This pattern is known as **continuous growth** and it usually gives an S-shaped or sigmoid curve.

Not all organisms undergo continuous growth. Insects grow in a series of **moults**. They shed one exoskeleton and then expand their bodies by taking in air or water and 'grow' whilst the new exoskeleton is soft. Once the new skeleton has hardened the air or water can be released, leaving room for the tissues of the insect to increase in size. This is known as **discontinuous growth** and gives a different growth pattern to that of organisms that grow continuously. If length is measured the arthropod appears to grow in a series of steps, as figure 5.1.14 shows.

The development of the embryo is the time when the largest amount of growth occurs, in terms of percentage of body mass. At this time mitosis occurs at an immensely rapid rate. Growth continues until the organism reaches maturity. At this point growth slows down or stops completely in many organisms. Another type of pattern in growth that can be observed and measured is the difference between **absolute** and **relative growth**. **Absolute growth** is the growth of the whole organism throughout the growth period.

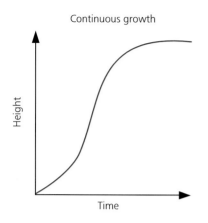

Continuous growth

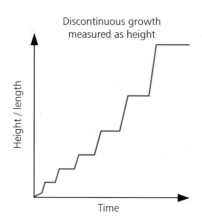

Discontinuous growth measured as height

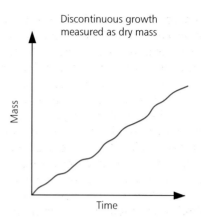

Discontinuous growth measured as dry mass

It gives the typical sigmoid growth curve which is found in almost all organisms. **Relative growth** occurs when a particular organ or part of the body grows at a different rate from the rest. When this happens a change in size is accompanied by a change in shape. This type of growth is particularly common in developing embryos of almost every type, and in mammals throughout their development. It is particularly clear in human beings during puberty, when the body proportions change quite dramatically and the external sex organs grow, as illustrated in figure 5.1.15.

Even when growth stops completely, mitotic divisions do not stop as cells are continually becoming worn out and being replaced. This continues until the onset of **senescence** or old age, when mitosis occurs less frequently and the dying cells begin to outnumber the new cells being formed. When this process reaches a certain point, death will occur.

Figure 5.1.14 Growth curves are usually measured by the linear dimensions. If dry mass is used the discontinuous growth curve becomes less pronounced.

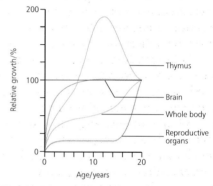

Figure 5.1.15 This graph shows relative growth rates of the human brain, thymus and reproductive organs beside the absolute growth of the whole person, which shows the typical sigmoid shape.

Cancer – when normal cells run amok

Cancers have affected the living world, plants and animals alike, for millions of years. Signs of cancers have been found in the bones of dinosaurs and in Egyptian mummies. As people live longer, and infectious diseases have been brought increasingly under the control of drugs, so the toll of cancers on human health have become more apparent. But what is cancer?

If the answer to this question was fully understood, then cancer would be curable in all its forms. Sadly this is not yet the case, but scientists and doctors are rapidly increasing their understanding of cancer. Cancer cells carry out many cellular functions as normal, but the transformation of a normal cell into a cancerous cell brings about some important changes. The most important of these is uncontrolled growth. When we cut ourselves, the cells on the edge of the cut undergo rapid mitosis until the cut is healed. The rate of mitosis is then restored to its normal level. In cancer cells mitosis simply goes on and on because the normal regulatory systems fail to work. The cancer cells do not respond to the normal mechanisms that control cell growth, so they divide rapidly to form a mass of abnormally growing cells called a **tumour** which invades the surrounding tissues. A tumour may split up, releasing small clumps of malignant cells into the blood or lymph systems where they circulate and then lodge in a different area of the body, continuing their uncontrolled division and forming a secondary tumour. This splitting and spreading is called **metastasis**, and a tumour that invades surrounding tissues and metastasises is termed a **malignant tumour**. Cancer cells live longer than ordinary cells, so the enlarging tumour or other malignant condition disrupts normal tissues, often to the point of killing the organism.

What causes cancers? Again, the answer is far from fully understood. Certain substances cause cancer – they are known as **carcinogens**. The tars in tobacco smoke, chemicals such as benzene, some dietary additives and many other substances may trigger the transformation of normal cells to cancer cells. Radiation, ultraviolet light from the Sun and X-rays can all have a similar effect. Some viruses are known to cause cancers in animals, and it is suspected that they play a role in some human cancers too. And finally, some people have genes which make them more vulnerable to cancer than others. **Oncogenes** which result in cancer, or **proto-oncogenes** which may become oncogenes if exposed to particular carcinogens, may prove to be the vital clues in the search for a cure – only time will tell.

Cancer and the Sun

Our knowledge about what causes cancer is increasing all the time. For many years people regarded getting a good suntan as a very healthy thing to do. Looking like a lobster for a few days was considered a price worth paying for a golden tan. As more and more people started to go abroad for holidays, the tans got deeper and redder! We may think a suntan looks good, but it is a sign that the cells of the skin have already been damaged and are making more melanin to try and protect themselves from any more burning.

It has long been known that farm workers and others who spend much of their working day out in the sunshine are more likely to get skin cancers than office workers. A few years ago it became increasingly clear that the ultraviolet light in the Sun's rays was causing mutations in the skin cells, and these mutations were leading to highly aggressive malignant tumours. Melanoma, a cancer of the cells that produce the pigment melanin, tends to metastase very rapidly and is often fatal. The number of cases of melanoma began to rise steadily and it became clear that getting sunburnt, particularly in childhood, was very dangerous indeed, as it greatly increased the risk of melanoma developing. Melanoma is not only a cancer of old age – relatively young adults can and do die from skin cancer.

This type of cancer is a particular risk for pale-skinned people – those with a brown or black skin have plenty of melanin which acts as a natural sunscreen and protects the skin from damage. Around the world, in countries such as Australia, the USA and the UK, there has been a strong move to persuade white people in particular to wear sunscreens when they go out in the Sun. These screens either absorb the ultraviolet radiation that causes the problem or reflect it back away from the skin, preventing damage. The level of ultraviolet radiation is increasing all the time as the ozone layer thins, so it is hoped that wearing sunscreen and covering up in the heat of the day will become a life-saving habit for those at risk.

SUMMARY

- **Asexual reproduction** involves one parent, is safe, certain and may produce many offspring which are genetically identical with the parent. **Sexual reproduction** is the meeting of **gametes** from two parents. It is less straightforward but produces genetic variety.

- Methods of asexual reproduction include **binary fission** – the splitting of an individual; **sporulation** – the production of asexual spores in organs called **sporangia**; **fragmentation** and **regeneration**; and **budding**, which is similar to fission except that the new organism is smaller than the parent.

- **Vegetative propagation** is asexual reproduction in flowering plants, and often involves **perennating organs** which store food and remain dormant in the soil. Methods of vegetative propagation include bulbs, corms, runners, rhizomes, stem tubers and root tubers.

- Asexual reproduction and growth result from cell division by **mitosis**, which produces two daughter cells with genetic material identical with that of the parent cell.

- Each species has a characteristic number of **chromosomes** in its body cells (46 in humans). This is the **diploid number**, made up of **homologous pairs** of chromosomes (23 pairs in humans). Chromosomes become visible during cell division and may be displayed as a **karyotype**.

- The **cell cycle** involves a period of mitotic division and a non-dividing state called **interphase**. Stages of interphase are G_1 when cell components are synthesised, S when cell components and DNA are replicated and G_2 when growth continues until mitosis occurs. The cell cycle can last for any period from about 24 hours to years.

- **Prophase** is the first stage of mitosis. The chromosomes become visible, made up of two **chromatids** joined at the **centromere**. The nuclear membrane breaks down and the nucleolus disappears. The centrioles (in animal cells) start to pull apart.

- In **metaphase** a **spindle** of microtubules has formed. The chromosomes jostle for position and line up on the **metaphase plate**.

- In **anaphase** the centromeres split and the chromatids separate to opposite poles of the cell.

- In **telophase** the spindle disappears and new nuclear membranes, nucleoli and centromeres form. The chromosomes disperse and the cytoplasm splits (**cytokinesis**).

- **Growth** is a permanent increase in the size of an organism. It involves **cell division**, **assimilation** and **cell expansion**.

- Growth may be measured by height or circumference or by mass, but none of these gives a very accurate picture. The **dry mass** is an accurate measure of the amount of biological material present but involves killing the organism.

- Organisms may show **continuous growth**, or **discontinuous growth** such as in insects which grow in a series of **moults**.

- **Absolute growth** measures the growth of the whole organism, while **relative growth** may occur if one organ or body part grows at a different rate from the rest of the body.

- Growth is greatest while the embryo develops. It continues to maturity when mitotic divisions are reduced and only replace worn-out cells. When this process slows down **senescence** occurs, followed by death.

QUESTIONS

1 a What are the advantages and disadvantages of asexual reproduction?

b What are the advantages and disadvantages of sexual reproduction?

c Produce a table summarising the main methods of asexual reproduction in both the animal and the plant kingdoms.

2 a What is the role of mitosis in growth?

b Describe mitotic cell division in animal cells.

3 a What are the difficulties of measuring growth in organisms?

b What is meant by:

i continuous growth

ii discontinuous growth?

c Explain what happens when control over cell growth is lost or altered in some way.

Developing Key Skills

Embryonic stem cells hold out the hope of potential cures for many different conditions. New nerve cells could be used to overcome paralysis, new brain tissue could mean that the dreadful degeneration of Alzheimer's and Parkinson's diseases could be avoided, new islets of Langerhans could free diabetics from the vital routine of insulin injections – the possibilities are almost endless. However, current source material for these potentially life saving stem cells is either the excess embryos produced during some forms of fertility treatment or embryos which result from medical abortions. For some people this is simply unacceptable for moral and ethical reasons, whilst others find no difficulty in the use of such materials.

The other alternative source of stem cells is from the umbilical cord. In Japan, each child is presented with its own umbilical cord in a decorated box, to remind it of the bond with its mother. At the end of the twentieth century there was a nuclear accident in Japan. The two workers who were most badly affected had most of their bone marrow destroyed. One received a transplant from his sister, the other had no relatives who matched his tissue type, so blood stem cells were retrieved from his preserved umbilical cord and infused to give him a chance of life. However, for umbilical tissue to be a useful source every individual umbilical cord would need to be saved in frozen form until it was required for stem cells. The implications of this are, at best, that it would only be available to people living in the developed world. At worst, it would be available only to rich people in the developed world.

Use this information, along with the Focus material for this chapter and anything else you can find out about these issues from the media or the Internet, to prepare a speech for a debate on the subject: 'This house believes that the use of human embryonic stem cells is unethical and should be banned.' You can choose to speak either for the motion or against it.

FIRST FIND YOUR MATE

Courtship

For many animals, sexual reproduction involves mating. To mate, you have to let another animal get so close to you that they could easily attack and harm you if they chose to do so. So most animals that mate have evolved courtship rituals which fulfil a number of roles, most importantly to deflect any aggression and make it possible for the animals to get close enough to exchange sex cells. Courtship displays may be physical, such as the bright plumage of birds or the antlers of deer, or they may be behavioural, such as the wrapping of a food gift by the male spider *Pisamura mirabilis*. He gives it to his mate to eat during copulation so she doesn't eat him!

Courtship behaviour is species specific, ensuring animals only mate with another member of the same species, increasing the likelihood of producing healthy, fertile offspring. If an animal makes a courtship gesture to another animal and does not get the expected piece of behaviour in return, it will move away and not attempt to mate.

Courtship behaviour in a particular species is triggered by specific stimuli such as day length, temperature or food availability. The stimulus has a direct effect on the physiology of the animals, and this in turn results in the appearance of courtship behaviour. This synchronisation of breeding behaviour means that all the animals of a particular species are fertile and receptive at the same time. The birth of offspring will also be synchronised, usually to the season of the year when the young are most likely to be reared successfully.

Figure 1 The male frigate bird with his 2.5 m wingspan has a very distinctive courtship display. He develops an enormous brilliant red inflated sac on his throat, which is displayed to the female until she has laid an egg. The sac then deflates and fades.

Which mate?

Another important element of courtship behaviour is that of sexual selection. Usually, although not always, the female selects which male she will permit to father her offspring. As a result it is usually the males that produce the most glamorous and exciting colours, body adaptations and behaviours in order to attract a mate. Once a mate has been selected, in those species where the male and female form a pair for at least a short time, courtship enables the formation of a strong pair-bond. Pair-bonding lasts at least until the male and female have mated, produced offspring and reared them.

The sense of smell is also very important in courtship. Fertile females and mature males may release **pheromones**, special chemicals that are often sexual attractants. The pheromone produced by the female silk moth can be detected by the male more than a mile away, and he flies along a concentration gradient to find his mate. Courtship is a very complex business, often ending with the termination signal of ejaculation in the male, though in many animals both parents go on to invest care and resources in the offspring that result from successful courtship displays.

Figure 2 The courtship display of the great crested grebe involves a highly complex series of movements often referred to as a 'dance'. Only after the full series of movements has been completed by both birds will mating take place.

5.2 Sexual reproduction

As we saw in section 5.1, sexual reproduction is the production of a new individual resulting from the fusing of two specialised cells known as **gametes**. The individuals resulting from sexual reproduction are *not* genetically the same as either of their parents, but contain genetic information from both. Sexual reproduction introduces variety – no two individuals (apart from identical twins, discussed in section 5.5) will have the same combination of genes.

As we have seen, asexual reproduction is a very successful process. A winning genetic formula is preserved and passed on to subsequent generations at minimum risk to the parental organism. It is often rapid and does not require any investment in specific reproductive organs. Whilst conditions remain stable all is well. However, populations with little or no genetic variability are vulnerable to new diseases or to environmental crises such as drought. Sexual reproduction, in spite of being more risky and expensive in terms of bodily resources, introduces genetic variety, and this variety enables organisms to adapt and cope with changing circumstances.

Gametes

What are gametes?

The nucleus of a cell contains the chromosomes. As we saw in section 5.1, the vast majority of the cells of an organism are **diploid** – chromosomes occur in pairs. However, if two diploid cells combined to form a new individual in sexual reproduction, the offspring would have two pairs or four sets of chromosomes,

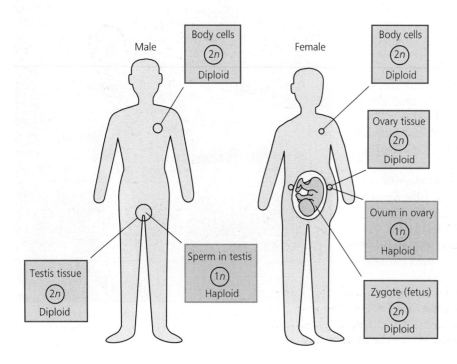

Figure 5.2.1 Diploid body cells, haploid gametes and the diploid zygote.

twice the characteristic number for the species. Subsequent generations would each have double the previous number of chromosomes. To avoid this, **haploid** nuclei with half of the full chromosome number are formed, usually within specialised cells called **gametes**. Sexual reproduction occurs when two haploid nuclei fuse to form a new diploid cell called a **zygote**, as figure 5.2.1 shows.

Types of gametes

For the gametes to fuse one of them at least must move to meet the other. In many organisms both gametes are motile and are released directly into the water, where they meet. Identical gametes such as these are known as **isogametes**. **Isogamy** is the production of these identical gametes. *Chlamydomonas* is an example of an isogamous organism.

In many other organisms the gametes are not identical. When the gametes differ from each other in size and structure they are known as **anisogametes**, and their production is known as **anisogamy**. The **female** gamete does not move. It is usually large and filled with food stores for the development of the embryo. The motile **male** gamete is much smaller and adapted for movement.

If one individual forms both male and female gametes it is said to be **hermaphrodite**. Plants in which both male and female gametes are formed on a single plant are called **monoecious**. Plants that form only male or only female flowers during their lifetime are known as **dioecious**. Examples are shown in figure 5.2.2.

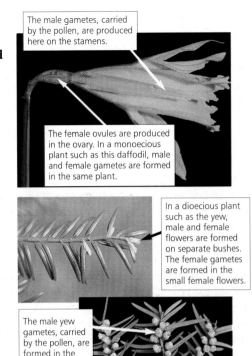

The male gametes, carried by the pollen, are produced here on the stamens.

The female ovules are produced in the ovary. In a monoecious plant such as this daffodil, male and female gametes are formed in the same plant.

In a dioecious plant such as the yew, male and female flowers are formed on separate bushes. The female gametes are formed in the small female flowers.

The male yew gametes, carried by the pollen, are formed in the male flowers.

Figure 5.2.2 A monoecious and a dioecious plant.

Sexual reproduction in bacteria

For many years it was assumed that bacteria reproduced only asexually. Then in 1946 Joshua Lederberg, a student at Yale University, and his professor Edward Tatum, performed an experiment which showed that some sort of genetic exchange must occasionally take place in these organisms.

They grew two strains of bacteria. Strain A could grow on a minimal medium as long as the amino acid methionine and the vitamin biotin were added. The bacteria could synthesise everything else they needed. Strain B could grow on the minimal medium as long as the amino acids threonine and leucine were added. Neither strain could grow on the medium alone. But after mixing the two strains together, about one in every 10 million bacterial cells could grow on the minimal medium without any additions. This was only possible if these cells had received some genes from strain A and some from strain B. The electron microscope has since shown clearly bacteria 'mating'

and exchanging genetic information through a strand of cytoplasm known as the **sex pilus**. This has been vital in the development of **genetic engineering**, which will be discussed in more detail in section 5.7.

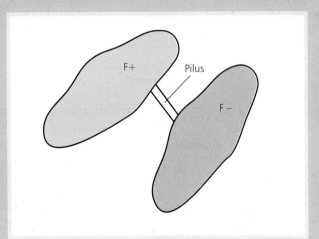

Figure 5.2.3 Bacterial conjugation – DNA is transferred from the male (F+) cell to the female (F–) cell through the pilus which joins them.

Where are gametes formed?

Gametes are formed in special sex organs. In some animals and plants these are often temporary, forming only as they are needed. In larger animals they tend to be more permanent structures and may be referred to as **gonads**. In flowering plants the sex organs are the **anthers**, where the male gamete carried in the **pollen** is produced, and the **ovaries**, where the female **ovules** are formed. In animals the male gonads are the **testes**, responsible for production of **spermatozoa**, the male gametes. The female gonads are the **ovaries** and they produce **ova**. The male gametes are frequently much smaller than the female ones, but are usually produced in much larger quantities.

The formation of gametes – meiosis

When cells divide by mitosis the number of chromosomes in each of the daughter cells is the same as the number in the original parent cell. However, in the cell divisions which lead to the formation of gametes the chromosome number needs to be halved to give the necessary haploid nuclei. The formation of the gametes must therefore result from a different process of cell division. This **reduction division** is known as **meiosis**, and in most organisms it occurs only within sex organs. Meiosis occurs infrequently in a small number of cells, whilst mitosis occurs regularly in very many cells. Meiosis is of great biological significance – it is the basis of variation and thus also of evolution.

The stages of meiosis

In mitosis a single nuclear division gives rise to two identical diploid daughter cells. In meiosis two nuclear divisions give rise to four haploid daughter cells, each with its own unique combination of genetic material. As in the case of mitosis, the events of meiosis are continuous but are divided into defined stages for ease of description and understanding. The stages of meiosis are shown in figure 5.2.4. As in mitosis again, the contents of the cell, and in particular the DNA, are replicated whilst the cell is in interphase.

Figure 5.2.4 These diagrams show the stages of meiosis in a simplified cell which has only two pairs of chromosomes.

Prophase I – each chromosome appears in the condensed form with two chromatids. Homologous pairs of chromosomes associate with each other.

Metaphase I – the spindle forms and the pairs of chromosomes line up on the metaphase plate. **Crossing over** occurs.

Anaphase I – the centromeres do not divide. One chromosome (pair of chromatids) from each homologous pair moves to each end of the cell. As a result the chromosome number in each 'cell' is half that of the original.

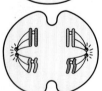

Telophase I – the nuclear membrane reforms and the cells begin to divide. In some cells this continues to full cytokinesis and there may be a period of brief or prolonged interphase. During this interphase there is *no further replication* of the DNA.

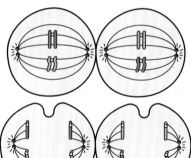

Metaphase II – new spindles are formed and the chromosomes, still made up of pairs of chromatids, line up on the metaphase plate.

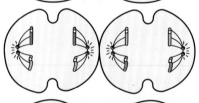

Anaphase II – the centromeres now divide and the chromatids move to the opposite ends of the cell.

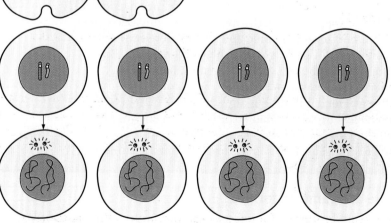

Telophase II – nuclear envelopes reform, the chromosomes return to their interphase state and cytokinesis occurs, giving four daughter cells each with half the chromosome number of the original diploid cell.

Prophase I

The chromosomes have replicated to form chromatids joined by a centromere just as in mitosis. However, in meiosis the two members of the chromosome pair associate together. Imagine the original pair of chromosomes in the parent cell as a pair of shoes – the 'left shoe' from the mother and the 'right shoe' from the father. After replication in interphase there are two identical pairs of shoes. The two right shoes are joined by the shoelaces – the centromere – as are the two left shoes. In prophase I of meiosis the two right shoes and the two left shoes are paired, giving a structure made up of four 'shoes' or chromatids. It is at this stage that **chiasmata** may be formed, resulting in **crossing over** (this is shown in figure 5.2.6 and explained overleaf). As in mitosis, the nuclear membrane breaks down, the nucleolus disappears and the centrioles pull apart to form the spindle.

Metaphase I

The homologous pairs of chromosomes line up on the metaphase plate of the spindle.

Anaphase I

One chromosome of each pair moves to one pole of the cell, whilst the other goes to the opposite pole. As the centromeres do not split, it is *pairs of chromatids* that move. To continue the shoe analogy, the laces are not untied, so two left shoes go one way and two right shoes the other.

Telophase I

The spindle fibres disappear and nuclear membranes form around the chromosomes. Cytokinesis begins, and there are half as many chromosomes in the new cells as there were in the original parent cell. In some cases the division is complete, but often prophase II begins almost immediately.

Prophase II

Dispersed chromosomes shorten and become visible again. They are still made up of two chromatids joined at the centromere as at the end of telophase I.

Metaphase II

A new spindle forms and the chromosomes (pairs of chromatids) line up on the metaphase plate.

Anaphase II

The centromeres finally divide (the 'shoelaces' are undone) and each chromatid moves to one of the poles of the cell.

Telophase II

The nuclear membranes reform as the chromosomes become invisible again. Cytokinesis occurs, resulting in four haploid daughter cells each with half the chromosome complement of the original parent cell. These daughter cells will then develop into gametes – spermatozoa, ova or the gametes in pollen grains – in the fullness of time.

The importance of meiosis

Having seen the stages of mitosis we can now look at the fundamental significance of the process. Firstly it reduces the chromosome number in gametes from diploid to haploid. But meiosis is also the primary means of generating new gene combinations.

Distribution of maternal and paternal chromosomes

The chromosomes from either parent are distributed in the new gametes completely at random. Taking the human situation as an example, each gamete receives 23 chromosomes. The parent cell which forms the gametes has 46 chromosomes, 23 from the original maternal gamete and 23 from the original paternal gamete, arranged in pairs. Any number of the 23 chromosomes which go into the gamete, from none to all 23, could come from either source. The most usual situation is a mixture of the two, as in figure 5.2.5. There are more than eight million potential chromosome combinations within the sperm or the egg.

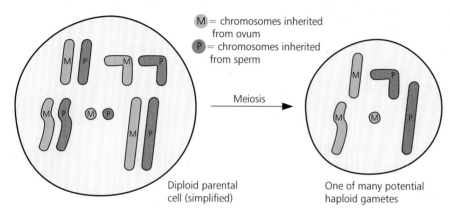

Ⓜ = chromosomes inherited from ovum
Ⓟ = chromosomes inherited from sperm

Meiosis

Diploid parental cell (simplified)

One of many potential haploid gametes

Figure 5.2.5 The set of single chromosomes in a gamete usually contains a mixture of the maternal and paternal chromosomes in the parent.

Recombination

Added to this is the phenomenon of **crossing over** or **recombination** shown in figure 5.2.6. Large, multienzyme complexes 'cut and stitch' maternal and paternal chromatids together during prophase I. The points where the chromatids break are called **chiasmata**. These are important in two ways. The exchange of genetic material produces new combinations of genes, as the recombined chromatids are unlike any other chromatids. Moreover, errors in the process lead to **mutation** and this introduces new genes into the genetic make-up of a species. We shall now go on to look at mutations in more detail.

Mutation

Mutations are changes in the chemical structure of an individual gene or in the physical make-up of the chromosome – in other words, changes in the arrangement of the genes on the chromosome. Mutations are the ultimate source of variation, but the vast majority of them are disadvantageous and so rapidly disappear. Many others are neutral – they neither improve nor worsen the chances of survival or reproduction. Very occasionally a mutation occurs which results in the production of a new and superior protein. The organism gains an advantage and so the mutation survives and remains in the gene pool of the species.

There are several different sorts of mutation. Some involve a change in the individual gene and are known as **point mutations**. If we consider genes as the letters of the alphabet and chromosomes as sentences, a point mutation is like changing a letter in one word. It may well still make an acceptable word, but the meaning will very probably be different. There are also a variety of mutations which involve changes in the position of genes within the chromosomes. These are known as **chromosomal mutations**. This is like rearranging the words within a sentence – if we are lucky they still make sense, but will probably not mean the same as the original sentence. Some examples of chromosomal mutations are shown in figure 5.2.7. And finally there are whole chromosome mutations in which an entire chromosome is either lost

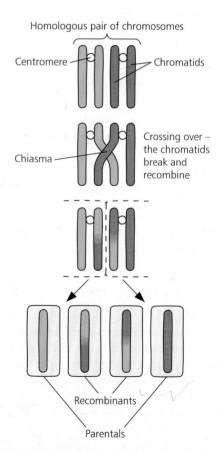

Homologous pair of chromosomes

Centromere — — Chromatids

Chiasma — Crossing over – the chromatids break and recombine

Recombinants

Parentals

Figure 5.2.6 Chromatids crossing over in meiosis. Recombinant chromatids are unlike any other chromatid in the organism.

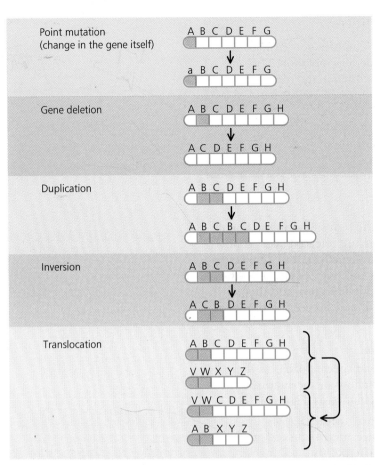

Point mutation (change in the gene itself)	A B C D E F G ↓ a B C D E F G
Gene deletion	A B C D E F G H ↓ A C D E F G H
Duplication	A B C D E F G H ↓ A B C B C D E F G H
Inversion	A B C D E F G H ↓ A C B D E F G H
Translocation	A B C D E F G H V W X Y Z V W C D E F G H A B X Y Z

Figure 5.2.7 Several processes can alter the arrangement of the genes on the chromosomes. These are some of the most common types of chromosomal mutation. The relative size of the genes is very much exaggerated in the diagrams – there are in fact very many more genes on each chromosome.

during meiosis or duplicated in one cell by errors in the process – the loss of or repetition of a whole sentence in our analogy.

Mutations occur all the time, but broadly speaking they are only of major importance when they occur in the gametes, for they may then be passed on to future offspring. Such natural mutations which are passed on do not occur very frequently (see box below), but exposure to ionising radiation and certain chemicals increases the rate at which they appear. Anything which causes an increased frequency of mutation is called a **mutagen** and is said to be **mutagenic**. Because genetic mutations can be lethal, and because many severe human diseases are the result of genetic mutation, these mutagenic substances are usually best avoided.

How often do mutations occur?

The frequency with which mutations naturally occur (the **mutation rate**) was first demonstrated by Herman J. Muller at Columbia University. He devised a way of measuring the mutation rate in the fruit fly *Drosophila* by observing the occurrence of lethal genes carried on the sex chromosomes. Lethal genes show up because the ratio of males to females is affected – the males inheriting the lethal gene died and so there was a higher than usual proportion of female offspring. The mutation rate of each individual gene was between 10^{-5} and 10^{-6} mutations per gene per generation. He subsequently showed that exposure to X-rays increased the mutation rate, and that the greater the dosage of X-rays the higher the rate of mutation.

Mutations are relatively rare events – even in our complex genetic make-up, each one of us will contain on average just one new mutation. If we are 'normal' and healthy, that mutation is probably hidden in the recessive form in our genes, and may never be expressed unless by chance we meet up with and have children by another individual with the same mutated gene. (A mutation on the X chromosome could be expressed in male offspring even if the father does not have this mutation. There is more about this in sections 5.6 and 5.7.)

Gametogenesis in humans

Sperm cells in the male mammal are produced in the testes. Ova in the female are produced in the ovaries. Many millions of sperm are released every time a male mammal ejaculates. The numbers of eggs in a sexually mature female are usually numbered in thousands, and will eventually run out. Special cells (the **primordial germ cells**) in the gonads divide, grow, divide again and then differentiate into the gametes. How are the events of meiosis used to produce two such different sets of gametes?

Spermatogenesis – the formation of spermatozoa

Each primordial germ cell results in large numbers of spermatozoa. As there are enormous numbers of primordial germ cells, millions of spermatozoa (commonly known as sperm) are produced on a regular basis. Figure 5.2.8 shows this process.

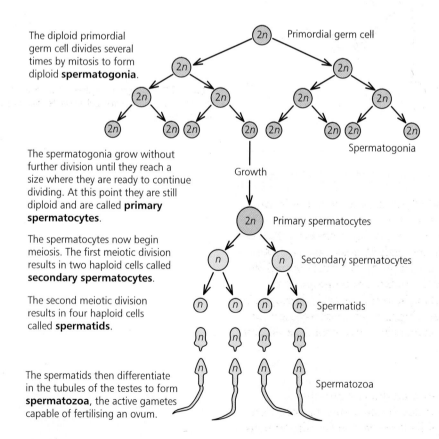

The diploid primordial germ cell divides several times by mitosis to form diploid **spermatogonia**.

The spermatogonia grow without further division until they reach a size where they are ready to continue dividing. At this point they are still diploid and are called **primary spermatocytes**.

The spermatocytes now begin meiosis. The first meiotic division results in two haploid cells called **secondary spermatocytes**.

The second meiotic division results in four haploid cells called **spermatids**.

The spermatids then differentiate in the tubules of the testes to form **spermatozoa**, the active gametes capable of fertilising an ovum.

Figure 5.2.8 The stages of spermatogenesis. Formation of sperm in the testes goes on from puberty to the end of life for most men.

Oogenesis – the formation of ova

Each primordial germ cell results in only one ovum. As a result the number of female ova is substantially smaller than the number of spermatozoa. As ova are much larger cells containing more cytoplasm than sperm, there is a much greater investment of resources in each one and therefore it would not make biological sense to produce too many. Figure 5.2.9 shows the process of oogenesis.

The diploid primordial germ cell divides several times by mitosis to form diploid **oogonia**.

Most of the oogonia do not develop any further. They simply degenerate. Only one continues to grow and substantial amounts of storage material go into the cell to make it very large compared with the spermatocytes. At this stage the large cell is known as a **primary oocyte**.

The oocyte now undergoes meiosis. The first meiotic division results in two haploid cells of very different sizes. The larger cell is the **secondary oocyte**. The other, much smaller cell sticks to it and is called the **first polar body**. At this stage the oocytes do not divide further until fertilisation. The ova in the ovary are secondary oocytes.

The second meiotic division occurs after fertilisation has taken place. The secondary oocyte divides to form the haploid **ovum** and another polar body, whilst the first polar body divides to form two more haploid polar bodies. The polar bodies do not have any function except to receive half the chromosomes in the meiotic divisions. They then degenerate as the ovum develops.

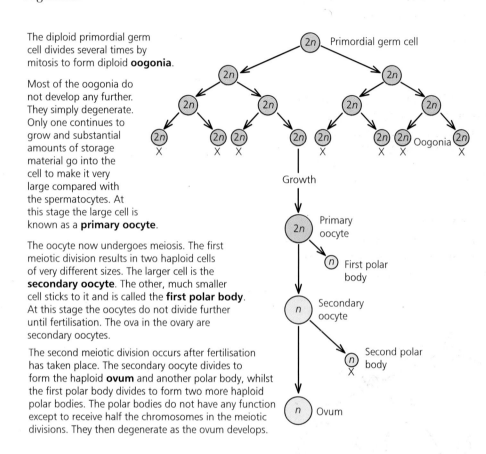

Figure 5.2.9 The stages of oogenesis. Maturation of ova in the ovary goes on from puberty to the menopause for most women.

Fertilisation

Asexual reproduction is a guaranteed method of passing on the genes from one individual into the next generation. For sexual reproduction to be successful, gametes must meet. If these gametes are coming from two different individuals, systems are needed to ensure the successful transfer of the male gamete to the female gamete. In plants, flowers either attract other organisms such as insects, birds or mammals to transfer the pollen from one plant to another, or they are arranged in such a way that the pollen is easily removed by the wind. In animals a wide variety of strategies have developed to ensure the meeting of gametes. They fall into two main categories – **external fertilisation** and **internal fertilisation**.

External fertilisation

This occurs outside the body, with the gametes shed directly into the environment. It is common only in aquatic species, because spermatozoa and ova are very vulnerable to drying and are rapidly destroyed in the air. Animals such as the coelenterates simply release copious amounts of male and female gametes into the sea and chance determines whether fertilisation takes place. Animals such as fish and amphibians have complex rituals which increase the likelihood of fertilisation by ensuring that the ova and sperm are released at the same time in close proximity to each other, as figure 5.2.10 illustrates.

In spite of strategies such as these, many of the gametes do not meet. External fertilisation can be very wasteful of resources, and is not an option for many of the organisms that have colonised the land.

Figure 5.2.10 The female frog carries the male around for several days prior to the release of gametes. The male develops special grasping areas (**nuptial pads**) on his forelimbs to help him remain in place. It is vital that the sperm are squirted onto the eggs as soon as they are laid so that fertilisation can take place before the protective coating of the eggs absorbs water and swells to form a layer of jelly.

Internal fertilisation

This involves the transfer of the male gametes directly to the female. Although this does not ensure fertilisation, it makes it much more likely. The way in which the sperm are transferred varies greatly, with many species producing packages of sperm for the female to pick up and transfer to her body. Many vertebrates have evolved a system whereby the male gametes are released directly into the body of the female during **mating** or **copulation**. This ensures that the ova and sperm are kept in a constantly moist environment and are placed as close together as possible, thus maximising the chances of fertilisation.

Fertilisation will not take place unless the spermatozoa meet a mature ovum. Many animals show complex behaviour patterns which help to ensure that mating only takes place at the time when the ovum is most likely to be fertilised. In many cases the female is only receptive to mating when she is fertile.

Inbreeding and outbreeding

Outbreeding means mating and reproducing with unrelated individuals. It has the great advantages of producing more new genetic combinations and reducing the likelihood that faulty genes will be expressed. Outbreeding results in fitter, healthier animals than those closely inbred. The offspring resulting from outbreeding have what is known as **hybrid vigour**. It is thought that many animals can sense, probably in response to chemicals picked up by the nose, when another animal has similar cell antigens. This means the chances that they are related are high, and the animals usually refuse to mate.

Inbreeding involves sexual reproduction between closely related individuals, or, in some plants and animals, self fertilisation. Inbreeding makes the appearance of homozygous characteristics much more likely – and these could be faulty genes inherited from both parents. Inbreeding reduces genetic variety and increases the likelihood of genetic defects and diseases. In most human societies inbreeding between close relatives is forbidden by social, sexual or religious taboos. When it occurs it is usually in small isolated communities of animals or plants, or carried out artificially by people to produce pedigree animals such as breeds of dogs, cats and horses.

Organisms which are dioecious, that is, have two separate sexes, must by definition have their gametes fertilised by another individual. They are termed **obligate outbreeders**. Organisms which are monoecious – produce male and female gametes in the same individual – have the potential to fertilise their own gametes. In spite of this, many monoecious organisms are outbreeders. However, inbreeding involving self fertilisation can be advantageous. Organisms which live extremely isolated lives, such as tapeworms in the gut, are inbreeders by necessity. Although they fertilise their own ova, variety still arises due to meiosis in the production of the gametes. However, this variety is limited compared with that which arises from fertilisation by another genetically different individual. The biggest disadvantage of inbreeding is that any harmful or disadvantageous genes are likely to be expressed in the offspring and successive generations will become weaker and less able to survive.

Self pollination and cross pollination

Self pollination happens when the pollen from a flower pollinates that flower, or another flower on the same plant. **Cross pollination** happens when pollen is brought in from a flower on another plant. Cross pollination – and therefore cross fertilisation – is ideal because it brings about variety. In self fertilisation the offspring will be genetically very similar to their parents. Plants are at higher risk of self fertilisation than animals, as a very large number of plant species are monoecious. However, most monoecious species have developed a variety of strategies to avoid self fertilisation except as a last resort.

The female gametes may mature before the male ones are ripe – this is **protogyny**. Equally the male gametes may mature before the female ones, in **protandry**. **Self sterility** may occur, in which case the male and female gametes of the same plant cannot fuse and fertilise each other: see section 5.3, page 385. The arrangement of the reproductive parts of a flower may be such that self pollination is most unlikely – for example, if the style is long so that the stigma is sited above the male anthers, then the likelihood of self pollination is substantially reduced.

Parthenogenesis – the redundant male

Parthenogenesis is not sexual reproduction, but it involves the same systems. In the females of some plant and animal species the ova can develop without fertilisation by the male. This may give rise to haploid offspring such as male honey bees (drones), or there may be an additional doubling of the chromosomes to give diploid offspring as occurs in aphids. Insects,

lizards, some relatives of the lobsters and even turkeys (artificially) are capable of parthenogenesis.

Like asexual reproduction or inbreeding, parthenogenesis is very successful when conditions are stable. Greenfly reproduce by parthenogenesis in the spring, giving a very rapid rise in the population at a time when food supplies are good. In the autumn when variety is needed to help ensure survival over the winter, sexual reproduction occurs again.

Variation

Different species of animals and plants are obviously very different from each other – consider a rabbit and a carrot – but individuals of the same species can also show remarkable variety or **variation**. This variation is very important to the success of a species.

The variety we see around us comes about in a number of different ways. The most important factor that makes us the way we are is the genetic information we carry, handed down from our parents and our grandparents before them. Our genetic information came from both parents when the gametes joined together at fertilisation to form a unique individual. The genetic information from our parents has been reshuffled and mixed up, introducing lots of new combinations of the same genes. Mutations may have occurred, permanently changing the way a gene works. Most of these mutations are harmful (making us ill or killing us) or neutral (not affecting us), but just a few of them might give us some benefits. On top of this, the environment in which we are brought up will affect our ability to fulfil our genetic potential. For example, we may have genes to make us very tall, but if we suffer malnutrition while we are growing we will not reach our full potential height.

Why does variation matter?

Variation is the key to a species coping with a change in its environment. If the climate changes, or a new disease appears, almost all of the individuals of a species may be destroyed. But because of variation in the genetic material, a

Figure 5.2.11 There are remarkable differences between people, even if they are all of similar ages. This variation between individuals is common to almost all species.

few individuals will almost always survive to breed and continue the species. This is the basis of natural selection, the driving force behind the evolution of all life on Earth.

Types of variation

In any population of organisms there are two types of variation – **continuous** and **discontinuous**. Characteristics that show continuous variation can have any value within a range, and include body mass and height in animals, or the number of leaves on a plant. Factors such as these are often determined by a number of genes (they are **polygenic**) but they are also very much affected by the environment – food availability, presence of disease and so on. Discontinuous variation, on the other hand, tends to describe features that are either present or not – for example, the ability to roll the tongue, blood groups, wing colour in the peppered moth *Biston betularia* and sex (male or female). Features such as these are generally affected by one or at most a very few genes, and the environment does not affect the appearance of any one individual – they are either male or female, their wings are either light or dark, etc.

When we study variation in a population we need to take large samples, because chance can make a big difference to the results. If we only take a small sample from one particular area we might, quite by chance, pick on the shortest people in the population or the most vivid coloured plumage. To look at variation within a species or population we need to look at a large sample that is collected randomly from the whole range of habitats of the organism. If we only collect from one area, we might find a regional effect due to climate or diet and think that this gives an accurate picture of the whole species. Once data about a particular characteristic have been collected they need to be displayed using a graph or histogram in order to show the frequency distribution of the characteristic clearly, as shown in figure 5.2.12.

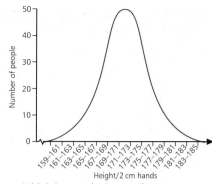

Height in human males shows **continuous variation** and gives a characteristic bell-shaped curve.

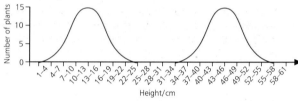

Height of pea plants shows **discontinuous variation**. There is no overlap between the two categories. Dwarf pea plants may vary in height in a bell-shaped curve, and tall pea plants vary in the same way, but there is no overlap between the two populations. A pea plant is either tall or dwarf.

Figure 5.2.12 Displaying data about the occurrence of a particular feature in this way shows clearly whether the feature shows continuous or discontinuous variation.

Normal distribution about a mean

If a feature of an animal or plant shows continuous variation, then the frequency distribution will be a **normal distribution curve**. This is the typical 'bell-shaped curve' which we can see in figure 5.2.12. To help us understand what this means we will take the example of height in the human female population. Common sense (as well as the distribution curve) tells us that most women in the population are going to be somewhere in the middle of the height range. At the extremes there will only be a few individuals who are very short or very tall. The mean height (the average height of all the women measured) will be found exactly at the centre of the normal distribution curve, so all the heights are distributed equally about the mean.

A useful concept in helping us to judge the amount of variation in our sample is the idea of **standard deviation**. The standard deviation is calculated from all the data collected and it gives a figure which we can then use to decide how much variation is in our population. Of the sample, 68% will be within 1 standard deviation of the mean, 95% will be within 2 standard deviations of the mean and almost 100% will be within 3 standard deviations of the mean. If the calculated standard deviation is small, then there is very little variation in our population because all the sampled individuals are very close to the mean. On the other hand, if the standard deviation is large this indicates a high degree of variation, because there is a wide range of measurements away from the mean. Figure 5.2.13 shows this difference.

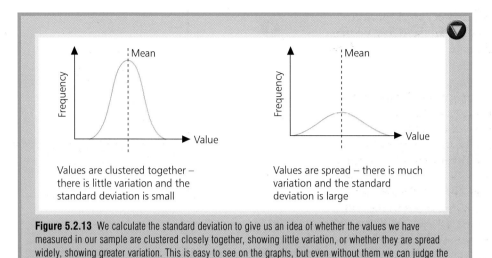

Figure 5.2.13 We calculate the standard deviation to give us an idea of whether the values we have measured in our sample are clustered closely together, showing little variation, or whether they are spread widely, showing greater variation. This is easy to see on the graphs, but even without them we can judge the variation in a population if we find a numerical value for the standard variation.

Standard error

As well as the normal distribution curve and the standard deviation, we can use another statistical tool to help us determine the accuracy of any results we may gather in scientific research. If we calculate the mean and then feed in all the data we have collected, we can calculate the **standard error**. This tells us that 68% of our results should fall within 1 standard deviation of the mean, and 95% of them within 2 standard deviations. If the standard error is small, our work is accurate and we can rely on the results. If the standard error is large, then the results are covering a wide range and so we should be wary of drawing too firm a conclusion from them.

So far we have looked at reproduction in a general sense – its purpose, and how cellular reproduction and gamete formation are brought about. In sections 5.3–5.5 we shall move on to consider in detail how sexual reproduction is brought about in both flowering plants and people.

5

SUMMARY

- The **gametes** are specialised cells which have half the normal number of chromosomes (23 in humans) – one chromosome from each homologous pair. They are **haploid**. In sexual reproduction two haploid nuclei fuse to form a diploid **zygote**.
- **Isogamy** is the production of identical gametes which are both motile. **Anisogametes** are different in structure and function. Usually the female gamete does not move, is large and contains food stores for the developing embryo. The male gamete is smaller and adapted for movement.

- **Hermaphrodite** organisms produce both male and female gametes. **Monoecious** plants form male and female gametes, while **dioecious** plants produce only male or only female flowers.

- Gametes are formed in specialised sex organs (**gonads**). In plants the anthers produce gametes carried in pollen and the ovaries produce ovules. In animals the testes produce spermatozoa and the ovaries produce ova.

- Cells in the gonads divide by reduction division or **meiosis** to produce haploid gametes. Meiosis results in four haploid daughter cells from one diploid parent cell.

- **Prophase I** is the first stage of meiosis. Homologous chromosomes, each made up of two chromatids joined at the centromere, pair up. The chromatids cross over (form **chiasmata**) which exchanges genetic material. The nuclear membrane breaks down, the nucleolus disappears and centrioles separate to form the spindle.

- In **metaphase I** the pairs of chromosomes line up on the metaphase plate.

- In **anaphase I** the chromosomes from each pair migrate to opposite poles of the cell.

- In **telophase I** the spindle disappears and nuclear membranes form around the chromosomes. Cytokinesis begins.

- In **prophase II** there is no further replication of DNA. The dispersed chromosomes shorten and nuclear membranes break down.

- In **metaphase II** a new spindle forms and chromosomes line up on the metaphase plate.

- In **anaphase II** the centromeres split and chromosomes migrate to opposite poles of the cell.

- In **telophase II** nuclear membranes reform, chromosomes disperse and cytokinesis occurs.

- Meiosis results in genetic variation because the parental chromosomes are distributed randomly in the gametes. **Recombination** (formation of chiasmata) exchanges genetic material, and **mutations** in the process increase variety further.

- **Point mutations** are changes in individual genes, while **chromosomal mutations** are changes in the positions of genes on a chromosome.

- **Fertilisation** is the meeting of gametes so that they can form the zygote. In **external fertilisation** the gametes are shed into the aquatic environment to meet by chance. In **internal fertilisation** the male gametes are transferred into the female, during mating in many land animals.

- **Obligate outbreeders** have their gametes fertilised by another organism, while **inbreeding** or **self fertilisation** involves the meeting of gametes from the same parent. To avoid self fertilisation in some flowering plants the female gametes may mature first (**protogyny**) or the male gametes may mature first (**protandry**).

- Individuals of the same species show variety or **variation**. This variation is very important to the success of a species. Characteristics that show **continuous variation** can have any value within a range, and are often determined by a number of genes (they are **polygenic**) and also affected by the environment. Features that show **discontinuous variation** are either present or not, and are determined by one or a few genes – the environment does not affect them.

1 a What are gametes?
  b How do gametes differ from normal cells?
  c Describe meiotic cell division.

2 a Where are the gametes formed in:
    i   the human male
    ii the human female?
  b Draw up a table comparing gametogenesis in the male and in the female.
  c Where does gametogenesis occur in plants?
  d What are:
    i   monoecious plants
    ii dioecious plants?

3 a What is mutation and why is it important?
  b What are the main problems to be overcome in reproduction for organisms living on the land rather than in the oceans?
  c What are the advantages and disadvantages of:
    i   inbreeding
    ii outbreeding?

Developing Key Skills

Find five very different examples of courtship displays or behaviours. Use them in the design of a poster for display in the public library during 'Wildlife Awareness Week'. The title of the poster should be 'The mating game'.

Around the world, organisms are becoming extinct increasing rapidly. It has been estimated that 25% of the world's flowering plant species could disappear within the next 50 years. Of the 242 000 species of flowering plants around at the moment, this means that 60 500 different types of plant could disappear within our lifetime. This would equate with the mass extinctions from the past, which have resulted in the loss of thousands of species now known to us only as distant fossil records, or not at all.

Would this loss of plant life really matter? Of course it would – as we saw in section 2, plants are of vital importance to all our lives, not just as producers of biomass and oxygen, not simply as suppliers of food, fuel, clothing and housing, but as a rich source of new medicines, pest control chemicals and industrial raw materials.

Figure 1 Wakehurst Place, home to the seeds of 4000 wild flowering plants.

Saving the seeds

With a view to conservation, the Royal Botanic Gardens at Kew set up a seed bank at Wakehurst Place in Sussex in the 1960s. In response to the ever-accelerating biodiversity loss, and in the light of global concerns about conservation, they have decided to extend this project considerably. A Millennium Seed Bank has been set up, with two main aims. The first was to collect and conserve the seeds of the entire UK native flora by the year 2000. Of the 1442 of these native plants, 300 are already threatened with extinction. The second aim is to conserve the seeds of an additional 10 per cent of the flora of the whole world by the year 2010, concentrating particularly on the drylands – arid, sub-arid and sub-humid regions – which are experiencing some of the most rapid loss of habitat.

Why seeds?

Setting up a seed bank is an ideal way of preserving plants in a state of effective suspended animation. Live seeds are collected from the wild, removed from the fruits and cleaned. They are screened using X-rays to make sure they contain fully developed embryos, and then they are dried. Finally they are stored in jars at between –20 °C and –40 °C. To the best of our knowledge they will survive in these conditions and remain capable of germinating for up to 200 years – time enough for people to sort things out and restore their habitats.

Plants make huge numbers of seeds, so they can be collected without damaging the natural population. Seeds are usually small, so large numbers of them can be stored cheaply in a small space, and they contain all the genetic material of the plant, so that they are a perfect record of the existing plant as well as a potential new plant for the future. With luck, other countries will set up similar projects – perhaps by the year 2010 seeds from all the plant species that can withstand drying and freezing will be safe in seed banks somewhere in the world, even if they are no longer safe in their natural habitats.

Figure 2 A DNA bonanza – jars of seeds in cold storage at a seed bank represent our hope of preserving plant species for the future.

5.3 Sexual reproduction in plants

The **angiosperms** or flowering plants reproduce by the production of flowers. As we have already seen in section 5.1, many flowering plants can reproduce asexually too. Evidence of sexual reproduction in plants is all around us – in the pollen which causes the misery of hay fever, in the flowers of the garden, the hedgerow and the rainforest, and in the fruits and vegetables which form a large part of our diet worldwide. What is the role of these various structures in the process of sexual reproduction?

Flowers

Flowers are some of the most beautiful manifestations of biological diversity. The range of colours, patterns, designs and scents is almost endless, as figure 5.3.1 illustrates. Flowers are collections of sex organs. Plants do not have sex organs as a permanent part of their structure – they are developed when conditions are appropriate. Many plants produce flowers which combine both the male and female reproductive parts. As mentioned in section 5.2, **dioecious plants** produce male flowers on one plant and female flowers on another. This prevents any problems of self fertilisation. **Monoecious plants** produce male and female gametes on the same plant. Flowers are very expensive in terms of the resources of the plant, so they are only produced at times when it is most likely that successful reproduction will result.

Each *Gazania* **flower** is made up of a large number of very small flowers. It is therefore a **composite** head of flowers, with individual flowers maturing over several days. Different pollinators therefore fertilise each egg cell.

The common garden tulip shows the bright colours and patterns frequently used to attract insects to flowers.

The male and female parts of this grass protrude beyond the dull-coloured petals.

Figure 5.3.1 Flowers are sexual structures with an almost infinite variety of shapes, colours and smells.

The structure of a flower

In spite of the great diversity shown in figure 5.3.1, most flowers are based on a very similar pattern. Flowering plants are divided into the monocotyledons and the dicotyledons – these terms are explained on pages 385–386. Both types of plants produce flowers, although those of the dicotyledons are generally larger and more colourful. In plants which produce separate male and female flowers, parts of the general design are present in the male flowers and other parts in the female flowers.

Flowers are a group of leaves modified for a particular function. A typical flower consists of four types of structure – **sepals**, **petals**, **stamens** and **carpels**. Their arrangement and functions are shown in figure 5.3.2.

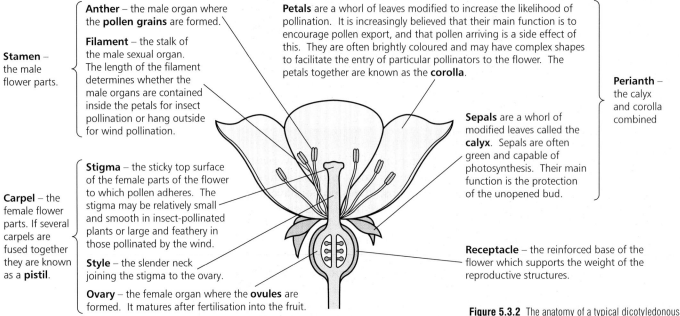

Stamen – the male flower parts.

Anther – the male organ where the **pollen grains** are formed.

Filament – the stalk of the male sexual organ. The length of the filament determines whether the male organs are contained inside the petals for insect pollination or hang outside for wind pollination.

Petals are a whorl of leaves modified to increase the likelihood of pollination. It is increasingly believed that their main function is to encourage pollen export, and that pollen arriving is a side effect of this. They are often brightly coloured and may have complex shapes to facilitate the entry of particular pollinators to the flower. The petals together are known as the **corolla**.

Perianth – the calyx and corolla combined

Sepals are a whorl of modified leaves called the **calyx**. Sepals are often green and capable of photosynthesis. Their main function is the protection of the unopened bud.

Carpel – the female flower parts. If several carpels are fused together they are known as a **pistil**.

Stigma – the sticky top surface of the female parts of the flower to which pollen adheres. The stigma may be relatively small and smooth in insect-pollinated plants or large and feathery in those pollinated by the wind.

Style – the slender neck joining the stigma to the ovary.

Ovary – the female organ where the **ovules** are formed. It matures after fertilisation into the fruit.

Receptacle – the reinforced base of the flower which supports the weight of the reproductive structures.

Figure 5.3.2 The anatomy of a typical dicotyledonous flower. These basic structures may be modified in a wide range of ways to adapt the flower to particular pollinators.

Pollination

Sexual reproduction is the fusing of two gametes to form a zygote, as we saw in section 5.2. The gametes in a flowering plant are in the pollen and the ovules. For the gametes to meet, **pollination** must take place – the pollen must be transferred from the male organs to the female organs. As inbreeding is generally avoided, most plants require their pollen to be transferred to another plant, and to receive pollen from elsewhere in return. A variety of strategies have evolved to ensure that this happens, two major groups being those plants which depend on insects or other living organisms to transfer pollen and those which rely on a physical medium such as the wind. Flower structures vary greatly between these categories.

Those flowers which are pollinated by insects or other animals must initially attract these **pollinators**, and so coloured and patterned flowers are produced. Some have attractive scents and most also have rewards for the pollinators such as the sugary liquid **nectar** found in the base of many flowers. Flower structures are designed to maximise the chance of pollen from another plant reaching the stigma, and equally the chance of pollen from the anthers being removed and carried to another plant.

Flowers which rely on the wind as a pollinator do not need attractive structures. Many monocotyledons are wind pollinated, including all the grasses and cereal plants. The size and arrangement of the parts of the flower are modified to maximise the chances of pollen being blown from the stamens, and also of pollen from another plant of the same species being trapped on the stigma. The main structural modifications seen in these two types of flower are summarised in table 5.3.1.

Feature of flower	Insect-pollinated flowers	Wind-pollinated flowers
Sepals	May be green and photosynthetic or may be indistinguishable from the petals, brightly coloured to help attract insects	Often absent
Petals	Usually large and conspicuous, with colours and patterns which may be visible only in ultraviolet light. May be arranged or shaped to encourage only specific pollinators	Small, inconspicuous, often green or brown
Scent	Often attract specific pollinators – insects very sensitive to scents	Usually absent
Nectar	May be produced by nectaries at the bases of the petals so that the pollinator must enter the flower to reach the nectar	None produced
Stamens	Usually enclosed within the flower	Long filaments usually protrude from the flower with loosely attached anthers so pollen is easily blown off even in light wind
Carpels	Flat, lobed and sticky stigma usually enclosed within the flower	Stigma protrudes from the flower, and is usually feathery and sticky to trap pollen from the air
Pollen grains	Relatively large, often sticky	Very small, light and powdery, sometimes with air bladders

Table 5.3.1 A comparison of the main adaptations of insect-pollinated and wind-pollinated flowers

The mechanism of reproduction

Formation of the gametes

The formation of gametes in flowering plants is made more complex by the fact that plants have two phases to their life cycles. The **sporophyte** generation is diploid and produces spores by meiosis. The **gametophyte** generation which results is haploid and gives rise to the gametes by mitosis. In many plants such as mosses and ferns these two phases exist as separate plants, as we shall see in section 6.3. In seed-bearing plants, the two phases have been combined into one plant. The main body of the plant which we see is the diploid sporophyte. The haploid gametophytes are contained in the anther and the ovary. They are produced by meiosis from spore mother cells, as described below.

In plants the male gametes are contained in the pollen grains formed by the anthers, and the female gametes are contained in the ovules formed in the ovary. The gamete carried by the pollen is known as the **microgamete** and the ovule as the **megagamete**.

The formation of pollen – microgametogenesis

The anthers are analogous to the testes of animals. Meiosis occurs within the anthers resulting in vast numbers of pollen grains which carry the male gametes.

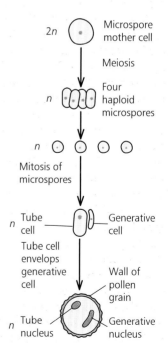

Figure 5.3.3 Microgametogenesis – the formation of the male gamete.

Each anther contains four **pollen sacs** where the pollen grains develop. In each pollen sac there are large numbers of **microspore mother cells**. These cells are diploid and they divide by meiosis as shown in figure 5.3.3 to form haploid **microspores** which are the gametophyte generation. The gametes themselves are formed from the microspores by mitosis. A haploid tube cell and a haploid generative cell result from the mitosis of the microspore, and the tube cell then envelops the generative cell to form the pollen grain. This pollen grain contains two nuclei, the **tube nucleus** and the **generative nucleus**.

The pollen grains that are produced have extremely complex cell walls with three-dimensional patterns, as can be seen in figure 5.3.4. These pollen surface patterns are unique and species specific. They are produced by polysaccharides and proteins deposited in the cell wall. Pollen grains are extremely tough and resistant to decay so they remain in the soil for thousands of years. An expert examining an ancient sample of soil or dust can identify the species of plant growing at the time, and even give an idea of how abundant the different species were, from the distinctive pollen grains that survive.

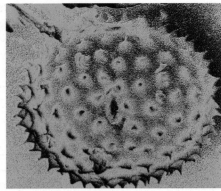
Figure 5.3.4 These fearsome looking pollen grains are from the common ragweed. They often cause the allergic reaction we call hay fever.

The formation of egg cells – megagametogenesis

The ovary of the plant is analogous to the animal ovary. Meiosis results in the formation of a relatively small number of egg cells contained within ovules (egg chambers). The site of egg development is within the ovary itself. Some plants, for example the nectarine, produce only one ovule, whilst others such as peas produce several.

The ovule is attached to the wall of the ovary by a pad of special tissue called the **placenta**. A complex structure of integuments (coverings) form around tissue known as **nucellus**, and in the centre diploid **megaspore mother cells** divide by meiosis to give rise to four haploid **megaspores**. Three of these degenerate leaving one to continue to develop. This megaspore undergoes three mitotic divisions which result in an **embryo sac** containing an egg cell (the **megagamete**), two **polar bodies** and various other small cells, some of which degenerate. This process is shown in figure 5.3.5.

Figure 5.3.5 Megagametogenesis – the formation of the egg cell – takes place in the ovary.

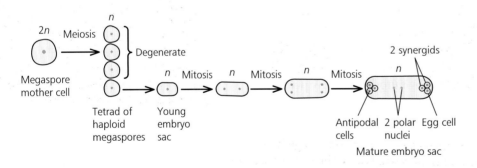

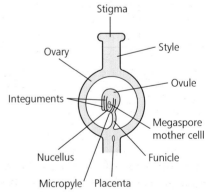

Pollination and fertilisation

Once pollen formation is completed the anthers ripen and their walls dry out and split. As a result the pollen is released for transfer to the stigma of another plant. As mentioned in section 5.2, self pollination is often avoided as far as possible by strategies such as a stigma positioned above the anthers, or female parts which mature either before or after the stamens. Most commonly the anthers mature first, described as **protandry**. Examples of protandrous flowers include white deadnettles and dandelions. **Protogyny** is the maturing of the stigmas first – an example is the bluebell.

Once a pollen grain has arrived on the stigma of a flower from another plant, transferred by either animals or the wind, **pollination** has taken place. The gametes must now fuse in the process of **fertilisation**.

The male gamete is contained within the pollen grain. The female gamete is embedded deep in the tissue of the ovary. To enable the two to meet an ingenious series of events takes place.

Molecules on the surfaces of the pollen grain and the stigma interact. If they 'recognise' each other as being from a compatible individual of the same species, the pollen grain begins to **germinate**. A **pollen tube** begins to grow out from the tube nucleus of the pollen grain, through the stigma into the style. It continues down towards the ovary, and the generative nucleus travels down it, dividing mitotically as it does so to form two **male nuclei**. Eventually the tip of the pollen tube passes through the **micropyle** of the ovule.

Once the tube has entered the micropyle, the two male nuclei are passed into the ovule so that fertilisation can occur. Angiosperms undergo what is known as **double fertilisation**. One of the male nuclei fuses with the two polar nuclei to form one **triploid** (with three sets of chromosomes) **endosperm nucleus**. The other male nucleus fuses with the egg cell to form the **diploid zygote**. This is shown in figure 5.3.6. At this point fertilisation has been completed and the development of the seed and the embryo within can begin.

The growth of the pollen tube is very fast due to the rapid elongation of the cells. If self pollination does occur in a plant which does not normally self pollinate, then **self incompatibility** (**self sterility**) means the pollen grain often does not develop or grows too slowly to bring about successful fertilisation. This is the result of self-incompatibility genes.

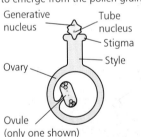
Chemicals on the surfaces of the pollen grain and stigma interact. A pollen tube begins to emerge from the pollen grain.

Generative nucleus
Tube nucleus
Stigma
Style
Ovary
Ovule (only one shown)

The pollen tube grows down through the style. The generative nucleus has divided to give two male nuclei which travel down the pollen tube.

Pollen tube
Male nuclei
Tube nucleus

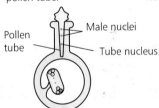
The pollen tube grows into the micropyle of the ovule. One male nucleus fuses with the two polar nuclei to form the endosperm nucleus and the other fuses with the egg cell nucleus to form the zygote.

Figure 3.5.6 A summary of the events which follow pollination and lead to fertilisation of the ovum.

Seed and fruit formation

Once the double fertilisation of the ovule has taken place, the next stage is the protection and dispersal of the embryo within the **seed**. Within the embryo sac two distinct processes take place which lead to the formation of the seed. First the endosperm nucleus divides repeatedly by mitosis and absorbs many of the nutrients produced by the parent plant. This gives rise to food-storage tissue known as the **endosperm**. Once this food source is well established, the zygote begins to undergo mitotic cell division to produce an embryo. The embryo plant consists of three main regions – the **plumule** (embryonic shoot), the **radicle** (embryonic root) and the **cotyledons** (embryonic leaves). It is the number of these embryonic leaves present which gives us the main division of the angiosperms into **monocotyledons** (with one seed leaf) and **dicotyledons** (with two seed leaves).

In monocotyledons the main food store is the endosperm and the cotyledon remains a very small part of the seed. In most dicotyledons the endosperm channels food into the cotyledons which become the main food store. By the time the seed is mature the endosperm has all but disappeared – the embryo with its food-swollen leaves takes up most of the seed, as shown in figure 5.3.7. Once the food store has been laid down and the embryo has developed the seed dehydrates, losing much of its wet mass, and with this loss of water the seed becomes dormant. The plant growth regulator abscisic acid (see section 4.5) appears to control this dormancy in seeds. The integuments of the ovule meanwhile become hardened to form the seed coat or **testa**.

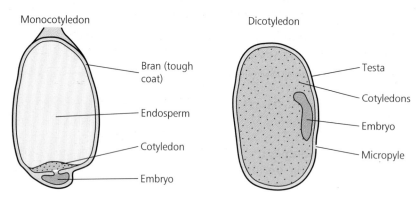

Monocotyledon — Bran (tough coat), Endosperm, Cotyledon, Embryo

Dicotyledon — Testa, Cotyledons, Embryo, Micropyle

Figure 5.3.7 The internal arrangements of monocotyledonous and dicotyledonous seeds look different, but their basic parts are the same – an embryo ready to develop, a food store to supply the energy needed and a protective seed coat.

Once the seeds have formed and the seed coat has developed, the fruit begins to enlarge around the seed. In most cases the fruit develops from the wall of the ovary, although in some cases it is the result of an enlarged receptacle. Fruits come in many forms – the succulent, juicy cherry and grape, the leathery pods of the pea and bean, the tough husks of the coconut and the papery thin wings of the fruits of the sycamore and ash trees. All fruits are adaptations to aid in the spread or **dispersal** of seeds, as illustrated in figure 5.3.8.

The dandelion 'clock' is in fact a mass of fruits. Each pappus of hairs acts as a tiny parachute, enabling the seed to be carried long distances on currents of air.

Sweet and fleshy fruits like these blackberries rely on animals and birds eating them. The seeds then pass through the digestive tract and the action of the enzymes there prepares the testa for germination. Land sprayed with treated human sewage tends to yield a high proportion of tomato plants as tomato seeds pass through the human gut.

The extremely hard fruits of *Banksia serratifolia* can float in the sea off Australia. Once they have drifted ashore, they will resist opening until fire heats the nut wall and causes it to split.

Figure 5.3.8 Fruit adaptations showing various methods of dispersal of seeds.

The need for seed dispersal

Any plant is in competition with other plants for soil nutrients, light and water. Tall plants with well established roots are at a great advantage over small unestablished plants in obtaining these resources. If the seeds of a plant simply fell off onto the ground beneath it, their chances of survival would be greatly reduced by competition with the parent plant and with each other.

The survival and successful germination of the seeds carrying the genetic material on into the next generation are very important. Resources are often used by the parent plant to produce fruits which not only protect the developing seed but also help to disperse the ripe seeds as far from the parent as possible. This increases the chance of successful growth of the seeds by reducing the likelihood of competition both with the mature plant and with other seedlings.

Methods of dispersal

Methods of seed dispersal range from the commonplace to the bizarre. Seeds that float in the air, pods that explode to expel the seeds and edible fruits are familiar to most of us. Tumbleweeds are less well known in Britain – the whole plant dies and is then uprooted and blown for miles in strong winds, scattering seeds as it rolls and tumbles along.

Dying with the dodo?

Theories about the calvaria tree of Mauritius show the vital role of dispersal. Calvarias used to be one of the most common trees on the island, but now only a few very ancient trees remain, in spite of the fact that the trees all produce their edible peach-like fruit each year. Why have no new trees developed? Some people believe that the calvaria trees relied on dodos for the dispersal of their seeds. The theory is that the passage of the seeds through the guts of these large birds native to Mauritius prepared the seeds for germination. Since the extinction of the dodos by sailors in 1681, calvarias have been unable to disperse their seeds – and now 300 years later the trees themselves face extinction.

Although this provides a neat and attractive explanation, and while dodos may indeed have played their part in calvaria seed dispersal when they were alive, it is actually far more likely that the ecology of the island has become so unbalanced with the introduction of increasing numbers of non-indigenous species that any seedlings produced cannot survive the competition.

Germination, development and growth

Seed dormancy

The plant embryo survives in a dehydrated condition in the seed by becoming **dormant**. The respiration and metabolic rates drop to very low levels, and in this state the seed can survive very adverse conditions. In some species the seeds can survive in this state for many years. During a Second World War air raid in London, some dried plant specimens at the Natural History Museum were accidentally sprayed with water. The seeds contained in the plants germinated – and the specimens were known to be 250 years old!

The main function of the period of dormancy is to allow seeds to germinate when conditions are most suitable. They remain dormant until they are triggered to germinate by an environmental stimulus. This may be the disruption of the seed coat as it passes through an animal, exposure to light as the fruit rots away, exposure to the colder temperatures of winter in temperate climates or the washing of substances from the seed coat by rain in desert plants. Even with the appropriate environmental trigger, seeds will not germinate in the absence of water, oxygen and a suitable temperature. Once all these requirements are met, a period of intense activity starts within the seed and growth of the embryo occurs.

Germination

Germination or the development of the embryo plant from the seed may be seen as a race against time. The seed contains the embryo plant and a food store. Once the process of germination begins, the seedling must develop to become capable of obtaining water and minerals from the soil and carrying out photosynthesis before the food store of the seed runs out.

Taking in water

The first step in germination is for the seed to absorb water. This is taken in through the micropyle, as the rest of the testa is waterproof. The water is

ABA and dormancy

Figure 5.3.9 Seeds often will not germinate for many months, even if conditions at times seem suitable.

It is important that seeds do not break out of dormancy just because there are a few warm, sunny days in winter. In many seeds there is an in-built control mechanism in the form of high levels of the plant hormone abscisic acid (ABA). This inhibits growth, and only breaks down slowly over a period of time. So until the ABA has broken down, the seed remains dormant whatever the external conditions.

Demonstrating conditions needed for germination

The conditions needed for seeds to germinate can be demonstrated by a simple series of experiments, as described in figure 5.3.10.

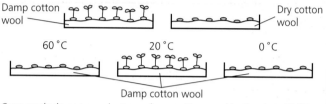

Cress seeds germinate readily on damp cotton wool at room temperature in the air. Dry seeds on dry cotton wool at room temperature in the air will not germinate – water is necessary for the process.

Cress seeds do not germinate on damp cotton wool in the air at 60 °C – the enzymes are denatured. At 20 °C they grow readily but not at 0 °C, although if this dish is subsequently warmed germination will occur. In the cold the enzymes are simply inactivated, not destroyed.

Cress seeds germinate readily on damp cotton wool at room temperature suspended in a sealed container over water. Those suspended over alkaline pyrogallol are deprived of oxygen and do not germinate, indicating that oxygen is required. As germination involves the rapid mobilisation and respiration of food stores to provide energy and materials for the growing embryo, this is not surprising.

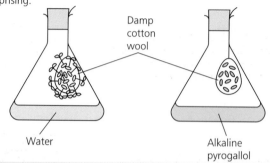

Figure 5.3.10 These simple experiments demonstrate the major requirements for the successful germination of seeds. If any of the elements is missing, germination does not take place.

absorbed by hydrophilic proteins within the seed and the large intake of water serves two major purposes. Firstly, the tissues of the embryo swell, and its enzymes can work again. Secondly, as a result of this swelling and the growth that occurs as the enzymes become active, the seed coat or testa splits.

The radicle emerges

The first structure to emerge from the ruptured seed coat is the **radicle**, the first short length of root. Once this has appeared the seed has germinated. The radicle, like all root tissue, is positively geotropic. This means that whichever way up the seed has fallen, the root will always grow downwards into the soil.

Development of the seedling

Up until the point where the radicle is growing down into the soil, germination is much the same in all plants. However, the way the seedling then continues to grow varies between monocotyledons and dicotyledons, and moreover dicotyledons may germinate in one of two different ways. In the developing seedling, the **hypocotyl** is the region beyond the radicle, that part of the seedling found *below* the cotyledons. The **epicotyl** is part of the developing stem *above* the cotyledons. The different processes involve different positions of these parts, as shown in figure 5.3.11.

Whatever the details of the development of the seedlings, the internal events are very similar. The food stores are mobilised to provide energy and materials for the rapidly growing and dividing cells. The rapid growth that is seen is largely the result of massive cell elongation. In monocotyledons the endosperm is used up and is then redundant. In many dicotyledons the cotyledons are brought up above the ground and once the food store inside them has been used up, they remain useful for some time as they photosynthesise until the seedling is well established with true leaves, when the cotyledons wither and drop off.

Primary growth – from seedling to mature plant

Once the seedling is well established, much growth is needed to give rise to a mature plant. In the growing regions of the stems and roots are regions known

In the germination of a monocotyledon such as maize the **coleoptile** leads the shoot through the soil and protects it. The food stores remain below the soil.

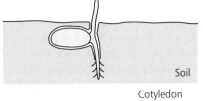

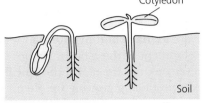

In many dicotyledons the cotyledons are brought above the ground, so that both the epicotyl and the hypocotyl emerge. This is known as **epigeal germination**.

Cotyledon

Soil

Soil

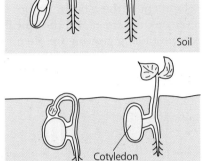

Some dicotyledons develop leaving the cotyledons, hypocotyl and radicle below the ground. This is called **hypogeal germination**.

Cotyledon

Figure 5.3.11 Whatever the method of germination and development, the race against time for the seed is completed when the root system is growing and the first true leaves are open and photosynthesising before the food store in the endosperm or cotyledons is used up.

as the **meristems**. It is here that rapid mitotic cell division occurs to generate new cells. These then undergo expansion and elongation by the uptake of water and the assimilation of new materials. The cells which result then differentiate into the different cell types needed within the stem or root. The growth which occurs at these growing root and shoot tips is known as **primary growth**.

Root growth

To make progress the growing root must probe through the soil. The delicate root cells are protected from damage by a tough **root cap**. There are three main zones in a rapidly growing root – the **meristematic region**, the **region of elongation** and the **region of differentiation**, shown in figure 5.3.12.

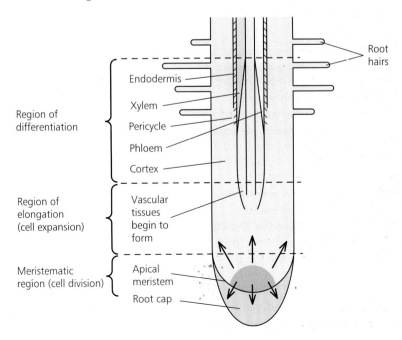

Region of differentiation

Root hairs

Endodermis
Xylem
Pericycle
Phloem
Cortex

Region of elongation (cell expansion)

Vascular tissues begin to form

Meristematic region (cell division)

Apical meristem
Root cap

Figure 5.3.12 The three major growth zones in a young root. New cells arise by mitosis in the meristematic region. They increase in size and particularly in length in the region of elongation. Finally they differentiate into epidermis, vascular tissue, etc. in the region of differentiation. The development of root hairs is one of the earliest signs of differentiation.

Shoot growth

Stems grow from dividing cells behind the tip known as the **apical meristem**. The stem does not have the equivalent of a root cap, because there is not as much risk of mechanical damage growing through air as through soil. The meristematic zone in stems has two regions, the **tunica** and the **corpus**. As in the root, cells are formed and then elongate and differentiate into the tissues needed within the stem. The tunica and the corpus are involved in the production of regular swellings called **leaf primordia**. These subsequently develop into leaves. Within the leaf primordia are **axillary bud primordia**. Auxin from the main stem tip inhibits the development of these buds. As the stem lengthens and they become further from the auxin source, or if the **apical dominance** is removed by pinching off the auxin-producing growing tip, then these axillary buds develop into lateral shoots as shown in figure 5.3.13.

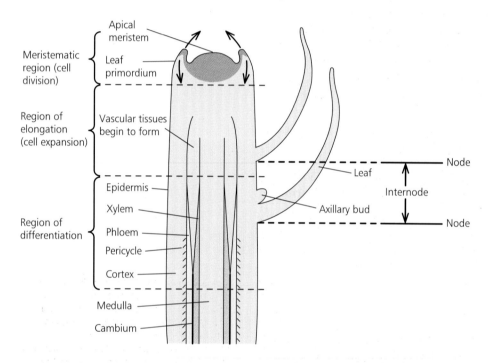

Figure 5.3.13 Cell division in the apical meristems results in stem growth. Most of the specialised tissues develop directly in the region of differentiation, except xylem and phloem – a procambial strand develops, and the xylem and phloem differentiate from this.

Life spans and lifestyles in plants

Angiosperms produce flowers and gymnosperms (conifers) produce cones, both forming seeds to reproduce. But they do not all grow, flower and set seeds in the same yearly pattern. There are three main divisions – **annuals**, **biennials** and **perennials**.

Annuals

Annual plants complete their life cycle within one year. The seed germinates and the plant grows and flowers, seeds develop and are dispersed and the parent plant dies, all in one growing season. The plant will survive the winter, or other adverse conditions such as drought, only as seeds. Annuals live for a relatively short time and much of their resources go into the production of flowers and seeds. Almost all the growth in these plants is primary growth. Many weeds, grains, garden flowers and vegetables are annuals. The major adaptive advantage of this lifestyle is that the plant can spread rapidly and produce many seeds in a short period.

Biennials

Biennial plants are less common than annuals. They complete their life cycles over two growing seasons. In the first season they germinate and grow, then the established plant overwinters. In the second season it produces flowers and seeds, and then dies. Parsley and foxgloves are typical examples.

Both annuals and biennials die after flowering because no more growth is possible. The apical meristem is converted into a flower, and once all the meristems have flowered the plant is doomed.

Perennials

Perennial plants may live for many years, and some such as trees have very large bodies which may survive for centuries. Sexual reproduction may not begin until a perennial plant is many years old. Although flowering does involve apical meristems, it takes place only on some of the lateral branches, and so growth can continue at the apical meristems of the rest of the branches.

Perennials can grow very large because of a process known as **secondary growth** or **secondary thickening** shown in figure 5.3.14. This occurs as a stem grows laterally, increasing its girth. This thickening of the stem involves production of secondary vascular tissues such as xylem and phloem and the laying down of lignified tissue, and enables the plant to withstand the added load of branches and leaves, and also to cope with the elements as it gets larger.

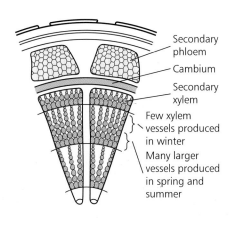

Secondary phloem
Cambium
Secondary xylem
Few xylem vessels produced in winter
Many larger vessels produced in spring and summer

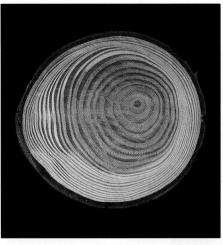

Figure 5.3.14 During autumn and winter the tree is becoming dormant and very few xylem vessels are produced by the cambium, giving narrow, dark rings. In spring and summer the cambium is reactivated and produces many larger xylem cells which gives the lighter regions in the rings. The photograph of a 24-year old pine tree shows how these rings appear in the wood.

Secondary thickening

The thickening of a stem or secondary thickening is brought about by two growth regions known as **lateral meristems**. One is called the **vascular cambium** and the other is the **cork cambium**.

The vascular cambium

The vascular cambium is the cylindrical layer of actively dividing cells that we saw when we considered the stem in section 2.2. As secondary thickening starts, a complete ring of cambium develops and its mitotic activity in turn results in complete cylinders of xylem and phloem, as shown in figure 5.3.15. The phloem cells die off and are regularly replaced, so there is only a narrow band of phloem around the edge of the stem. However, the lignified xylem vessels remain even when they have become blocked and non-functional, forming the wood which makes up the bulk of the stem. Because the activity of the vascular cambium is affected by environmental factors such as temperature and water availability the rings of growth recorded in the trunk of a tree reflect the environmental fluctuations over the years.

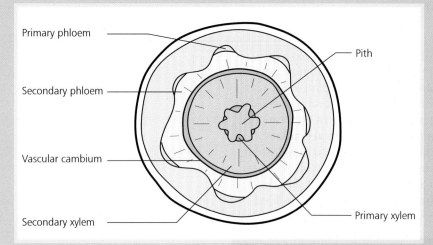

Primary phloem

Secondary phloem

Vascular cambium

Secondary xylem

Pith

Primary xylem

Figure 5.3.15 Apical meristems grow to increase the length of the roots or the height of the stem. Vascular cambium grows to increase the girth of the stem or root.

The cork cambium

The cork cambium is a layer of dividing cells found just below the epidermis, and the **cork** or bark which it produces replaces the epidermis as the stem gets larger and older. The cork cells become impregnated with suberin which makes them waterproof and prevents water loss. This also prevents the passage of oxygen and carbon dioxide into and out of the stem. Small openings called **lenticels** shown in figure 5.3.16 play the same role as stomata in leaves and allow gaseous exchange to occur.

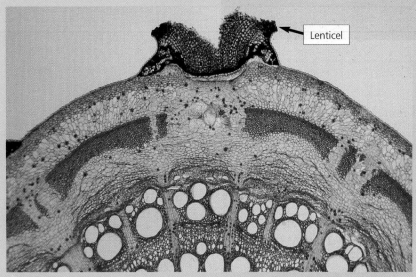

Lenticel

Figure 5.3.16 The waterproof cork produced by the cork cambium protects the stem from water loss. The lenticels perforate the layer to allow gaseous exchange.

Thus a variety of lifestyles and the strategies for asexual and sexual reproduction that we have seen enable plants to master an enormous range of habitats – their dominance over the surface of the land is such that the green colour they impart can even be seen from space.

SUMMARY

- **Angiosperms** or flowering plants reproduce by the production of flowers. Flowers have **sepals** which protect the bud, **petals** which may be brightly coloured, **stamens** which are the male flower parts and **carpels** which are the female parts, all supported on the **receptacle**.

- Stamens are made up of the **anther** where pollen grains are formed supported on the **filament**. The **carpel** is made up of the **ovary** where ovules are formed, the **stigma** where pollen grains land and the **style** which joins the stigma to the ovary.

- **Pollination** is the transfer of pollen from one flower to another. **Insect-pollinated** flowers have attractive flowers and scents and may produce nectar. Their stamens and flat sticky carpels are usually enclosed in the flower, and their pollen grains are large and sticky. **Wind-pollinated** flowers have small inconspicuous flowers with long filaments and feathery stigmas protruding outside the flower. Their pollen grains are small and light.

- Flowering plants have a diploid **sporophyte generation** and a haploid **gametophyte generation**.

- **Microgametogenesis** is the formation of pollen. Each anther has four **pollen sacs** containing diploid **microspore mother cells** which divide by meiosis to produce haploid **microspores**. Mitosis of these results in two cells combining to form a **pollen grain** with two haploid nuclei, the **tube nucleus** and the **generative nucleus**.

- **Megagametogenesis** is the formation of egg cells in the ovule, which is attached to the ovary wall by the **placenta**. The **nucellus** is covered by **integuments** and contains diploid **megaspore mother cells**. These divide by meiosis to give four haploid **megaspores**. Three of these degenerate and one undergoes three mitotic divisions to give an **embryo sac** containing an **egg cell**, two **polar bodies** and other small cells.

- On pollination, molecules on the surface of the pollen grain and stigma interact to recognise each other. The pollen grain **germinates** – a **pollen tube** grows from the tube nucleus into the stigma, through the style to the ovary. The generative nucleus divides on its way down to form two male nuclei which pass through the micropyle of the ovule.

- Double fertilisation occurs – one male nucleus fuses with two polar nuclei to form the triploid **endosperm nucleus**. The other male nucleus fuses with the egg cell to give the diploid **zygote**.

- The endosperm nucleus divides by mitosis to give endosperm food stores. The zygote divides to form the embryo plant containing the **plumule** (shoot), **radicle** (root) and **cotyledons** (seed leaves – one in **monocotyledons** and two in **dicotyledons**).

- The seed dehydrates and becomes **dormant**. The integuments form the **testa**, a seed coat to protect the seed.

- The seed may be dispersed by various methods involving wind and water, or edible or hooked **fruits** developed from the ovary wall or the receptacle.

- The seed **germinates** after an environmental trigger in the presence of oxygen and water. Water is taken in through the micropyle causing the embryo tissues to swell and the testa to split. The radicle emerges first.

- In monocotyledons the **coleoptile** leads the shoot through the soil. In dicotyledons germination may be **hypogeal** or **epigeal**.

- Stems and roots have **meristems** where primary growth occurs.

- A root has a **root cap** to protect it and has a **meristematic region**, the **region of elongation** and the **region of differentiation**.

- A shoot has an **apical meristem** with two regions – the **tunica** and **corpus** which produce swellings called **leaf primordia**. These develop into leaves, and have **axillary bud primordia** which are inhibited by auxin from the apical meristem.

- **Annual plants** complete their life cycle in one year. **Biennials** germinate and grow in the first season and flower in the second season, after which they die. **Perennials** live for many years and may have **secondary growth** – a thickened stem which has lignified tissue.

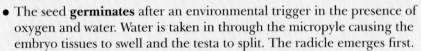

QUESTIONS

1 a Draw an annotated diagram of the structure of a flower, relating structure to function.

b Describe some of the modifications to the basic flower pattern that have evolved to enable different agents to pollinate the flowers.

c What is the difference between pollination and fertilisation in a flower?

2 a Describe the fertilisation of an ovule.

b After fertilisation, a fruit containing the seeds will form. What is the function of this fruit and why is it necessary?

3 a Under suitable conditions seeds will germinate. Describe the main events of germination.

b After germination a period of growth and maturation occurs within the plant. Explain the main stages of this growth which result in a mature plant.

Developing Key Skills

Use the information in the Focus material along with the resources of the internet to help with the following:

a What percentage of the native British flora is threatened with extinction at the moment?

b What are the main advantages of using seeds to preserve plant species and how is it done?

c Give three different UK plants that are in danger of extinction. Describe the plants, their habitat and why they are under threat.

d Give three different plants from around the world (not UK) which are similarly under threat of extinction. Again describe the plants, their habitat and the reasons for their endangered status.

e Explain why it matters if plants become extinct.

In sex education, and in everyday life, we make the assumption that producing babies is something that occurs very naturally and easily – indeed, at times almost too easily. For the majority of couples this proves to be the case, and they achieve a pregnancy within a few months of deciding to start a family. But at least one couple in 10 do not conceive after a year or more of trying. There are many reasons why a couple cannot produce children. In about 30% of cases there is a problem in the reproductive system of the female partner, and in another 30% the malfunctioning is in the male reproductive system. For the remaining couples both partners may be less fertile than average (**sub-fertile**), or both are infertile, or there may be no apparent reason why pregnancy does not occur.

Infertility in women …

A woman can have difficulty in conceiving for a great variety of reasons. If the ovaries do not contain ova, then pregnancy is obviously impossible. This is very rare, however. Far more commonly the ovaries contain ova, but they are not released in the normal monthly cycle – ovulation does not occur. The Fallopian tubes that carry the ova from the ovary to the uterus may be blocked or twisted. Blocked tubes may be the result of an infection such as *Chlamydia*, or some other sexually transmitted disease, or there may simply be an anatomical abnormality. The uterus itself may not accept a pregnancy due to an imbalance of hormones, or the lining may only grow in patches. Some women even make antibodies to the sperm of their partner, destroying them before they have the chance to penetrate an ovum.

… and infertility in men

Infertility in the male has been recognised only relatively recently. Before that it was assumed that any inability to have children was the woman's problem. We now know that men's reproductive systems are just as likely to go wrong as their partners'. The main problems are with the process of sperm production, known as **spermatogenesis**. Obviously if no sperm are produced, then fertilisation is impossible. More common than the complete absence of sperm is the presence of a high proportion of abnormal sperm. In the semen of a normal man, about 15 per cent of the sperm are abnormal. As this proportion rises, the chances of conception will fall.

Spermatogenesis takes about 70 days, and can be affected by a variety of factors such as the general health of the man, his alcohol intake and smoking. Spermatogenesis is under hormonal control, and so hormonal imbalance can affect sperm production. The testes need to be about 2 °C below body temperature for normal sperm production to occur, so if the testes are undescended (held in the body cavity) or if the temperature increases in any other way, sperm production drops. Even the wearing of tight underpants and trousers has been indicated as a possible cause of sub-fertility in men because of the effect on the temperature of their testicles. In some cases the sperm cannot be released due to a block in the vas deferens, the tube carrying them from the testes to the urethra. This is often the result of an earlier sexually transmitted disease.

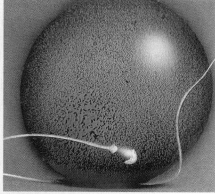

Figure 1 The moment of conception, when a sperm enters an ovum and a new life begins, is the result of a complex sequence of events in both female and male bodies co-ordinated by a number of hormones. It is not surprising that sometimes the system fails. So the causes of fertility are many – later on in the book we shall look at some of the possible solutions.

5.4 The mammalian sexual anatomy

Sexual reproduction is a process of paramount importance in the living world. It provides a way of introducing variety and change, allowing for the exploitation of new niches and the survival of organisms in difficult conditions. Sexual reproduction occurs in most groups of living things, and is carried out successfully by a wide variety of strategies. Of all the animal groups, mammals have perhaps the most sophisticated systems for ensuring both that fertilisation takes place and that the offspring survive the early stages of development, providing a ready supply of food for subsequent growth.

Reproduction in mammals

As members of the mammalian group we share many reproductive features with our nearest relatives. This means that as we look at the sexual anatomy and functioning of our own species we learn much of the reproductive physiology of others.

In mammals – including ourselves – it is very difficult to tell males from females in the early stages of embryo development. However, by the time of birth the external **genitalia** of the two sexes are quite obviously different, although otherwise the overall appearance is similar. The adult forms develop after a process of sexual maturation. The sexual anatomy of these adult males and females is very different. The differences are indicative of the distinct roles of male and female mammals in reproduction. What are these roles, and how is each anatomy designed to fulfil them? We shall look at the male and female in turn to answer these questions.

Reproduction and the male mammal

The male role

The male role is to provide the male sex cells or **spermatozoa**, commonly known as **sperm**, which are needed to fertilise the eggs within the female. Because most mammals live on land, it is important that these sperm are delivered inside the female reproductive tract at about the time of **ovulation** when a ripe egg is released. Spermatozoa cannot survive exposure to the air. As organisms evolved to colonise the land, systems developed by which the male gametes could be transferred to the female in a liquid environment. In mammals special glands provide a nutrient fluid containing the spermatozoa, known as **semen**.

In mammals the transfer of the gametes involves a specialised organ called the **penis** which, when engorged with blood and **erect**, is used to deliver spermatozoa into the female reproductive system. This takes place during **mating** or **copulation**, usually preceded by elaborate courtship displays to ensure that the female is both receptive and so will not attack the male, and fertile so that the spermatozoa are not wasted. In humans this element of the reproductive ritual has been, if not lost, at least substantially modified. Although it could be argued that in most societies sexual intercourse is still preceded by elaborate courtship displays (like buying rings, getting married, setting up home or other ritual behaviour), these displays are no longer linked to establishing whether or not a female is fertile – the sexual receptiveness of women is not linked to the time of ovulation.

For fertilisation to occur, vast numbers of spermatozoa need to be produced to allow for the enormous natural wastage which occurs, and to complete their task they need the right conditions – a moist environment, a supply of nutrients and the right temperature and pH.

Fulfilling the male role

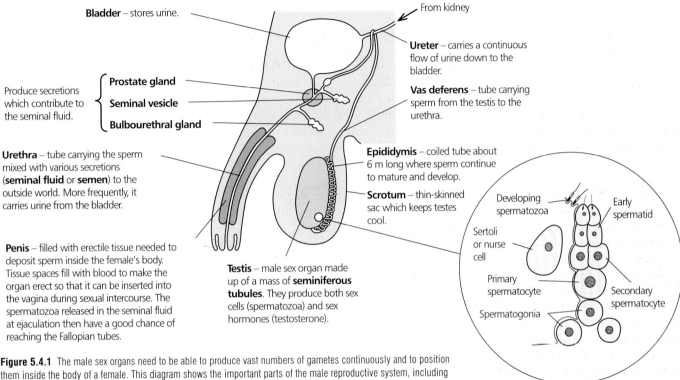

Bladder – stores urine.

From kidney

Ureter – carries a continuous flow of urine down to the bladder.

Produce secretions which contribute to the seminal fluid.
- **Prostate gland**
- **Seminal vesicle**
- **Bulbourethral gland**

Vas deferens – tube carrying sperm from the testis to the urethra.

Urethra – tube carrying the sperm mixed with various secretions (**seminal fluid** or **semen**) to the outside world. More frequently, it carries urine from the bladder.

Epididymis – coiled tube about 6 m long where sperm continue to mature and develop.

Scrotum – thin-skinned sac which keeps testes cool.

Penis – filled with erectile tissue needed to deposit sperm inside the female's body. Tissue spaces fill with blood to make the organ erect so that it can be inserted into the vagina during sexual intercourse. The spermatozoa released in the seminal fluid at ejaculation then have a good chance of reaching the Fallopian tubes.

Testis – male sex organ made up of a mass of **seminiferous tubules**. They produce both sex cells (spermatozoa) and sex hormones (testosterone).

Developing spermatozoa

Sertoli or nurse cell

Early spermatid

Primary spermatocyte

Secondary spermatocyte

Spermatogonia

Figure 5.4.1 The male sex organs need to be able to produce vast numbers of gametes continuously and to position them inside the body of a female. This diagram shows the important parts of the male reproductive system, including the links with the urinary system.

The male sex organs are the **testes**. In human males the testes are found outside the main body cavity in a thin-skinned sac called the **scrotum**, and the design of many other male mammals is similar. This external position makes these delicate organs vulnerable, but helps maintain the optimum temperature for the production of healthy sperm, about 2 °C lower than normal body temperature. Thus for the species as a whole, the advantages of having the testes outside the body outweigh the disadvantages.

It is the presence of testes which results in the development of all the other characteristics of maleness. The testes have two main functions, controlled by hormones produced by the pituitary gland in the brain. **Follicle stimulating hormone (FSH)** stimulates the development of spermatozoa. **Luteinising hormone (LH)** stimulates the testis to make testosterone.

The testes as chemical controllers

The testes are made up of several different types of cells, most of which are involved in sperm production. However, the function of the **interstitial** or **Leydig cells** is to manufacture the male sex hormone **testosterone**. Luteinising hormone is released by the pituitary and picked up by receptors in the interstitial cells. It stimulates the synthesis of enzymes which in turn make testosterone. Luteinising hormone is identical in males and females, but in males it is sometimes called **interstitial cell stimulating hormone (ICSH)**, describing exactly what it does.

Male characteristics

Figure 5.4.2 illustrates the human male secondary sexual characteristics which develop at the period of life known as **puberty**.

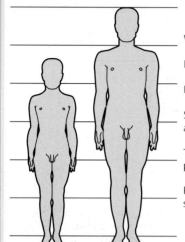

Whole body undergoes growth spurt.

Facial hair, pubic hair and body hair begins to grow.

Larynx enlarges and the voice deepens.

Shoulders and chest broaden – male musculature appears.

Testes grow larger, become active and start sperm production.

Penis enlarges and its skin, along with that of the scrotum, becomes more pigmented.

Figure 5.4.2 Puberty can be a trying time. The changes which occur over these troublesome years produce the physical and psychological differences between boy and man.

Testosterone is the main male hormone. It is partly responsible for the production of sperm and wholly responsible for the development and maintenance of the **secondary sexual characteristics** – those features which make the individual male. Before puberty the basic body shape of both boys and girls is very similar. In boys during adolescence (at the time of puberty) the brain starts to produce increased levels of ICSH and the testosterone level rises as a result. Sperm production begins and the entire physical appearance undergoes changes, some quite rapid, others taking years to complete. These physical changes all depend on a maintained level of testosterone. Other mammals show varying degrees of the same process, with adult males usually being easily recognisable from the females.

The testes as sperm producers

As figure 5.4.1 shows, the testes are extremely complex organs, consisting of a mass of seminiferous tubules. At the time of puberty they are 'kick-started' by a combination of follicle stimulating hormone from the pituitary and testosterone from their own interstitial cells. This sets in action the process of sperm production which normally continues throughout the life of the individual.

The testes contain germ cells which undergo the complex process of **gametogenesis** or **spermatogenesis** (see section 5.2, page 372), followed by a phase of differentiation called **spermiogenesis** before they become active fertile spermatozoa ready to fertilise an ovum.

Spermatozoa are produced in the epithelium of the seminiferous tubules. Many millions are made each day, and the maturation process takes about 70 days from the beginning of spermatogenesis to the end of spermiogenesis. **Sertoli** or **nurse cells** supply support, protection and nutrition to the maturing sperm. The glands along the system provide the nutrients and fluid that make up the seminal fluid released at ejaculation. The spermatozoa themselves make up only a tiny fraction of the 3 cm^3 of ejaculate – the remainding liquid helps to modify the pH of the vagina and maintain optimum conditions for the survival of the sperm.

The structure of a spermatozoon

The spermatozoa of most species are around 50 μm long. They have several tasks to fulfil. They must remain in suspension in the semen to facilitate transport through the female reproductive tract, and to carry out fertilisation they must be able to penetrate the protective barrier around the ovum and deliver the haploid genome into the cytoplasm of the egg. (This process is described in detail in section 5.5.) The close relationship between the structure of the human spermatozoon and its functions can be seen in the figure.

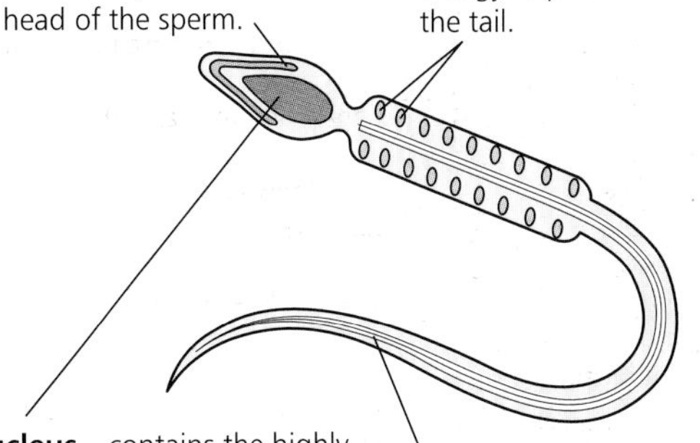

Figure 5.4.3 Millions upon millions of these motile gametes are produced in the lifetime of a human male, yet the average size of a family in the developed world is only around 2 children. Only one spermatozoon fertilises each egg. Biologists are currently considering several hypotheses about the role of the 'wasted millions'.

Acrosome – the storage site for the enzymes which digest the layers surrounding the egg and allow the penetration of the head of the sperm.

Mitochondria – tightly packed into the middle section of the spermatozoon, these provide the energy required for the lashing of the tail.

Nucleus – contains the highly condensed haploid set of chromosomes. The condensed state of the genetic material reduces the amount of energy needed to transport it.

Microtubules – produce the whip-like movements of the tail of a mature sperm which keep it in suspension and may help it 'swim' towards the egg.

Reproduction and the female mammal

The female role

The role of the female mammal in reproduction is to produce a relatively small number of large gametes or **ova**, to provide the developing embryo with food and oxygen, remove its waste products and, after delivering it into the world, provide it with a continued supply of food for a period of time.

Fulfilling the female role

The female sex organs are the **ovaries**. These are found low in the abdominal cavity and are very closely associated with, but not attached to, the **uterus** with its **Fallopian tubes**.

It is the presence of the ovaries which results in the outward signs of femaleness. The ovaries have two main functions and they are controlled by chemical messages from the pituitary gland in the brain just like the testes. Follicle stimulating hormone stimulates the development of ripe **ova**, the female gametes, within structures called **follicles** in the ovaries. FSH also stimulates the production of the hormone **oestrogen**. Luteinising hormone (LH) brings about the production of the hormone **progesterone**.

The ovaries as chemical controllers

Of the two hormones produced by the ovaries, oestrogen is mainly responsible for the secondary sexual characteristics, those physical attributes associated with femaleness. The changes in the female body shape during puberty tend to be more dramatic than those in the male and on the whole take less time to be completed. The role of the female hormones in regulating the reproductive cycle is described on page 402.

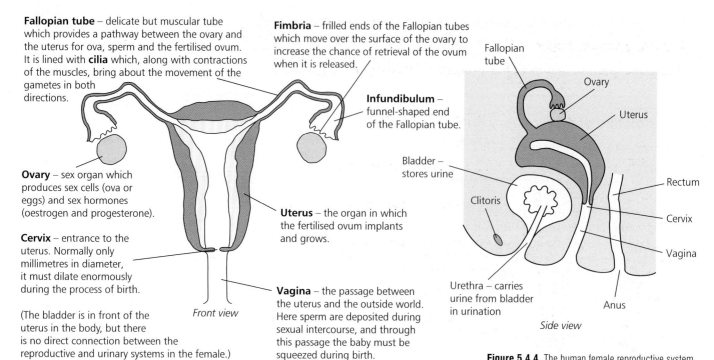

Fallopian tube – delicate but muscular tube which provides a pathway between the ovary and the uterus for ova, sperm and the fertilised ovum. It is lined with **cilia** which, along with contractions of the muscles, bring about the movement of the gametes in both directions.

Fimbria – frilled ends of the Fallopian tubes which move over the surface of the ovary to increase the chance of retrieval of the ovum when it is released.

Infundibulum – funnel-shaped end of the Fallopian tube.

Ovary – sex organ which produces sex cells (ova or eggs) and sex hormones (oestrogen and progesterone).

Cervix – entrance to the uterus. Normally only millimetres in diameter, it must dilate enormously during the process of birth.

(The bladder is in front of the uterus in the body, but there is no direct connection between the reproductive and urinary systems in the female.)

Front view

Uterus – the organ in which the fertilised ovum implants and grows.

Vagina – the passage between the uterus and the outside world. Here sperm are deposited during sexual intercourse, and through this passage the baby must be squeezed during birth.

Fallopian tube

Ovary

Uterus

Bladder – stores urine

Clitoris

Rectum

Cervix

Vagina

Urethra – carries urine from bladder in urination

Anus

Side view

Figure 5.4.4 The human female reproductive system produces relatively few, large gametes and provides a place for the growth and development of any that are fertilised – a strategy which has been enormously successful in evolutionary terms. These diagrams show the main parts of the female reproductive system.

The ovaries as egg producers

The production of ova begins in the fetus long before birth. By the time of birth about 2 million (2×10^6) immature ova-containing follicles are present in the ovaries of a baby girl. Only about 450 of these ova will ever be released from mature follicles, and a tiny fraction of these will be fertilised and develop into new human beings.

At puberty, the menstrual cycle begins and is repeated approximately every 28 days for the years of a woman's reproductive life – that is, until she runs out of ova. In each cycle several follicles begin to develop and ripen, and from one a mature ovum is released. Those follicles which ripen but do not release ova simply shrivel and atrophy. When there are no ova left to mature a woman enters what is called the **menopause**, and this marks the end of her ability to bear children.

The menstrual cycle

Once gamete production starts in men, it is a continuous process. In women and other female mammals the situation is very different. Mature ova are produced as the result of cyclical activity, so that females are only fertile for relatively brief but regularly spaced periods of time, compared with the constant fertility of the male. The way in which the reproductive cycle is organised varies, but in humans and their closest relatives it takes the form of the **menstrual cycle**.

The events of the cycle are controlled by the pituitary hormones and the hormones of the ovary itself. The menstrual cycle is measured from the first day of menstrual bleeding as this is an easy event to pinpoint. The old lining of the uterus breaks down and sloughs off. In the first stage of the cycle, follicles mature under the influence of follicle stimulating hormone from the pituitary gland (which seems to initiate the process). At the same time luteinising hormone, also from the pituitary, stimulates the cells of the developing follicle to produce oestrogen. Oestrogen suppresses the production of FSH by the pituitary through a negative feedback loop. Oestrogen also stimulates the

Female characteristics

Figure 5.4.5 shows the human female secondary sexual characteristics.

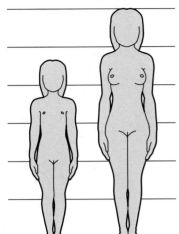

Whole body undergoes growth spurt.

Breasts develop.

External genitalia enlarge and become more pigmented.

Ovaries begin production of ova and menstruation begins.

Uterus grows and begins to produce thickened endometrium (lining tissue) in response to hormones from ovary.

Pubic hair grows.

Female deposition of fat develops on hips, buttocks and thighs.

Figure 5.4.5 The changes which take place during puberty in the human female.

lining of the uterus (the **endometrium**) to become thicker and more vascular in preparation for the arrival of a fertilised ovum. By about day 14 of the cycle oestrogen has reached a peak, FSH and particularly LH are released in relatively large amounts from the pituitary and **ovulation** occurs – a ripe ovum is released from a follicle and picked up by the fimbria to begin its journey towards the uterus.

After ovulation the cells of the empty follicle change to form a **corpus luteum**. The name literally means 'yellow body', from the yellow fat deposited in the empty follicle. The corpus luteum makes and releases the second ovarian hormone, progesterone. Progesterone maintains the endometrium in preparation for pregnancy and prevents the release of FSH and LH by the pituitary. However, if the ovum is not fertilised and pregnancy does not occur, then after about 11 days the corpus luteum atrophies and the level of progesterone drops. This has two effects – the lining of the uterus is shed in the menstrual bleeding and the levels of FSH and LH begin to rise again so that a new cycle begins. Figure 5.4.6 shows the events of the menstrual cycle.

The hormonal events of the menstrual cycle do not affect only the ovaries and uterus – they can have an effect on other parts of the body as well. As the hormones peak in the middle of the cycle, many women feel particularly well, although some experience some tenderness in their breasts. However, as the menstrual bleed approaches many women suffer a range of symptoms which are often referred to as **premenstrual tension** (**PMT**). These symptoms include water retention, so the woman feels bloated and her breasts may be swollen and tender, headaches, irritability, feeling emotional and tired, stomach cramps and backache. Some women suffer none of these symptoms, and many experience only some of them very mildly. But a few women are almost incapacitated each month by their menstrual cycle, and there are various hormone treatments available to help them.

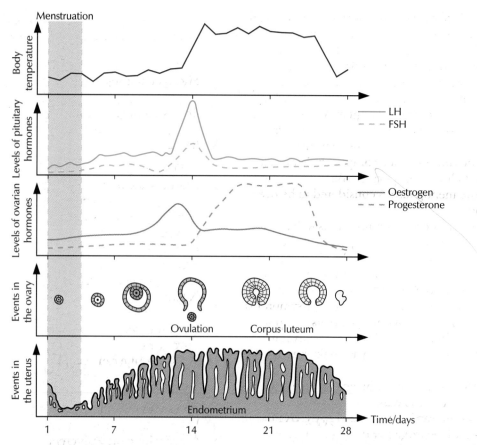

The structure of the ovum

While the spermatozoa of most animals are very similar in size, eggs vary greatly in both their diameter and their mass. The human ovum is about 0.1 mm across, whilst the ovum contained in the ostrich egg is around 6 mm in diameter.

The main difference between eggs of various species is the quantity of stored food they contain. In species such as birds and reptiles, complex development of the young occurs before hatching. Large food stores are therefore contained within the egg to supply their needs. In mammals, the developing fetus is supplied with nutrients from the blood supply of the mother and so large food stores are unnecessary. Figure 5.4.7 shows a human ovum.

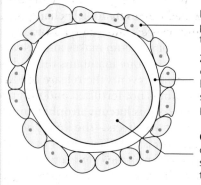

Follicle cells form a protective layer around the oocyte.

Zona pellucida – a clear jelly-like protective layer through which spermatozoa must penetrate.

Oocyte containing chromosomes which still have to complete their meiotic divisions.

Figure 5.4.7 The human oocyte is much larger than the spermatozoa and completely non-mobile. It relies entirely on beating cilia and muscular contractions of the Fallopian tubes to move it along towards the uterus.

The menopause and HRT

One of the landmarks of ageing for women is the **menopause**. This is the period of time, usually over several years, when biological changes happen which reduce and finally end the ability of a woman to have a child. The age at which the menopause occurs varies, but it is usually between 45 and 55 years of age. The ovaries contain only a limited number of ova, which are all present at the time of birth. Throughout the reproductive life many of these ova die, and some are released as part of a menstrual cycle. As the number of follicles becomes low, the ovaries become less sensitive to the pituitary hormones, so less oestrogen and progesterone are made. In turn, the levels of pituitary hormones drop, until a point is reached when hormone levels are no longer high enough to trigger ovulation. The endometrium may still build up enough to cause menstrual bleeding, but this then becomes less regular as the hormonal balance of the cycle is lost. For some women this means periods every couple of weeks for some time, but for the majority the menstrual bleeding becomes increasingly spaced out until it stops completely. Yet other women experience a sudden, complete halt in their periods. Because of the erratic nature of the physical change, the menopause is considered to be over one year after the last menstrual period.

The menopause has a number of other associated symptoms as well as the loss of fertility. Because the sex hormones also affect the vaginal mucus and the libido, some women find that their vagina becomes dry and thus love-making can be painful. The libido may also drop, though for many women the removal of any risk of pregnancy overcomes any hormonal decrease in desire. The fluctuating levels of sex hormones can also trigger mood swings and symptoms such as 'hot flushes' when massive vasodilation occurs, night sweats, sleeping problems, headaches, sore breasts, palpitations, irritability and depression. Very often those women who have most difficulties already in their lives are the ones most likely to suffer symptoms.

Most women find the menopause little more than an inconvenience, but about 30% experience symptoms severe enough to make them feel ill. The current medical practice is to offer **hormone replacement therapy** (**HRT**). This involves a regular dose of low levels of oestrogen and progesterone (not unlike the contraceptive pill) which help maintain an artificial balance until the menopause if over. HRT causes the woman to have periods for as long as she takes it, but she is not fertile. The use of HRT is still quite contentious, with some people arguing that it should be given to the majority of menopausal and post-menopausal women, and others that the the long-term effects are unknown and that it should be used only when absolutely necessary.

The oestrus cycle

In human beings, sexual activity is no longer closely tied in to the fertile parts of the menstrual cycle, but for most other mammals the situation is rather different. The females of most species of mammal come into heat (**oestrus**) at regular intervals which range from every few weeks to once a year. This is the time when they are both fertile and sexually receptive. The timing of oestrus tends to be such that the young are born at the time of year when the conditions are most favourable for their survival, or when conditions will be good and food plentiful at the time when their demands for milk and nourishment are at their highest. Either way the reproductive cycle works to maximise the chances of the offspring surviving and thriving.

For example, in the Northern Hemisphere, sheep are seasonal breeders. Their regular 16-day oestrus cycles start in the autumn, and if they are not mated will continue until early spring and then stop. The stimulus controlling the onset of oestrus is the length of daylight. The ewe shows oestrus behaviour for about 24 hours before the release of a ripe ovum – she produces pheromone-rich secretions from her vagina which tell the ram that she is ready to mate. She also walks in front of the ram, and stands with her back arched slightly to allow him to mount her and mate. If mating does not occur, the ripe ovum is reabsorbed and a new cycle begins. The endometrium does not begin

HRT and health

Many women swear by their HRT, feeling rejuvenated and full of energy. Others find it brings nothing but problems. But how does it affect our health?

HRT offers protection against heart disease by maintaining the levels of protective oestrogen. It also helps to prevent osteoporosis developing, because the oestrogen helps the body maintain a good calcium balance and it also slows the rate at which bone density is lost. Progesterone is given at the same time to reduce the risk of uterine cancer. There are concerns that HRT may increase the risk of breast cancer and endometrial cancer, but it certainly offers health benefits in return. Different groups present the evidence in different ways – so far the jury is still out on the overall long-term health effects.

to develop substantially until after fertilisation, so there is no 'menstrual bleed'. Most farmers put a harness on their rams with a dye marker on the chest, so the ram will mark the ewes as he mates with them, helping the farmer keep track of which ewes have been covered by the ram.

The sexual anatomy and the way it works to produce gametes in the right place at the right time is a complex system in both males and females. However the joining of these gametes and the forming and nurturing of the new life which results are even more complex, as section 5.5 will demonstrate.

Figure 5.4.8 The reproductive cycles of sheep ensure that lambs are born ready for the rich spring grass.

SUMMARY

- The mammalian male gametes are **spermatozoa**. They cannot survive in air so a nutrient fluid called **semen** is secreted to carry them inside the female.

- Spermatozoa are introduced into the female through the **penis** when **erect** (engorged with blood) during **copulation**.

- Spermatozoa are produced under the influence of FSH and testosterone in the **testes** which are positioned outside the main body cavity in the **scrotum**, to keep them cool. Spermatozoa pass into the **epididymis**, a coiled tube, and to the penis via the **vas deferens**. Along this tube the **prostate gland**, **seminal vesicles** and **bulbourethral gland** produce seminal secretions. Semen passes out of the penis via the **urethra**.

- The **interstitial** or **Leydig cells** of the testis produce testosterone under the influence of LH from the pituitary gland. Testosterone brings about the development of male secondary sexual characteristics at puberty.

- **Spermatogenesis** takes place in germ cells in the testis followed by **spermiogenesis** or differentiation. **Sertoli** or **nurse cells** support, protect and feed the large numbers of developing spermatozoa. The sperm cell has a head containing the **acrosome** (a storage site for enzymes) and the nucleus, a middle section containing large numbers of mitochondria and a long tail containing microtubules which enable it to whip backwards and forwards.

- The female gametes are **ova** or eggs, produced in **follicles** in the **ovaries** under the influence of FSH from the pituitary. The **uterus** or womb contains the developing embryo and the ova reach this via the **Fallopian tubes** which have frilled ends called **fimbria** to catch the ripe ova that are released. The **cervix** is the entrance to the womb, and the **vagina** leads to the exterior.

- The ovaries produce the hormones **oestrogen** under the influence of FSH and **progesterone** under the influence of LH. Oestrogen brings about the development of female secondary sexual characteristics at puberty.

- One ovum is released from either one of the ovaries once every 28 days, in the **menstrual cycle**. Day 1 is the beginning of **menstruation**, the shedding of the **endometrium** or vascular uterus lining. A **follicle** starts to develop in the ovary under the influence of FSH. The endometrium is built up again under the influence of oestrogen. At about day 14 **ovulation** takes place under the influence of LH and the ovum released from the follicle travels down the Fallopian tube towards the uterus. The empty follicle becomes a **corpus luteum** and produces progesterone. If the ovum is not fertilised, the corpus luteum atrophies and the level of progesterone falls, causing the endometrium to be shed again, and the cycle is repeated. If the ovum is fertilised, the corpus luteum is maintained and progesterone prevents menstruation.

- Ova are larger than spermatozoa. The central **oocyte** is contained inside the jelly-like **zona pellucida** and the **follicle cells**.

- During the **menopause**, the ovaries stop releasing ripe ova and the levels of hormones that control the menstrual cycle gradually fall, so the woman becomes infertile. Menstruation stops and other body changes are experienced.

QUESTIONS

1 a Draw the outline of an adult human male with details of the reproductive system, including the pituitary gland in the brain. Label it appropriately.

b Using annotated arrows, show the organ of origin, the receptor sites and the effects of the main male reproductive hormones.

c Draw the outline of an adult human female with details of the reproductive system, including the pituitary gland in the brain, and label the diagram.

d Using annotated arrows, show the organ of origin, the receptor sites and the effects of the main female reproductive hormones.

2 Describe the similarities and differences between:
  a mammalian testes and mammalian ovaries
  b mammalian sperm and mammalian ova.

3 Produce a simple and clear explanation of the events of the menstrual cycle that could be used on a leaflet in an infertility clinic. Remember that in this situation patients need to understand the details of the processes, but may have little or no scientific background.

Developing Key Skills

Your local network of GP practices is setting up a web site for its patients. Failure to conceive a baby quickly is a relatively common problem, so the GPs want to have several pages dedicated to the causes of infertility. They want lots of diagrams and language which is accessible to the majority of their patients (who are not studying AS or A2 biology!). However, they need the problems to be explained in a sufficiently scientific way for patients to be able to understand what is happening when they come to discuss possible solutions to their problems. Your brief is to design these web pages.

For some couples the heartbreak of infertility can now be overcome by one of a number of different techniques (see pages 424–426), but there is sometimes conflict between providing much-desired treatment to the individuals concerned and considering the benefit to society as a whole.

The technique of *in vitro* fertilisation has enabled many couples to conceive, but it has also resulted in a great many 'spare' embryos. What is to be done with them? In most cases the parents give permission for them to be used for experimentation, to further our knowledge of reproduction and development. In Britain and many other countries, a limit has been set on the age at which embryos can be used for experiments. At 14 days, the developing embryo is no longer likely to split and form identical twins, and the very beginnings of the nervous system are forming. Beyond this age no further experiments on *in vitro* human embryos are allowed.

Donating gametes, borrowing bodies

Some reproductive technologies involve using other people to help a couple produce a baby. For many years now artificial insemination by donor sperm has been available. One potential problem with this is that the offspring do not know who their biological father is, and so have the very remote chance of meeting, falling in love with and marrying a half brother or sister. However, this can happen with natural fathers too, so the situation is really very little different. More recently, it has become possible to harvest the eggs from one woman, fertilise them with sperm outside the body and implant them into a different woman who does not have any ova of her own. The moral issues involved in this are very similar to those involved in the donation of sperm, except that the process is much more complicated and invasive for the woman donor.

There are moves to make it easier for the children produced by these techniques to trace their biological parents. However, most gamete donors want to help an infertile couple, not to have a child themselves, so making it easier for offspring to trace their parents may reduce the already short supply of donors.

Another recent development has been the use of surrogate mothers. A surrogate mother carries a baby through pregnancy for someone else, and gives up the baby at birth. This has always been possible, but IVF has extended the possibilities. A surrogate mother may help a woman who has no uterus, either from birth or as a result of surgery. The technique is still relatively rare and often very controversial, particularly when women are paid for the use of their uteruses.

Strong opinions tend to be expressed in the media about paid surrogate mothers, or a surrogate mother who changes her mind and cannot give up the baby. A grandmother acting as surrogate mother for her childless daughter and son-in-law seems to meet more general approval, even though it involves the often frowned-on technique of restoring the fertility of a post-menopausal woman by using drugs. In society in general, discussion about such issues is rarely detached and based on science – it is more often stirred up by emotive and at times inaccurate reporting of both the situation and the science. The issues under discussion are too important to look at in this way – we must make the right ethical judgements now for the sake of the generations to come.

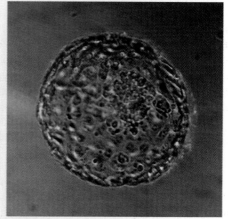

Figure 1 A 14-day human embryo – no experimentation is allowed beyond this stage. However, now the technology is available someone, somewhere might continue to experiment at later stages of development.

Figure 2 The ultimate gift? A mother acts as surrogate to her own grandchild when her daughter cannot carry a baby to term.

5.5 Reproduction in mammals

Reproduction in mammals depends on the production of haploid ova and spermatozoa within the bodies of sexually mature individuals. New life starts at **fertilisation**, with the union of the two germ cells. From that point onwards complex developments during the period of **gestation** or **pregnancy** result in the eventual birth of a fully formed, new individual. In this section we look into the events of fertilisation and beyond, while accepting that we can only scratch the surface of these incompletely understood areas of biology.

Fertilisation

The arrival of the ovum

During the 28-day human menstrual cycle, a follicle ripens and bursts to release an ovum. This is picked up by the fimbria of the infundibulum of the Fallopian tube. It is then moved along the tube towards the uterus by a cilial current and by the muscular contractions of the oviduct walls.

The human ovum begins to deteriorate only a few hours after ovulation, and is dead within 24 hours. For fertilisation to occur, spermatozoa must reach the ovum as soon as possible after ovulation, or must be already present in the Fallopian tube when the ovum is released. In most mammals the period of sexual receptiveness known as **oestrus** begins several hours before ovulation. This results in mating taking place before the ripe ovum leaves the ovary. However, in humans this link between mating and ovulation has been lost. Human females are, at least in theory, sexually receptive all the time and so there is no guarantee that sperm will be deposited at the optimum time for fertilisation to take place, in contrast to other mammals.

The journey of the spermatozoa

The movement of the spermatozoa from the testis to the site of fertilisation involves an epic journey. On leaving the testis the spermatozoa pass into the epididymis which consists of an extremely long, twisted tube. Here they are stored for a time. As the spermatozoa pass through the next tube, the vas deferens, they become **motile** or capable of moving themselves by the lashing of their tails. During sexual excitement the penis engorges with blood and becomes erect. This enables it to be positioned in the vagina of the female. The spermatozoa are mixed with secretions of the various glands to form **semen** and ejected into the female reproductive tract as the result of a brief series of muscular contractions known as **ejaculation**. Typically about 300–500 million sperm contained in 3–4 cm^3 of fluid will be deposited high up in the vagina.

The semen coagulates after ejaculation, which seems to help to prevent the loss of the fluid from the female reproductive tract. The sperm are then moved up through the cervix and the uterus into the Fallopian tubes very rapidly – spermatozoa reach the upper parts of the tubes between 5 and 30 minutes after intercourse has taken place. It was originally thought that they 'swam' but the current model is that the spermatozoa are moved mainly by contractions of the female reproductive tract. The movements of sperm which are observed seem to be more important for maintaining them in suspension in the semen and for the fertilisation of the egg than for movement. The difficulty of the journey undertaken is such that, in spite of the millions of sperm which start off, only a few hundred to a few thousand reach the ovum.

Copulation

Mating in most mammals is the result of instinctive behaviour patterns which occur when sex hormone levels reach a particular level and the environmental cues are appropriate. In humans the situation is more complicated, since mating (more commonly referred to as sexual intercourse or copulation in the human context) can take place at any time of year, regardless of the likelihood of ovulation occurring. Sexual arousal in the male causes the erection of the penis and the events already described. In the female, sexual arousal rather than simple hormone levels ensures the secretion of extra mucus in the vagina to make penetration by the penis easier. Also the **clitoris**, a tiny sexual organ similar in structure and sensitivity to the penis, gives sexual enjoyment when appropriately stimulated. It may be this level of voluntary rather than innate involvement of both partners which has freed human sexuality from the bonds of oestrus.

The female role in sperm movement

Once the sperm enter the female reproductive tract they are moved largely by the female system.

(1) Around the time of ovulation the vaginal mucus changes in pH in response to the changing levels of sex hormones. It is normally so acidic that it tends to kill sperm. At the fertile time it becomes more alkaline to prevent sperm damage.
(2) In a similar way, mucus which blocks the cervix preventing the entry of microorganisms becomes much less viscous, allowing the spermatozoa to move through it more easily.

(3) **Prostaglandins** (local hormones) in the semen and **oxytocin**, a hormone released from the female posterior pituitary gland during sexual intercourse, cause contractions in the uterus which move the semen towards the Fallopian tubes.
(4) Groups of cilia in the lower end of the Fallopian tubes appear to beat upwards, carrying the semen towards the ovum.

The meeting of the gametes

The female ovum is fully viable for only a few hours. The male sperm will survive a day or two in the female reproductive tract. There is little evidence to suggest that the sperm are attracted to the egg in any way. Yet, in spite of this, they frequently do meet and fuse. What happens when sperm meets egg?

During their passage through the female reproductive tract spermatozoa become fully activated in a process known as **capacitation**. This involves a change in the membrane covering the acrosome, after which the sperm are able to penetrate the egg. The ovulated ovum has not fully completed meiosis and is a secondary oocyte (see section 5.2, page 373). It is surrounded by a protective jelly-like layer known as the zona pellucida and also by some of the follicle cells. Many sperm cluster around the ovum, and as soon as the head of the sperm touch the surface of the ovum the **acrosome reaction** is triggered, shown in figure 5.5.1. Enzymes are released from the acrosomes which digest the follicle cells and the zona pellucida. One sperm alone does not produce sufficient enzyme to digest all the protective layers around the ovum, and the very large number of sperm initially released in ejaculation ensures that there are sufficient sperm present in the Fallopian tube to surround the ovum and digest its defences.

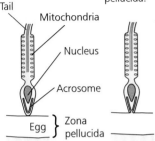

The front of a sperm touches the jelly coat of the egg and the acrosome reaction is triggered.

Tail
Mitochondria
Nucleus
Acrosome
Egg } Zona pellucida

Digestive enzymes pour out of the opened acrosome and begin to digest away the zona pellucida.

Projections of the sperm surface shoot forward as a result of actin-like proteins.

Fertilisation occurs when one projection touches the surface of the egg and the membranes fuse.

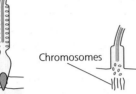

The sperm nucleus rapidly decondenses and the chromosomes are released into the egg cell to fuse with the female nucleus.

Chromosomes

Figure 5.5.1 The acrosome reaction plays a vital role in the fertilisation of the egg. It is thought that the enzymes from a number of acrosome reactions are needed to enable one sperm to eventually break through the protective layers.

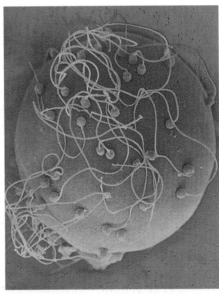

Figure 5.5.2 Sperm meets egg – and a new life begins. Once the head of a sperm has fused with the membrane of the egg a complex series of reactions takes place to ensure that no other sperm can enter, and the development of the new diploid zygote can begin undisturbed.

Eventually one sperm will wriggle its way through the weakened protective barriers and touch the surface membrane of the oocyte. This has several almost instantaneous effects. The oocyte undergoes its second meiotic division, providing a haploid egg nucleus to fuse with the haploid male nucleus. It is vital that no other sperm enter the egg, as this would result in triploid or polyploid nuclei (with several sets of chromosomes), and the other events that follow fertilisation prevent this possibility. There are immediate changes in the electrical properties of the cell surface membrane of the ovum so that the inside, instead of being negative with respect to the outside, becomes positive. This alteration in charge prevents the entry of any further sperm. It is a temporary measure until a tough **fertilisation membrane** forms which then repels other sperm as the electrical charge returns to normal. Fertilisation is also referred to as **conception** in the case of humans, and is shown in figure 5.5.2.

The head of the sperm enters the oocyte, and the tail region is left outside. Once the head is inside the ovum it absorbs water and swells up, releasing its chromosomes to join those of the ovum and forming a diploid **zygote**. At this point fertilisation has occurred and a new genetic individual has been formed.

Development of the embryo

Formation of the embryo

If the ovum is fertilised, a complex series of events is set in motion which in humans will lead to the birth of (usually) one fully formed new individual. The first stage of this process is known as **cleavage**. Cleavage involves a special kind of mitosis, where cells divide repeatedly without a substantial interphase for growth between the divisions. A mass of small, identical and undifferentiated cells results which forms a hollow sphere known as a **blastocyst**. Cleavage occurs as the zygote is moved along the Fallopian tube towards the uterus, which in humans takes about one week. A large number of small cells result from one large egg cell.

Figure 5.5.3 By the time a woman misses a menstrual period and begins to suspect that she might be pregnant, the fertilised ovum has undergone a series of rapid mitotic divisions to produce the hollow ball of cells known as the blastocyst, and this has begun to implant itself in the lining of the uterus.

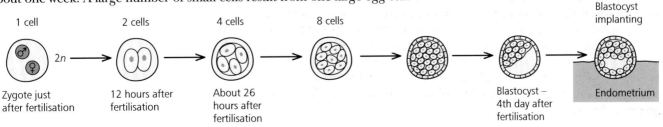

1 cell | 2 cells | 4 cells | 8 cells | | Blastocyst implanting

Zygote just after fertilisation

12 hours after fertilisation

About 26 hours after fertilisation

Blastocyst – 4th day after fertilisation

Endometrium

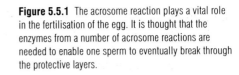

After several days in the uterus the 50–100-cell blastocyst must embed itself into the lining of the uterus for the pregnancy to be recognised by the body and development to continue. Finger-like projections (**trophoblastic villi**) grow out from the outer layer (**trophoblast**) of the blastocyst. These embed themselves into the lining of the uterus, usually at the top end of the uterus, and eventually form the site of the placenta. This is known as **implantation**. It is usually completed about 11 or 12 days after fertilisation, and from this time onwards the woman is considered to be pregnant. Figure 5.5.3 illustrates the events leading up to implantation.

In the development of the human embryo the major organ systems are completed by around the 12th week of the 40-week pregnancy. By the end of this time the embryo is a tiny but recognisable human infant as shown in figure 5.5.4, although totally incapable of life outside the uterus. During these weeks the embryo is particularly vulnerable to any harmful substances which the mother may take in. Eighty per cent of the birth defects which occur in live births are caused by **teratogens**. These are environmental influences which affect the development of the embryo, usually at the early stages when organ systems are forming. Drugs such as thalidomide (which affects the growth of the limbs), nicotine from cigarette smoking and alcohol, diseases such as rubella (German measles) which affects the ears and brain and ionising radiation such as X-rays can all cause irreparable damage in the initial stages of pregnancy.

From around 12 weeks onwards the developing individual is known as a **fetus**. The remaining time in the uterus is used mainly for growth and maturation of the tissues and the fetus is much less vulnerable to the influence of teratogens. The rate of growth in a developing embryo is phenomenal. Rat pregnancies last just 22 days from fertilisation to birth. In that time the embryo increases from one to three billion cells, as the result of simple, steady mitosis. Even this level of growth pales into insignificance compared with the development of the blue whale. A whale ovum is less than a millimetre in diameter and weighs a fraction of a gram. The newborn calf that results from the fertilisation of such an egg is 7 metres long and weighs 2000 kg, representing a 20 million-fold increase in mass.

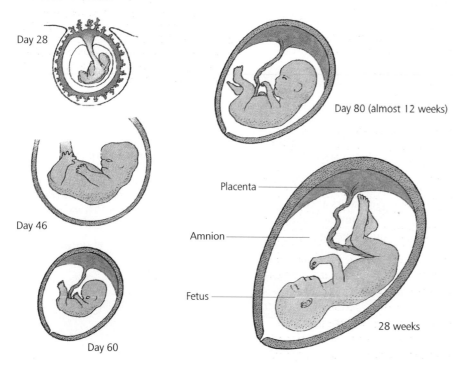

Day 28

Day 46

Day 60

Day 80 (almost 12 weeks)

Placenta

Amnion

Fetus

28 weeks

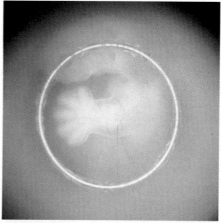

5 weeks

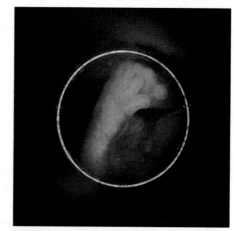

6 weeks

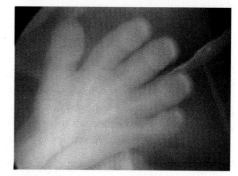

7–8 weeks

Figure 5.5.4 The human hand develops from a simple paddle to a sophisticated tool in just a few weeks, and the other systems of the body form similarly at the same time. Most of the period of gestation is spent in growth and maturation rather than in tissue differentiation.

Formation and functions of the membranes

The dividing mass of cells of the zygote in the early stages of gestation also forms the **extraembryonic membranes**. These membranes, shown in figure 5.5.5, play a vital role in the development of the fetus. They are present right up to the time of birth – the rupturing of the membranes and the subsequent release of the fluid they contain is a sign that the birth of the baby is imminent.

The membranes fold around the embryo to form the **amniotic cavity**. This is filled with **amniotic fluid** in which the embryo and fetus grows. The fluid supports the developing fetus, allowing it the freedom to move about easily. It provides a medium in which to practise swallowing and breathing movements and holds urine as it is voided. The amniotic fluid also cushions and protects the fetus from damage by external injury or impact to the mother – only a very violent blow would have any effect on the fetus. The inner membrane is the **amnion**, and the outer of the two is the **chorion**. After the initial implantation into the lining of the uterus by the blastocyst, it is the chorion that takes over the formation of the **placenta**, the area where the fetal and maternal blood exchange various substances (this is described below). Another cavity, the **allantois**, arises from the gut of the embryo and in humans this is destined to become the **umbilical cord** which links the embryo to the mother.

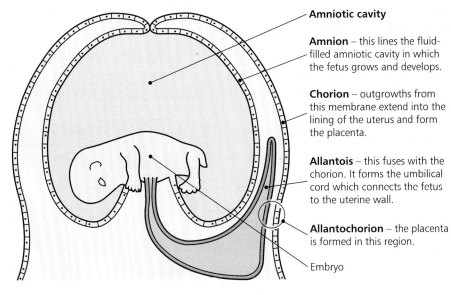

Amniotic cavity

Amnion – this lines the fluid-filled amniotic cavity in which the fetus grows and develops.

Chorion – outgrowths from this membrane extend into the lining of the uterus and form the placenta.

Allantois – this fuses with the chorion. It forms the umbilical cord which connects the fetus to the uterine wall.

Allantochorion – the placenta is formed in this region.

Embryo

Figure 5.5.5 The extraembryonic membranes in mammals are developed as part of the products of fertilisation – they are not produced by the maternal tissues. They play vital roles in the maintenance of the fetus during the period of development within the uterus. Babies are sometimes born still completely surrounded by these membranes – 'born in a caul'. This used to be regarded as a sign of good luck and an omen that the individual would never die by drowning. Now it is more likely to be regarded simply as a result of extremely tough membranes!

Formation and functions of the placenta

The surface of the chorion develops large numbers of finger-like projections into the endometrium, the maternal tissue lining the uterus. These form in the region shown in figure 5.5.5 as the allantochorion, and are known as the **chorionic villi**. They provide a vast surface area for the exchange of substances between the fetal and maternal blood. To make the exchange even easier the maternal blood vessels of the endometrium break down in the regions of the invading chorionic villi, so that the villi are bathed in maternal blood and the distance for diffusion of substances is only about 0.002 mm. A mature placenta towards the end of pregnancy is a disc about 20 cm across and 6 cm thick, with a surface area for exchange of 16 m² – equivalent to almost half a tennis court!

The site where the placenta forms is of great importance to the progress of the pregnancy. In the majority of cases it is in the upper third of the uterus, but sometimes the placenta forms lower down near the cervix (**placenta praevia**) when problems may arise at delivery. Without medical intervention the placenta would be delivered before the baby, which would then die from lack of oxygen.

The mother would also be at risk from loss of blood from the site of the placenta. Routine ultrasound scans in pregnancy now pick up this condition so that the pregnancy can be monitored and a Caesarian section carried out.

What are the substances that are exchanged across this organ made up partly of tissue from one individual and partly of tissue from another? Oxygen and dissolved food substances pass from the mother to the fetus. Waste products of metabolism such as carbon dioxide and urea pass from the fetus to the maternal system for removal from the body. Some antibodies may also pass from the mother to the fetus, providing it with temporary immunity to certain diseases. The placenta also acts as a barrier, protecting the developing fetus from many microorganisms and drugs which cannot cross from the mother to the fetus. Figure 5.5.6 shows how exchange takes place across the placenta.

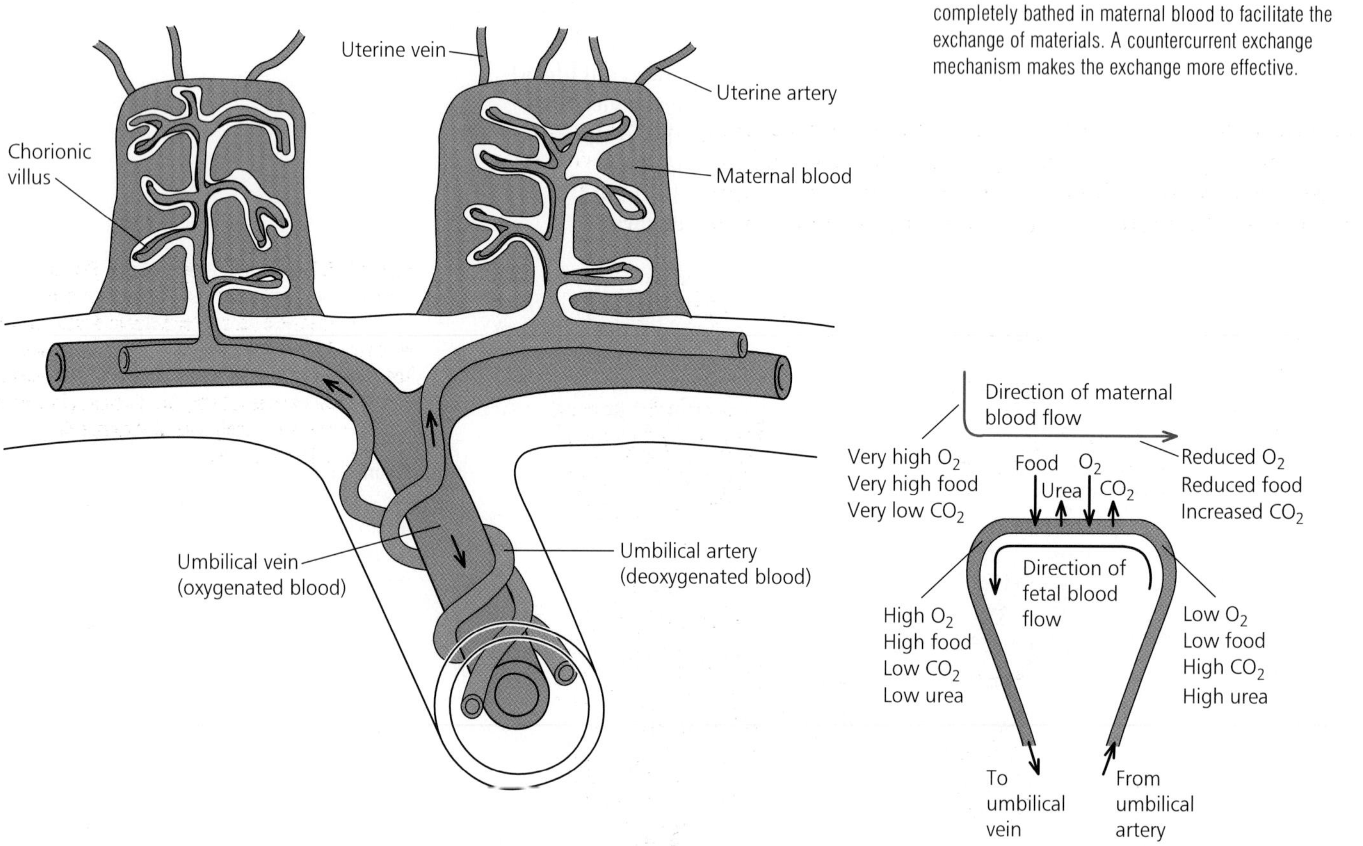

Figure 5.5.6 Within the placenta the fetal villi are completely bathed in maternal blood to facilitate the exchange of materials. A countercurrent exchange mechanism makes the exchange more effective.

Why the maternal and fetal blood are not mixed

It might be thought that the easiest way to supply the fetus with nutrients would be for maternal blood to flow through it. However, this would be disastrous for a number of reasons, detailed below.

(1) The maternal blood is under relatively high pressure compared with the fetal system which could damage the delicate tissues of the developing fetus.

(2) The maternal blood and that of the fetus may not be of the same blood group and so mixing would result in agglutination of one or the other.

(3) Most importantly, if the two bloods mixed the fetal blood would be recognised as foreign by the maternal blood. The maternal immune system would respond to and destroy the fetus. This is because half the genetic material in the fetus comes from the father and so the fetal cells are not identical to those of the mother. Surprisingly, the maternal system does not recognise and destroy the invading chorionic villi. They appear to be coated with special molecules which prevent the maternal blood from reacting adversely to them. The mechanism for this protection is not fully understood. When we understand how the fetus avoids rejection by the mother, then the treatment of skin grafts and organ transplants should be greatly improved if we can mimic this 'anti-rejection' message.

Multiple births

A **multiple birth** occurs when more than one fetus develops in the uterus at the same time. The most common type of multiple birth in humans is twins (two fetuses), which occur about once in every 90 births. Triplets (three fetuses) and quadruplets (four fetuses) may occur naturally but they are very rare.

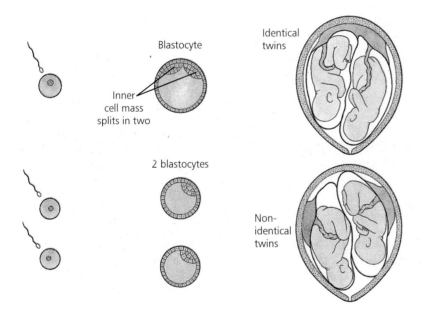

Figure 5.5.7 If twins are different sexes they are obviously the result of two fertilisations and non-identical. There is a genetic tendency to double-ovulate, which is why non-identical twins can run in families. The presence of one placenta rather than two suggests that identical twins result from the divisions of a single egg. No one is yet entirely sure what causes the formation of identical twins.

How do these relatively rare events come about? They are usually chance occurrences, happening either when more than one ovum ripens and is released at ovulation, or when a single ovum is fertilised but the zygote splits into two during the first two weeks of development. There is a genetic tendency to release more than one ovum at the fertile time of the menstrual cycle, but it can also happen randomly. The use of fertility drugs in the treatment of those with fertility problems often increases the likelihood of a multiple pregnancy by increasing the number of ova released, as does the technique known as *in vitro* fertilisation.

Twins may result from the fusing of one egg and one sperm (**identical** or **monozygotic twins**), or they may result from two quite different eggs and sperm (**non-identical** or **dizygotic**). The differences are shown in figure 5.5.7.

Hormonal control of pregnancy

As we saw in section 5.4 the female reproductive cycle is under the control of several hormones. When the cycle is interrupted by pregnancy, hormones again play a vital part. One of the most common causes of miscarriage – the spontaneous abortion of the embryo or fetus in the early stages of development – is insufficient production of hormones at the appropriate time.

Once the embryo has implanted it sends a hormonal message into the blood of the mother. This is **human chorionic gonadotrophic hormone** (**HCG**) and it stimulates the corpus luteum in the ovary to keep producing progesterone and so maintain the pregnancy. Some of this HCG is excreted in the urine of the mother, and this forms the basis for many of the pregnancy testing kits now available.

At the end of the first 12 weeks of pregnancy the production of HCG by the implanted embryo begins to decrease. This is a critical time for the pregnancy, because if the drop in the levels of HCG is matched by a corresponding drop in progesterone levels, then the lining of the uterus will be shed and the pregnancy lost in miscarriage. At the same time as the embryonic production of HCG falls away, the rapidly maturing placenta begins to manufacture and secrete large amounts of progesterone which carries on the role of maintaining the endometrium and inhibiting further menstrual cycles. In this way the pregnancy is maintained until the time of birth.

Pregnancy tests

When a woman thinks she might be pregnant, she (and often her partner too) will want to know for sure as soon as possible. Pregnancy tests have been available for some time, based on detecting the levels of pregnancy hormones excreted in the woman's urine. Some early tests involved applying the woman's urine to a certain type of toad. If the toad laid eggs, the woman was pregnant!

Modern pregnancy tests are extremely sensitive and can give an indication of whether a woman is pregnant as early as the day her period is due. A positive result means she is definitely pregnant, while a negative result may simply mean that the hormone levels have not built up enough to be detected and the test needs to be repeated a few days later.

The basis of most pregnancy tests is the use of monoclonal antibodies which bind to the hormone HCG produced by the embryo. The test consists of a special dipstick containing immobilised anti-HCG antibodies and also mobile anti-HCG antibodies which have coloured molecules attached to them. The woman dips the stick into a sample of urine. As the urine moves up the stick, any HCG molecules are bound by the mobile coloured antibodies. The resulting complex is carried to the static antibodies where it stops, forming a coloured line or spot which is visible through a viewing window and indicates a positive result. As a control to show that the test has worked, a line or spot forms at a different window if the result is negative.

Sometimes the HCG levels are too low to give a reliable reading, or there may be difficulties later in the pregnancy. In these situations a blood test can be carried out to measure accurately the levels of the hormones progesterone and HCG produced by the placenta.

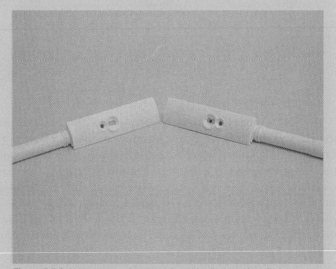

Figure 5.5.8 Home pregnancy tests such as this allow people to find out as soon as possible whether they are expecting a baby.

The effect of pregnancy on the mother

Pregnancy has a profound effect on the body, influencing almost every system of the woman who is carrying the developing fetus. It is also a remarkable experience psychologically, particularly once the developing baby is large enough to be felt moving and having hiccups, to have another person living within the same body. If the pregnancy is wanted and the woman is healthy, it can be a most exciting and rewarding time. Conversely, if the mother feels ill or the baby is not planned or wanted, then it can be a time of great hardship and distress.

One of the most obvious effects of pregnancy is a gain in body mass, starting around the 14th week of pregnancy and stopping at about week 36. The amount gained varies enormously from woman to woman and from pregnancy to pregnancy. Ideally the gain in mass should not be too large, because this can put a strain on the skeleton and joints and also on the cardiovascular system. By the end of the pregnancy most women will have gained around 10 kg, made up by the mass of the baby, the placenta, the amniotic fluid, the enlarged uterus and breasts and the increase in the circulating volume of blood. There may also be some extra fluid retention and some women gain fat, not least because as their pregnancy progresses they may become less active.

The average non-pregnant woman has about 5 dm^3 of blood circulating in her body. In pregnancy the need for blood increases – the uterus, placenta, breasts and other organs which are growing all need extra blood supplies. By around the 34th week of pregnancy the blood volume will have increased by about 30–40 per cent, giving a blood volume of 6.5–7 dm^3. It is important that it is not just the plasma volume that increases – the number of red cells must rise too as the growing fetus is also developing a circulation and making red blood cells. It is particularly important for pregnant women to have plenty of iron and vitamins in their diet, or they can become very anaemic. Once the hormone levels fall after birth, the blood volume rapidly returns to normal.

The heart too has to work very hard during pregnancy. The pulse rate changes very little but the heart itself enlarges so that the volume of blood pumped in every beat (the cardiac volume) is increased. The cardiac volume of the heart increases by about 30–40 per cent during pregnancy, but within days of delivery it has returned to its original value.

Another system affected by pregnancy is the kidneys. They have to filter an increased blood volume and also excrete the urea produced by the developing fetus as well as that from the mother. They have the capacity to do this without major structural change.

Figure 5.5.9 Pregnancy puts new demands on the female physiology, but most women cope with both pregnancy and getting on with their everyday lives without too much trouble.

Danger in the uterus

The body systems have evolved to keep a developing fetus safe in the uterus, protected from danger as it grows to full term. However, substances taken in by the mother can have a harmful effect on her developing infant, particularly during the first 12 weeks of pregnancy when the major systems are being formed.

Figure 5.5.10 The facial abnormalities that mark babies with FAS can be clearly seen in this child. The mother stopped drinking once she realised she was pregnant, but it was too late.

- **Alcohol** readily crosses the placenta into the blood of the developing fetus. The fetal liver cannot deal with alcohol properly, so the levels in its blood will be twice those in the mother's blood. Repeated exposure to alcohol causes fetal alcohol syndrome (FAS). Babies affected are born early and have a low birth mass, facial abnormalities, heart defects and, if exposed to alcohol in the last three months of pregnancy, they also have brain malformation, causing sight and hearing problems, fits and poor motor coordination.

- **Smoking** – after smoking a cigarette, up to 10 per cent of the haemoglobin in the blood of a smoker will be carrying carbon monoxide rather than oxygen. The haemoglobin of a pregnant woman is carrying oxygen not just for her own cellular respiratory needs but for her developing fetus as well. Fetal haemoglobin has a high affinity for oxygen so it picks up oxygen from the maternal haemoglobin in the placenta and carries it round the fetal circulation, supplying all the developing tissues. If the maternal blood does not contain enough oxygen as a result of smoking, the fetus suffers long-term oxygen deprivation and this can lead to growth problems, reduced development of the brain, and ultimately to premature birth, low birth mass and even stillbirth (the baby is born dead) or neonatal death (it dies soon after birth).

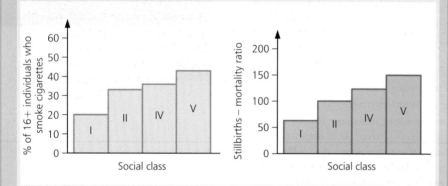

Figure 5.5.11 These graphs suggest a very close relationship between the incidence of smoking and the incidence of stillbirths.

- **Drugs** – medical drugs taken during pregnancy can cause huge problems, as thalidomide clearly showed. This drug was given to pregnant women in the 1950s and 1960s, and resulted in the birth of many babies with greatly reduced or missing arms and legs. Doctors are now very careful about what they prescribe to pregnant women, but it is best to avoid drugs if possible when pregnant. Illegal drugs can also cause great damage to unborn babies – for example, heroin increases the risk of spontaneous abortions (miscarriages), premature births and stillbirths. Drug users also run the risk that their babies will be born addicted to the same drug, and newborn babies suffering from drug withdrawal symptoms do not have a good start to life.
- **Food-borne organisms** – some of the organisms that can cause food poisoning in adults can infect unborn babies too. An example is *Listeria monocytogenes*, found in unpasteurised cheeses, ready-prepared chilled meals and ready-to-eat chicken. The symptoms of a *Listeria* infection are not usually severe in adults, but if a pregnant woman eats infected food early in her pregnancy she will probably miscarry, and later in the pregnancy it may cause the baby to be born severely ill and to die or be permanently damaged.

These are some of the main risk factors for a fetus in the uterus, although there are others. Pregnant women have to be vigilant and remember that what they put into their bodies can have very long-term effects on the baby they are carrying.

Initiation of birth

The most dangerous journey most of us will ever undertake is the short distance from the uterus of our mother to the outside world. It is a passage which, even today with advanced technologies, is fraught with difficulties and dangers for both mother and infant. At the end of the human gestation period, which lasts approximately 40 weeks, the fetus is outgrowing the uterus. The placenta becomes less efficient and space is at a premium. It is the increasingly cramped fetus rather than the mother which initiates the birth process.

Evidence for the role of the fetus in initiating birth

The importance of the fetal role in the birth process has been studied in a variety of ways, but some of the most interesting evidence came from simple observations of a natural phenomenon. Shepherds in Idaho noticed that certain pregnant sheep died with their lamb fetuses unborn but extremely large – up to two or three times the normal size. Careful observation showed that this occurred in sheep which had eaten large quantities of a certain weed (*Veratrum californicum*). When biologists investigated the weed they found that it contained a chemical which interferes with the pituitary and adrenal glands of the fetus. This in turn led to the discovery of the sequence of events which we now believe takes place to initiate and maintain birth.

The sequence of events which triggers the process of birth is believed to be as follows. The fetal pituitary secretes ACTH, which in turn stimulates the fetal adrenal glands to produce steroid compounds. These steroids affect the maternal cells of the placenta to produce substances called **prostaglandins**, which act as local hormones and cause the muscles of the uterus to contract. As the head of the fetus is pressed down onto the cervix, stretch receptors fire and send messages to the maternal brain causing the release of **oxytocin**. This also causes the uterine muscle to contract. The process is outlined in figure 5.5.12.

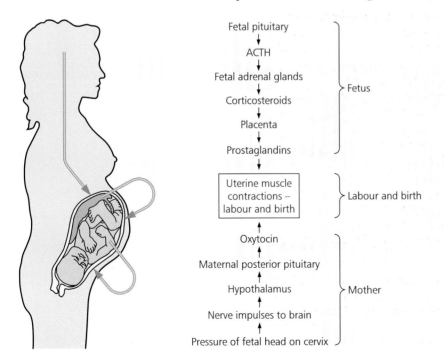

Figure 5.5.12 The fetus is believed to initiate the birth process. Hormones from the fetus, the placenta and the maternal brain all act together to bring about birth.

The stages of birth

To expel a fully developed fetus from the uterus into the outside world is no easy task. The process, known as **labour**, involves the contraction of the uterine muscles, which are the strongest in the body. The process is often lengthy and can be very painful.

There are three main stages. During the first stage of labour the uterine contractions increase in both frequency and strength. Their major function at this stage is to cause the dilation of the cervix from a gap of a few millimetres to the 10 cm needed to allow the passage of the head of the baby.

The second stage of labour occurs once the cervix is fully dilated. It involves the actual delivery of the baby. Both the involuntary muscles of the uterus and the voluntary muscles of the abdomen are used in a massive expulsive effort to push the fetus out from the uterus, through the cervix and out along the vagina.

The third and final stage of labour is the use of those same muscles to push the now redundant placenta out of the body after it has peeled away from the uterine wall.

The arrival of a healthy full-term baby is the hoped-for outcome of every planned pregnancy. It can be somewhat sobering to discover that it is not all that easy to achieve this target. From every 1000 human eggs exposed to sperm only around 310 live infants will result. Not all the eggs will be fertilised and many of those that are will be miscarried either before or after the pregnancy is recognised, due to hormone insufficiencies or abnormalities of the developing embryo/fetus. The result of this filtering is that the majority of fetuses which make it through the pregnancy to term are relatively free from abnormalities.

Changes at birth

As the fetus emerges at the moment of birth and the first breath is drawn into its lungs a new independent life begins. The transition from fetus to baby involves some very complex changes. Whilst in the uterus the fetus is supplied with all the food and oxygen it needs through the placenta. Waste products are removed in the same way. The body is cushioned and supported by the amniotic fluid. But after birth all these support systems are removed and the infant must perform their functions itself if it is to survive. What does this transition entail?

The heart and lungs

Some of the most critical initial changes occur in the cardiovascular system and lungs. In the uterus the lungs are filled with fluid and receive very little blood as they play no part in oxygenation. After birth they must immediately inflate with the first breath – this is made possible by the presence of **lung surfactant**, described in section 2.4. Changes must also take place in the circulation of the blood through the heart. The fetal heart differs from that of an adult in two main ways. The two sides of the fetal heart are not completely separate. They are joined by the **foramen ovale** and the blood in the two sides can mix relatively freely. Also, the pulmonary artery which leaves the right-hand side of the heart carrying blood to the lungs is joined to the main aorta by a small vessel called the **ductus arteriosus**. Up to 90% of the blood which enters the right atrium goes not to the lungs but into the aorta through the ductus, because the resistance of the fluid-filled lungs is much higher than that of the rest of the system. From the aorta blood flows to the placenta in the umbilical artery, where it will be oxygenated.

At birth this circulation must change to allow the blood to gain oxygen from the lungs rather than from the placenta. In the first few hours after birth the ductus arteriosus narrows and a flap descends to cover the foramen ovale.

Within minutes of birth 90% of the blood leaving the right atrium travels to the lungs, which have a much lower resistance now that they are inflated. This enables oxygenation of the blood to occur. Within a few weeks of birth both the ductus and the foramen have been permanently closed. If they do not close up properly, abnormal heart sounds and problems associated with ineffective oxygenation of the blood will be noticed. An incompletely closed foramen ovale, commonly called a 'hole in the heart', can be a life-threatening condition, but many people live long and healthy lives with a slight gap in their heart septum. The changes in the heart between fetus and child can be seen in figure 5.5.13.

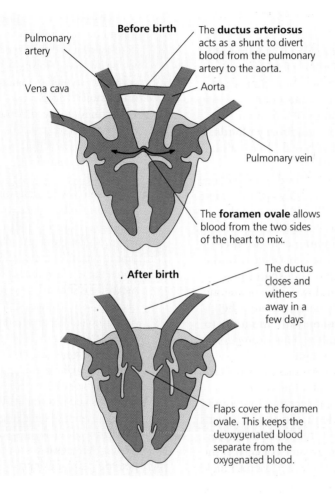

Before birth

Pulmonary artery

The **ductus arteriosus** acts as a shunt to divert blood from the pulmonary artery to the aorta.

Vena cava

Aorta

Pulmonary vein

The **foramen ovale** allows blood from the two sides of the heart to mix.

After birth

The ductus closes and withers away in a few days

Flaps cover the foramen ovale. This keeps the deoxygenated blood separate from the oxygenated blood.

Figure 5.5.13 The structure of the heart changes at birth.

The liver

The other major organ system which has a greatly increased workload after birth is the liver, which has to deal with the pigment bilirubin, one of the main breakdown products of fetal haemoglobin. The level of bilirubin in the blood increases to levels where it causes a yellowish tinge in the tissues of the newborn infant known as **physiological jaundice**. This is so common in newborn infants as to be normal, but the yellow colour may become very pronounced if the liver is slow to start bilirubin breakdown. If the bilirubin levels get too high, brain damage can occur. To prevent this babies are monitored carefully and treated by exposure to broad spectrum light if bilirubin levels rise too high. The light breaks down the bilirubin into substances which can be managed by the infant system until the liver becomes effective at breaking down haemoglobin.

Reproduction represents a considerable investment of biological resources, particularly for the female of the species. Many aquatic organisms which release their gametes directly into the water provide no care for their offspring. In other animals the parental involvement in the development of the offspring is greater, and the level of parental care once the offspring have hatched or been born is generally greater too. There are examples of fish, amphibians and reptiles which take great care of their young, and birds are well known for their extensive parenting, both in incubating eggs and feeding the offspring after hatching. Mammals show an even greater level of infant care.

Producing milk

Even the most prolific mammalian breeders produce a relatively small number of offspring. However, the mammals have evolved a method of providing almost guaranteed food for their offspring. This maximises their chances of survival and so minimises the wastage of resources. This evolutionary breakthrough is the production by specialised sweat glands of a protein-rich liquid to feed the offspring. The modified glands are the **mammary glands**, and it is the possession of these that provides the mammals with their name. The protein-rich liquid is more commonly known as **milk**.

In humans breast feeding provides infants with the ideal food – the balance of fats, proteins, carbohydrates, minerals and vitamins is exactly appropriate to the needs of a growing human baby (see figure 5.5.14). The balance of the different components varies with how long the baby has been suckling, the weather and the age of the baby to ensure that all the infant needs are met. Until the age of around six months, no additional feeding is necessary. In the developed world many people begin additional feeding earlier than this, though physiological rejection mechanisms in the infant have to be overcome before this can be done. As well as providing a perfectly balanced diet, the major advantage of breast milk is that it provides the infant with immunity to those diseases to which the mother has acquired antibodies. This protection can be very important in maintaining the health of the infant.

The World Health Organisation has produced some very strongly worded directives advising that all babies should be breast fed if at all possible. Unfortunately in the developed world there is often great pressure for women to bottle feed, using modified milk from cows to provide the nutritional needs of their babies. Whilst this is frequently done successfully, the immunological advantages of breast milk cannot be mimicked. Of even greater concern is the spread of bottle feeding to the developing world. Here the water used to make

Hormonal control of milk production

The production of milk is a complex process, precisely controlled by a number of hormones.

- During pregnancy the placenta produces **human placental lactogen**. Along with raised levels of oestrogen and progesterone, this hormone stimulates the development and growth of the mammary glands during pregnancy in preparation for milk production.
- **Prolactin** is produced by the anterior pituitary gland. It stimulates the milk ducts to make milk and maintains milk production.
- **Oxytocin** is produced by the posterior pituitary gland. It stimulates delivery of milk to the infant. Milk is produced all the time in the milk glands, and is stored there. When the baby suckles, this stimulates the release of oxytocin which causes the contraction of the myoepithelial cells surrounding the milk glands. The milk is squeezed out from the glands, through the milk ducts and into the baby's mouth. This process is known as the **let-down reflex**. It can take some time to be effective when a baby first starts feeding, but it gives a surprisingly powerful jet of milk once established. It rapidly becomes a conditioned reflex, and mothers will begin letting down milk as they prepare to feed or even when they hear their baby cry.

Figure 5.5.14 Milk production from the mammary glands is almost unaffected by the levels of nutrition of the mother, thus ensuring that the infant is adequately fed under most circumstances. Not content with human milk, we have attempted to modify the milk of cows to feed our offspring, in spite of the fact that the balance of protein, fats, minerals and vitamins in the two milks are very different as they are tailored to different needs.

up infant feeds may be infected by a variety of diseases, the feed is often not concentrated enough as the milk powder is expensive and the lack of immunological protection is particularly important.

Different milks for different mammals

The milk mammals produce for their young is uniquely adapted to the particular demands of the growth patterns of the species. For example, newly born whales and seals have to cope with living in very cold conditions. They need to develop a thick layer of blubber as rapidly as possible and therefore they need a very high calorie intake. The milk of female whales and seals is extremely high in fats – it is very, very thick and creamy and has the necessary high calorie content.

The young of grazing herbivores such as antelope and cows need to grow very rapidly to keep up with other members of the herd and to escape predators. The milk of these animals is relatively low in fats but high in the protein needed to produce new tissues.

Human milk is relatively low in both protein and fat. Human babies need to grow quite slowly to allow their brains to develop and assimilate the enormous amount of complex behaviour that allows human societies to function. Thus the milk of each mammal is tailored to meet the requirements of its growing offspring.

Contraception

As we have seen, humans appear to be the only mammal in which copulation and reproduction are no longer synonymous with each other. The human sexual drive or **libido** is not seasonal. Whilst tiredness, ill-health and many other factors may influence the frequency of copulation between a couple, in theory intercourse may occur at any time throughout the year. However, many people do not wish to risk pregnancy whenever they have sex, and for centuries various methods of **contraception** (ways of preventing conception) have been suggested. These have included vinegar-soaked sponges placed in the vagina before intercourse, mixtures of camel dung and various herbs similarly placed, and reusable condoms made from animal intestines.

At the present time methods of contraception fall into several categories. **Natural methods** are based on an understanding of the menstrual cycle and accurate predictions of the point of ovulation. Their major advantage is that they are accepted even by those religious groups which condemn other methods of controlling family size. **Physical** or **barrier methods** of contraception involve physical barriers which prevent the meeting of the ovum and the spermatozoa. **Chemical methods** involve chemicals which work in a variety of ways to do the same thing. **Sterilisation** is the ultimate form of contraception. By cutting or tying the tubes along which egg or sperm travel, conception is rendered almost impossible. This has the additional benefit of not having to remember to use contraception, the major cause of failure in the other methods. These methods of contraception are summarised in table 5.5.1.

Contraception is largely used by people in the developed world. A combination of factors, including a desire to have a large family for fear of children dying and therefore lack of support in old age, lack of medical supervision, expense and religious condemnation, mean that in the developing world contraception does not as yet play a major role.

Hormones and contraception

The hormones that are involved in the menstrual cycle and the maintenance of pregnancy can be used to prevent unwanted pregnancies.

The **combined oral contraceptive pill** (more commonly called just 'the pill') contains synthetic oestrogens and progesterones. It raises the blood hormone levels to those of the early stages of pregnancy, and so suppresses the secretion of FSH. In turn this means that no follicles – and therefore no ova – develop. The high progesterone levels also inhibit menstruation, but it was found that women felt it psychologically disturbing to have no periods at all, so the pill is taken for 21 days and then a break is taken for 7 days before beginning the next cycle of pills. This allows a 'breakthrough bleed' as the progesterone levels drop, but does not allow time for follicles to develop. The pill hormones also prevent the build-up of the endometrium, change the pH of the vaginal environment, making it inhospitable to sperm, and thicken the mucus of the cervix, forming a physical barrier to the passage of sperm. This multiple contraceptive effect makes the pill a very reliable form of contraception as long as it is taken regularly.

The **progesterone-only pill** or 'mini-pill' contains very low doses of hormones, mainly progesterone. The level is not sufficient to suppress ovulation, but it does affect the mucus at the cervix and the vaginal environment and prevents the endometrium from building up. **Injections** and **implants** have been developed so that women do not have to take contraceptive pills regularly. Progestogen, a synthetic progesterone, may be injected into the muscle of the buttock, from where it is slowly released into the bloodstream. The hormone is at a level that both inhibits FSH production and affects cervical mucus. Progestogen implants consist of six small rods which are surgically placed under the skin of the upper arm. They have a contraceptive effect for about 5 years, although the hormone is at a level too low to inhibit ovulation.

Table 5.5.1 A summary of the main available methods of contraception

Method of contraception	How it works	Advantages/disadvantages
Rhythm (natural) **method**	Depends on monitoring the menstrual cycle and pinpointing ovulation by the rise in temperature associated with it or by changes in mucus. Intercourse is then avoided for several days before and after the expected date of ovulation to prevent ovum and sperm meeting.	*Advantages*: No side effects and permitted by, for example, the Catholic church. *Disadvantages*: Depends on full co-operation of both partners. Not always easy to pinpoint ovulation so pregnancy can result.
Condom (barrier method)	A thin latex sheath is placed over the penis before intercourse to collect the semen and so prevent ovum and sperm meeting.	*Advantages*: No side effects, no medical advice needed, offers some protection against sexually transmitted diseases such as syphilis and AIDS. *Disadvantages*: Can interrupt intercourse. Sheath may tear or get damaged during intercourse allowing semen to get through. Gives better protection when combined with spermicide.
Diaphragm or **cap** (barrier method)	A thin rubber diaphragm is inserted into the vagina before intercourse to cover the cervix and prevent the entry of sperm.	*Advantages*: No side effects, offers some protection against cervical cancer. *Disadvantages*: Must be initially fitted by a doctor. May be incorrectly positioned or damaged and allow sperm past. Gives better protection when combined with spermicide.
Female condom (barrier method)	Fitted inside vagina to cover the cervix and vagina and anchored externally.	*Advantages*: No side effects, no need for medical advice, offers some protection against sexually transmitted diseases. *Disadvantages*: May be damaged and allow sperm through. Gives better protection when combined with spermicide.

Method of contraception	How it works	Advantages/disadvantages
Intrauterine device (IUD)	This does not prevent conception – the ovum and the sperm may meet – but it interferes with and prevents the implantation of the ball of cells. An IUD is a device made of plastic and a metal, frequently copper, which is inserted into the uterus by a doctor and remains there all the time.	*Advantages:* Once inserted, no further steps need to be taken. Relatively effective at preventing implantation. *Disadvantages:* Can cause pain and heavy periods. Can cause uterine infections which may lead to infertility. If pregnancy does occur it has a high chance of being in the Fallopian tubes (ectopic pregnancy).
Spermicides (chemical method)	Chemicals which kill sperm when they come into contact with them. Often used as creams, foams, gels or pessaries with barrier methods of contraception such as condoms or the diaphragm.	*Advantages:* Readily available. *Disadvantages:* Used alone they are relatively ineffective at preventing pregnancy.
Contraceptive pill (chemical method)	'The pill' consists of synthetic chemicals which mimic the effects of the sex hormones. The combined pill contains both oestrogens and progestogens, and this prevents pregnancy by inhibiting ovulation as well as altering the environment of the vagina and the consistency of the mucus. The progesterone-only pill does not inhibit ovulation and needs to be taken at very precise time intervals to be effective.	*Advantages:* The combined pill particularly is very effective at preventing pregnancy. The pill is taken at regular daily intervals and so does not interfere with intercourse. It may offer some protection against certain tumours. *Disadvantages:* The pill may increase the risk of certain tumours. It can cause raised blood pressure and an increased tendency for the blood to clot.
Sterilisation	In men the vas deferens is cut (**vasectomy**) preventing sperm from getting into the semen. In women the Fallopian tubes are cut or tied to prevent the ovum reaching the uterus or the sperm reaching the ovum.	*Advantages:* Almost 100% guaranteed to prevent pregnancy. Permanent control of fertility. *Disadvantages:* For women in particular it involves a general anaesthetic. Not easily reversible.

Table 5.5.1 continued

The social consequences of contraception

The social consequences of effective contraception are very far-reaching. As a country develops and becomes industrialised, and particularly as the women in the population become educated, the rate of population growth tends to fall. The use of contraception of various types rises, and the average family size drops. Eventually, as in the UK at the moment where the average family size is around 1.7 children, the population is no longer replacing itself. The long-term prediction is that population numbers will fall and that a decreasing number of young people will be supporting an increasing number of old people as advances in medicine promote longer lives.

In the developing world, the situation is very different. People in general have larger families, and the use of contraception is not widespread for a variety of reasons. In areas of the world where there is an imposed religion, particularly Roman Catholicism or Islam, active contraception is condemned.

In many places a large family is a positive choice. In areas where the childhood mortality rate is high, people want plenty of children to ensure that some of them survive to adulthood. If there is no state support for old age or infirmity, a large family is one way of ensuring that you will be cared for as you get older. In many societies, the number of children in a family is a status symbol, and those with the largest families are those who will be most successful. Added into this equation is natural birth control. In societies where mothers have only subsistence levels of nutrition, babies may be breast fed for several years. Prolactin suppresses FSH secretion, so ovulation and menstruation are inhibited in a breast-feeding mother. Thus extended breast feeding separates the children, often giving bigger family spacings than those seen in developed countries.

Abortion: the choice

One of the important issues of birth control, which is also central to some of the implications of genetic diseases, is that of **abortion**. Most abortions are spontaneous and natural, when for some reason an embryo or fetus is not carried to term but dies and is lost. Natural abortion or **miscarriage** is very common indeed in the first three months of pregnancy. Most women will experience at least one early miscarriage during their child-bearing years. Some of these are so early that the woman does not even realise that she is pregnant, simply that her period is a bit late. In many cases the embryo or fetus has some sort of genetic problem, but sometimes there is no apparent reason for the loss.

However, there are circumstances where an apparently healthy pregnancy will be ended deliberately in a medical abortion. This is usually carried out if there is a risk to either the physical or mental health of the mother, or if the baby is handicapped in some way. Depending on both the culture of the country involved and the attitude of the individual doctor, the interpretation of these criteria varies greatly. In some European countries where there is relatively little use of contraception, abortion is used as a method of limiting family size, and almost every woman will have had at least one or two abortions. In other countries abortion is illegal and women have to go to extraordinary lengths if they need to terminate a pregnancy. Southern Ireland is an example, where until recently even young girls who become pregnant by rape or abuse were denied abortion and had to travel abroad for help.

Most abortions are carried out in the first three months of pregnancy, when the embryo is still very small and a long way from being capable of independent life. The lining of the uterus, including the embryo, is removed either by vacuum extraction or by scraping away the uterine lining (a 'D and C', or dilatation and curettage). However, in many countries abortion is legal until 20 weeks or even later. This is a traumatic process as the woman has to give birth, and it is usually only used when serious genetic handicaps are identified by amniocentesis testing later in the pregnancy.

The ethics of abortion cause great divides. On one side are those who believe that women have a right to decide if and when they wish to have a baby, and that every child born has the right to be a wanted child. Whilst everyone would prefer it if abortions were not necessary, these people feel that if a woman is pregnant and does not wish to be, or if the fetus has a genetic disorder or some other developmental problem, then a termination of that pregnancy is the right course to take.

Other people feel equally vehemently that it is never right to take a human life, even that of an embryo a few weeks old. They believe that the rights of the unborn should be equal to or take priority over those of the parents and any other siblings who might already be in the family, and that abortion is always wrong.

These are issues of great sensitivity about which people feel very strongly. The views on both sides need careful consideration, and each individual must reach his or her own conclusion.

Treating infertility

While many couples the world over use contraceptives to prevent the birth of unwanted babies, or have abortions to terminate unwanted pregnancies, other couples struggle desperately to produce a child of their own. There are many causes of infertility (see page 395) and until relatively recently little could be done to overcome the problems. But over the last 25 years or so infertility treatments have moved forward at a tremendous pace. It is now possible for many couples (though not every couple) to produce their own child even if their reproductive systems are not working properly.

For many years the techniques available to help infertile couples were very limited. **Artificial insemination by a donor** (**AID**), or the insertion into the vagina of sperm donated by an anonymous donor, could help those couples where the malfunction was in the male sperm production. But AID could not help couples whose problem lay in the female reproductive system. In recent years, many new methods of treatment have become available. Some of these are outlined below.

Using drugs to stimulate ovulation

As our knowledge of the hormonal control of fertility has increased, so has our ability to manipulate it artificially. The inability to ovulate has been treated for some time now with what are commonly known as **fertility drugs**. These may be synthetic hormones such as clomiphene which stimulate the pituitary gland of the patient to produce more gonadotrophins (hormones such as FSH which act on the ovary to bring about ovulation), or they may be the gonadotrophins themselves, extracted from the urine of post-menopausal women. In the early days of this treatment the risk of multiple pregnancies was high, and women conceived as many as eight embryos at once. Although a few women did give birth to quads, quins and sextuplets, with most of the babies surviving, many more had their hopes dashed as they miscarried the unnaturally high number of embryos. However badly a couple wants children, four or five babies at the same time are an enormous physical, emotional and financial strain. Nowadays the treatment has been greatly refined and the drug preparations are far more sophisticated. As a result, although there is still a higher risk of twins and triplets resulting from treatment with fertility drugs than from an unassisted pregnancy, many couples are treated successfully and large multiple pregnancies are generally a thing of the past.

In vitro fertilisation – a major breakthrough

The biggest breakthrough in the treatment of human infertility problems, and the technology which has opened a Pandora's box of possibilities for the future, is known in the popular press as the 'test tube baby' technique. More properly described as ***in vitro* fertilisation (IVF)**, it involves the fertilisation of the ovum outside of the mother's body and then the replacement of the embryo into the uterus to implant and develop as normal.

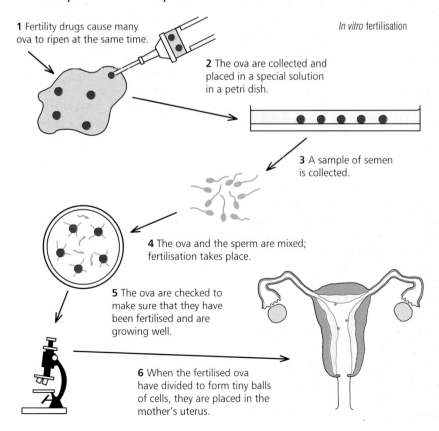

In vitro fertilisation

1 Fertility drugs cause many ova to ripen at the same time.

2 The ova are collected and placed in a special solution in a petri dish.

3 A sample of semen is collected.

4 The ova and the sperm are mixed; fertilisation takes place.

5 The ova are checked to make sure that they have been fertilised and are growing well.

6 When the fertilised ova have divided to form tiny balls of cells, they are placed in the mother's uterus.

Figure 5.5.15 The main steps in the process of *in vitro* fertilisation.

The first step in the process is to induce **superovulation**, giving fertility drugs to ensure that not just one but several ova ripen in the ovarian follicles. Just prior to natural ovulation these ova are harvested surgically and they are then mixed with sperm from the male partner in a Petri dish. Examination under a high powered microscope shows which ova have been fertilised, and those that appear undamaged are incubated until several cell divisions have occurred. The woman is meanwhile given further hormones to ensure that her uterus is ready to accept a pregnancy, and then several embryos are placed into their mother's body, as shown in figure 5.5.15. Different medical centres replace varying numbers of embryos. Some replace only one, but should that not implant the procedure needs to be repeated. Most replace two or three embryos, so that the failure of one or two to implant can still have a successful outcome. The risk of twins or triplets is thus increased when the technique works.

The technique of *in vitro* fertilisation was first developed by Patrick Steptoe and Robert Edwards in the 1980s. It is still very expensive, with a relatively low success rate, and is not widely available. Other easier and cheaper techniques have been developed from IVF, such as **gamete intra-fallopian transfer** (**GIFT**). Here the ova and sperm are collected and replaced immediately in the body again, but on the uterus side of the tube blockage. Several eggs are placed in the Fallopian tube in an attempt to ensure fertilisation, but of course no control can then be exercised over the number of embryos that eventually implant. Also, to enable couples to donate ova only once (it is a time-consuming, expensive and uncomfortable process), work has been done on the freezing of both ova and embryos. (Sperm have been successfully stored in liquid nitrogen for many years.) It is now possible for a couple to donate ova and sperm, have some of the fertilised ova implanted immediately and have the remainder frozen to be implanted later when they want another child. Even more recent developments include the ability to take a single sperm from a man who produces very few fertile spermatozoa and inject it directly into an ovum from the mother, which is then replaced in her uterus. Developing embryos have even been frozen, thawed and then developed into healthy babies in their mother's uterus.

Ethical issues of IVF

IVF has enabled many couples to overcome the heartbreak of being unable to have children. However, there are many implications and possible misuses of the technique. For example:

- If embryos are frozen for future use, what happens if the parents divorce? To whom do the embryos belong?
- If parents and their first child are killed, there could be great difficulties over the estate. Do the frozen embryos inherit, and if so should they be implanted in a surrogate mother and allowed to develop in order to collect their inheritance?
- In some countries, such as the USA and Italy, IVF is now being used to allow women who are past the menopause, in their 50s and 60s, to have babies. The treatment has been carried out with substantially higher success rates than IVF in younger, infertile women. IVF specialists in Britain feel that this is not an appropriate use of the technology because of the social issues it raises. What are these social issues? Men can father children into their 70s and even 80s – why should women not prolong their reproductive life too? The main concerns seem to be for the health of the mother and the mental wellbeing of the child, which is more likely than most to lose its parents whilst still relatively young.

The new reproductive technologies raise these and many other ethical questions, some of which are addressed on page 406. They need careful thought by all of us.

SUMMARY

- In most mammals except humans, **oestrus** is the period of sexual receptiveness in the female, which occurs just before ovulation.

- The spermatozoa are deposited high in the vagina by **ejaculation** during **copulation**. They are helped up through the cervix and uterus to the Fallopian tubes by contractions of the female reproductive tract. Sperm movements keep them in suspension in the semen.

- Many spermatozoa cluster round the ovum and as their heads touch its surface the **acrosome reaction** is triggered. Enzymes are released which digest the follicle cells and zona pellucida.

- One sperm touches the oocyte membrane and the oocyte undergoes its second meiotic division, producing a haploid egg nucleus to fuse with the haploid male nucleus. The oocyte membrane becomes positive on the inside to prevent any more sperm entering. A **fertilisation membrane** forms to repel further sperm as the electrical charge returns to normal.

- The head of the sperm enters the oocyte and its chromosomes fuse with the haploid egg nucleus to form the zygote.

- The zygote undergoes **cleavage**, repeated mitotic divisions to form a **blastocyst** or hollow ball of cells. During **implantation** this becomes embedded in the endometrium and **trophoblastic villi** grow out from the outer layer or **trophoblast**.

- From around 12 weeks the human embryo is called the **fetus** and its major organ systems are completed.

- The **extraembryonic membranes** (**amnion** and **chorion**) fold around the embryo to form the **amniotic cavity**, filled with **amniotic fluid**. The chorion forms the **placenta** and the allantois the **umbilical cord** which connects the fetus to the placenta.

- To make the placenta the chorion forms many **chorionic villi** which protrude into sinuses in the endometrium and are bathed in maternal blood. Oxygen, food and some antibodies pass from mother to fetus and carbon dioxide and urea from fetus to mother. The placenta is a barrier to some microorganisms and drugs.

- **Identical** or **monozygotic twins** result from a single egg and sperm, while **non-identical** or **dizygotic twins** result from two different eggs and sperms.

- Pregnancy is first maintained by progesterone from the corpus luteum under the influence of **human chorionic gonadotrophin** from the embryo. After about 12 weeks the placenta takes over secreting progesterone to maintain the pregnancy.

- Birth is initiated by fetal ACTH which stimulates the fetal adrenals to produce steroids. These cause the maternal placenta to secrete **prostaglandins** which cause contractions of the uterus. Stretch receptors in the cervix stimulate the brain to secrete **oxytocin** which also stimulates contractions.

- In the first stage of labour contractions increase in strength and frequency and the cervix becomes dilated. In the second stage the baby is pushed out through the cervix and vagina. In the third stage the placenta is expelled. ▼

- The baby's lungs inflate immediately after birth aided by **lung surfactant.** ▼ The sides of the fetal heart are connected by the **foramen ovale** which closes over after birth. The fetal pulmonary artery is joined to the aorta by the **ductus arteriosus** which bypasses the lungs, and this narrows after birth.

- The fetal liver starts breaking down fetal haemoglobin, increasing the level of bilirubin and causing **physiological jaundice**.

- The **mammary glands** of the mammals produce protein-rich **milk** to feed the young, which also confers maternal antibodies.

- Conception may be prevented by various **contraceptive** measures. These may be:

  natural methods – the rhythm method

  barrier methods – the condom, diaphragm and female condom

  the **IUD** which prevents implantation

  chemical methods – spermicides which are best used with barrier methods, and the contraceptive pill which prevents ovulation

  sterilisation – irreversible surgical techniques which involve cutting the Fallopian tubes or vas deferens.

- **Infertility** may result from problems with either the male or the female reproductive system. Treatments include **artificial insemination by a donor (AID)**, **fertility drugs** to stimulate ovulation, *in vitro* **fertilisation (IVF)** and **gamete intra-fallopian transfer (GIFT)**.

QUESTIONS

1 a Describe the journey of the human ovum from the ovary to the point of fertilisation.
  b How does the sperm arrive in the Fallopian tube?
  c Describe the events of fertilisation.

2 Produce a leaflet suitable for the antenatal clinic of your local hospital explaining the main stages of fetal development, the role of the placenta in supporting the fetus and some of the factors which may have an adverse effect on fetal development.

3 a Before birth, a fetus has all its requirements supplied by the maternal system. Once a baby is born it has to immediately adapt to independent life. Describe the changes which occur in a baby in the first few minutes after birth.
  b Discuss the advantages and disadvantages of different feeding methods for babies in the developed countries and the developing world.

Developing Key Skills

The use of surrogate mothers to enable infertile couples to have children, the restoration of fertility to older women using hormones and *in vitro* fertilisation, and the rights – or otherwise – of the excess human embryos created during fertility treatment are all major ethical issues of our time.

Select one of them and prepare two newspaper articles about the technology and the issues. One report is to be for a broadsheet paper such as *The Guardian, The Independent* or *The Telegraph*, whilst the other is for a tabloid such as *The Sun, The Daily Mail* or *The Mirror*.

NATURE VERSUS NURTURE

Some of our characteristics, such as that shown in figure 1, are very clearly the result of the genes we have inherited from our parents. However, the appearance of an organism is not the result of its genetic make-up alone. For example, genetically identical plants (clones) grow very differently when exposed to varying amounts of light and soil nutrients. The ability of animals to achieve their full genetic potential in terms of growth also depends heavily on the amount of food available.

It is therefore very important during any genetic experiment that all the organisms are subjected to the same conditions, so that as far as possible any differences between them can be seen as the result of genetic differences alone. When we look at an individual organism, the role of the environment in shaping the apparent phenotype cannot be ignored. Which is the more important – nature or nurture?

Twin studies

With many experimental organisms, we can take control of their environment and change it to suit our needs. But we cannot deliberately manipulate human environments for our genetic experiments. Many human traits are **polygenic** (the result of a number of different genes), and what is more the environment within the uterus, during childhood and at adolescence affects the appearance of many features. Thus deciding whether nature or nurture determines a certain phenotypic characteristic in humans is very difficult indeed. Twin studies are very useful to help us unravel some of these strands.

In twin studies the differences between identical (monozygotic) twins are studied. Occasionally identical twins have been separated at birth to be adopted by different families. If separated twins are compared with non-separated identical twins, with non-identical twins and with ordinary siblings, then some idea can be gained as to which traits are largely determined by genes and which are strongly affected by the environment. Sometimes separated twins show remarkable similarities – for example, wear the same jewellery, or have husbands and children with the same names – but hard scientific evidence is needed to analyse these similarities. The data in table 1 show that height appears to have a strong genetic component and is influenced relatively little by environmental factors. On the other hand, body mass seems to be much more affected by external factors such as learned eating habits, and IQ – one measure of intelligence – seems to be a combination of both, with environment playing a distinct and important role.

Our knowledge of the genetic basis of human traits is still far from complete, but work like these twin studies helps us move our understanding forward.

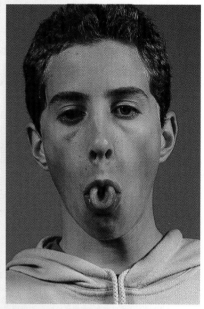

Figure 1 You can either roll your tongue or you cannot. This ability is related directly to genetic information in your cells.

Figure 2 Many identical twins brought up together show remarkable physical similarities. None of these children was told how to sit, yet each set of twins has placed their hands in a typical pose. However, these similarities could be due to being brought up in the same environment at the same time.

Trait	Identical twins reared together	Identical twins reared apart	Non-identical twins	Non-twin siblings
Height difference	1.7 cm	1.8 cm	4.4 cm	4.5 cm
Mass difference	1.9 kg	4.5 kg	4.6 kg	4.7 kg
IQ score difference	5.9	8.2	9.9	9.8

Table 1 The differences between twins, based on 50 pairs each of identical twins reared together, non-identical twins and non-twin siblings, and 19 pairs of identical twins reared apart.

Genetics

The fruit, vegetables and farm animals of several hundred years ago were very different from those we see today, as figure 5.6.1 illustrates. These differences have been brought about by a process of **selective breeding** – plants and animals with the desired features are bred to give offspring which also exhibit them.

For a long time these crosses were carried out without any real understanding of the mechanisms behind the breeding process. But over the last hundred years or so the underlying mechanisms of inheritance have been worked out and understood, and the science of **genetics** has emerged.

Ornamental cabbages add an extra dimension to the herbaceous border.

Figure 5.6.1 Selective breeding has taken the cabbage plant in a variety of directions to suit a variety of demands. The mechanisms by which such changes come about are now well understood.

A nineteenth century cabbage was a relatively unspecialised plant.

The familiar large round cabbage from the supermarket shelf fulfils the requirements of the British shopper.

The basis of inheritance

The physical and chemical characteristics which make up the appearance of any organism are known as its **phenotype** – for example, the shape of a cabbage, the scent of a flower and the colour of hair. This phenotype is the result of the genetic information handed on from parents to their offspring (the **genotype**) along with the effect of the environment in which an organism lives. The shape of a cabbage will depend on the levels of soil nutrients and sunlight as well as on the genetic make-up of the individual. For many characters, the phenotypic variation between individuals results largely from genetic differences between individuals. These genetic differences are due in part to the shuffling of genes which occurs during the process of meiosis, and in part to the inheritance of genes from two different individuals in sexual reproduction. How does the process of inheritance work?

As we have seen in sections 5.1 and 5.2, the cells of any individual organism contain a species-characteristic number of chromosomes. These occur as matching **homologous pairs**. One of each pair is inherited from the female parent and one from the male. Along each chromosome are thousands of **genes**, and the genes coding for particular characteristics or **traits** are always found in the same position or **locus** on a particular pair of chromosomes. A gene is a segment of DNA coding for a specific RNA molecule to give a particular characteristic. A gene may be one of two or more different **alleles**, each allele producing different alternative forms of the characteristic. An allele is a particular sequence of bases which may or may not result in a functional protein. For example, the common or garden pea plant has often been used as a subject for genetic experiments. The gene for the type of pea is always found at the same locus on the chromosomes, but either the allele for round peas or the allele for wrinkled peas (different sequences of base pairs) may be present at the locus.

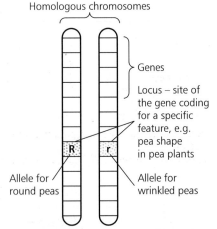

Homologous chromosomes

Genes

Locus – site of the gene coding for a specific feature, e.g. pea shape in pea plants

Allele for round peas

Allele for wrinkled peas

Note: The genes are shown much larger in relation to the whole chromosome than is actually the case.

Figure 5.6.2 In sexual reproduction it is the alleles passed on which determine the genotype and hence eventually the phenotype of the offspring.

Monohybrid crosses

If both of the alleles coding for a particular characteristic on a pair of homologous chromosomes are identical, then the organism is **homozygous** for that characteristic – it is a **homozygote**. Homozygotes are referred to as **true breeding**, because if two similar homozygotes are crossed all the offspring will be the same. The offspring of two homozygous parents are called the F_1 (**first filial generation**). If those offspring are crossed the next generation, the F_2 (**second filial generation**), will also have the same genotype and phenotype and this will continue on through the generations.

If the two alleles coding for a characteristic on a pair of homologous chromosomes are different, the organism is **heterozygous** for that feature and is referred to as a **heterozygote**.

Some alleles are described as **dominant**. This means that their effect is expressed even in the presence of another, **recessive** allele. Thus if one allele is dominant over another the individuals will show the dominant feature whether they are homozygotes or heterozygotes, as figure 5.6.3 shows. The dominant allele might result in the production of a particular protein – for example, a pigment molecule or an enzyme – whilst recessive alleles might result in a lack of that protein or in a different, non-functional protein. Recessive alleles are only expressed in the phenotype when they are present in the homozygous form. Dominant genes are usually represented by a capital letter, recessive genes by the lower case version of the same letter. When one genetic trait is considered at a time the cross is referred to as a **monohybrid cross**.

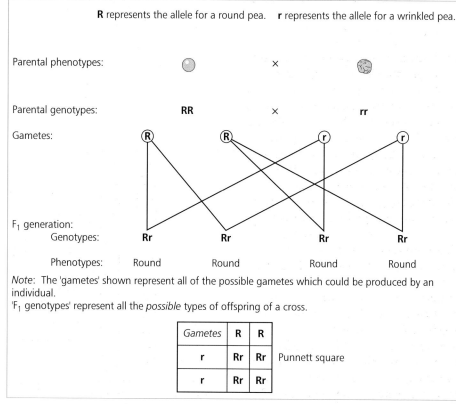

R represents the allele for a round pea.   **r** represents the allele for a wrinkled pea.

Parental phenotypes: ○ × 🟤

Parental genotypes: **RR** × **rr**

Gametes: Ⓡ Ⓡ ⓡ ⓡ

F_1 generation:
Genotypes: **Rr**   **Rr**   **Rr**   **Rr**

Phenotypes: Round   Round   Round   Round

Note: The 'gametes' shown represent all of the possible gametes which could be produced by an individual.
'F_1 genotypes' represent all the *possible* types of offspring of a cross.

Gametes	R	R
r	Rr	Rr
r	Rr	Rr

Punnett square

Figure 5.6.3 Pea plants were the first organisms to be studied in genetics, and they are still useful as we now know a great deal about their genetic make-up and the way different traits are inherited. This representation of a cross between a pea plant producing round peas and a plant producing wrinkled peas shows how to present a typical genetic cross. The Punnett square is not always needed in a monohybrid cross such as this, but becomes very important later when dihybrid crosses are considered. The cross also demonstrates the typical heterozygous genotype but dominant phenotype in the offspring from a cross between a homozygous dominant individual and a homozygous recessive individual.

Heterozygotes are not true breeding. If two heterozygotes are crossed then the offspring may include homozygous dominant, homozygous recessive and heterozygous types, as figure 5.6.4 shows.

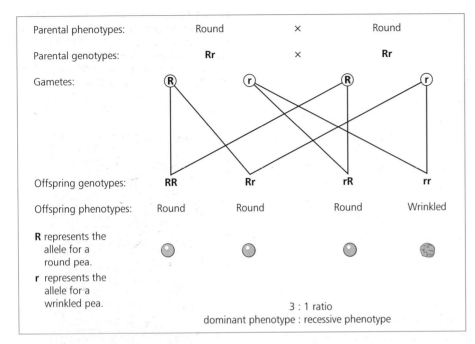

| Parental phenotypes: | Round | × | Round |
| Parental genotypes: | **Rr** | × | **Rr** |

Gametes: R r R r

Offspring genotypes: **RR** **Rr** **rR** **rr**

Offspring phenotypes: Round Round Round Wrinkled

R represents the allele for a round pea.

r represents the allele for a wrinkled pea.

3 : 1 ratio
dominant phenotype : recessive phenotype

Figure 5.6.4 The phenotypes of heterozygotes such as these parental peas show no evidence of their underlying genotype. However, when they are crossed, the occurrence of homozygous recessive forms reveals the hidden alleles.

Sampling errors

Considering genetic crosses in theory gives rise to *predicted ratios* for the proportions of different types of offspring. These ratios are seen in real-life genetic experiments, but they are unlikely to correspond exactly to the predictions. The ratios are only approximate due to a variety of factors, for example the death of some offspring before they can be sampled, or inefficient sampling techniques – for example, it is very easy to let a few *Drosophila* escape. Also, chance plays a large role in reproduction – the joining of particular gametes is a completely random affair. Thus **sampling error** must be taken into account when a cross is considered, and the smaller the sample, the larger the sampling error. Therefore the results of a genetical experiment with thousands of offspring will be much more predictable than those of an experiment with under 100 results.

The ratios of genotypes and phenotypes expected from genetic crosses are known as **Mendelian ratios** after Gregor Mendel, the Austrian monk who first developed the study of genetics (described later in this section).

Test crosses

As can be seen from figures 5.6.3 and 5.6.4, individuals which are homozygous dominant or heterozygous will have identical phenotypes. In practical terms this can present all sorts of difficulties for breeders of plants and animals. A breeder needs to know that stock will breed true – in other words, that it is homozygous for the desired feature. If the feature is inherited through recessive genes then the genotype can be seen from the phenotype. However, if the required feature is inherited through a dominant gene the physical appearance does not show whether the organism is homozygous or heterozygous. To find out the genotype of an individual showing the phenotype corresponding to a dominant allele, it is crossed with a homozygous recessive individual. The recessive genes have no effect on the phenotype of the offspring unless they are in the homozygous state, so this type of cross can reveal the parental genotype. If there are offspring with the recessive characteristic the parent must have been heterozygous, as figure 5.6.5 shows. Such a cross is known as a **test cross**.

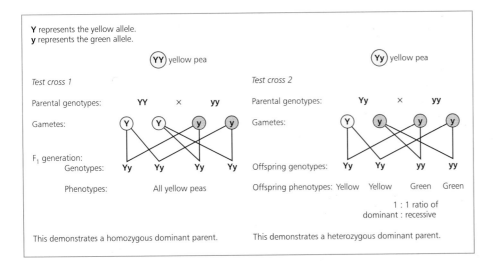

Y represents the yellow allele.
y represents the green allele.

(YY) yellow pea   (Yy) yellow pea

Test cross 1   Test cross 2

Parental genotypes: YY   ×   yy   Parental genotypes: Yy   ×   yy

Gametes: (Y) (Y) (y) (y)   Gametes: (Y) (y) (y) (y)

F₁ generation:
Genotypes: Yy   Yy   Yy   Yy   Offspring genotypes: Yy   Yy   yy   yy

Phenotypes: All yellow peas   Offspring phenotypes: Yellow Yellow Green Green

                                                                    1 : 1 ratio of
                                                                 dominant : recessive

This demonstrates a homozygous dominant parent.   This demonstrates a heterozygous dominant parent.

Figure 5.6.5 Test crosses are carried out to discover the unknown genotype of a parent. The colour of the pea seed is inherited as a dominant allele **Y** for yellow seeds or a recessive allele **y** for green seeds. Thus a plant producing yellow seeds could have the genotype **YY** or **Yy**. The phenotypic ratios of the progeny of the test cross reveal whether the yellow-seed producing parent was homozygous or heterozygous.

Codominance

When a pure-breeding red-flowered antirrhinum is crossed with a pure-breeding white-flowered antirrhinum, we might expect either all red- or all white-flowered offspring, depending upon which allele is dominant. In fact, pink flowers are the result – a 'mixture' of the two phenotypes. This is due to **codominance** between the alleles. Both alleles result in the production of functional proteins that interact in a specific way. Neither is dominant over the other, hence the term codominance. In antirrhinum the red-flower allele and the white-flower allele are codominant and so heterozygotes display pink flowers. This type of interaction between alleles is sometimes referred to as **incomplete dominance** as both alleles are represented, yet neither is completely dominant to the other.

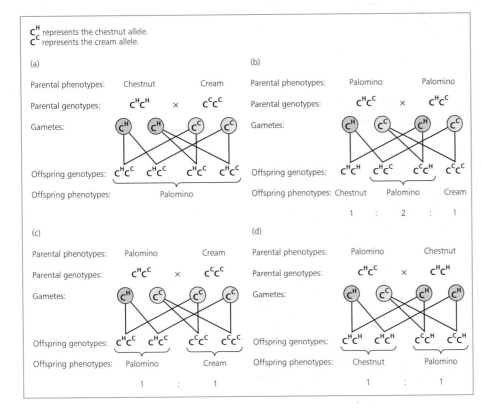

C^H represents the chestnut allele.
C^C represents the cream allele.

(a)

Parental phenotypes: Chestnut   Cream
Parental genotypes: $C^H C^H$ × $C^C C^C$
Gametes: (C^H) (C^H) (C^C) (C^C)
Offspring genotypes: $C^H C^C$ $C^H C^C$ $C^H C^C$ $C^H C^C$
Offspring phenotypes: Palomino

(b)

Parental phenotypes: Palomino   Palomino
Parental genotypes: $C^H C^C$ × $C^H C^C$
Gametes: (C^H) (C^C) (C^H) (C^C)
Offspring genotypes: $C^H C^H$ $C^H C^C$ $C^C C^H$ $C^C C^C$
Offspring phenotypes: Chestnut   Palomino   Cream
                        1   :   2   :   1

(c)

Parental phenotypes: Palomino   Cream
Parental genotypes: $C^H C^C$ × $C^C C^C$
Gametes: (C^H) (C^C) (C^C) (C^C)
Offspring genotypes: $C^H C^C$ $C^H C^C$ $C^C C^C$ $C^C C^C$
Offspring phenotypes: Palomino   Cream
                        1   :   1

(d)

Parental phenotypes: Palomino   Chestnut
Parental genotypes: $C^H C^C$ × $C^H C^H$
Gametes: (C^H) (C^C) (C^H) (C^H)
Offspring genotypes: $C^H C^H$ $C^H C^H$ $C^C C^H$ $C^C C^H$
Offspring phenotypes: Chestnut   Palomino
                        1   :   1

Figure 5.6.6 The photographs show, from the top, a chestnut, a cream and a palamino horse. The attractive golden colour with the white mane and tail which characterises the palomino horse is much sought after by some breeders. However, it is a difficult colour to obtain because it does not breed true. These genetic diagrams show the results of crosses between a) a chestnut horse and a cream horse, b) two palomino horses, c) a palomino horse and a cream horse, and d) a palomino horse and a chestnut horse.

When true-breeding cream horses are bred, cream foals result. When true-breeding chestnut horses are bred, chestnut foals result. But the result of a cross between a cream horse and a chestnut horse is a palomino – a horse with a very distinctive gold colouring and a white mane and tail. This again is due to codominance between the alleles and a specific interaction between the resulting proteins.

The example of the palomino horses is unusual – a heterozygote for codominant alleles usually shows a condition much closer to a simple mixture of the two codominant forms rather than the very distinctive coat colour shown in figure 5.6.6.

Both the human ABO blood groups (met in section 1.6) and the MN blood groups are examples of inheritance involving codominant alleles. In the ABO system there are three possible alleles – **A**, **B** and **O**. **A** and **B** are both dominant to **O**, but are codominant to each other so an individual with the genotype **AB** has the blood group AB. The MN blood group system is another way of tissue typing human blood, and just like the ABO system is dependent on the presence or absence of antigens on the surface of the red blood cells. In the MN system, homozygous **MM** individuals have blood group M. Homozygous **NN** individuals have blood group N. Heterozygotes carrying **MN** have blood group MN. Codominance may be considered as a possible explanation of the more unexpected phenotypic results of some genetic crosses.

Experimental species

To carry out genetic experiments, organisms are needed that are relatively easy and cheap to raise. They need to have short life cycles so that the results of crosses and/or mutations can be seen quickly. They also need to produce large numbers of offspring so that the results of any crosses can be checked statistically against the predicted ratios. For example, an expected 3:1 ratio of phenotypes in the offspring of a cross is unlikely to show itself if only four offspring are produced. With 400 offspring the likelihood of seeing the expected ratio is increased and 4000 offspring would be better still.

Commonly used organisms include the fruit fly *Drosophila melanogaster*, pea plants, fungi such as *Aspergillus* and a variety of bacteria. Specially bred 'fast plants' are now being used increasingly, particularly in schools and colleges. These are members of, for example, the cabbage family which have been bred to germinate, mature, flower and set seed in a matter of weeks. This means that they can be used in much the same way as *Drosophila*, without the problems of specimens getting stuck in the nutrient medium, dying or escaping!

Multiple alleles

Most of the traits we have considered so far are inherited as genes with a pair of possible alleles. However, this is not always the case. Sometimes there will be several possible alleles (**multiple alleles**) – even as many as 100 – all resulting in a slightly different phenotype for the same trait, and with varying degrees of dominance over each other. Of course, however many alleles there are, any one diploid individual will possess only two of them.

The human ABO blood group is determined by three alleles. I^O is recessive, and a homozygote is blood group O. I^A and I^B are both dominant to I^O, and are codominant to each other. Thus a genotype $I^A I^B$ gives an AB blood group, whilst either I^AI^A or I^AI^O gives blood group A and I^BI^B or I^BI^O gives blood group B. Figure 5.6.7 shows some genetic crosses involving human blood groups.

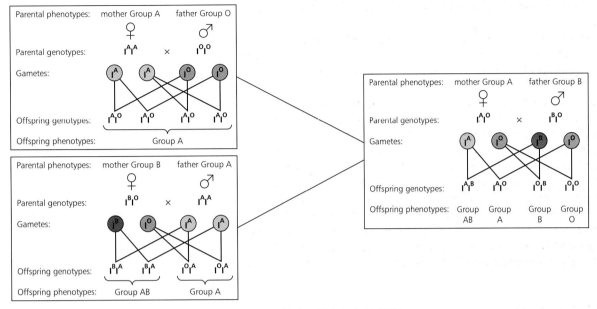

Figure 5.6.7 Crosses such as these can be used in determining the father of a child when this is in doubt. Whilst the genetics of blood groups can be used to show that a certain man is *not* the father of a child, it can never be used to prove that someone definitely *is* the father. Whilst possessing a particular blood group may make him a possible father, several million other men will also have the same blood group and so are, in theory at least, equally likely to be the father!

Genetic compatibility and transplant surgery

Earlier in this book (pages 81–83) we looked at the importance of the different human blood groups in blood transfusions. These blood groups are brought about by the genes inherited by each individual, and a level of genetic compatibility is important for a transfusion to be successful. The match does not have to be perfect – for example, blood from an individual with the genotype I^OI^O (group O) can be given to anyone else, regardless of their genotype. However, when we are dealing with the transplantation of whole organs, the problems of genetic compatibility become much more acute. All of our body cells are covered with **histocompatibility antigens** (sometimes known as the HLA system) and these are unique to each individual. These antigens are coded for by a group of genes known as the major histocompatibility complexes. In humans, these complexes contain at least four closely linked genes, with a selection of around 50 possible alleles in total. The possible combinations of these genes are to all intents and purposes limitless, and so are the numbers of the cell surface antigens they code for. This is why no two people, unless they are identical twins, are immunologically the same. Before an organ is transplanted, the genetic compatibility of both the blood group systems and the histocompatibility antigens is tested. The closer the match between antigens on the cell surfaces of the donor and the recipient, the more likely it is that a transplant will be successful.

Lethal genes

Manx cats originate on the Isle of Man. They are well known for the physical peculiarity of lacking a tail, and they are very difficult to breed. When a Manx cat is mated to a normal long-tailed cat approximately half the offspring will be Manx and half will have normal tails. This indicates that the Manx cat is heterozygous for a dominant mutant gene which causes the lack of tail. However, if two Manx cats are mated the expected Mendelian ratio for a heterozygote cross (3 dominant phenotypes to each 1 recessive) does not occur. The ratio is always 2:1. Why do Mendelian ratios not apply to Manx cats? The answer is that the homozygous form of the mutated Manx gene is **lethal**. Kitten embryos which inherit it fail to develop the entire back end of the body and usually die and are reabsorbed before birth. This means that one quarter of the expected progeny of the cross do not appear in the actual offspring, giving the distorted 2:1 ratio, as shown in figure 5.6.8.

Figure 5.6.8 The gene which causes the phenotype of the Manx cat is dominant. However, the lethal aspect of the gene acts as if recessive – when it is present in the homozygous form the kittens do not survive. It is an example of a single gene affecting several traits. True-breeding stock of Manx cats has never been achieved.

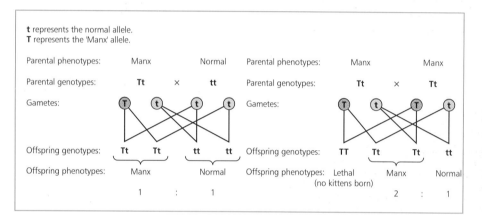

t represents the normal allele.
T represents the 'Manx' allele.

Parental phenotypes:	Manx	Normal	Parental phenotypes:	Manx	Manx	
Parental genotypes:	Tt × tt		Parental genotypes:	Tt × Tt		
Gametes:	T t	t t	Gametes:	T t	T t	
Offspring genotypes:	Tt Tt	tt tt	Offspring genotypes:	TT	Tt Tt	tt
Offspring phenotypes:	Manx	Normal	Offspring phenotypes:	Lethal (no kittens born)	Manx	Normal
	1 : 1				2 : 1	

Lethal genes usually occur as the result of a chance mutation. If they persist in a wild population they must be recessive for the lethal characteristic. This would enable them to be passed on in the heterozygous form, only causing problems when two heterozygotes breed giving rise to a homozygote which would then die as a result. A dominant lethal mutation would usually be wiped out instantly as all the offspring which inherited the mutation would die before reproducing. Most lethal genes take effect before the embryo is fully developed or in early life, although exceptions to this are seen where the lethal genetic disorder only manifests itself at a stage when reproduction has already occurred and the gene has been passed on.

A brief history of genetics

For centuries the theories developed to explain the inheritance by offspring of characteristics from their parents made the same fundamental error. The assumption was made that the characteristics of the parents in some way blended or fused so that the distinct characteristics of each were lost. Followed to its logical conclusion, this theory means that the offspring from mating a pure-breeding black dog with a pure-breeding white dog would always be grey. Not only is this rarely the case, but even if grey puppies do result they may produce black or white offspring at a later date. The birth of Gregor Mendel in 1822 was to herald the end of these ideas.

The remarkable physical differences between these two cats from the same litter of kittens are due to the difference in a single gene.

Mendel became a monk at the Augustinian monastery at Brunn, and here he formulated his ideas about the particulate nature of the hereditary material – what we now call genes. He was educated in maths, physics and statistics as well as botany, which may well explain his rigorous approach and analysis of his results. His abbot supported his research and had a large greenhouse built to grow the peas with which he worked. Much of his work was carried out using the features of peas shown in figure 5.6.9.

In 1866 Mendel presented his results and the two fundamental laws of heredity he had deduced from them. However, as has often been the case with great ideas, he was ahead of his time and the work was poorly received and almost ignored. Bear in mind that no one knew of the existence of chromosomes at this time, let alone genes, so Mendel's ideas were presented to a scientific community with no framework ready to receive them. Along with this, his statistical work was strange to many biologists of the time, and the full impact of his work was not recognised until 16 years after his death.

Both the male and female parts of the pea flower are held within a hood-like petal so that self fertilisation frequently occurs. Mendel opened the bud of one flower before the pollen matured and fertilised the stigma with pollen from another chosen flower. In this way he could control the cross.

Anther

Stigma

Mendel used seven clearly differentiated, pure-breeding traits of the pea plant for his experiments. They are show here in both their dominant and recessive forms.

Stems		Pods		Seeds/flowers		
Tall	Axial flowers	Green	Inflated	Round	Yellow	Red flowers
Short	Terminal	Yellow	Pinched	Wrinkled	Green	White

Dominant trait

Recessive trait

Figure 5.6.9 Pea plants were Mendel's main experimental organism, and by focusing on particular traits he was able to build up a mass of statistics about the various crosses he made.

By 1900 chromosomes had been discovered and meiosis had been seen and described. Hugo de Vries in Holland and Karl Correns in Germany discovered Mendel's work and duplicated his results. To their credit, they gave him the recognition he deserved. Then in 1902 it was suggested that Mendel's units of inheritance might be found on the chromosomes, and in the early 1900s Thomas Morgan and his team in the USA worked with *Drosophila* to gain evidence for this idea. From this point onwards the study of genetics snowballed. Today a complete unravelling of all the human DNA (the **genome**) is well on the way to becoming reality – and also the capability to alter and engineer parts of it, for good or ill.

Dihybrid crosses

In all the genetic crosses we have looked at so far, we have considered a single trait inherited on a pair of alleles. However, hundreds and thousands of genes go to make up the genotype of any one individual, and they are all passed on at the same time. **Dihybrid crosses** involve the inheritance of two different genes at the same time. Although still a very long way from the complexity of real events, this takes us one step closer to the real situation.

As we have seen, pea plants possess a variety of traits which are inherited through individual pairs of alleles. Mendel set up experiments to determine how two characters interact during inheritance, using the shape and colour of peas. Round peas (**R**) are dominant to wrinkled peas (**r**). Yellow peas (**Y**) are dominant to green peas (**y**). A dominant parent (round and yellow, **RRYY**) crossed with a recessive parent (wrinkled and green, **rryy**) gives rise to offspring which all display the dominant phenotype characteristics (round and yellow). A

Figure 5.6.10 In a dihybrid cross each of the two alleles of one gene may combine randomly with either of the alleles of another gene. As a result of this independent assortment, four possible phenotypes result when heterozygotes are involved, whether selfed or in a test cross.

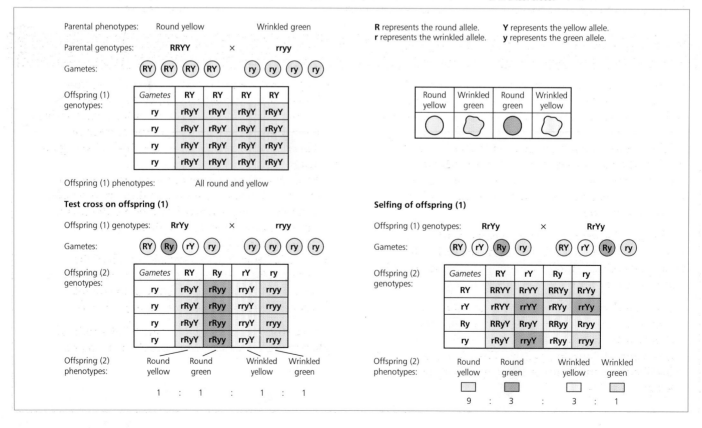

test cross with a homozygous recessive and a self cross between two of the offspring both give rise to four different phenotypes – round and yellow, round and green, wrinkled and yellow and finally wrinkled and green. Two of these – round and yellow, wrinkled and green – are the same as the original parents (**parental phenotypes**). The other two phenotypes – round and green, wrinkled and yellow – are different from the parents and have a **recombinant phenotype**. The ratios are different for the two types of cross. Figure 5.6.10 shows how such a dihybrid cross works in peas, and also demonstrates the value of a Punnett square in dealing with these more complex crosses.

The explanation for this situation is that the two sets of alleles are separated into the gametes quite independently of each other. In other words, four types of pollen and four types of egg are produced. Imagine the alleles as two pairs of shoes (pair 1 and pair 2, as shown in figure 5.6.11). If they are used to make a gamete (a single pair of shoes) it must contain one shoe from each pair. The possible combinations are two left shoes, two right shoes, a left shoe from pair

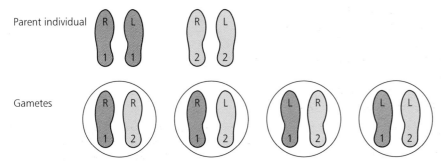

Parent individual

Gametes

The shoes represent the alleles. If the parent is homozygous for both genes then all the possible gametes will carry the same information.
If the parent is heterozygous for one of the genes then there will be two possible types of gamete.
If the parent is heterozygous for both genes then four possible gametes result.

Figure 5.6.11 Alleles are separated independently when the gametes are formed.

Using probability to predict the outcomes of complex crosses

As crosses become more complex, the use of simple diagrams to predict the possible offspring and their ratios becomes more difficult. However, it is possible to use probability to work out very simply what genotypes might be expected for any given cross. This only applies when the two characteristics are inherited independently of each other – in the case of gene linkage (see later in this section) these calculations need modification.

In the cross between the heterozygous grey-bodied long-winged *Drosophila* shown in figure 5.6.12, the probability of certain phenotypes occurring is worked out as follows:

- *Grey-bodied long-winged flies* – the grey allele is dominant, so $\frac{3}{4}$ of the F$_2$ offspring will be grey. Similarly long wings are dominant, so $\frac{3}{4}$ of the offspring will have long wings. Therefore the likelihood of any fly inheriting a grey body and long wings is $\frac{3}{4} \times \frac{3}{4} = \frac{9}{16}$.

- *Grey-bodied vestigial-winged flies* – as above, grey bodies have a $\frac{3}{4}$ chance of appearing in the offspring. The recessive character for vestigial wings has a $\frac{1}{4}$ chance of occurring in the phenotype. Therefore the probability of grey-bodied vestigial-winged flies appearing is $\frac{3}{4} \times \frac{1}{4} = \frac{3}{16}$.

- *Ebony-bodied long-winged flies* – the probability of ebony bodies appearing is $\frac{1}{4}$ as they are recessive, and that of long wings is $\frac{3}{4}$ as they are dominant. Thus the probability of this phenotype being inherited is $\frac{1}{4} \times \frac{3}{4} = \frac{3}{16}$.

- *Ebony-bodied vestigial-winged flies* – each of the vestigial characters has a $\frac{1}{4}$ chance of occurring in the offspring, so the probability of the double recessive phenotype being seen is $\frac{1}{4} \times \frac{1}{4} = \frac{1}{16}$.

Notice that this provides the same 9:3:3:1 ratio of phenotypes as was seen from the Punnett square.

1 with a right shoe from pair 2 or a right shoe from pair 1 with a left shoe from pair 2. Thus two of the pairs resemble the original shoes with a left and a right shoe, and two of the pairs are new combinations. In the same way, when gametes are formed in a dihybrid cross they segregate quite independently of each other and so recombine in all the possible ways.

Another example of dihybrid inheritance occurs in the fruit fly *Drosophila*. Grey bodies are dominant to ebony bodies, and long wings are dominant to the very short vestigial wings. A cross between two heterozygotes as seen in figure 5.6.12 shows again the use of a Punnett square to determine the results of dihybrid inheritance.

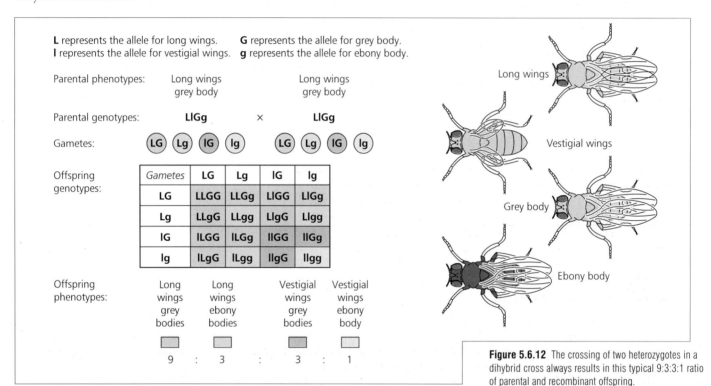

Figure 5.6.12 The crossing of two heterozygotes in a dihybrid cross always results in this typical 9:3:3:1 ratio of parental and recombinant offspring.

Mendel's laws of genetics

The contribution of the monk Gregor Mendel to genetics cannot be overstated (see box 'A brief history of genetics'). With his work on pea breeding he founded the subject, and arrived at two fundamental laws of heredity. He worked with pure-breeding strains of peas and carried out large numbers of crosses, followed as necessary by test crosses to determine whether individuals were homozygous or heterozygous. His results showed ratios which coincided remarkably well with the theoretical ones. It has been suggested that Mendel worked out in advance what he expected to happen and then either he or his helpers 'managed' the actual results to achieve the desired ratios. Even if this was the case, the ideas were correct and the laws, although oversimplifying matters, still apply today to all diploid organisms.

The law of segregation – Mendel's first law

The first law which Mendel presented is known as the **law of segregation**. It was the result of work with monohybrid crosses. The law states that in a diploid organism one unit or allele for each trait is inherited from each parent to give a total of two alleles for each trait. The **segregation** (separation) of each pair of alleles takes place when the gametes are formed.

Mendel himself knew nothing of the process of meiosis, but this is the modern-day explanation for his proposed segregation, as during meiotic division chromosome pairs are split and haploid cells produced. This idea of independent units of inheritance, some dominant to others, which are maintained throughout the life of an individual and do not fuse to form a homogeneous mass, was Mendel's real breakthrough.

The law of independent assortment – Mendel's second law

The **law of independent assortment** states that different traits are inherited independently of each other. What this means is that the inheritance of a dominant or recessive allele for one characteristic, such as grey or ebony bodies, has nothing to do with the inheritance of alleles of other genes, such as those for wing length or eye colour. Considering that Mendel formulated these laws so early in the history of our understanding of inheritance it is remarkable that they are still so relevant today, although we now recognise that the second law in particular has many exceptions. This is the result of gene linkage, discussed below.

Polygenic traits

When we consider monohybrid and dihybrid crosses we are looking at genetic traits which are inherited as the result of a single gene. However, many traits are **polygenic**. This means that they are controlled by several interacting genes, rather than one single gene. (This is distinct from multiple alleles for *one* gene seen in *Drosophila* eye colours.) Human eye colour is an example of a fairly simple polygenic situation – colour is controlled by two genes. Height, weight and intelligence involve the interaction of many more genes, and so the consideration of their inheritance is far more complex than the simple situation with round and wrinkled peas.

Gene linkage

In dihybrid inheritance we have seen how the alleles of the two genes segregate quite independently of each other. However, the situation is not always as predictable as this. When *Drosophila* with normal broad abdomens and long wings are crossed with flies displaying recessive narrow abdomens and vestigial wings, the first generation produced is as expected, with all the offspring showing the dominant phenotype but possessing the heterozygote genotype. However, when these first generation flies are crossed, the normal 9:3:3:1 ratio of parental and recombinant types does not occur, as figure 5.6.13 shows. Instead there is a 3:1 ratio of dominant:recessive phenotypes, which is what we would expect in a monohybrid cross. The explanation of this apparent discrepancy is that the genes are **linked** – that is, they are sited on the same chromosome and inherited as if they were one unit.

If genes are completely unlinked, approximately equal numbers of recombinants and parental type gametes are formed. But if genes are linked then they are inherited to a greater or lesser degree as if they were a single gene. When genes are closely linked recombinants rarely if ever occur. If the genes are more loosely linked then the number of recombinants which results will be higher. The tightness of the linkage is related to how close the two or more genes are on the chromosome – genes that are very close together are less likely to be split during the crossing over stage of meiosis than genes which are further apart (see section 5.2, page 370).

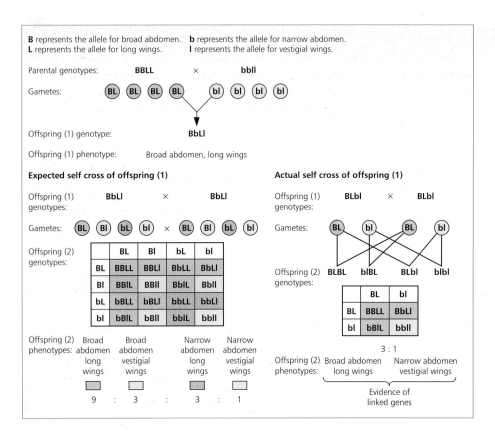

B represents the allele for broad abdomen.   b represents the allele for narrow abdomen.
L represents the allele for long wings.   l represents the allele for vestigial wings.

Parental genotypes: **BBLL**   ×   **bbll**

Gametes: (BL) (BL) (BL) (BL)   (bl) (bl) (bl) (bl)

Offspring (1) genotype: **BbLl**

Offspring (1) phenotype: Broad abdomen, long wings

Expected self cross of offspring (1)

Offspring (1) genotypes: **BbLl**   ×   **BbLl**

Gametes: (BL) (Bl) (bL) (bl) × (BL) (Bl) (bL) (bl)

Offspring (2) genotypes:

	BL	Bl	bL	bl
BL	BBLL	BBLl	BbLL	BbLl
Bl	BBLl	BBll	BbLl	Bbll
bL	bBLL	bBLl	bbLL	bbLl
bl	bBLl	bBll	bbLl	bbll

Offspring (2) phenotypes:
Broad abdomen long wings | Broad abdomen vestigial wings | Narrow abdomen long wings | Narrow abdomen vestigial wings

9 : 3 : 3 : 1

Actual self cross of offspring (1)

Offspring (1) genotypes: **BLbl**   ×   **BLbl**

Gametes: (BL) (bl)   (BL) (bl)

Offspring (2) genotypes: BLBL   blBL   BLbl   blbl

	BL	bl
BL	BBLL	BBLl
bl	bBLl	bbll

3 : 1

Offspring (2) phenotypes: Broad abdomen long wings   Narrow abdomen vestigial wings

Evidence of linked genes

Figure 5.6.13 These two genes are inherited as if they were one unit because they are closely linked on the same chromosome. The normal Mendelian ratios for a dihybrid cross only occur when the genes are on separate chromosomes.

Cross over values

If the linked genes are very close together on the chromosome they may be so tightly linked that they are effectively never split up during meiosis, and so the gametes formed will always be of the parental types. If the genes are further apart, crossing over between them is more likely to occur. Although in the majority of cases they will be passed on as a parental unit, sometimes they will be mixed and recombinant gametes will be produced, which will in turn be reflected in the offspring. This gives us a way of working out how close together various genes are on a chromosome – in fact, a genetic map of a chromosome can be built up by studying linked genes. To produce a genetic map the **cross over value** (**COV**) has to be worked out:

$$\text{Cross over value} = \frac{\text{number of recombinant offspring}}{\text{total number of offspring}} \times 100$$

Thus closely linked genes producing only small numbers of recombinant offspring will result in low cross over values. Genes which are further apart produce larger numbers of recombinants and have higher cross over values. This can be used to build up a chromosome map as shown in figure 5.6.14 and table 5.6.1. The clue that linkage is involved in a dihybrid cross is the absence of the expected 9:3:3:1 ratio. Whilst small differences in numbers may be put

Genes	Cross over value
X and Y	25%
Y and Z	5%
X and Z	20%

Table 5.6.1

Figure 5.6.14 To create a genetic map the cross over values are converted into arbitrary **map units**. The first cross over value positions genes X and Y relative to each other. However, the position of gene Z can only be decided by reference to its cross over values in relation to both gene X and gene Y. This technique can be very slow and laborious as most chromosomes carry thousands of genes, but it is vital in the process of altering individual genes or groups of genes.

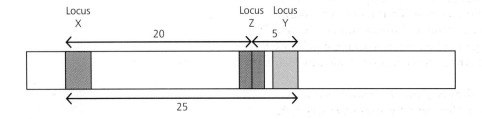

Locus X   Locus Z   Locus Y

20   5

25

Epistasis

In most of the examples of inheritance we have looked at, the genes involved work independently of each other. But sometimes genes interact, with one gene affecting or altering the expression of another. When the effect of one gene overrides or masks the effects of another, it is known as **epistasis** (meaning 'to stand over'). A common example of epistatic genes is seen in the appearance of the domestic cat. Cats have a number of genes that determine what their coats look like. Two of them in particular code for coat colour and coat pattern.

The coat colour alleles are **A** and **a**. The genotypes **AA** or **Aa** give rise to an **agouti** coat – grey hairs with a yellow band, which gives a brownish colour. The range of colour is enormous, depending on the width and position of the bands. The **aa** genotype gives a pure black coat.

The coat pattern alleles are **T** and $\mathbf{t^b}$. Genotypes **TT** or $\mathbf{Tt^b}$ give a mackerel-tabby coat pattern, with vertical curving black stripes, whilst $\mathbf{t^bt^b}$ gives a blotched-tabby coat, with swirls and whorls of black.

If an agouti, blotched-tabby cat is mated with a pure black cat, the situation shown in figure 5.6.15 may arise. All the kittens resulting from the cross shown in figure 5.6.15 have a mackerel-tabby pattern which they must have inherited from their black parent. The **aa** coat colour gene is epistatic to the coat-marking gene, so it was impossible to tell just by looking at the black cat what coat markings it might have had. The effect of the marking genes was masked by the black colouring, and revealed when the kittens inherited agouti-coloured coats.

Similar epistatic genes are seen in mice, when the albino gene is epistatic to the gene that gives banded coloured hairs. Epistasis should not be confused with dominance. Dominance relates to two alleles of the same gene. Epistasis occurs between two genes coding for quite separate phenotypic features, when one locus masks the expression of another.

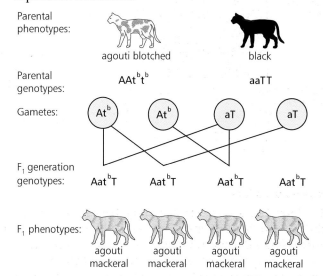

Figure 5.6.15 Epistatic genes determine the colour and pattern of cats' coats.

down to experimental error, larger discrepancies, with a heavy weighting to parental types, indicate that linkage between the genes is involved.

Sex linkage

The chromosomes in diploid organisms occur as homologous pairs. In organisms such as mammals where there are clear differences between the males and females, sex is determined by the chromosomes. As mentioned in section 5.1, all the pairs of chromosomes except one carry information about the general body cells and their biochemistry. They are known as the **autosomes**. The final pair of chromosomes carry information about the sex of the individual and are known as the **sex chromosomes**. In mammals the female has two large X chromosomes. Thus all of her eggs contain an X chromosome and she is referred to as **homogametic**. The male has one X chromosome and one much smaller Y chromosome. Thus half of the sperm will contain X chromosomes and half will contain Y chromosomes – the male is **heterogametic**. In humans there are 22 pairs of autosomes and one pair of sex chromosomes. In some organisms, for example birds, it is the male which is homogametic.

However, not all the genes on the sex chromosomes are concerned with matters related to sex. The small human Y chromosome seems to carry little but male sex information and a gene for very hairy ears, but the X chromosome carries a variety of other genes coding for traits such as clotting factors in the blood and the ability to see in colour. Genes which are carried on the X chromosome are said to be **sex linked**. Any recessive or mutant genes passed on the X chromosome from a mother to her sons will be expressed in the phenotype as there is no corresponding gene on the Y chromosome to mask them. Because of the importance of the X and Y chromosomes in sex linkage, they are shown on genetic diagrams.

Sex linkage in *Drosophila* was discovered by Thomas Morgan. In these flies eye colour is affected by sex, as shown in figures 5.6.16 and 5.6.17. In humans sex linkage leads to a variety of conditions known as **sex-linked diseases**, some of which will be considered in section 5.7.

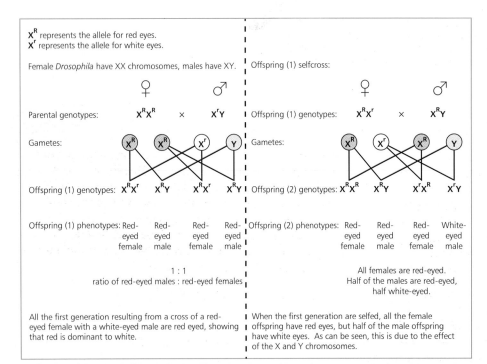

Figure 5.6.16 Sex-linked genes in *Drosophila* affect the eye colours which may be found in males and females.

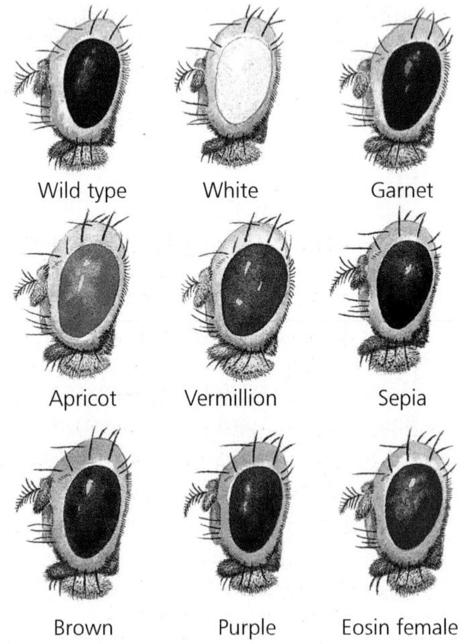

Figure 5.6.17 The normal *Drosophila* eye is red, but a whole range of mutant alleles can produce a great variety of other eye colours. These multiple alleles are sex linked.

Inactivation of X chromosomes

All the cells of a female mammal other than those of the ova contain two X chromosomes. However, during the early stages of development one of these X chromosomes is inactivated and coils up into a mass known as the **Barr body**.

Which X chromosome is inactivated in each embryonic cell seems to be a random event, but all the cells which are descended from that cell will have the same inactivated X chromosome. This means that females are made up of mosaics of cells, some with one X chromosome inactivated and some with the other. Tortoiseshell cats are a good example of this. Some of the X chromosomes carry the allele for black fur and some for orange. The mixture of colours on the cat reflects the mosaics of cells with different X chromosome inactivation. The situation is the same in all mammals, including humans. An example of human X inactivation is shown in figure 5.6.18.

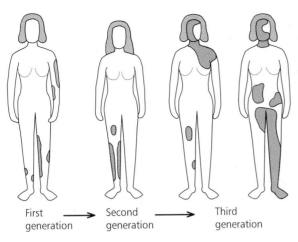

First generation → Second generation → Third generation

Figure 5.6.18 Anhidrotic ectodermal dysplasia is a mutation of a gene on the X chromosome which results in men without teeth, body hair or sweat glands. Heterozygous women have some missing teeth and patches of the body with no sweat glands, showing the random pattern of X inactivation. The last two women shown are identical twins, yet because the inactivation is random they do not show identical areas of skin without sweat glands.

The chi-squared test – getting it right

In genetics, as in many other areas of biology, we rely heavily on the results of practical experiments to test the validity of our ideas and hypotheses. When we carry out a genetic experiment such as the *Drosophila* cross shown in figure 5.6.12, we have a good idea of the results we are expecting. Even if we are carrying out a completely new experiment, we will have a hypothesis which we are hoping to prove or disprove.

But *Drosophila*, along with most other biological organisms, do not breed in neat multiples of 9, 3 and 1. So when we are faced with several hundred fruit flies with different coloured bodies and wings, how do we know if the results we observe are really close enough to our expected 9:3:3:1 ratio, or whether they are so far out that some other unexplained factor has come into play? Perhaps the hypothesis was wrong, or some flies escaped before being counted, or got stuck in the medium and died, distorting the results. The **chi-squared test** is used to analyse the results of such an experiment. This is a relatively simple

statistical method which will tell you if variation in your results from the expected values are significant, or if they are due to chance. It allows you to compare your actual results with the results you expected to see how well the real results fit your expectations. The procedure involves some fairly simple arithmetic followed by use of a chi-squared table. The formula for the chi-squared test is given below:

$$\chi^2 = \Sigma \frac{(O - E)^2}{E}$$

where O is the observed result, E is the expected result and the symbol Σ means 'the sum of'.

What does this mean in practice? Using the same example of the *Drosophila* cross, let us look at the results gained by one group of students working in the laboratory. We make the assumption that the observed results will show the expected ratio, and use the chi-squared test to show us if this assumption is correct. Table 5.6.2 shows the procedure.

Phenotype	Hypothesis	Observed	Expected	$O - E$	$(O - E)^2$	$\frac{(O - E)^2}{E}$
Long wings, grey body	9	101	99	2	4	0.04
Long wings, ebony body	3	31	33	−2	4	0.121
Vestigial wings, grey body	3	34	33	1	1	0.03
Vestigial wings, ebony body	1	10	11	−1	1	0.09
Total Σ		176				= 0.281

Table 5.6.2 These calculations allow us to carry out a chi-squared test

The table shows us that the value of chi-squared for this experiment is **0.281**.

We now need to know the number of **degrees of freedom** in the system. This is a measure of the spread of the data, and it is one less than the number of categories of observed information we are working with. So we find it by taking the number of pieces of observed information – in this case 4 phenotypes – and then subtracting 1 to give 3.

Once we have a value for chi-squared and the number of degrees of freedom, we can use a chi-squared table to find out the probability that our results are significant – in other words, that they support our hypothesis and are not just chance happenings.

We can see from figure 5.6.19 that with our result of 0.281, with 3 degrees of freedom, the probability that our results are significant is between 95% and 98%. Another way of putting this is to say that the probability that our results are due to chance alone is 2–5%. The accepted cut-off point is 5% – if there is a less than 5% likelihood that the results are due to chance, that is, a more than 95% probability that the hypothesis is correct, then it is accepted that the results are significant and show the biological effect we were looking for. If the results do not fall into these bands, then the results are not significant and we would need to look for some alternative explanation for them. This might mean looking for errors in the experimental technique, or it might involve revising the entire hypothesis.

Degrees of freedom	Probability, p	0.99	0.98	0.95	0.90	0.80	0.50	0.20	0.10	0.05	0.02	0.01	0.001
1		0.000	0.001	0.004	0.016	0.064	0.455	1.64	2.11	3.84	5.41	6.64	10.83
2		0.020	0.040	0.103	0.211	0.446	1.386	3.22	4.61	5.99	7.82	9.21	13.82
3		0.115	0.185	0.352	0.534	1.005	2.366	4.64	6.25	7.82	9.84	11.35	16.27
4		0.297	0.429	0.711	1.064	1.649	3.357	5.99	7.78	9.49	11.67	13.28	18.47
5		0.554	0.752	1.145	1.610	2.343	4.351	7.29	9.24	11.07	13.39	15.09	20.52

Figure 5.6.19 Part of a chi-squared table.

Genes in nature

As we saw on page 429, the phenotype of an organism is not the result of its genotype alone. The environment in which an organism or population grows will also have a major effect on the phenotypes expressed – for example, some mammals may have experienced more effective parenting, or some plants may have had more light, or less water. The variation that can be seen in a group of organisms is therefore the result of both the variation in their genotypes and variation in the environment. To take account of this, we can express the variation in a phenotype as the following equation:

$$V_P = V_G + V_E$$

where V_P is the variation in the phenotype, V_G is the variation in the genotype and V_E is the environmental variation.

E. coli and the lac operon

When we discuss the effect of the environment on the phenotype of an organism, we often use fairly loose and general terms about nutritional levels, temperature, etc. But in the phenotypes of some bacteria we can actually see the environmental effect taking place at a biochemical level. In the 1950s and 1960s two French geneticists, François Jacob and Jacques Monod, were working with the common gut bacteria *Escherichia coli*.

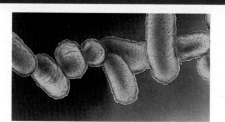

Figure 5.6.20 *E. coli* bacteria demonstrate the very direct effect the environment can have on the phenotype.

Lactose is a disaccharide which is broken down into galactose and glucose by the enzyme β-galactosidase. If there is no lactose present in the environment of the bacteria then there will be fewer than 10 molecules of this enzyme in each bacterial cell. But if lactose becomes available to the bacteria (as would happen in your gut if you ate ice cream or drank a milkshake) each bacterial cell will soon contain thousands of molecules of β-galactosidase along with two other related enzymes. The presence of the sugar **induces** the bacterial cells to make the enzyme. Jacob and Monod showed that this induction actually takes place at the level of the genes. They found a cluster of genes which function together to make the enzymes for breaking down lactose, and called the cluster the **lac operon**. They suggested that there might be a regulatory gene which produces a repressor substance when there is no lactose around. This repressor binds with the genetic material in the operator region of the gene (a part that can receive an off signal). This blocks the binding of RNA polymerase, preventing the code for the lactose-digesting enzymes from being transcribed. This means mRNA is not made, and so the enzyme cannot be made either.

When lactose is present, it binds to the repressor substance, causing it to change shape. This new shape cannot bind to the operator, so the RNA polymerase has free access to the DNA. Transcription takes place, closely followed by translation at the ribosomes to produce the enzymes. The bacterial cell can now use lactose as a food source. The change in phenotype from not producing β-galactosidase to active enzyme production is brought about purely in response to changes in the environment.

Operon systems like this give very sensitive control of the metabolism of the cell, allowing it to change in response to changes in the environment. They also provide an excellent research tool, because by manipulating the nutrients we provide to microorganisms growing in cultures, we can change their phenotypes and investigate further the mechanisms by which such changes come about.

The role of the environment in shaping an organism becomes even more important when we consider human development – an aspect which will be explored more fully in section 5.7.

SUMMARY

- The **phenotype** of an organism is made up of its observable characteristics. Its **genotype** is the genetic information in its chromosomes. The phenotype depends on the genotype and also on environmental conditions.

- A **gene** is a segment of DNA coding for a particular trait or characteristic, and is found at a particular position (the **locus**) on a specific homologous pair of chromosomes. Each homologous chromosome may carry different codings for this gene called **alleles**, and these produce alternate characteristics.

- An organism with the same allele for a particular gene on both homologous chromosomes is **homozygous** for that gene or characteristic.

- Homozygotes are **true breeding**. If two homozygous parents with the same characteristic are crossed and their offspring subsequently crossed, all generations of offspring have the same characteristics as each other and as the parents.

- The offspring of a cross between homozygous parents make up the **first filial generation** (F$_1$). The offspring all have the same phenotype. Crossing these offspring results in the **second filial generation**, and so on.

- An organism that has two different alleles for a particular gene on its homologous chromosomes is heterozygous for that gene or characteristic.

- A **dominant** allele expresses itself in the heterozygous state, masking the **recessive** allele. Recessive alleles are only expressed in homozygotes. Dominant alleles code for a particular protein, while recessive alleles usually code for its absence or an inactive protein.

- A **monohybrid cross** is a cross in which one genetic trait is considered. ▼ The predicted ratios of genotypes and phenotypes expected from a cross are known as **Mendelian ratios**, and the smaller the sample the larger the sampling error and the larger the error will be in applying these ratios.

- The Mendelian ratio for the phenotypes of a monohybrid cross between two heterozygotes is 3 dominant:1 recessive.

- A **test cross** is carried out to test whether a characteristic coded for by a dominant allele is the result of a homozygous or heterozygous genotype. The individual is crossed with a recessive homozygote. If the individual is heterozygous the offspring will have the ratio 1 dominant:1 recessive, while all will be dominant if it is homozygous.

- **Codominance** or incomplete dominance occurs when both alleles code for different proteins. The heterozygote has a characteristic in between those of the homozygotes. A heterozygote crossed with a homozygote results in offspring in the ratio 1 heterozygote:1 homozygote.

- **Multiple alleles** may result in several different phenotypes in different individuals.

- **Lethal genes** result in the death of individuals with particular gene combinations, for example homozygous recessive individuals may die before birth. This gives a ratio of 2:1 instead of the expected 3:1 for the first generation of a cross between two heterozygotes.

- **Dihybrid crosses** consider the inheritance of two traits at the same time. Offspring may show the same combination of traits as the parents (**parental phenotypes**) or they may show different combinations (**recombinant phenotypes**).

- The expected ratio for the second generation of a cross between two different homozygous parents is 9:3:3:1. A ratio of 3:1 in the second generation shows that the genes are **linked** (on the same chromosome).

- Mendel's **law of segregation**, in modern language, states that in a diploid organism one allele for each trait is inherited from each parent to give a total of two alleles for each trait. The pairs of alleles are separated during gamete formation (meiosis).

- Mendel's **law of independent assortment** states that different traits are inherited independently of each other.

- Exceptions to the law of independent assortment occur in **polygenic traits**, which are controlled by several interacting genes.

- Another exception to the law of independent assortment is genes being linked. This can happen to a greater or lesser extent, depending on how close together the genes are on the chromosome. Inheritance of linked genes can indicate how close together the genes are and hence the mapping of chromosomes, by working out the **cross over value**:

$$COV = \frac{\text{number of recombinant offspring}}{\text{total number of offspring}} \times 100$$

- Another exception to the law of independent assortment is **sex linkage**. Human males have one X and one Y chromosome, while females have two X chromosomes. Recessive alleles carried on the X chromosome will be expressed in the male since there is no other X chromosome to carry the dominant allele and mask them.

▼

- **Twin studies** give information about which aspects of a phenotype are caused by the genotype, and which by environmental influences. Studies on identical twins separated at birth and so subjected to different conditions have shown, for example, that height is largely genetically determined, unlike mass.

- The **chi-squared** test can be used to analyse the results of a genetic experiment, to show if variation in the results is due to chance or if it is significant.

QUESTIONS

1 As any gardener knows, F_1 hybrid seeds do not breed true. Thus plants raised from these seeds cannot be used as stock for the next year.

  a What is meant by the terms:
    i F_1 hybrid
    ii breeding true?

  b Why do F_1 hybrids not breed true if they are self-fertilised?

  c What is the advantage of using these hybrids?

2 **a** Human ABO blood types are determined by three alleles at one locus, I^A, I^B and I^0. I^A and I^B are codominant. What does this mean?

  b I^0 is recessive. Is it possible for one individual to carry all three alleles? Explain your answer.

  c What gametes will someone with blood type AB produce?

  d What gametes will someone with blood type O produce?

  e Produce a genetic diagram to show the possible outcomes of a couple with AB and B blood groups.

3 In *Drosophila melanogaster*, kidney bean-shaped eye is recessive to round-shaped eye and orange eye colour is recessive to red eye colour.
A fly, homozygous for both round-shaped eye and red colour, was crossed with a fly having kidney bean-shaped orange coloured eyes. The offspring (F_1) were allowed to interbreed and the investigator expected to find a 9:3:3:1 segregation for eye shape and colour in the F_2 generation. Instead, the following progeny were produced.

red colour, round-shaped eye	520
orange colour, kidney bean-shaped eye	180
red colour, kidney bean-shaped eye	54
orange colour, round-shaped eye	45

  a Account for the basis for the expected 9:3:3:1 segregation in the F_2 generation.   **(6 marks)**

  b Explain the observed result.   **(6 marks)**
              (Total 12 marks)
              (O&C June 1991)

Developing Key Skills

a Use the information given in the Focus material from twin studies and display it in a different form to make the variations and similarities between the experimental groups much clearer. Explain why it is considered that there is a strong genetic component in height, less genetic influence on body mass and a combination of genetics and environment affecting intelligence.

b Discuss some of the environmental factors that might influence body mass and intelligence.

c How might you set out to investigate which factors are most important in the development of intelligence? Is it possible to design an ethically acceptable experiment using humans and, if not, what alternatives are available?

THE HUMAN GENOME PROJECT

The **Human Genome Project** is a massive research programme set up with the aim of mapping the entire human genome – finding the positions of all the human genes on the chromosomes. In six countries, 265 laboratories are working towards determining the locations, DNA nucleotide sequences and functions of all the 100 000 or so human genes. It is estimated that the cost at completion will be around $3 billion. As this project moves forward it will be possible to identify the genes for all the single-gene genetic disorders, and doubtless provide screening tests for them. It should also clarify the situation in **multifactorial** diseases resulting from a number of genes and lifestyle factors too.

To know and to tell ...

All this knowledge will raise some tough issues for society to consider. For example, in a family affected by Huntington's disease, some individuals might find it unbearable to learn that they have inherited a completely untreatable disease which is fatal. An uncertain future with a degree of hope may be preferable to one filled with the knowledge of their own horrendous decline and death.

Another problem with the information being discovered by the Human Genome Project is who should have access to it. If an individual is screened and it is found that they either have a dominant allele for a specific disease like Huntington's, or that they are carriers of a recessive allele, then the information could remain confidential, available only to the individual concerned. This leaves it up to the individual to decide whether to tell partners, parents and friends, whether to have children and indeed, whether to tell their insurance companies. However, some people would argue that society has a right to know. You have a right to know that the person with whom you plan to have children is not going to knowingly pass on abnormal genes.

Most of us do not carry the allele for Huntington's disease, but in the UK one in 25 will carry the gene for cystic fibrosis. Should this affect our choice of partner? Information such as this will soon be available, affecting our life choices, and it would be better to decide how to deal with it now rather than later.

New treatments

The Human Genome Project also holds out the promise of a medical revolution, with drugs tailored to fit and interact with specific gene switches – for example, preventing genes that can cause breast cancer or heart disease from being turned on.

In another perturbing twist to the story, a commercial company claims to be racing the international scientists to map the complete human genome – and winning. Whereas the aim of the international effort is to provide the human genome free to everyone who needs it, the biotechnology company is attempting to patent thousands of genes, which could make any drugs produced in the future using these genes unrealistically expensive. So we now have to ask not only how society should use the information of the human genome, but should the fundamentals of our DNA be for sale?

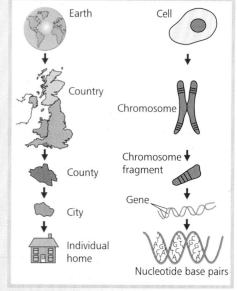

Figure 1 Identifying the DNA nucleotide sequence of every human gene is like taking a map of the world and homing in on someone's individual street address, allowing us to pinpoint exactly what our genetic make-up is.

Figure 2 Perhaps financial institutions should not be tricked into lending money or offering cheap life insurance to someone who knows they carry a genetic time bomb. However, on these arguments every one of us could be a bad risk, because no one has a completely perfect set of genes.

Human genetics

Although all human beings are members of the same species, there is tremendous variation between individuals. Height, weight, skin colour and many other features show an enormous range. Most families have particular genetic traits which can be traced back through the generations, such as unusually shaped noses, red hair or dimples. Some families have genetic traits which cause disorders such as colour blindness, haemophilia or Huntington's chorea (a disease characterised by involuntary muscular movements and mental retardation). The genetic principles which we have looked at so far also apply to our own genetics. However, like those of other complex organisms, many human features are polygenic, making working out the details of a human genotype considerably more difficult than understanding the genotype of *Drosophila*.

Figure 5.7.1 The variety within the human species is enormous, and the genetics behind this poses a complex puzzle.

Studying human genetics

Practical problems

A major problem in understanding human inheritance is that people are not available for experimentation. Apart from the obvious social and moral objections, humans are very poor laboratory animals! We have long life cycles, and only produce a very small number of offspring. The effects of any experiments would take a very long time to become apparent.

One of the main tools of genetic investigation is, as we have seen, the setting up of deliberate crosses between individuals – but humans do not reproduce to please geneticists. Secondly, it is frequently the second generation which reveals most about a particular cross. In humans a true F_2 generation almost never occurs, as it would be the result of a union between a brother and sister. Such relationships frequently result in children born with abnormalities due to the increased likelihood of two undesirable recessive genes coming together. Brother–sister marriages are taboo in most human societies. Finally, the sample size in human families is too small for statistical analyses – the average family in the UK is now less than two children per couple.

Bearing these problems in mind, how are human genetics studied? Much of the work done on human inheritance has involved studies of a genetic disorder. The production of a family tree or pedigree is one technique where a particular trait can be traced through several generations of a family and deductions made about the mode of inheritance. A **karyotype** or photograph of the chromosomes like that seen in figure 5.7.6 may be produced and used to uncover abnormalities involving whole chromosomes. Biochemical analysis of specific metabolic pathways can reveal the presence of mutant genes which cause severe genetic diseases. These techniques, along with the application of the Mendelian principles of genetics already considered earlier, and increasingly intricate gene mapping, are rapidly increasing our understanding of the human **genome** (the total number of genes). We shall now go on to consider these techniques, along with some disorders studied using them.

Family trees

The analysis of pedigrees or family trees can be very useful for deciding how a trait is inherited. Sex-linked diseases show up in the males rather than the females. Dominant genes express themselves in every generation whereas recessive genes may skip one or more generations, being passed on in the recessive states. A **carrier** is a healthy individual who possesses an unexpected recessive allele which would result in a genetic disease in the homozygous state or if inherited by a male. The use of a family tree allows potential carriers of a trait to be identified.

Genetic diseases

Genetic diseases may be caused by a single defective gene, leading to a reduced level of a particular enzyme. Alternatively, they may result from a whole chromosome mutation. Either type of problem can disrupt the entire biochemistry of the cell and cause major problems to the whole organism.

Aneuploidy

A change from the normal diploid chromosome number of 46 is the most common type of whole-chromosome genetic defect in humans. **Aneuploidy**, the absence of one or more chromosomes or the presence of one or more extra chromosomes, often results in a highly abnormal embryo which is spontaneously aborted at a very early stage. However, this does not always happen and some individuals with abnormal chromosome numbers survive to adulthood.

When cells in the ovaries and the testes undergo meiotic divisions to produce ova and sperm, the chromosome number of the original cells is halved. Each gamete formed should contain 23 chromosomes, including one sex chromosome, to pass on into the next generation. However, an error called **nondisjunction** can occur – during the reduction division of meiosis, individual members of an homologous pair of chromosomes fail to separate during anaphase. This means one of the gametes has two copies of that chromosome and the other has no copies of it. If one of the abnormal gametes joins with a normal one in fertilisation, an individual will result who is either **monosomic** for a particular chromosome (with only one member of the homologous pair present) or **trisomic** (with three rather than two chromosomes of a particular type). Most examples of aneuploidy are lethal and affected embryos abort, but some examples can and do survive.

Autosome abnormalities

The **autosomes** are all the chromosomes except the sex chromosomes – the 22 pairs of chromosomes that carry most of the information about you as an individual. Most autosome abnormalities are lethal, and the fetuses fail to develop to full term. Trisomy of chromosome 13 causes harelip, cleft palate and various eye, brain and cardiovascular defects. It only occurs in about one in every 10 000 live births and usually results in death within the first three months of life. Similarly trisomy of chromosome 18, found in one in every 5000 live births, causes malformation of almost every organ system. About 80% of the affected babies born are female – it is possible that males are so badly affected that almost all abort. Again, most of these afflicted babies die in the first few months of life. The most commonly occurring major autosome abnormality, and almost the only one compatible with continued life, is trisomy on autosome 21, known as **Down's syndrome**.

Aneuploidy of all kinds increases with maternal (and paternal) age. All the future ova of an individual woman become frozen in prophase I of meiosis while the woman herself is still an embryo. Meiosis is completed in the ovum only after ovulation and fertilisation by a sperm. Forty years or more of waiting and being exposed to all the chemical and radiation hazards of modern life appears to be too much for some of the ova and nondisjunction increases. This is

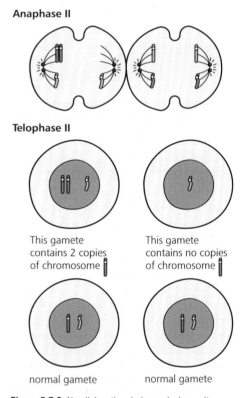

Anaphase II

Telophase II

This gamete contains 2 copies of chromosome ▌

This gamete contains no copies of chromosome ▌

normal gamete

normal gamete

Figure 5.7.2 Nondisjunction during meiosis results in gametes with an extra chromosome or a missing chromosome.

Figure 5.7.3 Down's syndrome results from trisomy (three copies) of chromosome 21.

demonstrated both by the raised level of spontaneous abortion of abnormal embryos in older women, and by the increased numbers of trisomic fetuses aborted after diagnostic tests and Down's syndrome babies born to older women.

Down's syndrome (see figure 5.7.3) causes mental retardation and abnormal physical development. The skull is small and flattened from front to back. The nose is short and flat, and the mouth cavity is small with an enlarged tongue. Other problems include squints, abnormal ears and teeth, cataracts and quite often an abnormal heart. There is also a substantial lack of muscle tone, which means that Down's syndrome individuals tend to lack facial expression, although most are capable of smiles. Most individuals with Down's syndrome are infertile, although babies have been born to women with Down's syndrome. Half of these babies are normal, half also have Down's syndrome, reflecting that half of the ova formed will contain one chromosome 21 and the other half will contain two. The level of mental retardation varies quite widely – many sufferers can learn to speak, and others can also write and read at a simple level and develop sufficient skills to be relatively independent. However, the majority are much less fortunate and most Down's individuals will need substantial care for the whole of their lives. Although their life expectancy is lower than normal, many Down's individuals outlive their parents, which can be very traumatic if they then have to be moved from loving care in a normal home into an institution. Many Down's syndrome individuals are very affectionate and loving, and this continues into adulthood. This is one of the major compensations felt by parents who are bringing up children disadvantaged in this way by their chromosomes.

Prenatal testing is widely used to discover if a fetus has Down's syndrome early enough in the pregnancy for the parents to be offered an abortion if they do not wish to continue with the pregnancy. In the UK a blood test is offered to all pregnant women at around 12 weeks of pregnancy. The levels of specific markers seen in the blood and the age of the mother allow an assessment of the risk that the fetus may be Down's syndrome. In addition, at 16 weeks of pregnancy the **alpha-fetoprotein** blood test is carried out. If the levels are low, this suggests an increased likelihood of a chromosome abnormality, particularly Down's syndrome. If the levels are raised, this can indicate that the fetus has spina bifida. Older mothers are offered testing automatically, as the risk of having Down's baby increases with age, as shown in figure 5.7.4, although the age at which testing is offered varies from area to area.

The least invasive procedure for finding out about the health of an unborn baby is the use of **ultrasound**. Very high frequency sound waves are bounced off the fetus and the reflected sound is used to build up a visual image. This shows whether the fetus is growing as it should and also checks for limb, heart and gross brain abnormalities. More information can be yielded by **fetoscopy**, where the fetus can be seen directly using a very fine fibreoptic telescope (fetoscope) inserted through the abdominal wall into the uterine cavity. However, to discover for sure the chromosomal make-up of the fetus, a **karyotype** (complete chromosome picture) needs to be made from the chromosomes of the fetal cells. The required fetal tissue can be obtained in one of two ways – chorionic villus sampling or amniocentesis. These are described in figure 5.7.5.

It may be difficult for parents to come to terms with the fact that the child they are expecting will not be the normal, healthy baby they had hoped for. Many parents who find that their fetus is affected by Down's syndrome decide to terminate the pregnancy, rather than condemn the child to a life of handicap and themselves and any other children they may have to a life of caring for the Down's child. Other parents either do not sanction abortion or choose to carry their child to term in spite of the genetic handicap it carries. For these couples

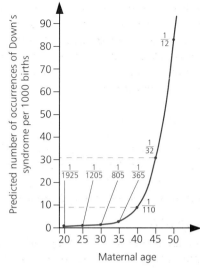

Figure 5.7.4 When chromosome 21 is 'sticky', two copies will be delivered to one gamete and none to another. If the first of these two gametes is subsequently fertilised the individual resulting will be trisomic for chromosome 21 and will have Down's syndrome. If the second is fertilised the zygote cannot survive and fails to develop. The likelihood of this 'stickiness' occurring increases with the age of the mother, particularly beyond the age of 40.

5

Amniocentesis involves removing about 20 cm³ of the amniotic fluid which surrounds the fetus. The fluid is withdrawn using a needle and syringe, at about the sixteenth week of pregnancy. Fetal epithelial cells and even fetal blood cells can be recovered from the fluid after centrifugation. After the cells have been cultured for several weeks, a number of genetic defects as well as the sex of the baby can be determined from examination of their chromosomes.
Disadvantages: Can only be carried out relatively late in the pregnancy, so that should termination of the pregnancy be necessary it is more traumatic. Have to wait several weeks after the test for the results. Carries about a 1% risk of spontaneous abortion following the procedure, regardless of the genetic status of the fetus.

Chorionic villus sampling involves taking a small sample of the embryonic tissue from the developing placenta. This makes a much bigger sample of fetal tissue available for examination. The embryonic cells are then tested for a wide range of genetic abnormalities. This technique can be carried out much earlier in the pregnancy, so that if a termination is necessary it is physically less traumatic for the mother. It yields information more rapidly.
Disadvantages: There is a risk that the embryo may spontaneously abort after the tissue sample is taken. All paternal X chromosomes are inactivated in fetal placental cells, so any problems in the genes on that chromosome cannot be detected by this technique.

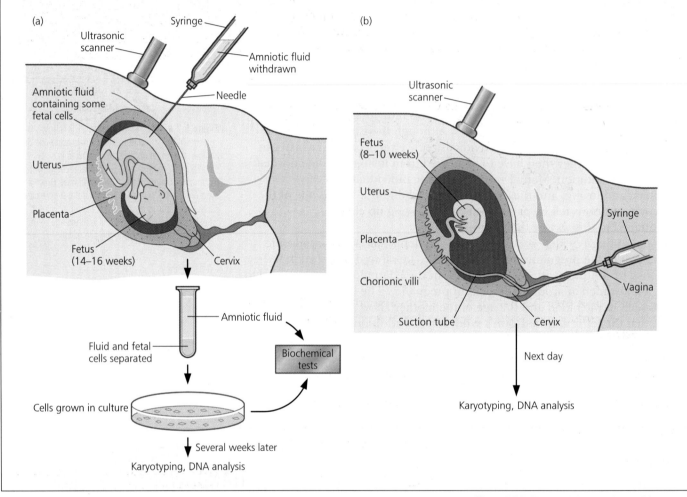

Figure 5.7.5 These techniques make possible an accurate diagnosis of Down's syndrome and other genetic disorders before birth.

too the testing is valuable. It allows them time to grieve the loss of the normal healthy baby they thought they were carrying and to come to terms with and welcome the child when it is born. The amniocentesis test only gives knowledge of Down's syndrome around half-way through a pregnancy, and so the abortion is late and therefore relatively traumatic if the parents choose to terminate the pregnancy. However, most people feel that the option of knowing should be available. Others feel that the view of society that the only acceptable baby is a perfect baby is a sad reflection of materialistic times.

Sex chromosome abnormalities

Very few embryos with aneuploidy of the autosomes survive even until birth, apart from those with Down's syndrome. In contrast, the absence of a sex chromosome or the presence of several sex chromosomes is less unusual and

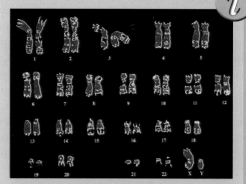
less life threatening, although in most cases there will be fertility problems. The presence or absence of the Y chromosome determines the route for sexual development in humans. Any embryo with at least one Y chromosome will develop male characteristics, whilst any embryo lacking a Y chromosome will develop female characteristics.

Sex chromosome abnormalities include:

- **Turner's syndrome** XO – the person is apparently female but infertile, and will not undergo puberty without extra hormones

- **Metafemales** XXX or more, resulting from nondisjunction during meiosis – the person is normal but there is a slightly raised incidence of mental illness

- **XYY men** – again these are normal and fertile individuals

- **Klinefelter's syndrome** XXY or XXYY again resulting from nondisjunction – these individuals appear normal males until puberty, but need hormone treatment to develop and are infertile.

The frequencies of the various chromosome abnormalities that result from nondisjunction discussed in this section are summarised in table 5.7.1.

Syndrome	Chromosomes	Average frequency at birth
Down's syndrome	3 copies of chromosome 21	Ranges from 1/2000 at maternal age 20 to 1/12 as maternal age approaches 50
Turner's syndrome	XO	1/5000
Metafemale	XXX	1/700
Klinefelter's syndrome	XXY, etc.	1/500

Table 5.7.1 Chromosome abnormalities as a result of nondisjunction

Genetic diseases that are not the result of aneuploidy

So far we have looked at genetic diseases in which there is an extra chromosome or a missing chromosome. However, most genetic diseases are caused by individual genes rather than entire chromosomes. In **Duchenne muscular dystrophy**, a mutated recessive gene is carried on one of the X chromosomes of the mother. If this fuses with a normal X chromosome from the father resulting in a girl, all will be well. But if a boy has an affected X chromosome, at around the age of seven or eight deterioration of the muscle tissue begins. The child becomes wheelchair bound and will die in the early teenage years. Girls do not suffer from this disease because affected boys die before they are capable of reproduction, so double recessive females with two affected X chromosomes are not conceived. It is possible that even if they were, the effect would be so catastrophic that the fetus would not develop to term.

This example shows that a mutation of just a single gene can cause far-reaching and even lethal damage to the physiology of the human body. New techniques for analysing DNA sequences and engineering genes have recently opened up the whole area of treatment of genetic diseases. Until very recently these diseases struck sometimes at random, sometimes following a family pattern, but nothing could effectively be done to cure them. Now, in some cases at least, problems can be detected before birth, and the chances of an apparently unaffected individual developing a disease or passing it on to another generation can be worked out. There is even the possibility of cures being developed. But these developments present us as individuals and as societies with some complicated ethical issues. We shall look at a number of genetic diseases, some more serious in their effects than others.

Red-green colour blindness

Family trees are useful for demonstrating the inheritance of some of the better known human sex-linked diseases – in particular red-green colour blindness and haemophilia. **Colour blindness** is due to a recessive mutation of a gene on the X chromosome. Around 8% of Caucasian males are affected by this, but only 1% of females. The gene does not markedly affect the chances of survival of an individual, and because the homozygous form is not lethal colour blindness does occasionally occur in women. This is explained in figure 5.7.7.

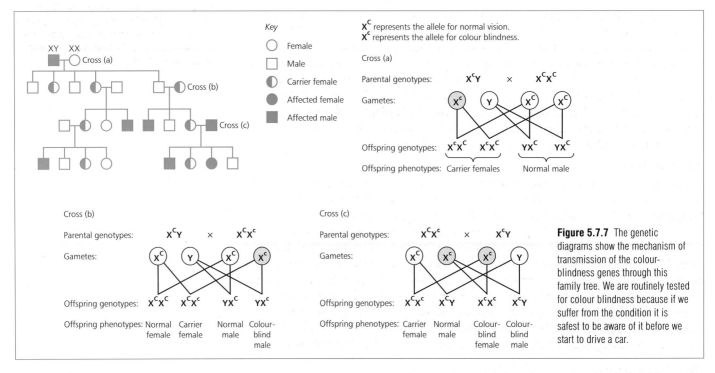

Figure 5.7.7 The genetic diagrams show the mechanism of transmission of the colour-blindness genes through this family tree. We are routinely tested for colour blindness because if we suffer from the condition it is safest to be aware of it before we start to drive a car.

Haemophilia

Colour blindness is usually an inconvenience but nothing more. **Haemophilia** is a much more severe sex-linked trait in which one of the proteins needed for the clotting of the blood (factor VIII) is missing. The mutated gene is carried on the X chromosome. The homozygous form is unlikely to arise since haemophiliac men rarely have offspring, but if it does it is lethal when the affected female reaches puberty if not before. In an untreated haemophiliac the slightest injury can lead to death through excessive bleeding – even exercise can result in internal bleeding of the joints. Haemophilia can now be treated by regular transfusions of factor VIII, and although this is expensive it can allow haemophiliacs to lead a more or less normal life.

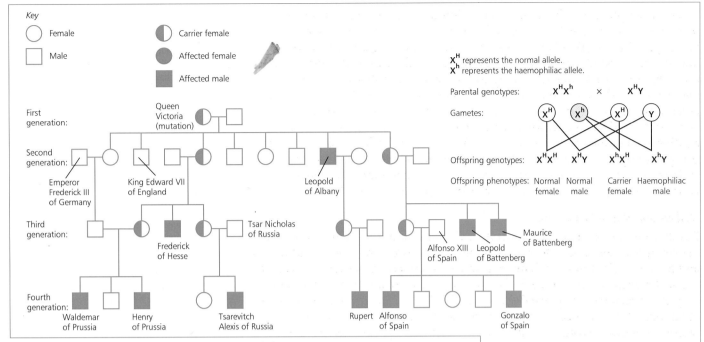

X^H represents the normal allele.
X^h represents the haemophiliac allele.

Parental genotypes: $X^H X^h$ × $X^H Y$

Gametes: X^H X^h X^H Y

Offspring genotypes: $X^H X^H$ $X^H Y$ $X^h X^H$ $X^h Y$

Offspring phenotypes: Normal female   Normal male   Carrier female   Haemophiliac male

First generation: Queen Victoria (mutation)

Second generation: Emperor Frederick III of Germany — King Edward VII of England — Leopold of Albany

Third generation: Frederick of Hesse — Tsar Nicholas of Russia — Alfonso XIII of Spain — Leopold of Battenberg — Maurice of Battenberg

Fourth generation: Waldemar of Prussia — Henry of Prussia — Tsarevitch Alexis of Russia — Rupert — Alfonso of Spain — Gonzalo of Spain

Figure 5.7.8 Haemophilia in the royal families of Europe – as a result of the wide-ranging intermarriages between the various royal families, haemophilia spread from the original mutation in Queen Victoria to most of the royal houses of Europe.

Haemophilia is caused by a mutation known since ancient times, and long before Mendel some idea of the genetics of the disorder was grasped. The primary source of Jewish law, the Talmud, specifies that if a boy dies of bleeding after circumcision, his younger brothers should not undergo the ritual and his male cousins on the mother's side were also exempt. This shows an understanding that blood which does not clot runs in families, and is inherited from the mother rather than the father. Haemophilia plagued the royal families of Europe after a mutation in the earliest stages of the embryonic development of Queen Victoria, as figure 5.7.8 shows.

Phenylketonuria

Biochemical analysis of certain biochemical pathways can uncover evidence for genes which cause severe problems. The metabolism of the amino acid phenylalanine is prone to errors. One of the most common is known as **phenylketonuria** (**PKU**), which is inherited as a recessive allele. Newborn infants who have inherited this condition have high levels of phenylalanine in their blood, but are not damaged. As the breakdown products of the amino acid build up, severe mental retardation results. Babies in the UK are routinely tested for PKU in the first few days of life. A few moments' discomfort can prevent a lifetime of brain damage and institutionalised care. If affected they can be given a diet almost free of phenylalanine so avoiding the problems of the defective metabolism and the child will develop more or less normally.

Tay-Sachs disease

Biochemical analysis has also been used to detect a genetic disorder known as **Tay-Sachs disease**. Particularly prevalent in the Ashkenazi Jews from central Europe, this is the result of a recessive allele which, when present in the homozygous form, prevents the production of the enzyme **hexosaminidase A**. This enzyme is required for lipid metabolism and without it the nervous system degenerates. This degeneration begins a few months after birth so that the infant becomes blind and deaf, suffers seizures and dies before reaching the age of five. Heterozygous carriers show no obvious symptoms, but it has been found that their blood levels of hexosaminidase A are reduced. Thus by testing

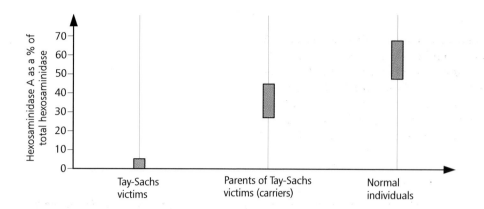

the blood, carriers in the 'at risk' group can be identified, as shown in figure 5.7.9. This information can be used to choose partners or have fetal screening as the identified carriers wish, in an attempt to eradicate this dreadful genetic disease.

Cystic fibrosis

Cystic fibrosis is a genetic disease that is usually carried by a recessive allele on chromosome 7. It occurs in about one in every 2500 babies born to white Europeans, but is much less common in other ethnic groups. Because cystic fibrosis is caused by a recessive allele, even if both parents are carriers of the disease they will only have a one in four chance of any particular pregnancy being affected, as shown in figure 5.7.10.

Cystic fibrosis causes severe respiratory and digestive problems, along with very salty sweat. The exocrine glands, including mucus-secreting and sweat glands, cannot reabsorb chloride and sodium ions, and this results in thick, sticky mucus secretions which obstruct the ducts in the exocrine glands and can cause irreversible damage. Clogged bile ducts can cause cirrhosis of the liver, and pancreatic tubules can rupture, releasing digestive enzymes into the body cavity which cause damage followed by the build-up of fibrous scar tissue. Without sufficient pancreatic enzymes, the digestion and reabsorption of protein and fats is often incomplete, so the individual can suffer from malnutrition. Thick sticky mucus accumulates in the small airways of the lungs, leading to severe coughing fits and breathlessness, and also leaves the respiratory system very vulnerable to bacterial infections, which can often be fatal. Physiotherapy may be needed at least twice a day to clear the lungs, and the effects on the digestive system can be controlled to some extent by taking replacement enzymes. With better management and drugs, more cystic fibrosis sufferers now lead relatively normal lives and grow up into early adulthood. However, most sufferers are infertile, as the mucus also clogs the tubules in the testes and affects the Fallopian tubes.

The position of the mutated gene on chromosome 7, which causes 70–5% of cystic fibrosis cases, was isolated by scientists in August 1989. Because it is recessive, the allele has to be inherited from both parents for the disease to manifest itself. Anyone with a single allele is simply a carrier, with the potential to pass the gene on to their own offspring. By 1990 the normal allele had been copied and added to cells affected by cystic fibrosis in the laboratory, where it proved effective in correcting the defective biochemical pathway. Throughout the 1990s work continued to find a way of converting this major discovery into a treatment to help cystic fibrosis sufferers, most of whom are young as the life expectancy of sufferers is severely reduced.

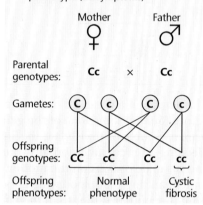

C represents the normal allele
c represents the allele for cystic fibrosis
Cc represents a carrier with a normal phenotype (no symptoms)

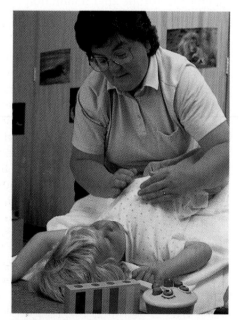

Figure 5.7.10 Individuals carry the recessive allele for cystic fibrosis without knowing it. If two carriers have a child which inherits both recessive alleles, it will have cystic fibrosis. The child will need several daily sessions of physiotherapy to keep the lungs clear, as well as constant medication.

Huntington's disease

Huntington's disease or **Huntington's chorea** is a genetic disease caused by a dominant allele. This means that anyone who inherits the allele will get the disease, and that any children of an affected parent will have a 50% chance of inheriting it too. Until very recently, the victims of Huntington's disease have only found they were affected when symptoms began to show at between 30 and 50 years of age, so many affected people have already had children before they discover their own disease. It is very rare, affecting about one in 20 000 of the white American population, for example.

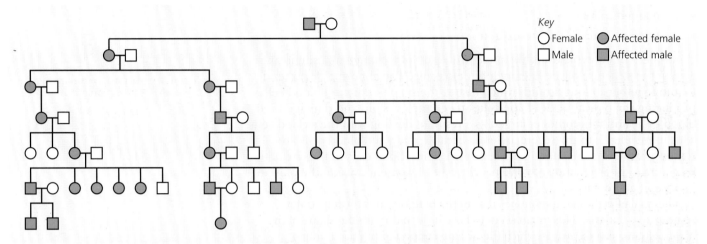

Key
○ Female   ● Affected female
□ Male   ■ Affected male

Figure 5.7.11 Because the symptoms of Huntington's disease do not appear until early middle age, and because the dominant genetic nature of the disease was only recognised relatively recently, the disease has devastated families for generations, as can be seen in the family tree of this American family.

Huntington's disease involves progressive degeneration of nerve cells in the central nervous system. The individual begins to have involuntary jerking or writhing movements of the arms and legs, and strange facial grimaces. Changes in personality occur, including inappropriate laughter and tears, anger, memory loss and bizarre, almost schizophrenic behaviour. The pattern of symptoms is very variable, but the patient usually sinks into a virtually vegetative state for several years before inevitable death. In 1983 Dr James Gusella working in Boston, Massachusetts decided to compare the DNA of family members affected by Huntington's disease with those who did not have the disease. He used gene probes to discover a genetic marker present only when the Huntington's disease allele was there in an individual. This discovery was the basis for a genetic test to be developed for use with families when one member develops Huntington's disease. If that family member is your parent, you are faced with many years of uncertainty before you know if you too have inherited the disease. The test opens the door for people to face and plan their own future, and also to plan whether and how to bring children into the world. For example, if one partner has the Huntington's allele, a couple may choose not to have children and thus risk passing on the allele. On the other hand they may have children, but choose to have the fetuses screened, terminating the pregnancy if the Huntington's allele is present.

As workers move closer to identifying the gene itself, the possibilities of genetic cures also move closer. But the new knowledge about Huntington's disease raises many difficult issues.

Pleiotropic genes and sickle cell anaemia

Many genes are **pleiotropic**. This means that one gene affects more than one phenotypic feature. A well researched example of pleiotropy in humans is a gene affecting the production of haemoglobin. The allele **Hb**^{A} allows for the

Figure 5.7.12 Normal and sickled red blood cells. Sickle cell anaemia is the result of a homozygous recessive gene. In the homozygous state it is usually lethal. However, in the heterozygous form it confers resistance to malaria, and so the gene is maintained in the population.

formation of normal haemoglobin. The mutant form **Hb^S** causes a disease known as **sickle cell anaemia** which usually results in an early death. This mutant allele is recessive and has at least five readily observed phenotypic consequences if it is inherited. These include:

- red blood cells which are sickle shaped instead of the normal biconcave disc, as shown in figure 5.7.12
- severe and eventually lethal anaemia – a greatly reduced number of red blood cells
- pain in the abdomen and joints
- an enlarged spleen
- resistance to malaria in heterozygotes.

All these phenotypic traits are in fact the result of a change in a single amino acid in the structure of the haemoglobin molecule. The abnormal form tends to join together in long strands which distort the shape of the red blood cells, producing the typical sickle shape. The spleen removes old and damaged red blood cells, and it becomes enlarged as a result of dealing with the sickled cells. This in turn leads to the severe anaemia because many red blood cells are removed from the circulation and destroyed. The sickled cells in the circulation block tiny capillaries and so starve nearby cells of oxygen, causing the pain in joints and abdomen.

The final effect of the mutation is that in the heterozygous form it confers resistance to malaria. This might seem to have little to do with the shape of the haemoglobin, and the way in which the two are connected has taken much unravelling by doctors, biochemists, population geneticists and electron microscopists. The heterozygous genotype **Hb^AHb^S** results in individuals who produce both normal and abnormal haemoglobin. Under normal body conditions their red blood cells are disc shaped. When malarial parasites are present in the blood cells the cells cannot cope with reduced oxygen tension, and they sickle as the oxygen level falls. These mis-shaped cells are then removed by the spleen, incidentally getting rid of the malarial parasites at the same time. Normal shaped, unaffected cells are unharmed. The result of this is individuals who might have slightly enlarged spleens or suffer a degree of anaemia – but who are resistant to malaria. The sickle cell gene is found in populations almost exclusively where malaria is also prevalent. The advantages it gives in terms of malarial resistance ensure that it is retained within the genetic mix of the population in spite of the problems it causes in the homozygous form, as demonstrated in figure 5.7.13.

Figure 5.7.13 Homozygotes for the sickle cell allele die as a result of it. Many of those homozygous for the normal gene will die or be seriously debilitated by malaria. Sickle cell heterozygotes usually survive both conditions.

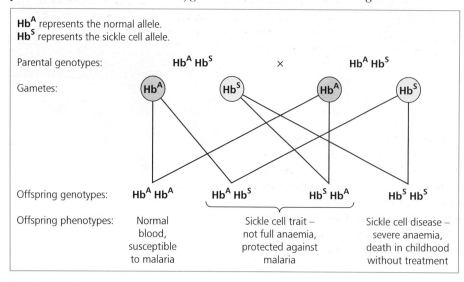

Multiple sclerosis – genetic disease?

Not all diseases can be described neatly as genetic, or environmental, or infectious. In spite of our greatly improved understanding of diseases, there are still some about which remarkably little is known. **Multiple sclerosis** (**MS**) is one such disease. It has an unknown cause, no known cure and an unpredictable course. It often starts when people are in their 20s and 30s, disrupting their lives but rarely shortening them. Multiple sclerosis causes inflammation of random patches of the central nervous system. The myelin sheath is damaged, causing permanent disruption and slowing of the conduction of nervous impulses. Symptoms include difficulty in walking, slurred speech, reduced vision, bladder dysfunction, spasticity (jerky movements) and tremors (shakes). It is most common in white Caucasians of Northern European ancestry, although it has appeared in all ethnic groups and about twice as many women as men are affected. Canada has a particularly high proportion of sufferers. About 15% of those with the disease have a close relative who is also affected. Diagnosis involves MRI scans and lumbar punctures in which cerebrospinal fluid is withdrawn from the spinal cord through a needle. The disease may be active, with very noticeable deterioration and great fatigue, or it may remain stable for many years. Treatment varies greatly and is mainly based on alleviating the symptoms as much as possible.

For some time an obscure viral infection was suspected of causing MS. Whilst this idea has not been eliminated, evidence is increasingly pointing to a number of genes interacting in individuals who have the disease. This means that the likelihood of any offspring inheriting all the affected genes is only 3–4%. Although this is higher than for the general population, it is a lot lower than for genetic diseases caused by one gene. Research into this mysterious and debilitating disease goes on.

Gene probes

Gene probes allow scientists to identify particular pieces of DNA in a cell, such as a piece of recombinant DNA in a microorganism such as a bacterium, or specific disease-causing genes in a human cell. Whatever the use, gene probes all use similar technology. To find a particular gene out of the hundreds of thousands present in the DNA of a human cell, a very specific probe is needed. The unique feature of any gene is the sequence of nucleotides of the DNA. This can be recognised by a stretch of RNA with the complementary sequence, in a process known as **DNA–RNA hybridisation**. The DNA is isolated from some cells and heated gently. This breaks open the weak hydrogen bonds holding together the two strands of DNA. Radioactively labelled mRNA for the required gene is added – this is the probe. Any DNA–RNA hybridisation that takes place indicates the presence of the required gene, and can be pinpointed by the radioactive label on the mRNA. Gene probes have been used to identify genetic markers in families with severe genetic problems such as Huntington's disease. They have also been used to identify and isolate genes that code for the production of antibiotics and hormones, which have then been used in genetic engineering to enable microbes to make, for example, human insulin. The use of gene probes in the identification of genetic traits in an individual and in the world of genetic engineering will surely continue to increase in the next decade as our knowledge of the human genome expands.

Genetic testing and screening – issues and ethics

Genetic testing involves the testing of the members of a family into which a child with a genetic disorder has been born, to try to estimate the risk of any further babies being affected and to identify the individuals who are carriers of the faulty gene. **Genetic screening** involves the genetic testing for a particular faulty gene of a large proportion of the population who are reproducing. At first sight the idea of genetic screening sounds excellent. Find out what your faulty genes are (and we all have some!) before you pass them on to any children you might have in the future. But what are the implications of this type of knowledge? And can genetic screening as it stands give us all the information we need? These questions need to be addressed. There is currently a major research drive known as the **Human Genome Project** which aims to produce detailed maps of all the genes on all the human chromosomes (see page 450).

The findings will make it possible for each of us to know our genetic make-up, and give us a baffling range of choices about partners, children, jobs and medication. It can certainly be argued that it is unfair to have children affected with a serious genetic disease when the knowledge is there to prevent it. But the knowledge does not solve the problems, it simply raises further dilemmas. Should all couples who plan to start a family – or indeed, who plan to have sex (as there is always a risk of pregnancy unless one of the partners is sterilised) – be screened to see if their genetic weaknesses are compatible? Amongst the Ashkenazi Jews of North America, Tay-Sachs disease is very common. The rabbis themselves have organised screening of each couple who plan to marry. If it is found that they are both carriers of the Tay-Sachs gene, then the marriage is forbidden. The distress for couples who find they are genetically incompatible must be great, yet the saving of human misery if Tay-Sachs disease can be reduced or removed from the population would be enormous. In the North American community the incidence of the disease has already been lowered by about 80%. Similarly, screening of couples for **thalassaemia**, a hereditary blood disease, has been extremely effective in countries where the risk is high for the whole population, such as the Mediterranean countries. It is less successful in countries like the UK where the affected group is a minority scattered through the rest of the population, and may be less aware both of the risks and of the screening that is available.

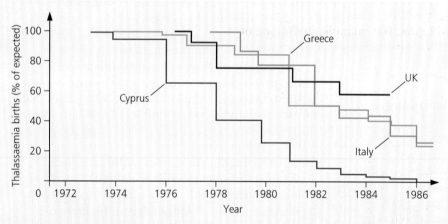

Figure 5.7.14 Results of thalassaemia control programmes in Cyprus, Greece, Italy and the UK.

Screening all couples to see if they are carrying a particular gene can be prohibitively expensive, and very much a blunt instrument in some cases. In Tay-Sachs disease the screening is limited to a relatively small community, so is viable. For cystic fibrosis, the whole reproductive population of Europe would have to be screened, and then only 70–75% of the possible cases of cystic fibrosis would be prevented because sometimes it is caused by a gene other than the one isolated on chromosome 7. The economic value of screening programmes can be studied for each disease to see if they are financially worth carrying out. For example, in 1979 it was estimated that it cost £20 000 to screen 15 000 babies for PKU, of which one was likely to suffer from the disease, and then to supply the affected baby with a special diet until adulthood, when the brain loses its sensitivity to high levels of phenylalanine. However, the treatment of a PKU baby who is not detected early and is therefore so severely handicapped that it will need institutional care throughout its approximately 45-year or so life cost £126 000, so the cost of the screening of all newborn infants was well justified. For cystic fibrosis screening, however, the cost benefit of whole-population screening would be much smaller (as calculated in 1989). The cost of screening 2000 fetuses to find and abort the one with cystic fibrosis was £80 000. The cost of treating a child suffering from cystic fibrosis throughout its relatively short life was £125 000. Figures like these look only at the medical costs – the human suffering of affected individuals and their families is not, and probably cannot, be quantified. Thus, partly because of economic analyses like these and partly because screening does not guarantee the correct answer as more than one gene may cause the same problem, cystic fibrosis screening is only offered to families in which the disease has occurred.

Couples who find they are at risk of producing children with genetic defects have several options open to them. They can go ahead and have a family, hoping that in the genetic lottery they are lucky and their children inherit healthy genes, but prepared to support and take care of them if not. They may decide not to have children at all, to prevent passing on a faulty gene even in a carrier. The third option is to go ahead with pregnancies but to have each pregnancy screened and terminated if the fetus is affected. This option can be very traumatic, and is not open to some individuals because of their beliefs about abortion issues, but it is effective at preventing the birth of children with genetic diseases. What it doesn't do is weed out individuals who are carriers, so the gene continues into the next generation. A more sophisticated version of this technique is to use IVF. The ova and sperm of a couple at high risk of producing offspring affected by genetic disease are fertilised outside the body. When the embryos are small balls of cells, a single cell is removed from each (this appears to cause no harm to the development of the embryo), and the genetic make-up is checked. Only those embryos free of the problem genes are placed in the mother's uterus to implant and grow. For example, in the case of sex-linked diseases such as haemophilia and Duchenne muscular dystrophy, only female embryos would be replaced.

Another aspect of this complex picture is that with techniques of genetic manipulation, inserting a healthy gene into the cells of an individual with a genetic disorder is becoming a possibility. Trials are already going ahead in people with cystic fibrosis, providing cells which can manage sodium and chloride ions appropriately and so allow normal, healthy mucus to be produced, and the results are promising. Another disease which is being considered for this sort of treatment is diabetes. If the gene for healthy islets of Langerhans can be inserted into sufferers' pancreas cells so that new insulin-producing islets are formed, the days of insulin injections for diabetics might be numbered. But as with most emergent technology, there are more ethical dilemmas here. At present, genetic manipulation of the germ cells is completely forbidden. The downside of this sensible decision is that whilst in the foreseeable future, affected individuals may be helped in their lifetime to be free from the effects of the genetic disorder they have inherited, they will nevertheless still be at risk of passing it on to their offspring. This means treatment has to be ongoing through the generations, which is an expensive option. It can only be a matter of time before it is suggested that manipulation of the germ cells as well as the somatic cells would treat not just the individuals concerned but all their potential future descendants too. Once it is permitted to manipulate the genes of the germ cells for medical reasons, there are those who fear this would lead to changes being made in the genes for intelligence, or beauty, or height, or aggression. The manipulation of the human breeding stock and the creation of sets of 'designer humans' might then become not science fiction but science fact.

These complex issues can arouse very emotional and not always scientifically informed debate. However, it is very important that we as a society address these problems with care in full and open debate before decisions are made for us behind closed doors without our understanding or consent.

Genetic counselling

For most people, finding out about genetic diseases in the family is very traumatic. Instead of seeing themselves as normal healthy people who will go on and produce a normal healthy baby, they suddenly realise that they carry a gene that could make them (or more probably their children) seriously ill or handicapped. All of the issues just discussed about whether to have children, to abort affected pregnancies, who to tell, etc. are suddenly of immediate and personal relevance. Because many couples first realise they have a problem when they are pregnant or shortly after their baby is born, the trauma is even harder to bear.

Genetic counsellors are trained to help people come to terms with carrying an abnormal gene that can cause genetic disease. They help people understand how the genetic information is passed from one generation to another, and the relevance of dominant and recessive characters. A family pedigree will be worked out, which may be useful in confirming the diagnosis and can also be used to indicate any other individuals who might unknowingly be affected as carriers. This however raises another difficult question – should those other potential carriers, some of whom may be quite distant relations, be told or not? Genetic counsellors help people come to a decision about issues like this. They also assess the statistical risk of a couple producing another child with the same defect. If the problem is caused by a single recessive or dominant gene then the risk can be calculated easily using Mendel's laws, and even if it is polygenic or the result of a whole-chromosome abnormality the risk can be calculated using accumulated medical data.

For most genetic defects, as already mentioned, the only real options are to avoid having children (or any more children) or to undergo prenatal screening and abort affected pregnancies. Again the role of the genetic counsellor is to help couples recognise the options and work their way through to the alternative that is right for them within their own framework of moral, family, religious and social beliefs and traditions. There are as yet no easy solutions to this problem. All that can be hoped for is that a couple reach as comfortable an acceptance of the facts as they can. Whether the advances promised by techniques such as genetic engineering and gene manipulation will bring real help and relief to families affected by genetic diseases is still to be seen. The problems such techniques themselves bring might be just as difficult for individuals and society to resolve.

Genetic engineering

What is genetic engineering?

Genetic engineering is a term used to describe the skills which have been developed enabling molecular biologists to move genes from one chromosome to another. They have made possible the creation of new genomes resulting in the production of altered organisms such as the giant mice shown in figure 5.7.16 and in bacteria which express human genes. Genetic engineering involves locating a desirable gene, isolating it and then moving into the genome of another organism (see section 7 for details of the technique). The proteins produced in response to the new piece of DNA will either have a useful effect in the host cell or may be harvested for use elsewhere.

Figure 5.7.15 Trained genetic counsellors can help couples to understand their choices when they become aware that they are carrying genes which could result in their children suffering genetic diseases.

Figure 5.7.16 One of these mice is quite normal. The other has the human growth-hormone gene in the chromosomes of its cells, inserted using the techniques of genetic engineering.

What is the value of genetic engineering?

Genetic engineering as a technique has or may have immense value to human beings in three main ways:

- Genes may be placed into microbes and the microbes will then produce large quantities of a desired substance. Examples of successes in this area include the production of human insulin by bacteria, reducing the need for insulin from other animals to be used.

- Engineered genes may be placed in domestic species of plants or animals to improve traits such as their growth rates or the protein quality produced. It may enable more plants to produce first class protein, or reduce the fat content of the protein-rich muscle tissues in animals. Engineered genes in crop plants have enabled the plants to synthesise chemicals which act as inbuilt pesticides, removing the need for extensive crop spraying.

- Gene therapy involves putting engineered genes into people to cure genetic diseases. As we have seen throughout this section, the human race is plagued by a large number of genetic diseases such as sickle cell anaemia, haemophilia, cystic fibrosis and thalassaemia. They affect about 1% of all children, placing a heavy burden of both care and cost on the individual families and on the society in which they live. The first few tests of gene therapy are currently being undertaken with genes to combat immune insufficiency and to alleviate cystic fibrosis. The day is getting ever closer when engineered genes will be inserted routinely into the relevant somatic (body) cells of an affected individual, allowing normal functioning of the cells to begin.

The genetic disorders of the human species may be inherited in a wide variety of ways. The lethal gene causing Huntington's chorea is a dominant gene that is only expressed later in life. Albinism and sickle cell anaemia are the result of recessive alleles on the autosomes, and haemophilia is caused by a mutation on the X chromosome – these are but a few examples. With the advance of screening techniques such as those described for Tay-Sachs disease, and the increasing use of gene manipulation and genetic engineering, we may hope to see a substantial reduction in the human suffering caused by these genetic diseases within the next 50 years. Perhaps one day they, like smallpox, will become a thing of the past.

Genetic engineering – the final step?

With time and technical advances, the insertion of healthy genes into the body cells of individuals suffering from genetic diseases may soon become an everyday procedure. However, this only alleviates the problem for each individual, and the therapy would need to be repeated in each succeeding generation. To eliminate the disease completely it would be necessary to engineer the germ cells so that the altered genome was passed on to subsequent generations. This is seen as a very major step – interfering with the inheritable material of an individual could open a Pandora's box of ethical and moral controversies. Some individuals might well demand 'intelligence' genes or 'good-looking' genes, and some societies might wish to engineer social classes... the implications for this area of biology are immense. At the moment any engineering of the germ cells is forbidden, but once the technology for engineering is in place, society has some very big decisions to make about what is to be done with it.

SUMMARY

- **Genetic diseases** may be carried by a single defective gene, leading to a reduced level of a particular enzyme. Alternatively, they may result from a whole chromosome mutation.

- **Family trees** are used to trace human genetic disorders through the generations and identify potential **carriers** who may be heterozygous for a particular harmful trait.

- **Aneuploidy** is the absence of a chromosome or presence of an extra chromosome. **Nondisjunction**, the failure of a homologous pair of chromosomes to separate during meiosis, can result in **monosomy** (only one of a pair of chromosomes) or **trisomy** (three of a type of chromosome instead of two). Examples include **Down's syndrome**, caused by trisomy on chromosome 21, detected by amniocentesis or chorionic villus sampling. Nondisjunction of the sex chromosomes may result in **Turner's syndrome**, **metafemales**, **XXY men** and **Klinefelter's syndrome**.

- **Duchenne muscular dystrophy** is a paralysing disease caused by a single recessive allele on the X chromosome.

- **Red-green colour blindness** is caused by a recessive mutation on the X chromosome and so affects more males than females, though recessive homozygotes (colour-blind women) do occur.

- **Haemophilia** is a sex-linked recessive trait carried on the X chromosome in which a protein needed for blood clotting is missing. The homozygous recessive condition in females is rare and lethal.

- **Phenylketonuria** is a recessive allele that causes defective metabolism of the amino acid phenylalanine. The condition is detected by **biochemical analysis**.

- **Tay-Sachs disease** is caused by a recessive allele that prevents the production of the enzyme hexosaminidase A, required for lipid metabolism. Without this enzyme the nervous system degenerates. Carriers can be identified by biochemical analysis as they have reduced blood levels of hexosaminidase A.

- In **cystic fibrosis**, again caused by a recessive allele, the exocrine glands produce sticky mucus, resulting in severe respiratory and digestive problems.

- **Huntington's disease**, caused by a dominant allele, leads to degeneration of the nerve cells in middle age.

- A **pleiotropic gene** affects more than one phenotypic feature. The recessive mutant allele for **sickle cell anaemia** causes sickle-shaped red blood cells, severe anaemia, pain in the abdomen and joints, an enlarged spleen, and resistance to malaria in the heterozygous state. These all result from a change in a single amino acid in the haemoglobin molecule. The trait is selected for in areas where malaria is prevalent.

- In **genetic engineering**, a desirable gene is removed from its chromosome and joined into the genetic material of another organism, for example into a bacterial plasmid. In **gene therapy** the recombinant DNA is used to cure genetic diseases in people.

QUESTIONS

1 A fairly common sex-linked trait in humans is colour blindness. The allele for normal vision is dominant. In the United States 6% of males are colour blind, compared with fewer than 1% of females. Explain why there are more colour-blind males than females. Does every colour-blind male have a colour-blind parent? Does every colour-blind female? Use genetic diagrams to explain your answer.

2 Discuss the difficulties of investigating human genetics and comment on some of the techniques used.

3 Select two different human genetic diseases and discuss the impact genetic engineering might have on such diseases in the future.

Developing Key Skills

You are due to appear on a radio programme about the Human Genome Project. Choose one of the following three topics and prepare your talk, which should last no less than three minutes and no more than four and a half minutes. You also need to be prepared to answer questions from the presenter when you have spoken.

a The potential benefits of the Human Genome Project.

b The potential problems generated by the Human Genome Project.

c The ethics of patenting human genes.

1 The drawings show the sperm and eggs of three different animals.

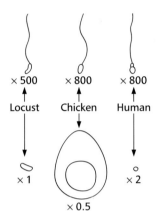

a i How many times longer than the chicken sperm is the chicken egg? **(1 mark)**

ii Calculate the actual length of the head of the chicken sperm in millimetres. Show your working. **(2 marks)**

b What is the main advantage to the locust in producing eggs which are much larger than sperm? **(2 marks)**

c Explain why human eggs are smaller than chicken eggs even though adult humans are much larger than adult chickens. **(2 marks)**

(AQA specimen 2000)

2 a Explain why root tips are particularly suitable material to use for preparing slides to show mitosis. **(1 mark)**

b Give a reason for **each** of the following steps in preparing a slide showing mitosis in cells from a root tip.

i The tissue should be stained. **(1 mark)**

ii The stained material should be pulled apart with a needle and gentle pressure applied to the cover slip during mounting. **(1 mark)**

c The drawing has been made from a photograph showing a cell undergoing mitosis.

i In which stage of mitosis is the cell shown in this drawing? **(1 mark)**

ii What is the diploid number of chromosomes in this cell? **(1 mark)**

(AQA specimen 2000)

3 In the human thyroid gland the amino acid, tyrosine, is converted by a series of reactions into the hormone, thyroxine. Insufficient thyroxine production may affect mental and physical development.

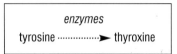

In about 1 in 5000 children, one of the enzymes involved in thyroxine production does not function effectively. The enzyme is ineffective because of a gene mutation.

a i Describe **two** changes in a gene which may have resulted in a mutation. **(2 marks)**

ii Give **one** factor which might increase the frequency at which gene mutation occurs. **(1 mark)**

b Explain how a gene mutation may result in the formation of an ineffective enzyme. **(3 marks)**

(AQA specimen 2000)

4 People suffering from cystic fibrosis have a faulty CFTR gene which produces a defective form of the protein CFTR.

a i What is the difference between a CFTR protein molecule in an unaffected person and a CFTR protein in a person with cystic fibrosis? **(1 mark)**

ii What causes this difference? **(1 mark)**

b i Describe the function of the CFTR protein in an unaffected person. **(2 marks)**

ii Explain how the symptoms of cystic fibrosis result from CFTR protein molecules which do not function. **(4 marks)**

c i American doctors have succeeded in curing mice with cystic fibrosis. The healthy CFTR gene was introduced into embryo mice by a virus while the embryos were still in the uterus of the mother. Suggest how enzymes might be used to isolate the healthy gene that makes correct CFTR protein and to insert it in a virus. **(4 marks)**

ii Why must great care be taken before a similar technique is tried out on humans? **(3 marks)**

(AQA specimen 2000)

5 The histogram below shows the height of wheat plants in an experimental plot.

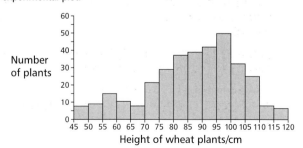

a What evidence from the data suggests that there are two strains of wheat growing in the experimental plot? **(1 mark)**

b i Which type of variation is shown by the height of each of the strains of wheat plants? Give the reason for your answer. **(2 marks)**

ii Explain why the height of the wheat plants varies between 45 cm and 120 cm. **(1 mark)**

(AQA specimen 2000)

6 The inheritance of colour in sweet peas is controlled by two pairs of alleles (**A** and **a**, and **B** and **b**) at two gene loci on different chromosomes. The diagram below shows how the dominant alleles at these two gene loci determine flower colour by controlling the synthesis of a purple pigment.

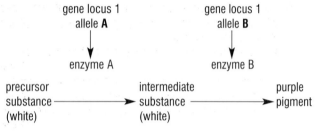

a Use information in the diagram to explain why plants homozygous for the mutant allele, **a**, have white flowers. **(3 marks)**

b Use a genetic diagram to explain the genotypes and the expected phenotypes when plants with the genotypes **Aabb** and **aaBb** are crossed. **(4 marks)**

(AQA specimen 2000)

7 Rats and mice are common pests. Warfarin was developed as a poison to control rats and was very effective when first used in 1950. Resistance to warfarin was first reported in British rats in 1958 and is now extremely common. Warfarin resistance in rats is determined by a single gene with two alleles **W^s** and **W^r**. Rats with the genotypes listed below have the characteristics shown.

W^{s}W^s Normal rats susceptible to warfarin.

W^{s}W^r Rats resistant to warfarin needing slightly more vitamin K than usual for full health.

W^{r}W^r Rats resistant to warfarin but requiring very large amounts of vitamin K. They rarely survive.

a Explain why:

i there was a very high frequency of **W^s** alleles in the British population of wild rats before 1950 **(1 mark)**

ii the frequency of **W^r** alleles in the wild rat population rose rapidly from 1958. **(2 marks)**

b Explain what would be likely to happen to the frequency of **W^r** alleles if warfarin were no longer used. **(2 marks)**

c In humans, deaths from conditions where blood clots form inside blood vessels occur frequently in adults over the age of fifty. These conditions may be treated successfully with warfarin. However, some people possess a dominant allele which gives resistance to warfarin. Why would you not expect this allele to change in frequency? **(2 marks)**

(AQA specimen 2000)

8 The table below shows the mean values of some features of the blood and circulation of groups of pregnant and non-pregnant women.

	Women at 32 weeks of pregnancy	Non-pregnant women
Total volume of blood/cm^3	5400	3800
Red blood cell volume as percentage of total blood volume	30	35
Plasma protein concentration/g 100 cm^3	3.7	4.2
Pulse rate/beats minute^{-1}	82	70

a Calculate the mean total volume of red blood cells in each of the two groups. Show your working.

i Mean total volume of red blood cells in women at 32 weeks of pregnancy. **(1 mark)**

ii Mean total volume of red blood cells in non-pregnant women. **(1 mark)**

b Suggest how the change in pulse rate helps the mother to meet the demands of pregnancy. **(2 marks)**

c Explain how the structure of the placenta provides a large surface area for the exchange of materials between the mother and the fetus. **(2 marks)**

d Suggest how the fall in the concentration of plasma proteins may cause accumulation of tissue fluid during pregnancy. **(2 marks)**

(AQA specimen 2000)

9 The graph below shows changes in the concentration of two female sex hormones involved in controlling the menstrual cycle.

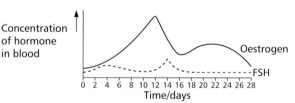

a i What is the main function of FSH? **(1 mark)**

ii Describe the effect of oestrogen on the concentration of FSH during days 4 to 10 of this cycle. **(1 mark)**

iii How might the information on the graph be used to work out the most likely time for conception? **(1 mark)**

b Use the information in the graph to explain one way in which oral contraceptives might act to prevent fertilisation taking place. **(2 marks)**

(AQA specimen 2000)

10 The hormonal control of reproduction in birds is similar to that in mammals. The diagram below shows some of the factors affecting the reproductive behaviour of doves.

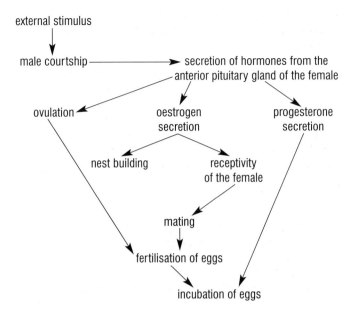

a Suggest a likely external stimulus for male courtship behaviour.
(**1 mark**)

b Which hormone from the anterior pituitary gland is mainly responsible for stimulating ovulation? (**1 mark**)

c Give the site of secretion of progesterone. (**1 mark**)

d With reference to the above diagram, explain the importance of courtship in doves for successful reproduction. (**2 marks**)

(AQA specimen 2000)

11 The figure shows the changes in the size of a bacteria population with time when grown in a flask containing a sterile solution of glucose.

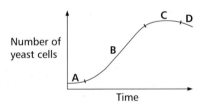

a Name the phase of growth and explain the shape of the curve at each of the periods **A** to **D** in the figure. (**6 marks**)

b With reference to a **named** example, explain how limiting factors determine the final size of populations in nature. (*In this question, 1 mark is available for the quality of written communication.*)

(**9 marks**)

(OCR specimen 2000)

12 Guinea pigs, which were homozygous for long, black hair were crossed with ones which were homozygous for short white hair. All the F₁ offspring had short, black hair.

a i Using suitable symbols, draw a genetic diagram to explain this result. (**3 marks**)

ii Draw a genetic diagram to show the results of interbreeding the F₁ offspring. (**5 marks**)

b State the ratio of phenotypes expected in the F₂ offspring.
(**1 mark**)

OCR specimen 2000)

13 a i State **three** ways in which meiosis can lead to variation.
(**3 marks**)

ii Explain why variation is important in selection. (**2 marks**)

Rye, *Secale cereale*, is a cereal crop which is widely cultivated. It is believed to have originated over 2500 years ago in Asia Minor from *Secale ancestralis*, a wild species with a fragile stem but fairly large grains. When the cultivation of wheat, *Triticum* sp., spread, wild rye accompanied the wheat as a weed. The ability of wild rye to thrive on poor soil, and to resist frost and drought better than wheat, resulted in it being subjected to selection pressures such that it yielded a crop when the wheat failed. Climatic and soil factors eliminated the wheat, leaving rye as the sole cereal crop in northern upland regions. Artificial selection of rye has favoured the varieties with the highest grain yield.

b Explain why *Secale ancestralis* and *Secale cereale* are classified within the same genus but as separate species. (**2 marks**)

c With reference to the passage:

i explain what is meant by the term *selection pressures*
(**2 marks**)

ii suggest how natural selection has led to rye becoming 'the sole cereal crop in northern upland regions'. (**3 marks**)

d Explain how artificial selection of rye could have been achieved.
(**4 marks**)

(OCR specimen 2000)

14 The diagram represents a plant cell in which the diploid number of chromosomes is six.

a Draw a diagram to show:

i this cell during anaphase of mitosis (**2 marks**)

ii the chromosomes in a gamete produced from this cell by meiosis. (**1 mark**)

b Asexual reproduction involves only mitosis. Give **one** reason why offspring produced by asexual reproduction may vary in:

i genotype (**1 mark**)

ii phenotype but not in genotype. (**1 mark**)

c The formation of gametes during sexual reproduction involves meiosis. Give **two** ways in which meiosis results in genetic variation in the gametes produced. (**2 marks**)

(AQA March 1999)

5

6 POPULATION BIOLOGY

Introduction

Much of biology focuses on individual organisms, and even on particular small parts of individual organisms. It is easy to lose sight of the fact that whole living organisms of almost infinite variety live together with others of their own species, and also with many other organisms, to make up the natural world.

Over the years there have been many attempts to explain where the huge variety of life on Earth has come from, and to try and classify all its organisms into ordered groups. Such classification makes it much easier to compare and contrast the different types of organism, and also to communicate with other scientists. However, living organisms do not exist in a vacuum – they are constantly interacting with each other and with their surroundings, and those interactions can sometimes determine the types of organism that evolve. Populations of organisms change in response to stresses in their environment, and if the stress is so severe that only a few members of a population survive, then the genetic profile of that whole population will change. By looking in detail at population genetics, the concept of evolution becomes easier to understand.

Animals depend on plants as a source of food and oxygen. Plants depend on animals as a source of fertiliser and carbon dioxide – and often as helpers in the process of reproduction. The types of animals and plants found in any one place will be determined by a complex mixture of factors such as the soil type, the rocks, the weather and the hours of daylight. The study of the interaction between these factors and the living organisms is known as **ecology**, and it is of central importance to our understanding of how the living world works.

The number of animals or plants living in any particular habitat will depend on a whole range of different ecological factors. By developing an understanding of those factors that affect population growth and population density for different organisms, scientists can begin to understand how best to manage threatened environments. Many ecosystems are no longer wholly natural – they are affected to a greater or lesser degree by human activity. All over the world there are also many ecosystems that are entirely managed by people, such as farms, forests and fisheries. Human management in the form of farming is essential in order to feed the Earth's population, but there is also great potential for damage. Increasingly there is a worldwide move towards sustainable management of the land.

Human beings have not been on the Earth for long, but our activities have had an immense impact on the environment. We need to understand how human activities damage and pollute the Earth – but also to consider the many ways in which human effort helps to conserve environments and species which might otherwise be lost forever.

Figure 1 A huge population of trevally fish move as one in their watery environment.

EXTINCTION IS FOREVER

Throughout the history of the Earth, it is thought that about 4 billion different species have existed. Yet only about 2 million species of living organism are present on the Earth today – what has happened to all the others? The answer is **extinction**. The great majority of life forms thrown up by the process of evolution reach a point where they can no longer survive on the Earth. Extinction means the permanent loss of all members of a species. As new species evolve that are better fitted to survive in a particular set of conditions, other, perhaps older, species that are less well adapted cannot compete with the newcomers and die out.

Mass extinctions provide opportunities for others

The competitive extinction just described has been occurring since the earliest days of life. But throughout the history of life on Earth **mass extinctions** have occurred at intervals. At the end of the Permian period, 96 per cent of all the then-living marine invertebrate species became extinct. At least five such mass extinctions appear to have occurred. Even species that are well adapted under normal circumstances may be wiped out as their adaptations become irrelevant under extreme environmental stress. Major eradications of large numbers of species seem to have cleared the way for the evolution of new and opportunistic groups, and thus have had a major effect on the pattern of life on Earth.

An escalating disaster

At the present time extinctions are still occurring, and much of this loss of species diversity is as a direct result of human activity. This is not a recent problem – well-respected theories suggest that the loss of the mammoths and the sabre-toothed tiger was largely due to hunting by humans. The dodo met its end because it was an easy target for hungry sailors, and many other island and mainland species have gone the same way. What is new is both the scale of the extinctions and the speed at which they are happening. Some scientists have calculated that, if the present levels of habitat destruction and pollution continue, more than a million species will be lost in the 30 years leading up to 2010. That is 25 per cent of all the species on Earth. This sort of loss of diversity would be without parallel in the history of the Earth – whilst there have been greater overall losses, they have spanned millions of years, not decades. Moreover, the effect of the loss of all this life would be to change the climate and the ecosystems of the planet in such a way that more extinctions would follow – the mass extinction to end all mass extinctions. Many of the species being lost are not yet known or studied, and they may contain the answer to our food needs, or drugs to cure our most feared diseases. Extinction is forever – we need to act now to try and conserve as many species as we can, before it is too late!

Figure 1 Grey squirrels are successful in Britain – they eat a varied diet and are very disease resistant. They have contributed to the decline in numbers of the red squirrel (shown above), which, with its restricted diet and poor disease resistance, might have become extinct in the UK without the intervention and protection of people.

Figure 2 When the vast domination of the dinosaurs came to an end, new mammalian species took advantage of many of the niches vacated by the reptiles both large and small, launching the Age of Mammals from the death throes of the Age of Reptiles.

Life on Earth comes in an amazing variety of forms, many of which interact successfully to form thriving ecosystems. But where have they all come from – and how can we bring order out of the chaos of living organisms?

Figure 6.1.1 The diversity of life – the biosphere contains millions of different organisms which are interdependent in many ways, and can colonise even the most daunting of habitats.

The origins of life

For some, the origins of life on this planet are a matter for religious faith rather than scientific thought. But for many others the events of the beginning of life on the Earth offer the challenge of a puzzle which can never be completely solved. Theories about the origins and evolution of life are still being discussed, although amongst most scientists a consensus has been reached on the most probable pattern of events, which is described here. Around 4500 million years ago there was no life on Earth. To date more than four billion species of living organisms have appeared, most to disappear again in the mists of time and others to persist until the present day.

The formation of monomers

Before life emerged on the planet, the organic molecules which are the building blocks of life had to be formed. In the 1920s two scientists – the Russian Aleksandr Oparin and the Briton J. B. Haldane – developed a revolutionary theory that the energy of ultraviolet light, heat, other radiation or massive lightning discharges could have catalysed the formation of small organic molecules or **monomers**. In the 1950s these predictions were tested experimentally by Harold Urey and Stanley Miller using the apparatus shown in figure 6.1.2, and large quantities of amino acids and simple sugars were produced.

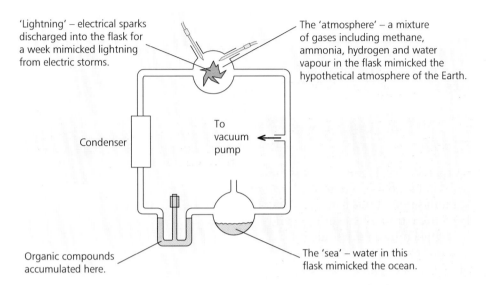

'Lightning' – electrical sparks discharged into the flask for a week mimicked lightning from electric storms.

The 'atmosphere' – a mixture of gases including methane, ammonia, hydrogen and water vapour in the flask mimicked the hypothetical atmosphere of the Earth.

Condenser

To vacuum pump

Organic compounds accumulated here.

The 'sea' – water in this flask mimicked the ocean.

Figure 6.1.2 The successful production of organic compounds by Miller and Urey in this apparatus gave support to the theory of chemical evolution.

Current evidence suggests that the atmosphere of the early Earth was in fact much more similar to the present atmosphere, though without the oxygen, than was hypothesised by Miller and Urey. By using various combinations of gases up to 100 monomers have been produced – almost all the building blocks of living cells.

From monomers to cells

The chemical mix of monomers which, in theory, formed in the earliest stages of the development of life moved on with the formation of **polymers**. These long-chain molecules could have been produced using the energy of the Sun or the heat of the Earth as an energy source. Alternatively, ATP is one of the chemicals produced in a Urey–Miller chamber, and this could have supplied the chemical energy for polymerisation.

Polymers may form aggregates, groups of molecules which begin to exhibit some of the characteristics of living things – for example, aggregates of lipids will show membrane-like properties. From then on, through a series of steps open to hypothesis, what we consider to be 'life' emerged. It seems to have been the inevitable consequence of a variety of physical and chemical processes, though no one will ever know for certain when, where and how life on Earth began.

The earliest cells

The oldest remains of living organisms are fossil rod-shaped structures found in rocks in Australia which have been dated as 3.5 billion years old. The first cells were almost certainly anaerobic and heterotrophic. They would have fed on the organic chemicals which formed spontaneously in the atmosphere and waters of the Earth. Mutations occurred which resulted in cells with the ability to exploit another energy source – sunlight. These cells would have been the first autotrophs. From single-celled organisms such as these early microbes it appears that all subsequent life on Earth has evolved.

The diversity of life

The range of organisms on the Earth is vast (see pages 480–492). There are microorganisms, so small that their existence only became known with the development of the microscope. They are capable of life in almost every available niche, and yet we are usually unaware of them except when they cause disease. Fungi of different types decompose dead and dying organic material. Trees form forests, produce oxygen and provide timber. Birds fill the air, fish and many other diverse creatures fill the seas, lakes and rivers. Animals and plants of every description are part of our lives, and we in turn are part of the great diversity of living things. How has this diversity of life come about?

Theories of evolution

The background to evolutionary theory

For many years the commonly held belief was that the Earth and all that is on it were spontaneously created by God over a period of six days, as described in the first chapter of Genesis in the Bible. The implication of this belief was that all of the species present on the Earth had been there from the beginning and were unchanging. However, by the end of the eighteenth century some scientists were beginning to put forward a scientific explanation for the existence of life on Earth. Simple observation of the development of farm animals seemed to indicate that living things could and did change from generation to generation. In 1809 (the year Darwin was born) Jean Baptiste de Lamarck presented a new evolutionary theory. He accepted the idea that life forms evolve, and proposed that the driving force behind this evolution was the **inheritance of acquired characteristics**. In other words, organisms change physically as they struggle to meet the demands of their environment, and these advantageous changes are passed on to their offspring. His classic illustration was the evolution of the giraffe as he saw it, as shown in figure 6.1.3.

Figure 6.1.3 'Use it or lose it' and 'Use it and it may improve' were the key ideas of Lamarck's theory. His idea was that over a series of generations the neck got longer and longer as giraffes stretched to reach the topmost leaves.

We now know that Lamarck's theory is not correct, because activities such as stretching to feed do not affect the germ cells or the gametes. However, research such as the work on learning behaviour in flatworms (section 4.3, page 284) has led to recent discussion that there may be unexpected Lamarckian elements in the process of evolution after all.

Darwin's theory of evolution

Charles Darwin set off on the surveying ship *HMS Beagle* when he was in his early twenties. The ship circumnavigated the world, taking five years to do so. During that time Darwin read, amongst other things, books on geology by Lyell speculating that, on the basis of the fossil record, animal and plant species arose, diversified and then died out. Darwin also spent hours observing the wide range of living organisms, both plant and animal, in the various countries where they stopped. His most famous observations were made on the Galapagos archipelago (group of islands). On returning to England Darwin read an essay by Thomas Malthus proposing that populations grow faster than their food supplies and so organisms are forced into a 'struggle for existence'. There followed a long period of thought, during which Darwin made copious observations on breeding pigeons and other domestic animals, until eventually he wrote his now famous work *On the Origin of Species by Natural Selection, or the Preservation of Favoured Races in the Struggle for Life*, published in 1859. A large part of Darwin's book argues that **evolution** has taken place. He then explains a possible mechanism by which evolution has come about, and that is **natural selection**.

The main argument put forward by Darwin was as follows. Living organisms which reproduce sexually show great variety in their appearance (or phenotype as we would now describe it). Also, more offspring are produced than survive so that there is always a struggle for existence, a competition between members of the same species. Those organisms which inherit characteristics that put them at an advantage in this struggle are most likely to survive and reproduce, passing on the desired feature to their offspring. Organisms that possess features which put them at a disadvantage will be more likely to die out and thus fail to reproduce themselves. This can be summed up in the phrase 'the survival of the fittest', where fitness is the ability of an organism to survive and reproduce in the environment in which it is living. He called this process **natural selection**, and the long-term changes in organisms which occur as a result of natural selection are **evolution**. Alfred Wallace, another British naturalist, proposed a very similar theory at the same time as Darwin, but Darwin's ideas were backed up by a far greater bank of research and observations and so it was he who received most of the accolades (and criticisms) which went with the theory.

Figure 6.1.4 Darwin's ideas in many ways reflected the changing mood of his times. But for some of the more traditional thinkers and the hierarchy of the Church, his ideas were heretical and damaging to the status quo.

Darwin speaks

Charles Darwin was a modest and retiring man who spent most of his time at home with his wife and children. Yet his mind was continually active and he produced one of the most revolutionary biological ideas of all time – the theory of evolution by natural selection has affected all subsequent studies. In the summary of his work *On the Origin of Species* he writes:

As more individuals are produced than can possibly survive, there must in every case be a struggle for existence, either one individual with another of the same species or with the individuals of a distant species, or with the physical conditions of life … Can it therefore be thought improbable seeing that variations useful in some way to each being in the great and complex battle of life, should sometimes occur in the course of thousands of generations? If such do occur, can we doubt (remembering that many more individuals are born than can possibly survive) that individuals having any advantage, however slight, over others would have the best chance of surviving and of procreating their own kind? On the other hand, we may feel sure that any variation in the least degree injurious would be rigidly destroyed. This preservation of favourable variations and the rejection of injurious variations, I call natural selection.

(Charles Darwin, *On the Origin of Species*, 5th edition 1896)

Darwin's book was an immediate success – every copy of the first edition was sold the day it was published. When we remember that Darwin's ideas were formulated with no knowledge of genetics, his perceptiveness and vision become more remarkable. He is rightly remembered as one of the truly great figures in biology.

Neo-Darwinism

Throughout the twentieth century our knowledge of genetics, molecular biology, ecology and palaeontology have grown at an astonishing rate. As a result of some of this knowledge, Darwin's theory has been slightly modified to give what is called **neo-Darwinism**. Neo-Darwinism considers that the evolution of organic forms occurs as a result of the **differential survival and fertility** of organisms with different genotypes (and therefore phenotypes) within an environment. In other words, a disadvantageous trait need not mean that those individuals are wiped out, simply that they are less reproductively successful than others, for evolution to occur. It also indicates that what constitutes an advantageous or disadvantageous trait will differ with the environment. We have only to think of the sickle cell allele considered in section 5.7 to recognise the truth of this.

Continuing evolution

Where Darwin leads...

The importance of Darwin's ideas in the study of ecology and the changing populations of organisms on Earth today will be considered in section 6.6. Here we shall go on to look at the picture of evolution which has emerged over the years since Darwin published *On the Origin of Species*, and the various strands of evidence which support the ideas.

The evolution of the different phyla – reptiles, fish, mammals, angiosperms, etc. – can be seen as the result of many small changes resulting in new species. These major changes or **macroevolution** occurred over millions of years, in a time scale measured by geologists going back to the beginnings of the planet Earth. The most important developments are summarised in figure 6.1.7. The information in a diagram such as this comes from a variety of sources, relying very heavily on information from the fossil record. As you can see, human beings have been on the Earth for a very short time. If the history of the Earth was represented by one year, the first bacteria appeared around March, and the first photosynthesisers arrived in the sea in May. In contrast the first vertebrates, primitive fishes, appeared around 20 November. Amphibians crawled onto the land around 30 November. The reptiles became dominant around 7 December and the mammals became common by 15 December. The human genus *Homo* did not arise until 11 p.m. on 31 December!

Evidence for evolution

There are many strands of evidence which can be applied to evolution. Some of these are outlined below.

- **The fossil record** – fossils are the remains of the hard body parts of living organisms, or the remains of their imprints (tracks, burrows, faeces, etc.) preserved in rocks, amber, ice, etc. The study of fossils is called **palaeontology**. The fossil record depends on chance preservations, and does not record soft-bodied creatures, so it can only give us a tantalising and fragmented picture of the evolution of living organisms (see figure 6.1.5). The finding of fossils is also largely dependent on chance, and they are difficult to date accurately because of their great age.

- **Distribution studies** look at how organisms have evolved differently after being separated geographically. The continents were originally joined in one supercontinent called **Pangaea**. As this supercontinent broke up and the continents drifted apart, the same ancestral forms evolved differently to fill a variety of niches. This type of evolution is called **adaptive radiation** – the Australian marsupials are a good example. Australia split from the other land masses early in mammalian evolution. In isolation, marsupials evolved to fill all the 'mammalian' niches as there was no pressure from better adapted placental mammals. The Galapagos islands, and many other island communities, also show clearly the effect of isolation. However, geographical isolation does not always result in very different forms of organism. **Parallel evolution** happens when very similar organisms evolve quite independently from the same ancestral forms but in very different places (an example is shown in figure 6.1.6).

- **Comparative anatomy** uses the similarities between organisms to deduce how recently they had a common ancestor. **Convergent evolution** results in structures that are **analogous** – they perform the same function but have evolved independently. Examples include the wing of a bird and the wing of an insect, or the streamlined body shape of a dolphin (a mammal), a swimming penguin (a bird), a shark (a fish) and *Ichthyosaurus* (a prehistoric reptile). On the other hand, **divergent evolution** results in features that have similar anatomical features but perform different functions – they are **homologous**. For example, the pentadactyl (five-fingered) limb is adapted as an arm and hand in humans, a leg with a single hoof in the horse, a flipper in the whale and a wing in birds and bats, along with many other shapes and arrangements throughout the vertebrate world.

- **Embryology** can reveal relationships between organisms that are not obvious in the adults. It can be a fascinating science – for example, the human embryo passes through a stage with fish-like gills – and has a place in helping to determine evolutionary relationships, but it needs to be used with care.

- **Cell biology** and **biochemical analysis** can reveal differences and similarities between organelles and chemicals within cells, confirming whether different organisms had a recent common ancestor. The more similarities there are between the biochemistry of different organisms, the more closely they are related in evolutionary terms. For example, the vertebrates and the echinoderms appear, from the evidence of comparative anatomy and embryology, to come from one line of ancestors and the annelids, molluscs and arthropods from another. Biochemical evidence shows that the two different groups have different **phosphagens**, the phosphate group needed for the synthesis of ATP. The vertebrates and echinoderms have **phosphocreatine**, whilst **phosphoarginine** occurs in the other groups. Analysis of the amino acids in particular proteins is also useful evidence – mammalian relationships have been mapped out using analysis of fibrinogen.

Figure 6.1.5 Fossils provide us with useful insights into early life but the record is limited and fragmented – we need evidence from other sources.

New World American porcupine

Old World porcupine

Figure 6.1.6 More than 70 million years ago, when the land masses of South America and Africa separated, both contained the same large, furry, rat-like animal. Today these two remarkably similar animals have evolved to fill a similar niche in the different continents in a striking example of parallel evolution.

Era	Period/epoch		Millions of years ago	Geological events	Biological events – plants	Biological events – animals
C E N O Z O I C	QUATERNARY	Holocene		Cooling after middle of period. Glaciations. Continents separate.	Conifers and flowering plants become widespread. Grasslands and forests expand.	Modern *Homo sapiens* arises 0.135 million years ago.
		Pleistocene				
			2			Mammals diversify, primates arise.
	TERTIARY	Pliocene Miocene Oligocene Eocene Palaeocene				
			65			
M E S O Z O I C	CRETACEOUS			Last expansion of shallow seas. Rocky mountains arise and climate cools.	Flowering plants arise and diversify.	Major extinction event. Most large reptiles and ancient birds extinct.
			136			
	JURASSIC			Very stable climate.		Teleost fish diversify. Dinosaurs dominant. Modern crustaceans present.
			190			
	TRIASSIC			Land high, widespread deserts.	Conifers and ferns dominant.	Dinosaur ancestors. First mammals and birds.
			225			
P A L A E O Z O I C	PERMIAN			Cold climate slowly warming.	Conifers appeared.	Mammal-like reptiles common. Major extinction of the invertebrates and amphibia.
			280			
	CARBONIFEROUS			Lowland forests, coal swamps, mountain building.	Forests widespread – coal deposits formed.	First reptiles. Amphibians diversify.
			345			
	DEVONIAN			Continents rising. Appalachian mountains forming. Cooler climates.	First forests. Vascular plants and seeds present.	Fish diversify. First insects, sharks and amphibians.
			395			
	SILURIAN			Land uplifting slowly. Still extensive seas.	Green, red and brown algae common.	First land arthropods. Jawed fish arise.
			430			
	ORDOVICIAN			Warm shallow seas extensive. Warming continues.	First vascular land plants probably appeared.	Second major extinction event. Jawless fish and molluscs diversify. Large invertebrates present.
			500			
A R C H A E O Z O I C	CAMBRIAN			Warm climate. Huge equatorial shallow seas.	Algae dominant.	First major extinction event. Trilobites common. Evolution of many phyla.
			570			
	PRECAMBRIAN		1500		Algae abundant. Cyanobacteria diversified. Eukaryotes present.	Worm-like animals and cnidarians.
				Atmosphere oxidising. Shallow seas.	Origin of life. Prokaryotic heterotrophs, chemical evolution.	
			2500			
	Origin of Earth		3000 3500	Earth's crust hardens. Sea, atmosphere and rocks develop?		
			4000	Formation of the Earth?		

Figure 6.1.7 A summary of the main events in the evolution of life on Earth.

Is evolution the whole story?

Although the majority of the scientific community of the developed world accept the ideas of Darwin as the basis for the evolution of life on Earth, the discussions continue. There will always be some who *believe* in Creation – as they have every right to do, for belief and science are very different things and belief requires no evidence. Many other scientists accept the evidence available for evolution, yet still believe in God. Yet others *believe* in evolution, and regard God as a figment of the human imagination. And many individuals have different views on the details of the process by which life has evolved on Earth. Whilst these diverse viewpoints continue to exist, discussion and indeed argument will always be maintained.

Ordering the products of evolution

The result of millions of years of evolution has been an enormous variety of living organisms. Along with this great diversity of life on Earth goes a diversity of names. The same organism will have a wide variety of names not only in different countries but also within different regions of the same country and even depending on whether it is a child or an adult who is speaking. When biologists from different countries discuss a particular organism, they need to be sure exactly which organism is being referred to. This problem is solved by using names given to organisms as a result of their place in a system of **classification**. The names are in Latin, which avoids the problem of choosing and thus favouring any single living language.

Taxonomy – categorising living things

Attempts to categorise living things in an orderly way have been made since before the time of the Greek philosopher Aristotle. However, it was not until the work of the Swedish botanist Carolus Linnaeus in the eighteenth century that real progress towards a universal classification system was made. The aim of a classification system is to represent the true ancestral relationships of living things. Such a system must be based on homologous features (see page 477). If analogous features were used then all wriggly worm-like organisms (including worms, slugs and snakes) would be grouped together, as would bats, birds and flying insects. A valid classification must be based on careful observation and the use of structures which genuinely demonstrate a common ancestry. Linnaeus achieved such a classification and nomenclature system which is still relevant today in spite of the fact that he was working before the time of Darwin.

Linnaeus published a book called the *Systema Naturae* in which he organised and named all the animals and plants known at the time. He introduced a system known as the **binomial system of nomenclature** by which all organisms were assigned two Latin names. The first name indicates the **genus** to which the organism belongs (a genus is a group of very similar species). The second term indicates the **species** of the organism. A species is a specific group of closely related individuals which are all capable of interbreeding to produce fertile offspring. All the members of a species are potentially capable of interbreeding, although the geographical spread of the species may substantially reduce the chances of members from one environment meeting members from another. The full binomial (two-part) name of an organism always includes both genus and species, for example *Homo sapiens* (human being), *Equus caballus* (domestic horse), *Zea mays* (maize or sweetcorn) and *Lumbricus terrestris* (earthworm).

When Linnaeus devised his classification system the number of known species was much smaller than it is today. The only way of differentiating between them was by their physical appearance or **morphology**. However, since the eighteenth century many more species have been discovered and there are many more ways of identifying differences between organisms.

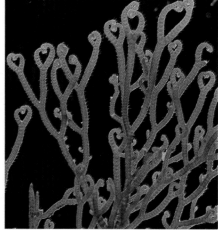

Figure 6.1.8 Red algae with their cocktail of photosynthetic pigments which allows them to photosynthesise deep in the oceans; liverworts – plants with no true stems, roots or leaves; and jellyfish which float aimlessly yet are ferocious carnivores – these three organisms represent just a tiny part of the variety of life which needs ordering and naming to help us study it.

Taxonomic groups

The discovery of many more organisms has led to the development of broader groups. Similar genera are arranged into **families**; similar families are placed in the same **order**; similar orders go in the same **class**; similar classes into a **phylum**; and finally, the largest division of the living world, similar phyla are placed into the same **kingdom**. This arrangement is illustrated in table 6.1.1, along with the classifications of several common organisms. Named groups within the classification hierarchy (such as the phylum Chordata or the order Hymenoptera) are known as **taxa** (singular **taxon**).

Taxon	Human	Honeybee	Corn	Mushroom
species	*Homo sapiens*	*Apis mellifera*	*Zea mays*	*Agaricus campestris*
genus	*Homo*	*Apis*	*Zea*	*Agaricus*
family	Hominidae	Apidae	Poaceae	Agaricaceae
order	Primates	Hymenoptera	Commelinales	Agaricales
class	Mammalia	Insecta	Monocotyledoneae	Basidiomycetes
phylum	Chordata	Arthropoda	Angiospermophyta	Basidiomycota
kingdom	Animalia	Animalia	Plantae	Fungi

Table 6.1.1 The classification of organisms still follows the basic hierarchical system devised by Linnaeus in the eighteenth century, although the classification criteria used today are different from those on which Linnaeus relied

Classification today

Modern classification systems are no longer based purely on simple morphological observations such as the number and type of limbs possessed by an organism. There have been two major developments since Linnaeus's time which have altered the way in which organisms are compared in taxonomy. One of these is Darwin's theory of evolution, which we have already considered in some detail. The other is the development of new techniques in physiology, embryology and biochemistry which have revealed similarities between living organisms which the most careful external observer could not hope to discover.

One of the most vexed issues of taxonomy has concerned the broadest level of classification of organisms into kingdoms. From the original two kingdoms Plantae and Animalia, proposed by Linnaeus and maintained for many years, the general consensus at present is that there should be five kingdoms, as detailed below. Not all biologists accept this, however, and some still refer to the original two kingdoms only. Even five kingdoms do not provide an entirely appropriate niche for all living things – more kingdoms may yet need to be created.

The kingdoms

The five kingdoms in most common use for classification purposes are:

- **Prokaryotae** – the single-celled prokaryotic organisms (bacteria)
- **Protoctista** – often single-celled eukaryotic organisms including protozoa and some of the algae
- **Fungi** – eukaryotic organisms with non-cellulose cell walls, from the single-celled yeasts to the more complex toadstools

- **Plantae** – eukaryotic photosynthetic organisms including multicellular algae
- **Animalia** – non-photosynthetic multicellular organisms with nervous coordination.

When biologists set out to identify organisms which they have not met before, they rely largely on observation as a first step in the classification process. The following summaries of the kingdoms of the living world highlight the major features enabling the identification of the organisms within each kingdom.

Prokaryotae

The prokaryotic cells which make up bacteria are smaller and simpler than those of any other type of organism, as described in section 1.1 (see box 'Eukaryotic and prokaryotic cells', pages 13–14). They obtain their nutrition in a wide variety of ways – it has been said that bacteria exploit every energy-yielding reaction in nature.

Bacteria are unicellular, although the cells may be grouped together to form chains or clumps. They occur in a variety of shapes and sizes. Some feed autotrophically by chemosynthesis or photosynthesis, others are heterotrophs. Bacteria may therefore be classified as photosynthetic or non-photosynthetic. Bacteria usually reproduce by binary fission, although sometimes a simple form of sexual conjugation occurs. Some bacteria are pathogenic (cause disease), for example *Streptococcus*, others are beneficial to humans, for example nitrifying bacteria and gut bacteria.

The photosynthetic bacteria include the cyanobacteria, which used to be called the blue-green algae. They are pigmented and occur as unicells or filamentous organisms.

Figure 6.1.9 Many different forms of bacteria colonise almost every known habitat on Earth. Within the last few years scientists have found bacteria in deep vents almost 3000 m below the surface of the ocean. Conditions in the mineral-rich water in these 'black smokers' are extreme – temperatures of around 350 °C and high pressures. 'Black smoker' bacteria stop reproducing if the temperature falls to 100 °C! These bacteria challenge many of the accepted theories about the biochemistry of enzymes and cells, and also illustrate the ability of bacteria to take advantage of environments in which nothing else can survive.

Protoctista

The protoctists consist of unicellular eukaryotic organisms that have a variety of methods of nutrition and reproduction. These organisms come in an enormous range of shapes and life styles – from amoebae to diatoms, including plant-like cells that swim, animal-like cells that cannot move, cells shaped like bells or fans or shells, and cells grouped into colonies. The number of phyla within the kingdom varies from expert to expert up to 45, but only a small sample will be considered here. Within the protoctista are organisms which make up the greater part of the plankton of the oceans, and a few which cause some of the most serious diseases to affect the human race.

The Protoctista kingdom includes the phylum Rhizopoda, single-celled amoebae which are common in both fresh and salt water as well as in the soil. They move and capture their prey by means of temporary **pseudopodia**. One group of Rhizopoda are parasitic – for example, dysentery in humans is caused by *Entamoeba hystolytica*, a gut parasite.

The phylum Zoomastigina are also protoctista. These 'animal flagellates' have one or more flagella at some stage of their life cycle. They do not contain chlorophyll. They are heterotrophs, absorbing their food through the cell membrane or taking it in by phagocytosis. An example is *Trypanosoma*, a blood parasite causing the disease African sleeping sickness.

The members of the protoctistan phylum Apicomplexa (or sporozoans) all move by wriggling. They reproduce by producing spores, and most importantly they are parasitic, using animals as their hosts. *Plasmodium*, the blood parasite responsible for the human disease malaria, is perhaps the best known sporozoan. There are more details of malaria in section 7.

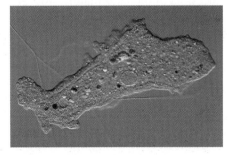

Figure 6.1.10 *Amoeba* is a well used experimental organism, as its responses are readily seen.

The Ciliophora are unicellular protoctistans covered by cilia, whilst the Euglenophyta include the 'plant flagellates' which are predominantly plant-like. They contain chlorophyll and feed by photosynthesis. Euglenophyta have flagella used for locomotion at some stage of their life cycle. Phytoplankton (plant plankton) are at the base of many marine and aquatic food chains.

The members of the phylum Oomycota are important because they are the cause of a variety of serious plant diseases, including potato blight (*Phytophthora infestans*) which resulted in the Irish potato famines in 1845 and 1847. Oomycetes are in many ways similar to the fungi (see below).

The green algae Chlorophyta may be unicellular or filamentous protoctistans. They are photosynthetic, and the main photosynthetic pigment is chlorophyll. Both chlorophyll *a* and chlorophyll *b* are present in the green algae, as they are in the higher plants – the green algae are the most likely ancestors of the land plants. Most green algae are found in fresh water or damp places, with only a few such as the sea lettuce inhabiting the sea. The classic example is *Spirogyra*, a single chain of identical cells found in freshwater ponds.

The red algae Rhodophyta, on the other hand, are mainly marine algae found in tropical waters. Their photosynthetic pigments are the red **phycoerythrin** and the blue **phycocyanin** as well as chlorophyll *a*, but they have no chlorophyll *b*. These pigments give them characteristic red-purple colours, and also enable them to absorb the blue and green wavelengths of light which filter through to deeper water – the rhodophytes can live 150m deeper than any other algae (see figure 6.1.8). They are used to produce agar and the stabilising agent carrageenan used in paints, ice cream and cosmetics.

The brown algae Phaeophyta are the giants of the algal world. They are the most complex with considerable cell differentiation, containing chlorophylls *a* and *c* and the brown **fucoxanthins**. They are generally familiar as seaweeds. The brown algae frequently show differentiation into a **holdfast** for clinging to rocks or the sea bed, a **stipe** or stem equivalent and **fronds** or leaf equivalents. It appears some vessel cells may be present which allow the transport of the products of photosynthesis – necessary in species such as kelp, shown in figure 6.1.12, which may grow up to 100 m long!

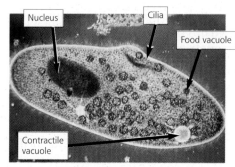

Figure 6.1.11 The coordinated beating of the cilia on the surface of ciliates such as *Paramecium* allows directional movement to take place.

Figure 6.1.12 The Phaeophyta are the 'trees' of the algal world, with complex structures needed to support the functions of large organisms.

Fungi

For many years the fungi were classified as an unusual sort of plant. Now the great differences between fungi and true plants are recognised and they have a kingdom of their own. Fungi are eukaryotic and frequently multicellular. They are heterotrophic, digesting food extracellularly and then absorbing the nutrients. They play a vital role within ecosystems as **decomposers**.

In most fungi the body structure is made up of thread-like **hyphae** which have walls usually made of chitin. These hyphae form a tangled network known as the **mycelium**. Reproduction is usually by the production of spores or by simple sexual conjugation. The kingdom of the fungi contains a wide variety of organisms and some of the main divisions are considered here. Fungi are of immense importance in the ecology of the Earth. In their role as decomposers they prevent the build-up of the bodies of dead animals and plants by digesting them and returning nutrients to the soil. They provide the human race with food and with vital drugs such as penicillin. Conversely, fungi cause major human problems. They destroy vast quantities of crops and food worldwide, as well as causing a variety of diseases in both people and domestic animals.

Phylum: Zygomycota

The zygomycetes are all terrestrial and are largely saprophytic. The main body of the fungus, the mycelium, is haploid. They reproduce asexually by non-motile spores which form in a tough spore case known as the **sporangium**. They reproduce sexually by conjugation between neighbouring hyphae. Typical examples are the pin-moulds such as *Mucor* which form on rotting fruit and vegetables. Zygomycetes are also very important for their role in the symbiotic relationships which they form with the roots of the vast majority of other plants. These associations between roots and fungi are known as **mycorrhizae**. The masses of fungal hyphae increase the surface area of the roots for the absorption of water and nutrients, and the saprophytic activity of the fungus also increases the availability of these mineral nutrients. The plant in turn supplies the fungus with the products of photosynthesis.

Phylum: Ascomycota

The ascomycetes form the largest group of fungi. Asexual reproduction involves the formation of spores called **conidia**. These are produced in large quantities and are frequently the cause of human 'hay fever'-type allergies. Sexual reproduction involves conjugation followed by the production of **ascospores** inside a sac-like **ascus**.

The yeasts, which are useful to us in the fermentation reactions which produce alcoholic drinks and leaven bread, are rather atypical members of the ascomycetes. Yeasts are unicellular fungi which usually reproduce asexually by budding. Occasionally, however, two cells fuse and form an ascus and ascospores.

Some ascomycetes form toxins which cause hallucinations and can be fatal – LSD is derived from an ascomycete which attacks rye. Ascomycetes also include the *Penicillium* moulds which have played a vital role in reducing the impact of bacterial diseases. These fungi have also been used for centuries to ripen and impart flavour to many cheeses such as Camembert and Roquefort.

The attraction of the truffle

Many fungi are used as human food, but the most highly prized and expensive of all is the truffle. Truffles are the fruiting bodies of members of the ascomycetes. Known as the Tuberales, these rare fungi live in mycorrhizal symbiosis with the roots of oak and beech trees. The fruiting bodies are formed underground. The spores are only released as the truffle slowly decays, or if a burrowing animal breaks it apart. Truffles usually have strong and pungent smells, ranging from rich garlicky odours to the smell of sewer gas, depending on the species. Only a small number are edible.

To harvest these elusive fungi, European truffle hunters have traditionally used pigs to sniff out and dig up the fruiting bodies. A well trained truffle pig will dig down to a metre to seek out truffles. What stimulates a pig to be this persistent? It seems unlikely that it is the taste of the truffles. Researchers have discovered that truffles produce a highly volatile pig sexual attractant, usually found in the testes of boars. Androstenol is released in the saliva during pre-mating behaviour. It seems that truffles have evolved to attract sows, ensuring that the spore case is broken open and the spores dispersed. Androstenol is also produced by the human testes and released in the sweat glands of male armpits. Perhaps this explains why people are prepared to pay high prices for such an unlikely delicacy!

Phylum: Basidiomycota

The basidiomycetes are the best known of the fungi, including mushrooms, toadstools, puffballs and bracket fungi. Most of the basidiomycetes form large conspicuous fruiting bodies from a mass of hyphae buried within the soil or in a plant body such as a tree. Whilst the hyphae are haploid, the fruiting body is the result of sexual conjugation and consists of diploid hyphae. Meiosis results in haploid **basidiospores** which are formed in microscopic club-shaped **basidia**.

Plantae

The plant kingdom encompasses a variety of organisms which range from the simple liverworts to the giant redwoods. They are multicellular eukaryotic organisms relying on photosynthesis for their nutrition. A typical plant cell (see section 1.1) has a cellulose cell wall, sap vacuole and chlorophyll *a* along with other photosynthetic pigments and plastids (structures such as chloroplasts). Plants reproduce in a variety of ways, both asexually and sexually (see sections 5.1 and 5.3). Plant reproduction is characterised by **alternation of generations** – the haploid **gametophyte** generation and the diploid **sporophyte** generation. So far botanists have identified around 300 000 living plant species, with over 80% of these being flowering plants.

Phylum: Bryophyta

The bryophytes are the simplest land plants. They do not have vascular tissues and so are unable to transport material around the body of the plant. They are small – the largest species is less than 60 cm tall – and are found in damp places. A large percentage of bryophytes live in tropical rainforests.

The life cycle shows a clear alternation of generations. The haploid, gamete-forming gametophyte is usually the more prominent phase with the diploid spore-forming sporophyte attached to and dependent on it. The gametophyte usually shows differentiation into **stem**, **leaves** and **rhizoids** for anchorage. Bryophytes are limited in their colonisation of the land by their dependence on water for their swimming sperm, their lack of vascular tissue for transport and lack of stomata to prevent water loss. The best known bryophytes are the liverworts (class Hepaticae) and the mosses (class Musci).

Figure 6.1.13 The classic toadstool of fairytales is the fly agaric, a basidiomycete producing a toxin which is a powerful hallucinogenic chemical and can be fatal. Reindeer are very fond of eating fly agaric.

Class: Hepaticae

The liverworts are made up of a flat, lobed gametophyte **thallus**. On the thallus forms the **antheridium**, a sperm-producing chamber, and the **archegonium** which produces eggs. Sometimes both these structures form on a single gametophyte, sometimes they form on two different thalli. Water is needed for the sperm to swim to the egg and fertilise it. The fertilised egg develops into a diploid sporophyte dependent on the thallus. Meiosis occurs within the mature sporophyte to produce haploid spores. When released, these develop to form new haploid gametophytes.

Class: Musci

The mosses are similar to the liverworts, but the gametophyte is always differentiated into simple stems and leaves rather than a thallus. The rhizoids are multicellular rather than unicellular. Mosses form velvet-like carpets wherever the air is moist and clean. Like the liverworts, mosses produce sperm and eggs in antheridia and archegonia, and depend on water from rain, streams or other sources to carry the male gamete to the female one.

Phyla: Lycopodophyta, Sphenophyta and Filicinophyta

In these phyla **true leaves**, **stems** and **roots** occur. The two generations exist as separate plants, but the sporophyte is the larger and dominant plant, with the gametophyte reduced to a small, simple prothallus.

The Lycopodophyta are the club mosses, the Sphenophyta the horsetails and the Filicinophyta are the ferns. Horsetails are an ancient group, dating back to the Carboniferous swamps. They have a spore-bearing cone at the top of the stem. The club mosses are small-leaved plants with sporangia arranged between the leaves. By far the largest group is the ferns (Filicinophyta). They usually have large, lacy, prominent fronds which are true leaves. The dominant sporophyte generation is diploid. At maturity sporangia form in clusters called **sori** on the undersides of the fronds. Meiosis takes place within these sporangia to give rise to haploid spores. The spores are discharged into and dispersed by the air. A spore then develops into a small heart-shaped **prothallus** with no vascular tissue. Antheridia and archegonia form and give rise to male and female gametes. Because the sperm need water to swim to the egg, ferns are most commonly found in moist environments. The fertilised egg gives rise to a new diploid sporophyte, as shown in figure 6.1.15.

Figure 6.1.14 Liverworts and mosses are not waterproof and have no water transport systems, so they need to live in damp places.

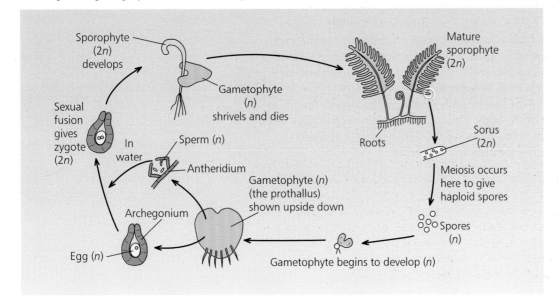

Figure 6.1.15 The life cycle of *Dryopteris*, a typical fern.

The seed-bearing plants

The seed-bearing plants include the vast majority of plant species. They have enormous economic and ecological significance. They provide the human race with much of its food, drink, cloth, building material, drugs and more. Fossil evidence suggests that the seed-bearing plants have been the most widespread and abundant land plants for 250 million years. In seed-bearing plants the gametophyte generation is part of the physiology of the sporophyte generation which is completely dominant (for life cycles see section 5.3). There are two phyla of seed plants, the Coniferophyta and the Angiospermophyta.

The Coniferophyta (conifers) or 'naked seed plants' include pine trees, spruces and cedars. They are characterised by narrow needle-like leaves, no vessels in the xylem tissue (only tracheids, lignified single cells) and most of all by their reproductive structures which are carried on spore-bearing leaves arranged into **cones**. Conifers are usually the dominant vegetation in cold and mountainous regions.

In contrast the Angiospermophyta or flowering plants have their reproductive structures carried in flowers. The ovules occur in an ovary and after fertilisation this develops into a fruit. Angiosperms also have vessels in their vascular tissue, making it much more effective at transporting substances. The two classes of the angiosperms are the monocotyledons and the dicotyledons. In monocots the embryo has a single seed leaf (cotyledon). Leaves generally have parallel veins and the stem contains scattered vascular bundles. As there is no cambium, no secondary thickening takes place and so monocotyledons do not generally reach great sizes. Palm trees are one of the better known exceptions to this rule. In dicots the embryo has two seed leaves (cotyledons). The leaves usually have a network of veins and the stem contains a ring of vascular tissue. Cambium is present so secondary thickening can take place and some dicotyledons reach great sizes.

Animalia

The majority of the species on Earth are the complex eukaryotic organisms we know as animals. There are around 2–12 million known species of animals alive today. They feed heterotrophically and reproduce mainly sexually. Here we shall consider a few of the main animal phyla.

The multicellular state has allowed great diversity of form to evolve, but also imposes certain limits. As a result of surface area:volume constraints the cells of most animals are very similar in size. This means that the major difference between a flea and an elephant is the number of cells, not the size of the cells. As animals get larger, more powerful muscle systems are needed to move them around. Fewer of the cells are in contact with the external environment and so respiratory and transport systems must become more sophisticated. Communications systems need to be more highly developed in larger animals to supply information to all areas of the body. Thus as we consider increasingly more complex animals, it is necessary to bear in mind the developments in these systems which make the increasing sophistication possible.

Phylum: Cnidaria

The cnidarians include some exceptionally beautiful creatures and also some very poisonous ones. Sea anemones, hydra, jellyfish and coral are among the members of this phylum. They have a sac-like body cavity called the **enteron** with only one opening and a **diploblastic** or two-layered structure to the body wall. The outside layer is called the **ectoderm** and the inner layer is the **endoderm**. The body plan of these animals demonstrates **radial symmetry** – they look circular when viewed from above or below and body structures radiate in all directions from the centre, as shown in figure 6.1.16.

Figure 6.1.16 Though relatively unspecialised, with no organs to perform specific tasks, the cnidarians achieve a much higher level of organisation than the sponges.

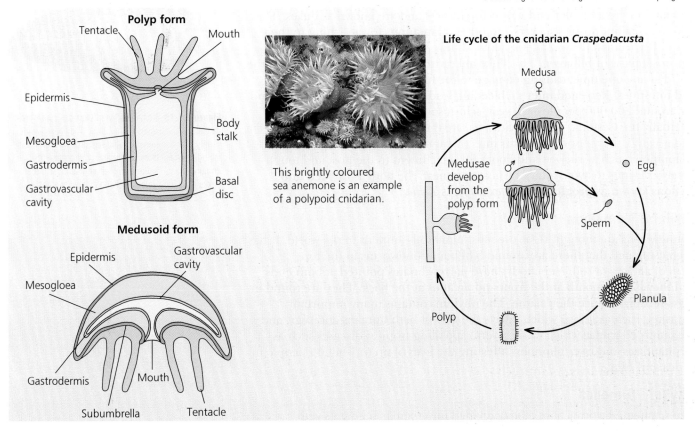

Polyp form

Tentacle · Mouth · Epidermis · Mesogloea · Gastrodermis · Gastrovascular cavity · Body stalk · Basal disc

Medusoid form

Epidermis · Gastrovascular cavity · Mesogloea · Gastrodermis · Mouth · Subumbrella · Tentacle

This brightly coloured sea anemone is an example of a polypoid cnidarian.

Life cycle of the cnidarian *Craspedacusta*

Medusa ♀ · Medusae develop from the polyp form · Egg · Sperm · Planula · Polyp

Most cnidarians exist in two forms, as **polyps** and **medusae**, and these forms alternate in the life cycle. This is an example of alternation of generations in the animal kingdom. Most cnidarians are carnivorous, trapping and killing their prey by means of special stinging cells on the tentacles known as **nematoblasts** (see figure 4.1.1, page 242). A simple nerve net over the entire body coordinates movement and response. These animals do not have a front and back, and they do not move in a single direction.

Phylum: Platyhelminthes

The flatworms show a much greater level of organisation. They possess a front end where the mouth, major sense organs and the main integrating region of the nervous system is sited. This anterior moves forward first and so is the first to encounter new situations. Such front-end specialisation is known as **cephalisation**. Along with the development of the front end, flatworms show **bilateral symmetry**. This means that the right and left sides of the animal are mirror images. Platyhelminthes are also the first major group to have organs rather than simply specialised tissues.

Flatworms range from 1 mm to 30 cm in length. They are dorsoventrally flattened, have a mouth but no anus and many blind-ending branches to the gut. They develop from three embryonic layers. **Ectoderm** gives rise to the surface layers, **mesoderm** to muscle fibres, excretory organs known as **flame cells** and the reproductive parts, whilst the **endoderm** lines the gut. There are no respiratory or circulatory systems – flatworms are so thin and flat that diffusion can fulfil these needs. The majority of flatworm species are parasitic. They are **hermaphrodite** – they possess both male and female reproductive organs, although self fertilisation is rare.

Turbellarians are free-living platyhelminths, found in fresh and salt water. Trematodes are all either endo- or ectoparasites and are known as flukes. They have no cilia but possess suckers and other adaptations for attaching to their hosts. The trematode *Schistosoma*, a blood fluke, causes the disease schistosomiasis or bilharzia. This fluke affects around 200 million people in the world at any one time, causing damage to the bladder, kidneys, liver, spleen and intestines. Repeated internal bleeding leads to weakness and anaemia and for around 200 000 people each year, schistosomiasis results in death.

Finally the Cestoda, all endoparasites, are the tapeworms. They have no cilia and no gut – they absorb nutrients directly from their host's gut. They have adaptations such as suckers and hooks for attachment to the host and tough outer coverings to avoid attack by host enzymes. The body is divided into sections known as **proglottids**. An example is *Taenia*.

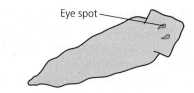

Figure 6.1.17 *Planaria*, a typical turbellarian.

Figure 6.1.18 Trematode liver flukes can cause great damage to the tissues of their host. They have a wide variety of adaptations to avoid rejection by their hosts, including in some cases the ability to change the immunological markers on their cell surfaces. Most flukes have life cycles involving at least two hosts.

Phylum: Nematoda

Roundworms are thought to be the most numerous animals in the world. It has been estimated that there are around 5 billion roundworms in the top 7 cm of an acre of soil. Nematodes have narrow bodies pointed at both ends, and they have a mouth at the front and an anus at the back. They are round in cross-section – hence their name. The phylum contains many important parasites, such as *Ascaris* which infects the guts of both humans and pigs, and the family Filariidae which cause several appalling tropical diseases such as elephantiasis and river blindness affecting the lives of up to 1 billion people in Africa and Asia.

Phylum: Annelida

The segmented worms have a body divided into regular segments with structures and organs repeated along the body. The segments are separated from each other by **septa** – thin sheets of membrane – and as a general rule each segment has bristle-like **chaetae** used for locomotion. **Nephridia**, specialised organs for excretion and osmoregulation, are also present in each segment. There is a closed circulatory system. The development of segmentation in this phylum seems to be an important step towards the evolution of larger animals, giving the potential for increased body size, efficient movement and specialisation of particular areas for particular tasks. The annelids have a true body cavity or **coelom**. They include the familiar earthworm, *Lumbricus terrestris*, ragworms, lugworms and leeches.

Phylum: Mollusca

The molluscs encompass a wide range of lifestyles and include the most intelligent of the invertebrates. Some molluscs have shells, and molluscs may live in the sea, in fresh water or on land. The main features of the molluscs include a soft muscular foot on the ventral side of the body, and a dorsal visceral hump containing the organs of the body which is often protected by the shell. Respiration is carried out by **gills** in the **mantle cavity**. There are several classes of molluscs, which include the Gastropoda or 'stomach-foots' (snails, slugs and whelks are examples). They have a large flat muscular foot and often a coiled shell.

The Pelycopoda or bivalves are molluscs which have shells secreted in two halves. Examples include oysters, scallops and mussels such as *Anodonta* the freshwater mussel and *Mytilis* the marine mussel.

The Cephalopoda or 'head-foots' have a foot which is reduced and incorporated in the head, and 8–10 tentacles. The members of this class are not typical molluscs. They include squids (the largest invertebrate on Earth is the giant squid), nautiluses and octopuses. The squids and octopuses have well developed eyes and octopuses in particular have large brains with areas not unlike cerebral hemispheres. They can be taught to run mazes and distinguish shapes – they are the most intelligent invertebrates.

Phylum: Arthropoda

The arthropods are the most varied animals on the Earth, with around 3–12 million different species, though some estimates are as high as 30 million. They have made use of a wide range of available ecological niches – the only stumbling block to their total dominance of the planet has been their inability to reach great sizes, as the exoskeleton limits growth.

Arthropods have jointed appendages, both legs and antennae. One of the most distinctive features of the arthropods is their rigid exoskeleton, the result of a chitinous cuticle which is hardened to various degrees. Muscles are attached to the exoskeleton, which is shed periodically in the process of moulting (ecdysis) to allow for growth. The body cavity is a blood-filled haemocoel. They show bilateral symmetry and a degree of segmentation, although the segments are often modified for special functions. Some of the groups have compound eyes. The enormous number of arthropod species are arranged in a number of classes, four of which are described below.

The crustaceans (Crustacea) are mainly aquatic with two pairs of sensory antennae and jaw-like mouthparts called **mandibles**. The dorsal surface of the body is usually covered with a tough protective **carapace** which in some cases completely covers the ventral surface as well. Examples include *Carcinus* (shore crab), woodlice and shrimps.

The centipedes (Chilopoda) are carnivorous arthropods with a pair of poison claws. The body is flattened dorsoventrally. They have one pair of legs per segment, whilst the millipedes (Diplopoda) are herbivores with rounded bodies, no poison claws and two sets of legs on each body segment.

The arachnids (Arachnida) are the spiders, scorpions, mites, ticks and harvestmen. They have several simple eyes, a **cephalothorax** and an **abdomen**, and poison glands. Most of them have eight legs.

The insects (Insecta) include around 900 000 named species, which have adapted successfully to life on land, in fresh water and in the air. Their bodies are divided into **head**, **thorax** and **abdomen**. The legs and wings are carried on the thorax. They have a single pair of antennae and well developed compound eyes. Gas exchange occurs within a tracheal system and they have Malpighian tubules for excretion. Insects are resistant to water loss and have efficient muscles. They also have life cycles which in general involve changes in form (**metamorphosis**) (see figure 6.1.20). This allows them to exploit different food sources and to avoid competition between adults and immature forms. Many insects exhibit extremely complex behaviour patterns on both social and individual levels which enable them to survive and reproduce in a wide variety of situations.

Nudibranch mollusc, a marine gastropod

A blue-ringed octopus – a cephalopod, this is one of the smallest but most poisonous of the octopuses.

Figure 6.1.19 The molluscs – a phylum containing the largest and the most intelligent of the invertebrates.

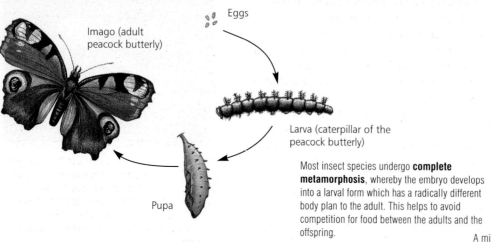

Imago (adult peacock butterfly)

Eggs

Larva (caterpillar of the peacock butterly)

Pupa

Most insect species undergo **complete metamorphosis**, whereby the embryo develops into a larval form which has a radically different body plan to the adult. This helps to avoid competition for food between the adults and the offspring.

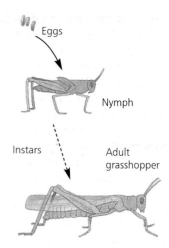

Eggs

Nymph

Instars

Adult grasshopper

A minority of the insect species, including grasshoppers and cockroaches, have a development pattern known as **incomplete metamorphosis**. The embryo develops into a **nymph**, an immature version of the adult form. The nymph undergoes a series of moults through stages called **instars** until the adult finally emerges with fully mature organ systems.

Figure 6.1.20 The insects are the most diverse group in the animal kingdom. Their complex life cycles are part of the key to their success.

Phylum: Chordata

The invertebrates make up more than 99.9% of the animals alive on Earth today. Yet most people, when asked to name ten animals, would suggest ten from the remaining 0.1% – the vertebrates. The vertebrates are in fact one subphylum of the **chordates**. Chordate features include **gill slits**, a **notochord** (a dorsally situated strengthening rod), a **hollow nerve cord** and a **tail and associated muscle blocks**. All chordates, including ourselves, possess these features at some point during their life cycle. The chordate phylum is divided up into two subphyla, the non-vertebrate chordates and the vertebrate chordates.

The non-vertebrate chordates have a notochord, but are all aquatic or marine organisms which seem to have been evolutionary 'dead ends'.

The vertebrate chordates

The true vertebrates possess all of the chordate features at some stage of their development. In addition, the notochord occurs only in the embryo form and is replaced in the adult by a **vertebral column**, with the brain developed and enclosed in a protective case called the **cranium**. The fossil record suggests that the early jawed fish were the first of the modern vertebrates to evolve, and that they gave rise to all the other vertebrate groups.

The cartilaginous fishes (Chondrichthyes) include the sharks, skates and rays. The class is almost entirely marine. These fish show several of the chordate features even into adulthood, with gill slits, tails with distinctive muscle blocks and hollow nerve cords. Their skeleton, made of **cartilage**, is light and strong. It is combined with large oil-storing livers so that many cartilaginous fishes have almost neutral buoyancy and need to expend very little energy to keep afloat. They have five pairs of gill slits.

The modern bony fishes (Osteichthyes) also have gill slits, tails with associated muscle blocks and hollow nerve cords. They have four pairs of gill slits which are covered by a flap called the **operculum**. They also usually have an **air sac** (the swim bladder) to control their buoyancy in the water. Within the bony fish is a small group of fleshy-finned fish. Extinct *Rhipidistans* of this type in Devonian times were probably the ancestors of the land vertebrates. The few modern forms include the lungfish and coelacanths.

The amphibians (Amphibia) were the first vertebrates to colonise the land. They have simple sac-like lungs (which are not very efficient) and smooth, moist skin which is used as a supplementary respiratory surface. Their life cycle includes metamorphosis, and they need water for successful reproduction as fertilisation is

Figure 6.1.21 Species of bony fish have colonised both fresh and salt water, although the salmon is unusual in that it can live in both!

Figure 6.1.22 Although the amphibians are no longer a large group on Earth, their ancestors took the first steps towards life on land for other animals to follow.

external and the larval form (tadpole) is aquatic. Gills are only present in the larval forms. Examples include frogs, toads, newts and salamanders.

The reptiles (Reptilia) are mainly terrestrial animals which were for many millions of years the dominant species on Earth. They have dry skin with **scales** and their gas exchange takes place exclusively in the **lungs**. They have developed **internal fertilisation** and lay eggs on land which are enclosed within a leathery shell. Some reptiles retain the eggs within the body and give birth to fully developed young. These reproductive developments have freed the reptiles from the need to return to the water to breed, and so have enabled them to colonise dry and hot environments. The gill slits which are a chordate feature are seen only in embryonic development. Examples include snakes, crocodiles and lizards.

Birds (Aves) are thought to have evolved from the reptiles or even the dinosaurs, and indeed they have many features in common. Instead of scales birds have **feathers** over most of the body. The forelimbs have been adapted as **wings** which in most cases are used for flight. The sternum or breastbone has been enlarged into a big keel shape for the attachment of the wing muscles, particularly in those birds which fly. The jaws are toothless and are covered by a horny beak. Reproduction involves the production of a well developed egg with a hard shell and in many cases considerable parental care is invested in the raising of the young. Birds have light skeletons and are endothermic. Of the four main chordate features, only the hollow nerve cord remains in the adult bird.

Figure 6.1.23 Crocodiles are some of the best known reptiles, but the group has a wide range of body forms which includes creatures as diverse as snakes and chameleons. Yet in spite of their obvious differences, the most important aspects of their biology – embryonic development, reproduction and breathing methods – are the same.

Class: Mammalia

A true mammal is distinguished by the production of milk for its young in **mammary glands**, a high internal body temperature and the presence of **hair**. Most mammals also produce live young which have developed for a time within the body of the mother in a structure called the **uterus**. As with the birds, chordate features are only plainly visible in embryonic development when gill slits, tails with segmental muscles and notochords may be seen. The mammals include organisms of an enormous range of sizes, from tiny shrews to elephants and whales. Their sophisticated temperature control and reproductive capabilities have made it possible for them to live in almost all of the Earth's environmental niches. Human beings are just one example of this highly developed class of animals.

The mammals are in fact divided into three subclasses based on the sophistication of the reproductive processes. These are:

- **Subclass: Monotremes** include the duck-billed platypus and the spiny anteaters. They are between the true mammals and the reptiles. The fertilised egg and early embryo are kept in the uterus for about two weeks. A reptilian type of egg is then built round the embryo and the egg is laid and incubated for a short time. A primitive newborn then emerges from the egg and suckles milk from the mother's mammary glands.

- **Subclass: Marsupials** are pouched mammals. Here the embryo grows for three to four weeks in the uterus before being born whilst almost still a fetus. The blind and tiny infant crawls from the vaginal opening through the fur of the mother to the **marsupium** or pouch. Here it latches on to the teat of a mammary gland and feeds, grows and develops until large enough for life outside the pouch. The length of time for which a marsupial can develop in the uterus is limited by the lack of a placenta in most species. Marsupial mammals include the kangaroo and the opossum.

- **Subclass: Eutherians** or placental mammals make up the majority of the mammals. The formation of a placenta which provides nourishment for a fetus and prevents immunological rejection by the maternal tissues allows the developing fetus to reach a large size and a high level of development before birth. In terms of evolutionary success this is of enormous significance. The mother remains freely mobile during pregnancy without the need to incubate eggs, and the mammary glands provide a guaranteed source of food for the offspring after birth. In view of all these factors the rapid rise of the placental mammals as a group is easily understood.

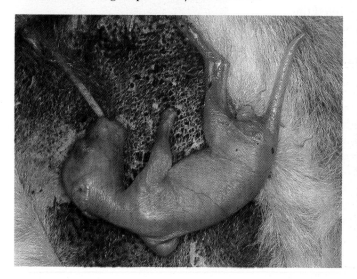

Figure 6.1.24 A kangaroo and a cow are of comparable size, yet there is an enormous discrepancy between the size of their newly born infants. A newborn kangaroo is about the size of a bean and weighs around 0.1 g, whilst a newborn calf weighs around 45 kg. The comparatively large size of the calf is largely due to the role of the placenta in its development.

SUMMARY

- The organic molecules that make up life could have been produced by the action of lightning or radiation from the Sun on the early sea and atmosphere, as demonstrated by Miller and Urey.

- The earliest known cells were anaerobic and heterotrophic. These cells subsequently evolved to form all the life now present on Earth.

- Lamarck's evolutionary theory proposed that evolution takes place by **the inheritance of acquired characteristics**. This is now largely disproved.

- Darwin's theory says that due to the variety within a species, those organisms best suited to their environment are most likely to survive and reproduce because of **the struggle for existence** – more offspring are produced than ever survive into adulthood. The favourable characteristics are thus passed on to the next generation. Changes in the environment will bring about a change in the characteristics by selecting for favourable characteristics within the variation normally present. **Evolution** is brought about by **natural selection**.

- **Neo-Darwinism** considers that evolution occurs as a result of the **differential fertility** of organisms with different phenotypes – those that reproduce the most successfully will be selected for, and advantageous features vary according to the environment.

- Evidence for evolution is provided by **palaeontology** (the study of fossils), **distribution studies** (after being separated, species may evolve differently to fill the same niches in **adaptive radiation**, or similar organisms may evolve independently in **parallel evolution**), **comparative anatomy**, **embryology**, **cell biology** and **biochemical analysis**.

- Organisms are classified according to the **binomial system of nomenclature**, in which each organism is given a **genus** and **species** name. Organisms are grouped together in further **taxa** (groups) – **families**, **orders**, **classes**, **phyla** and **kingdoms**. These classifications are given in table 6.1.2.

Kingdom	Phylum	Class	Example
Prokaryotae	(Non-photosynthetic bacteria)		*Staphylococcus*
	(Photosynthetic bacteria)		*Oscillatoria*
Protoctista	Rhizopoda		*Amoeba*
	Zoomastigina (flagellates)		*Trypanosoma*
	Apicomplexa (sporozoans)		*Plasmodium*
	Ciliophora (ciliates)		*Paramecium*
	Euglenophyta		*Euglena*
	Oomycota		*Phytophthora infestans*
	Chlorophyta (green algae)		*Spirogyra*
	Rhodophyta (red algae)		*Chondrus*
	Phaeophyta (brown algae)		*Laminaria* (kelp)
Fungi	Zygomycota		*Mucor*
	Ascomycota		*Penicillium*
	Basidiomycota		*Agaricus* (mushroom)
Plantae	Bryophyta	Hepaticae (liverworts)	*Pellia*
		Musci (mosses)	*Bryum capillare*
	Lycopodophyta (club mosses)		*Selaginella*
	Sphenophyta (horsetails)		*Equisetum*
	Filicinophyta (ferns)		*Dryopteris*
	Coniferophyta (conifers)		*Pinus* (Scots pine)
	Angiospermophyta (flowering plants)	Monocotyledoneae	*Triticum* (wheat)
		Dicotyledoneae	*Rubus fructicosus* (bramble)
Animalia	Cnidaria		*Aurelia* (jellyfish)
	Platyhelminthes (flatworms)	Turbellaria	*Planaria*
		Trematoda (flukes)	*Schistosoma*
		Cestoda (tapeworms)	*Taenia*

Kingdom	Phylum	Class	Example
	Nematoda (roundworms)		*Ascaris*
	Annelida		*Lumbricus terrestris* (earthworm)
	Mollusca	Gastropoda ('stomach-foot')	*Helix* (snail)
		Pelycopoda (bivalves)	*Mytilis* (marine mussel)
		Cephalopoda ('head-foot')	*Loligo* (squid)
	Arthropoda	Crustacea (superclass)	*Carcinus* (crab)
		Chilopoda (centipedes)	*Lithobius* (centipede)
		Diplopoda (millipedes)	*Lulus* (millipede)
		Arachnida	*Scorpio* (scorpion)
		Insecta	*Locusta* (locust)
	Chordata	Chondrichthyes (cartilaginous fishes)	*Scyliorhinus* (dogfish)
		Osteichthyes (bony fishes)	*Clupea* (herring)
		Amphibia	*Rana* (frog)
		Reptilia	*Lacerta* (lizard)
		Aves (birds)	*Columba* (pigeon)
		Mammalia	*Homo* (human)

Table 6.1.2

QUESTIONS

1 a What features distinguish prokaryotes from eukaryotes?
b In what ways are some protoctista like plants, some like fungi and some like animals?

2 a Why are the fungi known as the great decomposers?
b Compare the vascular and non-vascular groups of land plants, indicating the major differences in their structures and lifestyles.

3 a What are some of the innovations of reptiles which freed them from dependence on a very moist environment?
b The three lines of modern-day mammals are the monotremes, the marsupials and the placentals. What features distinguish each group?

Developing Key Skills

Across America, in a number of states, any mention of Charles Darwin, the theory of evolution and associated ideas such as extinction is being removed from biology text books. This is in reponse to objections from fundamentalist Christians who believe in creation as described in the first book of the Bible. Write to the state governor explaining why you agree or disagree with this decision.

When the first antibiotic drugs were discovered, it must have seemed like the beginning of a brave new world in which dreaded infectious diseases would no longer kill thousands of people each year. But antibiotics are not the whole answer to bacterial diseases, and problems are now arising which result directly from the over-use of these valuable drugs.

Each antibiotic is only effective against certain bacteria. This is because the metabolic process or biochemical pathway with which it interferes does not occur in all bacteria, or because there is no binding site for the drug, or because some bacteria naturally produce enzymes that destroy the drug. This in itself is not a major problem, because many different antibiotics have been developed, so there should be an antibiotic effective against every pathogen. However, antibiotics have been used widely and freely, exposing many pathogens to a wide range of our antibacterial weaponry. They have often not been used properly, with people not completing their course of drugs, and they have been fed to farm animals on a daily basis. As a result, increasing numbers of pathogens are becoming resistant to the effects of many common antibiotics.

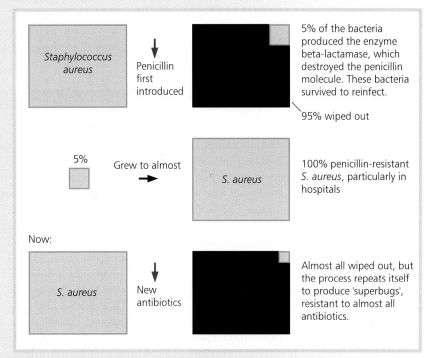

Figure 1 *Staphylococcus aureus* causes boils and abscesses. The balance of power between this bacterium and penicillin has swung first one way and then the other since the introduction of the drug. In hospitals at least, the bacterium is now on top and penicillin has little or no effect, because almost all *S. aureus* strains produce an enzyme which destroys the structure of the antibiotic.

How does resistance come about?

Resistance develops through chance mutation giving a bacterium that can withstand an antibiotic. It may become impermeable to the drug, or it may develop a new biochemical pathway, or most commonly it switches on or acquires a gene for the production of an antibiotic-destroying enzyme. This mutant will rapidly become the main form, because non-resistant strains of the bacteria will be wiped out by antibiotic therapy, as shown in figure 1.

Superbugs

Some bacteria have become resistant to the effects of many different antibiotics. These are sometimes referred to as 'superbugs', and they can be killers. One of the more frightening aspects of this problem is that superbugs are most often found in hospitals, where drug use is at its highest. The only way to prevent this trend continuing is to use antibiotics only when strictly necessary, and to use as few different antibiotics as possible, holding some in reserve to treat diseases that have not responded to the usual drugs.

Figure 2 The agricultural community has long been using antibiotics to promote faster growth. This practice is finally being stopped, removing a source of antibiotic-resistant bacteria.

6.2 Population genetics

The complexity of the evolutionary events leading to the development of the vast array of modern species can seem overwhelming. Looked at from the viewpoint of individuals in populations the mechanisms of evolution become easier to understand.

Populations

Defining terms

Before we begin to look at population genetics, we need to know what is meant by the term 'population'. In biological terms, a **population** is a group of individuals of the same species occupying a particular **habitat**. The habitat of an organism is the place where it lives, and takes into account both the physical and biological elements of the surroundings. This will be discussed in more detail in section 6.4.

In population genetics the gene is taken as the unit of evolution. The genetic make-up of a population evolves over time. The sum total of all the genes in a population at a given time is known as the **gene pool**. For all the genes contained within the genome of a population the gene pool will run to millions or even billions of genes. However, at any one time it is usually the gene pool for a particular trait that is considered. This tends to be a more manageable number of genes of around several thousand. At any point in time a population of organisms will have a particular gene pool, with different alleles occurring with varying frequencies. Evolution may be considered as a permanent change in **gene frequencies** within a population. What does this mean and how is it measured?

Gene frequencies

The **frequency** of a particular allele in a population is a statement of how often it occurs. This is usually expressed as a decimal fraction of 1. Surprisingly, the frequency with which a gene occurs within the population has little bearing on whether it is a dominant or recessive allele, as figure 6.2.2 illustrates. Take an imaginary gene with two possible alleles **X** and **x**. If all of the individuals in a breeding population of 100 are heterozygous, then the frequency of each allele is 100/200 or 0.5. For example, tests were done on a sample of white Caucasians living in the USA to determine the frequencies of the alleles for the MN blood groups, L^M and L^N (see section 5.6, page 434). These turned out at L^M 0.539 and L^N 0.461.

There is a general formula which can be used to represent the frequency with which the dominant and recessive forms of an allele occur in the gene pool of a population. The frequency of the dominant allele is represented by the letter p and the frequency of the recessive allele is represented by the letter q:

$$p + q = 1$$

The frequency of the dominant allele plus the frequency of the recessive allele will always equal 1. Thus for the MN blood group:

$$0.539 + 0.461 = 1$$

Evolution involves a change in the allele frequencies within a population.

Figure 6.2.1 When the frequencies of the genes within a population change, favouring one phenotype over another, then evolution can be seen to be taking place. These photographs show the white and blue forms of the lesser snow goose.

Figure 6.2.2 The frequency of a phenotype in a population is the result of the frequency of particular alleles and that is independent of the dominant or recessive nature of the allele. Thus blue-eyed, blond-haired children (both features the result of recessive alleles) are not uncommon in this country, and in Scandinavia they are the most common phenotype.

This simple equation is of very limited use as it stands, because it is almost impossible to measure the frequencies of alleles or the ways in which they change. What can be observed readily in a population is the distribution of phenotypes. In 1908 the British mathematician G. H. Hardy and the German physician W. Weinberg independently developed an equation for stable gene frequencies within a population, which can be solved using observable phenotypes.

The Hardy-Weinberg equilibrium – an ideal case

The algebraic equation developed by Hardy and Weinberg describing stable gene frequencies is:

p^2	+	$2pq$	+	q^2	=	1
Frequency of homozygous dominant individuals in population		Frequency of heterozygous individuals		Frequency of homozygous recessive individuals		Total

One of the main problems in finding gene frequencies is that it is not possible to distinguish between the homozygous dominant and the heterozygote based on the appearance of the individuals. However, using the Hardy-Weinberg equation these gene frequencies can be calculated from the number of homozygous recessive individuals in the population. The number of homozygous recessive individuals gives us q^2. From this, q is readily obtained by finding the square root. The result gives the frequency of the recessive allele and by substituting this figure into our initial formula of $p + q = 1$, the frequency p of the dominant allele can be found.

The Hardy-Weinberg equation was developed to describe the situation in a stable equilibrium, where the relative frequencies of the alleles and the genotypes stay the same over time. The implication is that in the absence of any factors which affect the equilibrium, gene frequencies will remain constant within a population from generation to generation. However, this is only true for an ideal population. An ideal population is one in which:

- there is random mating – there are no factors at work to cause the choice of mates to be non-random
- the population size is large
- the population is isolated so that there is no exchange of genetic material with other populations
- there are no mutations
- no natural selection takes place – in other words, all alleles have the same level of reproductive advantage or disadvantage.

In the real world these ideal conditions rarely if ever exist, and it is the upsetting of the gene-pool equilibrium which results in evolution. We shall examine each of these conditions in turn.

Using the Hardy-Weinberg equation

In the case of the MN blood groups, the frequency of the NN phenotype in American Caucasians is 0.21. Thus q^2 is 0.21 giving q as $\sqrt{0.21}$ or 0.461. The frequency of the $\mathbf{L^N}$ allele is 0.461, and this can then be used to find the frequency of the $\mathbf{L^M}$ allele:

$$p + 0.461 = 1$$
$$p = 1 - 0.461 = 0.539$$

By substituting these values into the Hardy-Weinberg equation, the frequency of homozygous MM individuals [$(0.539)^2$ or 0.29] and heterozygous MN individuals ($2 \times 0.539 \times 0.461$ or 0.5) can be calculated. As the L^M and L^N alleles show incomplete dominance, these theoretical frequencies can be confirmed by phenotypic observations.

The mechanisms of evolution

Upsetting the Hardy-Weinberg equilibrium

The Hardy-Weinberg law is never really valid as the ideal conditions it demands cannot be met in real situations. Mutation occurs constantly in any population and many other factors also influence the gene pool. However, the equation is invaluable as a way of measuring evolutionary change, and also as a way of demonstrating that evolution is a constantly occurring feature of the living world. Deviations from the Hardy-Weinberg equilibrium show that species, far from being unchanged since time immemorial, are in a continuous state of evolutionary flux. The factors which result in deviations from the hypothetical equilibrium state are the factors which bring about a long-term change in the gene pool and so drive evolution forward.

Non-random mating

One of the most important requirements for a gene pool to remain in equilibrium is for **random mating** to occur. Random mating means that the likelihood that any two individuals in a population will mate is independent of their genetic make-up – for example, the pollen from a wind-pollinated grass flower is likely to blow to any one of thousands of other similar grass flowers. **Non-random mating** occurs when some feature of the phenotype affects the probability of two organisms mating.

Animals in which the male displays in some way to attract the female do not show random mating. The male peacock with the most impressive tail, the stag with the largest antlers and most effectively aggressive nature and the male stickleback with the brightest belly and most available nest will all appear to be more attractive than average to the females of the species. As a result they will be more likely to have the opportunity to mate and pass on their genes, ensuring that their offspring in turn are likely to carry these attractive characteristics. In plants and some animals self fertilisation or other forms of inbreeding mean that mating is not random and this affects the genetic ratios.

Within human populations non-random mating is the normal state. In every human culture value judgements of one sort or another are used in the selection of a partner. The selection may be made by the family or social groups to which the individuals belong, in which case the professional and social standing of the prospective partners and their families will be weighed in the balance. Equally the selection may be made by the individuals concerned and called 'falling in love', but even this seemingly random process is governed by choices based as much on society and peer group pressure as on the perceived attractiveness of the proposed partners. In different populations different traits are regarded as desirable and so the gene pool shifts, as figure 6.2.3 illustrates.

A large population

The Hardy-Weinberg equation is only valid if it is applied to a large population, that is, one with several thousand individuals. This is because the maintenance

Figure 6.2.3 In the general human population albinism occurs in one person out of every 30 000. However, albinos are highly esteemed in certain Native American tribes and as a result the trait occurs in one out of every 240 individuals. This is a remarkable shift in the gene frequency within the population and shows the effect of non-random mating on the gene pool equilibrium.

of genetic equilibrium depends on random assortment of the genes. Compare the situation with tossing a coin. In theory, every time a coin is tossed it has a 50/50 chance of landing with the 'heads' side upwards. In practice, if a coin is tossed 20 times it could land 'tail' side up every time. If it is tossed 200 times, then at least some 'heads' will almost certainly occur. By the time 2000 tosses have been carried out the number of 'heads' and 'tails' resulting will be nearing the expected 50/50 ratio.

A similar situation exists in populations. If an allele occurs in 10% of the population and that population has only 10 individuals, then only one will carry the allele. Should a calamity befall that individual, the gene will be lost from the population completely. In a population of 5000 individuals, 500 will carry the allele in question and the likelihood of all of these being destroyed is remote.

A clear example of the importance of large populations in the maintenance of stable genetic frequencies occurs in the reverse situation, that is, when a small number of individuals leave the main population and set up a separate new population. Any unusual genes in the founder members of this new population will be amplified as the population grows. This is known as the **founder effect**, which is demonstrated clearly amongst the Amish, an American religious sect which exists in three isolated communities. One of the groups has a high frequency of a very rare genetic disorder known as Ellis-van Creveldt syndrome, because one of the founder members carried the gene. More cases of Ellis-van Creveldt syndrome have been found in this one small population than in the whole of the rest of the world (for more details see box below).

The founder effect

When Mr and Mrs Samuel King emigrated to Pennsylvania in 1744 as members of a small group of 200 souls who founded an Amish community, they can have had no idea of the legacy they took with them. One of them was heterozygous for Ellis-van Creveldt syndrome. This rare genetic disease results in a type of dwarfism – the limbs are shortened, there may be extra digits and as a result of associated problems the victim usually dies in the first year of life. The Kings produced many children, who in turn were also particularly prolific. This raised the frequency of the allele within the population way above its normal level. Purely by chance at least one other of the founding group also possessed this recessive gene in the heterozygous form. As a result of interbreeding in this isolated Amish community, one in 14 individuals in the population now carry the gene. This results in a distressingly high number of affected births – in 1964 there were 43 cases of Ellis-van Creveldt syndrome in a population group of 8000.

Gene flow – a lack of isolation

One of the constraints on a population in order to maintain the Hardy-Weinberg genetic equilibrium is that it should exist in isolation. There should be no migration of organisms either into or out of the population. Of course, this is very rarely the case in the living world. Insects carry pollen from one population of flowers to another, and the wind can carry it for miles. Male animals frequently leave their familial groups and go in search of other populations to find a mate. Many simple organisms release their gametes directly into the water to be carried great distances before fertilisation occurs. In all of these cases migration of either the whole organism or the genetic material into or out of the population takes place. As a result of this, **gene flow** occurs, tending to make the individual populations more alike. In extreme cases of isolation such as the Amish described above, this gene flow effect is missing.

Mutations

For the Hardy-Weinberg equation to apply to a population, no mutations must occur within that population. This is because mutations involve changes in the inheritable material, that is, the alleles are altered. As we have seen in section 5, a mutation-free situation is an unrealistic expectation as mutations occur within a population all the time. Mutations in the somatic cells of animals will not be passed on to their offspring. They may or may not affect the individual themselves. The only animal mutations which are passed on to the next generation (and so affect the gene pool) are mutations in the cells of the germ line – in other words, those cells which will form the eggs and sperm. In plants there is no germ line – any of the shoots of a plant may develop into a flower bud – and so any mutation may become part of the gametes.

Although mutations occur continuously, they do not happen very rapidly. In a single generation each gene has between a 1 in 10^4 and a 1 in 10^9 chance of mutation. For human beings with a structural gene pool of around 10^6 this probably means that each of us contains only one new mutation. The vast majority of these will be recessive and are unlikely to be expressed, but occasionally mutations arise which confer benefits to an individual and may eventually become entrenched within the gene pool.

Natural selection

Survival of the fittest

To quote Stephen Jay Gould, a leading authority on evolution: 'The essence of Darwin's theories is his contention that natural selection is the creative force of evolution – not just the executioner of the unfit.' Natural selection acts at the level of each individual organism. Some individuals carry alleles that result in phenotypes which provide them with some sort of advantage. These phenotypes can vary from the very obvious traits which make them more likely to be selected as mates or less likely to be eaten by predators, through to more subtle features such as forms of enzymes which allow them to digest food more effectively. Any individual with advantageous alleles will be more likely to survive and reproduce – in other words, they will be selected for over other less well adapted individuals. Thus natural selection means that the best adapted organisms are more likely to survive and reproduce, and as a result the frequencies of those advantageous alleles within the population increase, as illustrated in figure 6.2.4.

Natural selection

Within any natural population selection is always occurring as some phenotypes are more advantageous than others and are therefore selected for.

Figure 6.2.4 The ptarmigan is a member of the grouse family found in the Scottish Highlands. After the autumn moult the plumage regrows almost white. This is the result of natural selection – those birds which produced lighter feathers for the winter were less likely to be seen and eaten by predators during the snowy winter months than darker birds and so stood a greater chance of surviving to the spring and reproducing those advantageous alleles. Over many years this has become the normal state for the ptarmigan and almost all birds become white in the winter as the frequency of the allele controlling this feature has risen within the population. Similar colour changes can be seen in the Arctic hare.

Natural selection works in several different ways to affect gene frequencies within a population, and we shall consider the main methods below.

Stabilising selection

Natural selection is often thought of as the selection of some new and advantageous features into a population. This is far from the truth – often natural selection acts to preserve what is already present in a population. This **stabilising selection** has resulted in many organisms which have changed little from the relatively early days of their history, for example ferns, sharks and lungfish. Wherever the environment of an area has been stable for a long period of time, then the effect of stabilising selection can be seen, as figure 6.2.5 shows.

Directional selection

This is the 'classic' type of natural selection, involving a change from one phenotypic property to a new one more advantageous in new circumstances. There are many excellent examples of this type of evolution in progress. One of the best known is the story of the peppered moth *Biston betularia* which underwent natural selection in response to environmental changes caused by industrial processes (**industrial melanism**). *Biston betularia* is a creamy speckled moth found in British woodlands. In the eighteenth century the relatively rare black specimens resulting from a random dominant mutation were very popular with butterfly collectors of the day. Their dark colour made them easily visible against the pale bark of the trees for both human collectors and birds looking for a meal, and so the dark allele was selected against and its frequency in the population remained low.

Then in the mid-nineteenth century the Industrial Revolution changed the face of much of Britain and Europe. The soot and smoke from the factory chimneys darkened the bark of the trees and the surfaces of buildings. As a result the dark melanic form of *Biston betularia* was at a selective advantage and the frequency of the allele within the population began to increase as more and more of the light-coloured moths fell prey to predators.

Now that there is considerably less industry in Britain, and the remaining industries produce much less pollution, trees and buildings are becoming cleaner and paler again and the selection pressure is beginning to move back in favour of the paler moth. Figure 6.2.6 shows the forms of the peppered moth.

Another example of directional selection is the oysters of Malpeque Bay, Prince Edward Island, Canada. In 1915 the oyster fishermen of Malpeque Bay

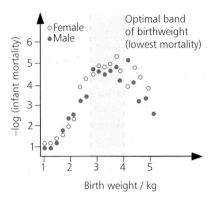

Figure 6.2.5 This graph shows the negative log of human infant mortality plotted against birth weight. The higher the vertical axis, the lower the death rate. The evidence demonstrates the effect of stabilising selection on the birth weight of babies. Babies with very low birth weights (often also born very early) have a high death rate. Very large babies may well endanger the mother at the time of birth and may also have some metabolic disorders. They too have a relatively high death rate. Those babies born in the 2.7–4 kg (6–9 lbs) range are most likely to survive and reproduce themselves, and this is by far the most common birth weight range.

Figure 6.2.6 The two main forms of *Biston betularia* on the bark of a clean tree and a polluted tree. In the 1950s H. B. D. Kettlewell of Oxford University set up several experiments to examine the selection of the two forms. In an unpolluted area with clean trees he released equal numbers of light and dark moths. 12.5% of the light moths were subsequently recaptured, but only 6% of the dark ones were retrieved. In another series of observations birds were seen to eat 26 light moths and 164 dark ones as they rested on a light tree trunk. In an industrial area 40% of the dark moths were recaptured but only 19% of the light ones. Of the moths picked off the blackened trees from equal releases, 43 were light and 15 were dark. In recent years the move has been back in favour of the paler moth and the frequency of its allele in the population has begun to increase again.

began to notice that amongst their usually healthy catches there were a few diseased oysters, small and flabby with pus-filled blisters. By 1922 the oyster beds had been all but wiped out by this Malpeque disease. However, a small number of the millions of offspring produced by each oyster each year carried an allele giving resistance to the disease. Not surprisingly the frequency of this gene in the population increased rapidly – by 1925 a small oyster harvest was again possible and by 1940 the beds were as prolific as ever, as figure 6.2.7 shows. However, there was now a rather different gene pool, the new one containing a high frequency of disease-resistant alleles.

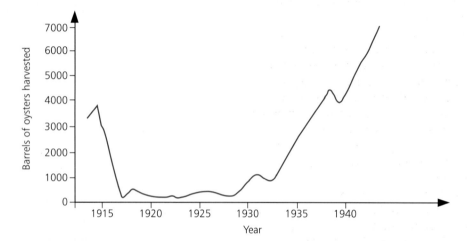

Figure 6.2.7 Oyster yields from Malpeque Bay, 1915–40. Disease devastated the populations but as a result of the increased selection of the disease-resistant allele within the population, healthy oyster beds developed.

Directional selection occurs whenever environmental pressure is applied to a population. It is frequently seen in populations of insects and plants that are regarded as pests and sprayed with chemical insecticides or herbicides. The chemicals may have a devastating effect initially, but directional selection ensures that within relatively few generations resistant individuals become more common within the population. Because a few plants or insects contain the random mutation that makes them resistant to the effect of the chemical toxin, they will survive the spraying. When they reproduce, they will pass on those successful genes – far fewer of the 'normal' genotype will have survived to breed, so the resistant form becomes the norm. This resistance to pesticides and herbicides is becoming a major agricultural problem all over the world. Stronger chemicals, chemical 'cocktails' – mixtures of a number of toxins – and a constant race to produce new and better poisons have resulted from the development of resistant strains. However, these chemicals can be toxic to the animals and plants that we are trying to produce – and to human beings as well. Now people are looking increasingly to genetic engineering (see Section 7) and biological pest control (see pages 548–552) to solve the pest problem. This, like the peppered moths, is just one of many examples of the effect of human activities on natural selection. The introduction of the rabbit disease myxomatosis into this country almost wiped out the rabbit population 40 years ago, but rabbits are now common once more. Many of them carry alleles which render them immune to myxomatosis – the frequency of such alleles in the rabbit gene pool has increased enormously.

Disruptive selection

Disruptive selection, also known as **diversifying selection**, is another variation of directional selection. The difference is that the outcome is an increase in the diversity of the population rather than a trend in one particular direction. This occurs when conditions are very diverse and small subpopulations evolve different phenotypes suited to their very particular surroundings. Darwin's finches are a good example of diversifying selection.

Balancing selection

Here natural selection maintains variety, keeping an allele within the population even though it might seem to be disadvantageous. One clear example of **balancing selection** we have already come across is the sickle cell allele for human haemoglobin. Although the homozygous form of the allele is usually lethal, the heterozygous form gives protection against malaria and so the allele remains at a relatively high frequency within the population. This is known as **heterozygote advantage** or **hybrid vigour.**

The effect of this hybrid vigour is clearly seen in domestic dogs and cats. Pure breeds of dogs and cats have frequently been highly inbred over the generations to arrive at and maintain the particular features required for the breed. However, this also concentrates 'disadvantageous' genes and highly inbred animals are frequently relatively low in overall resistance to disease and also particularly prone to particular problems – Labradors tend to get arthritis, spaniels have ear problems, etc. On the other hand cross-bred cats and mongrel dogs, whilst of a far less predictable phenotype, tend to have much higher disease resistance and a much reduced tendency to succumb to inherited diseases – they are full of hybrid vigour.

Natural selection then can take a variety of forms. It may result in populations with a smaller gene pool or it may produce populations with such increased variety that two new populations or even species result. Along with all the other factors we have considered, natural selection occurs constantly in the living world, bringing about evolution. Some of the ways it does this are shown in figure 6.2.8. It is interesting to note how environmental factors can act as stabilising or evolutionary forces of natural selection, either maintaining a feature which is well adapted to a stable environment or driving through change when it is needed to adapt to different conditions.

Figure 6.2.8 The effects of stabilising, directional and diversifying selection on populations. The shaded areas represent the alleles selected against, and their loss results in the next graph down. Natural selection, acting in these different ways, is a major factor in the evolution of life on Earth.

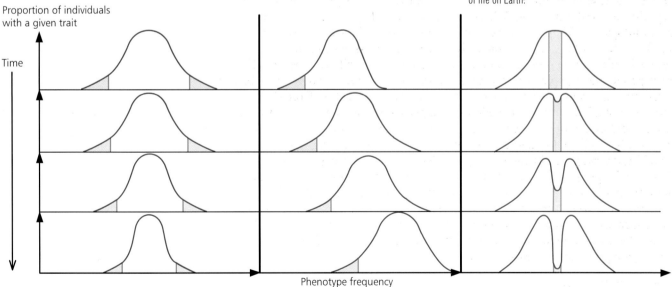

Proportion of individuals with a given trait

Time

Phenotype frequency

Stabilising selection tends to reduce variety so that only the phenotypes best adapted to a particular set of circumstances are maintained within the population.

Directional selection leads to a change in the phenotypes of a population in a particular direction, making them better suited to their environment.

Disruptive or diversifying selection increases the variety within a population – if the selection pressure is strong two non-overlapping populations may result which could end up as two new species.

How species are formed

Changes in populations of animals and plants are very interesting, and they can tell us a great deal about the process of natural selection. But a species is usually a much bigger entity than a population, and will often consist of a large number of populations. How is a new species formed?

A species is a group of organisms sharing a number of structural and evolutionary features which are capable of interbreeding to produce fertile offspring. **Speciation** (the formation of a new species) usually happens in the following way. Part of a population becomes isolated in some way (see box below). The two isolated populations experience different conditions, and this in turn means that natural selection will act in different directions on the two populations. As a result, over time both the genotype and the phenotype of each isolated group will change. This can continue to the point where, even if members of the split population are reunited, they can no longer successfully interbreed.

Another way in which new species can form is by **hybridisation**. Sometimes two closely related species may interbreed and in fact form fertile hybrids which may be successful in their own right. These hybrids may not be fertile if crossed back with their original parent species. This type of hybrid speciation is particularly common in plants.

Isolating mechanisms

There are a number of ways in which parts of a population may become isolated, leading to the formation of new species. These isolation mechanisms include:

- **geographical isolation** – when a physical barrier such as a river or a mountain range separates two populations originating from the same stock
- **ecological isolation** – when two populations inhabit the same region but develop preferences for different parts of the habitat
- **seasonal isolation** – when the timing of flowering or sexual receptiveness in some parts of a population drifts away from the norm for the group, this can

eventually lead to the two groups reproducing several months apart

- **behavioural isolation** – when changes occur in the courtship ritual, display or mating pattern which means some animals do not recognise others as being potential mates, such a change might be a mutation which changes the colour or pattern of markings
- **mechanical isolation** – a mutation may occur which changes the genitalia of animals, making it physically impossible for them to mate successfully, or which changes the relationship of the stigma and stamens in the flowers of plants, making pollination unsuccessful.

Allopatric speciation takes place when populations are physically separated in some way. This has been of enormous importance in the history of evolution, when great land masses were moving and separating. It is still enormously important as physical isolation of populations occurs both as a result of natural changes and also as a result of human intervention – changing the course of rivers, or building structures such as dams, roads or cities.

Sympatric speciation takes place when two populations are geographically still close to each other but for other reasons – mechanical, behavioural, genetic – reproductive isolation develops. It explains, for example, the mechanism by which the various finch species of the Galapagos Islands evolved.

SUMMARY

- A **population** is a group of individuals of the same species occupying a particular **habitat**. The habitat includes the geographical place where an organism lives and its interactions with other organisms.

- The **gene pool** is the sum total of the genes in a population at a given time. **Evolution** is the permanent change in **gene frequencies** within a population.

- If p represents the frequency of a dominant allele and q the frequency of a recessive allele, then $p + q = 1$. p and q are impossible to measure because heterozygotes and homozygous dominants have the same phenotype.

- The **Hardy-Weinberg equation** can be solved to give the genotypes by observing the number of individuals with the recessive phenotype (homozygous recessives): $p^2 + 2pq + q^2 = 1$. The Hardy-Weinberg equilibrium only occurs where the gene frequencies are **stable**, i.e. the population is not evolving.

- Factors which result in evolution in a population are:

  non-random mating, where the phenotype affects the chances of mating

  small isolated populations, where unusual genes have a greater effect than would normally be the case due to the **founder effect**

  gene flow – migration to or interbreeding with different populations

  mutations – changes in alleles.

- **Natural selection** results in an increase in the proportion of advantageous alleles in a population.

- **Stabilising selection** maintains advantageous characteristics already present in a population.

- **Directional selection** results in a change to a new phenotype better suited to a changing environment.

- **Diversifying selection** results in different subpopulations with their own phenotypes suited to different habitats.

- **Balancing selection** maintains variety, where a disadvantageous allele is kept in a population, e.g. by being advantageous in the heterozygous state.

- **Speciation**, or the formation of new species, may occur when a population is broken up and parts of it are isolated from each other, be it geographically or in some other way that prevents then breeding together. Over time, the separated populations evolve differently, to the point that if reunited they could no longer interbreed.

QUESTIONS

1 Define the following terms and give examples where appropriate:
  - **a** adaptation
  - **b** gene pool
  - **c** population
  - **d** allele frequency
  - **e** genetic equilibrium
  - **f** founder effect.

2 **a** What conditions must operate to maintain the Hardy-Weinberg equilibrium?
  b Do these conditions occur in nature?
  c What conclusions can you draw from your answers to **a** and **b**?

3 What is meant by the term 'natural selection'? Explain how it is implicated in the evolution of new species.

 ## ISLAND ARKS

Islands have played an important part in the development of biology as we know it today. The islands of the Galapagos archipelago fascinated Charles Darwin and were instrumental in the development of his theory of evolution through natural selection. Wallace, Darwin's fellow thinker in evolution, was similarly inspired by the plants and animals of the Indonesian Spice Islands.

Unique and fragile ecosystems

Islands, because of their geographical isolation, tend to have a rich variety of plants and animals not seen anywhere else. Because they are often relatively small in size, island ecosystems are extremely vulnerable to interference and damage by humans. Out of a recorded 484 animal extinctions in the last 400 years, 75% of them have been of island species. An analysis of modern species under threat shows that one in six of all plant species grow on oceanic islands, and 33% of these are threatened with extinction. Of all bird species, 17% are confined to islands, and 23% of these are at risk. In the Pacific islands alone 110 species of bird face possible extinction.

The Solomon Islands – biodiversity at risk

There is a global move to preserve biodiversity – everyone is becoming increasingly concerned about the loss of species to extinction all over the world. Many ecosystems and habitats are at risk, and it is impossible to save them all. How do we decide where to act? Increasingly some scientists are arguing that conservation efforts should be concentrated in island areas such as the Solomon Islands.

The Solomon Islands are a little-known archipelago off the eastern tip of the much bigger island of New Guinea. There is evidence of much speciation and population variation between the islands, even though some of them are only 40–50 km apart. They contain a number of the rarest fruit bat species in the world, and all but one of the five species of monkey-faced flying foxes are found only in the Solomons. They carry an astonishing variety of bird life. Plants are prolific too – so far 230 species of orchid have been recorded and 50 per cent of these are unique to the Solomons. But island species such as these have a small gene pool, and they have nowhere else to go if their habitat is threatened. When people begin to clear areas of forest to build hotels or to use the timber, or deepen natural harbours to take larger boats, there is not enough alternative habitat for the island flora and fauna, and so they are at risk of dying out. Species that are introduced to a small island by humans can also wreak untold damage. The ground-nesting chisel pigeon of the Solomon Islands, the most spectacular bird of the area, is already extinct following the introduction of pet cats. The unique giant rats of the islands, the emperor rat and the king rat, which can grow as long as 34 cm, are also threatened by the cat population. Some of the rare bats are dying because of a new disease which seems to have arrived with some imported coconut plants. But scientists are working with the local people to try and establish sustainable use of the forests and teach them an appreciation of the importance of the biodiversity of the islands. By saving small island ecosystems, with their rich variety of unique animals and plants, and also other areas of specific biological interest such as the mangrove swamps of India, we may be able to preserve at least some of the habitats and thus the diversity of living organisms on the planet Earth.

Figure 1 Perhaps the best known of all extinctions, the dodo lived on the island of Mauritius until it was hunted to extinction by sailors.

Figure 2 The Solomon Islands – home to many species found nowhere else in the world.

6.3 Ecology

In our society the term 'ecology' often carries emotive meaning. It may conjure up pictures of brave (or foolhardy) conservationists in small rubber dinghies sailing in front of ships carrying toxic waste. It may be associated with earnest biologists, frequently sporting bushy beards and sandals and eating a vegetarian diet. Ecology is intimately linked in the public mind with the best and the worst of our efforts to undo some of the damage human beings have inflicted on our planet. These images are far from the true definition of ecology. The word comes from the Greek *oikos* meaning 'house', and ecology is the study of the interactions that determine the distribution and abundance of organisms within a particular environment. Information gained from the study of ecology may be useful to those involved in conservation, but ecology and conservation are not the same.

Figure 6.3.1 The largest ecosystem is the biosphere. It has many parts, each of which can be considered as an ecosystem in its own right. These range from the frozen Arctic wastes to the richness of a tropical rainforest, from the depths of an underground cave to a lush grassy meadow. All the ecosystems within the biosphere are dependent on the input of energy from the Sun.

Ecosystems

What is an ecosystem?

An **ecosystem** is a life-supporting environment. It includes all the living organisms interacting together, the nutrients cycling through the habitats in the system, and the physical and chemical environment in which the organisms are living. An ecosystem consists of a network of several habitats and the communities associated with them (see box below). Particular emphasis is placed on the energy flows and links between the various components of the ecosystem. The largest ecosystem is the **biosphere** – the life-supporting seas, soils and atmosphere of the planet Earth and the organisms which live upon it, as illustrated in figure 6.3.1.

The terminology of ecology

Figure 6.3.2 Within a diverse habitat such as a tropical rainforest, many different populations of organisms live interdependently as part of a complex community. These populations occupy all the available niches, unless circumstances change either to create a new niche or to empty an old one, when different species may enter the ecosystem.

Like any other area of scientific study, ecology has its own specific terms. Here are definitions of some of the most common terms you will meet.

- **Environment** – the overall physical features of a biome or ecosystem (although the term is often used very generally in everyday language.
- **Habitat** – the place where an organism lives. An organism's habitat can be considered as its address. Examples of habitats include a freshwater pond, a deciduous woodland or a rocky seashore. Many organisms live and move only in a small part of a particular habitat, such as a tree in a woodland or a rock on the seashore, and these are referred to as **microhabitats**.
- **Population** – a group of organisms, all of the same species, living together in a particular habitat. The three-spined sticklebacks in a particular pond and the skin mites in your mattress are examples of populations.
- **Community** – the total of all the populations of animals and plants living in a habitat at any one time. For example, in a habitat such as a rock pool there will be populations of seaweeds of various types, of sea anemones, of shrimps, of small fish such as gobies, and of crabs to name but a few. This collection of populations makes up a community.
- **Niche** – the ecological niche of an organism is difficult to define. It can best be described as the role of the organism in the community, its way of life. If the habitat is the address of the organism, the niche describes its profession. A niche can be broken down into specific elements, for example the **food niche** or the **habitat niche**.
- **Biome** – one of the world's major ecosystems – grasslands, forests, deserts and oceans are a few examples.
- **Abiotic factors** – these make up the non-living elements of the habitat of an organism. Abiotic factors include the amount of sunlight and rainfall experienced by a habitat, the water currents in an aquatic habitat, and all the chemical nutrients available to organisms along with the pH of a habitat. Abiotic factors can determine the ability of an organism to succeed within a particular habitat.
- **Biotic factors** – these are the living elements of a habitat which affect the ability of a group of organisms to survive there. For example, the presence of suitable prey species will affect the numbers of predators in a habitat.

Biomes – the major ecosystems

The biosphere is, as we have said, the largest ecosystem associated with the planet Earth. However, the biosphere is so large that it is very difficult to study as a whole. The biosphere is divided into smaller ecosystems, each readily visible around the planet. These major ecosystems or biomes are frequently further subdivided many times for ease of study. The major biomes around the world are shown in figure 6.3.3, and a summary of their features follows.

Tropical rainforests

Tropical rainforests have become part of our everyday language through high-profile international conservation efforts. Tropical rainforests occur at low latitudes where the rain falls abundantly all year long and the temperature is warm. The high humidity, warmth and sunlight provide ideal growing conditions so that trees grow very tall, supporting many species of orchids,

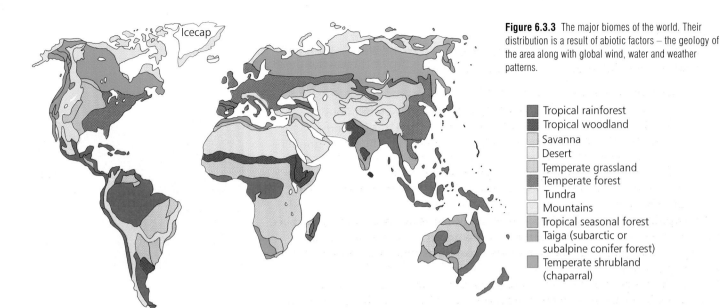

Figure 6.3.3 The major biomes of the world. Their distribution is a result of abiotic factors – the geology of the area along with global wind, water and weather patterns.

- ■ Tropical rainforest
- ■ Tropical woodland
- □ Savanna
- □ Desert
- □ Temperate grassland
- ■ Temperate forest
- □ Tundra
- □ Mountains
- □ Tropical seasonal forest
- ■ Taiga (subarctic or subalpine conifer forest)
- ■ Temperate shrubland (chaparral)

vines and fungi. Animal species tend to be concentrated either in the canopy 40 m or so above the ground, or on the forest floor, which is relatively clear of vegetation because very little light penetrates the dense canopy. There is a great richness and diversity of species in tropical rainforests.

Tropical seasonal forests

Tropical seasonal forests occur where the climate is rather drier than in areas of rainforest. The trees may lose their leaves when the drier seasons come, so the rate of growth is lower than in the rainforests, but these forests are nevertheless a very diverse ecosystem.

Savannas and tropical woodlands

Savannas are the great tropical grasslands, well known in Africa. The driest savannas consist almost entirely of grasses, though with increasing rainfall they support increasing numbers of trees until they merge into **tropical woodlands**. Savannas support enormous herds of grazing animals and their predators, as well as many invertebrate species. Tropical woodlands are made up largely of thornwoods, bushes and trees such as the *Acacia* protected with long spines. They grow rapidly during the short rainy seasons but then frequently lose their leaves and grow very little during the dry seasons.

Deserts

Deserts are areas of very little rainfall. Some are almost entirely barren, while others have seasonal rainfall and so can support some vegetation. Relatively few species can cope with the extremes of a habitat such as a desert and most have very specific adaptations to allow them to succeed in harsh conditions.

Temperate grasslands, shrublands and forests

Temperate grasslands are similar to savannas but occur in cooler climates. Examples are the American prairies, the Eurasian steppes and the pampas of Argentina. They usually have rich, deep soil and are often used for human agriculture. **Temperate shrublands** grow where there are hot, dry summers and cool, wet winters. **Temperate forests** include deciduous and evergreen forests but contain far fewer species than a tropical rainforest.

Figure 6.3.4 The grasslands of the savannas support large herbivores and large carnivores in clearly defined predator–prey relationships.

Taiga and tundra

Taiga is evergreen forest which is found in subarctic and subalpine conditions. The number of tree species found is usually very low – two or three – but there is a greater variety of animal life, frequently including animals such as wolves, elk, moose and jays.

Tundra is found in the Arctic and on the world's highest mountains. It consists of treeless plains with grasses, lichens, sedges and mosses as the predominant species. Many migrants use the tundra during the short summers.

Aquatic biomes

As well as land biomes, there are several aquatic biomes. **Freshwater biomes** include **lentic** (lake and pond) communities and **lotic** (stream communities). **Marine biomes** include **shorelines** both sandy and rocky, **marshes**, **coral reefs**, **open ocean** communities and **benthic** communities (bottom dwellers).

This brief review of some of the major ecosystems shows something of the variety of habitats existing on the Earth. The make-up of a habitat is affected both by the climate – the wind, rainfall and sunlight it receives – and by the populations of living organisms which make that habitat their home. For any ecosystem to survive there must be a through-flow of energy and a renewal of resources. We shall consider these vital aspects of an ecosystem next.

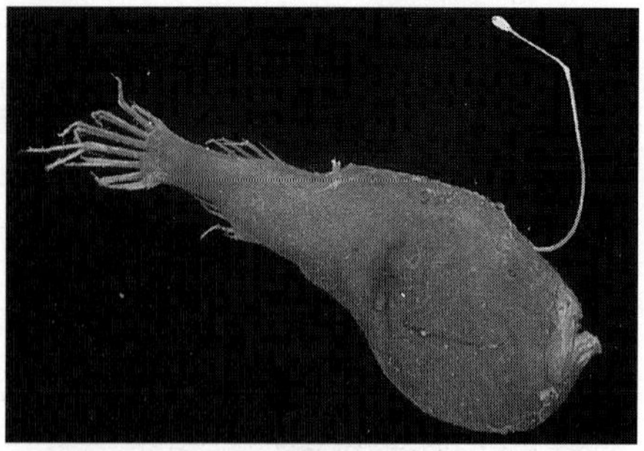

Figure 6.3.5 The biome of the deep ocean is one of the least understood. Many of the species show strange adaptations to their extreme environment, and there are probably many other populations as yet undiscovered in this major ecosystem.

The evolution of ecosystems

How ecosystems evolve

The major biomes just described are the results of processes occurring over long stretches of time, changing the original bare rock of the Earth into the ecosystems of today. This change has been brought about by **succession**, a process by which communities of animals and plants colonise an area and then over time are replaced by other, more varied organisms. Succession can be observed everywhere – the species composition of the community of any habitat is gradually changing all the time.

New communities are usually started by plant species known as **opportunists** or **pioneers**. These plants interact with the abiotic environment and thus change the habitat. Other organisms, both plants and animals, then enter the community until finally a stable community is reached. This is known as the **climax**. The complete sequence of succession is sometimes called a **sere**, with the different stages of the succession called **seral stages**. There are two main types of succession, **primary succession** and **secondary succession**, which we shall go on to look at in more detail.

Primary succession

Primary succession occurs from the starting point of bare rock. This type of succession is seen after the eruption of a volcano or a landslide, or after the emergence of a new volcanic island such as Surtsey. The first organisms are known as **pioneer species** and usually include lichens, algae and mosses which can penetrate the rock surface and trap organic material to begin the formation of humus. Other pioneer species such as grasses and ferns then take advantage of the pockets of soil formed, and the death and decay of several generations of these pioneers adds to the accumulating soil, as shown in figure 6.3.6. More water and nutrients gradually become available for plant roots so that other species can survive and the succession moves on. Gradually the diversity of species increases and larger plants can be supported. An increasingly diverse assortment of animals also colonises the environment, changing along with the dominant plant types. Eventually a climax community is reached, where the species are regarded as being stable until the environment changes again.

A specialised form of primary succession is aquatic succession when a lake or pond silts up and a new terrestrial habitat is formed. Although in the formation of the biosphere primary succession must have been of prime importance, today it is relatively rare as volcanic eruptions and earthquakes are not everyday events in most parts of the world.

Volcanic eruptions result in bare rocks on which a primary succession starts.

The appearance of mosses and lichens on bare rock is the beginning of a primary succession.

A few years after the emergence of bare rocks an increasing diversity of plant species is beginning to colonise the new habitat.

Figure 6.3.6 Primary succession is the gradual progression from bare rock to a full and diverse ecosystem such as a woodland, coral reef or tundra. The first stages are illustrated here.

Secondary succession

Secondary succession is the evolution of an ecosystem from bare existing soil, as illustrated in figure 6.3.7. It occurs as rivers shift their courses, after fires and floods and after disturbances caused by humans. The sequence of events is very similar to that seen in primary succession, but because the soil is already formed there are much larger numbers of plants and animals present at the beginning of the succession.

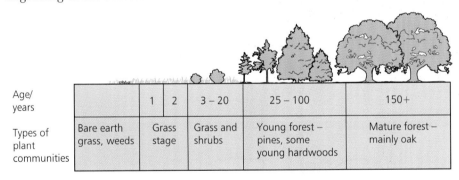

Age/ years		1	2	3 – 20	25 – 100	150+
Types of plant communities	Bare earth grass, weeds	Grass stage		Grass and shrubs	Young forest – pines, some young hardwoods	Mature forest – mainly oak

Figure 6.3.7 The stages of a secondary succession from bare earth to an oak woodland are shown here. The time scale is very approximate – it will depend on many factors including rainfall and temperature – but the types of plants found at different stages can be seen. The types of plants found at the end of a secondary succession vary greatly. Simply digging a patch of earth and leaving it allows the beginnings of a secondary succession to be observed.

All ecosystems are dynamic and change over time. These 'successions' do not always start from bare earth or bare soil. If any piece of land becomes abandoned, most of the stages of a secondary succession will be seen. Grassland, farmland, parks, even houses or whole villages, if left for around 100–150 years, will evolve into a climax community. All over the country are examples of this, such as a few ruined brick walls remaining among the trees to stand witness to a thriving community of many years ago.

Farming the land results in a **deflected succession** – instead of progressing towards a climax community, the ecosystem is kept the same. Most of the hard work of farming goes towards preventing natural succession from taking place, and when that control of the land ceases the natural sequence rapidly follows.

Figure 6.3.8 Fires frequently denude areas of heath, moor and forest of their vegetation. Pioneer plants such as this rosebay willow herb are adapted to germinate rapidly and take advantage of the newly created habitat.

6

Climax communities

The final community of plants at the end of an ecological succession is known as the **climax community**. A climax community is stable and reproduces itself, and it is the most productive group of plants that the particular environment can sustain. It will be rich in species variety. In 1916 F. E. Clements proposed the idea that climate is the major factor in determining the make-up of the climax community in a particular place. He said that for any given climate, there was only one possible climax community, and that this should be known as the **climatic climax community**. This view has been modified over time, with the recognition that many factors interact to determine any given climax. So a climatic climax community is now defined as one that stands the test of time – it is the final climax community for that location and it remains stable over many years.

However, in the modern landscape there are many examples of another type of climax. These climaxes are stable, reproduce themselves and have stayed the same over many years – but they are not entirely natural. People have intervened in the landscape – clearing woodland, grazing domestic animals and so on – and this has changed the ultimate climax community. A final community like this that is partly the result of human management is known as a **plagioclimax**. Examples include chalk grassland and lowland heaths. Much of the British countryside today, even many of our woodlands, are plagioclimax communities rather than climatic climaxes.

Succession in the sand dunes

Observing succession is not easy, because it occurs over very many years. However, Gibraltar Point on the east coast of England is one of several places where sand dunes hold a complete record of the stages of the succession. The oldest dunes, those furthest from the sea, are in the late stages of the succession. Nearest to the sea are the youngest, newly formed dunes which are in the very earliest stages of the ecological succession process. The gradual change from sand to a more mature soil, and the differences in the plants and animals making up the communities populating each habitat, can readily be observed in figure 6.3.9.

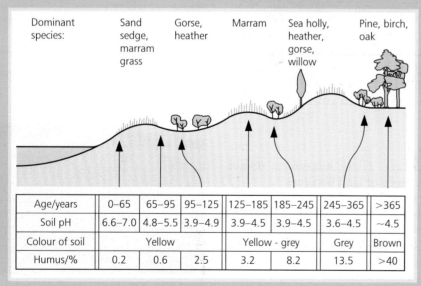

Age/years	0–65	65–95	95–125	125–185	185–245	245–365	>365
Soil pH	6.6–7.0	4.8–5.5	3.9–4.9	3.9–4.5	3.9–4.5	3.6–4.5	~4.5
Colour of soil	Yellow			Yellow - grey		Grey	Brown
Humus/%	0.2	0.6	2.5	3.2	8.2	13.5	>40

Figure 6.3.9 Studying sand dunes shows how the plants growing at each stage alter the environment and make it suitable for different plants in the later stages.

Diversity and the stability of ecosystems

When studying an ecosystem, one of the best ways of determining the type of ecosystem and the health of the ecosystem is to measure the variety of organisms living in it. The **diversity index** measures both the number of different species in the ecosystem and also the population numbers of each there. The following formula gives the diversity index:

$$d = \frac{N(N-1)}{\Sigma n(n-1)}$$

where:

d = diversity index

N = the total number of organisms of all species

n = the total number of organisms of each individual species.

A simple example is shown below.

In a sample from a stream, the species shown in table 6.3.1 were found.
The diversity index for this sample is calculated as follows:

$$d = \frac{40 \times 39}{(4 \times 3) + (12 \times 11) + (3 \times 2) + (4 \times 3) + (17 \times 16)}$$

$$= \frac{1560}{12 + 132 + 6 + 12 + 272}$$

Diversity index = 3.60

The higher the value of the index, the greater the variety of living organisms found in the area.

In general, when an environment has extreme conditions and is difficult to live in, the diversity of the organisms living there is low. Abiotic factors dominate the population numbers, determining both the abundance of the organisms and their distribution. This type of ecosystem tends to be unstable and susceptible to change. A particularly severe frost, a flood or a new bacterium could devastate or even wipe out one or more populations. Equally such an environment is likely to have unfilled niches, so that an incoming organism might rapidly become established and overpower an existing species if they are competing for food or territory. In such an ecosystem with little species diversity, a small change in a population will have a relatively large effect. This sort of ecosystem might be seen in the early stages of the colonisation of new land, or of bare earth, or in areas of the world where conditions are particularly harsh, such as the Arctic or the deep sea vents.

On the other hand, in less hostile environments the diversity of organisms will be very high. Biotic factors rather than abiotic will determine the numbers and distribution of the different organisms. High diversity results in a stable ecosystem, because a new species moving in or out will have little effect on the overall picture. If one species suffers a setback, another is ready to step in and take over its niche. The most stable and diverse ecosystems are usually climax communities. During the process of succession towards the climax, succeeding types of organisms make the physical environment less and less hostile and so diversity increases.

Species	Number of organisms
Stickleback	4
Mosquito larvae	12
Water boatman	3
Pond skater	4
Cyclops	17
Total number of organisms:	**40**

Table 6.3.1 Data used for calculating the diversity index.

The idea of energy transfer

In the 1920s a young Oxford biologist called Charles Elton began to study the relationships between the animals in the Arctic tundra of Bear Island (off the northern coast of Norway) and the scarce food resources there. The relatively few available plant food species probably made his study easier and more effective than studying a more diverse habitat. The main carnivores he observed were the arctic foxes, which ate birds such as sandpipers and ptarmigan. These birds, mainly summer migrants, ate the leaves and berries of the tundra plants or, in some cases, ate insects which in turn fed on the plants. Elton referred to this series of feeding interactions between organisms as a **food chain**.

A model for a food chain

Elton then proposed a general model for a food chain. The first stage involves the trapping of solar energy by a plant in photosynthesis. Some of the energy from the Sun is converted into stored chemical energy within the structure of the plant cells and for this reason plants are known as **producers**. This energy is then passed on from the plant to the herbivore (known as a **primary consumer**) which eats it. The energy within the herbivore is, in its turn, passed on to the carnivore (a **secondary consumer**) which eats the plant eater, and this continues along the chain. At the end of every chain are the **decomposers**, bacteria and fungi which break down the remains of animals and plants and return the mineral nutrients to the soil. From here they will be absorbed again and recycled into new plant material. Each link in the food chain represents a specific **trophic** (or feeding) **level**, as shown in figure 6.3.10.

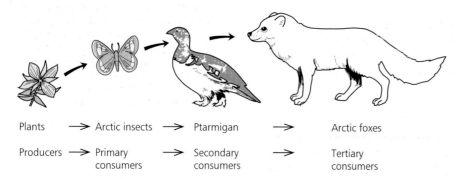

| Plants | → | Arctic insects | → | Ptarmigan | → | Arctic foxes |
| Producers | → | Primary consumers | → | Secondary consumers | → | Tertiary consumers |

Figure 6.3.10 A food chain is the simplest representation of the feeding relationships and therefore the energy flow within an ecosystem.

Food webs within an ecosystem

The description of a food chain makes sense and is relatively simple to understand. It is easy to think of all the organisms in a habitat taking part in a whole range of food chains. However, further thought suggests that this must be an oversimplification. Few animals eat only one single food – giant pandas eating only bamboo and koala bears feeding only on eucalyptus are two of a small number of examples. Most animals have a variety of food sources and exist not in simple food chains but as part of complex interconnected **food webs**. This is precisely what Elton went on to observe on Bear Island and a representation of some of the feeding relationships he observed is shown in figure 6.3.11.

In situations involving a simple food chain, such as the giant panda with its diet almost exclusively of bamboo, the ecosystem is very easily destroyed. Any event which reduces the availability of the bamboo will also threaten the

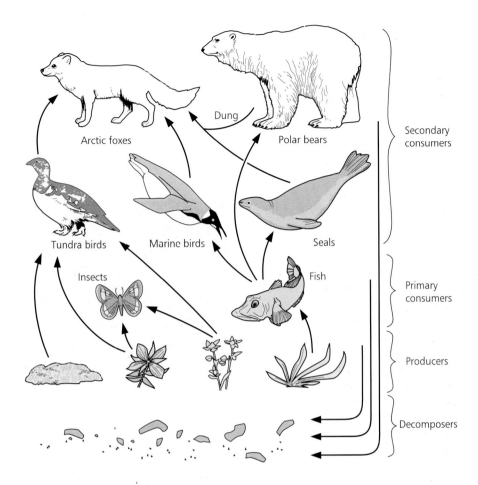

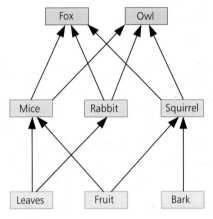

Figure 6.3.11 A food web is a complex system of interrelated food chains. This example of a food web from a tundra biome is still very much simplified, but begins to show how energy moves through the system.

Figure 6.3.12 A web such as this simplified one for an English deciduous woodland represents a relatively stable system. For example, when rabbits were decimated by myxomatosis, owls did not die out but survived by eating more of their other prey species. Whilst squirrels and mice were more heavily predated as a result, they also gained the benefit of reduced competition for plant resources so they in turn could reproduce more successfully. Thus the change in the rabbit population did not, in the long term, inflict any major damage on the rest of the community.

pandas, making them very vulnerable to habitat destruction. When an organism is part of a complex food web a change in any one component, whilst potentially affecting the balance of the ecosystem, is far less likely to have catastrophic effects and so the system will be more stable, as illustrated in figure 6.3.12.

Ecological pyramids

Since Elton first began to consider the transfer of energy through ecosystems, much work has been done in a wide variety of habitats to look at the feeding relationships between the members of the various communities. A common observation is that in most communities there appear to be more plants than herbivores, more herbivores than small carnivores, more small carnivores than large carnivores, and so on. These observations are represented at their simplest as a **pyramid of numbers**, as in figure 6.3.13.

However, in many instances a simple pyramid of numbers is not helpful in demonstrating the flow of energy through an ecosystem. For example, a single rose bush will support a very large population of aphids which in turn will be eaten by a smaller population of ladybirds and hoverfly larvae, which are the prey of a few birds. A more realistic picture is gained by considering a **pyramid of biomass**. This shows the combined mass of all the organisms in a particular habitat measured in grams. Either wet or dry biomass may be used – dry mass eliminates the inaccuracy of variable water content but involves destroying the material. To avoid destruction of the habitat a small sample is usually taken and measured and the total biomass of the population then calculated. It is much more time consuming to produce a pyramid of biomass than a simple

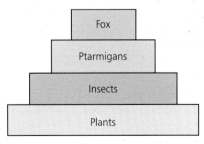

Figure 6.3.13 For the simplified food chain showing the feeding relationships on Bear Island a pyramid of numbers such as this can be built up. The number of individuals falls as we move further along the chain.

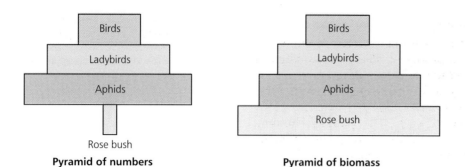

Pyramid of numbers   Pyramid of biomass

Figure 6.3.14 Considering the biomass of the organisms rather than their physical numbers gives a more accurate picture of what happens in the food chain.

pyramid of numbers, but it gives much more accurate information about what is happening in an ecosystem, as figure 6.3.14 shows.

Even pyramids of biomass do not always supply us with the information we need about a particular ecosystem. For example, when a sample of water from the English Channel is analysed and the biomass of the organisms found, there appears to be a greater mass of zooplankton than of the phytoplankton on which it feeds. The reason for this is that the sample represents a picture of the water only at the moment the sample is taken – it is in effect a still photograph of the ecosystem. What is really needed is a moving film of the system, and a repeated sampling procedure shows that the phytoplankton reproduce much more rapidly than the zooplankton. Thus although the total population of phytoplankton at any one time (the **standing crop**) is smaller than that of the zooplankton, the turnover of phytoplankton is much higher and so the biomass over a period of time is greater. An analogy is a bowling green. The smooth closely cropped grass does not seem to represent a very large standing crop of grass. But at the height of the growing season a bowling green will be cut several times a week, and only if all the piles of grass clippings are taken into account will the true productivity of the grass be seen. A pyramid made up from observations taken over time is called a **pyramid of energy** and this gives the most accurate picture of energy flows within an ecosystem, as figure 6.3.16 shows.

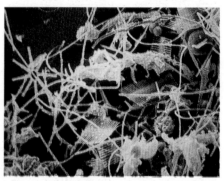

Figure 6.3.15 When we think of plants capturing the energy of the Sun, we tend to think of land plants, but phytoplankton such as these produce vast amounts of biomass by photosynthesis.

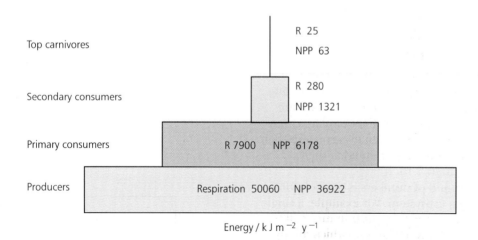

R = respiration, NPP = net primary production (see text)

Figure 6.3.16 A pyramid of energy such as this one for a pond ecosystem in Florida is difficult to produce, as it makes allowances for energy gains and losses over a period of time, but it gives the most accurate picture of the energy flows within a food chain or web.

Energy relationships within ecosystems

The transfer of energy through an ecosystem leads to the accumulation of biomass as new plant and animal material is produced. There are two kinds of production in an ecosystem – **primary production** is the synthesis and storage of organic molecules as a result of photosynthesis, and **secondary production** is the processing and storage of organic material by herbivores and carnivores. All the consumers in a food chain ultimately depend on the photosynthesisers for energy. The rate at which producers convert the Sun's energy into organic material determines the flow of energy within an ecosystem.

As we have seen in section 3.1, only a very small percentage of the energy from the Sun is transferred into plant material. Similarly, not all the organic material produced by photosynthesis is available to secondary consumers. Only about 10% of the material is passed on, the remainder being dispersed in a variety of ways, mainly by respiration and metabolism. Thus the net rate of production can be described as:

$$\text{Net primary production} = \text{gross primary production} - \text{respiration and metabolism}$$

The **net primary production** or **NPP** of different biomes has been estimated and is shown in table 6.3.2. The enormous productivity of the tropical rainforests can clearly be seen. Although only about 5% of the surface of the Earth is covered by tropical rainforest, it yields about 28% of the total NPP. For this reason alone the continuous massive deforestation presently taking place is a major cause for concern. The human population of the world is growing at a very rapid rate, as we shall see in section 6.4, and even at its current level humans are consuming up to 40% of the NPP of the planet.

Habitat	Mean net primary production/ $g\ m^{-2}\ y^{-1}$
Terrestrial	
Tropical rainforest	2200
Temperate evergreen forest	1300
Temperate deciduous forest	1200
Savanna	800
Taiga	800
Cultivated land	650
Temperate grassland	600
Tundra and alpine communities	140
Desert and semidesert scrub	90
Extreme desert	3
Aquatic	
Algal beds and coral reefs	2500
Estuaries	1500
Upwelling zones	500
Continental shelf	360
Lake and stream	250
Open ocean	125

Table 6.3.2 Net primary production of a variety of ecosystems (*after R.H. Whittacker*, Communities and Ecosystems, *2nd edition, Macmillan 1975*)

Energy budgets in ecosystems

As in any budget, the outgoings from each trophic level of an ecosystem need to be balanced by the incomings. This means that all the energy entering one trophic level must be accounted for when considering the transfer to the next trophic level. The energy bound up in plant material, the NPP, is transferred to heterotrophs. At this and every subsequent step, relatively little of the energy (around 10%) is used for producing new animal material. What happens to the rest?

As we have seen, the energy used to make a new animal is known as secondary production. Much of the energy passed on from plants to consumer or from one consumer to another is used for respiration, and most of this is consequently transferred to the atmosphere as heat.

Yet more of the energy will be lost as metabolic waste products and heat in the urine of the animal, and as undigested and therefore unused material in the faeces, as illustrated in figure 6.3.17. Thus relatively little of the Sun's energy that reaches the Earth is used to produce plant material, and increasingly small amounts of that energy find their way into the individuals of a food chain or web. This is why the biomass and energy content of a food chain decreases along the chain.

However, the role of the decomposers must not be forgotten in this energy budget. They break down the bodies of animals and plants when they die, thus releasing and utilising much of the energy held within them. Decomposers also feed on and digest the faeces produced by living animals and thus make use of this energy too.

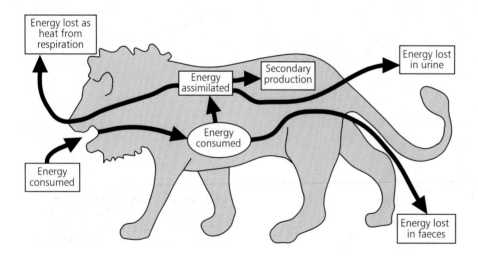

Figure 6.3.17 The fate of the food eaten by a consumer – a lion is shown but the situation is similar in any herbivore, omnivore or carnivore. Much of the food consumed is assimilated by the lion, but only a small proportion (about 2%) is used to produce new lion tissue. Some of the food is never assimilated at all and is simply lost as faeces – this proportion will be significantly larger in a plant-eater than in a carnivore.

The relatively inefficient transfer of energy through food chains and webs limits the number of trophic levels. Usually by the fourth or fifth level at most, harvesting the energy becomes too inefficient to be biologically worthwhile. This is why, for example, the killer whale at the top of a food chain (killer whale → seal → large fish → small fish → shrimp → phytoplankton) has no real predators of its own – an animal large enough to capture and kill a killer whale would need to expend so much energy hunting that it could not realistically survive.

Cycles within ecosystems

An ecosystem is defined as a life-supporting environment which has both living and non-living elements. We have considered the main ecosystems found on Earth, how those ecosystems have evolved by succession, and the transfer of energy through an ecosystem from plants into animals and decomposers. However, for organisms to survive they need other materials as well as the organic compounds we refer to as 'energy'. We shall now consider how inorganic elements cycle through ecosystems and so remain constantly available to all the organisms that require them.

Energy is constantly entering ecosystems from the Sun and then being very inefficiently transferred through food chains and webs. The inefficiency does not matter, as there is a constant supply of energy from the Sun. However, the same is not true for other ingredients of life such as water, and also carbon and nitrogen, vital components of the chemicals which make up the structure of living cells. Complex cycles have evolved which result in the chemical constituents of life being used, and then returned to the various ecosystems of the world to be used again. These cycles involve a **biotic phase** where the inorganic ions are incorporated in the tissues of living things, and an **abiotic phase** where the inorganic ions are returned to the non-living part of the ecosystem.

The carbon cycle

As we saw in sections 1.2 and 1.3, carbon is the element that is crucial to the formation of the complex organic molecules – carbohydrates, proteins, lipids and nucleic acids – which are the building blocks of life. There is a massive pool of carbon in the carbon dioxide present in the atmosphere and dissolved in the water that makes up rivers, lakes and oceans. This carbon dioxide is taken up and the carbon incorporated into plants in the process of photosynthesis. The carbon is then passed into animals through food chains. At all stages, carbon dioxide is returned to the atmosphere or water during the process of respiration and by the actions of decomposers. The interactions of the **carbon cycle** can best be summarised in a diagram such as that shown in figure 6.3.19.

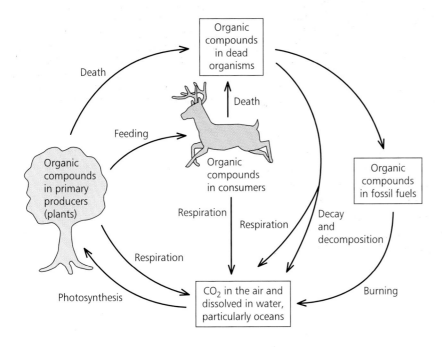

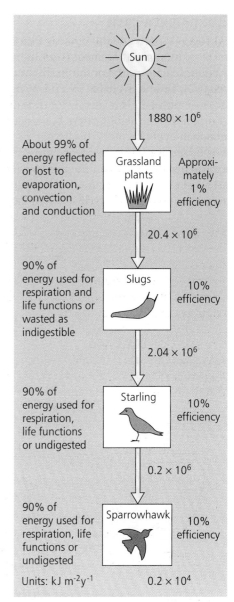

Figure 6.2.18 Living organisms are alone in their ability to convert the energy of the Sun into living tissue, but the process is not particularly efficient because each organism needs to use energy to live.

Figure 6.3.19 The carbon cycle. Left to itself the cycle is self regulating – the oceans act as massive reservoirs of carbon dioxide, absorbing excess when it is produced and releasing it when it is in short supply. However, the enormous increase in the production of carbon dioxide by people is now threatening the balance of the carbon cycle, and the results could be disastrous for many forms of life.

The nitrogen cycle

Nitrogen is probably the limiting factor on the production of new biomass in most ecosystems. It is a vital constituent of amino acids and therefore of proteins. Although almost 80% of the Earth's atmosphere is made up of nitrogen, relatively little is available in a form which can be used by living organisms because nitrogen is relatively inert. It does not naturally combine with other components of the biosphere but is actively 'fixed' by microorganisms. The **nitrogen cycle** involves this 'fixing' of nitrogen from the atmosphere into a form which can be utilised by plants and animals to produce proteins. The nitrogen is eventually released from the tissues of living things and returned to the atmosphere by the action of more microorganisms, the decomposers. The main stages in the nitrogen cycle are summarised in figure 6.3.20.

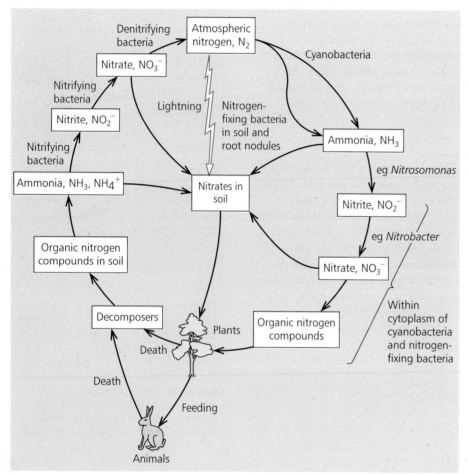

Figure 6.3.20 The nitrogen cycle. Nitrogen from the air is fixed by bacteria, then processed through plants, animals and more bacteria before being returned to the atmosphere.

The majority of plants obtain their nitrates from the soil. The nitrogen in the air is converted or **fixed** into useful nitrates in several ways. This nitrogen fixation is an energy-requiring process – it uses ATP. Nitrogen fixation is carried out by **nitrifying bacteria** and, to a much smaller extent, by the action of lightning on the atmosphere. The bacteria involved include cyanobacteria and organisms such as the *Rhizobium* bacteria in the root nodules of leguminous plants. The product of the initial stages of nitrogen fixation is ammonia. In the soil ammonia is then rapidly converted to nitrites by bacteria such as *Nitrosomonas* and then to nitrates by other bacteria such as *Nitrobacter*.

In leguminous plants, amino acids are synthesised directly using the ammonia resulting from the initial nitrogen fixation. The nitrates produced by nitrogen fixation are used to form the protein of plant and subsequently animal tissues. The nitrogen is eventually released from the dead and decaying tissues of both plants and animals by the action of yet more bacteria such as *Thiobacillus denitrificans*.

By considering the energy flows within ecosystems and the cycling of essential nutrients, we can build up a picture of some of the factors which influence life within those ecosystems. In section 6.4 we shall consider in more detail the survival of populations within their specific habitats, and the factors influencing their growth or decline.

SUMMARY

- **Ecology** is the study of the interactions that determine the distribution and abundance of organisms within a particular environment. An **ecosystem** is a life-supporting environment consisting of organisms, nutrients and the physical and chemical environments. The biosphere is the largest ecosystem.

- A **habitat** is the place where an organism lives. A **population** is a group of organisms of the same species living in a habitat. A **community** is all the different populations living in a habitat. The ecological **niche** of an organism describes its role in the community. **Abiotic factors** make up the non-living elements of a habitat, and **biotic factors** its living elements.

- A **biome** is one of the world's major ecosystems.

  The major biomes of the world include:

tropical rainforests	temperate grasslands
tropical seasonal forests	temperate shrublands
savannas	temperate forests
tropical woodlands	taiga
deserts	tundra.

- **Aquatic biomes** include **freshwater biomes** (**lentic** or lake and pond biomes, and **lotic** or stream biomes) and **marine biomes** (shorelines, marshes, coral reefs, open ocean and benthic or bottom-dwelling biomes).

- Ecosystems evolve over long periods of time by a process called **succession**. New communities are started by **pioneers** or **opportunists** which change the habitat so that other organisms can occupy it. After a series of stages or **seres** a stable **climax community** is reached.

- **Primary succession** is the evolution of an ecosystem starting from bare rock, while **secondary succession** starts from bare existing soil.

- A **food chain** represents the feeding relationships between organisms. **Producers** convert solar energy into chemical energy. Producers are eaten by **primary consumers** (herbivores), which in turn are eaten by **secondary consumers** (carnivores). **Decomposers** break down the remains of dead animals and plants. Each link in the chain represents a **trophic level**. Food chains are interconnected in complex **food webs**.

- Feeding relationships can be represented by **pyramids of numbers**, **pyramids of biomass** and most accurately by **pyramids of energy**.

- **Primary production** is the synthesis and storage of organic molecules by producers, and **secondary production** the processing and storage of organic molecules by consumers. Organic material and therefore energy is dispersed at each trophic level, in the processes of respiration and metabolism, such that only about 10% of the energy gained by the organisms at one trophic level is passed on to the organisms of the next trophic level. This limits the number of trophic levels in a food chain.

- **Net primary production** (NPP) of a biome = gross primary production − (respiration + metabolism).

- Supplies of inorganic materials on the Earth are finite, and such materials are recycled through ecosystems. These cycles involve a **biotic phase** where the materials are incorporated into the bodies of living organisms, and an **abiotic phase** where they are returned to the non-living part of the ecosystem.

- In the **carbon cycle** the abiotic phase is carbon dioxide in the air and dissolved in the oceans. Photosynthesis fixes carbon in organic compounds, which are then eaten by consumers. Respiration, death of plants and animals and decay by decomposers, and combustion of fossil fuels all recycle carbon dioxide.

- In the **nitrogen cycle** the main abiotic phase is nitrogen gas in the atmosphere. This is turned via a series of stages involving **nitrogen-fixing microorganisms** to nitrates in the soil. Nitrates are taken in by plants, which form organic nitrogen compounds. Animals eat these, and death and decay of plants and animals results in organic nitrogen compounds in the soil. The action of **denitrifying microorganisms** returns nitrogen to the air, again via a series of stages.

QUESTIONS

1 a What is meant by the term:
  i ecosystem
  ii community
  iii niche
  iv biome?
  b Select three of the major biomes of the Earth, and for each describe its main features.
  c Discuss the interactions between the living and non-living components of any ecosystem.

2 a What is meant by the term 'ecological succession'?
  b What is the difference between primary succession and secondary succession?
  c Describe an example of:
  i primary succession
  ii secondary succession.

3 Explain how energy flows through an ecosystem, using food webs and ecological pyramids in your answer.

Developing Key Skills

Plans for a major bypass around the nearest town mean that a small river will have to be re-routed and an area of climax woodland will be cut down. You are chairing the local action group set up to object to the plans and have been invited to speak on the local radio station to outline your main objections against the proposed bypass and explain how the campaign hopes to stop the building of the road.

Plan your talk and if possible record it. Be prepared for a studio debate to follow.

MIRACULOUS JOURNEYS

One of the most dramatic ways in which populations change is in **migration**. Whole populations of animals appear or disappear over a short space of time.

Summer birds, winter visitors

Swallows are perhaps the best known summer visitors to the UK. In early spring these graceful birds begin arrive in flocks, and by the end of April they are a common sight in the countryside where they build their nests and breed. In late September and October the days become noticeably shorter, and the evening temperature begins to drop quite sharply, leading in many places to early frosts. Annual plants are killed off and the number of flying insects begins to fall. All of these changes have an impact on the swallows, particularly the day length which affects the secretions of the pineal gland. The birds are seen in large flocks on telegraph wires and then suddenly, they have gone. They fly non-stop, feeding as they fly, all the way to South Africa where they overwinter before, in response to further environmental cues, they make the return flight to the UK the next year. Africa is the overwintering place of a great number of British summer birds, including blackcaps, chiffchaffs, whitethroats and sand martins.

Thanks to the warm waters of the Gulf Stream, the UK enjoys a relatively mild winter climate. So just when many summer birds are leaving Britain many other species are arriving from colder places such as Iceland, Greenland, Siberia and Finland to take advantage of our 'warm' winters. These birds include many species of ducks and geese, as well as songbirds. The trigger that stimulates these birds to migrate is also shortening day length, but ambient temperature plays an important role as well – as temperatures begin to plummet, migration begins.

Migration involves a long and dangerous journey, with such hazards as being blown off course by storms, losing direction and starvation. It puts an enormous strain on the physiological resources of the animals, particularly summer visitors that start to breed straight after arriving. The advantage is, of course, that the animals are in a place where food is more abundant and conditions are more favourable for survival. Natural selection ensures that animals only migrate when the pay-off is worth the cost, so birds of the same species may be migratory in some parts of the country and not in others. For example, song thrushes in northern Scotland migrate to the Mediterranean in winter, but those living in the warmer south stay in the UK.

Navigating through the sky

How do birds navigate on their great migrations? Evidence suggests they use the magnetic field of the Earth along with the position of the Sun to help them find their way. There also seems to be an annual clock mechanism which prepares birds twice a year, in spring and autumn, for their massive flights, and innate behaviour patterns are also very important. The great migratory journeys produce some of the most fascinating population shifts known, and they will surely be the subject of research for a long time to come.

Figure 1 There is an old country saying 'One swallow doesn't make a summer', but the arrival of these visitors in the UK is a sure sign that summer is on the way.

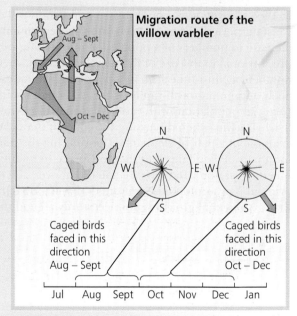

Migration route of the willow warbler

Figure 2 It has been shown that willow warblers have an innate pattern of behaviour. In cages removed from the stimulus of the seasons, they still face south-west for about a month in autumn, long enough to fly from Germany to Spain, and then face south-east for three months, the time needed to fly from Spain to South Africa. Their innate programming gives them both direction and distance – but how this works no one is yet quite sure.

The ecology of populations

A population is a group of individuals of the same species living in the same habitat. For ecologists to develop effective models of how ecosystems work, studying the growth of populations and the factors affecting that growth is extremely important.

Population growth

As far as geneticists are concerned, a population is a group of interbreeding or potentially interbreeding individuals. For the ecologist, the word 'population' has a rather wider meaning – a group of interbreeding organisms that take up or provide a habitat and produce or consume resources. Members of a population occupy a particular ecological niche.

Populations grow, and also become smaller, at various rates – they may be relatively stable for a long period of time, they may grow rapidly or slowly, or they may become extinct. Such growth can be expressed mathematically. Population growth is affected by a wide variety of factors, and as a result the maximum possible rate of growth is rarely achieved.

Exponential growth

In theory, given ideal conditions, a population will double in size during a constant period of time. This is known as **exponential growth**. The rate of increase in numbers of a population undergoing exponential growth is proportional to the size of the population, and when plotted on a graph of numbers against time such a population gives an **exponential growth curve**. Such optimum growth rarely occurs, although it can be seen occasionally in bacterial populations with carefully managed environments, as shown in figure 6.4.1. Darwin, when discussing the concept of exponential growth, used the example of a pair of elephants. Considering the minimum reproductive rate for a pair of elephants and their offspring (6 infants per pair in a 60-year breeding period), Darwin calculated that over 750 years the descendants of an original pair would number around 19 million elephants. Thus it can be seen that exponential growth is not necessarily a good thing!

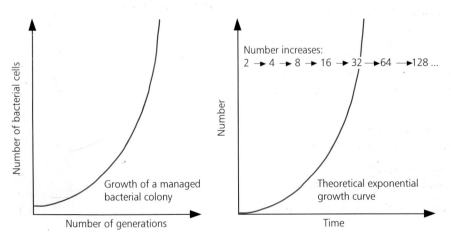

Growth of a managed bacterial colony

Number of generations

Number increases:
2 → 4 → 8 → 16 → 32 → 64 → 128 ...

Theoretical exponential growth curve

Time

Figure 6.4.1 An exponential growth curve for a population of bacteria. The rate of population growth increases as the number of individual bacterial cells, each capable of dividing, increases.

One of the few situations in which natural populations may undergo exponential growth is when colonising a new habitat. Sooner or later, however, the period of exponential growth ends and the population numbers increase more slowly, or even decrease. A look at figure 6.4.2 showing population growth in a variety of organisms demonstrates clearly how far the situation is from exponential growth. Why is this?

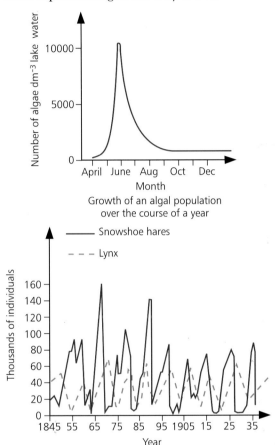

The interrelated populations of snowshoe hares and lynxes in Canada between 1845 and 1935

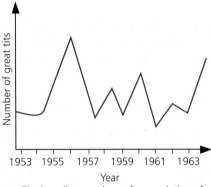

The breeding numbers of a population of great tits in Sweden between 1953 and 1964

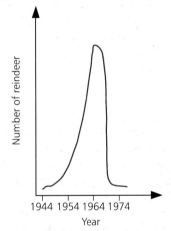

Growth and decline of the reindeer population on a small island in the Bering Sea

Changes in population size

Organisms enter a population either when they are born or by immigration into one group from another. They leave by dying or by emigrating to a different group. These changes affect the **population density**, that is the number of individuals per unit area.

The rate at which organisms are born or die changes according to various factors, largely concerned with the food supply and the build-up of wastes. These two factors have a direct effect on both the reproductive activity and the success of a population (its **birth rate** or **natality**) and also on the **death rate** (**mortality**) of the group:

$$\text{Birth rate} = \frac{\text{number of births}}{\text{number of adults in the population}}$$

$$\text{Death rate} = \frac{\text{number of deaths}}{\text{number of adults in the population}}$$

The effects of immigration and emigration on a population are more complex – see the box that follows.

Figure 6.4.2 The population numbers of these organisms fluctuate in patterns that are very different from the exponential pattern of growth. A variety of factors, both biotic and abiotic, are behind these peaks and troughs of population.

Immigration and emigration

It is easy to consider populations as stable entities, affected only by the birth and death rates of the organisms within them. However, the real-life situation is rather different. Organisms leave and enter a population by means other than birth and death. In plants this happens as a result of successful seed dispersal, and in animals the movement of individuals away from their original population or the movement of new individuals into a population can take place for a variety of reasons. For example, in mammalian populations groups of young adult males tend to leave their original population (emigrate) and subsequently enter another population to find mates (immigrate). Immigration and emigration can be affected by many factors, and because of this unpredictability generalisations cannot readily be made. Each population must be considered separately.

The factors influencing the growth of a population can be divided into two categories – abiotic and biotic. The interaction of these elements of an environment determine how many individuals of a population can live in a given area, as illustrated in figure 6.4.3. The upper limit of the population size, which can never be exceeded on a permanent basis, is known as the **carrying capacity** of the environment.

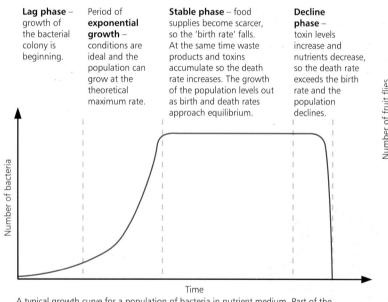

Lag phase – growth of the bacterial colony is beginning.

Period of **exponential growth** – conditions are ideal and the population can grow at the theoretical maximum rate.

Stable phase – food supplies become scarcer, so the 'birth rate' falls. At the same time waste products and toxins accumulate so the death rate increases. The growth of the population levels out as birth and death rates approach equilibrium.

Decline phase – toxin levels increase and nutrients decrease, so the death rate exceeds the birth rate and the population declines.

A typical growth curve for a population of bacteria in nutrient medium. Part of the curve follows the theoretical exponential path, but other factors intervene and the population stabilises and dies.

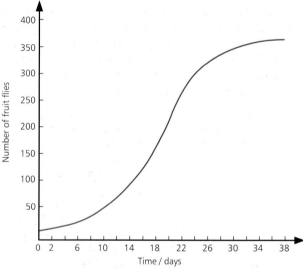

This **logistic growth curve** demonstrates the most common pattern for population growth in a wild population. The early rapid growth phase is replaced by the stable situation, with births and deaths approximately equal. If no other factors intervene the stable phase will occur at the carrying capacity of the environment.

Figure 6.4.3 Common patterns of population growth.

A dramatic example of how the growth of a population can be affected by environmental factors occurred in 1944, when United States coastguards introduced 29 reindeer to a small island in the Bering Sea off the coast of Alaska. The reindeer had plenty of food and no predators whatsoever, and as a result the population numbers climbed steadily until in 1963 there were 6000 animals on the island. However, this number of reindeer strained the food resources of the island – particularly the winter fodder plants – to their limit. The death rate rocketed and the birth rate plummeted. As a result the reindeer population was decimated and in 1966 there were only 42 reindeer left (see figure 6.4.2). In this extreme example, as in all populations, it is the complex interaction of a variety of factors that determines the number of individuals which thrive in a particular environment.

Way Kambas and the Javan rhino

The most endangered species of mammal in the world is the Javan rhino. One group of around 50 individuals inhabits a small peninsula in Java. Although the population is slowly increasing, it is vulnerable to rapid extinction from the outbreak of disease or an eruption of nearby Krakatau.

In a combined operation the Indonesian government, the WWF and the IUCN are hoping to relocate a small breeding nucleus of the rhino to another reserve in Indonesia. Way Kambas, a national park of great importance because of the rare habitats and endangered species it already supports, seems likely to be chosen. Javan rhino used to live there but became extinct in the region in 1961 as a result of poaching. Stricter controls mean that poaching is no longer a major threat. However, before an introduction is attempted, a detailed piece of field research was undertaken in 1993. The aim of this was two-fold – to see if Way Kambas does offer a viable second home to these rarest of mammals, and to attempt to estimate the impact of a rhino introduction on the other endangered species there. These include Asian elephants, Malay tapirs, Sumatran tigers, clouded leopards and white-winged wood duck. What type of questions would need to be asked before the project went ahead, to avoid the possibility of an ecological disaster?

Population distributions

Some populations naturally have high densities, such as nematode worms in rich soil, ants in an ants' nest and people in a city. Other species, for example eagles, cheetahs and polar bears, have very low population densities and individuals are found widely scattered through the habitat. The members of populations are generally found distributed in one of three ways in the environment. These are **clumped**, **uniform** and **scattered** distributions, illustrated and explained in figure 6.4.4.

Clumped species are most common – herds of animals or groups of plants and animals that have specific resource requirements and therefore clump in areas where those resources are found, for example a herd of elephants, a school of dolphins or a stand of pines.

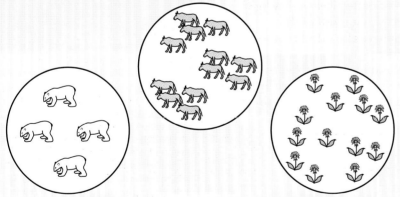

Uniform distribution usually occurs when resources are thinly but evenly spread, or when individuals of a species are antagonistic to each other as in the case of many large carnivores. A territory is often defended for example by bears and hawks.

Random dispersal patterns are the result of plentiful resources and no antagonism, for example dandelions on a lawn.

Figure 6.4.4 Dispersal patterns of different populations of organisms.

We have already seen in figure 6.4.3 that populations tend to grow most rapidly in the earlier stages of their colonisation of an environment. Dense populations have lower birth rates, higher death rates and slower growth than less dense populations, as illustrated in figure 6.4.5. This suggests that there is an optimum population density. Factors affecting the size and therefore the density of the population are in some cases **density dependent**. Predation, disease, parasitism and most importantly competition increase with the density of the population and so control the size of that population. **Density-independent** factors such as earthquakes, unusual extremes of weather and fires also act to control population sizes, but in a much more random and unpredictable way.

Abiotic factors affecting population size

What are abiotic factors?

As we have seen in section 6.3, the abiotic factors affecting a population are the non-living elements of its environment. These include physical factors such as the amount of sunlight, the wind speed and direction, water currents and seasonal variations in rainfall and temperatures, along with chemical factors such as soil pH and the chemical input into the environment by human beings. The distribution of a species will be determined to a large extent by the abiotic factors in the environment. For example, for both plants and animals temperature is frequently the factor which determines whether or not they can grow in a particular environment. There is a range of temperatures at which a particular organism can grow and successfully reproduce, but above or below that range reproduction does not occur even if the organism survives. Abiotic factors exert a density-independent effect on populations – the effect is the same regardless of the numbers of organisms in a particular area.

Light

Light has a more direct effect on the growth of plant populations than on that of animals. Plants are dependent on light for photosynthesis, and so populations living in habitats with low light levels have evolved strategies for coping with this situation. Some plants simply reproduce early, which avoids the shade caused by larger plants, as illustrated in figure 6.4.6. Others have evolved to be able to photosynthesise and reproduce effectively in low light levels. Animals are affected by light levels indirectly as a result of the distribution of food plants, and seasonal light changes also affect reproductive patterns, as we have seen in section 5.2 (page 366).

Some plants that live in shaded situations have larger leaves. Nettles growing in a shady woodland have a much larger average leaf surface area than nettles in open sunlight, and this allows the population to thrive in both habitats as shown in figure 6.4.7.

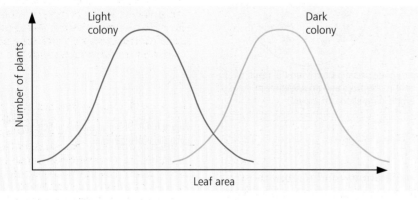

Temperature

The temperature of the environment affects the rate of enzyme-controlled reactions in plants and ectothermic animals. Thus in general populations grow more rapidly in warmer regions. This is demonstrated by the simple

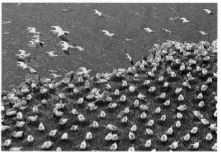

Figure 6.4.5 Population density affects population growth. Many sea birds nest in immense colonies, each with its own very small territorial area. However, if the number of birds in a given area gets too high then reproductive success is affected and egg production drops, as can be seen from the data on great tits in figure 6.4.2.

Figure 6.4.6 Although light levels are generally far higher in summer than they are in early spring, plants growing on the woodland floor are in deep shade in the summer once the tree canopy is fully developed. Thus plants such as bluebells produce leaves very early in the year in spite of low temperatures. They photosynthesise and prepare to reproduce, flowering as insect numbers are increasing with the raised temperatures of late spring. After flowering the plant dies back and becomes dormant through the shaded summer months. This strategy is used by a number of woodland plants to overcome the problem of shading under trees.

Figure 6.4.7 The bell-shaped normal distribution curves show the ranges of leaf areas which might be expected in two different nettle populations. The leaves of nettles grown in the shade are on average considerably larger in area than those of a nettle grown under normal conditions.

experiment of keeping frogspawn in two different situations, some outside and some inside. The spawn inside hatches sooner and the development of the tadpoles is more rapid due to the higher temperature. Similarly, by travelling the length of Britain in early spring the stages of development of plant leaves and flowers can clearly be seen, and the retarding effects of the cooler northern temperatures observed.

The reproductive behaviour of populations is also affected by temperature. Many migratory birds undertake their epic journeys across the world to reach an area where the temperature is suitable for their reproductive patterns.

Wind and water currents

Wind adds to environmental stress, as it increases water and heat loss from the bodies of organisms. In areas with strong prevailing winds the numbers of species which can survive are reduced, and those that do survive have reduced populations. Occasional gales and hurricanes can devastate populations. Whole woodlands may be destroyed along with the communities of plant and animal life within them, as shown in figure 6.4.9.

In water, currents affect the type of organisms that can populate a region, and the numbers within those populations. A strong current will dislodge organisms not well adapted by having a strong attachment or by being extremely good swimmers. Currents are most damaging to populations when the strength increases suddenly, as is the case when flooding occurs.

Water availability

In most aquatic environments the availability of water is not a problem (see section 4.6). In a terrestrial environment the availability of water is affected by a variety of factors including the amount of rainfall, the rate of evaporation and the rate of loss by drainage through the soil. Water is needed for the functioning of the cells of an organism, for excretion and for the transfer of gametes. Any situation of limited water supply will put stress on populations. If the water stress becomes too severe the organisms will die unless, like camels and cacti, they have special adaptations to enable them to cope. Equally, an increase in the availability of water can lead to a massive increase in populations such as that seen in deserts after a long period of drought. After a little rain has fallen, the seeds of many desert plants germinate, grow and flower in a very short space of time, in the phenomenon known as the 'flowering of the desert', as shown in figure 6.4.10.

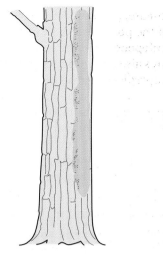

Figure 6.4.8 The higher temperatures on the south side of the tree trunk affect the growth of the mosses and algae colonising the bark – the populations are more successful on the cooler, damper north side. Careful observations in a woodland will show that all tree trunks show a similar pattern of colonisation, the result of the temperature and light differences.

Figure 6.4.9 The wind can cause great damage to populations of both plants and animals, as this picture shows. The damage seen here was caused by very high winds which swept Britain in the autumn of 1987. However, although many populations were greatly depleted or destroyed in the aftermath of the wind, other opportunistic species could take advantage of the new, empty habitats created and their populations increased rapidly.

Figure 6.4.10 The effect of water availability on the ability of populations to survive is graphically illustrated by some of the plants living in the extremely hostile environment of the desert. The seeds survive the hot, dry conditions by remaining dormant for years at a time. Then when water availability suddenly increases after a fall of rain these seeds can progress through germination and growth very rapidly – in a matter of days – to give a large population of reproductive individuals which in turn produce the hardy seeds needed to survive dormant until water becomes available again.

6

Oxygen availability

There is never a shortage of oxygen in the air, but it can be in short supply in both water and the soil. When water is cold, or fast flowing, sufficient oxygen dissolves in it to support life. If the temperature of the water rises or it becomes still and stagnant, then the oxygen content drops and this affects the survival of populations within it.

Similarly, the environment within the soil is usually well aerated. The spaces between the soil particles contain air and so there is plenty of oxygen for the respiration of plant roots and thus the maintenance of plant populations. If the soil becomes waterlogged, the air spaces are filled with water and the plant roots may be deprived of oxygen.

Soil structure and mineral content

The structure of the soil on which organisms live and grow affects the success of the various populations associated with it. Sand has a loose, shifting structure which allows very little to grow on it. Plant populations which are linked together by massive root and rhizome networks can and do survive, reproducing successfully and also binding the sand together, making it more suitable for colonisation by other species. One of the best known organisms for colonising shifting sand in Britain is marram grass. Marram has an extensive interlinked rhizome network and is also, as we have seen in section 4.6 (pages 324–325), well adapted to survive the physiological drought conditions present on the seashore.

Sandy soils are light, easily worked and easily warmed. However, they are also very easily drained. Water passes through them rapidly, carrying with it minerals useful to plants. This leaching of minerals reduces the population density of plants growing in the soil. Conversely, soils made up predominantly of **clay** particles are heavy, cold, hard to work and readily waterlogged as the drainage is very poor. Leaching of minerals is not a problem in soil of this type,

---

Oxygen from water?

The levels of oxygen in fresh water can vary quite considerably, from the high oxygenation of a mountain stream through to the low levels of a stagnant pond. This has led to some diverse adaptations in the invertebrates that live in fresh water.

Many freshwater invertebrates, particularly larval forms, bypass the water altogether as a source of oxygen and rely on breathing tubes which they stick up through the surface. The rat-tailed maggot, larva of the drone fly, has a telescopic breathing tube at its rear end which it can extend up to breathe air. Many mosquito (and other) larvae have adaptations of the spiracles and tracheae of their anus or rectum to breathe air through their bottoms!

Other insects have evolved tracheal systems at the body surface, where they act as gills to obtain oxygen from the water. In the larvae of the midge *Chironomus*, the blackfly *Simulium* and other insects, the whole body surface acts as a gill, whilst in *Elmis* anal gills have developed and in some dragonfly larvae the gills are in the rectum. Many adult insects collect air at the surface and carry it with them, replacing the bubble once it is used up. They may, like the great silver beetle, carry bubbles of air trapped on specialised body hairs, or keep it in specialised wing cases, like the water scorpion.

Yet other invertebrates found in water with relatively little oxygen have evolved special haemoglobin-like blood pigments which allow them to extract oxygen from the water very efficiently. These are just a few of the many invertebrate adaptations to cope with the fluctuating oxygen levels of freshwater environments.

Carrying an oxygen supply with them is an adaptation that frees aquatic invertebrates from the restrictions of changing oxygen concentrations.

but the populations it will support are still limited. The ideal soil, **loam**, has particles of a wide range of sizes. It is heavier and less prone to leaching than sandy soils, yet easier to warm and work than clay. As a result both the plant populations growing in a loam soil and the populations of animals associated with them will be larger and more successful.

The mineral content of the soil is vital to the successful growth of plants. A variety of minerals are needed for healthy root and shoot development. In a natural ecosystem, many of these mineral requirements are taken up from the soil by plants and incorporated into the material of the plant body. The minerals are then returned to the soil either directly when the plants die and are decomposed, or indirectly as animals eat the plants and they and their waste products are decomposed in turn. This is the basis of the carbon and nitrogen cycles described in section 6.3.

This natural replenishment of resources is undermined when humans grow crops. Most crop plants are grown as **monocultures** – that is, a field full of a single species of plant. Thus all the plants are removing the same minerals from the soil and yet, because the crop is removed long before the plants die and decompose, virtually nothing is returned to the soil. Farmers can apply artificial fertilisers to help supply the mineral needs of their crops. Even so, maintaining this pattern of agriculture over a period of years results in soil becoming relatively barren, with increasing amounts of expensive chemicals being applied to maintain the fertility of the soil.

These problems may be minimised by **crop rotation**. This involves growing a series of different crops in a particular field each year in rotation, thus altering the mineral demands made each year. Also, natural fertilisers such as farmyard manure supply the required minerals in a slow release form as they decay, and they also improve the structure of the soil. By careful management, soil fertility can be maintained and crops taken off at regular intervals.

Microclimates

Within a particular habitat or area, we might expect the abiotic factors to be fairly constant. In reality abiotic factors can vary quite markedly within a particular habitat to produce **microclimates**. These are very important in determining the distribution of different species or populations within the habitat. For example, logs may be placed for seating on a grass area. Whilst the area will be largely dry and well-lit, under a log it will be damp and shady, allowing very different organisms to grow and thrive compared with those in the grassy areas. A large stone, a dead animal, a hollow in the ground or a wall are just some of the many features that can lead to the creation of microclimates.

Biotic factors affecting population size

What are biotic factors?

Biotic factors are all the living elements of the environment of a plant or animal. These include predation, parasitism and disease, and most importantly competition for resources. In many cases it is difficult to distinguish clearly between biotic and abiotic factors affecting a population as they are frequently interlinked – for example, the carbon and nitrogen cycles covered in section 6.3 involve both abiotic and biotic elements. Biotic factors exert a density-dependent effect on populations – the more animals or plants there are in a population, the more of them will be affected by the biotic factor.

6

Competition

Competition seems to be the major biotic factor determining the density and growth rate of populations. The competition may be directly for resources such as sunlight, minerals and food, or it may be for position, nest sites or mates. **Intraspecific competition** is competition for resources between members of the same population or species (see the example in the box below). When there is competition like this between members of the same population for the same resources, some of the population may not survive, or may not reproduce, and so the growth of the population slows as a consequence. Equally, if resources are plentiful and there is no competition for them, then the numbers of individuals will increase more quickly.

In some cases competition occurs not between members of the same population, but between different species within the community for the same scarce resources. This is known as **interspecific competition**. All the competing populations grow more slowly under these conditions than they would otherwise, and if one species has a high starting density or a superior reproduction rate, then one or more of the competing species may be removed. If this happens on a large scale, extinctions can occur. For example, years ago sailors released goats on Abingdon Island which is part of the Galapagos Archipelego. Goats are relatively large fast-breeding mammals with appetites to match. Over the years the growing goat population consumed so many of the plants previously eaten by the giant tortoises of the island that the reptiles could not survive the competition and in the 1960s became extinct on the island.

Competition within a population may be very obvious, such as blackbirds fighting over territories in a garden or tomcats fighting over a female on heat. The winning competitor gains the resource. This is referred to as **contest competition**. In other cases, many individuals all compete for, and gain some of, a relatively scarce resource – for example, lions squabbling over a carcase, as shown in figure 6.4.11. This is known as **scramble competition**.

Many modern ecologists hypothesise that competition is the major factor in the maintenance of stable communities in natural equilibrium, particularly for those organisms higher up the food web or chain. The role of competition in both population ecology and the structure of complex communities is currently the subject of much research and discussion, but there can be no doubting that it has a major role in the balance of nature.

Predation

Interactions of predators and prey are a factor in the regulation of population size. For the purposes of population studies a predator is any organism which feeds on another living organism, so for ease of discussion herbivores and parasites are regarded as predators too.

The obvious conclusion is that predators must be involved in regulating the population numbers of their prey species. Horses grazing a field must reduce the reproduction of the grass by eating the potentially flower-forming parts, and a fox family must reduce the numbers of the local rabbit population. However, things are rarely as simple as this. A mathematical model has been developed which attempts to describe the relationships between predator and prey populations. The prediction was that the populations would oscillate in a repeating cycle. The reasoning underlying this model is straightforward. As a prey population grows it provides more food for the predators and so, after an interval, the predator population grows too. The predators increase to the point where they are eating the prey species faster than it can reproduce, so the numbers of the prey population fall. In turn, this limits the food supply of the

Figure 6.4.11 In scramble competition, all the individuals compete for part of a resource. Although some individuals will fare better than others, in times of relative plenty the whole population will survive. When prey is harder to come by, all the members of the group get less to eat and the population grows more slowly. Only in times of severe shortage will some weaker members of the population get so little to eat that they cannot survive.

Intraspecific competition in Puerto Rican frogs

In the tropical rainforests of Puerto rico there is a species of frog known as *Eleutherodactylus coqui*. These frogs feed on insects and are active at night, hiding during the day to avoid predators. It appeared that the amount of food available should support a larger population of frogs than in fact exists, so scientists set about discovering the limiting resource. Competition for space as a factor limiting the population size was investigated, dividing the study area into 100 m^2 plots. In some areas the frogs were provided with many small bamboo shelters to hide in, whilst in others the habitat was left unchanged. All the shelters in the test plots were rapidly occupied and the population density increased accordingly, whilst the population density of the frogs in the control plots remained the same. The population size of the frogs was therefore controlled by competition between them for the one relatively scarce resource – sites in which to hide from predators and breed.

Territorial behaviour

One of the most clearly defined forms of both intraspecific and interspecific competition is territorial behaviour. A territory is an area held and defended by an organism (usually an animal) or a group of organisms against other organisms. These may be of a different species (interspecific competition), but very often the animals are of the same species (intraspecific competition). Territories have different functions for different types of animals, but they are always used in some way to make sure that a breeding pair has sufficient resources to raise their young. In birds such as penguins that need a relatively small nest area for their egg and chick, and have the whole ocean to feed from, territories are small. On the other hand, an animal like a tiger, which needs a large area in which to hunt, will have a very large territory indeed.

Most animals, particularly the males, are very aggressive in defence of their territory. This involves great displays but only relatively rarely actual violence, which would waste valuable resources for healing and resting. Meerkats, a type of mongoose, work as groups and both the males and females will defend their territory against other groups of meerkats wanting to forage there. Many animals mark their territory in some way – songbirds use their songs to mark the boundaries of their territory, whilst many carnivores mark their large territories with a scent trail by urinating or rubbing scent glands on particular marking posts.

Organisms that cannot win themselves a territory are marginalised in the society and are much less likely to reproduce successfully, so this type of competitive behaviour also helps regulate population size.

Figure 6.4.12 When a tiger marks his territory it is best not to be too close, for a whole variety of reasons!

predators and so their numbers will fall as well, allowing the prey to increase again and so on, as shown in figure 6.4.13.

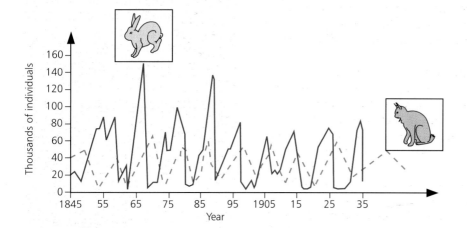

Figure 6.4.13 The data in this graph come from the records of pelts kept by the Hudson's Bay Company in Canada. They appear to confirm the theoretical model of predator and prey populations oscillating in a regular pattern. The peaks and crashes in the lynx population are certainly dependent on the snowshoe hare population. However, the hare population has been shown to follow a similar pattern even in areas where there are no lynxes. The hares are responding to cycles in their own plant 'prey', which themselves seem to reflect climatic variations and changes in insect pest populations. The interrelationships of predator–prey populations are clearly not as simple as it might at first seem.

The difficulty with using predator–prey relationships to understand the population balance of communities is that very few animals rely on only one food source. As we have seen in section 6.3, food webs are complex and many organisms are interlinked and interdependent. Thus one species may prey largely on another in times of plenty, but if the normal prey is in short supply it will switch readily to alternative food sources, thus affecting population numbers in another group but remaining stable itself, as shown in figure 6.4.14. As a result of a variety of studies it appears that the main effect of predators on a prey population is seen when that prey population is in some way weakened, perhaps by lack of food or disease. When this situation arises the inroads made by predators cannot readily be made up by increased reproductive activity and the prey population 'crashes'. In a healthy community predator–prey relationships do have a role to play in maintaining the overall balance of species within the system, but their importance is probably not as great as might at first seem to be the case.

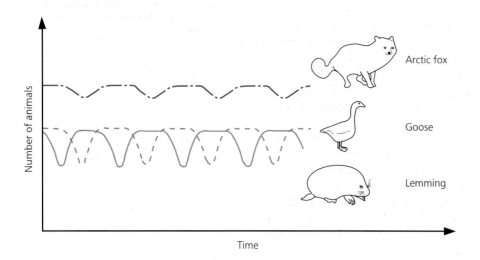

Figure 6.4.14 In a natural environment a crash in the population numbers of one organism may not lead to a delayed crash in the predator population, as the predator may simply switch to another source of food. In this example the major component of the diet of Arctic foxes changes from lemmings to geese.

Parasitism and disease

The size of populations and their growth are both affected by parasitism and disease. Infectious diseases are far more likely to be spread when there is a high population density, as individuals are in much closer proximity to each other. This is well documented in the social history of human diseases. Plague, cholera, smallpox, 'flu and chickenpox are passed on far more readily when people live and work closely with others.

The effect of a disease on populations depends to some extent on the community structure and on the populations within it. A virus which attacks an agricultural monoculture such as fields of corn or a bark beetle invading a woodland with little diversity in the number of species present will have a devastating effect. This is because any other populations within the community will depend heavily on the one affected by the disease. In a richer and more diverse community, although the effect on the particular population attacked by the disease will be as great, the effect on other populations within the habitat will be much less, as they will have many other potential sources of food.

Parasites also play a role in the success or otherwise of populations. Parasites feed off the living body of their host. Some (**endoparasites**) live within the body of their host and others (**ectoparasites**) are external, sometimes living on the outside of the host and sometimes simply visiting when they need a feed.

The major effect of a parasitic infestation on an individual is to weaken it. If all the individuals of a population are heavily infested by parasites then the rate of growth will slow. Many more individuals will be susceptible to predation and disease and reproduction will be less successful – the population as a whole will be checked. As in the case of infectious diseases, parasitic infections are more likely to be passed from one individual to another in situations of high population density than when the individuals are more spaced out, as illustrated in figure 6.4.15.

The human population

Human beings have been present as a species on the Earth for a very small part of the history of the planet. For thousands of years the human population has grown slowly, with increases due to improved weapons for hunting, tool making or crop growing being cancelled out by catastrophes, diseases and war. At the time of the agricultural revolution there were about 133 million people in the world. Since then the human population has ballooned, with the time taken for it to double getting less and less, as shown in figure 6.4.16. The point is now in the foreseeable future when the ecosystems of the Earth will no longer be capable of supporting the numbers of human beings – a situation which in any other species would result in an enormous population crash. Whether this will be the case for human beings is as yet a case for conjecture. Perhaps we shall control our population growth, or develop an as yet untapped food source. Certainly something will have to be done. Already people are placing enormous strains upon the planet in a variety of ways and to maintain population growth on this scale will require the careful use of all the Earth's resources.

Food production will become a major problem – many people already do not have sufficient to eat. Urbanisation will continue. It is estimated that early in the 21st century, over 50% of the population of the world will live in cities, and this causes enormous social problems of hygiene, shelter and disease. As people take up more and more space, other species will be marginalised and habitats lost.

More people will mean increased use of energy. Reserves of fossil fuels cannot last forever, and if they are burned increasingly rapidly then the gases they produce will add further to the greenhouse effect. Growing food will become more difficult if the climate of the Earth becomes hotter and drier as a result of such human pollution.

Figure 6.4.15 Food availability obviously has an effect on the individuals shown here, but more than that the feral dogs will be riddled with parasitic worms which use up many of their resources. Most wild dogs can find sufficient food to survive – it is the parasites which are largely responsible for their emaciated appearance. The same species, kept in a human home and devoid of parasites, utilises the food it is given to produce a well-covered frame.

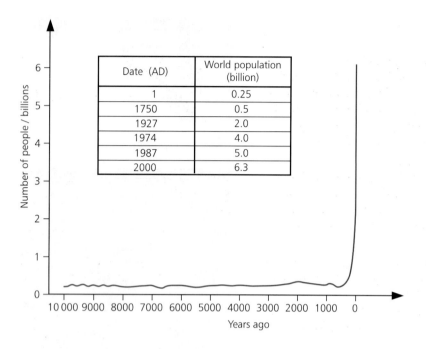

Date (AD)	World population (billion)
1	0.25
1750	0.5
1927	2.0
1974	4.0
1987	5.0
2000	6.3

Figure 6.4.16 The world human population has increased enormously in the last centuries, falling only briefly in the fourteenth century due to the many deaths from the Plague. The question must remain – where do we go from here?

If any other species showed a boom in population of the type seen in human beings, natural checks and balances such as we have considered in this section would ensure that the explosion was slowed and stopped if not reversed. In our position as manipulators of nature and controllers of our own environment, will we be able to cope with the results of our own success?

The structure of a community within a particular habitat can be seen as the sum of all the different populations within it. Those populations are affected by many factors – their growth is to some extent self limiting, and both biotic and abiotic factors act to increase or limit the numbers of a particular type of organism. Add to this the interactions between the various populations of an ecosystem and the cycling of minerals within it, and ecology can be seen as an immensely complex area of study. As a result of our own role within the biosphere, it may well be the most important area of biological knowledge for the future of the planet.

Figure 6.4.17 Alternative energy sources, like wind power, along with other measures such as improving methods of agriculture and limiting the size of families to two (replacement fertility), are all important aspects in the battle to maintain the ecosystems of the Earth, and enable them to continue to support the human population.

SUMMARY

- A population that doubles in size in a constant time period shows **exponential growth**. Most populations do not live in ideal conditions and their growth is **limited** by various factors. The upper limit of a population in a habitat is the **carrying capacity** of the habitat, reached after a slow initial **lag phase**, an **exponential phase**, and then a **stable phase** at the carrying capacity. **Decline** follows when resources run out or toxins build up.

- The **population density** is the number of individuals per unit area. The population density is affected by increases in numbers (caused by **birth** or **immigration**) and decreases in numbers (caused by **death** or **emigration**). The **birth rate** is given by the number of births divided by the number of adults in the population, and the **death rate** similarly by the number of deaths per adult in the population.

- The **distributions** of populations may be **clumped**, with organisms living in groups such as herds, **uniform**, with individuals in their own territories, or **scattered**, with individuals randomly dispersed.

- **Density-dependent** factors affecting population growth include predation, disease, parasitism and competition. Density-independent factors include unusual extremes of weather, earthquakes, etc.

- **Abiotic factors** affecting population size include:
  light   water availability
  temperature   oxygen availability
  wind   soil structure and mineral content.
  water currents

- **Biotic factors** affecting population size include **competition** for sunlight, food or other resources. Competition may be **intraspecific**, between members of the same species, or **interspecific**, between different populations. In **contest competition** individuals fight over a resource such as territory, and the winner gains the resource. In **scramble competition** many individuals compete for and gain part of a resource, such as food.

- **Predator–prey relationships** are biotic factors often changing in a cyclical pattern, the prey fluctuating between higher and lower numbers and the predators following a similar pattern but lagging behind slightly. The availability of more than one prey species in a complex food web and seasonal changes in resources complicate this pattern.

- Parasites and disease are biotic factors particularly affecting dense populations, generally weakening them.

- After an initial steady increase, the **human population** has increased extremely rapidly over the last 200 years or so. Measures will have to be taken to conserve the Earth's ecosystems in order to prevent a human population crash.

1 a In theory, populations of organisms can increase exponentially. What does this mean and why is it rarely seen in nature?

b What is meant by the 'carrying capacity' of a habitat?

c How can abiotic factors affect the size of populations?

2 Discuss the ways in which competition, predation, parasitism and disease limit the size of natural populations.

3 Of all the different species present on the Earth, human beings have had perhaps the greatest impact. The human population, after a long period of slow growth, is now increasing very rapidly. Why is this happening and what are the implications for the ecology of the planet?

Developing Key Skills

Using the internet and other resources, research the migration patterns of a type of bird and a mammal. Put together a presentation to show the scope of the migration, the theories on how the organisms navigate on their journeys and the similarities and differences between the two species.

THE DISAPPEARING HEDGEROWS

Hedgerows are an integral part of the British countryside, one of the unique features that make it different from the landscape almost anywhere else in the world. Many hedgerows are thousands of years old – there are hedges around Dartmoor that can be traced back to our Bronze Age ancestors 3500 years ago! But since the Second World War they have been disappearing fast.

Hedges have been planted for two main reasons – to enclose livestock and to mark out the boundaries of property. They also provide shelter for the animals they enclose and can be a source of firewood. But modern fences are more effective at keeping animals enclosed and are cheaper to maintain than hedges, which also get in the way of large agricultural machinery. Over the last 50 years a huge proportion of hedges have been uprooted and destroyed all over Britain. In some counties, particularly in East Anglia, hedgerows have all but disappeared and huge prairie-like fields are the norm. However, in recent years the value of hedges has begun to be recognised, and the tide is slowly turning.

Figure 1 Hedgerows are not only attractive, they also form an important habitat in our countryside.

Why do hedges matter?

Hedges are important for two main reasons. First, they provide a very important habitat amidst fields of monoculture. The species recorded in association with hedgerows number 600 flowering plants, 1500 insects, 65 birds and 20 mammal species. Of the species threatened in the UK, 47 are hedgerow dwellers, including 13 species that are globally recognised as being at risk of extinction. These include some very rare species, such as the Plymouth pear, the cirl bunting and the burberry carpet moth, but also some more familiar creatures such as the dormouse and the song thrush.

Some hedges contain more diverse species than others, and the oldest ones have the widest variety of both plant and animal life. In general, the more woody species present in a hedge, the greater the variety of other organisms that will be found living or feeding there. But even younger hedges provide a microclimate, sheltering several species of animals and plants.

The second important function of hedges was not fully recognised until many of them had been uprooted. Hedgerows help prevent soil being eroded by the action of the wind and the rain, and without them the fertility of the soil is reduced. Recognising this, some farmers have begun to manage and restore their remaining hedgerows, and even replace those that have been destroyed.

In the final years of the twentieth century, action was taken to try and protect our most ancient hedges by legislation. The UK Biodiversity Action Plan has also targeted this habitat, in particular ancient hedgerows (those present before the 1720 and 1840 Enclosure Acts) and species-rich ones (containing five or more native woody species in a 30-metre length). They aim to provide financial help to encourage farmers to manage their ancient and species-rich hedgerows. With luck, our landscape complete with hedgerows, with their beautiful displays of flowers and berries as the seasons change, along with the birds, insects and mammals that live in them, will continue to be part of our heritage for centuries to come.

Figure 2 Hedgerows provide the main nest sites for many songbirds.

6.5 Managed ecosystems

Around the world many ecosystems are simply the result of millions of years of evolution. Many others owe at least as much to human intervention as they do to natural selection. All the farms, fisheries and forestry plantations around the world are **managed ecosystems**, and the way in which they work – or don't work – is down to human beings.

Farming

As recognisable modern human beings evolved, they lived as nomadic hunter/gatherers. Part of the social group – usually the men – would hunt for large animals to provide meat for everyone. The remainder of the group – the women and children – would gather fruits, nuts, berries, roots and any other plant material, as well as insects or eggs, to form the staple part of the diet. The first industry to emerge was farming, and this allowed people to begin to settle into more stable social groups. They began to grow 'crops' – plants that provided edible roots or shoots, including the wild grasses that were the forerunners of our modern cereals – and to rear animals to provide a renewable source of protein. This in turn led to the construction of more complex homes, and became part of the human evolutionary pattern.

Increasing numbers of people have meant increasing demands for food, and in the last century or so both the human population and the demand for food have risen to an all-time high. The effects of managed ecosystems have a major impact on other ecosystems as well. There are grave concerns at the moment both about the ability of the planet to provide enough food for all the people who now live on it, and about the effect of current farming techniques on the ecosystem as a whole. For the Earth to survive and prosper, a balance between these apparently conflicting demands must be found.

Farming methods

More food was produced in the last 30 years of the twentieth century than ever before, although food production is still not keeping up with population growth. This increased production was largely the result of technological developments in farm machinery and of scientific research into and selective breeding of crop plants and animals. Growing crops on a farm or raising livestock creates an ecosystem that is very different from those found naturally. As seen on page 517, the **net primary production** of an ecosystem or of an individual type of organism can be expressed as the amount of new biomass formed minus the losses used up in respiration and metabolism. Comparing the net primary production of different biomes shows that tropical rainforests have the highest productivity, followed by temperate evergreen and deciduous forests. The productivity of cultivated land is only a little higher than that of natural temperate grassland (650 compared with $600\,\text{g}\,\text{m}^{-2}\,\text{y}^{-1}$), but farmers and crop breeders are working to increase this productivity level.

The yield of a crop is rather different from the overall productivity of the plant. What farmers want to increase is the **harvest index** – the mass of the usable part of the crop relative to the total mass of the crop, which often

Figure 6.5.1 In some areas of the world, farming has changed little with the centuries. In other parts it has become a highly mechanised and cost-efficient process.

includes material that is of no commercial value. There are two main ways of doing this. One is to alter the biochemistry of the plant to make the energy conversion within the leaf more efficient – for example, attempting to combine some of the benefits of both C_3 and C_4 plants in one leaf. Another is to direct more of the food produced by the plant to the parts of the plant that are harvested. Yet another is to improve the **leaf area index**. This is a measure of leaf area per unit of ground area. Most of the sunlight that reaches the surface of the Earth does not fall on the leaves of plants – it falls on the ground and so is lost as a source of net primary production. The bigger the leaf area index of the plant, the more of its leaf area covers the ground and the more sunlight it will absorb. This means that breeding plants to have larger leaves, or to have their leaves arranged in such a way as to be more effective at trapping the sunlight, will increase their overall photosynthetic productivity.

The amount of light falling on the fields is something farmers can do little about, so the initial energy input to a farming ecosystem is similar to the input to any other area of land in the region. However, the farmer uses fertilisers, irrigation if necessary and pest control to try and make sure that the productivity of the farm is as high as possible. The price that is most often paid in the ecosystem is the loss of both species variety and genetic variety, as huge areas of land are all planted with the same plants or grazed by cattle of one particular type. This is the price we pay for plentiful and relatively cheap food.

Some of the main methods used by arable farmers to grow crops, with their advantages and disadvantages, are summarised below.

Ploughing

Ploughing breaks up the soil to produce seed beds for the new crops. It also incorporates the remains of the previous crop into the soil, and can be used to convert grassland into farmland. In developed countries large metal ploughs are pulled by powerful tractors which cover huge fields easily and quickly, but can cause problems because of their great weight compressing the soil. In the developing world ploughs are more often wood or wood and metal, and pulled by people, oxen, or horses more often than by tractors. The process is very slow, but works well for small fields.

Direct drilling

In **direct drilling**, which is often carried out after a cereal crop has been harvested, the stubble (remains of the old crop) is left in place and the ground is sprayed with a powerful weedkiller. Then the seeds are planted directly into the undisturbed soil using a seed drill. This reduces costs because spraying is much quicker than ploughing, and it removes the need for spraying again at a later date.

Monoculture

Many farmers nowadays in the developed world grow only a very narrow range of crops. They operate a system of **monoculture**, whereby large areas of land are all planted with the same type of crop plant. The vast wheat-growing areas of the world such as the US prairies are perhaps the biggest monocultures on Earth. This has many advantages – the plants will all look the same and go to the same markets, and the farmer only has to buy fertiliser and pest-control chemicals for one type of crop. But there are some serious disadvantages – for example, lack of genetic variation leaves the crops vulnerable to a change in conditions or the introduction of a new disease. In a monoculture all the plants could be affected and lost.

Figure 6.5.2 Ploughing the fields before planting new crops is an ancient farming practice, now done with less effort and far faster than our ancestors could ever have imagined.

The Irish potato famine

For centuries Ireland remained an undeveloped country, using crude methods of ploughing and harvesting and suffering from a difficult climate and geographical isolation. When the potato reached Ireland, almost everyone could suddenly grow enough food for their families, and the population exploded, growing from 2.6 million to 5 million in under 20 years. But in 1845 potato blight (a disease caused by *Phytophthora infestans*, an oomycete member of the protoctista which is very like a fungus) wiped out the crop, and suddenly people were starving all over Ireland. Over a million people died in the years after 1845, when the crop first failed badly, of starvation or diseases such as cholera that accompany it. Many more left the country, largely heading for America and changing the make-up of American society for good. The relationships of both Ireland and the USA with Britain were permanently changed by the potato famine and its aftermath. The potato has caused as much suffering and political difficulty as any other plant on Earth and the events of nineteenth-century Ireland illustrate perfectly the dangers of depending on monoculture.

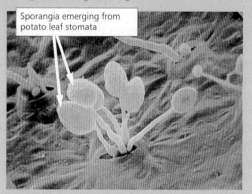

Sporangia emerging from potato leaf stomata

Figure 6.5.3 The effect of the potato blight, caused by this oomycete, was far-reaching. Of an Irish population of around 9 million, a million men, women and children died of famine or associated disease. A further 1.5 million left Ireland for America, and by the time of the First World War about 5.5 million Irish people had emigrated.

Long term it is very important that plant breeders do not lose the genetic variation that allows organisms to adapt to changing conditions, and also allows the organisms to be adapted for changing markets. The maintenance of seed banks (see page 380) and of specialist growers who keep a wide range of old varieties will be of vital importance in years to come for the continued genetic health of our crop plants. To this end, varieties of the world's major crops are held in international gene banks established by the Consultative Group on International Agricultural Research (CGIAR) which was set up by the United Nations. These gene banks are preserving an enormous number of genes – for example, there are 12 000 different varieties of potato at the International Potato Centre in Peru! Another by-product of the large fields often used for monocultures has been the removal of hedgerows, with the accompanying loss of genetic variety and loss of soil fertility due to erosion (see page 539). Currently many farmers are working hard to restore some habitat diversity to their farms, leaving hedges and small stands of trees, providing nest sites for barn owls and generally attempting to restore some ecological balance whilst still making a profit.

Harvesting

In the developed world cereal crops are **harvested** by huge combine harvesters. Harvesting the crops has to be done at exactly the right time and in the right conditions to ensure that the crop is in a suitable state to go to the shops or be stored safely. The moisture content of cereal crops has to be at exactly the right level both for them to be ground successfully to make flour, and for any long-term storage. This used to be a major problem for farmers, and it still can be in some areas of the world. In developed countries where most of the intensive cultivation goes on there are huge commercial grain dryers that enable the moisture content of the cereal crops to be controlled artificially.

Storage

After harvesting, some crops are sold immediately either for food or for further processing (such as sugar cane and sugar beet). However, many crops need to be **stored** for some time before they are used, and it is at this point that a high percentage of the world's food production is lost. Insects and fungi between them destroy millions of tonnes of stored food every year all over the world. To limit this type of damage, food may be dried, or the surrounding temperature may be kept relatively low. An atmosphere with a high proportion of carbon dioxide may be used, and fungicide sprays can help prevent damage by moulds and other fungi. The battle to prevent damage while in storage is continual, and as always it is the developed countries that have the most appropriate and pest-free storage facilities.

Figure 6.5.4 When people are dying of starvation in the world it becomes a priority to prevent stored food being lost by mould damage like this.

The farmer's dilemma

In most countries people want both plant-based food and meat. In some areas of the world every family group grows the food that it will eat for itself, but in most societies there are also farmers, individuals who grow crops or raise animals to provide food (at a price) for the rest of their community. This farming may be on a small scale or a vast industry, but the issues for farmers are basically the same everywhere.

- People want and need food to eat, and want at least the basic foodstuffs to be as cheap as possible.

- The demand for food all over the world is rising. In the developing world there is a higher demand for the basic foodstuffs. In the developed world people want more varied food, they want it fresher and increasingly they are beginning to want to know how it is produced – what chemicals are sprayed onto crops and how animals are reared, fed and treated during their lives.

- Farming takes up land, and the more demand there is for food production the more land has to be found to grow food.

- Farmers need to make a living, to be able to provide for themselves and their families, so they need to be paid a realistic amount for the food that they produce.

- For the long-term health of the farmer, the community and the planet, farming needs to be a sustainable activity – one that can be repeated over and over again. This raises serious concerns, as some modern farming practices are damaging to the environment. Some farming techniques actively destroy the ability of the land to produce food, and these need to be identified and stopped if farmers are to feed the growing human population in the future.

There are a number of problems in farming, but the solutions have the potential for causing damage to the environment. These need to be considered in detail by both farmers and society around the world to decide what is acceptable and what is not.

Slash and burn – a policy of destruction

In many areas of the world currently covered by tropical rainforests, one of the most devastating types of farming is taking place. In a desperate attempt to grow food for themselves many people are simply cutting down great areas of the forest and clearing it for use as farmland. There is very little topsoil in a tropical rainforest, and what soil there is is relatively infertile – all the nutrients are bound up in the living organisms. After being cut down the trees are burned, which releases many nutrients into the thin soil and allows crops to be grown successfully for a few years. But once those minerals have been depleted the soil becomes totally infertile. It is rapidly eroded by rain in the absence of the tree cover.

The people then move on to slash and burn another area of forest, while the area left behind will take at least 80 years to regain its fertility to the point where it could once again support a rainforest – and by then it may well be too late. The same policy has been carried out to provide grazing land for cattle, to produce cheap beef for the burger market in the USA and across Europe. If farming policies like these continue we will destroy the ecology of the Earth (see section 6.6).

Fertilising the soil

The factor limiting the production of new biomass in most ecosystems is the level of nitrogen, in the form of nitrates in the soil, and this is just as true of a managed farm ecosystem as any other. For many centuries soil fertility on farms was maintained by a combination of ploughing back the remains of the previous year's crop, ploughing in lots of well rotted farmyard manure, and the use of crop rotation systems. In **crop rotation**, different plants are grown and harvested on a field in a three- or four-year cycle. One year of the cycle, legumes (peas, beans or clover) are grown. They fix nitrogen and add greatly to the fertility of the soil. In each of the other years different crops are planted, including one year of roots and another of cereals, making sure that the resources of the soil are never drained and always replaced. Crop rotation also reduces the likelihood of diseases causing problems, because the same plants are never grown in the same soil twice in succession. This method of farming is still used successfully today in countries in the developing world.

In years gone by, many UK and USA farmers were 'mixed' farmers – that is, they ran relatively small farms and both grew crops and raised livestock. The manure from the livestock was used to fertilise the land that was to be used for growing crops, and when the land was rested and lay fallow the livestock could feed on it.

This type of farming still exists in many areas of the world, but in most developed countries farming is now on a far bigger scale, and many farmers are now specialists – they produce only certain crops, or they are dairy farmers, or they farm sheep or fruit. As a result there is often no manure available on crop-growing farms.

Crop farmers are using their land more and more intensively. To replace the nutrients used by the plants, and to compensate for the fact that the crops are not left to rot and return minerals to the soil, farmers apply artificial fertilisers. Artificial fertilisers are particularly rich in very soluble nitrates, along with phosphates and potassium. These increase the crop yields, but the quantities of expensive fertilisers used need to be carefully calculated. Increasing dosages of fertiliser cannot increase the yield indefinitely, not least because other factors such as availability of light come into play and become limiting. The overuse of artificial fertilisers causes environmental problems (see also section 6.6). If the fertilisers are leached from the soil by heavy rain and carried into local waterways, then **eutrophication** is the likely result.

Figure 6.5.5 It takes plenty of livestock to provide enough manure to fertilise fields for growing crops.

If minerals such as nitrates and phosphates are leached into rivers, streams and ponds, they provide nutrients for the water plants, algae and photosynthetic bacteria present in the water. These grow very rapidly, making the water appear cloudy and scummy with a luxuriant growth of plants. The death of these photosynthetic organisms then provides a rich food source for the decomposers. The decomposers use up large quantities of oxygen from the water in the process of decay, which in turn may deprive other organisms such as fish and crustaceans of oxygen, causing them to die. Their bodies add to the organic material available to decomposers and so the situation gets worse. This process is known as eutrophication. Although it can happen quite naturally, the overuse of fertilisers has increased the occurrence of eutrophication and has led to the death of many rivers and streams, which have ended up devoid of all animal life.

This problem can be solved – if organic fertilisers such as manure are used on the land, the decomposition and thus the release of minerals into the soil is relatively slow, and so the nutrients are not readily leached away. There are moves towards greater use of organic manure in farming in the UK, and farmers are ploughing in stubble again to add to the humus content of their soil. However, around the world the drive to produce more crops still results in the overuse of artificial fertilisers, and so to the death of many waterways.

Figure 6.5.6 With the increase in intensive agriculture the number of dead rivers, ponds and streams has increased throughout the developed world.

Farm waste and eutrophication

The use of excess fertilisers by farmers is not the only farming activity that puts rivers, streams, ponds and lakes at risk of eutrophication. British livestock farmers produce about 1000000 tonnes of beef, 400000 tonnes of lamb, 750 tonnes of pork and 15000000 tonnes of milk every year. Whilst sheep are generally reared out in pastures for almost all of their lives, cattle are usually kept in barns during the winter months and pigs may well be kept inside for their whole life. This means that there is an enormous amount of **slurry** (a mixture of urine and dung, with variable amounts of bedding material depending on the farming methods used) that has to be disposed of – about 200 million tonnes in all! This slurry is often spread on the land as a fertiliser, but if it gets into a waterway it can cause major problems. Slurry is 100 times more polluting than raw, untreated domestic sewage. Silage effluent is even worse. This is the liquid produced when crops that have been harvested whilst they are still green are preserved as fodder for the animals. **Silage** effluent is up to 200 times more polluting than sewage. Slurry and silage effluent are both very rich in nitrogen, and so they cause eutrophication on a massive scale. The problem is particularly severe in Wales and the west of England. These areas have very wet climates, which means they grow lots of grass and so are popular areas for dairy farms. The wet weather leads to higher levels of slurry – eating wet grass means

more urine is formed – and so a higher pollution risk. The British Government, through the Ministry of Agriculture, Fisheries and Food (MAFF), has taken a number of steps to encourage farmers to manage their livestock waste effectively. Two million pounds each year is being spent on research to investigate ways of maximising the benefits of using animal waste on the land whilst minimising the risk of pollution. There are a number of laws which make it an offence to pollute the waterways or to cause continual offensive smells, and farmers can be fined up to £20000 if they are found guilty of these offences. Legislation also sets standards for the containers used to store both slurry and silage. In addition there are Codes of Good Agricultural Practice for the Protection of Water and the Protection of Soil, which give farmers advice and guidance on the best ways to maintain the health of the soil while avoiding polluting their local waterways.

As a result of these types of intervention, and of increased awareness in farmers, the incidence of severe water pollution resulting from agricultural activities in the UK has fallen substantially. In 1989 there were 4141 reported incidents of water pollution by agriculture. By 1996 this had fallen to 2111, and of those only 28 were serious, resulting in the death of large numbers of fish. With the continued commitment of the farming community, the pollution of our waterways as a result of farming activities should continue to fall.

6

Pest control

Another very important aspect of farming is pest control. Up to a third of the crops grown worldwide are spoiled by pests. A growing crop will grow less well if it is competing against weeds, plants that are often opportunistic and therefore grow very fast, depriving the crop plants of nutrients, water and light. Growing crops are also vulnerable to damage by animal pests, particularly insects. Insects can affect the yield of crop plants in two main ways. They may have a very direct effect – grain weevils and other such insects feed on the seeds of cereal plants, thus reducing the crop yield. Other insect pests including caterpillars have a more indirect effect – they feed on the leaves of the crop plant, thus reducing the surface area available for photosynthesis. This in turn reduces the biomass that the plant is able to produce, and so reduces the crop yield. Plant leaves and seeds are also vulnerable to damage from moulds and bacteria.

So in order to prevent the loss of their crops, farmers apply **pesticides**. Those that target other plants are known as **herbicides**, and they come in a variety of forms. The original herbicides were known as **contact herbicides** such as sodium chlorate. These damaged or killed the leaves of plants when they came into contact with them. More recently these have been superseded by **systemic herbicides**. These are chemicals such as auxins which are taken into the bodies of the weed plants and disrupt their biochemistry, destroying the natural control of growth and eventually causing the death of the plant (see page 298). Paraquat and diquat interfere with photosynthesis whilst atrazine and simazine remain in the soil, preventing seed germination.

Fungicides are pesticides that affect fungi and prevent their growth, reducing the damage done by moulds. Perhaps the most important group of pesticides is the **insecticides**. These are chemicals that have been developed to protect crop plants from the ravages of insect pests which can greatly reduce or completely destroy a crop if they are not controlled in some way. However, the chemicals used to destroy insect pests are toxins; these toxins can have unexpected effects on the environment. For example, when DDT was developed it was hailed as a great success. It was only after some time that scientists began to be aware of the problems it was causing in the environment.

The DDT story

Biological magnification occurs when materials present only in minute amounts in the environment accumulate in increasing quantities in the members of a food chain or web. Examples are seen when chemicals added to the environment by humans accumulate in other organisms and cause damage.

DDT is an extremely effective pesticide, but it is not readily excreted. In many animals it is stored in the body fat. Insects killed by DDT and zooplankton living in contaminated water are eaten by small fish, which in turn are eaten by larger fish. Finally the larger fish are eaten by top carnivores, fish-eating birds such as ospreys and herons.

When DDT was introduced as a pesticide in this country it was observed that the numbers of large fish-eating birds began to decline. The tissues of the birds were analysed and found to contain high concentrations of DDT, particularly in the fat, muscles and livers. The levels of DDT were not high enough to kill the birds, but were affecting their ability to reproduce. The eggs laid had very thin shells which broke readily, so many fewer offspring than normal were hatched and raised. Although the chemical was accumulating in the tissues of the entire food chain, it was only in the top consumers that it reached high enough levels to have an effect. These effects were noticed in the 1960s and 1970s. Since that time the use of chemicals such as DDT has been banned in most of the developed world. However, because they are very effective pesticides they are still in use in much of the developing world, where the priorities for disease vector control are very much higher.

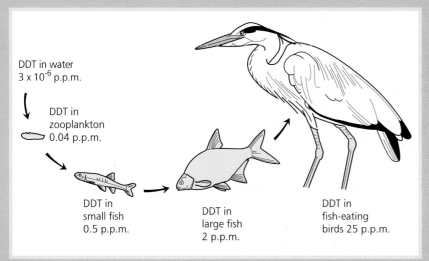

DDT in water
3×10^{-6} p.p.m.

DDT in zooplankton
0.04 p.p.m.

DDT in small fish
0.5 p.p.m.

DDT in large fish
2 p.p.m.

DDT in fish-eating birds 25 p.p.m.

Figure 6.5.7 Biological magnification or bioaccumulation is demonstrated clearly in the concentration of chemicals such as DDT in the tissues of organisms in the higher trophic levels.

The ideal pesticide should be toxic only to the pest organisms it is designed to kill, should not persist in the environment after it has done its job (it should be **biodegradable**, broken down by the action of bacteria or other organisms into harmless chemicals) and should not accumulate in food chains. Unfortunately most pesticides are not completely specific in their toxicity and many of them show some degree of persistence either in the soil or in food chains. When pesticides are being developed, these aspects of their performance are weighed up in a cost–benefit exercise. For example, it is often decided that a highly toxic chemical that does not persist in the environment will do less long-term damage than a slightly less toxic chemical that persists in the environment and could undergo biological magnification. What also has to be decided is the strength of pesticide to spray – the idea is to kill as many pests as possible for as low a cost as possible. Pesticides are rarely sprayed at a high enough concentration to make them 100% effective. This means not only that they are accumulating in food chains all over the world (residues of organochlorines, the group of chemicals that includes DDT, have been found in the body fat of Antarctic penguins!) but also that increasing numbers of insects and other pests are developing resistance to the most commonly used pesticides. The organisms that survive spraying are likely to have a resistance gene that allowed them to survive, and when they reproduce they pass this resistance on to their offspring. If a pesticide persists in the environment long after spraying, then it will increase the likelihood that the only surviving pest organisms will be those resistant to the chemical. In a relatively short time a whole population of predominantly resistant pest organisms develops. Most pests have short life cycles and produce a lot of offspring, so this does not take long. Farmers then need to change the chemical they use to protect their crops – and another resistant population will eventually be the result.

For many years now the main weapons turned on crop pests have been chemical. Early solutions involved tar sprays – still used by some fruit farmers – and copper sulphate ($CuSO_4$), which offered some protection against problems such as potato blight. The complex chemical cocktails currently used have been very successful at reducing crop damage and have played an important part in increasing crop yields all over the world. However, for all sorts of reasons there is now a move towards alternative methods of controlling pests. One of the most promising of these is **biological pest control**.

Biological pest control

Biological pest control involves using one living organism to control the activities of another. In the developed world we have become increasingly concerned about the long-term effects that chemical pesticides and herbicides may have on us. We have also become progressively 'greener' over recent years, with more and more people expressing concern over the future of the Earth and our effect on it. Substituting biological control for chemical intervention therefore seems like a very good idea.

The developing world cannot yet afford such concerns – the main struggle for many developing nations is to be able to feed all the hungry mouths. But in these countries too the cost of chemical control and the increasing resistance of pests to the expensive chemicals is adding another powerful voice to the arguments in favour of biological control as an integrated part of pest management.

So how does biological control work? In a natural ecosystem a balance is set up between the plants that provide the primary source of food (the producers), the animals that eat the plants (the primary consumers) and the animals that eat the animals that eat the plants (the secondary consumers). Chemical pesticides destroy this delicate balance. Biological pest control attempts to deal with the pest without destroying this balance. There are three different approaches, discussed below.

Encouraging natural enemies

If the natural enemies of a pest species can be conserved and encouraged, they may well control the pest as effectively as any spray, and far more cheaply. A good example of the effectiveness of this approach is the control of rice pests in Indonesia. In the 1970s the development of high-yielding strains of rice and increasing use of fertilisers and pesticides allowed two rice crops to be grown each year instead of one. Unfortunately it also led to an enormous growth in the population of the brown planthopper (*Nilaparvata lugens*) which is a devastating pest of rice plants. Farmers were spraying up to eight times a season to try to reduce the damage done by this pest, with huge Government subsidies to help with the cost. It was then shown that spraying had caused the problem in the first place!

The sprays had wiped out all the natural predators of the brown plant-hoppers, particularly spiders, and yet had only limited effect on the pest itself. An **integrated pest management** (IPM) system was introduced. The Indonesian Government reduced the subsidies on chemical sprays and banned the use of 57 insecticides on rice. A nationwide training programme was set up to help farmers conserve predators such as spiders. It only costs about £10 to train each farmer – but there are about 7 million farmers in Indonesia alone! In spite of this, by the third year following the ban, pesticide use had been

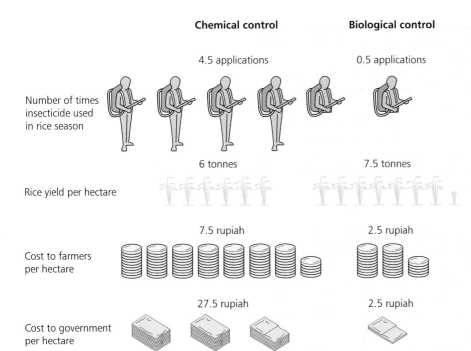

Chemical control	Biological control

4.5 applications   **0.5 applications**

Number of times insecticide used in rice season

6 tonnes   **7.5 tonnes**

Rice yield per hectare

7.5 rupiah   **2.5 rupiah**

Cost to farmers per hectare

27.5 rupiah   **2.5 rupiah**

Cost to government per hectare

Figure 6.5.8 These charts show the effect on rice farming in Indonesia of introducing an integrated pest management system.

reduced by 90% with large savings in cost for both the farmers and the Government – and the yields of rice were increasing. Spraying is now only considered as a last resort. Similar IPM programmes for rice are being introduced successfully in Bangladesh and India.

At Southampton University there is a team investigating the possibility of biological control of the grain aphids which damage our wheat crops by sucking the sap. The larvae of hoverflies are voracious predators of aphids. The plan is to have strips of 'weeds' in and around fields of growing grain. The 'weeds' will be flowering plants that attract female hoverflies, which need protein from pollen to produce eggs successfully. The plan is that the flies will move out into the crop after feeding and lay their eggs near the aphids.

Once the larvae hatch they attack and destroy the aphids with ever-increasing enthusiasm. The older larvae can each eat between 30 and 40 aphids a day. The cost of using land for flowering plants to attract hoverflies rather than to grow crops should be more than regained by savings on chemical pesticides. If the idea is shown to work, it would be yet another example of successful IPM – and would also add extra colour to the countryside!

When the use of biological control and chemical control can be integrated to minimise the use of chemicals but maximise their effect when they are brought into play, the well-being of the farmer, the consumer and the land can all be protected.

Biological pesticides

Simulium posticatum is a tiny black fly, known locally in Dorset as the Blandford fly. It infests the river Stour and has a vicious bite. A blister and swelling form around the site of the bite and some people suffer fevers, swelling of the lymph glands and dizziness.

A method of biological control was tried on a small tributary of the Stour. A biological pesticide was introduced to the water in the form of *Bacillus thuringiensis israelensis* (BT). This bacterium kills the larvae of the Blandford fly in the river without damaging other forms of life or polluting the water. BT is a

Figure 6.5.9 The attentions of these tiny insects can severely reduce the yield of wheat. It is hoped that weeds and hoverflies between them will control the problem in years to come – resulting in more food for all.

6

biological pesticide which has a variety of forms. It has been used internationally with a great deal of success against many of the appalling fly-borne diseases of the developing world. A particular success story has been its use to clear thousands of square miles of West Africa of the organism which carries river blindness, a disease that has affected almost every family in the past. Best of all, in removing river blindness, the African waterways have not been chemically polluted and the remaining fauna is unharmed.

Exotic enemies

The third, and perhaps best known, form of biological control is the release of an exotic species from one country to control a pest in another. The introduction of the vedalia beetle from Australia onto the citrus groves of California saved the Californian citrus growers from destruction by the cottony cushion scale, a pest that was completely destroying the fruit trees. This happened a century ago and since then exotic species have played their part in the battle to preserve our food from the multitude of pests who would like to share it with us.

Nowadays the introduction of a new exotic species to a country is only carried out after extensive research to make sure that it will do the job required and nothing else. It would be catastrophic if a beetle introduced to control a plant pest turned out to prefer a diet of corn or potatoes and laid waste to acres of food crops!

Biological control of weeds by the introduction of herbivorous insects has been successful in many parts of the world. Australia in the 1920s was threatened with a take-over by the prickly pear cactus *Opuntia*. It was controlled by the introduction of the Argentinian moth *Cactoblastis cactorum* which cleared over 60 million acres. When biological control of weed pests is achieved it is permanent, very cost effective and environmentally friendly.

Exotic and alien organisms have been used for biological control for over a century now. To begin with, introductions were not screened thoroughly and problems arose, but lessons have been learned and several thorough steps now have to be taken before the release of an exotic organism can be considered.

How is a biological control system developed?

When a new system of biological pest control is considered, a great deal of background work is necessary to discover whether the pest organism is a suitable target for this type of control. Research is expensive, and an initial study is needed to determine whether the money will be well spent. Then a range of possible control organisms are collected. As far as possible, these need to be species specific and unlike any naturally occurring organism in the country affected by the pest. Laboratory trials demonstrate the effectiveness or otherwise of the control organism, the specificity of its action and its effect on the environment as a whole. Only after the successful completion of all of these tests and meeting international safety guidelines will a biological pest control organism be released.

People are increasingly aware of the value of integrated pest management systems, where natural predators are preserved and chemical sprays used as a last resort. This puts management of the land back in the hands of individual farmers. It is cheaper both for the individual farmer and for governments freed from subsidising the purchase of expensive chemicals, and the lowered doses of pesticides make the prospect of eating the food more pleasant too.

One area associated with biological control that does raise some important questions is the use of genetically engineered organisms in pest control.

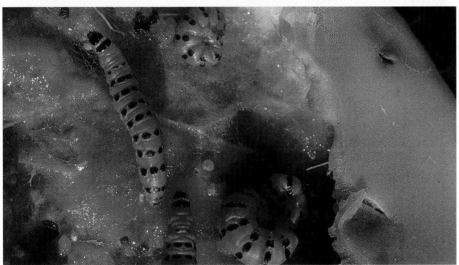

Figure 6.5.10 In 1920 these large cacti were taking over the Australian countryside in much the same way as bracken is spreading in Britain today. The introduction of an Argentinian moth controlled the situation. In Britain it is hoped that the caterpillar of the *Conservula cinisigna* moth will perform a similar function in controlling the spread of bracken.

A plague for locusts

For thousands of years, the arrival of a plague of locusts has meant fear and possible starvation for the local people. Locusts devour all the crops across broad areas of the countryside in Africa, leaving the land bare. Control of these locust swarms has been difficult if not impossible. But over the last ten years a possible form of biological control has been developed.

Research workers from Britain, Niger and Benin have worked with the fungus *Metarhizium flavoviride*, a naturally occurring fungus that infects insects. Its spores will normally only germinate in moist conditions, which are unfortunately rare in many areas of Africa. The scientists have solved this problem by trapping the fungal spores in droplets of oil which seem to absorb moisture. The spores are

then sprayed over populations of locusts. Once the spores germinate, the fungus forces its hyphae

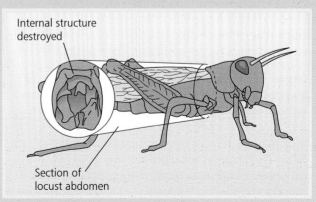

Internal structure destroyed

Section of locust abdomen

Figure 6.5.11 The locust has no defences against the ravages of the fungus, which attacks it from within.

6

through the external skeleton of the insects. It then grows inside the body of the insect, digesting away the internal organs to leave a hollow dead skeleton. It takes two to three weeks for the fungus to kill the locust, so swarms need to be sprayed when the immature hoppers are still on the ground, before they take to the air and fly to their feeding grounds. The work is now in its final stages, and it looks as if biotechnology may provide a plague to threaten locusts as they have for centuries threatened us.

What is the aim of manipulating genes to produce biological control agents? The work is very much concentrated on pathogens. Some of the gene manipulation is designed to increase the virulence of existing pathogens – creating 'super-pathogens' which are much more effective at attacking the pest. Other engineering work is designed to increase or change the range of organisms affected by the pathogen.

The other thrust of genetic engineering is to introduce genes from insect pathogens into plants, so that when an insect feeds on a plant, it also takes in a dose of toxin. Genes from *Bacillus thuringiensis* (BT) have been introduced into various crop plants, including cotton, potatoes and tomatoes. Although very effective, a problem has arisen. Following the repeated exposure of the insects to the toxin, for the first time resistance to a biological control method has been found. This poses profound difficulties, because BT is potentially one of the most useful organisms for biocontrol when targeted against very specific pests. It would be a tragedy if this potential were lost due to the injudicious use of engineered crop plants.

This area of biological control obviously opens up many avenues of exciting research. The answer to many pest problems may well lie with engineered organisms. But it does seem important that stringent safety measures are applied when introducing totally new and alien genetic material into the environment. Up until now biological control has an excellent safety record, with over 4000 introductions of exotic agents against insects and 1000 against weeds worldwide, and with no major accidents (although the control has not always worked as well as expected!). In fulfilling all the hopes for a pest-free, well-fed world, long may that record continue.

Organic farming

In parts of the world such as the UK, some people have become reluctant to eat food produced by modern farming methods, as they are concerned about the chemicals sprayed onto crop plants and the treatment of livestock. There has been a movement towards 'organic food' and 'organic farming'.

Organic farming means farming without the use of artificial fertilisers or pesticides and rearing animals without the use of hormone growth promoters or antibiotics in their feed. To be allowed to market food as 'organic', a farmer must be registered with the Ministry of Agriculture, Fisheries and Food (MAFF) and must comply with their strict guidelines. Organic farmers also have to belong to farming organisations such as The Soil Association, whose criteria must agree with those set down by MAFF, but may be even more rigorous. When converting land from conventional to organic farming, the produce cannot be labelled as organic for several years because the land will still have traces of artificial fertilisers and pesticides. Conventional chemicals cannot be used to increase yields during this period, so this is often a time of great financial difficulty, though there are grants to help. Organic farming is generally much more labour intensive than conventional farming – for example, manure is more bulky and more difficult to apply than artificial fertilisers. Biological pest control is permitted, but without the use of chemical herbicides weeds have to be controlled by regular hoeing and applying mulches around the growing plants. Yields of crops are generally lower than those produced using conventional intensive farming methods, and if the farmer at any time reverts to the use of forbidden chemicals which are then detected in or on the crop, the farm will lose its organic status. So with all these apparent disadvantages, why do farmers go organic? There are a number of reasons. First, there is an increasing demand from consumers for food produced by organic methods – even supermarkets are stocking more and more organic produce. People are prepared to pay a premium price reflecting the extra effort that goes into the production of the food. Because of this, the organic farmer's income does not have to suffer – indeed it may even increase.

Another reason why many farmers turn to organic methods is that they are themselves concerned about the environmental issues and welcome the opportunity to farm in a more ecologically friendly way, perhaps returning to mixed farming to provide themselves with manure as well as a different strand of income. Thus in spite of the practical disadvantages of a return to farming by more old-fashioned methods, the advantages seem to have the upper hand and an increasing number of UK farmers are making the move to become organic growers.

Figure 6.5.12 Organic produce tastes good and is produced in an environmentally friendly way, and that is why customers will pay more for it.

Sustainable agriculture – is there a future?

There are many problems with food production in the world. Most of the food is produced by the countries with the smallest populations, and many of the countries with the largest populations cannot produce enough food for themselves. Buying food from the developed countries simply increases their debts. Some of the agricultural techniques being used around the world are leading to the permanent destruction of ecosystems and the production of sterile areas where nothing will grow.

For farming to be viable it must be efficient – in other words, the cost of the inputs must not be greater than the overall value of the output (the total crop). In achieving this efficiency, a balance must be struck between **intensive** and **extensive** farming. **Intensive farming** involves growing the maximum amount of product in the minimum amount of space. Modern intensive farming uses expensive labour saving machinery, fertilisers and pesticides to get the maximum yield from the land. When land is expensive and at a premium, this is a valid policy. Many people dislike the idea of intensive farming, but in practice it provides much of our cheap and readily available food. To maintain our present standards of eating, and to help feed the whole of the world, some intensive methods are needed. Used wisely and with full monitoring, intensive farming does not have to be unsustainable. A certain amount of highly intensive farming can also free up land for more extensive methods.

Extensive farming takes up more space but involves less intervention. When land is cheaper and plentiful, it may well be economic to spend less money on increasing the yield per hectare, but simply to plant up more hectares. Traditional dairy farming, in which the cattle graze pastures full of a wide variety of wildflowers, insects and small mammals, is an example of extensive farming. Extensive farming needs to be productive – the farm must be economic to run – but leaves enough space for increased variety of wildlife species.

It is important that society rewards farming methods that do not lead to soil erosion and other environmental problems. On a global scale, this could mean giving financial or practical aid to developing countries that implement sustainable agriculture programmes instead of slash and burn, or at a more

6

local level it might involve paying a premium price for food produced by organic farmers. It is vital that financial and technological aid is provided to poorer countries so that they can learn about sustainable agriculture and set up suitable methods of farming and food production. The less developed nations can also be encouraged to grow food crops for themselves rather than cash crops such as coffee, tea and tobacco for the wealthier nations. Finally there could be a global move towards the use of new varieties of crop plants produced by selective breeding and/or genetic engineering that will survive and give good yields in a variety of different conditions. So the cereal crops grown in the UK would be very different from the varieties grown in Africa or India, because different plants maximise their net primary production in the different conditions in each area.

Controlling the growing environment

Farmers can maximise the growth of their crops by improving the fertility of the soil, by controlling the numbers of pests and by providing irrigation (extra water) when it is needed. However, across enormous fields farmers can have little effect on other abiotic factors. Growing plants indoors in massive greenhouses or sheds allows the grower to take control and influence almost every aspect of the growing environment of the plants to ensure maximum yields. Factors that limit the rate of photosynthesis, such as carbon dioxide levels, light levels and temperature (see pages 185–186), can be artificially manipulated to make sure that the plants are photosynthesising and growing at the optimum rate all the time.

Plants such as lettuces and tomatoes are usually grown in massive greenhouses which may cover several hectares of land. Every aspect of the growing conditions is carefully controlled and kept at optimum levels, from germination of the seeds through to harvesting, using computer systems linked to sensors throughout the greenhouse. Heaters raise the temperature when needed and vents are opened if it gets too warm. The carbon dioxide in the air may also be kept at a level suitable for the plants being grown, so that carbon dioxide is never a limiting factor. Gas heaters are often used to warm the greenhouse, which also produce extra carbon dioxide. The plants are kept well watered, although moisture levels in the air are kept reasonably low to avoid mildew and other fungal diseases developing on the leaves, so along with other data, humidity levels are monitored every 15 seconds or so. Young plants are often planted under white plastic sheeting, which keeps their leaves clean and reflects light back onto the leaves – this can increase yields by up to 15 per cent. In large greenhouses the soil is fertilised at least twice a year, and levels of nitrates, phosphates and potassium are monitored so that fertiliser sprays can be applied if necessary. In some greenhouse systems the lighting is natural, but in others extra lighting is given on dull days, or the pattern of light and darkness that the plants experience can be changed to alter their flowering or fruiting times. Combinations of light-proof blinds and powerful lights producing a broad spectrum of frequencies can simulate summer – or winter – at any time of the year.

Pest control in these large areas of monocultures can be a problem. Robot sprayers apply insecticides and fungicides evenly and at controlled doses. There is legislation to make sure plants do not receive doses of toxic chemicals near to the time of harvesting. In some greenhouse situations, biological control can work effectively – for example, ladybirds and other insects that eat aphids can be used to control aphid populations on plants such as tomatoes in which the fruits are harvested, leaving the leaves and stems behind. These methods are not used for crops such as lettuces, as people tend to object to finding either ladybirds or dead aphids in their salad leaves!

Figure 6.5.13 Controlling the environment in a greenhouse allows farmers to maximise production every minute of the 24-hour day.

An even more intensive method of greenhouse farming, which can more than double production levels, is the use of **hydroponics**. The plants are not grown in soil – instead they are set in gravel to anchor the roots and then water containing all the minerals needed for optimum growth is constantly circulated around the roots. The levels of minerals are constantly controlled to make sure that maximum growth is always possible, as well as the light levels, carbon dioxide levels and temperature as in ordinary greenhouse horticulture. The result is that crops grow rapidly and are kept very clean, ready for the supermarket shelves. More and more types of plants are being grown intensively in this way all the time. However, the method is very expensive – it requires a massive investment in technology and then constant care and monitoring to make sure that the system runs properly. If the temperature is much too high or too low for just a few hours, literally millions of plants could be destroyed. So intensive greenhouse systems are used to produce plants that will give a good return on the investment, such as plants grown out of season, luxury items and other similar markets that command a good price.

In spite of intensive greenhouse techniques such as these, the term 'farming' still conjures up visions of tractors in fields and cows coming home for milking. However, the boundaries of farming have been extended and harvests may be of fish or trees rather than wheat or rice. The techniques needed for such 'farming' are very different from those used on a conventional farm.

Managing the countryside

As well as growing crops and raising animals, farmers and other big landowners also manage huge areas of grassland, moorland and heathland. Each of these habitats can be rich in biodiversity or, with neglect and mismanagement, species deficient and threatened. Farmers and landowners can act to maintain or even increase biodiversity using a combination of the following methods:

Figure 6.5.14 Beautiful plants like these used to be a common sight in our meadows and grasslands. With careful management, some of them will still be there for years to come.

- Grasslands and meadows should be kept down, by grazing or cutting for hay or other winter fodder. Keeping the grasses short allows other plants to thrive and flower. Ancient meadows may have up to 100 different plant species growing in them, including different species of orchid and cowslip. Modern grass meadows planted by farmers may have as few as 10! To increase the numbers of species the grassland must also be spared any fertiliser – most grassland plants prefer poor soil. The policy of grazing land for a few years, then ploughing up, fertilising and reseeding should be avoided, and no herbicides should be applied to the land. Using this type of management, even new grassland will soon see an increase in species diversity of both plants and the animals that arrive to feed on them.

- If grassland is not grazed, then the seedlings of trees and shrubs rapidly begin to grow and the land becomes scrub rather than grassland. The shade from the scrubby bushes stops many natural grassland plants from growing. To restore it to its original state involves scrub clearance – digging out the bushes and young trees, and restoring the land to a cycle of mowing or grazing.

- Moorlands and heathlands are areas of land with peaty soil covered with short vegetation, often predominantly heather. They are often the result of deforestation many years ago, and have become important habitats in their own right. They are particularly rich in invertebrates and birds, including some of our rarest birds such as the curlew and the golden eagle. At times species such as gorse and bracken may begin to take over the heath or moor.

The most effective way of conserving these habitats is the use of controlled burning. This returns nutrients to the soil, and the moorland grasses and heathers recover and recolonise far more quickly than the invading gorse or bracken. As long as the burning is carefully controlled and carried out outside the breeding season, the animals suffer little damage, because they can simply flee to nearby habitat which is left alone by the fire.

Figure 6.5.15 It may seem drastic, but burning is the most effective way of maintaining species diversity and biological health on moorlands and heaths.

Woodland management

Woodlands are immensely productive communities, and wood is a vitally important resource. We use it for construction, joinery, furniture, toys and paper. In the UK alone every man, woman and child uses about 1 tonne of wood per year in various forms. The warm, wet UK climate is ideal for growing trees, and with appropriate management woods and forests can become a sustainable resource. Much of Britain was covered by trees for thousands of years, but indiscriminate felling of trees for timber and paper meant that by the end of the First World War only four per cent of the country remained forested. Increased awareness of the need to 'farm' wood with care and to produce a sustainable crop has increased this to eleven per cent, but Britain is still one of the least wooded countries in Europe.

Many woodlands are not used to provide a regular timber crop. Broad-leaved woodlands containing oak, beech, ash, alder and birch trees have been part of the British landscape for centuries. A few of these woodlands are remnants of ancient forests, but most of them have grown up over centuries on sites which people have at some time cleared and the trees have then recolonised. These broad-leaved woodlands have the potential for enormous species diversity, and are often rich in species such as lichens that are slow growing and only flourish in areas with low pollution levels.

Traditional woodland management – pollarding and coppicing

In the past, woodlands in the UK have traditionally been managed by people in one of two ways. In wood pastures, often in areas with relatively poor soil, livestock grazed the lower tree branches as well as the grass, and the constant grazing meant that seedlings stood little chance of surviving. To provide a crop from these trees they were regularly **pollarded** – their tops were cut off about 2 metres above the browse line. This encouraged the growth of new lateral branches which could be harvested after a few years, when the trees were pollarded again. Woodlands managed in this way have limited species diversity, because the grazing kills off many species, and only tough plants such as holly and hawthorn thrive in the space below the tree canopy.

Another traditional form of woodland farming was found in areas with richer soils. **Coppicing** was used with species such as ash and hazel, and the tree is cut down almost at ground level every 5–20 years. This promotes the growth of lots of vertical straight shoots. The length of time between coppicing varied depending on what the wood was to be used for. For building materials, furniture or fencing the coppices were left for up to 20 years, but for making baskets, sheep hurdles (woven fence panels), thatching or for wattle to build wattle-and-daub houses, the coppicing cycle was much shorter to provide thin flexible branches. These woods would also provide fuel, and some trees were left to grow to full size to be felled for large timber. Because this style of woodland management often left the woodland floor exposed to sunlight, many small plants could photosynthesise and grow there, and because grazing was confined to natural members of the food chain, coppiced woodlands became habitats of immense species richness. By the end of the nineteenth

Figure 6.5.16 The New Forest in Hampshire is an ancient forest which has been used as wood pasture for centuries. Although pollarding is rare now, grazing by cows, ponies, pigs and deer is still common and keeps down the species numbers.

century coppicing was dying out, because society no longer demanded the type of wood it produced. Former coppiced woodlands grew and thickened and after 50 years or more of neglect, much of the species diversity had disappeared. However, in the later years of the twentieth century people became increasingly aware of this loss, and coppice cycles have been re-established in many places, often by conservation groups and volunteers. Because of the long survival period of seeds, many of the old species are reappearing and species diversity is being restored.

Commercial forestry

The biggest increase in forestation and tree farming in the UK is not, however, due to increased use of old woodlands. It is the result of massive tree-planting programmes by individual landowners and, most importantly, the Forestry Commission. Growing trees is a long-term activity – there are high costs associated with planting and managing woodlands, and the crop takes at least 40 years to mature! Government grants help to overcome the cash-flow obstacles, and help to encourage farmers to consider trees as a possible crop – in the UK we produce only about 25 per cent of our paper and timber needs. Commercial woods and forests are largely of softwoods, mainly conifers. These trees grow to maturity relatively rapidly and their straight and narrow growth habit means they can be grown relatively close together.

At the beginning of the development of commercial forestry in the UK, around 80 years ago, large areas were densely planted with conifers. Virtually no light penetrated the evergreen tree canopy, and so hardly any plants could grow and survive on the woodland floor. The species diversity was very poor, and the forests were dark and almost lifeless monocultures in the landscape. However, since then the Forestry Commission has done a great deal of research and very positive work, and now woodland and forestry management looks both to produce a sustainable crop and to manage the environment to ensure maximum species diversity. At the end of the twentieth century, 6.7 per cent of the total land area of Britain was covered by productive conifer woodlands, much of it in Scotland where the mountainous land has poor soil that is not suited to many other forms of agriculture. These modern forests are managed in a way that attempts to balance the demand for timber with the needs of the landscape, biodiversity, habitats for wildlife and, where possible, the recreational needs of people, providing walks and trails through the woods and forests. But most importantly, the forests are managed as a sustainable resource. Felling can only take place if licences are granted, and new planting must replace the trees felled to ensure that the forests are still supplying timber in 40, 50 and even 100 years' time. The UK Woodland Assurance Scheme has been set up to ensure that woodlands are managed as far as possible to protect existing ecosystems, and in many cases to restore native woodland habitats. The Forestry Commission is working with all its landowners to identify sites of environmental interest to ensure that they are protected, and to restore and manage both existing and new woodlands to increase species diversity. This will be approached in a number of ways, including the creation of glades and open spaces that will allow seedlings to develop and enable a variety of plant (and therefore animal) life to thrive. It also involves planting more broad-leaved trees, sometimes interspersed with conifers or in small copses. These and other strategies allow the woodlands to provide rich species diversity within a sustainable and economically successful system of silviculture (tree farming).

Figure 6.5.17 The Woodmark is a registered trademark to show that a piece of wood comes from a sustainably managed forest. It is even possible to trace the wood back to its original woodland home.

Fishing

People fish for food all over the world. On a small scale, individual fishermen with small boats provide food for their families and their own communities, while at the other end of the spectrum massive factory ships of the developed world bring in thousands of tonnes of fish for the international market. Most commercial fishing takes place at sea, harvesting from a natural ecosystem. Developments over the twentieth century have made it possible for fishing vessels to travel further and faster, and to pull larger nets. Radar enables large shoals of fish to be detected, and refrigeration techniques allow the harvest of fish to be processed and frozen either on board the fishing boat or on a larger accompanying 'factory ship'. This means that the catch does not have to be rushed immediately back to harbour, fishing can continue for longer and more fish can be taken home from each trip. The effect of these changes in fishing practices can clearly be seen both in the size of the fish caught and in the size of the total catches made worldwide – both have been getting progressively smaller. It is significant that both figures peaked again after the two World Wars, when fishing was severely curtailed.

Figure 6.5.18 Harvesting fish from the sea is a difficult and dangerous job, but restrictions are necessary to protect against overfishing.

In an undisturbed fish population, the number of fish in the population is increased by the fish breeding, but is decreased by fish dying of age, predation or disease. Once a fish population has reached the carrying capacity of the habitat (see page 526), it will remain fairly stable. When considering the effect of fishing on a population, biologists look at not only the numbers of fish but also their size. So the mass of the fish stock at the end of a year is equal to the mass of the fish stock at the beginning of the year plus the mass of new fish produced and the increase in mass as the fish grow through the year. This is the productivity of the fishery. However, subtracted from that must be the mass of the fish that die from natural causes and the mass of fish removed by fishing. For fishing to be a sustainable activity, the fish stocks need to stay approximately the same from year to year – in other words, the catch must equal the natural yield of the population. This is the **maximum sustainable yield**. As fishing has increased, this natural balance has become lost. Overfishing – removing more than the natural sustainable yield – tends to remove most of the older, bigger fish, leaving only very small ones behind. Left for just a year or two, many of the fish that have been removed would grow considerably and make much better catches for sale. If the fish are caught before they are even mature enough to reproduce, the breeding rate falls and the population of the fish goes into decline. Unfortunately, for some fishermen the temptation of money for fish caught today overrides the knowledge that waiting a year or two would result in bigger fish, a sustainable population and more money. Ultimately this can lead to the complete loss of fish stocks in areas of the ocean.

In an attempt to conserve fish stocks and manage the ocean resources as well as possible, a number of international measures have been introduced. These attack the problems from several fronts. **Net size restrictions** mean that in any given area there is a minimum mesh size allowed for the fishing nets, so that only fish above a certain size may be caught, depending on the state of the fish population. **Quotas** may be imposed, so that fishermen are only allowed to catch a certain mass of a particular type of fish from a particular area. Again quotas can be varied to protect vulnerable populations. If fish are constantly disturbed by fishing, they will not breed. To make sure that the populations have a chance to renew themselves, **close seasons** are imposed – in other words, fishing is banned at the times of year when particular fish populations will be breeding. And finally, to try and ensure that overfishing is not a problem, **exclusion zones** may be imposed. This means either that all fishing boats are banned from a particular area, or that only boats from a particular country can fish there. Exclusion zones are quite common close to the coastline of many countries, to protect the local fish stocks and make them available to local small-scale fishermen. Using a combination of these factors, it is hoped to protect stocks of popular fish such as cod and haddock and keep them available as foods for years to come. But the situation is complicated by pricing factors – biologically optimal fishing rates may glut the market at times and cause low prices. On the other hand, small quotas can leave fishermen and their vessels with no work to do. Deciding who can fish what and from where can set up international tensions, such as the 'cod wars' between the UK and Spain. Nevertheless, if the bounty of the oceans is to be conserved, then compromises must be reached.

Fish farming

Closed-system fish farming

An alternative to fishing wild fish stocks can be the process of **fish farming**. The farming of fish has taken place since ancient times. The early forms of fish farming involved **closed systems**, with the fish kept in specially dug ponds or in tanks. In many parts of the world today the basic earthen pond is still the basis of much fish farming, but the technology is rapidly changing.

There are a number of problems involved in closed-system fish farming. Like any other monoculture, such a system is very vulnerable to disease, which can wipe out whole ponds of fish in a very short time. Also, keeping many fish together in a small space can lead to fighting and inappropriate mating. Finally, waste products and uneaten food can build up in the water. The waste water needs to be disposed of very carefully – it is very high in nitrates and could cause eutrophication if released directly into local water supplies.

To raise large numbers of fish (such as the popular tilapia) or crustaceans (particularly shrimp), the animals are moved from pond to pond at different stages of their lives. Ponds are designed and dug to a size that depends both on the type of fish being farmed and on the number of grow-on stages in their development. The eggs hatch in a hatchery, and the very young fish are kept in brood tanks. Varying numbers of tanks are then used for the growing and developing adults. Each tank needs a supply of clean, fresh water and an outlet so that spent water can be removed. Efficient filters can be used to remove waste products and help to keep the water clean, and each time a batch of fish is moved out the tanks are cleaned before a new batch is moved in. If disease is suspected – or even simply as a precautionary measure – the fish farmer may include drugs such as antibiotics in the water to prevent disease.

The great advantage of fish farming is that it provides a constant and sustainable source of fish without the danger and uncertainty of fishing. The farmer can control exactly the amount of food the fish receive at each stage of their lives to ensure maximum growth, and as soon as they are the ideal size for market they can be harvested to make room for another batch. The fish can be bred to restock the hatcheries, or eggs can be bought in from specialist breeders.

Open-system fish farming

An increasingly popular alternative to closed-system fish tanks is **open-system** fish farming. This uses large cages made of wire, metal bars or nets, which are placed in the middle of lakes, rivers or the open sea. Fish are hatched in hatcheries and reared to a certain size in brood tanks, but from then on they are held in these large enclosures in natural water supplies. These open systems have huge potential for the production of human food, and the costs of running such a system are reduced because clean water is constantly supplied for free, and the waste from the fish simply falls through the cage. Such systems can be used for farming both fresh and marine fish, including salmon and trout. As well as the reduced investment in tanks and lower running costs due to the water supply, the advantages include the following:

- The fish can be supplied with optimal food levels.
- They have more space to move than in a closed system.
- It can be argued that the fish are being kept in a more natural environment.
- Harvesting the fish is easier than traditional fishing.
- Minimal cleaning is necessary before a cage is reused.

However, there are some disadvantages, both to the farmer and to the environment. The farmer still has a monoculture of fish, and out in the uncontrolled environment of the sea or lake they are more likely to be exposed to diseases than in a closed system. Also, accidental damage (a particular risk at sea) or deliberate sabotage of the cages could result in the release of the fish before they are ready to be harvested. Overall, the farmer has less control over the environment of the fish. From the environmental point of view, all the waste from this intensive collection of fish is constantly being released into the water, along with any uneaten food. This may be picked up by wild species, changing the natural food chain. Any antibiotics or other drugs used to control disease in the fish will be released into the water and so could lead to the development of bacterial resistance or damage the ecosystem in some other way. If issues such as these are dealt with, fish farming, particularly as it moves into the sea, could have a very big impact on food production in the twenty-first century and beyond.

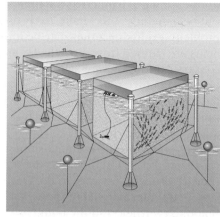

Figure 6.5.19 There are predictions that 40 per cent of our sea food will need to come from ocean ranches by the year 2020. Massive open-ocean aquaculture systems like this will be needed to provide production levels on this scale.

SUMMARY

- Farming methods have evolved from early hunter/gatherers to the specialised management of areas of land to grow crops and raise animals.
- Modern farming aims to increase the **harvest index** – the mass of the usable part of the crop relative to its total mass. In arable farming, the methods used to grow crops include ploughing, direct drilling, monoculture (which has disadvantages in terms of the vulnerability of the crop), harvesting and storage.
- **Fertilisers** increase the yield of crop from an area of land. Fertilisers include manure and other natural nitrogen-rich materials, and artificial fertilisers. Leaching of fertilisers into waterways can cause **eutrophication**.
- **Pesticides** are chemicals applied to crops to control pests – species that compete with the crop. **Herbicides** are used to kill competing plants (weeds), and include **contact herbicides** and **systemic herbicides**. **Insecticides** control insects that feed on the crop or otherwise damage it. Pesticides can cause problems in the environment, particularly if they are not biodegradable, and **biological pest control**, the use of natural predator species to control a pest, is often a preferred approach.

- **Sustainable** farming does not damage the ecosystem, and provides food without destroying the soil. **Intensive farming** aims to maximise the yield from an area of land, while **extensive farming** uses more land to achieve the yield.

- In greenhouses and sheds, the limiting factors of photosynthesis can be controlled, including the carbon dioxide, water, temperature and light levels. **Hydroponics** involves growing plants not in soil but in a solution of minerals, which gives an even greater level of control.

- Natural ecosystems such as grassland, moorland and heathland must be managed appropriately to conserve biodiversity.

- Traditional methods of woodland management include **pollarding** and **coppicing**. **Commercial forestry** grows fast-growing softwood species in a way that both provides a sustainable resource and preserves biodiversity.

- Fishing is controlled to avoid overfishing – that is, removing more fish than the maximum sustainable yield. Control measures include net size restrictions, quotas, close seasons and exclusion zones. **Fish farming** methods may be **closed systems**, with the fish in ponds or tanks, or **open systems**, in cages kept in natural water in lakes or the sea.

QUESTIONS

1 a What are the main differences between farming at the beginning of the twentieth century compared with the twenty-first century?

  b Explain the advantages and disadvantages of monoculture as a method of modern farming.

2 All over the world crops are affected by pests that either reduce the yields or damage the crop once it has been harvested.

  a Explain how plant and animal pests can affect the yields of a crop.

  b How does conventional pest control work, and what problems are associated with it?

  c What is biological pest contol and what are the advantages and disadvantages of such systems?

3 Choose either forestry or fish farming as an example of sustainable agriculture. Describe the crop, what it is used for, how it is farmed and harvested, and any problems that have to be solved for the venture to be both sustainable and successful.

Developing Key Skills

Produce a leaflet for your local NFU (National Farmers' Union) encouraging farmers to consider becoming organic producers. You need to put forward both ecological and economic arguments for the change, whilst being realistic about the level of commitment that such a move would mean.

FOCUS — LOOK TO YOUR LIZARDS!

When scientists are looking to see if a particular human activity has had an effect on an environment, one of the tools they use is **indicator species**, also known as **bioindicators**. In any environment there are some species of animals or plants that are commonly found, but that are particularly sensitive to changes in conditions. Some of these bioindicator organisms are unicellular, semi-microscopic or small invertebrates. But sometimes much larger organisms may give useful indications regarding the state of the ecosystem.

Lizards are very common animals in sub-Saharan Africa, and in many tropical, subtropical and warm, temperate climates of the world. Lizards, like all reptiles, are ectothermic – they are largely dependent on the external temperature for their body heat – and they eat insects. They have also been shown to be sensitive to many pesticides. They have low metabolic rates and relatively simple enzyme systems, so they cannot detoxify complex pesticide chemicals if they breathe them in or eat them in contaminated insects. Pesticide residues accumulate in their body fat, particularly the organochlorides such as DDT. Because lizards are themselves eaten by birds and small mammals, they are an important part of many food chains. If pesticides build up in their bodies, then bioaccumulation is much more likely, with possible devastating effects on large birds of prey or carnivorous mammals further up the food chain.

The obvious advantage of using lizards as bioindicator species is that they are relatively large and easy to see. But does the use of pesticide sprays in an environment affect their behaviour in ways that can be monitored?

In Zimbabwe, observers counted the tree-dwelling lizards *Mabuya striata wahlbergii* before and after the trees were sprayed with DDT. This was done to control the tsetse flies that cause sleeping sickness in cattle and people. In the untreated area, 6.1–19.3 lizards were recorded per hour of observation, but in the treated areas there were only 1.3–12.2, showing a significant drop in numbers. A different pesticide, deltamethrin, had no significant effect on the lizard population. Another interesting bioindicator was the effect of spraying on the frequency of *Mabuya striata wahlbergii* within the total lizard population. In untreated woodland, they made up 76 per cent of the population. In areas treated up to three times their frequency dropped to 72 per cent of the population, but in areas given between 4 and 6 treatments the proportion of *Mabuya striata wahlbergii* fell to only 48 per cent. Thus this species of lizard not only gives an indication of the presence of the pesticide in the environment, it also reflects the intensity of the contamination.

Similar stories have been found in other countries – in southern Mauritania a different species of lizard, *Agama boulengeri*, was identified as a useful indicator species of contamination by the pesticides used against locusts and weaver birds. Lizards are not very good at moving away from polluted areas or at adapting to rapid changes in their habitats, and combined with their important role in a number of food chains, this makes them very good bioindicators of pesticide contamination.

Figure 1 Lizards as bioindicators provide data that can be observed with the naked eye.

Figure 2 The mopane trees of Zimbabwe house the tsetse flies that carry sleeping sickness, and spraying them with DDT to a height of 3 metres gets rid of the flies. But the trees and the area are home to many other species as well.

6.6 Pollution and conservation

People have lived on the Earth for a relatively short period in its existence, but our impact on the environment has been enormous. Even back in our early history, it now appears that we may have hunted species such as the mammoth to extinction. In the years of the twentieth century the effects of human beings on the planet became increasingly obvious as the human population soared while science and technology blossomed as never before. Some of the actions of the human race can only be seen as damaging to the biosphere, whilst in other ways we have made efforts to manage wisely the only home currently available to us.

Pollution

Industry and technology provide the answers to many human problems, but widespread damage to the environment often results too. **Pollution** is the release of substances (or energy, such as heat or light) into the environment which cause damage either directly to people or to the environment. Pollutants are usually either present in very large amounts or they are very poisonous and do not degrade. Pollution has been brought about in a number of different ways, some of which have been considered already and some of which will be dealt with here.

Water pollution

For many years water has been regarded as the perfect place to dump chemical and body waste, but this cannot go on for ever.

Sewage

In section 6.5 we looked at how waterways can become polluted by excess fertilisers and farm waste, and the eutrophication and death of rivers and lakes that can result. However, agriculture is not the only source of water pollution. Human sewage is regularly dumped into waterways – raw sewage in some parts of the world, as used to be the case in the UK until relatively recent times. In Britain, sewage has to go through a number of treatments before being released into a river or stream, but the discharged liquid is still high in nitrates, phosphates and other minerals which can contribute to eutrophication. Untreated sewage contains a high level of disease-causing organisms, and whilst the dumping of sewage into rivers is now controlled in Britain, the dumping of sewage into the sea in a relatively raw state still continues at present, although there are plans to stop this practice. In many areas of the world it is unsafe to swim in the sea or drink the water because of the high risk of catching a disease, from relatively simple gastroenteritis (a killer if not correctly treated) through throat infections to serious diseases such as hepatitis. Even on many UK beaches the microbe count of the water is far higher than is desirable for bathing.

Biological oxygen demand

The amount of oxygen needed by the organisms living in water gives us a good idea of how polluted the water is. Contamination with sewage, farm effluent or fertilisers increases the nitrate levels in the water, and this results in a population boom in the photosynthetic organisms living in the water (see page 545). These organisms use large amounts of oxygen compared with the smaller number of organisms living in an unpolluted sample of water. The oxygen required by organisms in water is called the **biological oxygen demand** (**BOD**) and is measured as follows:

- A sample of water is taken and the oxygen content measured using a biosensor.
- The sample is sealed and kept in the dark for 5 days at 20 °C, to make sure no photosynthesis takes place (this would add more oxygen into the water).
- After 5 days the oxygen content of the water is measured again and compared with the original level.
- The rate at which oxygen has been used up gives the BOD.

For example, in unpolluted river water the BOD is around 3 mg of oxygen per dm^3 of water per day, whereas in raw domestic sewage the BOD is 250–350 $mg\ dm^{-3}\ d^{-1}$. In farm waste or silage effluent, the BOD is many times higher still. The BOD is a very useful tool when looking at the level of nitrate or phosphate pollution in water. By repeatedly checking the BOD of a particular waterway scientists can monitor any changes after an event such as, for example, the release of treated sewage into a river.

Figure 6.6.1 Many British waterways, like this river in Berkshire, remain largely free of pollution and support a wide variety of wildlife.

Industrial waste

Effluent flows into rivers and the sea from many of our major industrial plants. Some of them simply discharge hot water, but even that alters the habitat and changes which organisms can live near the outfall. Others discharge chemicals, including the detergents that produce the browny-cream froth commonly seen in the sea and rivers today. Much of the chemical waste released into rivers is discharged legally – at low concentrations it is felt that the ecosystem can cope with it. Whether this is true or not remains to be seen. Sometimes high levels of chemicals are accidentally released into a river or the sea, and on other occasions chemicals have been released into water before anyone recognised the potential for damage.

If heavy metal ions such as mercury and copper are passed out into the environment in industrial effluent, they can be very damaging. In high enough concentrations these ions can have a severely disruptive effect on the metabolism, and they tend to persist in living organisms, accumulating in the body tissues as they pass up through the food chains and webs. For example, in the 1950s, a terrible disease occurred in the Japanese coastal town of Minamata. Domestic animals fed on fish, and people who also ate fish, particularly the fishing community, developed symptoms including loss of balance, muscle wasting, paralysis and eventual death. Babies were born suffering terrible physical deformities and mental retardation. Eventually the cause was pinned down to the discharge from a factory making chlorine from sea water. It used a process known as a mercury cell, and mercury had contaminated the effluent. The metal had entered the food chain and through a process of biological magnification it reached sufficiently high levels in the fish to poison the people who ate them. Some mercury compounds are harmless, but it has been shown in recent years that even these supposedly harmless mercury compounds can be turned into biologically active molecules as they pass through food chains, so no discharge of mercury compounds into the environment can be said to be safe.

Other metals can cause problems too. In 1988, a batch of the aluminium compounds used in water purification treatments (see page 566) was dumped into the wrong tank at the treatment works and high levels of aluminium found their way into the water supply of Camelford, a Cornish town. It affected the health of many of the inhabitants and they continue to struggle with the after-effects to this day.

Oceans and seas have long been regarded as ideal dumping grounds for anything people prefer not to dispose of on land. In the UK most forms of waste disposal at sea have been or are being phased out, to be replaced with safe and practical land-based disposal instead (which brings its own problems!). Disposal of radioactive waste at sea was stopped at the end of 1982, and of industrial waste in 1992. At the end of the 1990s the disposal of sewage sludge at sea was being phased out.

Monitoring pollution levels

There are a number of tools for assessing the levels of pollution in water. One is the measurement of **BOD** described above. Another is the use of **indicator species**. Certain species of microorganisms and larger invertebrates and vertebrates are found in water of different levels of cleanliness. For example, trout are only found in water that has a high level of oxygen and contains little or no polluting chemicals. On the other hand, various species of worm are found in water of much poorer quality and can survive in relatively low oxygen concentrations. So the presence or absence of certain species can give us clues about the state of the water. Table 6.6.1 shows some of these indicator species.

Table 6.6.1 Invertebrate bioindicators and their pollution tolerances

Type of invertebrate	Tolerance of pollution
Most caddisfly larvae	Low tolerance, only found in water of good quality
Dragonfly larvae	Sensitive – need fairly good quality water
Freshwater shrimps	Fairly sensitive but will tolerate some pollution
Leeches	Tolerant – found in water of relatively poor quality
Many worms	Very tolerant – found even in highly polluted water

Species diversity is another important indicator – in polluted water, fewer species will survive and thrive. A comparison of the species diversity (see section 6.3) of different stretches of the same river, or of the same stretch of water at different times of the year, gives an indication as to whether pollution levels are rising or falling. Finally, **chemical analysis** of a water sample, testing for a range of common chemical pollutants, gives a clear picture of the state of the aquatic environment.

Oil pollution

Ships sometimes discharge crude oil into the sea as a deliberate but illegal action to get rid of waste oil, or to wash out oil tanks. Pipelines and storage tanks may leak, as may off-shore drilling operations. However, the biggest and most dramatic spills happen when massive oil tankers run aground and spill the contents of their tanks on the coastline.

Most oil spills do not have long-lasting effects. The oil is gradually broken up and dispersed by the action of the sea, and then microbes digest the oil and release harmless molecules as waste. But in the short term, and to vulnerable coastal ecosystems, an oil spill has a major impact. The animals that suffer most are the shore creatures such as crabs and limpets, and the sea birds. Their feathers are coated in oil, making it impossible for them to fly or swim properly, they breathe in oil and in their efforts to clean themselves they ingest it, damaging their respiratory and digestive systems. These birds are therefore likely to drown, to die of pneumonia or to starve. Detergents are used both to clean the birds and to break up the oil slick, but these can cause as much damage as the oil itself. Research is beginning to suggest that the environment recovers as well if not better when left to its own devices, although this may interfere with commercial concerns, leaving holiday beaches disfigured for longer.

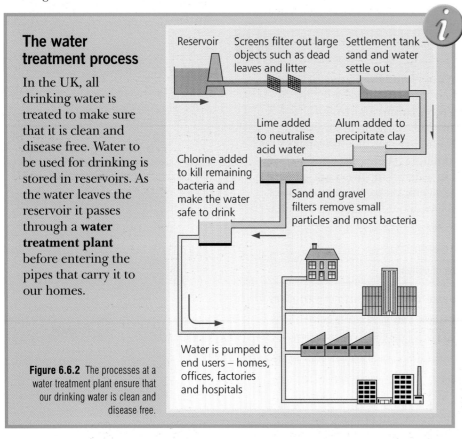

The water treatment process

In the UK, all drinking water is treated to make sure that it is clean and disease free. Water to be used for drinking is stored in reservoirs. As the water leaves the reservoir it passes through a **water treatment plant** before entering the pipes that carry it to our homes.

Reservoir

Screens filter out large objects such as dead leaves and litter

Settlement tank – sand and water settle out

Lime added to neutralise acid water

Alum added to precipitate clay

Chlorine added to kill remaining bacteria and make the water safe to drink

Sand and gravel filters remove small particles and most bacteria

Water is pumped to end users – homes, offices, factories and hospitals

Figure 6.6.2 The processes at a water treatment plant ensure that our drinking water is clean and disease free.

Air pollution

Many of the activities of human beings release chemicals into the air. A number of major environmental problems are now recognised as a result of these polluting activities. One of the best known of these is the phenomenon known as **acid rain**.

Acid rain

When fossil fuels are burned, carbon dioxide is produced along with sulphur dioxide and various nitrogen oxides. These gases then react with the water in the atmosphere to produce **acid rain**. Sulphur dioxide produces sulphuric acid and

Figure 6.6.3 As well as killing trees and lake organisms, acid rain damages buildings and monuments that have stood for centuries.

nitrogen oxides result in nitric acid. The end result is rain with a greatly lowered pH. In heavily industrialised areas of the north-eastern United States, women have reported holes appearing in their tights when acid raindrops have fallen on them.

In areas with plenty of limestone rocks, the effect of acid rain is small as the acid reacts with the rocks and the pH is maintained at neutral levels. However, in other areas without the limestone buffer lakes become acidic, leading to the death of wildlife. Trees are killed by the direct action of acid rain. In Germany in the early 1980s, up to 40 per cent of fir trees were shown to be sick or dying.

The acidic rain causes the leaching of minerals from the soil, including magnesium, calcium and aluminium and some heavy metal ions. Phosphates may be precipitated out of solution in the soil. These changes greatly reduce soil fertility and also cause toxic pollution to the lakes where all the mineral ions end up. If levels of aluminium or the heavy metals get too high, they will poison those organisms that survive the high pH.

It is interesting to note that it is often not the countries that produce the most polluting emissions that suffer most of the acid rain damage. Because of the prevailing high-level winds, many relatively 'clean' countries suffer acid rain from the emissions of others.

The long-term effects of acid rain pollution cannot yet be calculated. Even more disturbing is the fact that many governments and industries are ignoring the warnings of the scientific community, turning down the opportunity to control the emission of the damaging gases before it is too late. The immediate cost of preventative action is financial, and this is why it is avoided, but the eventual cost for the planet could be incalculably higher.

Country	Mass of sulphur dioxide emitted/kg head of population $^{-1}$ year $^{-1}$
East Germany	240
Czechoslovakia	201
Hungary	153
Yugoslavia	133
Finland	119
Bulgaria	112
Spain	99
Soviet Union	91
Italy	90
Denmark	89
Britain	83
Belgium	82
Poland	76
France	60
Sweden	60
West Germany	58
Netherlands	31
Switzerland	18

Table 6.6.2 These sulphur dioxide emissions from 1986 show the source of much acid rain. In the final years of the twentieth century some of these countries united or fragmented, and many began to control sulphur dioxide emissions more closely.

Figure 6.6.4 The amount of acid rain produced by a country is not necessarily the same as the amount of acid rain which falls upon it. The acidic gases may be carried by prevailing winds and the bulk of the acidic precipitation may occur many miles from the site of the original pollution.

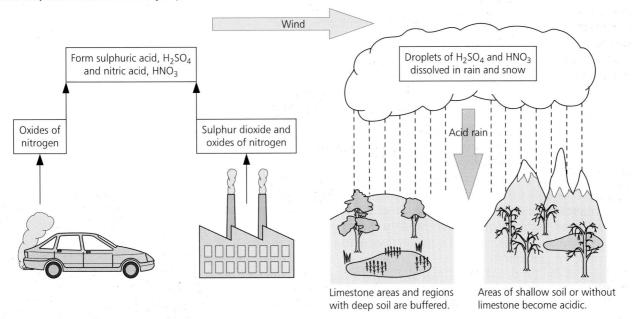

Greenhouse gases

Another form of air pollution is caused by the build-up of **greenhouse gases**. The burning of fossil fuels leads not only to the formation of acid rain but also to many other problems of air pollution. The fossil fuels coal, oil and gas are burned in industries, in our homes, to produce electricity and to power cars.

The other major fuel in the world is wood. These fuels all contain hydrocarbons – molecules containing hydrogen and carbon – and when burned in air they release carbon dioxide, carbon monoxide and water. Releasing large amounts of carbon-containing gases into the atmosphere interferes with the natural carbon cycle, and this may well turn out to be a great mistake.

People increase the amounts of carbon dioxide being returned to the atmospheric pool in two main ways. One is by the burning of fuels, and the other is by the cutting down and burning of tropical rainforests to make way for agriculture. This latter activity causes two-fold damage, releasing carbon dioxide gas by the combustion process and also reducing the number of photosynthetic fixers of carbon dioxide. The rise in atmospheric carbon dioxide levels resulting from these activities can be seen clearly in figure 6.6.5.

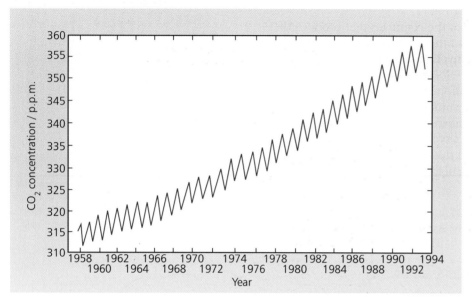

Figure 6.6.5 The burning of fossil fuels and extensive deforestation are leading to a long-term increase in the level of carbon dioxide in the atmosphere. The readings for this graph were taken on a mountaintop in Hawaii. The regular annual fluctuations in the levels of carbon dioxide seem to be the result of seasonal differences in the fixation of carbon dioxide by plants.

The long-term effect of this increase in carbon dioxide levels is not yet known, but it is speculated that temperatures at the surface of the Earth will be raised as a result of the increased **greenhouse effect**. Carbon dioxide in the atmosphere normally acts as a **greenhouse gas** and prevents heat loss from the surface of the Earth, just as the glass of a greenhouse prevents heat loss from the interior. Increased levels of carbon dioxide will cause this effect to escalate, resulting in higher temperatures which could radically change the climate of the planet. Partial melting of the polar icecaps would result in many countries being at least partly flooded. Climatic changes could also cause many vital crop-producing regions to become virtual deserts. Diseases that have been limited to tropical areas, such as malaria, will spread across the world. We have yet to see what will happen – whether the Earth will restore its own balance, or whether the worst of the predicted calamities will come about. The evidence available at the end of the 1990s suggested that global warming was becoming a fact, icecaps and glaciers were melting and the climate around the world was changing. In the meantime, scientists are almost unanimous in their advice to reduce the burning of fossil fuels in an attempt to prevent a continuing escalation in the carbon dioxide levels of the atmosphere.

Greenhouse gases

Carbon dioxide is not the only greenhouse gas – methane, oxides of nitrogen and chlorofluoro-carbons (CFCs) also increase the greenhouse effect. Human actions are adding an excess of 3000 million tonnes of carbon dioxide to the atmosphere each year. Added to this are steadily rising methane emissions resulting from changing agricultural practices, waste disposal and mining. Oxides of nitrogen result from combustion in cars and in power stations, and CFCs are synthetic compounds which have many uses due to their inert nature.

The effect of these gases on the Earth is shown in figure 6.6.6.

Figure 6.6.6 Sunlight passes through the atmosphere and warms the Earth. The warm Earth emits infra-red radiation, which is trapped by the greenhouse gases and keeps the Earth warmer.

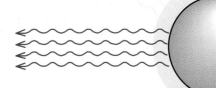

Visible radiation (sunlight) penetrates the atmosphere and warms the Earth.

Some sunlight is reflected.

Infra-red radiation is emitted by the Earth. Some infra-red is trapped by greenhouse gases in the atmosphere which act as a blanket, keeping the heat in.

Worldwide action

There have been a number of attempts to reach international agreement on the issues of carbon dioxide emissions, the burning of fossil fuels and the build-up of greenhouse gases. It is a difficult subject because whilst almost everyone agrees that there is a problem, no one wants to give up driving their car or using electricity whenever they feel like it!

The first conference on world climate change was called by the United Nations Environment Programme (UNEP) in 1979. In 1988 the Toronto Conference called for the reduction of carbon dioxide emissions by 20 per cent of the 1988 levels by the year 2005. In the same year the Intergovernmental Panel on Climate Change (IPCC) was set up, a group of 2500 international scientists and technologists around the world with a brief to monitor and assess climate change. Perhaps the best known attempt at international action on global warming was the UN Conference on the Environment and Development (UNCED) held in 1992 in Rio de Janeiro, generally referred to as the Rio Summit. The result was the Framework Convention on Climate Change, and by 1994 this had been signed by 166 states.

> The ultimate objective … is to achieve … stabilization of greenhouse gas concentrations in the atmosphere at a level that would prevent dangerous anthropogenic interference with the climate system. Such a level should be achieved within a time-frame sufficient to allow ecosystems to adapt naturally to climate change, to ensure that food production is not threatened and to enable economic development to proceed in a sustainable manner.
>
> *Information Unit on Climate Change 1992*

Whilst the summit had a great impact and filled many people with hope, results from it are somewhat slow in coming. The different countries were asked to make commitments about the reduction of emissions of greenhouse gases, but there were no specific timetables. Many countries set themselves targets for the year 2000 or 2005, but few seem likely to achieve the reductions on time or in full. In 1995 structures were set up to try and tighten up the commitments of the various parties to the agreement, and the decisions taken at Rio will affect governmental policy on greenhouse gases for a number of years to come.

The ozone layer

When **chlorofluorocarbons** (**CFCs**) and other similar halogen compounds were first developed, scientists thought they had found some extremely useful chemicals – they were inert, they were inflammable, they were not toxic or corrosive and they were cheap to make. The compounds were soon widely used as coolants in fridges, as propellants in aerosol cans and in the production of Styrofoam, a widely used packaging material. However, in time scientists discovered that CFCs released into the air rise slowly up into the stratosphere where they interfere with the **ozone layer**.

The ozone layer is a layer of ozone gas found in the upper atmosphere of the Earth. Ozone is a form of oxygen containing three oxygen atoms in each molecule rather than the two of ordinary oxygen. The ozone layer in the atmosphere absorbs short wavelength ultra-violet light very strongly, and prevents it from reaching the surface of the Earth. This short-wavelength ultra-violet radiation is harmful to living organisms, causing cell mutations in the skin which can lead to cancer and damage to the eyes which can lead to cataracts and blindness.

We now know that the ultra-violet light of the upper atmosphere breaks down the CFC molecules to release highly reactive chlorine atoms. These chlorine atoms have an unpaired electron (they are radicals) and they react with ozone, splitting the molecule into an unpaired oxygen atom and an oxygen molecule. Radical reactions such as this produce more radicals, causing an escalating problem. The effect of each CFC molecule will continue breaking down the ozone layer for many years.

Reduced ozone concentrations in the ozone layer were first suspected by scientists in the late 1970s, and these have since been confirmed. The most massive changes happen over Antarctica, where ozone concentrations fall temporarily each spring, resulting in an ozone 'hole'. The size of this hole appears to be increasing, and now a similar one seems to be appearing over the Arctic as well.

In 1987 an international treaty called the Montreal Protocol set out plans for a reduction in the use of CFCs. In 1989 a further 93 nations agreed to phase out their production and use of these chemicals. However, current levels of CFCs in the atmosphere will remain for a very long time. The rate of ozone depletion will not start falling until well into the twenty-first century. In the meantime, we are faced with increased exposure to ultra-violet light which will further increase the incidence of skin cancers. All over the world people need to take precautions, using sunscreen, covering their skin and protecting their eyes from the increased ultra-violet radiation.

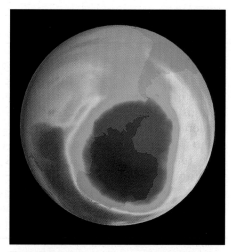

Figure 6.6.7 Every year the ozone hole gets bigger, and the risk of damage to people and other organisms from ultra-violet radiation increases.

Deforestation and desertification

Apart from pollution, humans destroy their habitat in many other ways. One of these is **deforestation**, and this impinges on many issues involving pollution as well.

Deforestation – the destruction of the rainforests

Tropical rainforests are the most productive and diverse of the land biomes. They have formed over millions of years and although they cover only a relatively small percentage of the surface of the Earth, they play a vital role both in maintaining species diversity and in absorbing carbon dioxide from the atmosphere for photosynthesis. During the latter part of the twentieth century a combination of world overpopulation, poverty and greed have driven people to ever-increasing destruction of these vital ecosystems. Rainforests have been destroyed to provide hardwoods such as mahogany for furniture and for other artefacts to supply the developed world. They have also been cut down and burned to make way for agriculture, both for growing crops and for rearing beef cattle. By 1980 around 44 per cent of all the tropical rainforest had been destroyed, and in the 1990s this destruction was continuing at the rate of around 35 acres every minute – if it continues at this rate, in about 90 years' time there will be no tropical rainforests left.

Why does this deforestation go on? Apart from demands for tropical hardwoods as timber, the need for agricultural land might be expected to be finite. However, the result of deforestation is only a temporary gain in agricultural land. After a few years of supporting crops or cattle the land structure breaks down. Without the roots of the massive trees to hold the soil together, rain and wind cause extensive erosion and the land rapidly becomes barren. At this point another massive tract of forest has been destroyed.

What effects could deforestation have? The projected loss of around a million species by the year 2010 (that represents about 25 per cent of the estimated diversity of life on Earth) would be a catastrophe in biological terms. Previous mass extinctions have occurred over millions of years rather than a few decades. Of equal importance is the effect of the loss of vast acreages of tropical rainforest on the world climate. The forests fix substantial amounts of carbon dioxide in the process of photosynthesis. If the forests are destroyed, not only will the carbon dioxide remain in the atmosphere, but burning the trees will release even more, feeding the greenhouse effect further. Deforestation is one of the biggest ecological issues we face, and if not addressed quickly it could have catastrophic effects on the climate and agriculture throughout the world. It is vitally important for the developed world to encourage sustainable forest management in the developing world, while recognising that the local people need to earn money to support themselves, their families and their communities. One approach is to encourage them to plant trees as well as harvesting them at a rate that enables the ecosystem to cope and continue providing wood for many generations. Another idea is to pay rainforest communities for any new medicines that are developed from plants in the undisturbed forest – a kind of 'rainforest tax' paid by developed countries to help maintain the biological variation that will very probably hold the answer to many of our health problems. Eco-tourism is also becoming increasingly popular and can provide a source of income for local people. A local economy based around tourism can be built up as an alternative to slash-and-burn farming.

Another development which may help to save trees in some parts of the world at least is the possibility of using a different plant as a source for paper. Paper is recycled and sustainable forests are used as far as possible for papermaking, but still many forests are permanently destroyed to provide paper all over the world. A woody annual plant called kenaf, which grows very quickly, can provide the same amount of paper in a year per hectare as a pine tree would produce after 50 years' growth. At the moment the processing of kenaf is twice as expensive as processing wood, so the paper produced is expensive, but as the technology develops this may save many woodlands and forests from destruction.

Desertification often follows deforestation, and also occurs all over the world for other reasons. Desertification results from excess soil erosion and it is defined as a process that reduces the productivity of a hot, dry area by 10 per cent or more. Moderate desertification reduces fertility by 10–25 per cent, and severe desertification by 25–50 per cent. In extreme circumstances desertification can create deserts where little or nothing can grow.

Figure 6.6.8 To provide the developed world with goods such as mahogany toilet seats and cheap beefburgers, rainforest destruction is occurring at a frightening rate. In less than 100 years' time there may be no rainforests left, and the effects of this both on the gene pool of the planet and on its climate are as yet unknown. Only concerted conservation efforts by all parties – both the owners of the forests and the consumers of the developed world – can prevent the long-term loss of this irreplaceable biome.

Soil is eroded by the action of wind blowing or water washing the fertile topsoil away. In undisturbed ecosystems, the soil is tightly bound together by the roots of plants, and soil is formed by the addition of humus at about the same rate as soil is lost. If the plants are removed or the soil is loosened and damaged, erosion begins. This can happen as a result of farming, overgrazing, deforestation, physical damage by vehicles or walkers, fire or surface mining. Each year worldwide about 25 billion tonnes of topsoil are lost to farmers by erosion, making it ever more difficult to feed the population.

There are a number of ways of cultivating the soil that minimise loss of topsoil, and they include:

- ploughing with rather than across the contours of a hill

- planting alternate strips of crop plants and soil-preserving plants such as grass or fruit bushes (strip or alley cropping)

- in the USA, water-holding gels have been used in irrigation programmes, and this has been shown to reduce soil erosion by about 80 per cent.

Deforestation almost always leads to desertification, either immediately if the wood is simply cleared for timber, or after a few years of fertility in slash-and-burn programmes. Only by education and human effort can this trend be stopped.

Conservation

The human race has caused many problems in the ecosystems of the world, but climates changed and organisms became extinct long before the earliest people walked the Earth. Whilst it is certainly important to recognise the ways in which people are damaging the environment, it is also valuable to consider the ways in which we work to conserve the world around us.

What is conservation?

Conservation means keeping and protecting a living and changing environment. It takes place when people manage the resources around them in order to give all living organisms the best chance of a successful, shared future. Conservation is a very active, dynamic process which can involve an enormous range of activities, from reclaiming land from industrial use to helping set up sustainable agriculture systems in the developed world, from the protection of a single threatened species to global legislation on greenhouse gas emissions. Conservation is not the same as **preservation**, which means saving something exactly as it is now. Conservation offers considerably more opportunity for change.

Conservationists aim to create healthy ecosystems in the belief that they will support all life on the planet, including human life, for the foreseeable future. Long-term, successful conservation and the success of the human race are tightly linked. The problem for conservationists is that in the short term, economic and political realities can make the two appear to conflict.

Many people involved in conservation are driven by strong ethical feelings that we have a duty to manage and protect the environment of the Earth not only for the benefit of all the organisms that share the planet with us, but also so that future generations will have a healthy planet on which to live. As well as the ethical considerations, there is also an economic necessity for conservation-friendly policies. We have already looked at the impact of the ozone hole, acid rain and global warming due to greenhouse gases, to name just a few of the problems humans have created. If the economics of the world are to stay in balance, if farming and other industries are to continue to function effectively, we must look to environmentally friendly policies. Conservation takes place at many levels and in many ways. Some of them are explored below.

Species conservation

The rate of extinctions is now higher than at any other time in the history of the Earth, and with these extinctions comes a loss of biological diversity which is of vital importance to survival and evolution. In recognition of this, efforts have been made to protect endangered species the world over and help their numbers to recover. This help has taken a variety of forms. For example, the giant panda has been given a small step back from extinction by the setting up of protected forest reserves by the Chinese Government, and by a captive breeding programme aided by the very best of modern reproductive technology.

Pandas are very poorly adapted animals. They are solitary, only meeting up to mate. They eat only arrow bamboo, a plant which dies off at intervals, leaving the pandas to die of starvation. Even when plentiful, the bamboo is very difficult for the panda to digest as its gut is better suited to eating meat than to a herbivorous diet. Pandas are poor parents – the mothers often put their tiny babies into their mouths to keep them warm, and then forget about them and eat them! Yet with all these disadvantages, with human support the numbers of pandas are slowly increasing.

Another example of an endangered species is the Tibetan antelope or chiru. These animals live on the vast, snowy and desolate Tibetan plateau, where bushes grow no more than a few centimetres high. The Tibetan antelope is on the verge of extinction due solely to hunting – they are killed for their fine, light, soft wool which is used to make shahtoosh shawls. These shawls are so fine they can be passed through a wedding ring. They are worth large sums of money and around 80 000 people make their living in Kashmir from making these shawls. The wool is smuggled from Tibet over the Himalayan passes and bartered for tiger bones, much valued in Tibetan medicine. This increases the pressure on the tiger, another threatened species.

There are now a number of national and international organisations set up with the express purpose of protecting endangered species such as these. These include the Worldwide Fund for Nature (WWF), the International Union for the Conservation of Nature and Natural Resources (IUCN) and the United Nations Convention on International Trade in Endangered Species (CITES). IUCN has the Tibeten antelope on its published *Red List of Threatened Animals*. CITES has the antelope on its Appendix 1 list, which means it is illegal to trade in any part of the animal anywhere in the world. Meanwhile the Wildlife Protection Society of India is making strenuous efforts to stamp out the trade in shahtoosh shawls, and has offered an alternative to the buyers and manufacturers of the shawls. Shahmina is the wool of a pure-bred pashmina goat, which can be bred in captivity and which sheds the wool annually without any harm to the animal. Shahmina shawls are almost as fine as shahtoosh, but they are a sustainable commodity. If this alternative is adopted, jobs will be preserved, beautiful shawls can still be made and the rare Tibetan antelope will be saved from extinction.

There are many other organisms on the endangered lists around the world. Dugongs (whale-like mammals), whales and hippopotami are just some of the species that the WWF is working to conserve. Plants too are endangered – cycads, the oldest group of seed plants in existence, are threatened with extinction. Fifteen per cent of them are found in South Africa, where land use changes and the collection of the plants for ornaments and medicines threatens their survival in the wild. WWF is supporting conservation moves

Figure 6.6.9 These beautiful antelopes are on the verge of extinction for the sake of fine shawls.

with South Africa to protect the habitat needed by the cycads, and at the same time is working to prevent the illegal trade and collection of these rare and ancient plants.

Biological conservation

Another strand of conservation work is **biological conservation**, or maintaining the diversity of living organisms within individual habitats. Examples of this type of work are the moves to maintain diversity on farmland by the conservation and restoration of hedgerows (see page 539), and the work on conservation of fishing stocks and minimising the impact of fishing on the marine environment (see pages 558–560).

Environmental conservation

Conserving the environment involves focusing not just on organisms but also on the abiotic factors of whole ecosystems. For example, changing the course of a river will change the availability of water to a large area of land. Similarly, clearing an area of trees changes the light levels available to plants growing in the area. So conserving an area often involves opposing new development, or working for development in a way that will have a minimal effect on the environment of the area.

Nature conservation organisations

NNRs and SSSIs

Sometimes conservationists work to conserve whole areas of countryside, encompassing entire habitats and even ecosystems. Such large-scale protection requires government involvement, and in Britain there are a number of different ways in which areas of land can be conserved, protected from development and allowed to sustain a rich and varied population of animals and plants. The National Parks and Access to the Countryside Act of 1949 gave the Government power to declare **National Nature Reserves** (**NNRs**) and to set up and safeguard **Sites of Special Scientific Interest** (**SSSIs**). It also gave local authorities the power to establish Local Nature Reserves. In 1990 there was an Environmental Protection Act which established the bodies English Nature, the Countryside Council for Wales and Scottish National Heritage. These organisations also work together as the Joint Nature Conservation Committee.

At the end of 1998 there were 196 NNRs covering 80 827 hectares of English countryside. These are relatively large areas of the countryside with high conservation status, but they are often on private land. At the same time SSSIs covered about 7 per cent of England's total area. SSSIs are usually relatively small areas containing a particularly rich diversity of life or a group of endangered plants or animals which thrive in the conditions of that area. Almost half of the SSSIs are owned by public bodies such as the Forestry Commission and the Ministry of Defence, but there are around 23 000 different owners in total. The sites are visited regularly and their status reviewed to see if conditions are improving, staying the same or declining. Advice on management is given where necessary to help conserve the site. The range of SSSIs is enormous, including such places as Appleby Fells in Cumbria, Leeks Moors in Derbyshire, Deadman mire in Somerset and Portsmouth Harbour in Hampshire. SSSIs play an important role in the conservation of many habitats in the British countryside.

The RSPB

Government agencies are not the only bodies that play an important role in the conservation and protection of ecologically important areas of the country.

Figure 6.6.10 There is only one National Marine Reserve, found at Lundy Island where there is an extremely wide variety of sea birds.

Voluntary organisations, financially dependent on their members and on charitable giving, also play a very important role. One of the most active in the UK is the **Royal Society for the Protection of Birds** (**RSPB**). The society has over a million members and owns 140 reserves covering 240 000 acres of land. The reserves cover a wide range of excellent wildlife habitats, from sea-bird friendly cliffs in Yorkshire through dense reedbeds in Cornwall to heathlands in Dorset and flood meadows.

The RSPB aims to try and conserve pockets of remaining habitats, protecting them from the damage so often brought about by changes in land use. This conservation is a very active process – in some places they are changing a habitat to improve it for a particular species. For example, ash and hazel trees are being coppiced to encourage nightingales, and clearings for nightjars are increasing breeding numbers of this rare bird. The RSPB is also working to expand the remaining remnants of the Caledonian pine forest in Scotland, where they own about 12 per cent of Britain's rarest habitat. The work of the RSPB goes far beyond simply an interest in birds – they are a major influence on conservation in the UK.

Figure 6.6.11 The RSPB reserve at Arne in Dorset contains a number of varied habitats including rare lowland heathland and part of a natural marine harbour.

National Parks

The biggest units of protected land in Britain are the **National Parks**. Set up over 50 years ago, they represent 14 000 km^2 of the most beautiful countryside in Britain. The mountains of Snowdonia, the Lake District in Cumbria, the Norfolk Broads, the Derbyshire Peak District, the North York Moors and the wild sweep of Dartmoor are just some of the outstanding areas that became the 11 National Parks in Britain. These areas are not removed from human habitation and life – they are home to farming communities, villages and towns – but they are managed with a view to the best possible compromise between economic demands and the conservation of the countryside and the wildlife that lives there. Unfortunately the National Parks are coming increasingly under threat. The money provided for them by the Government is not enough to pay for all the maintenance and conservation work that needs to be done. Environmental threats to the parks include quarrying, clay mining, commercial forestry using non-native conifers, acid rain, military exercises, noisy boats on waterways, overgrazing by livestock, traffic jams, pollution, unsightly fencing and massive erosion in some areas brought about at least in part by the feet of the visitors who come to visit these lovely areas. It falls to the National Park Authority of each area to manage the park and try to deal with the problems as they arise. The National Parks work closely with many other organisations such as English Nature, the RSPB and the Forestry Commission to try and conserve these ecosystems for generations to come.

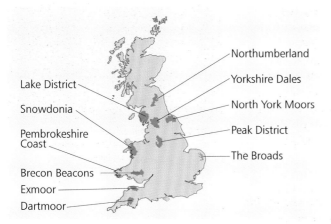

Figure 6.6.12 Almost 10 per cent of England is part of a National Park.

The Peak District National Park

The Peak District National Park is situated largely in Derbyshire. Some of the hills are of millstone grit, a very hard stone which lies under the Dark Peak and the bleak, exposed moorlands. Softer shale lies under the more fertile valleys whilst limestone is the rock under the White Peak, with its grassy plateaux and steep-sided dales. Most of the Peak District has been influenced by people at some time in its history, though much of the countryside is more or less natural. The major problems that face the Peak District are unfortunately the result of human activity. In the wild moorland in the area of the Dark Peak, there are substantial areas where the peat soil is being eroded. This is due to a number of different factors:

- The harsh climate (an altitude of 500–600 m above sea level and low temperatures) means damaged plants regrow only very slowly.
- Summer fires, started by thunderstorms or by careless visitors, kill the plants and can remove the top layers of peat, which take years to recolonise.
- Pollution, particularly acid rain, has affected the moorlands for years. The increased numbers of visitors in cars increase pollution damage further.
- Overgrazing by sheep – local farmers have to be persuaded to manage the numbers and grazing sites of their flocks to aid conservation.
- Trampling – the boots of thousands of tourists hiking across the moors wears away the plants and exposes the soil, and erosion quickly follows.

The woodlands of the Peak District are managed well.

The major threat to their wellbeing comes from sheep grazing the tree seedlings, so fencing to keep out the sheep helps conserve the woodlands.

The limestone peaks and dales are one of the most beautiful regions of the Peak District. The grasslands and woodlands are ancient, and so of particular interest to conservationists. The landscape with its rich variety of flora and fauna is the result of centuries of sheep grazing.

Figure 6.6.13 Many thousands of people visit the Peak district each year, and the paths are being destroyed more rapidly than they can be preserved and protected.

As the number of sheep farmers has fallen over the last century, so the grazing level has dropped. This allows small bushes and trees to grow, shading out the flowering plants. To maintain the environment, sheep farming is strongly encouraged in these areas.

Tourists bring money to the area, providing employment and paying for accommodation, food and souvenirs. However, across the park erosion of footpaths is a problem – too many people can destroy the very ecosystem they have come to enjoy, yet the whole rationale of the National Parks was to provide countryside with open access to the population as a whole. Building up and restoring the most damaged paths while encouraging people to use as many different routes as possible all help to maintain the balance within the Park.

EU conservation measures

As well as conserving habitats at national level, international efforts are also being made to protect different habitats and the organisms that live in them. In recent years the European Union (EU) has set up some major projects to help identify threatened areas and protect them throughout the continent. The 15 member states of the European Union cover the major part of western Europe, and contain several thousand different types of natural and semi-natural habitats, home to around 150 species of mammals, 520 species of birds, 180 reptiles and amphibians, 10 000 plant species and 10 000 invertebrates. Over the twentieth century this diversity has become increasingly threatened by industry, agriculture, urban development and the human population. Half of the mammal species and a third of the birds, fish, reptiles and plants are now endangered. To try and protect both habitats and living organisms the EU has taken three major steps.

- In 1979 the Birds Directive was added to Community legislation. This is concerned with the long-term protection and management of all the bird species of the EU and their habitats. The legislation required member states to identify all their species and then set up measures to protect the habitats of birds that were becoming endangered. Around 1600 sites have been classified as special protection areas, but there is still much to be done.

- In 1992 the Habitats Directive was adopted as a community strategy for safeguarding biodiversity in western Europe. Member states are obliged to identify threatened habitats and species that are of community interest, and to set up special areas of conservation to protect them. The directive lists about 200 different types of habitat in particular, including heathlands, peat bogs, dunes, coastal and freshwater habitats and areas such as the Alpine larch forests and Atlantic salt meadows.

- The most recent EU conservation measure has been the setting up of the **Natura 2000** project in 1997. The aim of this major initiative is to consolidate the work started by the Birds and Habitat Directives and to move further and faster to protect the natural habitats, flora and fauna of the European Union. The member states must select sites of community importance, many of which will be sites already identified by the previous directives. The importance of these sites will then be assessed by the European Commission, along with the member states, and they will form the Natura 2000 network of protection areas. Each country will be expected to declare its sites special areas of conservation by the year 2004, taking the most endangered or most important sites first. They will then be obliged to manage and conserve these sites for the benefit of the biodiversity of the whole European Community. Whilst each member state is free to manage and conserve its sites in its own way, they all have an obligation to the whole community to prevent deterioration of the habitat and repair any damage that is done.

Figure 6.6.14 The European white stork is one species of bird that has already benefited from the European Birds directive – numbers are beginning to climb in its protected habitat.

Initiatives such as these represent a real change in the way people are viewing issues of conservation. The maintenance of biodiversity is recognised as a priority by international and national institutions. Putting such ideals into practice still often meets with opposition from people with vested interests in other developments, but projects such as Natura 2000 offer hope for a future with rather different priorities.

Global conservation

Global conservation aims to keep the atmosphere and the oceans as clean and pollution-free as possible. These conservation measures have already been considered when looking at the problems of ozone depletion, global warming and water pollution. They all have to be tackled on an international scale, as any one country acting alone would have insufficient impact on pollution on a global scale.

Recycling and reclaiming – mimicking nature

Most of the commodities we produce are made by using up natural resources. Much of the paper used in offices, for newspapers, books or even as toilet paper, is made from the pulp of once-living trees. It is manufactured using considerable amounts of energy, provided either directly or indirectly from fossil fuels. Not only are these fuels a finite resource, but also burning them releases greenhouse gases into the atmosphere.

Aluminium is a widely used metal – bottle tops, drinks cans and aluminium foil are all common in everyday life – but extracting this metal from its ore is a very energy-intensive process. Glass too requires a large input of energy to make from its raw materials.

In nature materials are always **recycled** – the dead bodies of animals and plants pass through the nitrogen cycle and restore fertility to the soil. Humans too are now starting to recycle some of their waste materials, helping conserve the ecosystems of the Earth. Recycling paper can save trees and energy, and recycling aluminium or glass is far less energy demanding than making them from first principles. So recycling these materials, or buying recycled goods, will reduce the use of fossil fuels, reduce the emissions of greenhouse gases and, in the case of paper, help save forests from destruction.

Another form of conservation involves **reclaiming** (or recycling) land that has been damaged by industrial use. Mining of any kind has many damaging environmental effects, which include severe soil erosion, nutrient loss, sedimentation and water contamination. Underground coal mining has resulted in large 'slag heaps' – mounds of spoil which grow up around the colliery. The slag heaps near collieries became notorious after the disaster that occurred in Aberfan in South Wales in 1966. A massive slag heap above the village became unstable in a period of prolonged heavy rain and finally slipped, swamping the village school and other buildings and killing 144 people, including 116 school children. By the early 1990s deep mining was phased out in Britain, but opencast mining (excavating from the surface) continues, leaving great open quarries on the landscape. The china clay industry in Cornwall and other areas of the country has produced white 'hills' of waste. China clay is kaolin, a non-toxic, non-polluting mineral that is widely used in paint, plastic, rubber, cosmetics, toothpaste and ceramics. For every tonne of clay extracted, 7–8 tonnes of waste are produced.

Increasingly land used for mining is being reclaimed in Britain with government support, but this is often not as easy as it sounds. In areas used for opencast mining, and sometimes deep mining, lakes can be made within the site, and the spoil treated to grow a variety of plant life. Such reclaimed areas are often used as a leisure resource for the local population, providing walks, nature reserves and, when lakes are involved, fishing and water sports. The most common techniques for reclamation include preparing the site, treating the soil, and then monitoring and maintenance.

Figure 6.6.15 Green thinking – recycling materials makes good use of the Earth's resources, saves energy and helps reduce pollution.

Reclaiming the soil from the spoil

At most mining sites the soil is compacted and in huge piles. The rain penetrates the compacted earth slowly, so the runoff of water is increased, making it difficult for seedlings to become established. The first step in the reclamation process is to backfill the mine with the spoil and soil previously removed, contouring it carefully both to allow drainage and to blend with the surrounding countryside. During this process the spoil is churned up to mix it with the soil. The pH of the spoil is often too low for plant growth, and the most common treatment is to plough in lime and also organic materials, because mining waste is often low in humus. Chemical fertilisers are also used sparingly to help establish a healthy nitrate/phosphate balance. In the state of Georgia, USA, the waste from paper mills and chicken farms is being used to improve the structure and fertility of the spoil mix from china clay mines, and this is so far proving very successful. Much reclaimed land is then planted with grasses, to make it look more attractive quickly, and clover and other legumes are also some of the first plants to be grown. Then tree seedlings are planted, often a mixture of native and non-native species. In Britain, native species such as hawthorn, oak and ash do particularly well. Once plants have become established on reclaimed land, animals will quickly follow. Insects colonise the plants to feed on them, along with birds and small mammals. Within a relatively short time the eyesore of mine spoil can become an area of natural-looking beauty with a wide variety of wildlife making the most of the new habitat. In the USA, mined areas have been transformed not only into recreational lakes and parks, but also into land for agricultural use. Pasture land has been produced for farming, and forests have been formed which as well as being used for public enjoyment can also be harvested as a sustainable source of timber.

Figure 6.6.16 An example of successful reclamation of old gravel works in Blashford Lakes in Hampshire, now a wildlife haven.

Figure 6.6.17 Reclaiming worked-out china clay mines like this one in Georgia, USA can lead to new recreational areas.

When we look at the world from an ecological point of view there is much to be concerned about, and many conflicts to resolve. Perhaps the most serious of these are the conflict between the need to feed the world population and the need for conservation, and the conflict between the ever-escalating energy demands of both the developed and developing worlds and the need to reduce the damage we are doing to our environment. But people are becoming more and more aware of the damage we are causing, and increasingly putting pressure on politicians, agriculturists and industrialists to carry out their business with an eye to the effect it will have on all our futures.

SUMMARY

- **Pollution** is the release of substances or energy into the environment which cause damage either to people or to the environment.
- Common causes of water pollution include sewage and agricultural wastes, which can cause **eutrophication**. Sewage also contains disease-causing microorganisms. In Britain sewage is treated before being discharged, though it still increases the nutrient levels in water.
- Industrial effluents are discharged into water, including warm water which can cause **thermal pollution**. **Heavy metal ions** persist in organisms and can be toxic to higher members of food chains. Crude oil spills at sea affect coastal ecosystems, particularly sea birds.
- The purity of water can be assessed using the **biological oxygen demand** (**BOD**), **indicator species** of animals or plants, a **species diversity index** or **chemical analysis**.

- Gases produced by the combustion of fossil fuels, including sulphur dioxide and nitrogen oxides, form acids when dissolved in water in the atmosphere. These fall as **acid rain**, often far away from where they were produced. Acid rain upsets the balance of minerals in the soil and affects soil fertility, kills trees and lake life and damages buildings.

- **Greenhouse gases** are also emitted from burning fossil fuels. These gases include carbon dioxide, carbon monoxide and water vapour. Greenhouse gases increase the natural greenhouse effect of the atmosphere – more heat energy is kept around the Earth, and this is thought to be having major effects on the world's climate. International efforts are being made to reduce the emissions of greenhouse gases.

- **Chlorofluorocarbons** and other compounds react with the ozone layer in the upper atmosphere, breaking it down. This is leading to increased levels of ultra-violet radiation at the Earth's surface.

- **Deforestation** and **desertification** can result from unsympathetic agricultural practices such as slash and burn. Sustainable agriculture and eco-tourism are being encouraged to conserve rainforest areas.

- **Conservation** is the protection of a living environment in a dynamic and active way. Different facets of conservation include species protection, biological conservation (maintaining the diversity of species within a habitat) and environmental conservation (conserving the abiotic factors such as light levels and water availability).

- Organised conservation measures in Britain include the setting up of **National Nature Reserves** (**NNRs**) and **Sites of Special Scientific Interest** (**SSSIs**). Voluntary organisations such as the RSPB play a large part. **National Parks** conserve large areas in Britain and all over the world. The EU has directives such as **Natura 2000** to conserve important sites in western Europe. On a global level, international efforts are being made to reduce the emissions of greenhouse gases and protect the ozone layer.

- **Recycling** paper, aluminium and glass conserves not only the trees and other resources used to produce them, but also cuts down the amount of energy used. **Reclaiming** land used for industrial processes or mining can provide areas for leisure or for agriculture.

QUESTIONS

1 Explain the damage done to the waterways by
   a sewage pollution
   b industrial pollution
   c oil pollution.
   d For each type of pollution, explain how it might be prevented.

2 Pollution of the air has led to a number of potentially very serious environmental situations. Choose two examples from acid rain, greenhouse gases and CFCs. For the pollutants you have chosen explain where they come from, their effect on the environment, why this is a cause for concern and what, if anything, can be done about it.

3 Conservation is a big issue in the UK and Europe – what does it mean and what can be done?

Developing Key Skills

Design a poster for display in UK National Parks that will bring the key elements of environmentally friendly behaviour home to visitors without making them feel unwelcome!

6 QUESTIONS

1 The table shows data collected from a coastal area. A belt transect was used from the high tide line, inland across sand dunes, to a woodland behind the dunes. Quadrats were taken at five metre intervals. The dominant species in each quadrat was recorded.

quadrat number	sand couch grass	marram grass	lichens and mosses	heather	rye grass	birch	oak
1	+						
2	+++	+					
3							
4	++	++					
5		+					
6		+++					
7		+++					
8		++	+				
9			++	+			
10			+++	+			
11			+++	+++			
12			+++	+++			
13			+++	+++			
14					+++		
15					+++		
16					+++		
17					+++		
18					+		
19					+		
20						++	+
21						+	+
22							++

Key:
+
++   Increasing abundance of plants concerned.
+++

a The plants recorded at this site illustrate a succession. With reference to the figure, explain what is meant by the term *succession*. **(4 marks)**

The quadrats containing rye grass are in an area used for agriculture. This section of the transect illustrates a deflected succession.

b i Explain what is meant by a *deflected succession*. **(2 marks)**

ii Suggest how the deflected succession at this site may be maintained. **(2 marks)**

The numbers of a certain species of ground beetle in the woodland were estimated using a *capture–recapture* method. This involves catching a sample, counting the number caught, marking them in some way and releasing them (sample 1). After a period of time, a second sample (sample 2) is then captured and the number again counted, making a note of the number which are marked from the first sample. At one time of year, in the habitat under investigation, the figures recorded for samples of beetles were as follows:

    number in sample 1   :   284
    number in sample 2   :   267
    number found marked in sample 2   :   63

c Use these figures to estimate the population size of beetles at this time. Show your working. **(2 marks)**

d Suggest how the beetles in sample 1 might have been marked. **(1 mark)**

e State **two** assumptions that are made when interpreting data from the capture–recapture method. **(2 marks)**

(OCR specimen 2000)

2 The figure shows the concentration, in parts per million, of carbon dioxide from the atmosphere which has dissolved in glacier ice over the last 250 years. The carbon dioxide in the ice provides a relevant indicator for conditions in areas far from where these measurements were taken.

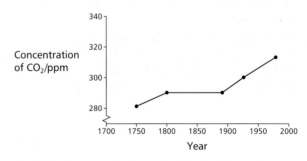

a i With reference to the figure, describe the changes in concentration of carbon dioxide in the glacier ice since 1750. **(3 marks)**

ii Explain how carbon dioxide produced far away from the glacier may become dissolved in glacier ice. **(2 marks)**

iii Explain the likely cause of the changes in the concentration of carbon dioxide shown in glacier ice since 1990. **(3 marks)**

b Suggest **three** measures that could be taken by countries to reduce carbon dioxide emissions. For each measure, explain why it might prove difficult to implement. **(6 marks)**

c Explain how an increase in the carbon dioxide concentration of the atmosphere may affect the temperature of the air above the surface of the earth. **(3 marks)**

(OCR specimen 2000)

3 Read carefully the following passage and answer the questions that follow.

The peach potato aphid, *Myzus persicae*, attacks a wide range of host plants such as potatoes and chrysanthemums. In Britain, the aphid overwinters on peach and nectarine trees. Alternatively, it can survive as active breeding populations in heated glasshouses and protected situations outdoors, especially in mild winters.

Like other aphids, *M. persicae* feeds by inserting its stylets (mouthparts) into phloem sieve tubes, and then relying on the pressure of the phloem sap to force food through its stylets and into the intestine. Phloem sap is rich in sugars, but poor in amino acids which the aphid needs to support growth. Aphids ingest a very large amount of food but as much of it is sugar, they egest this as a sugary solution known as honeydew.

The peach potato aphid spreads through a crop very quickly, although there are never many individuals on any one plant. While feeding on potatoes, the aphid picks up viruses from the host. These are often just transferred from one host to another on the stylets, but the potato leaf roll virus passes through the wall of the intestine of *M. persicae*, through the blood, and then enters the salivary glands. The aphid can carry potato leaf roll virus for a long time.

Field crops, such as potatoes, are protected against aphids by non-specific organo-phosphorus insecticides. These interfere with synaptic transmission in the aphid resulting in paralysis.

Biological control is used in glasshouses. The parasitic wasp, *Aphidius matricariae*, is used to control peach potato aphid in glasshouses where all-year-round chrysanthemums are grown.

a Explain why *M. persicae* spreads very quickly through potato crops. **(3 marks)**

b Describe the ways in which *M. persicae* may reduce the yield of potato crops. **(3 marks)**

c Suggest **two** disadvantages of using organo-phosphorus insecticides in controlling aphids in fields of potatoes. **(2 marks)**

d i Define the term *biological control*. **(1 mark)**

ii State **two** features of biological control agents, such as *A. matricariae*, that make them effective at controlling pests. **(2 marks)**

e Explain why a low population of the peach potato aphid has to be tolerated in glasshouses if *Aphidus matricariae* is used as a means of control. **(2 marks)**

f Suggest **two** problems that might be encountered in using *A. matricariae* in the control of peach potato aphids on field crops, such as potatoes. **(2 marks)**

(OCR specimen 2000)

4 a i Distinguish between *preservation* and *conservation*. **(2 marks)**

ii Outline **two economic** reasons for the conservation of species. **(2 marks)**

In Devon and Cornwall, a large area of land has been made derelict by the extraction of china clay. Once this had been extracted for use in chinaware and paper making, the waste is left as huge tips of white sand. The tips are low in nutrients, such as nitrogen, phosphorus and potassium, and are also low in silt and clay. The natural colonisation of the tips by plants is very slow. It takes about twenty years for even the base of a tip to develop a plant community.

b i Suggest **two** reasons why the base of a china clay tip is the first part to become colonised by plants. **(2 marks)**

ii Outline the methods by which china clay tips could be reclaimed. **(3 marks)**

(OCR specimen 2000)

5 The figure shows a section of a river that flows through rural and urban areas.

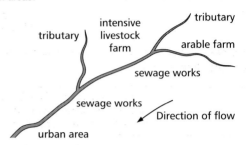

a Explain how the biological oxygen demand (BOD) of water samples taken from the river depicted in the figure could be measured. **(4 marks)**

b Outline **three other** ways in which the quality of the water in the river may be assessed. **(6 marks)**

c Explain the sequence of events that may lead to the eutrophication of the river shown in the figure. (*In this question, 1 mark is available for the quality of written communication*.) **(9 marks)**

(OCR specimen 2000)

6 The National Parks and Access to the Countryside Act, 1949, made provision for the setting up of different types of conservation areas in England and Wales. These included National Parks and Sites of Special Scientific Interest (SSSIs). Under this Act, about 2600 sites were given the status of being an SSSI.

a State **three** features used in determining whether a site should be given SSSI status. **(3 marks)**

b Explain how a National Park **differs** from a Site of Special Scientific Interest. **(4 marks)**

There are conflicts of interest within National Parks between farmers, foresters, conservationists and visitors.

c Discuss these conflicts and the measures that can be taken to resolve them. (*In this question, 1 mark is available for the quality of written communication.*) **(10 marks)**

(OCR specimen 2000)

7 The diagram below shows the way in which four species of monkey are classified.

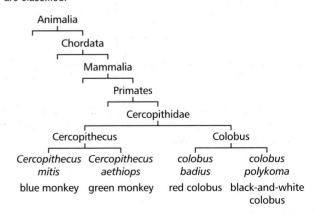

a This system of classification is described as hierarchical. Explain what is meant by hierarchical. **(1 mark)**
b i To which genus does the green monkey belong? **(1 mark)**
   ii To which family does the red colobus belong? **(1 mark)**
c What does the information in the diagram suggest about the similarities and differences in the genes of these four species of monkey? **(2 marks)**

(AQA specimen 2000)

8 The table below shows some figures relating to the flow of energy through a grassland ecosystem.

	Insect primary consumer	Mammal primary consumer	Insect secondary consumer	Mammal secondary consumer
Consumed as food	4.1	24.9	0.17	0.16
Absorbed from gut into body	1.6	12.5	0.14	0.13
Egested as faeces	2.5	12.4	0.03	0.03
Production of new tissue	0.64	0.25	0.05	0.01
Respiration	0.96	12.25	0.09	0.12

a Suggest units for the figures in the table. **(1 mark)**
b i In primary consumers, what percentage of the energy absorbed from the gut into the body is lost in respiration in:
      1. an insect
      2. a mammal? **(1 mark)**
   ii Suggest a reason for the difference in these figures between the two animals. **(2 marks)**
c Explain why the total energy consumed as food by the secondary consumers is less than the total energy consumed as food by the primary consumers. **(2 marks)**

(AQA specimen 2000)

9 A group of students was asked to investigate the factors affecting the distribution of plants in part of a woodland habitat. They decided to use a transect. The group first measured some of the abiotic factors along the transect. Their results are shown in the diagram below.

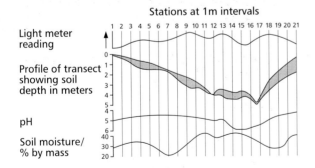

Stations at 1m intervals

Light meter reading

Profile of transect showing soil depth in meters

pH

Soil moisture/ % by mass

They then used a point quadrat to measure the distribution of plants along the transect. Below is an extract from the field notebook they used to record their results.

	Percentage hits at station																			
	1	2	3	4	5	6	7	8	9	10	11	12	13	14	15	16	17	18	19	20
Speedwell	20	5	15	5									5							
Dog's mercury		15		50	30	30			35	30										
Stinging nettle										60										
Bare ground		5	30	15		60	65	25		20	75	20		15		50	80	55	80	

a i Describe how a point quadrat is used to measure the frequency of plants along a transect. **(2 marks)**
   ii Construct a kite diagram to show the distribution of dog's mercury along the transect. **(2 marks)**

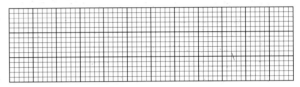

b From these data suggest and explain **one** reason for the distribution of speedwell along the transect. **(2 marks)**

(AQA specimen 2000)

10 Most cereal fields in Britain are sprayed with selective herbicides. In order to conserve wildlife, farmers are recommended to leave unsprayed a 6 metre strip, called a headland, around each cereal field.
a Explain how spraying selective herbicides on a headland might affect the number of insects living there. **(2 marks)**
b The table below shows the results of an investigation to find the effect of leaving headlands unsprayed on the populations of butterflies living there.

Butterfly species	Number of each species recorded on headland sprayed with selective herbicide	Number of each species recorded on headland not sprayed with selective herbicide	χ^2	Significance (NS = not significant)
Small kipper	2	41	35.4	$P<0.001$
Large kipper	1	17	14.2	$P<0.001$
Large white	38	56	3.4	NS
Holly blue	13	29	6.1	$P<0.05$
Hedge brown	59	93	7.6	$P<0.05$
Small heath	0	11	11.0	$P<0.01$
Ringlet	23	52	11.2	$P<0.01$

i Why was a X^2 (chi-squared) test applied to the results? **(1 mark)**
ii What conclusions can be drawn from the results of the χ^2 test? **(3 marks)**

(AQA specimen 2000)

7 MICROBES AND BIOTECHNOLOGY

Introduction

The lives of human beings and microorganisms are closely interlinked. The relationship is very positive in many ways, but has also caused untold death and devastation. The types of microorganisms that have an impact on human life include bacteria, viruses, fungi and protoctists. Each has its own characteristic structure and biochemistry, and the more we understand about these organisms the better able we are to use them to the benefit of the human race. Microbiologists have developed a number of techniques that make it possible to study these organisms.

One of the most obvious interactions between microorganisms and people is disease. Viruses, bacteria, fungi, protoctista and larger animals such as worms all attack people in different ways, but each type is capable of causing death. In the battle against disease we need to understand how microorganisms spread from one individual to another, how they invade and cause symptoms of illness and how they can be destroyed. Malaria, AIDS, TB, tonsillitis, 'flu, the common cold – the list of infectious diseases is almost endless. But the impact of many diseases is slowly being reduced as vaccination programmes, public health awareness, clean water sources and effective drugs are reducing erstwhile killers to mere inconveniences. However, we should never underestimate the power of disease – even today, more children die each year from sickness and diarrhoea than from any other cause.

Not all diseases are caused by microorganisms. Aspects of human lifestyle, both in the developed and the developing world, can lead to life-threatening diseases. Yet even where the causes of such diseases as lung cancer and heart disease are well understood, many people refuse to adapt their lifestyles to avoid the known risk factors.

Microbes may cause disease, but through the ages people have also managed to use them in a variety of beneficial ways. Making wine and baking bread are examples of biotechnology that have been around for centuries, whilst newer technologies include the treatment of sewage, the manufacture of penicillin and the use of isolated enzymes in industrial processes. Using microorganisms in industrial scale reactions brings its own difficulties, and special bio-reactors have been designed to carry out the task. Moving ever forward, biotechnologists can manipulate the DNA of a variety of organisms in the process known as **genetic engineering** (now often called genetic modification). A new and rapidly growing area of science and technology, genetic manipulation has great potential both to benefit and to damage the human population. In this area of biotechnology more than in any other, ethical issues are an important part of the discussion about how far and how fast the technology should develop.

Figure 1 Biotechnology – the area of science and technology that has given us bread, sewage treatment and Dolly the genetically engineered sheep.

FOCUS 'FLU'S DEADLY SECRET

Influenza – more commonly referred to as 'flu – is a relatively common respiratory disease that can be a killer. It is highly infectious and has a very short incubation period. These two factors mean it can cause huge epidemics and even pandemics, affecting people in many countries at the same time. Three 'flu pandemics have been recorded in this century alone, in 1918, 1957 and 1968.

'Flu is caused by a virus which occurs in three strains – influenza A, B and C. Strain A in particular causes severe disease. 'Flu infects the ciliated epithelial cells of the respiratory system, causing them to die. This leaves the airways open to infection, and many of the deaths associated with 'flu are from severe secondary bacterial infections on top of the original viral invasion. The people most likely to die of 'flu are the elderly and anyone who is prone to asthma or heart disease.

Each year the 'flu virus is subtly different: it mutates rapidly so that the antigenic structures on the surface of the virus change. The change is usually quite small, so having 'flu one year leaves you with some immunity against infection for the next. But every so often there is a major change in the surface antigens, and this heralds a 'flu epidemic or pandemic because no-one has any 'almost right' antibodies ready.

Fighting 'flu

The symptoms of 'flu include fever, often accompanied by shivering and sweating, feeling very unwell and unable to do anything, loss of appetite, aching muscles and painful joints. In addition many people suffer from severe headaches, sore throats and shortness of breath. If no secondary infection sets in the disease lasts for about 5–7 days before the fever goes down and convalescence begins. The lungs and the heart can both be severely affected. The exhaustion which follows a bout of 'flu can last from 6–12 weeks, even in patients without secondary infections.

Any secondary bacterial infections can be treated using antibiotics but there is as yet no specific drug to tackle the 'flu virus itself. A major pharmaceutical company claims to have developed a drug to reduce the severity of the disease, but initial trials in the UK gave inconclusive results in the most vulnerable groups. There are 'flu vaccines, but because of the changing nature of the virus, a different vaccine is needed each year. A cocktail is made up of the type A and B strains thought most likely to cause disease in any one year, and this vaccine is then made available to those in high risk groups.

'Flu viruses seem to originate or mutate in other species, particularly birds and pigs, and then cross the species barrier to humans. The great pandemic of Spanish 'flu that struck after the First World War led to around 40 million deaths around the world, and scientists fear that the same thing may happen again.

No-one yet fully understands why this Spanish strain was so virulent, but the answer now seems near at hand. Tissue has been recovered from the bodies of some of its victims buried in permafrost in Norway and Alaska, along with lung tissue from a First World War soldier who was also a 'flu victim. The genetic code that caused 40 million deaths can now be unravelled, and it is hoped that this will make it possible to prepare suitable vaccines, and possibly drugs, for when a similar deadly virus appears again. The question is not if, but when – and we must be prepared.

Figure 1 So far the only effective treatment for 'flu is rest, warmth, plenty of fluids (to avoid dehydration) and mild painkillers. However, it will surely not be long before some strains of 'flu, at least, become vulnerable to drugs.

Figure 2 In 1918–19, the nations that were already tired and weary from the bloodbath of the First World War were particularly vulnerable to the most virulent 'flu pandemic ever recorded.

7.1 Microbiology

In the air, in the water, all over the surface of your skin and virtually everywhere on the Earth's surface, millions of microorganisms exist. We are usually unaware of their presence, except for some that play a role in maintaining the nitrogen cycle and other nutrient cycles for all other living organisms, or others that cause diseases in animals or plants. Microorganisms are ancient – it seems likely that they were the earliest forms of life on Earth. Recent evidence from meteor fragments has even led some scientists to suspect that microorganisms (nanobacteria) may also have existed on other planets, in the past if not at present. In this chapter we shall be looking in more detail at different types of microorganisms.

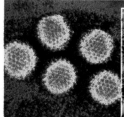
A respiratory tract virus

Bacteria which causes pneumonia and bronchitis

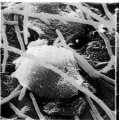
Athlete's foot fungus

A protozoan that causes a sexually transmitted disease

Figure 7.1.1 The organisms grouped together in the study of microbiology – viruses, prokaryotes, protoctists and fungi – are very diverse, with few structures in common. They are classified separately and do not form a single group.

Microbiology is the study of microorganisms which are classified in four groups:

- viruses
- prokaryotae (prokaryotes)
- protoctista (protoctists)
- fungi.

The great majority of these organisms, with the exception of some of the fungi, are so small that they can only be studied using a microscope.

Viruses

What is a virus?

Viruses are the smallest of all the microorganisms, and the least well understood. They range in size from 20 nm to 300 nm – about one fiftieth of the size of the average bacterium. It is still a matter of some debate whether they should be classified as living organisms or not. Viruses are not cells, but arrangements of genetic material and protein which invade other living cells and take over their biochemistry in order to reproduce themselves. It is because of this reproduction, and the fact that they change and evolve in an adaptive way that viruses are sometimes classed as living organisms. The presence of viruses as disease-causing agents was suspected by biologists in the late nineteenth century, but it was not until 1935 that the first virus was extracted, purified and studied by Wendall Stanley, an American biochemist. The leaves of tobacco plants are prone to an unpleasant blotchy disease, and no one could find its cause. Stanley pressed the juice from around 1300 kg of diseased tobacco leaves and after extraction and purification he produced pure needle-like crystals. If these crystals were dissolved in water and painted onto tobacco leaves, they caused the disease. The particles were called **tobacco mosaic virus** (TMV). It was obvious that the crystals were not living in the usual sense of the word, yet they retained the ability to cause disease. Viruses cannot be seen using a light microscope because they are usually smaller than half a wavelength of light. With the development of the electron microscope, the TMV particles were shown to be rod-like structures made up of a protein coat formed around a core of RNA.

The structure of viruses

Viruses usually have geometric shapes and they share a similar basic structure, made up of genetic material, a protein coat and sometimes an envelope. There is considerable variation in the sort of genetic material they possess, the structure of their protein coat and whether or not they have an envelope. The protein coat or **capsid** is made up of simple repeating protein units known as **capsomeres**, arranged in different ways. This structure of repeating protein units means that less genetic material is needed to code for the production of the protein coat, so the assembling of the protein coat in the host cell is kept as simple as possible.

Because viruses invade and take over living cells to reproduce, they all cause damage and disease of some sort. Many viruses can withstand drying and long periods of storage without losing their ability to infect cells – they are remarkably persistent in both the laboratory and in nature. There are very few drugs that have any effect on viruses, and those that do only work in very specific instances – for example, the drug acyclovir can help prevent herpes (cold sores and genital herpes) by inhibiting the enzyme DNA polymerase of the herpes simplex virus, preventing it from replicating within the host cells. In some viruses the genetic material and protein coat are covered by a lipid envelope, produced from the host cell. The presence of the envelope makes it easier for the viruses to pass from cell to cell, but it makes them vulnerable to substances such as ether which dissolve the lipid.

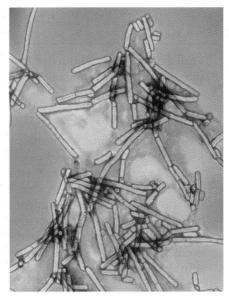

Figure 7.1.2 The tiny rod-shaped particles of the tobacco mosaic virus have a devastating effect on the leaves of the tobacco plant, destroying the crop and causing financial hardship to the growers.

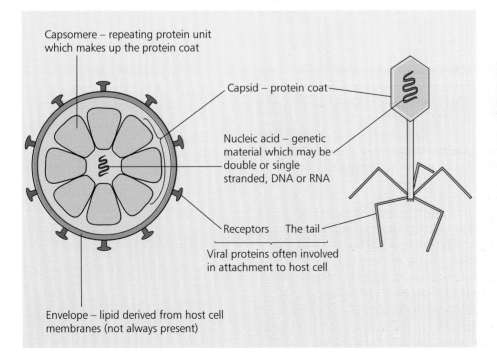

Capsomere – repeating protein unit which makes up the protein coat

Capsid – protein coat

Nucleic acid – genetic material which may be double or single stranded, DNA or RNA

Receptors   The tail

Viral proteins often involved in attachment to host cell

Envelope – lipid derived from host cell membranes (not always present)

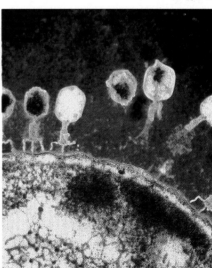

Figure 7.1.3 The general structure of a virus. T-bacteriophage is a virus that infects bacteria. It injects its genetic material into the bacterium.

Viral genetic material can be DNA or RNA, and the nucleic acid is sometimes double stranded and sometimes single stranded. The way in which the viral genetic material is used in the host cell to make new viruses depends on whether the virus has DNA or RNA as the genome. If the virus contains DNA, this acts directly as a template both for new viral DNA and for the mRNAs needed to synthesise viral proteins. Such viral proteins include new capsid molecules and also enzymes that bring about the assembly of the new virus particles, or that break down the host cell DNA to provide new nucleotides. Examples of DNA viruses include the smallpox virus, adenoviruses (which cause colds) and bacteriophages (viruses which infect bacteria) such as λ-phage. If, on the other hand, the viral nucleic acid is RNA, there is a different sequence of events. The viral RNA directs the synthesis of an enzyme called **reverse transcriptase** which makes DNA molecules corresponding to the viral genome. This DNA is then used as a template to make new viral proteins and ultimately a new viral RNA genome. Examples of RNA viruses include tobacco mosaic virus and HIV (human immunodeficiency virus).

Viruses attach to their host cells by means of specific proteins (antigens) known as **virus attachment particles** (VAPs). These respond to particular receptor molecules on the host surface, and because of this viruses are often quite specific in the tissue they attack.

Virus life cycles

Viruses attack their host cells in various ways. Phages (viruses that infect bacterial cells) such as T2 bacteriophage inject their genetic material into the host cell, leaving the bulk of the viral material outside the bacterium. The viral DNA forms a circle or **plasmid** within the bacterium, and then the infection can take two possible routes.

The lysogenic pathway

Many viruses are **non-virulent** when they first enter the host cell. They insert their DNA into the host DNA so that it is replicated every time the host cell divides. This inserted DNA is called a **provirus**. mRNA is not produced from the viral DNA because one of the viral genes codes for a repressor protein, which makes it impossible to translate the rest of the viral genetic material. During this period of **lysogeny**, when the virus is part of the reproducing host cells, the virus is said to be **dormant**.

The lytic pathway

Under certain conditions, the amount of repressor protein decreases, and the viral genetic material is then replicated independently of the host DNA. Mature viruses are made and eventually the host cell bursts, releasing large numbers of new virus particles to invade other cells. This destruction of the host cell is called **lysis**. The virus is said to have become **virulent** (disease causing) and the process of replicating and killing cells is known as the **lytic pathway**. The two pathways are shown in the life cycle of the T2 bacteriophage shown in figure 7.1.4.

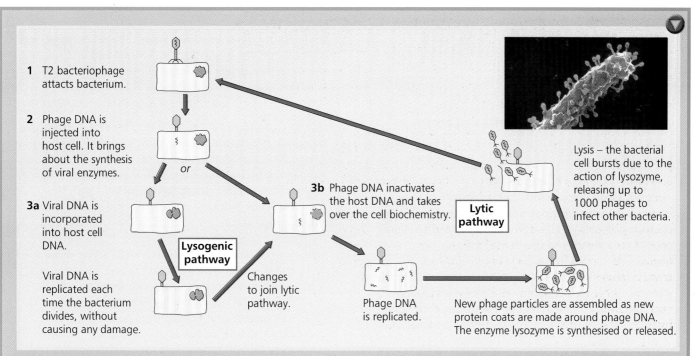

1. **T2 bacteriophage attacts bacterium.**

2. **Phage DNA is injected into host cell. It brings about the synthesis of viral enzymes.**

or

3a Viral DNA is incorporated into host cell DNA.

Viral DNA is replicated each time the bacterium divides, without causing any damage.

Lysogenic pathway

Changes to join lytic pathway.

3b Phage DNA inactivates the host DNA and takes over the cell biochemistry.

Phage DNA is replicated.

New phage particles are assembled as new protein coats are made around phage DNA. The enzyme lysozyme is synthesised or released.

Lytic pathway

Lysis – the bacterial cell bursts due to the action of lysozyme, releasing up to 1000 phages to infect other bacteria.

Figure 7.1.4 The life cycle of the T2 bacteriophage.

Retrovirus life cycles

Other viruses, particularly those with RNA as their genetic material, have a rather different life cycle. For example, the **retroviruses**, which include the HIV virus which causes AIDS, have RNA as their genetic material. This viral RNA cannot be used as mRNA, but is translated into DNA by the specific enzyme **reverse transcriptase** in the cytoplasm of the host cell. The viral DNA made in this way then passes into the nucleus of the host cell, where it is inserted into the host DNA. Then the host transcriptase enzymes make viral mRNA and new viral genome RNA. New viral material is synthesised using the mRNA, and the new viral particles leave the cell by **exocytosis** – they are emptied out from membrane-lined vesicles at the surface of the cell. The host cell continues to function as a virus-making factory.

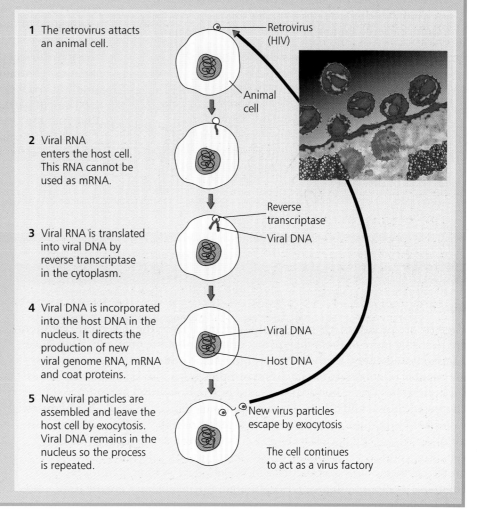

1. The retrovirus attacts an animal cell.

Retrovirus (HIV)

Animal cell

2. Viral RNA enters the host cell. This RNA cannot be used as mRNA.

3. Viral RNA is translated into viral DNA by reverse transcriptase in the cytoplasm.

Reverse transcriptase
Viral DNA

4. Viral DNA is incorporated into the host DNA in the nucleus. It directs the production of new viral genome RNA, mRNA and coat proteins.

Viral DNA
Host DNA

5. New viral particles are assembled and leave the host cell by exocytosis. Viral DNA remains in the nucleus so the process is repeated.

New virus particles escape by exocytosis

The cell continues to act as a virus factory

Figure 7.1.5 The life cycle of a retrovirus.

Viruses and disease

Viruses cause disease in the animal, plant or bacterial cells that they invade. They bring about disease in several ways. The most obvious is by the lysis of the host cells. Some viruses cause the host cells to release their own lysosomes, enzymes that digest the cells from the inside. Other viruses cause the production of toxins which inhibit the host cell metabolism.

Viral infections are often specific to particular tissues – for example, the adenoviruses that cause colds affect the tissues of the respiratory tract, but do not damage the cells of the brain or the intestine. This specificity seems to be due to the presence or absence of specific receptors on cell surfaces to which viruses bind. Each different type of cell has its own receptors and different types of virus can only bind to certain receptors. The presence or absence of these receptors determines whether a group of living organisms is vulnerable to attack by viruses at all. For example, the angiosperms (flowering plants) are vulnerable to viral diseases, but the gymnosperms (conifers and their relatives) are not.

Viruses are well known as the causative agents of diseases such as 'flu, measles and AIDS. Research also shows that in some cases they seem to play a role in the development of cancers. Certain animal cancers have been clearly linked to viral infection – for example, the human papilloma virus responsible for warts on the skin, including genital warts, has been linked with precancerous and cancerous changes in the cells of the cervix.

Treating viral diseases is extremely difficult because so far no one has found the viral equivalent of antibiotics, the drugs that miraculously enabled us to overcome many bacterial diseases. The present approaches which have had some limited success are:

- drugs that interfere with viral enzymes – for example acyclovir which inhibits DNA polymerase
- preventing replication and transcription – research is underway to develop drugs with a nucleotide sequence complementary to part of the viral genome, thus blocking replication and transcription
- interferons – these are part of the body's natural defences against viruses which render cells next to virus-infected cells immune to attack by the virus. When they were first discovered interferons caused a great deal of excitement, but so far they have not had a major impact on the battle against viruses
- antiviral vaccines containing weakened or dead viruses are already in common use against diseases such as polio and rabies, and the vaccine against smallpox was a major factor in the worldwide eradication of that disease. However, there is always a risk of active viral particles being given in the vaccine, causing the very disease against which you are seeking immunisation. Research is underway to produce vaccines that contain only the virus attachment particles on the outer protein coat, so that immunity can be given with no risk of the disease. The technique should allow us to produce safe vaccines for a wide range of pathogenic viruses.

Prokaryotes

About bacteria

Bacteria are prokaryotic organisms that are invisible to the naked eye, yet there are probably more of them than of any other form of life on Earth. They have adapted to fill almost every niche from the Arctic wastes to hot springs. They are capable of obtaining energy by autotrophic nutrition – some directly from sunlight by bacterial photosynthesis, and others from inorganic substances in chemosynthesis – and also by heterotrophic nutrition from organic substances. Compared with most eukaryotic cells, bacteria are very small. For example, the average volume of a bacterial cell is 1–5 μm^3, whereas the smallest eukaryotic cells (yeasts) have a cell volume of 20–50 μm^3 and the smallest algal cells are around 5000 μm^3 in volume. All bacterial cells have certain features in common, as shown in figure 7.1.6, although the details vary greatly from one type to another.

Prokaryotic and eukaryotic cells

Living organisms are made up of cells. Those cells, and therefore the organisms which they make up, can be divided into two major groups – the **prokaryotes** and **eukaryotes**. The prokaryotes (which include bacteria) are the oldest group, thought to have appeared about 3500 million years ago. The eukaryotes arrived about 2000 million years ago, and include all the other groups of living organisms. There are many differences between them, the main one being that although prokaryotes contain genetic material, they lack the membrane-bound nucleus typical of eukaryotic cells.

The main differences between the two types of cells are summarised in table 7.1.1.

	Prokaryote	Eukaryote
Cell size	0.5 – 5.0 μm in diameter	> 40 μm in diameter
Genome	Circular DNA in the cytoplasm with no nuclear membrane	Linear DNA forming chromosomes contained in a nuclear envelope
Protein synthesis	Smaller ribosomes than those of eukaryotes, no endoplasmic reticulum	Ribosomes may be attached to endoplasmic reticulum
Organelles	Few	Many
Cell walls	All have rigid walls made of peptidoglycan, a crosslinked substance containing polysaccharide and peptide chains	Many have no cell walls. Plant cell walls are made of rigid polysaccharide with cellulose for strength. Fungal cell walls are made of rigid polysaccharide with chitin for strength
Flagellae	Simple, no tubules, 20 nm in diameter	Complex, 9 + 2 tubules, 200 nm in diameter
Site of respiration	Cytoplasmic membranes, or possibly mesosomes	Mitochondria
Photosynthesis	No chloroplasts	Chloroplasts with complex internal structure

Table 7.1.1 Prokaryotic and eukaryotic cells

Nutrition in microorganisms

Autotrophic organisms make organic compounds from carbon dioxide, mostly by **photosynthesis**, using solar energy and transferring it to chemical energy in the bonds of glucose molecules. A few organisms are **chemosynthetic**, using chemical energy to synthesise organic compounds. **Heterotrophic** organisms take in organic compounds by feeding on autotrophs or other heterotrophs.

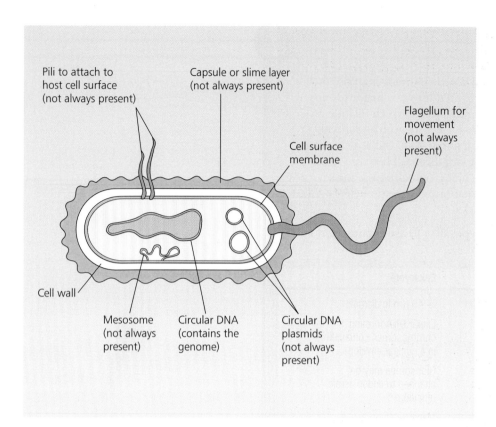

Figure 7.1.6 Structure of a typical bacterium.

Pili to attach to
host cell surface
(not always present)

Capsule or slime layer
(not always present)

Flagellum for
movement
(not always
present)

Cell surface
membrane

Cell wall

Mesosome
(not always
present)

Circular DNA
(contains the
genome)

Circular DNA
plasmids
(not always
present)

Bacterial cell walls

All bacterial cells have a cell wall. Bacterial cells usually contain a higher concentration of solutes than the medium around them, so water tends to move into the cells by osmosis. The cell wall prevents the bacterial cells swelling and bursting. It also maintains the shape of the bacterium and gives support and protection to the contents of the cell. Bacterial cell walls are made up of the cell surface membrane and a layer of **peptidoglycan**, also known as **murein**. Peptidoglycan consists of many parallel polysaccharide chains with short peptide cross-linkages, forming an enormous molecule with a net-like structure.

There are two distinct types of bacterial cell wall. The differences affect the way bacteria react to antibiotics, and also the way they take up stains. An important method of distinguishing different types of bacteria is based on the way they take up **Gram's stain**. This staining technique, developed by Hans Christian Gram in 1884, is still in use today. It involves treatment with a blue/purple stain called crystal violet, a decolorisation stage using an alcohol/acetone mixture, and then a red stain called safranine. Before·staining bacteria are colourless. **Gram-positive** bacteria such as *Staphylococcus aureus* take up the crystal violet and are not affected by the rest of the process, so they appear bluish purple under the light microscope, as shown in figure 7.1.7.

The cell walls of Gram-positive bacteria have two basic layers, the plasma membrane and a thick layer of peptidoglycan which contains a substance called **teichoic acid** within its net-like structure. The crystal violet binds to the teichoic acid and resists subsequent decolorisation giving the positive blue/purple colour at the end of the process. In **Gram-negative** bacteria, the cell wall has three basic layers – the plasma membrane, a thinner layer of peptidoglycan with no teichoic acid, and then an outer membrane-like layer

Figure 7.1.7 Gram-positive bacteria stain violet, a clear indication of the structure of the cell walls. This Gram stain of a smear from a mouth shows a mixture of Gram-positive and Gram-negative cocci and bacilli.

made up of lipopolysaccharides. Any crystal violet which does bind is readily decolorised and replaced with red safranine dye, so the treated bacterial cells appear red under the light microscope. The different structures of Gram-positive and Gram-negative bacterial cell walls are shown in figure 7.1.8.

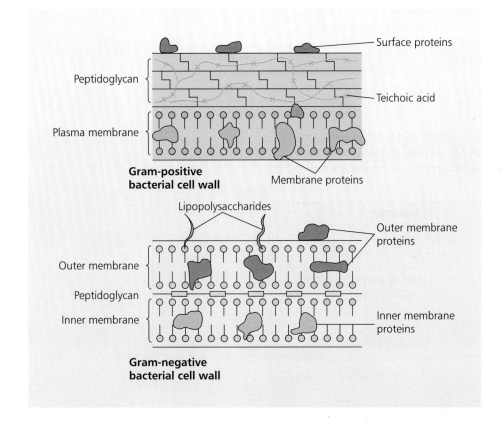

Figure 7.1.8 The structure of Gram-positive and Gram-negative bacterial cell walls.

Within the bacterial cell wall is the cell surface membrane. This is very similar in both structure and function to the membranes of eukaryotic cells, but in bacteria the cell surface membrane is also the site of some respiratory enzymes (bacteria have no mitochondria). In some bacterial cells, such as *Bacillus subtilis*, a common soil bacterium, the membrane shows infoldings known as **mesosomes**. There is still some debate about their function. Some people think they may be simply an artefact that results from the drastic treatment cells undergo before an electron micrograph can be made. Others believe mesosomes are associated with enzyme activity, particularly during the separation of DNA strands and the formation of new cross-walls during replication.

Some bacteria have a **capsule** or **slime layer** around their cell wall. The capsule may be composed of starch, gelatine, protein or glycolipid (a lipid containing a sugar molecule). The capsule protects the bacterium from phagocytosis by white blood cells, and also prevents the bacterial antigens from activating a response in the host immune system. In these ways a capsule helps a bacterium to be pathogenic (to cause disease) and some very unpleasant human diseases are caused by bacteria with capsules, as shown in table 7.1.2. However, there are many bacteria with capsules that do not cause disease, and it seems likely that capsules evolved originally in response to very dry conditions, enabling some bacteria to survive.

Species of bacteria	Diseases caused
Streptococcus pneumoniae	Pneumonia, meningitis, septicaemia
Neisseria meningitidis	Meningitis, septicaemia
Haemophilus influenzae	Meningitis, septicaemia
Klebsiella pneumoniae	Pneumonia, septicaemia, wound infection
Escherichia coli	Meningitis, septicaemia, gastrointestinal infections
Bacillus anthracis	Anthrax

Table 7.1.2 Some diseases caused by capsulated bacteria

Classifying bacteria

Grouping the many different types of bacteria simply as Gram-positive or Gram-negative is of limited use. Another way to identify bacteria is by their shape. Some bacteria are spherical, some rod shaped, and others are twisted or comma shaped, as shown in table 7.1.3.

Type of bacteria	Typical shape	Examples
Coccus (plural cocci)		*Streptococcus pneumoniae* (see table 7.1.2) *Staphylococcus aureus* (often present on skin, causes boils and abscesses)
Bacillus (plural bacilli)		*Bacillus anthracis* (anthrax)
Spirillum (plural spirilla)		*Treponema pallidum* (syphillis) *Campylobacter* (food poisoning)
Vibrios		*Vibrio cholerae* (cholera)

Table 7.1.3 Classification of bacteria based on their shape

Finally, bacteria are sometimes grouped by their requirements for respiration. **Obligate aerobes** need oxygen for respiration. **Facultative anaerobes** use oxygen if it is available but can manage without it, and many pathogens which infect humans fall into this group. **Obligate anaerobes** can only respire in the absence of oxygen.

Attachment and movement

Another structural feature seem in some bacteria are **pili** (also called **fimbriae**). There may be any number from one to several hundred of these threadlike protein structures projecting from the surface of the bacterium. They seem to be used for attachment to a host cell, for binding to specific antigens and for sexual reproduction in bacteria. However, they also make bacteria more vulnerable to virus infections, as bacteriophages can use pili as an entry point to the cell. Bacteria with pili include *E. coli* and *Salmonella*.

Some bacteria cannot actively move themselves at all. They are dependent on air and water currents or the actions of other organisms to get them from one place to another. Other bacteria can move themselves towards positive stimuli such as light and dissolved food substances, and away from negative stimuli such as dissolved toxins. They do this using **flagella**. Bacterial flagella are very different in structure to the flagella of eukaryotic cells. They are little bigger than a single one of the microtubules contained in a eukaryotic flagellum, and they are made of a many-stranded helix of the protein flagellin. The flagellum moves the bacterium by rapid rotations – about 100 revolutions per second – rather like a very rapid propellor. When the flagellum rotates clockwise, the bacterium moves forward. When the rotation is anticlockwise, the bacterium tumbles about chaotically.

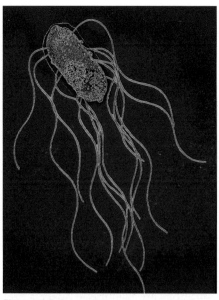

Figure 7.1.9 *Salmonella* bacteria possess both flagella, which are clearly visible on this photograph, and pili, so small that they can hardly be seen.

Reproduction in bacteria

The genetic material of bacteria is not contained in a nucleus like that of eukaryotic cells. It consists of a singular circular strand of DNA, which contains the genes for the bacterium (the genome), and in addition some bacterial cells contain one or more much smaller circles of DNA known as **plasmids**. These plasmids code for particular characteristics such as the production of a particular toxin or resistance to a particular antibiotic.

The growth of bacterial colonies

Bacteria can reproduce at quite astonishing rates. The small size and relative simplicity of these prokaryotic cells means that they can undergo asexual reproduction – binary fission (or splitting in two) – every 20 minutes when conditions are favourable. The time between cell divisions is known as the **generation time**. The implications of this rapid rate of reproduction are enormous. If a single bacterium had unlimited space and nutrients, and if all its offspring continued to divide at the same rate, then at the end of 48 hours there would be 2.2×10^{43} bacteria which would have a mass 4000 times the mass of the Earth! Clearly this sort of growth never takes place, for although the number of bacteria in a colony can increase exponentially at first, limited nutrients and a build-up of waste products always act as a brake on reproduction and growth.

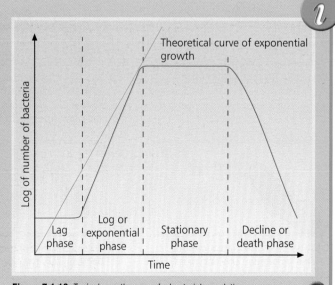

Figure 7.1.10 Typical growth curve of a bacterial population.

Figure 7.1.10 shows a typical bacterial growth curve, demonstrating four distinct phases:

- the **lag phase** when bacteria are adapting to their new environment and are not yet reproducing at their maximum rate
- the **log** or **exponential** phase when the rate of bacterial reproduction is close to or at its theoretical maximum
- the **stationary phase** when the total growth rate is zero – the number of new cells formed by binary fission is cancelled out by the numbers of cells dying, this state may arise due to a number of factors such as competition for food, lack of essential nutrients, an accumulation of toxic waste products and possible competition for oxygen
- the **decline** or **death phase** when reproduction has almost ceased and the death rate of cells is increasing.

A log scale is used for the curve because it allows very small and very large numbers to be shown easily on the same graph.

Binary fission

Bacteria can reproduce in two ways. By far the most common is by simply splitting in two (**binary fission**), which can take place very rapidly when conditions are favourable. Once a bacterium reaches a certain size, determined by the ratio of nucleic acid to cytoplasm, the DNA is replicated and the old cell wall begins to break down around the middle of the cell. While this happens the DNA appears to associate with the cell surface membrane, and it may be held in position by the mesosome if one is present. Enzymes break open the circular DNA, allowing the strands to unwind and be replicated. New cross-walls are laid down between the two new daughter cells, and again the mesosome appears to play a part in this where it is present. New cell surface membrane and cell wall material extend inwards, forming a septum which eventually divides the cell into two daughter cells, each containing circular DNA attached to the cell membrane. Plasmids often divide at the same time as the main DNA of the cell, so the daughter cells usually each contain a copy of both the original DNA and any plasmids present in the parent cell. The process of binary fission is shown in figure 7.1.11.

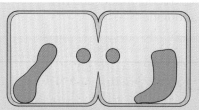

1 Bacterium reaches a critical size.

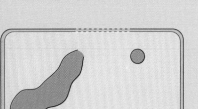

2 DNA becomes associated with the plasma membrane and enzymes break it open to allow replication. Cell wall begins to break down in centre.

3 Two sets of genetic material are associated with the plasma membrane. Plasmids often replicate as well. New cell wall and membrane begins to form at the centre.

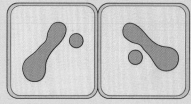

4 Two identical daughter bacterial cells results.

Phage therapy – a last resort?

We now face the terrifying prospect of bacteria existing that are resistant to all known antibiotics as a result of mutations (see p. 495). However, a new form of therapy holds out some hope. Used for some time in the countries of the former USSR, it has recently been tried in Australia. A woman was dying of a 'superbug' infection and all conventional cures had been tried. Finally, doctors infected the woman with yet another microorganism – this time a phage virus, which attacks bacteria. The virus destroyed the bacteria without affecting the human cells of the woman. Against all the odds, she recovered. A major research programme into phage therapy is to be set up. Will viruses be the new antibiotics?

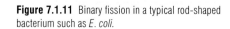

Figure 7.1.11 Binary fission in a typical rod-shaped bacterium such as *E. coli*.

Transformation, transduction and conjugation

In certain situations, some types of bacteria can reproduce using what appears to be a primitive form of sexual reproduction. There are three ways in which genetic material from one bacterium can be taken in and used as part of the DNA of another bacterium. None of these methods is common – in fact they are very rare events – and none of them involves the formation and transfer of gametes from one individual to another as happens in sexual reproduction in many eukaryotic organisms.

Fungi

Fungi are eukaryotic organisms that have a unique cellular structure. They are all heterotrophic – they do not make their own food but absorb it from outside the body. Many fungi have a multicellular structure of tangled threads; some, like the yeasts, are unicellular. Fungi are of immense importance in the decomposition of dead animal and plant material, and thus in the recycling of many valuable nutrients within ecosystems. Fungi have many uses:

- mushrooms and toadstools can be used as human food
- yeasts have been used for thousands of years in the production of alcoholic drinks such as beer and wine and to make bread rise
- certain moulds are used to produce antibiotics.

However, some fungi cause human disease – these tend to infect the skin, hair and nails, although they can also cause whole-body diseases in areas such as the lungs and give severe problems to patients whose immune system is impaired, such as AIDS sufferers. Examples of fungal diseases include athlete's foot and farmer's lung. There are also about 5000 species of fungi which attack agricultural and garden crops, causing billions of pounds worth of damage to food crops and stored food and thus causing food shortages in many areas of the world.

Fungal structure

Most fungi, with the exception of the yeasts and a small number of unicellular forms, are multicellular and **filamentous**. The basic structural units of filamentous fungi are thread-like cylinders known as **hyphae**. These hyphae grow to form a mass of threads known as the **mycelium**.

The hyphae grow from their tips and may or may not be divided by septa into cell-like compartments. Those that are divided up have many pores in each septum so there is cytoplasmic continuity and communication between the compartments. Fungal cell walls are thin and rigid made of the polysaccharide **chitin**, which is also found in the exoskeletons of some arthropods but does not occur in plants. Fungal hyphae contain many nuclei and also most of the usual eukaryotic organelles such as mitochondria, ribosomes, endoplasmic reticulum and vacuoles, although few fungal cells contain basal bodies or centrioles.

Figure 7.1.12 The fungal mycelium of this pin mould is made up of a mass of tiny thread-like hyphae.

Fungal hyphae may form a very loose mycelium, or they may be packed tightly together to form a fruiting body such as a mushroom. Fungal hyphae have no differentiated cell types – the cells are not specialised to perform particular functions – but in some species some of the hyphae themselves become specialised. For example, groups of hyphae may act as rhizoids, anchoring the fungus rather like roots, whilst others known as **haustoria** act as feeding structures, penetrating the cells of other living creatures and absorbing nutrients to be used by the whole fungus. Most fungi have hyphae that become specialised for spore production.

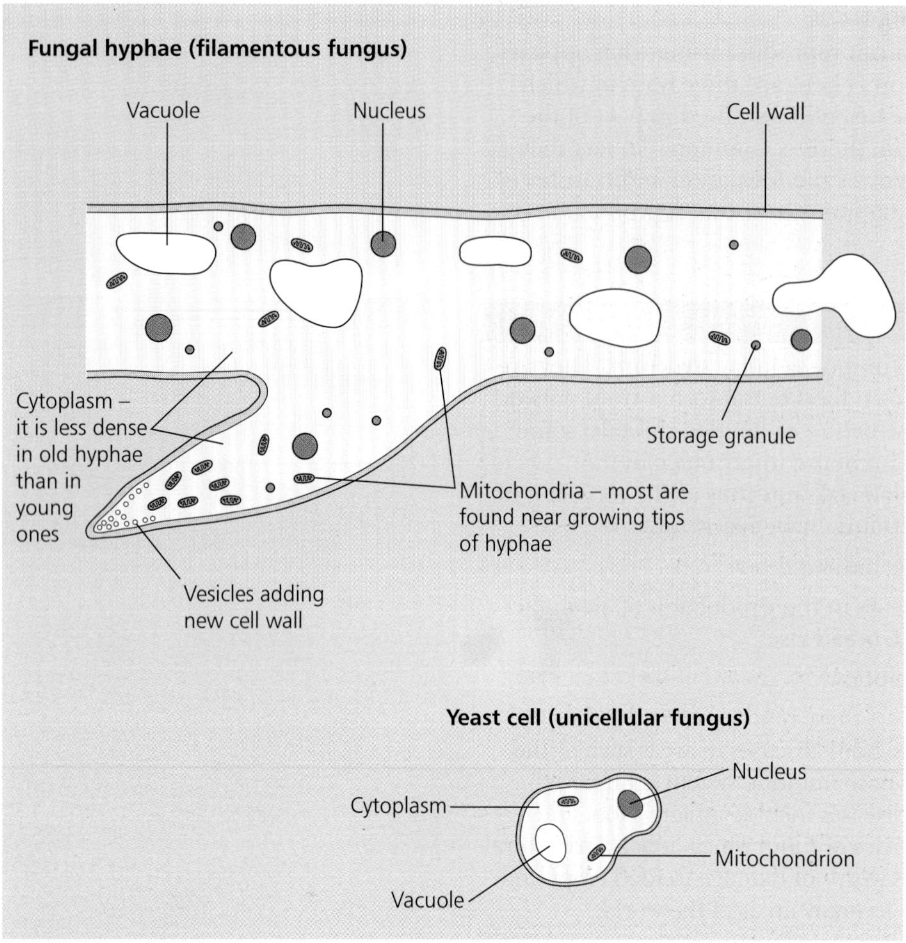

Fungal hyphae (filamentous fungus)

Figure 7.1.13 The structure of a fungal hypha and a unicellular fungus.

Vacuole

Nucleus

Cell wall

Cytoplasm – it is less dense in old hyphae than in young ones

Storage granule

Mitochondria – most are found near growing tips of hyphae

Vesicles adding new cell wall

Yeast cell (unicellular fungus)

Nucleus

Cytoplasm

Mitochondrion

Vacuole

Fungal nutrition

All fungi are heterotrophs, and they obtain their food from other organisms without the benefit of a gut. One way they do this is by absorbing food that is already digested, or in a form that is immediately useful to the fungus. Another way is by producing extracellular enzymes to break down the food outside the body. These enzymes are secreted onto the food and the digested products are absorbed into the hyphae. Fungi produce a range of different digestive enzymes, and which enzymes they can produce will determine what they feed on. Fungi that produce a wide range of carbohydrases, proteases and lipases can utilise a wide range of substrates, but those that produce a much more restricted range of enzymes are found only on very specific substrates. If a fungus stores carbohydrate it is kept in the form of glycogen, the carbohydrate storage molecule found in animals, rather than the starch found in plants.

A large proportion of fungi are **saprobionts** – they gain their food molecules by decomposing dead plant or animal material. A number of these saprobionts can secrete the enzymes cellulase and ligninase from their hyphae. Fungi that secrete cellulase can break down cellulose, a major constituent of plant cell walls, and those that secrete ligninase can break down lignin, present in wood. Most living organisms cannot digest either cellulose or lignin. Thus the fungi that produce cellulase and ligninase are extremely important in the decomposition of dead plants including trees; in fact the role of all saprobionts as decomposers is vital in the recycling of nutrients and the removal of dead material. *Saccharomyces* (yeast) and *Penicillum* (the mould that produces the antibiotic penicillin) are both saprobionts.

Yeasts and moulds – the difference

Yeasts and moulds are fungi that have a major impact on human life. They are both members of the same group of fungi – the **Ascomycota**. The ascomycetes form the biggest group of fungi. They reproduce asexually forming enormous numbers of spores known as **conidia**, which often trigger hay-fever type allergies in humans. In sexual reproduction hyphae conjugate and form **ascospores** inside a sac-like **ascus**. Most ascomycetes have hyphae that are divided up by partitions called **septa**.

The moulds are some of the best known ascomycetes. They have significant effects, both good and bad, on human life: they destroy vast quantities of food worldwide, but valuable antibiotics such as penicillin are also derived from moulds.

Yeasts are rather unusual members of the ascomycetes because they are unicellular fungi that almost always reproduce by budding. They fall into this group because very occasionally two cells fuse to form an ascus containing ascospores. They are used to make bread and alcoholic drinks.

Not all fungi feed on dead matter, however. Many get their food from living organisms. Fungi that obtain their food from the living are either **parasites** (if their actions cause damage to their hosts) or **mutualists** (if they bring their host some benefit). Fungal parasites are more likely to affect plants than animals, although there are examples of fungal parasites of animals such as athlete's foot. Many parasitic fungi that attack plants produce pectinases, which digest a vital part of plant cell walls and can reduce the entire plant tissue to a soft mush.

Protoctists

The protoctists are a kingdom consisting of eukaryotic organisms that have a variety of methods of nutrition and reproduction, described on p. 483.

Laboratory techniques

Culturing microorganisms

Most microorganisms are so small that they are impossible to see with the naked eye. In order to investigate microorganisms, for example for the medical diagnosis of a disease or for scientific experiments, we need to **culture** them. This means growing large numbers of the microorganisms so that we can see colonies of them with the naked eye.

Great care must be taken when culturing microorganisms because even if the organisms being cultured are usually completely harmless there is always the risk of a mutant strain arising which is pathogenic. Also, an otherwise harmless culture may have been accidentally contaminated with pathogenic microorganisms from the environment. Equally, if you are trying to grow a pure strain of a bacterium, it is important to avoid your culture becoming contaminated by any of the millions of other bacteria in the air and on your skin. For these reasons, health and safety precautions must always be followed when handling, culturing or disposing of microorganisms. It is particularly important that once a culture has been grown it does not leave the laboratory. All cultures should be disposed of safely by sealing them in plastic bags and sterilising them for 15 minutes before they are thrown away. An **autoclave** is

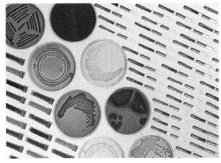

Figure 7.1.14 Culturing microorganisms like these different types of bacteria allows us to see what we are working with.

used to sterilise cultures – this uses steam under high pressure to kill any microorganisms.

Choosing a medium

Culturing microorganisms involves a number of steps. First the organisms to be cultured must be chosen and obtained. Then they need to be provided with the right food in order to grow. Most microorganisms require a good source of carbon and nitrogen as well as specific mineral resources. This food (the **nutrient medium**) can be either in liquid form (**nutrient broth**) or in solid form (usually **nutrient agar**). Agar is extracted from seaweed, and it has the useful property of setting as a jelly at 50 °C but not melting again until heated to 90 °C. Its higher melting point makes agar a much better medium for growth than gelatine, which was used originally, because bacterial cultures are usually grown at relatively warm temperatures which speed up their growth. Agar was first introduced into microbiology by Robert Koch, who heard of a woman in Jakarta who made jellies using a seaweed extract because normal gelatine-based jellies tended to melt in the tropical temperatures. Koch realised the potential of this new setting agent, and his work revolutionised microbiology.

Some microorganisms will grow on pure agar, but in most cases nutrients are added to provide a better growing medium. For some microorganisms to grow the balance of nutrients has to be very precise, but often the medium is simply enriched with good protein sources such as blood, yeast extract, meat, heart or brain. Liquid nutrient broths are usually enriched in a similar way. In such enriched nutrient media, samples initially containing only a very small number of organisms can multiply rapidly. Whatever medium is used, it is vitally important that it is kept **sterile** (free from contamination by microorganisms) until it is ready for use.

Introducing the microorganisms

Having prepared a suitable medium for your culture, the next step is to introduce the microorganisms (usually bacteria). This process is called **inoculation**. To inoculate a broth, a suspension is made of the bacteria to be grown and a known volume of this is mixed with the sterile nutrient broth in the flask. The flask is then stoppered again with cotton wool as quickly as possible, to prevent contamination from the air. The flask is incubated at a suitable temperature and may be shaken or agitated regularly to make sure that the broth is aerated, allowing oxygen to reach the growing bacteria. Solid media are also inoculated using a suspension of bacteria, but the process is slightly more complicated, as shown in figure 7.1.16.

Culturing viruses

Bacteria and fungi are relatively easy to culture in the laboratory – given a nutrient medium and the right oxygen concentration and temperature they will survive and grow. It is much less easy to culture viruses, because they can only survive as intracellular parasites, needing a living cell in which to reproduce. To culture viruses, living cells or tissues are used as the culture medium. The living cells may be extracted directly from a particular organ, or may come from cell cultures that are maintained in laboratories for long periods of time. The cells are usually cultured in a single layer at a temperature of about 37 °C in a humid atmosphere. When such cell cultures are inoculated with viruses, the viruses infect and take over the cells just as they would in their normal animal or plant host. The action of the viruses on the cells may be observed directly – for example, by the cells bursting or the formation of giant cells as the infected cells join up together – or using signs such as changes in

Figure 7.1.15 Cultures grown in broth are usually prepared in flasks or test-tubes, whilst agar-based cultures are prepared in Petri dishes. The hot sterile agar is poured onto the plates which are immediately resealed and cooled to set ready for use.

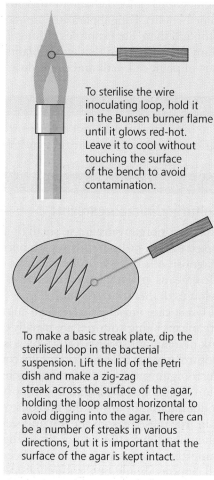

To sterilise the wire inoculating loop, hold it in the Bunsen burner flame until it glows red-hot. Leave it to cool without touching the surface of the bench to avoid contamination.

To make a basic streak plate, dip the sterilised loop in the bacterial suspension. Lift the lid of the Petri dish and make a zig-zag streak across the surface of the agar, holding the loop almost horizontal to avoid digging into the agar. There can be a number of streaks in various directions, but it is important that the surface of the agar is kept intact.

Figure 7.1.16 Inoculating an agar plate.

pH or the presence of viral antigens shown up by immunological techniques. Viral culture is considerably more difficult than culture of other microorganisms and is only carried out in specialist laboratories.

Limiting factors

Bacteria can reproduce at enormous rates, as described on pages 595–596, but although the number of cells in a colony can increase exponentially at first, there are several **limiting factors** that can prevent this continuing. One is the amount of nutrients available. At the start of the culture, there is more than enough food for all the microorganisms, but as the numbers multiply exponentially in the log phase of growth the excess is used up. Unless fresh nutrients are added, the level of nutrients will become too low to support further growth and reproduction and so will limit the growth of the microorganisms. Similarly, the level of oxygen can become limiting as the population, and hence the demand for respiratory oxygen, rises.

Temperature is another limiting factor. The enzyme reactions within microorganisms are affected by the temperature of the culture medium. For most bacteria, a low temperature will slow down enzyme reactions and therefore growth, and a warm temperature will speed them up. Bacterial enzymes, like any other, are made of protein, so an excessive rise in temperature will denature the proteins, stopping growth and reproduction completely and killing the microorganisms.

Toxic waste products can also limit bacterial growth. The amount of waste produced at the beginning of a bacterial culture is very small, but as cell numbers rise, the build-up of toxic material (and hence the pH, see box below) starts to inhibit further growth and even to poison and kill the culture.

pH in bacterial cultures

As a bacterial colony grows, there is a build-up of carbon dioxode produced by respiration, along with other acidic waste products. The pH of the culture falls as the colony numbers rise until the low pH acts as a limiting factor and brings about the decline of the population.

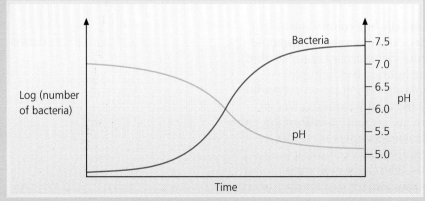

Figure 7.1.18 As time goes on, the number of bacteria rise and the pH falls. Eventually the pH is too low for the bacteria to tolerate, and their numbers tail off.

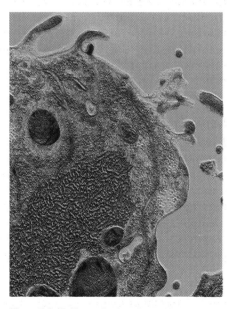

Figure 7.1.17 Viruses (such as these which cause measles) seem to have no difficulty growing in the cells of living organisms. However, persuading viruses to grow in laboratory cultures is much more difficult.

Tolerating high temperatures

Temperature has long been recognised as one of the limiting factors on the growth of a colony of bacteria. Low temperatures mean very slow growth. High temperatures kill bacteria so they are used to destroy bacteria and to make sure that culture media and medical instruments are sterile. However, within the last few years this accepted view of the effect of temperature on bacteria has been somewhat shaken by the discovery, in deep vents almost 3000 m below the surface of the ocean, of bacteria living in the most extreme conditions. In the mineral-rich waters of the vents the pressure is high and the temperature is around 350 °C. Not only do 'black smoker' bacteria thrive in these conditions, they actually stop reproducing if the temperature falls below 100 °C! These bacteria challenge many of our accepted theories about the biochemistry of enzymes and cells, and illustrate the ability of bacteria to take advantage of environments in which nothing else can survive.

Counting microorganisms

In order to monitor the growth in the population of a bacterial culture, a measure of the number of cells present at regular time intervals is needed. Cells are too small to count with the naked eye, but several other methods of counting the bacteria, either directly or indirectly, are available.

How many cells?

A **haemocytometer** may be used to count bacterial or fungal cells directly. This technique uses specialised slides originally designed for counting blood cells, which is how the name came about. A haemocytometer consists of a specialised microscope slide that holds a standard volume of liquid 0.1 mm deep. The slide may be marked with a grid, or a special lens with a grid marked on it may be fitted to the microscope. The microorganisms in the central panel of the grid are counted, and the number of cells in a standard volume of broth can be calculated from this. The count is usually made at least three times and the average calculated. Haemocytometer measurements taken at regular time intervals throughout the life of a bacterial colony give a picture of the changing cell numbers.

How cloudy is the culture?

An alternative way of measuring the number of cells in a culture is by **turbidimetry**, a specialised form of colorimetry. As the number of bacterial cells in a culture increases, the medium becomes increasingly cloudy (**turbid**). As a solution gets more turbid, it absorbs more light, so less light passes through it. Using a colorimeter to measure how much light passes through a sample tells us how much light is absorbed by the sample, and so gives an indirect measure of how many microorganisms are present. A **calibration curve** is produced by growing a control culture and taking samples at regular intervals. The turbidity of each sample is measured and a cell count is also made for each sample using a haemocytometer. The calibration curve produced can be used to convert a turbidity measurement to a number of cells for that particular organism. Cultures can then be grown under different conditions and the effect of the conditions on the growth of the microorganisms can be measured using turbidimetry.

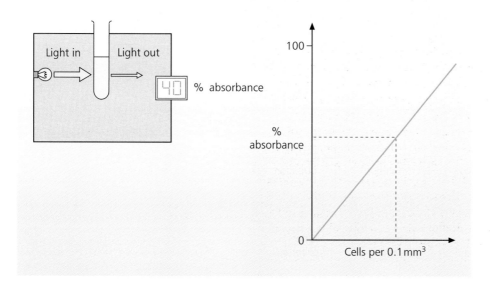

Figure 7.1.19 Turbidimetry is a quick and easy way to measure the cell population of a culture once the initial calibration curve for an organism has been set up.

How many colonies?

Yet another way of counting the microorganisms in a culture involves **dilution plating**, which is used to find a **total viable cell count**. This technique is based on the idea that each of the colonies on an agar plate has grown from a single viable microorganism on the plate. Thus if two bacterial colonies can be seen after culturing there were two living bacteria on the plate when it was inoculated, and if 50 patches of fungal mycelia form there were 50 fungal cells on the plate. However, in most cases a solid mass of microbial growth is present after culturing so it is not possible to work out the number of individual colonies. This problem is solved by repeatedly diluting the original culture in stages until a point is reached when the colonies can be counted. If the number of colonies is multiplied by the dilution factor, then a total viable cell count for the original inoculation can be found. There are often two or more plates on which the individual colonies can be counted, so an average can be calculated, giving a reasonably accurate picture of the number of cells in a particular culture. The accuracy can be checked from time to time using a haemocytometer to count the cells in the original culture.

How much dry mass?

In order to find the best concentration of nutrients or the optimum pH at which to grow fungi, the simplest method is to test the dry mass of the microorganism. Samples of broth may be removed a regular intervals during the culture and the fungi separated from the liquid by centrifugation or filtering. The fungal material is then dried thoroughly to the point where no more loss of mass is recorded (for example, in an oven overnight at around 100 °C). This gives the dry mass of biological material in a certain volume of the culture medium, and a change in the dry mass from one sample to another gives an indication of the change in the number of cells. The conditions that produce the greatest dry mass of fungus are the optimum conditions for growth.

Obtaining a pure culture

When culturing microorganisms it is often difficult to obtain a pure culture of a single type of bacterium or fungus. Soil, air, water and body fluids all contain a range of microorganisms. To isolate one in particular takes quite some time. The most commonly used way of isolating an organism is to use information

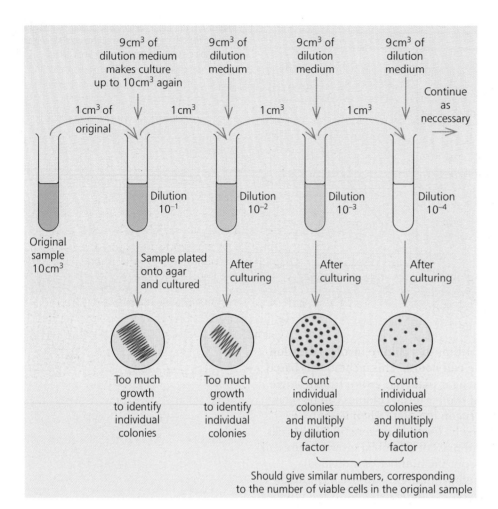

9cm³ of dilution medium makes culture up to 10cm³ again

1cm³ of original

9cm³ of dilution medium

1cm³

9cm³ of dilution medium

1cm³

9cm³ of dilution medium

1cm³

Continue as neccessary

Original sample 10cm³

Dilution 10⁻¹

Dilution 10⁻²

Dilution 10⁻³

Dilution 10⁻⁴

Sample plated onto agar and cultured

After culturing

After culturing

After culturing

Too much growth to identify individual colonies

Too much growth to identify individual colonies

Count individual colonies and multiply by dilution factor

Count individual colonies and multiply by dilution factor

Should give similar numbers, corresponding to the number of viable cells in the original sample

Figure 7.1.20 Dilution plating allows the number of colonies to be counted, which is a measure of the number of viable cells in the original sample.

either about the needs of the desired organism, or about the needs and weaknesses of the other organisms with which it is likely to be contaminated.

- If the bacterium or fungus to be cultured has a distinctive colour, this fact can be used. Serial dilutions will give a manageable number of separate colonies, and a colony of the appropriate colour can then be isolated and used to inoculate a sterile flask or plate to produce a pure culture.

- If the organism to be isolated does not need oxygen for respiration, then growing the culture in anaerobic conditions would enable only anaerobic bacteria to survive. Similarly, growing organisms with oxygen enables only aerobic organisms to survive. This may not give a complete separation of microorganisms for a pure culture, but it does reduce the spread considerably.

- The most effective way of producing a pure culture from a mixture of microorganisms is to manipulate the medium in which they are grown. The requirements of microorganisms vary greatly, and so a medium that favours the growth of the desired organism and inhibits the growth of others will encourage the desired microorganism to grow colonies. A colony can then be isolated and re-inoculated to produce a single pure culture. The changes made to the medium to encourage one particular organism to grow may be in the range of nutrients available, or in the presence of selective growth inhibitors such as antibiotics or antifungal chemicals which will reduce or prevent the growth of all but the desired microorganisms.

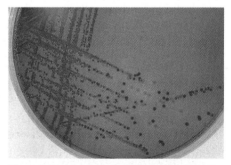

Figure 7.1.21 Colonies of lactose-fermenting *E. coli* bacteria are stained red on this indicator agar, whilst the other gut bacteria in the mixture that do not ferment lactose form colourless colonies. It would be a simple step from here to isolate and further culture either type of bacteria.

- Indicator media, which cause certain types of bacteria to change colour, are also available. Using such a medium allows the affected bacteria, or the colonies not affected by the indicator, to be isolated and cultured, as shown in figure 7.1.21.

It is particularly important to be able to isolate disease-causing microorganisms from those that normally exist on and in the human body (the normal body flora), so that both diagnosis and appropriate treatment can be planned. The techniques described above are used to isolate these organisms as pure cultures.

Chemicals that kill microorganisms

Antiseptics, disinfectants and antibiotics

Chemicals used to destroy bacteria in the environment are referred to as **disinfectants**, and those used directly on people as **antiseptics**.

It was not until well into the twentieth century that drugs became available that could be used to treat a patient once a bacterial infection has already taken hold.

All modern antimicrobial drugs have their effect because of the principle of **selective toxicity** – they interfere with the metabolism of the microorganism with minimal damage to the human host. The most commonly used and best known antimicrobial drugs are the **antibiotics**. The first discovered and best known antibiotic is penicillin, which is still used to combat bacterial infections today although many other antibiotics have been discovered since.

Killing and controlling

Research scientists are continually looking for and developing new chemicals that will destroy microorganisms. Before a chemical can be developed as a new antiseptic, disinfectant or antibiotic it must be shown to prevent the growth of microorganisms. Chemicals that do not kill a microorganism but prevent its growth are known as **bacteriostatic** or **fungistatic**. Chemicals that actually kill the microorganisms are known as **bactericidal** or **fungicidal**. Some chemicals halt growth at weaker concentrations and kill the microorganisms at stronger ones. There are several ways of investigating and demonstrating the effect of a chemical on a pure culture of a microorganism.

The following technique demonstrates how effective an antiseptic, disinfectant or antibiotic is and can show at what concentration it completely inhibits growth and at what concentration it completely kills the microorganisms. Increasingly dilute concentrations of the test chemical are inoculated in a nutrient broth with the same amount of microorganism. The tubes are cultured for a time and observed using turbidimetry to assess whether any microbial growth has taken place. The tubes are then subcultured onto nutrient agar which is free from the test chemical. If the chemical has killed the microorganisms there will be no growth on the place. If it has only inhibited growth, then colonies will develop on the agar. If the test chemical has not affected the microorganisms, or is at too low a concentration to have an effect, the tubes will appear turbid and colonies will appear on the agar.

The concentration of a chemical needed to inhibit microbial growth is known as the **minimum inhibitory concentration (MIC)**, whilst the concentration needed to kill a specific type of bacterium or fungus is known as the **minimum lethal dose (MLD)** or **minimum bactericidal concentration (MBC)**. These concentrations are shown on figure 7.1.22.

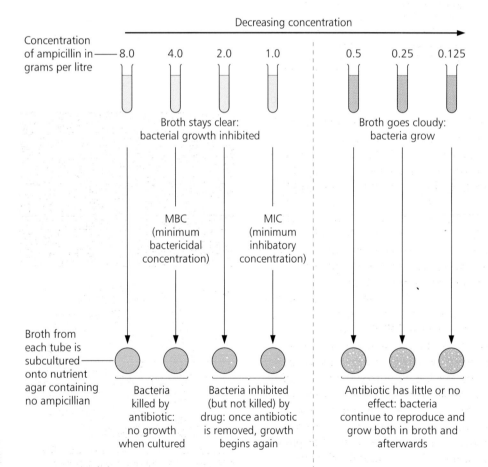

Figure 7.1.22 Testing ampicillin against bacteria to find the **MIC** and **MBC**.

Figure 7.1.23 The antiseptic dilution plate technique.

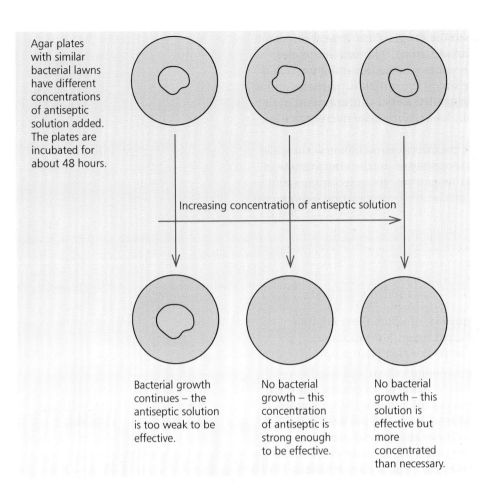

Agar plates with similar bacterial lawns have different concentrations of antiseptic solution added. The plates are incubated for about 48 hours.

Increasing concentration of antiseptic solution

Bacterial growth continues – the antiseptic solution is too weak to be effective.

No bacterial growth – this concentration of antiseptic is strong enough to be effective.

No bacterial growth – this solution is effective but more concentrated than necessary.

A simpler version of this test to look at the effectiveness of disinfectants and antibiotics can be done using a bacterial 'lawn' – an agar plate covered with a wide spread of bacterial growth. The antimicrobial chemical is added and swirled over the surface of the lawn, and different concentrations have different effects. This is called the **antiseptic dilution plate technique**, shown in figure 7.1.23.

When a new compound is found that appears to be effective against bacteria, one way of testing it is to rate it against one of the oldest disinfectants, phenol. The concentration of a new compound that kills the bacteria after being in contact with them for 10 minutes is compared with the concentration of phenol needed to do the same, and a **phenol coefficient** is found. If the phenol coefficient is high, the chemical is good at killing bacteria; if it is low the opposite is true and it will not be developed further. The test is usually carried out at either 20 °C (around room temperature) or at 37 °C (around body temperature), which mimic the two most likely conditions for use.

Antibiotics became increasingly important in the battle against bacterial diseases during the second half of the twentieth century. Not all bacteria are sensitive to all antibiotics, and some bacteria are resistant to the majority of antibiotics. New chemical compounds that show potential as antibiotics are constantly being looked for both in extracts from plants and animals and by manipulating computer-generated molecules. To determine if a particular bacterial culture is sensitive to an antibiotic, the simplest tests use filter paper discs impregnated with different concentrations of the antibiotic, or with similar concentrations of different antibiotics. The discs are laid on top of bacterial culture on agar plates, so that the antimicrobial chemicals diffuse into

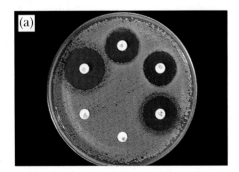

(a)

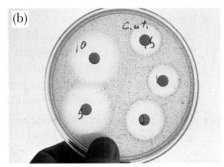

(b)

Figure 7.1.24 Plate (a) shows the effect of *different* antibiotics on the growth of a culture of bacteria. Plate (b) shows the effect of different concentrations of the *same* antibiotic.

the agar. If the microorganism is sensitive to the drug, a clear zone will form in the bacterial lawn around the disc as the culture grows. The size of this clear zone depends on a number of things – how water soluble the antibiotic is and so how far it diffuses through the agar, the size of the antibiotic particles and so the rate at which they diffuse through the agar, the initial concentration of the antibiotic in the disc and, most importantly, how sensitive the microorganism on the plate is to the antibiotic.

Whether scientists are trying to find out the effectiveness of a new chemical compound at inhibiting the growth of microorganisms, or the effectiveness of current compounds against particular microorganisms, these techniques and others like them allow them to build up a picture of the interaction between the chemicals and the microbes.

SUMMARY

- Microbiology is the study of **microorganisms**, of which there are four groups: viruses, prokaryotes, protoctists and fungi. Most of these organisms are very small and can only be seen with a microscope.

- **Viruses** are 20–300 nm across, and are sometimes classed as non-living. They usually have geometric shapes and are made up of genetic material (DNA or RNA) inside a protein coat (the **capsid**, made up of repeating units called **capsomeres**), sometimes surrounded by a lipid envelope. Viruses attach to living cells by means of **virus attachment particles**, which are specific to receptors on the host cell surface. They enter the cell and use its resources to reproduce themselves, thereby causing disease.

- Phages such as lysogenic bacteriophage λ attack bacteria, injecting their DNA into the host cell, where it forms a circle or **plasmid**. In the **lysogenic pathway**, the plasmid is incorporated into the bacterial DNA and is replicated along with the host cell. This dormant virus may then enter the **lytic pathway**, when the viral DNA is replicated independently and many mature viruses are formed in the host cell. They cause the cell to burst (**lysis**) and the viruses are released.

- Retroviruses such as HIV have RNA as their genetic material. Once inside the host cell, DNA is made alongside this RNA by the enzyme **reverse transcriptase**. The viral DNA is inserted into the host DNA, and viral mRNA is made from it, from which new viruses are built up. These leave the cell by exocytosis and the cell continues to produce more viruses.

- **Bacteria** are prokaryotic cells. Their genetic material is DNA, which is not enclosed in a nucleus. They have cell walls that contain peptidoglycan. Bacterial cells may also have **pili** to attach to the host cell surface, **mesosomes** thought to be involved in respiration, circular DNA **plasmids**, **flagellae** for movement and a **capsule** or slime layer. Some bacteria are autotrophic, other are heterotrophic. Some bacteria cause disease.

- Bacteria can be classified as **Gram negative** or **Gram positive**, depending on how their cell walls take up Gram's stain. They can also be classified according to their shape: spherical (**cocci**), rod-shaped (**bacilli**), spiral (**spirilla**) or comma-shaped (**vibrios**). Some bacteria are **aerobic** (need oxygen to respire); others are **anaerobic** (respire in the absence of oxygen).

- **Fungi** are made up of eukaryotic cells which have cell walls reinforced with chitin, and use glycogen to store carbohydrate in the cell. Fungi may be unicellular or multicellular. The multicellular fungi are filamentous, made up of threads called **hyphae** forming a mass called a **mycelium**. Fungi are heterotrophic – they absorb nutrients into their cells. **Saprobionts** secrete enzymes to digest dead materials extracellularly, and then take in the digested molecules. They play an important role in the decomposition of dead materials. Other fungi obtain food molecules from living cells, in either mutualistic or parasitic relationships. A few fungi cause disease. Fungi reproduce by means of **spores**, which may be produced sexually or asexually.

- **Protoctists** are eukaryotic organisms with many different methods of nutrition and many different structures and lifestyles.

- Scientists **culture** microorganisms in order to study them. There are health and safety risks associated with culturing microorganisms, and all cultures must be sterilised before being disposed of.

- Cultures are grown on a **medium** which provides nutrients. These may be liquid (**broth**) or solid (usually **agar**). The microorganisms are introduced or **inoculated** into the medium, which is then **incubated** (kept at a suitable temperature).

- Viruses are difficult to culture, and a single layer of living cells is used as the medium. The viruses may be observed by their direct effects on the cells, or indirectly by monitoring a side-effect of their actions.

- Bacteria can reproduce very quickly when conditions are favourable. The **generation time** is the length of time between cell divisions. Typical bacterial growth curves in a closed system show four stages:
  - the **lag phase** before the bacteria start reproducing at their maximum rate
  - the log or **exponential phase** when the bacteria are reproducing as quickly as they can, as they have plenty of space and nutrients
  - the **stationary phase** when the number of new cells is matched by the number of cells dying
  - the **decline** or **death phase** when many cells are dying and reproduction has almost stopped.

- **Limiting factors** which prevent exponential growth of microorganisms and bring about the stationary phase of growth include lack of nutrients or oxygen, a temperature that is too high or too low, lack of essential nutrients or an accumulation of toxic waste products.

- It is necessary to have a measure of the number of cells in a culture in order to monitor its growth.
  - A **haemocytometer** allows microorganisms to be counted under a microscope against a grid background, so that their concentration in the medium can be calculated.
  - **Turbidimetry** involves measuring how cloudy or **turbid** a culture is. When compared with a calibration curve the turbidity gives a measure of the number of microorganisms in the culture.
  - **Dilution plating** gives the number of viable cells in the culture. Each viable cell gives rise to an individual colony after repeated dilution and reculturing.
  - Growth of fungi can be monitored by measuring the dry mass of the microorganism.

- Sources of microorganisms usually contain many different microorganisms, and various separation techniques are used to obtain a pure culture. These include:
  - separation of coloured cultures if the microorganism has a distinctive colour
  - culturing in aerobic conditions to remove anaerobic microbes, or aerobic conditions to remove anaerobic ones
  - manipulating the medium so that it contains a limited range of nutrients, or contains antibiotics to prevent growth of unwanted microorganisms

- **Antiseptics** are chemicals used on people (for example on the skin) to destroy microorganisms. **Disinfectants** are used in the environment, for example on surfaces and instruments. Antiseptics and disinfectants are used to prevent infections during surgery and to stop diseases spreading.

- **Antibiotics** are drugs used to treat bacterial or fungal infections in humans and animals. They are **selectively toxic** – they have a damaging effect on the microorganisms but do not affect the host cells adversely. **Bacteriostatic** chemicals prevent the microorganisms growing and spreading, while **bactericidal** chemicals kill the microorganisms. The lowest concentration of a chemical that will inhibit microbial growth is the **minimum inhibitory concentration (MIC)**, and the lowest concentration that will kill the microbe is the **minimum lethal dose (MLD)**.

- Antibiotic properties may be identified in a chemical by impregnating paper discs with the chosen chemical, placing them on agar plates containing microorganisms, and observing the resulting cultures. A clear area around a disc indicates antibiotic activity. To test a new antibiotic for effectiveness, its activity is compared with that of phenol, giving the **phenol coefficient**.

QUESTIONS

1 Make a table to compare and contrast the main features of bacteria, fungi and viruses. The table should include both structural features of the different pathogens and methods of nutrition and reproduction.

2 a Describe two methods for culturing bacteria in the laboratory.
  b What safety precautions should be taken when handling microorganisms in the laboratory, and why?
  c Why is it important to be able to measure the growth of a culture of microorganisms? Summarise the ways in which the growth of microorganisms can be measured.

3 People are involved in a constant battle against the microorganisms which cause disease.
  a What are disinfectants and how do they work?
  b What are antibiotics and how do they work?
  c How is the effectiveness of antiseptics and antibiotics measured?

Developing Key Skills

If a patient has a viral infection, a doctor does not prescribe antibiotics, and usually gives no drugs to cure the disease at all. However, many patients are quite put out if they are not given antibiotics when they are feeling unwell. Produce a poster or leaflet to be used in a GP's waiting room or surgery which explains, in a clear, simple and accurate way, why antibiotics are only prescribed for bacterial infections and why viral diseases are rarely given any treatment at all, except perhaps to relieve some of the symptoms. The poster or leaflet needs to be bright and interesting to make sure that patients actually read and take in the information before they see the doctor.

FOCUS · THE DEMISE OF THE GUINEA WORM

The guinea worm has been active as a human parasite since ancient times. Adult worms have been found in Egyptian mummies and they were mentioned in the Sanskrit Rig-Veda in approximately 1350 BC. Yet thirty years ago the worm was still a scourge of the rural communities in India, Pakistan, Yemen and most of sub-Saharan Africa – there were an estimated 10–15 million human infections each year.

The mature female guinea worm is found in the connective tissue just beneath the skin. A mature female can be up to 80 cm long, although only 2 mm in diameter. The body of the mature female is filled with about 3 million larvae. Eventually a few larvae are released through the head into the flesh of the host, which reacts by forming a burning, painful blister which bursts after a few days to give a shallow ulcer. If the ulcer is placed in water the pain is relieved – and about a million first stage guinea worm larvae are released into the water. The dangling empty bit of worm dries up, and then if the ulcer is later plunged into water again more worm emerges and more larvae are released. The water used to soothe the ulcers is usually found in the local pond or drinking well.

The larvae are then eaten by predatory water fleas, and they develop inside their new hosts for two weeks. Then when the water fleas are taken in by a human as they drink the water, the guinea worm larvae have found their new host. They burrow through the intestine to reach the body wall in the chest area. Here males and females mate, and then the males die off. The females continue to grow slowly and migrate to the extremities of the body, especially the legs and feet, emerging about a year after the original infection.

The biggest health problem caused by the worms is that up to 50 per cent of the worm tracks become infected, leaving many people in the community either temporarily or permanently disabled by the infections.

Figure 1 Guinea worms can actually be wound out of the body onto a small stick, a few centimetres a day, to remove them.

Beating the worm

Thanks to some dedicated work over the last 20 years, the eradication of the guinea worm now seems within reach. In 1979 Ralph Muller was the first to suggest that the total elimination of the guinea worm was possible. As for many diseases, the first and major step in the process was the provision of safe, clean drinking water. Bore holes and narrow brick-lined wells (with inadequate light for water fleas to breed) were dug all over rural India and Pakistan, using funding from governments, charities and international agencies. Rain water is now collected and stored for use rather than using water sources such as ponds. The other important strand of the attack has been education. People have had the life-cycle of the worm explained, so they realise why it is so important to sieve drinking water and not to bathe ulcers in water sources. Also a larval insecticide with relatively little environmental impact has been used to kill off water fleas. The manufacturer has donated sufficient insecticide to treat all of the ponds in the affected areas of Africa.

Guinea worm has now been completely eradicated from Pakistan and 37 other countries. In Africa, the levels of infection have dropped dramatically and eradication is feasible within the foreseeable future. Guinea worm and its trail of disability and distress have been controlled using remarkably simple measures, mainly education and clean drinking water.

Figure 2 When everyone in the world has access to clean, safe drinking water, many diseases will loosen their grip on the human population.

Health and disease

The state of our health is very important to us. 'How are you?' or its equivalent is the most common greeting in many languages. We also spend a great deal of time and money on our health – getting healthy, keeping healthy, returning to health. But what do we mean by 'health'? The World Health Organization (WHO) defines health as *a state of complete physical, mental and social well-being which is more than just the absence of disease*. This is a relatively rare state which is also very subjective – for example, less than 10% of the British population claim to be completely healthy at any one time! Is health more than simply the absence of disease?

Figure 7.2.1 One of these people could have a mental illness, another be affected by parasitic worms and a third have a dietary deficiency disease. You cannot always tell by looking at people whether or not they are healthy.

Defining health and disease

Can you measure health?

Health is difficult to define and can be even more difficult to measure, either qualitatively or quantitatively. **Qualitative** measures (how people feel) are dependent on people's perceptions of their own health, and these are notoriously variable. Some people rarely if ever judge themselves as feeling healthy, even when they are perfectly well in a medical sense. Others who actually do suffer from medical problems may almost always describe themselves as feeling well. Perceptions of health also depend on the social context in which they occur. If you wake up with a slight headache on a school day you may feel so unwell that you stay in bed. A similar sensation at a weekend or during a holiday might be ignored!

Quantitative descriptions of health, involving precise measurements, are no easier to define. If someone feels well, they are unlikely to look for signs of ill health. Similarly, if someone feels ill, it is very hard to convince them that they are in fact healthy, and all the quantitative data in the world are unlikely to do this. Fortunately, although health is very difficult to measure, 'non-health' is rather easier to quantify. The opposite of health must be lack of health or non-health, usually referred to as dis-ease of the body, or **disease**.

There are different levels of disease, ranging from a general feeling of dissatisfaction with life, through **sickness**, when we feel something is wrong and treat it ourselves, into **illness**, when we feel unwell enough to seek help from a qualified health professional. This will often be a doctor, but it may be a nurse, a physiotherapist or a chiropodist. Increasingly, people are also consulting practitioners of alternative medicine such as a chiropractor or acupuncturist. A **disease** is a diagnostic label given to a set of signs and symptoms by a health professional. The **symptoms** of the disease we notice ourselves make us decide to visit our doctor, but there are often clinical **signs** unknown to us which the doctor will look for to aid diagnosis. For example, the symptoms of measles that we notice are the fever, irritability, cough and rash. But a doctor will look for Koplik's spots, white lesions inside the mouth, a clinical sign which confirms the diagnosis.

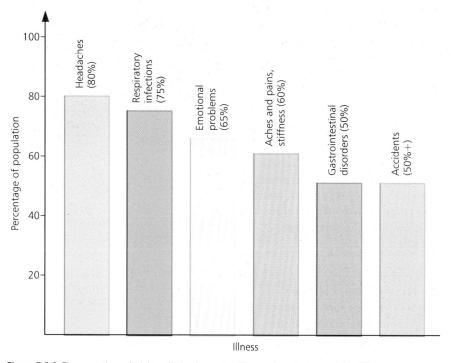

Figure 7.2.2 The proportions of adults suffering from minor illnesses in a single year in the UK.

Types of disease

Physical illness

A **physical illness** affects the body, with symptoms either associated with a particular organ system or more generally spread throughout the body. **Coronary heart disease** is an example of a physical illness, and so is **osteoarthritis**. The majority of patients in a doctor's waiting room will be suffering from physical illnesses. Such illnesses vary in severity from trivial to those that are likely to cause death. A disease may have different effects depending on the reaction of the patient to it, or where in the world it is experienced. In many developed countries such as Britain and the USA, **measles** is an unpleasant childhood disease which very occasionally causes serious side-effects or even death (see figure 7.2.3 overleaf). Yet in parts of the developing world, measles is a regular killer disease of children – there is an Arab proverb which roughly translates as 'Don't count your children until they have had measles'.

Figure 7.2.3 In recent years, the incidence of measles in many developed countries has been greatly reduced by vaccination programmes. A measles epidemic was predicted in Britain in 1994 which, because of the size of the population likely to catch it, would have killed a number of children. Mass vaccination of virtually all school children was introduced by the Government and as a result the epidemic did not materialise.

Mental illness

Mental illness affects the ability of the mind to function within a normally accepted range of behaviours. Some such illnesses arise when people find their circumstances difficult or very unsatisfying, and the reaction of the body is to rebel by producing a range of nervous and emotional reactions. Other mental illnesses seem to arise more as a result of inherited information, biochemical disturbances in the body and the physical processes of ageing. Like most health problems, mental illnesses (also referred to as **psychiatric disorders**) range from relatively common conditions like **depression** through to much rarer diseases such as **schizophrenia** and **manic depression**.

Aetiology – the causes of disease

What causes disease? People have sought the answer to this question for thousands of years. Earliest records of modern human beings show evidence of attempts at medical care. In more recent years, our understanding of the causes of disease has developed greatly, yet there are still illnesses whose causes we do not know or do not fully understand. However, most human diseases can be described as either **infectious** or **non-infectious**. We shall look at each of these main groups in more detail.

Infectious diseases

An infectious disease is caused by the invasion of a **pathogen**. A pathogen is an organism capable of invading our bodies and causing disease. We are host to a huge number of microorganisms which have colonised the outside or inside of our bodies. These **normal flora** do not cause disease; in fact they often benefit us by competing with potential pathogens for sites on our bodies and for nutrients, and even in some cases by producing chemical substances which are toxic to pathogens. Pathogens, in contrast, cause tissue damage as they rapidly reproduce themselves in or on the body. They are often microorganisms such as **bacteria**. By definition, an infectious disease must obviously also be **infectious** – in other words, it must be possible to pass the pathogen from one individual to another. Infectious diseases include **colds**, **influenza** ('flu), **cholera** and **measles**.

Parasitic diseases are a subset of infectious diseases. A **parasite** is an organism which lives on or in another organism, gaining benefit from it and causing it harm. Not all parasites harm their hosts seriously – in fact, a successful parasite does the minimum damage to its host whilst gaining maximum benefit itself – but many parasites do cause serious diseases.

Disease-causing bacteria are parasitic, but the diseases they cause, such as tonsillitis, are not usually referred to as parasitic diseases. The term is usually reserved for conditions such as **schistosomiasis** and **threadworms**, which are caused by relatively large multicellular organisms.

Another subset of infectious diseases are described politely as **social diseases**. These are sexually transmitted diseases such as **syphilis**, **chlamydia** and **AIDS**. Caused by a variety of bacteria and viruses, sexually transmitted diseases are so called because the method of transmission of the pathogen from one person to another is usually by sexual activity.

Non-infectious diseases

Not all diseases are caused by pathogens. A substantial number of the diseases that affect the population of the world are not caused by microorganisms but by lifestyle, ageing, starvation or genetics.

Degenerative diseases often, but not always, affect people as they get older. Common examples of degenerative diseases include **osteoporosis**, **osteoarthritis** and **Alzheimer's disease**. Such diseases are frequently seen as the result of ageing. However, research into these diseases, particularly when they occur in younger people, suggests that many of them are caused by the failure of particular biochemical pathways. Whilst this failure may be a result of ageing, it can also be triggered by genetic information, or a particular type of lifestyle behaviour, or even an infection.

At the moment of conception when a sperm fuses with an ovum, a new genetic individual is formed. Some people's genetic combination causes them to suffer from an **inherited** or **genetic disease** (see section 5.7). These include conditions such as **Down's syndrome**, **Tay-Sachs disease** and **cystic fibrosis**. Genetic diseases are part of the fundamental nature of every cell in the body of an individual, so there are no cures for such diseases – yet. However, the relatively new science of genetic engineering does offer some hope for genetic diseases that affect only part of the metabolism.

Another group of non-infectious diseases is the **deficiency diseases**, which result from dietary deficiencies. Lack of certain vitamins or minerals, or a long-term imbalance in the diet, can lead to disease and ultimately death if the deficiency is not made up. Examples of such diseases include **rickets**, **beri beri** and **scurvy**. The term 'deficiency disease' tends to conjure up images of starving children or adults in the developing countries of the world. However, deficiency diseases are reappearing in developed countries, particularly among individuals who eat large amounts of highly processed food.

A final category of non-infectious diseases is those diseases which are **self inflicted**. These include diseases related to alcohol and illegal drug abuse, along with food disorders such as **anorexia** and **bulimia**. This category is growing as research continues to reveal lifestyle factors in a wide range of diseases. The role of smoking in the development of lung cancer and heart disease is now well known, so it is possible to argue that in smokers these diseases are at least partially self inflicted. There are interesting social implications for the future as it becomes increasing likely that many of the major diseases affecting the developed world may have an environmental element in their aetiology.

What about cancer?

One of the most common and feared diseases in the developed world is **cancer**, yet apart from a mention of lung cancer it does not appear in any of our categories. This is because there does not seem to be a single 'cause' for cancer. Certain changes in the metabolism of cells are typical of all cancers, but the

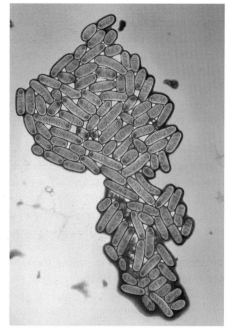

Figure 7.2.4 We can only see bacteria like these *Escherichia coli* in detail with the aid of electron microscopy. Pathogenic bacteria cause disease, suffering and death to millions of people the world over.

Figure 7.2.5 If it is possible to inflict disease on yourself, is it also possible to inflict health? These people working hard to increase their fitness and decrease their body fat obviously hope so!

cause of those changes is not always known. In some cancers, virus infection seems to play a part – can we say these cancers are infectious? In other cancers, substances we take into our bodies, such as cigarette smoke or alcoholic drinks, seem to be major triggers. Are these cancers therefore self-inflicted diseases? Yet other cancers seem to occur mainly in ageing cells in older people. Is cancer a degenerative disease? The answer is that cancer is all of these things, but none of them describes the disease fully. There are many different types of cancers, and as yet there is no simple answer to what causes them.

Detecting disease

There are many occasions when we have no difficulty in detecting and diagnosing our own diseases – for example, the runny nose and headache of a cold are easy to recognise. However, detecting disease is not always so simple. A set of symptoms can have a variety of causes, and it is obviously vitally important that the right disease is treated. A simple example is vomiting. When people are sick, it may be the result of a 'stomach bug' – bacteria or more probably viruses infecting the gut and irritating the stomach, causing the vomiting. However, the same symptoms can be the result of poisoning, drinking too much alcohol or pregnancy. Poisoning requires very specialist medical treatment; drunk patients need careful monitoring to make sure they do not become unconscious and drown in their own vomit; and a pregnant woman should not be given anti-sickness drugs without careful checking that they will not harm her developing baby. In some cases, it is important not only to detect the cause of the symptoms, but to do so quickly – with problems such as heart disease and a wide range of cancers, early detection can mean the difference between life and death.

The first and most important link in the detection of disease is the relationship between the patient and doctor. A doctor has been through long training at medical school along with experience of diagnosis in practice, and when a patient turns up with a range of symptoms, the doctor uses a variety of tools to help detect the cause.

Listening and looking

Listening to patients describing their symptoms, watching them during consultation and carrying out physical examinations are the oldest tools in the diagnostic kit bag. During this process a skilled doctor will be forming a mental diagnosis, or a list of possible diagnoses, and then looking for evidence to confirm the presence or absence of a particular disease. A surprising amount of evidence can be gathered simply by this process of observation and examination, but if more detail is needed then other methods are available.

Biochemical testing

Disease often results in biochemical changes within the body, which cannot always be detected by simple observation and examination. The need for biochemical testing was recognised long ago – urine from pregnant women was used on toads, which laid eggs if the woman was pregnant, and more adventurous doctors used to taste the urine of patients with suspected diabetes to see if it tasted sweet! Things have come a long way since then.

If a patient is breaking down protein as an energy source, the breath may have a distinctive smell of pear drops from the ketones formed in the process. A good doctor would notice this. However, there are a variety of causes for this symptom, one of the most common being untreated diabetes. A simple biochemical test helps in the diagnosis, without anybody having to taste urine!

Normally our bodies conserve glucose. The hormone **insulin** is secreted by the islets of Langerhans in the pancreas, in response to a high level of glucose

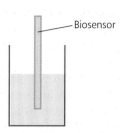

Plastic stick coated with a mixture of the enzymes **glucose oxidase** and **peroxidase** and a blue **chromogen dye** is dipped into a urine sample collected from the patient.

If there is no glucose in the urine the dye stays blue.
If there is glucose in the urine, the glucose oxidase breaks it down in the presence of oxygen and water (both in urine):

$$\text{Glucose} + \text{oxygen} + \text{water} \xrightarrow{\text{glucose oxidase}} \text{gluconic acid} + \text{hydrogen peroxide}$$

The blue chromogen dye is oxidised by the hydrogen peroxide in a reaction catalysed by peroxidase. The dye turns from blue to green to brown depending on the amount of hydrogen peroxide present.

$$\text{Blue chromogen dye} + \text{hydrogen peroxide} \xrightarrow{\text{peroxidase}} \text{green-to-brown chromogen dye} + \text{water}$$

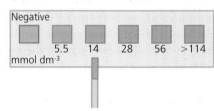

Negative

| | 5.5 | 14 | 28 | 56 | >114 |

mmol dm^{-3}

Comparing the colour of the test stick with a scale shows not only if glucose is present in the urine, but also at what concentration.

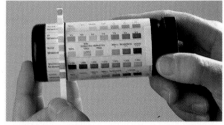

Figure 7.2.6 This simple, non-invasive biochemical test allows medical practitioners to detect early signs of diabetes. It also helps doctors, nurses and patients to check the effectiveness of any treatment for diabetes, which might be a carefully controlled diet, drugs or insulin injections.

in the blood. Insulin lowers the blood glucose level by causing the liver to convert glucose to glycogen, by stimulating fat cells to convert glucose to fat and by stimulating muscle and other tissues to absorb and respire glucose. In an undiagnosed diabetic, insufficient insulin is produced. This means that the level of glucose in the blood climbs higher and higher.

In the kidney, glucose is first filtered out of the blood into the filtrate and is then returned to the blood by an active transport system, so that no glucose normally appears in the urine. In an untreated diabetic, the concentration of glucose in the blood becomes so high that in the kidney, no further glucose can be reabsorbed into the blood. This means that increasing amounts of glucose appear in the urine, providing a useful diagnostic tool. The biochemical test for diabetes therefore detects the level of glucose in the urine. A small stick tipped with an indicator is dipped into a sample of the patient's urine. The tip changes colour, registering not only the presence or absence of glucose in the urine but also the concentration of glucose present (see figure 7.2.6).

Biochemical testing is now relatively common, with tests available for a wide range of diseases from PKU (phenylketonuria) in newborn babies to prostate cancer in older men.

Enzyme-linked immunosorbent assay (ELISA)

There are many variations on ELISA, all of them diagnostic techniques based around the same principles. They depend on the reaction between an antibody and an antigen. Either the antibody or the antigen is bound to a solid phase, usually the wall of the vessel that contains the reaction mixture. When a sample from a patient is added, any relevant antigen or antibody will bind to its opposite on the solid phase. Then another molecule is added which in turn binds to the molecule from the patient. This last molecule is labelled with an enzyme. The final stage is for the plates to be washed with a substrate for the enzyme, and the enzyme–substrate reaction causes a colour change. This colour change indicates a positive test result. The process is illustrated in figure 7.2.7.

Figure 7.2.7 Using ELISA (enzyme-linked immunosorbent assay) to detect a particular antibody.

1 Coating

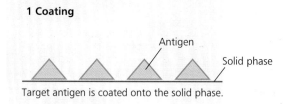

Target antigen is coated onto the solid phase.

2 Specimen added

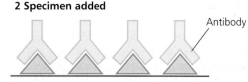

The patient's serum is added and incubated. If the specific antibody is present it is captured by the antigen.

3 Antibody detection

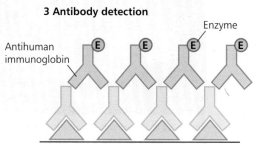

Enzyme-labelled antihuman immunoglobin binds to the captured antibody.

4 Substrate addition

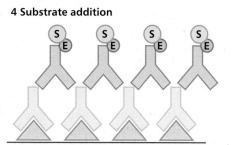

A substrate is added which reacts with the enzyme label to produce colour.

5 Colour detection

The optical density is measured. This is proportional to the amount of antibody bound.

ELISAs have many advantages:

- they use relatively cheap reagents
- they do not need expensive detection systems
- they can be automated easily
- the reagents have long shelf lives and are easy to store.

As a result, ELISAs are widely used in the diagnosis of bacterial, viral and parasitic infections.

X-rays and scans

For thousands of years of human history, the only ways of knowing what was going on inside the body were to feel it from the outside or to cut it open to see inside. The latter was a particularly traumatic procedure in the days before effective anaesthetics became available. However, in 1895 Wilhelm Röntgen discovered X-rays by accident. Their penetrating power and their ability to blacken photographic emulsions led rapidly to their adoption by doctors for examining suspected internal injuries, especially broken bones (the skeleton shows up particularly clearly on X-ray photographs of the body).

X-ray radiation can knock electrons out of atoms, **ionising** them. This can damage many of the chemicals inside cells, including the DNA. The damage done to the body by the strongly ionising effects of X-rays was not recognised for many years. This led to quite inappropriate uses of X-rays – 40 years ago shoe shops had X-ray machines to take pictures of children's feet inside new shoes, to check that the shoes fitted properly and their feet were not being squashed! Later, doctors and nurses who had been exposed to significant doses of X-rays began to develop serious illnesses induced by the ionising radiation, and the dangers began to be recognised. There are strict regulations now governing both the operators of X-ray machines and the doses given to patients. This means the benefits of using X-rays to detect damage and disease can be enjoyed whilst keeping the health risks to a minimum.

The use of X-rays in the detection of disease has become very much more sophisticated in recent years. X-rays are used to detect internal infections as well as skeletal problems. In addition to the simple single-image X-ray like that in figure 7.2.8, **CAT** (computer-assisted tomography) scanners have been developed. These machines take a series of X-ray 'slices' through the body and then, with the aid of computer technology, produce images which detect disease hidden deep inside the body without resorting to surgery.

A further step in the diagnosis of disease has been the development of **MRI** (magnetic resonance imaging). Instead of X-rays, this uses radio waves in a strong magnetic field to produce images of the inside of the body. Because MRI does not use ionising radiation, it has safety benefits over CAT scanners, and provides clearer and more useful images for many types of diagnosis. However, both play a major role in the early diagnosis of many diseases, particularly cancers which can grow unnoticed within the cavity of the body giving few symptoms until the disease is widely spread. CAT scanners and MRI both also show the swelling that often accompanies internal injury or infection, allowing the appropriate treatments to be given rapidly.

Ultrasound monitoring and diagnosis

The use of ultrasound in the detection of disease has become very common in recent years. The technique is based on the same principles as echo-location in bats and depth sounders in submarines. Very high-pitched sound, above the level of human hearing, is directed into the body and the reflected sound from various organs is then converted into an image of the inside of the body.

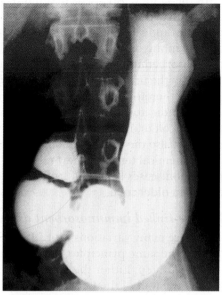

Figure 7.2.8 X-rays diagnose broken bones and skeletal problems such as arthritis, and are also used to identify problems in the heart and cancers in the lungs and other areas. In this X-ray of a patient after a barium meal, the stomach is clearly visible. The barium porridge is radio-opaque, and so shows up on the X-ray as the barium flows into various parts of the gut.

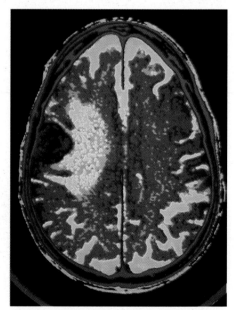

Figure 7.2.9 The ability to see a slice through the human body without resorting to the surgeon's knife has been a major step forward in the battle against disease. This CAT scan through the brain clearly shows a tumour (blue) on the left-hand side of the brain.

One of the best known and most common uses of ultrasound technology is in the monitoring of the developing fetus during pregnancy. Until ultrasound scanning became possible, the growth of a developing fetus was monitored by external manipulation and measuring the size of the mother's 'bump'. This is not necessarily an accurate measure of the size of the fetus. The only way of actually 'seeing' the fetus and checking it was developing normally was to use potentially harmful X-rays, and so this was done as little as possible. Now ultrasound scans are carried out at least once during most pregnancies, and the accurate measurements produced make it easier to predict when the baby will be born. It is also possible to monitor the growth of the fetus if there is any concern about it, and also to check that the limbs, heart, brain and spine are forming properly. Some voices of concern have been raised about the absolute safety of using ultrasound during pregnancy, but at present the consensus of opinion among doctors and scientists is that the value of the information gained from at least one scan during a pregnancy far outweighs any possible risks.

Lights, camera, action!

All of the techniques described so far which are used to help medical professionals 'see' inside their patients give an image of the internal organs which usually needs expert interpretation. But techniques such as **endoscopy** allow doctors to see literally inside their living patients. A tiny fibre-optic light source and camera are fed directly into the body cavity being investigated, such as the gut. The patient is conscious but tranquillised to keep him or her relaxed, to make sure that the throat remains open and to help the endoscope tube to be swallowed down into the gut. A picture is relayed back onto a screen so that the doctor can see the living, moving gut. The technique is shown in figure 7.2.10. This technology not only allows ulcers, tumours and other problems to be seen directly, but also makes it possible to take samples of tissue at the same time. Variations of this technique enable different areas of the body to be investigated. Surgery can be carried out using an endoscope without cutting into the patient, or through a very small incision just large enough to admit the camera unit. This is often referred to as keyhole surgery.

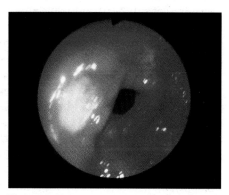

Figure 7.2.10 Endoscopy techniques allow pictures from inside the body to be seen directly. Because the patient is often conscious, some people actually see inside their own bodies! The photograph shows a stomach ulcer seen through an endoscope.

Studying disease

As we saw on page 612, it is very difficult to measure health, or even to define it. Most of the information we have about health comes from studying disease. Diseases that cause easily defined and measured symptoms are much easier to quantify than the subjective feeling of being healthy.

The study of patterns of disease is known as **epidemiology**. There are three main questions that drive epidemiology:

1 Who gets ill? This is the major epidemiological question, answered by looking at the distribution of a particular disease within a population, a country or across the world.

2 Why do they get ill? This considers the **aetiology** (cause) of a disease. A classic example of this was the work done by Richard Doll who linked data on the prevalence of lung cancer with data on smoking habits and was the first to suggest a link between smoking and lung cancer.

3 How should they be treated? This aspect of epidemiology evaluates the effectiveness of different types of treatment.

Two main aspects of disease are recorded in epidemiological studies. One is the **morbidity** of the disease. This is the number of people who are made ill by the disease. Morbidity has to be carefully defined, as it is dependent on how the measurements are made. For example, measuring the number of hospital admissions for asthma would not necessarily give a clear picture of the number of people whose lives are affected by the condition. The other aspect of a disease that is measured is the **mortality** of the disease – that is the number of deaths resulting from it. Mortality is obviously easier to measure than morbidity, but can only be used for diseases that are severe enough to cause death. The information for epidemiological studies comes from analysing data from specific surveys, from doctor's surgeries, from hospital admissions, from registers of births and deaths and from sociological studies.

Epidemiological studies provide us with a wide range of information which can be used in a variety of ways for scientific, medical, financial (insurance) and political ends. Epidemiology provides explanations of disease which take both social and biological factors into account. However, there are limitations to these studies. There must be a strict definition of the disease or symptoms being investigated. A choice has to be made about which social and biological factors to focus on, and this choice will almost inevitably affect the eventual results of the study. Because there is a need to simplify the situation and only consider certain factors, an epidemiological study may fail to take account of multifactorial causes or of the interaction between factors. Finally, and in some ways most importantly, an association being identified between two factors does not necessarily mean that one causes the other, so the results must be looked at with great care.

There are several clearly defined factors which epidemiology has shown to be closely associated with the state of health or disease of the individual. These are age, gender, marital status, ethnic background, place of residence and social class and occupation. We shall briefly consider these in turn.

1 Age affects all sorts of areas of our health. An example is the data in figure 7.2.11 showing the relationship between cause of death and age in females in the UK.

2 Health also varies with gender. On average, males die younger than females. Men are significantly more likely to die of coronary heart disease and cancer than women. Males are also more likely to suffer from genetic diseases caused by problems on the X chromosome. Epidemiology can help to decide how much this difference between males and females is due to intrinsic maleness, and how much to patterns of male behaviour common in different societies.

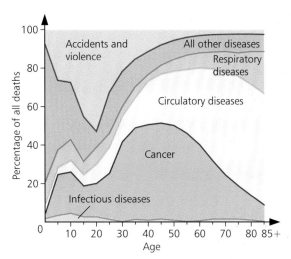

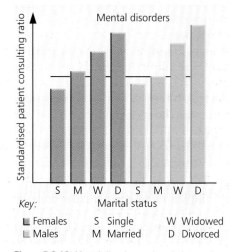

Figure 7.2.11 Causes of death for females in the UK, 1980.

3 Marital status seems to affect health, although as more people live together in long term stable partnerships without becoming legally married, these differences may well appear to decline. For example, the effect of marital status on the incidence of mental disorders in the UK is quite striking, as shown in figure 7.2.12.

4 Ethnic origins can be used to identify groups particularly prone to certain diseases. However, as with all epidemiological evidence, these data need to be handled with care. Some classic research in 1981 showed patterns in the incidence of heart attacks and strokes in people of white European, Asian and West Indian background, as shown in figure 7.2.13.

The graph suggests that clear conclusions can be drawn about the ethnic groups and these particular diseases. But the data take no account of the social classes and occupations of the individuals, and therefore of the health status and health care received by individuals before attacks, or of the same ethnic groups living in other countries like the USA.

Figure 7.2.12 Mental disorders and marital status in the early 1980s.

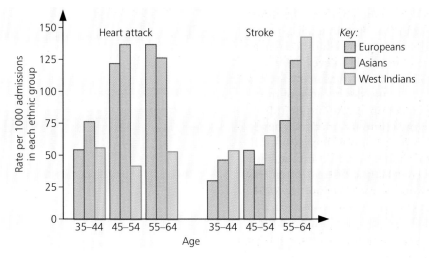

5 Where you live has a major influence on your projected health. The main causes of death in adults in England and Wales in 1982 are shown in figure 7.2.14, compared with the main causes of death in Africa, Asia and Latin America in 1978.

Infant mortality rates are a very good indicator of the state of health of a nation or a social group. The chances of a newborn baby surviving the first year of life varies enormously depending on where in the world it is born, as shown in table 7.2.1.

Figure 7.2.13 Heart attacks and strokes for different ethnic groups, 1981.

Country	Infant mortality rate per 1000 live births
Egypt	110
Kenya	92
Sierra Leone	215
Bolivia	138
Brazil	82
Cuba	22
Jamaica	30
USA	14
China	49
India	129
Japan	9
United Arab Emirates	57
Sweden	8
UK	14
Yugoslavia	35
New Zealand	14
Papua New Guinea	111

Table 7.2.1 Infant mortality rates in different countries, 1975–80

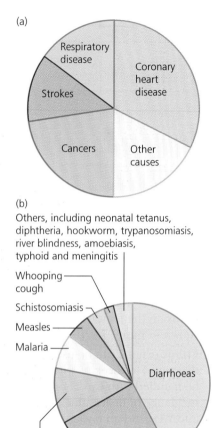

Figure 7.2.14 (a) Causes of death in adults in England and Wales, 1982. (b) Causes of death in developing nations, 1978.

The same disease can have a very different impact in different parts of the world. For example, as mentioned on page 613, measles is a highly infectious and potentially dangerous disease, linked with severe and debilitating fevers, a high risk of secondary bacterial respiratory infections and post-measles encephalitis (inflammation of the brain). In most developed countries, measles is now a relatively rare disease thanks largely to intensive vaccination programmes aimed at young children, the most vulnerable members of the population. Even if children in a developed country do catch measles, improved health and hygiene conditions mean that the mortality ratio has fallen from one child dying in every 100 in 1940 to 0.02 dying in every 100 in 1989. This probably has many factors. Children tend to be older now when they catch measles because of the relatively isolated way they live in developed countries. Alongside this, drugs to control fever and antibiotics to fight secondary infections have improved beyond recognition. In the developing nations, measles is still one of the main causes of childhood death. Epidemics are common, and children tend to be very young when they contract the disease, often less than one year old. The extended families common in developing world communities mean that young infants and children spend considerable amounts of time together, giving rise to pools of infection. Many of these children already have their health challenged in other ways, for example by parasites, malaria or malnutrition, so the measles virus is devastating. In addition, neither the vaccine nor the antibiotics to treat secondary infections are widely available or affordable. Thus on a global scale, measles is now largely a disease of the developing world, although it is difficult to eradicate completely even in the developed world because it is so highly infectious.

6   Finally, social class and occupation are very important in determining health. The graphs in figure 7.2.15 show the relationship between social

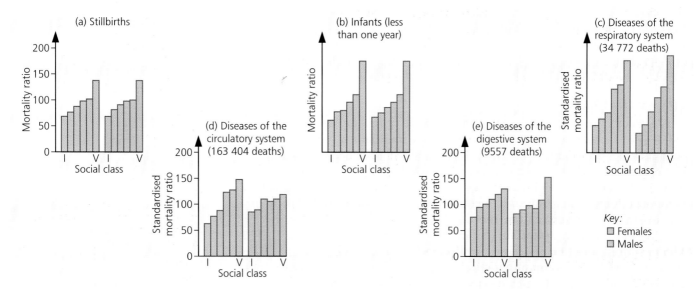

(a) Stillbirths

(d) Diseases of the circulatory system (163 404 deaths)

(b) Infants (less than one year)

(e) Diseases of the digestive system (9557 deaths)

(c) Diseases of the respiratory system (34 772 deaths)

Key:
□ Females
□ Males

Figure 7.2.15 Incidence of stillbirths, deaths in the first year of life and diseases of the respiratory system, the circulatory system and the digestive system related to social class.

class and mortality for a range of conditions in the UK from stillbirths to diseases of the digestive system. The graphs reveal how the dice are loaded against those born into the poorest groups in society. Epidemiological data such as these may be used to argue for social change in an attempt to improve the living conditions and thus the health of those in our society least able to help themselves.

Mortality ratios and social classes

Statistics on mortality often refer to the number of deaths per 1000 people. However, sometimes that is not the most useful measure and a **mortality ratio** is used instead. A mortality ratio compares the number of people in a particular group who have died of a particular cause with the total number of deaths from that cause. For example, in figure 7.2.15(a) the figures show the total number of stillbirths of girls or boys which occurred in each social class. Age is not a factor, as stillbirth can only happen at one particular stage of life. However, when looking at other diseases age is one of the variables. Therefore if we are concentrating on a variable other than age – in this

case, social class – the data are **age standardised**. This means the total number of deaths from the disease across the age range is used – there is no age selection.

Social class is a way of dividing people into groups based on their socioeconomic status. Thus people in social class I are the wealthiest and those in social class V are the poorest. People in social classes I and II are generally well educated and have professional jobs, while those in class V have few qualifications and may have a very low paid job or no job at all. The divisions are quite artificial, but they are used by epidemiologists and social scientists to investigate the effects of different ways of life on health.

Infectious diseases

Infectious diseases are diseases that can be transmitted from one person to another. They are caused by invading microorganisms known as **pathogens** which do not belong to the normal body flora. The invading microorganisms often cause tissue damage, though in some cases they produce a toxin and it is this that causes the symptoms of disease, rather than the microorganisms themselves. Infectious diseases range from being so mild we hardly notice them to those that may cause death. So what are the pathogens that cause disease?

Different pathogens, different diseases

There are five main groups of pathogens: viruses, bacteria, fungi and protoctists and larger organisms such as parasitic worms. Each type of pathogen is capable of causing serious disease. An example of disease caused by each of the different types of pathogen is described below.

AIDS – a viral killer

In 1981, doctors in America reported a new disease. It first became apparent in the homosexual community of Los Angeles, where unusually high numbers of young men developed a type of cancer, Kaposi's sarcoma, which was usually only seen in very elderly patients. Eventually a whole range of common symptoms (fevers, persistent diarrhoea, loss in body mass, TB, a rare type of pneumonia, Kaposi's sarcoma and infections that rarely affect healthy people) were recognised as resulting from infection by one particular virus. The end result for those showing symptoms was usually death. This disease was **AIDS (acquired immune deficiency syndrome)**, and the pathogen responsible is known as **HIV (human immunodeficiency virus)**. Infection by HIV does not necessarily lead to AIDS. People infected by the virus who do not display the symptoms of AIDS are referred to as **HIV positive**. When tested, their blood shows the presence of HIV antibodies. **UNAIDS**, the Joint Nations Programme on HIV/AIDS, estimates that currently about 33 million people throughout the world are infected by HIV/AIDS, about 90% of whom live in the developing world. More than 14 million people have already died from the disease.

The human immunodeficiency virus is very fragile and cannot survive in the air. It must be contained in human body fluids. HIV infection may come from either an individual who is HIV positive (who may be without symptoms and quite possibly unaware of their infection) or someone with AIDS. The virus can be transmitted from person to person in one of three ways, each of which involves contact between the body fluids of two individuals. The first and most common means of transmission is by sexual contact, between both homosexuals and heterosexuals. So far in the developed world homosexual sex has been more likely to transmit the disease, with relatively few cases of infection via heterosexual intercourse in the developed countries, but on a global scale heterosexual intercourse is responsible for over 70% of all HIV infections.

The second way in which HIV is spread is through infected blood. Intravenous drug users have appeared as a high risk group, due both to infection from shared needles and to the prostitution often undertaken to pay for the drugs. HIV has also been spread through the use of infected blood products. Haemophiliacs need transfusions of factor VIII to enable their blood to clot normally, and numbers of them, along with their families, became infected with the virus before the risk was recognised. In America and much of Europe, blood is now treated to destroy HIV before it is used for transfusions. However, in much of the developing world, blood for transfusions is bought from unscreened individuals and is frequently not treated in any way, so transmission through blood products continues.

Third, HIV can cross from a mother to her fetus in the early stages of pregnancy. Infection of the baby may also occur during birth, and the virus has been shown to be present in breast milk, so infants may be born free from HIV but become infected through breast feeding.

Most of the clinical symptoms of AIDS are the result of the profound effect HIV has on the immune system of the body. It leaves individuals vulnerable to a whole range of infections which might be trivial in a healthy person but which, in an AIDS sufferer, may mean death. The immune system (see section 1.6) has evolved to destroy and eliminate invading pathogens such as HIV, but it

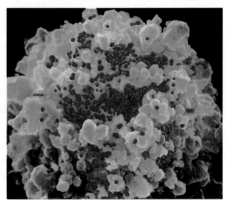

Figure 7.2.16 A scanning electron micrograph showing the AIDS virus (red) attacking a helper T-cell.

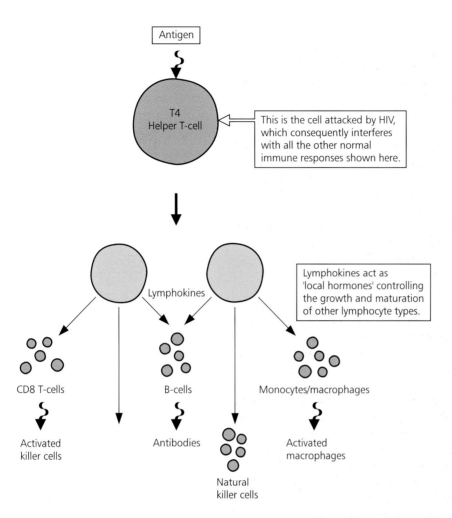

Antigen

T4
Helper T-cell

This is the cell attacked by HIV, which consequently interferes with all the other normal immune responses shown here.

Lymphokines

Lymphokines act as 'local hormones' controlling the growth and maturation of other lymphocyte types.

CD8 T-cells

B-cells

Monocytes/macrophages

Activated killer cells

Antibodies

Natural killer cells

Activated macrophages

Figure 7.2.17 The effect of HIV on the immune system cascade.

does not produce sufficient antibodies to overwhelm the virus because of the action of the virus itself. An important part of the immune system is a group of cells known as **T4** or **helper T-cells**. They have been termed 'the leaders of the immunological orchestra' because of their central role in the immune response. Helper T-cells support and amplify the response of other cells within the immune system, in particular the killer T-cells and some B-cells.

However, on the surface of the cell membranes of the helper T-cells is a specific glycoprotein called CD4. This is recognised by HIV, and the viruses attach to the CD4, after which they can infect the helper T-cells. As a result of the HIV infection, the normal functioning of the helper T-cells is lost or impaired. This undermines the ability of the entire immune system to react to the invasion of the body by other pathogens (see figure 7.2.17).

At the moment AIDS is still an incurable disease. A variety of methods of attack are currently under investigation and perhaps the most important of these is the attempt to limit the spread of the disease. As can be seen from figure 7.2.18, there are now millions of AIDS and HIV positive individuals throughout the world. Whilst the problem was first identified in America, there are now high numbers of affected people in the African and Asian continents. Education programmes have been set up to help people to understand the ways in which HIV is spread, and how to prevent it. Less promiscuous sex, the use of condoms to prevent internal contact between partners and the dangers of sharing needles in drug abuse are three of the main messages in the battle to contain this modern-day plague.

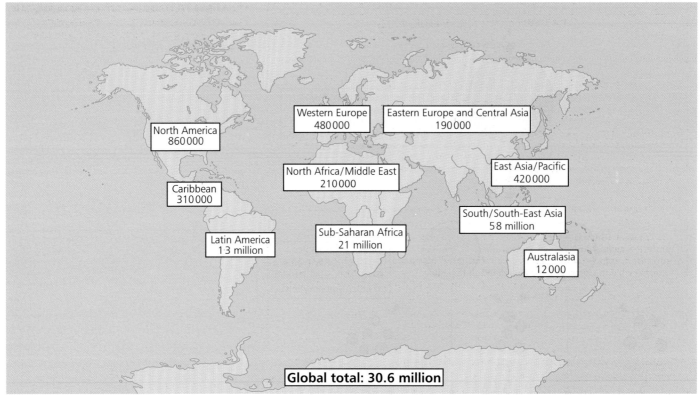

North America	860 000
Western Europe	480 000
Eastern Europe and Central Asia	190 000
Caribbean	310 000
North Africa/Middle East	210 000
East Asia/Pacific	420 000
South/South-East Asia	58 million
Latin America	1.3 million
Sub-Saharan Africa	21 million
Australasia	12 000

Global total: 30.6 million

Figure 7.2.18 The estimated numbers of people living with HIV/AIDS at the end of 1997. The effect of the disease in Sub-Saharan Africa and South/South-East Asia is catastrophic. It is hoped that a combination of behavioural and social changes, along with possible new vaccines and drugs, may yet prevent HIV from becoming even more destructive than at present.

Many specialists feel that the development of an effective vaccine is crucial to the containment of the AIDS epidemic, but producing a vaccine against an organism whose target is actually part of the immune system is very difficult indeed. Protection is needed against all strains of the virus, and HIV is a very variable virus. So far, insufficient detail is known about the infective mechanism of HIV to decide which part of the virus should be used as the basis for a vaccine. Added to this, AIDS is a peculiarly human disease. Chimpanzees seem to be the only other animals that are susceptible to the virus, and so work on animals to develop vaccines is limited. An effective vaccine is still only a hope on which much research is currently focused, although in the late 1990s a vaccine emerged with sufficient potential for a number of American doctors to offer themselves as human guinea pigs in a clinical trial.

Finally, drug therapy has a role to play. Although a variety of drugs have been tried so far, none has been found to be truly effective in either preventing the shift from HIV positive status to full-blown AIDS, or in slowing the progress of AIDS once it begins. Antiviral drugs are largely ineffective in the treatment of AIDS, and although drugs to stimulate the immune system have produced a short-lived improvement in killer T-cell functions, this improvement has not as yet been maintained over a longer period of time. However, towards the end of the twentieth century, combined drug therapies (where three or more drugs are used in a cocktail) began to offer hope. Patients are living longer and remaining more healthy. If the current progress continues, AIDS may become a treatable disease in the not too distant future.

Salmonella and friends – bacterial invaders

There are about 2200 different types of *Salmonella* bacteria which infect animals, and most of them are capable of causing disease in humans. Poultry is the most common source of human salmonellosis, as up to 60% of poultry meat

STATUTORY INSTRUMENTS

1995 No. 1763

FOOD

The Food Safety (General Food Hygiene) Regulations 1995

Chapter IX
Provisions applicable to foodstuffs

1. No raw materials or ingredients shall be accepted by a food business if they are known to be, or might reasonably be expected to be, so contaminated with parasites, pathogenic microorganisms, or toxic, decomposed or foreign substances, that after normal sorting and/or preparatory or processing procedures hygienically applied by food businesses, they would still be unfit for human consumption.

2. Raw materials and ingredients stored in the establishment shall be kept in appropriate conditions designed to prevent harmful deterioration and to protect them from contamination.

3. All food which is handled, stored, packaged, displayed and transported, shall be protected against any contamination likely to render the food unfit for human consumption, injurious to health or contaminated in such a way that it would be unreasonable to expect it to be consumed in that state. In particular, food must be so placed and/or protected as to minimize any risk of contamination. Adequate procedures must be in place to ensure pests are controlled.

4. Hazardous and/or inedible substances, including animal feedstuffs, shall be adequately labelled and stored in separate and secure containers.

Figure 7.2.19 Health regulations such as these are designed to avoid the spread of food poisoning such as salmonellosis. Health inspectors regularly check workplaces where food is prepared, sold or served to the public.

is contaminated with the bacterium, and so are many egg shells and the contents of some eggs. Relatively large numbers of the *Salmonella* bacterium need to be ingested to cause symptoms (in contrast to a disease such as typhoid, where only a very small number of infective organisms can cause disease). The disease is usually spread either by eating infected food which has not been properly cooked, or by eating cooked food which has been contaminated after cooking, during storage or preparation. If contaminated food is stored without refrigeration, the microorganisms multiply until their numbers are high enough to cause disease. Salmonellosis usually occurs in small outbreaks, either within a single household or within a group of people who have all attended the same party, wedding or other function and eaten the same food. In 1995/6, 50 people in Britain died of salmonella food poisoning.

There is an incubation period of 18–36 hours after the infected food is eaten, and the severity of the disease that follows is very variable. Typical symptoms include feeling unwell, nausea, vomiting and often a fever followed by diarrhoea. This is the main symptom of the disease and can continue for some time after the other symptoms have gone. Elderly people can be particularly at risk in *Salmonella* infections as they cannot cope easily with dehydration.

In (relatively) mild cases, rehydration fluids are given whilst the diarrhoea lasts, and occasionally these need to be given intravenously. Most patients recover on their own, but if the symptoms continue for several days, antibiotic treatment may be used. A major problem with antibiotic treatment is that *Salmonella* bacteria are common in farm animals as well as people, and they have developed resistance to many of the antibiotics used by vets, farmers and doctors. There is a very limited selection of effective antibiotics to choose from.

Careful management of food hygiene both in the home and in commercial kitchens are the main features of *Salmonella* control. After an attack of salmonellosis, an individual will excrete *Salmonella* bacteria in the faeces for up to four weeks. Although the numbers of the microorganism in the faeces are too low to cause a high risk of infection, infected children cannot return to school until they have shown three consecutive clear faeces samples, and the same applies to any adult whose work involves the handling of food.

Athlete's foot – a fungal infection

Athlete's foot is a fungal infection of the feet. In the developed world, human fungal infections are generally fairly superficial, affecting the skin, hair or nails. They tend to cause local inflammation and damage at the site of the invading mycelium. Athlete's foot is a common fungal infection, often found on the warm, often slightly sweaty, skin between the toes. Fungal spores are picked up from the air or the floor, and they germinate and thrive in these warm moist conditions. The fungus penetrates and digests the outer layers of the skin. These layers die and slough off, leaving the skin underneath raw and vulnerable to further attack.

Treatment of athlete's foot is usually by a topical (local) antifungal drug. A cream which can be bought over the counter at a pharmacy is rubbed into the infected area. If the infection is very entrenched in the skin, a course of oral antifungal drugs may be prescribed by a doctor so that the drug is within the system and the fungus is attacked from all sides.

Malaria – protoctistan death

Malaria has been around for centuries, and at present shows no signs of loosening its grip on the human race. At any one time the disease affects 267 million people over 103 countries, and results in around 107 million clinical cases and up to two million deaths each year. It is largely, but certainly not entirely, found in the developing world.

The *Plasmodium* parasite causes malaria. This parasite is a protozoan with a complex life cycle involving two hosts, the *Anopheles* mosquito and people. The mosquito, shown in figure 7.2.21, is the **vector** for the disease – it transmits it from one person to another. Only female mosquitoes bite people, because they need a blood meal before laying their eggs, and it is at this point that they pass on the protozoan.

Malaria begins with 'flu-like symptoms which develop 8–30 days after the infected bite, and the disease progresses to a regular cycle of severe fevers, shaking chills and drenching sweats. Figure 7.2.22 shows the life cycle of the *Plasmodium* parasite.

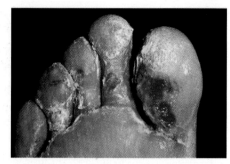

Figure 7.2.20 For most sufferers athlete's foot is itchy and perhaps sore at times. It is only after a long period of neglect that athlete's foot looks like this.

Figure 7.2.21 This scanning electron micrograph shows the mouthparts of the female *Anopheles* mosquito, the vector for malaria which kills over two million people each year.

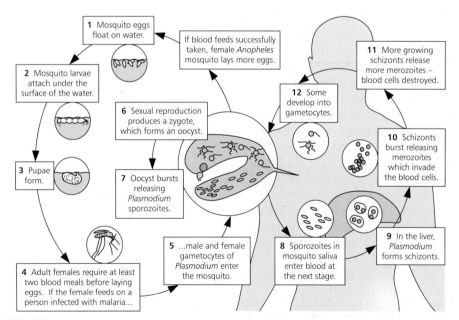

Figure 7.2.22 The symptoms of malaria coincide with the multiplication of the malarial parasites and the destruction of red blood cells. This may lead to long term weakness, anaemia and death.

Malaria has always been associated with rivers and ponds, sources of water where the mosquito larvae can grow. But as millions of people flock to the shanty towns surrounding the new megacities of the developing world, fresh opportunities are arising for the mosquitoes. Strains are emerging that can breed rapidly in a tiny amount of water, such as a bottle top, a water-filled footprint or a blocked drain, threatening a new surge of the disease. Many people in Africa have become at least partly immune to malaria, carrying it but showing no symptoms. However, the increased exploitation of resources in areas such as the Amazon basin, Ethiopia, Madagascar and Sri Lanka has led to susceptible people moving into these areas and local epidemics occurring.

No really effective treatments against malaria have emerged so far. This is in part due to the nature of the organism involved, and partly because those countries most affected by malaria are also generally very poor. Potential profits for a company marketing a cure are limited, and so the investment in research has been limited too. There are no drugs to destroy the parasite once in people's bodies. Vaccines are extremely difficult and expensive to make because the protozoans keep changing their outer coats, but recent developments mean that an effective vaccine may not be too far away.

Controlling the mosquito vectors has resulted in some success, by spraying waterways with DDT to kill the mosquito larvae, but the environmental effects can be grave. Controlling the environment by improving public and environmental health is an important factor. In Singapore, a law was passed making it illegal to have any standing water on property where mosquitoes might breed. People removed old tins, bottle tops, etc., and as a result the incidence of malaria has been substantially reduced. However, malaria is on the increase in the developed world as a result of climatic and social changes. Investment has increased and there is now the possibilty of a successful vaccine, based on an antibody to a vital *Plasmodium* protein. Malaria, the ancient scourge of the human race, may yet be defeated.

Multicellular parasites

Multicellular parasites are animals with organ systems of their own. They are usually **helminthes** or worms that are internal parasites. They may be roundworms or flatworms. People are the only hosts for some of these parasitic worms, but others have complicated life cycles in which humans are only part of the story. Helminthic diseases range from relatively mild problems such as **threadworms** in the large intestine which are common throughout the world, through to some of the most debilitating diseases of the developing world such as **schistosomiasis** caused by blood flukes and **river blindness** caused by a parasitic worm. The life cycle of the guinea worm, another parasite, is described on page 611.

Parasitism, disease and the human population

Parasitism and disease play an important role in destroying the well-being of the human population of the biosphere. In the developed world the treatment of diseases such as cancer, heart failure and AIDS involves great financial expenditure by both governments and individuals. In the developing world the tropical diseases such as malaria (which affects 267 million people in 103 countries!), yellow fever, river blindness and Chagas' disease cause untold suffering. These diseases, many of which are the result of parasitic infestations, weaken the population of many developing countries thus making it harder for them to utilise their natural resources. They cannot afford the treatments which would keep the population healthy, yet the parasitic infestations make them poorer. It is a vicious circle from which there is at present no escape.

Disease	Cause	Vector	Numbers affected	Symptoms
Malaria	*Plasmodium* – a single-celled protozoan parasite	The female *Anopheles* mosquito	267 million people in 103 countries	'Flu-like symptoms to begin with, then cycle of severe fevers, shaking chills and sweats which cause serious weakness and sometimes death
Schistosomiasis	Trematode flatworms (flukes)	Infected aquatic snails	200 million people in 76 countries	The body tissues react to eggs which become lodged in them. Causes debilitating diseases of the urinary tract and gut
Filariasis	Parasitic nematodes	Mosquitoes	90 million people in 76 countries	Blocked lymph vessels – in later stages painful and disfiguring swelling of the limbs known as elephantiasis
Onchocerciasis	Parasitic nematodes	*Simulium* blackflies	17.6 million people in 34 countries	Immature worms lodge in the skin and eyes, eventually causing blindness (river blindness)
Chagas' disease (South American trypanosomiasis)	Protozoan parasites – trypanosomes	The faeces of assassin bugs – large blood-sucking bugs which live in cracks in house walls	16–18 million people in South and Central America	Shortly after infection – by faeces through a bite – fever develops which can be fatal. Followed by symptomless period of months or years when parasite invades most body organs – causing chronic weakness and death

Table 7.2.2 Although the diseases of the developed world cause suffering to the individuals concerned, it is the parasitic tropical diseases which are the major scourge of the human population

Passing it on

Will it spread?

All pathogens *can* cause disease, but that is not to say they always will. Infectious diseases are **communicable** – the infection is spread from one person to another. The likelihood of any particular infectious disease being passed from one person to another will depend on the **pathogen**, the **host** and the **environment**.

- The **virulence** of a particular pathogen can vary. Virulence is the power of the pathogen to cause severe disease. An example of variable virulence is shown by the influenza virus. The virus is constantly changing slightly, producing different strains of 'flu, some of which are relatively mild but others of which are highly virulent, causing severe disease and death. Also, different pathogens adapt to new environmental conditions and respond to drugs and the body's immune response with varying levels of success.

- The behaviour and general health of potential hosts will also affect the likelihood of disease being passed on. Travelling to countries where particular diseases are common obviously increases the risk of infection, as does irresponsible sexual behaviour. Some occupations, especially those in the field of medicine, also increase the risk. Crowded living conditions, poor hygiene, poor nutrition and existing disease all increase the risk of infection. Conversely, previous immunity, from either a full infection or vaccination, can reduce the risk of a new infection.

- Many disease-causing organisms have to withstand a period of time outside their hosts in order to be communicated from one person to another. This transmission time varies in duration, but it is always a vulnerable time for the pathogen. Environmental factors such as temperature, dust and humidity levels, the availability of water and the use of antibiotics and pesticides can all affect the ability of a pathogen to survive outside its host.

How does it spread?

Diseases can spread in many different ways. They can spread **horizontally** through the members of the same population, or **vertically** from one generation to the next, as an infection passes from a mother to her child during pregnancy and birth. In some cases an animal disease can spread to humans. Such a disease is called a **zoonosis**. People like farmers and vets who work with animals are particularly at risk of catching these diseases, as to a lesser extent are people who breed birds or simply have a houseful of pets.

Table 7.2.3 (overleaf) outlines the main transmission methods. An understanding of the way a disease is transmitted from one individual to another is extremely important in helping to prevent the spread of the disease through a community.

Outbreaks of disease

Many diseases occur at low levels within a population all the time. Sometimes, there is a sudden increase in the incidence of a particular disease. At a localised level, such an increase is called an **outbreak**. On a national level, an increased incidence of a disease is known as an **epidemic**. On very rare occasions, an epidemic will affect many of the countries of the world at the same time. This situation is known as a **pandemic**. Only four infectious diseases are known to have caused pandemics – influenza, cholera, plague and acquired immune deficiency syndrome (AIDS). Some diseases are common in the population all the time, for example, malaria in West Africa, and these are referred to as **endemic**.

An outbreak of disease can start in several ways.

1 There may be a single **point source** of infection, and a group of people are exposed to it at one time. For example, if some food at a party is infected with *Salmonella*, everyone who ate that food will develop the symptoms of food poisoning within a few days of each other.

2 There may be a **common-source outbreak**, involving a source of infection to which several individuals are exposed over a period of time. For example, if an ear- and body-piercing establishment used contaminated equipment which was not sterilised properly between clients, then many people going there could be infected with the same disease.

3 Many outbreaks of disease are simply the result of **person-to-person contact**. There is a chain of transmission from one person to another, with apparent gaps in the chain caused by the incubation period. An outbreak of chickenpox in a primary school is a good example of this, with waves of children becoming spotty as the infection sweeps through the classes.

Each of these different types of outbreak gives a different distribution pattern, as shown in figure 7.2.23.

Natural defences

The human body has a number of lines of defence against the invasion of pathogens. Our defences can be considered in two parts – the non-specific defences and the specific immune system.

Non-specific defences

Non-specific defences against disease are part of the normal functioning of the body. The first is the **skin**, which forms a natural barrier surrounding the body, preventing the entry of microorganisms to the body. The oily substance called

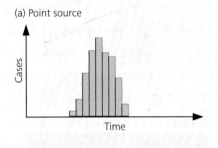

(a) Point source

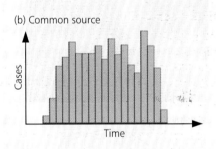

(b) Common source

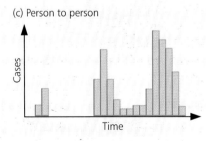

(c) Person to person

Figure 7.2.23 Recording case numbers over time gives these distinctive patterns of infection. Recognition of a disease as a point-source or common-source outbreak using this kind of analysis can help identify the source of the infection, preventing further outbreaks.

Type of transmission	How transmission occurs	Examples of diseases
Vectors	A living creature which transmits infection from one host to another is known as a **vector**. Many arthropods are vectors of disease. *Anopheles* mosquitoes which spread malaria are one of the best known examples of vectors.	Malaria, dengue, yellow fever, bilharzia
Fomites	Fomites are inanimate objects that carry pathogens from one host to another, for example, hospital towels and bedding or using someone else's make-up.	*Staphylococcus* infections
Direct contact	Direct contact can often spread skin diseases in small children. Many sexual diseases are also spread by direct contact of the genital organs.	Impetigo, gonorrhoea, syphilis
Inhalation	Whenever we cough, sneeze or talk, millions of droplets are expelled from our respiratory tract. If we have an infection of the respiratory system, those droplets all contain pathogens. Some of the water in the droplets evaporates, leaving tiny droplets full of pathogens which are small enough to remain suspended in the air for a long time. These tiny droplets may be inhaled by another individual, introducing the pathogens to a new respiratory tract.	Influenza, measles, tuberculosis
Ingestion	Many of the pathogens that cause gut diseases are transmitted by contaminated food or drink. These organisms are usually destroyed when the food is heated thoroughly, so the risk of infection is greatest when we eat raw or undercooked food. In the case of some disease-causing organisms, only a small number need to be taken in to result in disease so hands should be washed after handling raw meat or eggs to avoid contaminating cooked food. Pathogens from faeces, urine and vomit can also be spread by ingestion, by transferring from contaminated hands to the mouth.	Most forms of diarrhoea, hepatitis A, salmonellosis
Inoculation	A pathogen can be inoculated into the body directly through a break in the skin. This can happen via an injury from contaminated medical instruments, or by sharing needles for drug abuse. An infected animal may bite, lick or scratch you, or you may pick up pathogens through a puncture wound from a contaminated thorn or stone.	Hepatitis B, AIDS, rabies, tetanus

Table 7.2.3 How diseases are spread

sebum produced by the skin contains substances which inhibit the growth of microorganisms. The sebum does not harm the natural skin flora (the microorganisms which live on our skin without causing us any damage). These natural skin flora themselves play a role in preventing disease by competing successfully for position on the skin and also, in some cases, themselves producing substances which inhibit the growth of other microorganisms. The pharynx and the large intestine have protective coverings similar to the skin.

When we cut ourselves, we become vulnerable to infection by skin pathogens such as staphylococci or herpes viruses, and also to more invasive organisms such as *Clostridium tetani* which causes tetanus. Some organisms such as hookworms, ticks and biting insects can penetrate the unbroken skin for themselves, either causing disease directly or introducing disease-causing pathogens as in malaria. If the skin is damaged, the first response of the body is to seal the wound through the mechanism of **blood clotting** (see section 2.4, page 148).

Following damage to the skin, the **inflammatory response** (see page 635) brings phagocytic white blood cells to the site of damage. They ingest any microorganisms that have entered the bloodstream.

The surfaces of our internal tubes and ducts are covered in epithelia which are much thinner than our skin and are not toughened with keratin. However, these epithelia often secrete substances which protect against invasion. Many produce mucus, a sticky substance which traps microorganisms. It also contains lysozymes, enzymes capable of destroying microbial cell walls. Phagocytic white blood cells which can engulf pathogens are often present on epithelial surfaces. In the respiratory system mucus is secreted and constantly swept upwards by cilia, either out of the body or down into the gut. The epithelium of the urinary system is constantly washed through with urine. These mechanisms are so successful that there are usually no bacteria in either the respiratory system or the urinary system, except for the areas nearest to the outside world. However, if microorganisms are present in sufficient numbers they may breach these defences, as the cold and influenza viruses often do.

The **gut** is an opening through which pathogens can enter. It has defensive mechanisms – the saliva in the mouth can kill some bacteria, and the acid in the stomach destroys the majority of ingested microorganisms. Throughout the gut, the natural flora usually competes successfully for both nutrients and attachment sites with any microorganisms that pass through the stomach, and like the skin flora the gut flora produces anti-microbial compounds.

There are large concentrations of phagocytic white blood cells at all the lymph nodes, and their task is to ensure that if one organ becomes infected, the infection does not spread throughout the body. This is one reason why your 'glands' become enlarged when you are unwell. Even your eyes have their own defences against entry by pathogens. Tears contain lytic enzymes, which destroy bacteria before they attack the tissues of the eye.

Should any pathogen manage to breach all these non-specific defences, it will then meet the system which has evolved specifically to deal with the invasion of disease-causing organisms: the immune system.

The immune system provides a series of defensive responses to an invading pathogen (see section 1, pages 76–79). The pathogen is recognised as foreign material because of its antigens – specific proteins on its outer surface. Once the immune system is activated it usually destroys all the foreign material carrying those antigens, as a result of the activity of the T-cells, B-cells (which make antibodies) and phagocytes. Also, as part of the humoral response, **memory cells** are produced. These are specific B-cells which provide the body with a long-term **immunological memory**. As soon as you encounter the disease-causing antigen again, your body produces antibodies against it so quickly that the pathogens will all be destroyed before they have time to cause the symptoms of disease. This explains why you usually only get a disease such as chickenpox or measles once. However, some pathogenic organisms such as cold and 'flu viruses are constantly mutating and changing their antigens very subtly. This means that you can be reinfected with another strain of the same virus, because your body does not recognise its changed antigens.

Natural killer cells are another strand of the immune system. They do not need to be exposed to antigens – they bind to any infected or otherwise changed cells and activate the cell's own self-destruction mechanism.

The pathogens fight back

What makes a successful pathogen?

A successful pathogen exploits its host as effectively as possible. It is good at surviving and reproducing itself, and also at spreading to further hosts. In general, this does not mean killing the host, as a dead host is not very good at spreading pathogens! This ability of a pathogen to survive, spread and therefore cause disease is known as its **pathogenicity**. There are many adaptations of pathogens that help their success.

A pathogen has to be able to survive in the environment between hosts. Many microorganisms are killed by drying, by ultra-violet light and by high or low temperatures. However, some strategies have evolved which overcome these difficulties. Many microorganisms form very resistant **spores** which withstand drying and changes in temperature for many years.

Some pathogens are transferred from one host to another enclosed in droplets. Others, like the very delicate bacterium *Neisseria gonorrhoeae* which causes a sexually transmitted disease, cannot survive outside their host and are passed on directly through moist mucous membranes during sex.

Large pathogens like the helminthes often have very specialised body parts such as hooks, jaws or suckers which attach them to their host. Some bacteria also attach themselves to their host. A strain of *Escherichia coli* which causes urinary infections is not flushed out in the urine because it attaches itself to the epithelium of the urinary tract using pili. Being able to attach itself physically to its host obviously helps a pathogen to be successful.

Microorganisms that can defend themselves against their host's immunological attack are likely to be very successful pathogens. Bacterial capsules can act as a defence against some host antibodies. Other microorganisms, such as *Mycobacterium tuberculosis*, actually colonise host phagocytes during their life cycle. Yet other microorganisms, such as *Toxoplasma gondii*, have specialised biochemistry which helps overcome the host reaction.

Changing surface antigens is an excellent way of beating the host immune system. By the time one set of antibodies is in place, new microorganisms are being reproduced with a different set of antigens. The *Plasmodia* that cause malaria produce individuals with new antigens every few days. The influenza virus changes its surface antigens less frequently than that, but new antigenic strains to which no one has immunity evolve regularly.

Some microorganisms have a high pathogenicity because they suppress the activity of the host immune system. They are then free to reproduce and invade host cells, and so are other infections as well, because the suppressed immune system cannot fight any new invading pathogen. African trypanosomiasis (sleeping sickness) and AIDS are both caused by such **immunosuppressant pathogens** – the patient is often attacked by other microorganisms whose pathogenicity is increased because of the suppressed immune system.

The pathogenicity of many microorganisms depends on the **toxins** (poisonous substances) they produce. These toxins are usually produced as part of the

Figure 7.2.24 The Scottish island of Gruinard was infected with anthrax spores during an experiment on germ warfare early in the Second World War. It was to be 50 years before the island was passed as safe and free from the risk of infection.

microbial life cycle, and are frequently responsible for the symptoms of disease.

Some bacteria produce **exotoxins**. These are toxic substances excreted by the microbe. Bacteria of the *Staphylococcus* family produce a variety of these exotoxins. Some cause fever and a red rash and damage cell membranes. Others are involved in food poisoning, when the toxin stimulates the vomiting centre, causing sickness.

Endotoxins, in contrast, are chemicals within the structure of the bacterium itself which have a toxic effect on the host. A lipopolysaccharide in the wall of bacteria of the *Salmonella* family acts as an endotoxin in *Salmonella* food poisoning, irritating the lining of the gut.

Symptoms of infectious diseases

The symptoms of infectious diseases are many and varied, but the human body responds to invading pathogens in certain ways which are common to many infections.

The first and most common response to infection is to develop a **fever**. Normal body temperature is maintained by the hypothalamus, a small area of the brain above the pituitary gland. The body temperature varies slightly throughout the day, being lowest in the early hours of the morning and highest at about 10 p.m. When a pathogen infects the body it causes the hypothalamus to reset to a higher body temperature, so that we become aware of 'running a temperature' – in other words, we have a fever. A raised temperature seems to help the body combat infection in two ways. First, many pathogens reproduce best at 37 °C or lower. Thus a raised temperature will reduce their ability to reproduce effectively, and so they cause less damage. Second, the immune system works better at higher temperatures, and so will be more successful at combating the infection even if the pathogen is unaffected by the raised temperature.

Although fevers can be beneficial, they can also be damaging and even fatal if they become too high. Some enzymes denature at a body temperature above 40 °C, and permanent tissue damage may occur. If the temperature is not lowered fairly quickly, death may result.

Inflammation is another common way in which our bodies respond to infection. It tends to occur when the infection is more localised. The local blood vessels vasodilate, causing heat and redness, and fluid is forced out of them causing swelling and often pain. Phagocytic white blood cells called neutrophils and macrophages accumulate at the site to engulf the invading pathogens, and can often be seen as pus. A third common response is a rash, which is a form of inflammation or tissue damage that particularly affects the skin. An example is shown in figure 7.2.25.

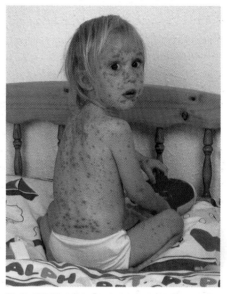

Figure 7.2.25 Many rashes are quite distinctive, like the chickenpox shown here, but general red rashes may accompany a wide range of bacterial and viral infections.

Controlling disease

The idea that diseases can be caused by microorganisms is central to our view of health and medical treatments, yet people have only known of the existence of bacteria, viruses and other microorganisms since the middle of the nineteenth century. Once the role of these organisms in causing disease was recognised, steps were taken to prevent their spread. For thousands of years people had used herbs, muds, prayers and infusions to try and overcome the ravages of disease and some of these methods had some success. But from the middle of the nineteenth century, in the developed world at least, the battle against disease became more focused. Today modern techniques such as monoclonal antibodies can identify specific pathogens, giving rapid and accurate diagnoses. As a result, appropriate treatments can be started quickly to maximise the chances of success. A chemical substance is usually used to prevent or treat a disease – this is called **chemotherapy**.

Monoclonal antibodies – medicine's magic bullets

In 1977 two research scientists at Cambridge University discovered a way of obtaining large amounts of a single known type of antibody. The Nobel prize-winning technique takes advantage of the special properties of two different types of cells.

A mouse is injected with a particular labelled antigen. **B-cells** (see pages 77–78) that make the appropriate antibody are then removed from its spleen and fused with a **myeloma**, a type of cancer cell which divides very rapidly. The fused cell is known as a **hybridoma**. Each hybridoma can produce many antibody molecules specific to the antigen, and the hybridoma itself reproduces very rapidly to give millions of 'living factories'. The technique is outlined in figure 7.2.26.

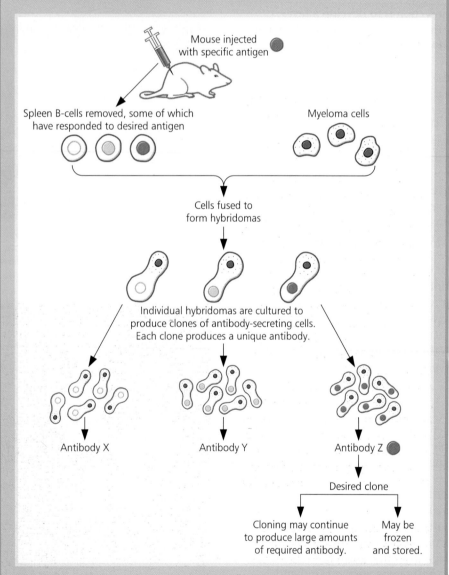

Mouse injected with specific antigen

Spleen B-cells removed, some of which have responded to desired antigen

Myeloma cells

Cells fused to form hybridomas

Individual hybridomas are cultured to produce clones of antibody-secreting cells. Each clone produces a unique antibody.

Antibody X

Antibody Y

Antibody Z

Desired clone

Cloning may continue to produce large amounts of required antibody.

May be frozen and stored.

Figure 7.2.26 Monoclonal antibodies allow us to produce extremely specific diagnostic tests and therapies.

A large number of medical benefits have already resulted from this technology. Monoclonal antibodies tagged with radioactive or fluorescent labels can be used in medical research to identify specific cells and tissues. They have been used in research into areas such as hormone action, diabetes, cancer, heart disease, rheumatoid arthritis, allergies and the functioning of the brain. They can provide extremely sensitive diagnostic tests – for example, the many pregnancy tests on the market which can give an indication of pregnancy on the very day a woman is due to have her period rely on monoclonal antibodies. Monoclonal antibodies also provide an accurate diagnostic tool for specific viruses, bacteria, fungi and parasites. In some cases, monoclonal antibodies can provide an effective therapy. The possibilities of these 'magic bullets' continue to stretch ahead – it is hoped that in years to come many cancers and other diseases will be treated by these versatile fused cells.

Chemical control – antiseptics

Some of the earliest steps in the control of bacterial diseases are hard to believe nowadays. In 1847 Ignaz Semmelweiss substantially reduced the number of cases of childbed fever (infections which frequently killed women in the few days after giving birth) by encouraging doctors to wash their hands between deliveries!

Subsequently the use of **antiseptic** techniques and **disinfectant** solutions also began to reduce the number of deaths from infectious diseases. Surgery in those days was very much a last resort, usually to remove parts of the body that had become gangrenous in an attempt to stop the infection killing the patient. Such surgery was often ineffective. However, it was noticed that if a surgical wound was coated in coal tar it was less likely to become infected. The coal tar kept out the air, and any microorganisms present in it, and also contained an unrecognised antiseptic chemical, **phenol** (also known as carbolic acid). By 1860 the Scottish doctor Joseph Lister had started using pure phenol as an antiseptic during and after surgery. Doctors started to observe stricter codes of personal cleanliness, medical instruments were sterilised and antiseptics were used more. The number of deaths from infectious diseases began to fall, and medical intervention became much safer for the patient.

Phenol did have some drawbacks. It is an acidic compound, and while it prevented wounds from becoming infected, it could also prevent them healing because of its corrosive effects on the skin. Many modern antiseptics are phenol derivatives, but they are much more effective at destroying bacteria and kinder to human tissues. We now have a range of chemicals used to destroy bacteria – those used in the environment, for example to sterilise equipment, are usually referred to as **disinfectants**, while those used directly on people are **antiseptics**.

Chemical control – antimicrobial drugs

Although antiseptics were used during the nineteenth century to prevent the spread of infection, it was not until well into the twentieth century that drugs became available to treat a bacterial infection once it had taken hold. In 1935 Gerhard Domagk used a new drug called Prontosil on his youngest daughter, and prevented her dying from a severe streptococcal infection. In 1936 it was shown that the effective part of the drug was a chemical compound known as a sulphonamide. This interfered with the metabolism of the bacteria without

Figure 7.2.27 Professor Gerhard Domagk at the Nobel prizewinner's traditional banquet.

Figure 7.2.28 Alexander Fleming, Howard Florey and Ernst Chain were awarded a Nobel prize in 1945 for their work on the discovery of penicillin.

disrupting human cells. All modern antimicrobial drugs have their effect because of this principle of **selective toxicity** – they interfere with the metabolism of the microorganism but cause minimal damage to the human host.

The most commonly used and best known antimicrobial drugs are the **antibiotics**. These are antimicrobial compounds made by microorganisms, or similar compounds synthesised by chemists. Antibiotics can be used against both bacterial and fungal diseases. Alexander Fleming is usually credited with the discovery of penicillin, the first modern antibiotic. He noticed the *Penicillium* mould infecting his bacterial plates, and observed a clear area of agar jelly around the mould where it had destroyed the bacterial culture. However, it was not until 1940 that the Australian Howard Florey and the German Ernst Chain, working in England, developed penicillin as an antibiotic. This new drug had an almost magical effect, curing patients who were seriously ill with previously uncurable bacterial diseases. Many other antibiotics have been discovered since, but penicillin is still commonly used to combat bacterial infections. The main classes of antimicrobial drug and the way they affect microorganisms are summarised in table 7.2.4.

Antimicrobial action	Examples
Antimetabolites interrupt the metabolic pathways of the microorganism, causing death.	Sulphonamides
Cell wall agents prevent the formation of cross-linking in bacterial cell walls. This weakens the cell walls so the bacteria are killed by lysis (bursting).	Beta-lactams, e.g. penicillins Glycopeptides, e.g. vancomycin
Protein synthesis inhibitors interrupt or prevent the transcription and/or translation of microbial genes, causing the genetic code to be misread and the wrong protein made in the bacterial cell.	Tetracyclines Chloramphenicol
DNA gyrase inhibitors damage the tertiary structure of bacterial DNA – they stop it coiling up so that it can no longer fit within the bacterial cell.	Quinolone

Table 7.2.4 Action of the main types of antimicrobial drug

The majority of antibiotics can be used to treat many different types of bacteria – they are known as **broad-spectrum antibiotics**. However, some antibiotic drugs are effective against only very few types of bacteria or even one particular type. These are known as **narrow-spectrum antibiotics**. When choosing an antibiotic, a doctor will consider carefully the pathogen likely to be causing the symptoms, and prescribe the cheapest antibiotic likely to be effective against it.

The effectiveness of any antimicrobial drug depends on a variety of factors. One such factor is the concentration of the drug in the area of the body infected. This depends on the dose, on how easily the drug can reach the tissue and on how quickly it is excreted. The effectiveness of the drug also depends on the pH in the body. Both the pathogen and the host tissue may destroy the antibiotic, which obviously makes the drug less effective. But one of the most important factors is the susceptibility of the pathogen to the particular antibiotic used. If the standard dose of a drug (in other words, what a doctor would normally prescribe) successfully destroys the pathogen and cures the disease, then the pathogen is **sensitive** to that antibiotic. If the standard dose is not completely successful but an increased dose of the antibiotic treats the disease, the pathogen is **moderately sensitive**. However, there are increasing numbers of cases where a particular microorganism is not affected by an antibiotic, sometimes even an antibiotic which has treated that disease successfully in the past. In these cases the microorganism has become **resistant** to the antibiotic.

An antibiotic may have one of two different effects on the pathogen. The drug, or the dose of the drug administered, may be **bacteriostatic**. This means that the antibiotic prevents the growth of the microorganism. This level of treatment is usually sufficient for the majority of everyday infections, because combined with the immune system it ensures that the pathogen is destroyed and removed. However, sometimes a particular drug, or the dose of the drug that is given, will be **bactericidal**. This means it will kill 99.9% of the pathogens present. This type of treatment is particularly important in severe and dangerous infections, and also for treating infections where the immune system is of limited use or suppressed through disease. The effect an antibiotic will have on a particular microorganism can be determined by a sensitivity test. Discs containing known concentrations of antibiotics are placed on an agar plate covered with the test bacterium. The inhibition of bacterial growth, shown by clear patches on the agar, gives a measure of the effectiveness of the drug.

Antiviral drugs – a long time coming

Whilst antibiotics have provided a vital weapon in the battle against bacteria, they are of no help at all in the viral war. Viruses are non-cellular, so how do we kill them? Because they do not have membranes or their own biochemistry, the problem of destroying the virus without harming the host becomes particularly acute. There are several lines of research which show promise, but there is still no group of antiviral drugs to treat the majority of everyday viral infections. Methods of attack which are showing promise include:

- **interfering with viral enzymes** – some viruses use host cell enzymes for reproduction; others cause the host cell to make viral enzymes. The latter type of virus can be attacked by drugs that inhibit viral enzymes, such as **acyclovir**. The drug is only activated in the presence of a viral enzyme, so it does not attack uninfected host cells. Once activated, it binds to DNA polymerase enzymes, making sure

that the virus cannot replicate. Acyclovir is used against genital herpes, cold sores and shingles, and it is hoped that other antiviral drugs with a similar action will be developed soon.

- **interfering with viral genes** – this involves introducing complementary stretches of DNA or RNA into infected host cells, interfering with the viral genes and preventing them from being replicated or transcribed. Work is in progress on treatments based on this theory.

- **using interferons** – interferons are part of the body's natural defence system. They are glycoproteins that are made and released by virus-infected cells to make neighbouring cells resistant to infection by the virus. The prediction is that genetic engineering will enable bacteria to produce large quantities of interferons, and their use as drugs may then become practicable.

Vaccination

Drugs are used to treat microbial infections once they are present in the body. An alternative approach to breaking the cycle of disease is to prevent it happening in the first place. This is what vaccination programmes aim to do. The history of vaccination is long, going back to Edward Jenner in 1796 with his pioneering work on smallpox vaccination. Over 100 years later, Louis Pasteur moved vaccination forward again by demonstrating that a modified technique could provide protection against a variety of diseases, not just smallpox.

When we are exposed to a pathogen and suffer from a disease, we develop a natural immunity to that pathogen. Having dealt with the pathogen once, our immune systems can destroy it before it causes disease on a subsequent infection. Vaccination enables us to develop that immunity artificially, by exposing our immune systems to the pathogen in a safe way so that antibodies and memory cells can be prepared without us having the real disease.

The aim of immunisation on a personal level is to protect individuals against diseases which might kill or harm them. However, immunisation also has a wider role in society. It is used to control diseases that cause large numbers of deaths, disabilities or illnesses within a population, and therefore place a strain on that society. Smallpox is the only disease that has been completely **eradicated** by vaccination. Eradication means that the organism is no longer found in people, in animals or anywhere in the environment. Once a disease has been eradicated, immunisation can stop. Smallpox was a very recognisable disease which had no long-term carriers, visible evidence of immunisation (see figure 7.2.29), no non-human hosts and a long incubation period. These features all helped make eradication possible.

Polio has many of the same infective features as smallpox, and the World Health Organization hoped to eradicate the disease worldwide by the year 2000. This target turned out to be too ambitious, but polio has been removed from many parts of the world including the USA, China and most of Europe. Major efforts in the early years of the twenty-first century should see the end of this killer disease. However, for many other diseases – for example, where the pathogen survives in soil or water or animal hosts – eradication is not realistically possible. This is true for:

- measles, where infection is rapid, the incubation period short and the disease is not regarded as serious by many in the developed world
- tuberculosis, which is caused by airborne pathogens and can be present in a host without showing symptoms
- cholera, caused by a water-carried pathogen which is highly infectious and has a very short incubation period
- malaria – the insect vector (female *Anopheles* mosquito) is difficult to control and the infective organism changes the antigens on the surface of the cells, making vaccines very hard to develop.

For such diseases, elimination or control have to be the aims of any immunisation programme. **Elimination** means that the disease has disappeared but the pathogen remains in animals, in the environment or in sub-clinical infections (without showing symptoms), and so immunisation must continue even when no clinical cases are being seen. A disease that is **controlled** still occurs, but not often enough to be a significant health problem. For some serious infectious diseases such as malaria, it has proved impossible to develop a vaccine that is effective against all the different forms of the pathogen, because it changes its antigens so rapidly.

Today, many different types of vaccine are available for use. **Live vaccines** use **attenuated** (weakened) strains of pathogens which can stimulate an immune

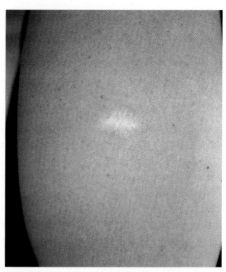

Figure 7.2.29 For years, people all over the world could prove they had been vaccinated against smallpox by showing the scar left by their body's reaction to the vaccine. But since 1979, children's arms have been scar free. Smallpox has been officially eradicated so worldwide immunisation is no longer necessary, as the smallpox virus only exists sealed up in two top security laboratories.

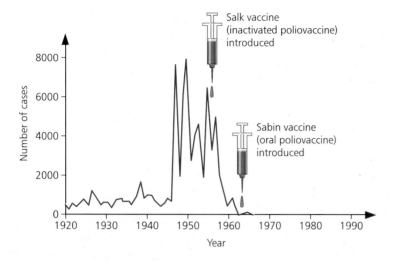

Salk vaccine
(inactivated poliovaccine)
introduced

Sabin vaccine
(oral poliovaccine)
introduced

Figure 7.2.30 The graph shows cases of poliomyelitis in England and Wales that have caused paralysis, 1914–92. The vaccination programme has not completely eradicated polio. Because live vaccine is used, in rare cases infants develop the disease, and very occasionally adults have caught polio from changing the nappies of their recently vaccinated infants. However, the impact of the disease on the population as a whole has been reduced to a minimal level.

response but are virtually incapable of causing active disease. A single dose of a live vaccine usually provides long-lasting immunity. Common examples of this type of vaccine include rubella, oral polio, measles and yellow fever.

The poliovirus does not simply paralyse the legs and arms. The muscles needed for breathing and swallowing can be affected too. Polio epidemics in the UK in the 1940s and 1950s left many young people confined to an 'iron lung' which artificially expanded and contracted their chests to enable them to breathe, and polio vaccines were developed in response to these human tragedies. The potential effectiveness of a vaccination programme is shown by data from the poliomyelitis vaccination programme in England and Wales from 1914 to 1992, shown in figure 7.2.30.

Other vaccines are produced from killed virulent organisms, for example, the whooping cough (pertussis) vaccination. There is no risk of causing the disease, but the vaccination may have to be repeated, giving 'boosters' to top up the immune response from time to time. This is true for all vaccines that do not contain living pathogens.

Some pathogens cause disease as a result of a toxin they produce. In such cases, the vaccine may be a modified version of the toxin molecule, capable of stimulating an immune response without causing disease. The diphtheria vaccine is an example of this type.

In modern 'flu vaccines, the protein–polysaccharide antigens from the viral coat are separated and inoculated. Again there is no risk of developing the disease, but an effective immune response is stimulated.

Finally, genetically engineered bacteria can produce certain antigens which can then be used for vaccines. The vaccine against hepatitis B is produced in this way.

Vaccination programmes

For a vaccine to be effective in preventing epidemics of disease, a large proportion of the population needs to be vaccinated. Otherwise, a large pool of infection remains in the community and a drop in vaccination levels can lead to an epidemic. This is known as the **herd effect** – if enough of the 'herd' is protected by vaccination, the disease can only affect isolated individuals, and is unlikely even to do that. To try and achieve vaccination of a very large proportion of the population against the most common infectious diseases, many countries target small children for vaccination. This increases the likelihood of uptake, as parents are more likely to take their children for vaccinations and health checks than to have such vaccinations themselves. In the UK, the target coverage for

Figure 7.2.31 Successful vaccination programmes around the world are reducing deaths from diseases such as polio and measles.

childhood vaccines is 95% of all children at two years of age. Most of the vaccination programme is carried out at GP surgeries under the National Health Service, and in the 1990s there were financial rewards for surgeries that achieved the vaccination targets set by central Government. The childhood immunisation schedule in Britain in the mid-1990s was quite extensive, as can be seen from table 7.2.5. Some of the vaccines were delivered to pupils in schools, but the majority were for pre-school children.

It is interesting that not every vaccination given is needed by the individual concerned. For example, rubella (German measles) is a relatively mild infection accompanied by a rash and feeling slightly unwell. The disease often passes almost unnoticed, yet the aim is for the entire population of children to be vaccinated against it. This is because if a pregnant woman becomes infected by rubella in the early stages of her pregnancy, the developing embryo may become deaf, blind or possibly brain damaged. Immunising young children against rubella protects pregnant women, as it greatly reduces the pool of infection. Also, the vaccinated girls of today are the pregnant women of tomorrow, so they will already be immune to rubella long before they are likely to be carrying a fetus.

The whole population of children is targeted for vaccination, boys as well as girls. This benefits society by reducing the pool of rubella infection, but does it give any benefit to each male child as an individual? It can be argued that by reducing the likelihood that a future partner carrying his child will become infected by rubella, the boy is in fact receiving the same protection for his future children as girls. However, if *all* girls were immunised against rubella it should not in theory matter if boys were not immunised. Like any medical procedure, all vaccines carry an element of risk. Some individuals may be allergic to components of the vaccine, or show unexpected sensitivity to it and become ill. So this vaccination programme can be viewed as protecting society as a whole, rather than being for the good of the individual.

Immunisation programmes can also be used to prevent potential epidemics, and again individuals may be revaccinated with no value – and indeed an element of risk – to themselves for the good of society as a whole. A prime example of this was seen in the UK in 1994. It was predicted that a measles epidemic was likely in Britain which would potentially lead to the death of around 15 children, mostly teenagers who had not previously been vaccinated. As a result, a mass immunisation programme was put in place to immunise every school child in Britain. Many of the younger children had already been vaccinated against measles once, and in some cases twice (when the MMR was introduced). To convince people that their children should be vaccinated again, statistics were put out showing that up to 1 in 10 children would not have developed immunity to measles after their first vaccines. The risks of death and disability from measles were also given high-profile coverage.

Just before the vaccination programme started, certain sections of the British media published some of the risks allegedly associated with the vaccine. It is always extremely difficult to prove that a child's reaction following a vaccine is actually a response to that vaccine and not a coincidental alternative infection. However, some children were severely brain damaged by events immediately following vaccinations, and their parents were convinced that the vaccine was to blame. Their points of view were widely publicised, resulting in a great deal of agonising for many parents. The immunisation programme went through, a few people withdrew their children – and the great measles epidemic did not occur. However, after the media circus preceding the vaccination programme, there was very little media presentation of either the effectiveness of the campaign in preventing an epidemic or the damage done to children by the vaccine.

Age	Vaccines
2 months	Diphtheria/tetanus/pertussis (whooping cough) (**DTP**) Oral polio (**OPV**) *Haemophilus influenzae* (bacterial meningitis) (**Hib**)
3 months	DTP OPV Hib
4 months	DTP OPV Hib
12–15 months	Measles/mumps/rubella (**MMR**)
4–5 years	Diphtheria/tetanus OPV
10–14 years	Bacille Calmette-Guérin (tuberculosis) (**BCG**)
15–18 years	Tetanus/low dose diphtheria OPV

Table 7.2.5 British immunisation scheme, mid-1990s

Change the world – prevent disease?

We tend to think of medical intervention (drugs, vaccines, etc.) as the main method of preventing and curing infectious diseases. Important as the medical developments of the late twentieth century certainly are, other changes are at least equally important in the prevention and even elimination of some infectious diseases. Data collected on the numbers dying of infectious diseases against which many of us have been immunised are shown in figure 7.2.32.

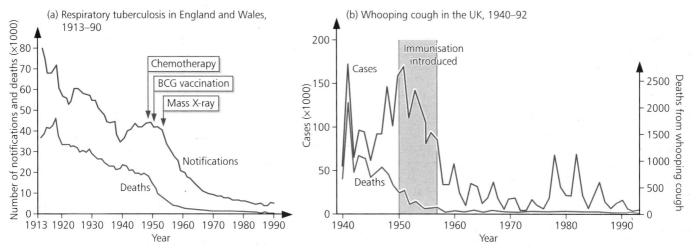

Over the last 150 years the population size, social structure, working conditions, affluence and health awareness of the general population of the British Isles have changed dramatically. Housing has improved, water supplies have been purified, sewage is removed and treated, diet has improved, children are no longer part of the workforce and health and safety regulations govern the working conditions in factories and other places of work. Add to this smaller average families, child welfare programmes and the Clean Air Act, and a whole range of reasons for the decline of many infectious diseases becomes apparent. For some diseases like smallpox, effective vaccination was almost the sole cause of its eradication. For most diseases, a drop in the death rate from the disease is due not to one specific reason but to a general improvement in nutrition and public health. Antibiotics and/or immunisation programmes can often be seen as the final piece of the jigsaw, reducing the levels of serious infections to a point where they no longer have a major impact on public health.

Figure 7.2.32 These data show that deaths from these major infectious diseases in the UK had started to fall substantially before the introduction of either antibiotics or immunisation programmes. What caused these large drops?

A closer look at some more infectious diseases

A few specific infectious diseases are described in more detail below, giving more insight into the problems surrounding their control, and into how their impact on individuals and populations may be lessened.

Tuberculosis (TB)

Tuberculosis is one of the most common human infections, with millions of people infected around the world. The majority of these cases are in the developing world, although TB ('consumption') used to be rampant in Europe and the UK. It is relatively rare in the western Pacific regions. In many developed countries, the number of cases of TB has fallen dramatically over the last 150 years due to a combination of social and medical reasons. However, the numbers are beginning to increase again, probably as a result of deteriorating social conditions, refugees, the spread of HIV and intravenous drug use.

TB comes in many forms, but it is most commonly caused by infections of *Mycobacterium tuberculosis*. It is transmitted by droplet infection and so crowded living or working conditions help it spread from person to person. The other common source of infection worldwide is from *Mycobacterium bovis*. This bacterium affects cattle, and people can become infected from drinking infected milk in areas where the disease has not been controlled in cattle and where milk is drunk unpasteurised.

Tuberculosis can affect many areas of the body, including the bones and the lymphatic system, but the most common forms of TB affect the respiratory system. The bacteria damage and destroy the lung tissue, and also suppress the action of the immune system, making the body less able to fight the disease.

Typical symptoms of TB are fever, night sweats, anorexia (inability to eat) and loss of weight. Coughing produces sputum from which *M. tuberculosis* can be cultured. However, in the developed world at least, the blood-stained phlegm of Victorian consumptives is rarely seen now as people are generally healthier and effective treatment is available. X-rays of the lungs give a picture typical of the disease – opaque areas and large, thick-walled cavities resulting from the bacterial damage, as shown in figure 7.2.33.

The main treatment for tuberculosis is with antibiotics. For the first couple of months a cocktail of different antibiotics is used, to destroy any mycobacteria that are resistant to some of the drugs. This cocktail kills not only the rapidly reproducing microorganisms, but also those that are metabolising slowly, hidden in cysts or within the immune system. This initial treatment is followed by another four to seven months of treatment with just two drugs, rifampicin and isoniazid. Following this treatment regime, most patients will be completely free of TB in about nine months, but it can take a year to 18 months before all traces have gone, particularly if the TB has infected other tissues such as the joints or the kidneys as well as the lungs.

Although treatment is available, it is long term and expensive. It is therefore widely used in the developed world, but in countries like India where levels of TB are still very high, there is insufficient money to treat all the people who need it.

The most effective ways of controlling TB relate to improved living standards. Less crowded housing and working conditions mean people are less likely to pass on the disease. Generally healthier and better fed people are less likely to develop debilitating TB even if they meet *M. tuberculosis*. Preventing and treating the disease in cattle and pasteurising or heating milk before it is drunk both prevent the spread of *M. bovis*.

A small but important factor in the control of TB in countries where it is rare is **contact tracing**. When a patient turns up with active TB, attempts are made to contact all the people who are in regular close contact with the patient so that they can be tested for TB and either immunised or treated as appropriate.

Immunisation has been very effective in the final reduction of the number of cases of TB in countries like the UK. The BCG (bacille Calmette-Guérin) vaccine is a live attenuated strain of the mycobacterium, given as a single injection. This is also more suitable for use in developing countries, as vaccines are much cheaper than treatment. In countries where TB is still very common, the vaccine is often given to very young babies. In the UK it is given to school children of 10–13 years old, and also to any adults in high-risk jobs such as teachers and health care workers. Before older children and adults are given the BCG, they are tested to see if they are already immune to or infected by tuberculosis. Between one and two per cent of all the children tested give a positive test and need further investigation.

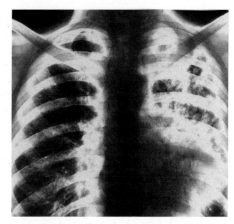

Figure 7.2.33 This X-ray of the lungs of a tubercular patient shows a shadowed area over the right-hand side of the chest where the disease has damaged the lung.

Change society – or buy medicine?

The role of different factors in the control of tuberculosis are difficult to interpret from data, as shown in figure 7.2.34. There is understandably a great tendency to credit the development of drugs and vaccines with the control of disease, and to forget general social improvements that might also have an effect. It is also easier to fund a programme of medical aid than to attempt to improve the social conditions of large populations of people.

Information on death rates is often used as evidence to back up proposals for medical intervention.

However, by presenting the same data in different ways we can paint two different pictures of the role of modern interventions in the fall in the death rate from tuberculosis. Is the transition of TB in the developed world from a feared killer disease to a rare and treatable disease due to modern medical intervention or social factors? The same figures can be used to support an argument in either direction.

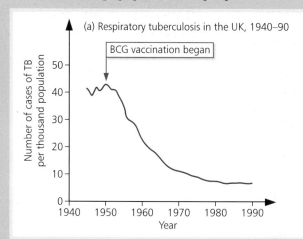
(a) Respiratory tuberculosis in the UK, 1940–90

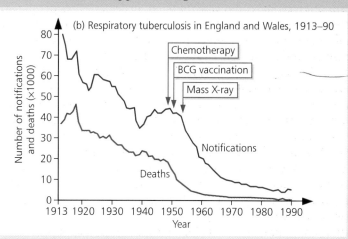
(b) Respiratory tuberculosis in England and Wales, 1913–90

Figure 7.2.34 Looking at the same data in different ways can lead to different conclusions, and as a result to different emphases in health care programmes. Should social change or immunisation be the real priority for the eradication of TB?

Typhoid and cholera

Typhoid and cholera are both transmitted by drinking water contaminated by faeces, so they spread in conditions of poor sanitation. In previous centuries these diseases were found everywhere, thriving on the non-existent personal and public hygiene of the times. In the twentieth century both diseases have become rare in the developed world, with the development of extensive sewage treatment systems and better understanding of hygiene. But in the developing world, they are still epidemic. Whenever a society suffers trauma such as war, famine, earthquake or flood which disrupts normal living and forces people to live in crowded and makeshift camps, then typhoid and cholera claim lives and cause great suffering. In the slums of the megacities forming in some areas of the world, lack of proper sanitation again encourages the diseases to spread.

Typhoid is caused by the bacterium *Salmonella typhi*. Only a few bacteria need be ingested to cause infection, as they replicate very rapidly in the body. The incubation period is about two weeks, after which the disease starts like 'flu with high fever, headaches and feeling generally unwell. Diarrhoea does not start until a week to 10 days after the fever begins, but if the typhoid is not treated the diarrhoea becomes life threatening. It causes dehydration, and moreover the bacteria attack and damage the gut wall, causing bleeding and sometimes even perforating the gut. Typhoid can be treated by antibiotics taken over about two weeks to prevent a relapse, but it is important to begin treatment before serious damage to the gut lining has occurred.

Typhoid can be prevented by adequate sanitation, but without this it is necessary to avoid high risk foods like shellfish and drinking contaminated water. This advice may be fine for travellers, but is less useful to the indigenous population. Vaccines against typhoid are available, but they generally only offer protection for one to three years. Again, these are useful for travellers from developed countries, and can be provided in the wake of a natural disaster or a war, but they are less useful on a day-to-day basis in the countries most affected by typhoid.

Cholera is a disease caused by the response of the body to the toxin produced by a comma-shaped bacterium *Vibrio cholerae*. In the nineteenth century cholera was feared right across the world, but in the twentieth century it has, like typhoid, remained common only in the poorer developing nations and among travellers who visit these countries.

Cholera is spread mainly through drinking water contaminated with infected faeces or by eating raw or lightly cooked shellfish which have grown in contaminated water. It has a relatively short incubation period of just a few days before the victim begins to produce copious amounts of highly infectious diarrhoea. There are very few other symptoms. The diarrhoea has a typical appearance – pale fluid containing a little mucus and dead cells – and is known as 'rice water stools'. Rapid dehydration is the result which can lead to death if untreated.

V. cholerae do not damage the gut as typhoid does, so if patients can be given rehydration treatment (which is very cheap and becoming available all over the world), most will survive and recover after four or five days. Because of this, antibiotics are only used for the most seriously ill and vulnerable patients. There is a cholera vaccine but it only gives about 50% protection and only lasts about six months, so is of very limited use. Like typhoid, the best advice is to avoid taking in contaminated food and drink.

In this chapter we have had a brief look at some of the many infectious diseases in the world. Doctors now know how to reduce or eliminate many of these diseases, but in many areas of the world neither the will nor the resources are available to do so. In spite of all our advances in antimicrobial drugs and immunisation programmes, the sad fact is that one of the biggest killers in the world is diarrhoea. Simple gut infections causing diarrhoea still kill millions of people each year, many of them babies and young children who cannot cope with the rapid dehydration. Figure 7.2.35 shows the problem.

In spite of some notable successes in the fight against infectious diseases in the developed world, on a global scale at the moment the pathogens are still winning.

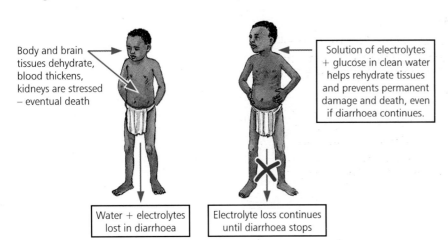

Body and brain tissues dehydrate, blood thickens, kidneys are stressed – eventual death

Solution of electrolytes + glucose in clean water helps rehydrate tissues and prevents permanent damage and death, even if diarrhoea continues.

Water + electrolytes lost in diarrhoea

Electrolyte loss continues until diarrhoea stops

Figure 7.2.35 The main cause of death due to diarrhoeal illnesses is the loss of body fluids and electrolytes (ions such as Na^+ and Cl^-). Keeping people hydrated through a diarrhoeal illness greatly increases their chances of complete recovery, and the manufacture and distribution of cheap rehydration packs is helping to reduce the impact of these diseases, still a major global cause of death in children.

SUMMARY

- **Health** is a state of physical, mental and social well-being which is more than just the absence of disease. This is very difficult to measure. A **disease** is a label given to a particular set of symptoms. A **physical** illness affects the body, while a **mental** illness affects the ability of the mind to function within the normally accepted range of behaviours.

- An **infectious disease** is caused by an organism (a **pathogen**) that invades the body and causes the symptoms of the disease. The pathogen can be passed from one person to another. Infectious diseases include those caused by bacteria and viruses, and also the **parasitic diseases** caused by larger multicellular organisms.

- **Non-infectious diseases** are not caused by pathogens but by lifestyle (such as coronary heart disease), ageing (**degenerative diseases**), starvation (**deficiency diseases**) or genetics (**inherited diseases**).

- The detection of disease may involve physical examination, biochemical tests such as the ELISA technique, X-rays, CAT or MRI scans, ultrasound scans and endoscopy.

- **Epidemiology** is the study of patterns of disease. The distribution of a disease is studied, the **aetiology** (cause) of the disease suggested and the effectiveness of different treatments assessed. The **morbidity** of a disease is the number of people made ill by the disease, and the **mortality** of the disease is the number of deaths it causes. There are many social as well as biological factors that determine whether someone is likely to suffer from a particular disease.

- Infectious diseases are **communicable** (spread from one person to another). The likelihood of a disease spreading depends on the pathogen, the behaviour and general health of the potential host and environmental factors.

- Disease can spread **horizontally** through members of a population or **vertically** from one generation to the next. Animal diseases may spread to humans (**zoonosis**). Diseases may spread by:

  vectors – other organisms, such as the *Anopheles* mosquito which transmits malaria
  fomites – objects such as towels and bedding
  direct contact – touching, also by sexual contact
  inhalation – breathing in droplets containing the microorganism
  ingestion – contaminated food or drink
  inoculation – through a break in the skin.

- A localised increase in the incidence of a disease is called an **outbreak**. An increase on a national level is an **epidemic**. An epidemic affecting many countries at the same time is a **pandemic**. A disease that is common in a particular population all the time is **endemic**.

- An outbreak of a disease can start from a single **point source**, and people exposed to the point source will develop the disease at the same time. There may be a **common source**, to which people are exposed over a period of time, or the disease may spread by **person-to-person contact**, where there is a chain of transmission with gaps while the disease incubates.

- The body is protected from pathogenic invasion by the skin, the blood-clotting mechanism, mucous membranes, phagocytic white blood cells, the acid in the stomach and competition from the natural flora (bacteria) on the skin and in the gut.

- The **immune response** enables the body to recognise and remove foreign material. The body recognises the material as foreign by its **antigens** – proteins on the cell surface membranes.

- **Lymphocytes** are white blood cells that each recognise one particular antigen. There are two types of lymphocytes – **T-cells** and **B-cells**.

- T-cells bring about the **cell-mediated response** to invasion by a foreign antigen. A T-cell binds to and destroys the antigen and then divides to produce a clone of **killer T-cells** which all destroy the same type of antigen.

- B-cells bring about the **humoral response** by producing **plasma cell clones** and **memory cells**. Plasma cell clones produce **antibodies**, proteins which bind to the antigens and destroy them. Memory cells convey **immunological memory** so that plasma clone cells are produced rapidly next time the antigen is met.

- The **pathogenicity** of a pathogen is its ability to survive, spread and cause disease. A successful pathogen needs to survive between hosts, successfully invade new hosts and survive the immune response. Some pathogens suppress the action of the host immune system.

- Common symptoms of infectious diseases include fever, inflammation and rash.

- Chemicals used to control the spread of disease include **antiseptics** (used on people) and **disinfectants** (used to sterilise equipment).

- **Antimicrobials** are drugs which are **selectively toxic** – they destroy bacteria inside the body without harming the human cells. **Broad-spectrum antibiotics** can be used to treat many types of bacteria; **narrow-spectrum antibiotics** are effective against a few or even just one type of bacterium. Bacteria may become **resistant** to an antibiotic, when they are no longer affected by it. **Bacteriostatic** antibiotics stop the microorganisms growing and multiplying; **bactericidal** antibiotics kill the microorganisms.

- **Vaccination** lets the body develop immunity to a pathogen without suffering the disease. **Live vaccines** use attenuated (weakened) strains of the pathogen. Other vaccines include killed pathogens, toxins or antigens from the viral coat.

- A disease has been **eradicated** when the organism is no longer found anywhere in hosts or the environment. It has been **eliminated** when people no longer suffer from the disease, but the organism is still around and so immunisation has to continue. A **controlled** disease still occurs, but not often enough to be a significant health risk.

QUESTIONS

1 a What is meant by the term 'health' and why is it so difficult to measure?

   b What is meant by the term 'disease'?

   c Make a table summarising the main types of disease with their causes, giving a specific example of each type of disease.

2 Explain the use of the following techniques in the diagnosis of disease:

   a observation   **c** ELISA

   b X-rays and ultrasound   **d** biosensors.

3 Epidemiology is a relatively new science. What is it, and how is it useful to our understanding of diseases and their causes?

4 Infectious diseases are caused by invading pathogens which may be viruses, bacteria, fungi, protoctista or multicellular organisms. Choose three of these groups of pathogens and for each describe:

   a one pathogen

   b the symptoms of the disease it causes

   c the treatment.

5 a Describe briefly the main body defences against disease.

   b How do pathogens attempt to overcome these defences?

6 Summarise the main methods of chemical control against disease and describe how they work.

7 For major diseases in the world, one of the main lines of research is usually for an effective vaccine.

   a What is vaccination and how does it work?

   b What are the main advantages of using vaccination programmes to control a disease?

   c What are the main disadvantages of vaccinations?

Developing Key Skills

A major charity is planning a campaign to reduce the numbers of children dying of diarrhoea in the developing world. The approach is to be three pronged – providing clean supplies of drinking water, making rehydration packs readily available and educating people so they can understand how the infection is picked up and passed on. Your task is to plan a presentation which could be given in an assembly, at a youth group or at an open evening to convince people that it would be a good idea for the school, college or youth group to support this cause and help to raise money. Use the information in the Focus material and the rest of the chapter, as well as information from other sources, including the internet, to build up evidence that will demonstrate to your audience that this is a worthy cause which has every chance of success if the resources are made available. You can produce posters and a talk, or a PowerPoint presentation, or a piece of drama – whatever you feel will carry the most information and have the most impact on your target group.

CAFFEINE – A MODEL OF ADDICTION

Many of the illnesses we suffer in the developed world can be described as 'lifestyle diseases'. They occur as a result of the way we live and the substances we take into our bodies. Heart disease, strokes, lung cancer, emphysema, bowel cancer, throat cancer and cirrhosis of the liver are all linked closely to substances we choose to put into our bodies. Many people continue to smoke and drink knowing it is not good for them, because they are addicted to the drugs contained in cigarettes and alcohol. But what is addiction and how does it work? By looking at caffeine, a widely used drug that is legal and has no stigma attached, we can build up a picture of how addiction works.

Figure 1 One of the most accepted drugs in our society is caffeine, often taken in the form of coffee.

A cup of caffeine

The drug that is probably used most commonly in modern society is taken regularly every day by millions of us. Many people find it hard to get going in the morning without their first fix of caffeine – more commonly known as a cup of tea or coffee. Caffeine is a mild stimulant, which is why tea or coffee helps you to wake up in the morning or to keep going during the day if you feel sleepy. As well as stimulating the brain, it also has an effect on the body, increasing the heart rate and blood pressure. For most people this physical effect is of little consequence, but it can be damaging to people with heart disease or high blood pressure, who should cut down on the amounts of coffee and tea that they drink or change to decaffeinated brands. Also, as with most drugs, some people are more sensitive to caffeine than others and find that drinking coffee in the evening prevents them sleeping properly. Caffeine is legal, socially accepted and widely enjoyed, but like many other drugs it can be addictive, particularly if taken in large amounts. It is easy to drink lots of strong coffee to cope with extra pressure of work or to concentrate late at night. However, when coffee-drinking drops back to normal levels, feelings of tiredness and headaches may result – withdrawal symptoms brought on by an addiction to caffeine. If these symptoms are ignored the addiction is soon broken and the person feels normal again, but many people in this situation simply make another cup of coffee without thinking! The way caffeine becomes a part of our lives, leaving a void if we try to give it up, gives us a working model of what happens when we use other, more damaging drugs.

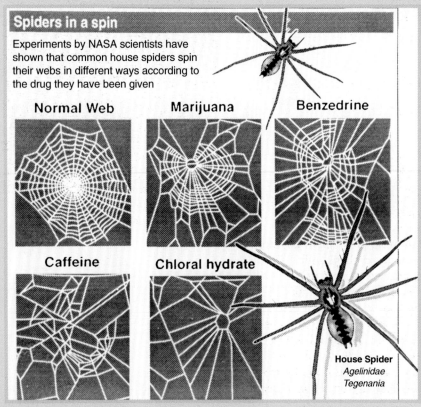

Spiders in a spin

Experiments by NASA scientists have shown that common house spiders spin their webs in different ways according to the drug they have been given

Normal Web   **Marijuana**   **Benzedrine**

Caffeine   **Chloral hydrate**

House Spider
Agelinidae
Tegenania

Figure 2 The action of caffeine on the web-spinning ability of a spider! In this experiment spiders were exposed to minute amounts of several different drugs and the effect on their nervous system was demonstrated by the disruption of the web. It is interesting to note that, for spiders, caffeine has a more disruptive effect than several other drugs.

7.3 Lifestyle diseases

Many of the infectious diseases described in section 7.2 are at least in part the result of lifestyle. The poor living in slums in the developing world are exposed to many infectious diseases, and their inadequate diet may result in vitamin and mineral deficiency diseases. On the other hand, those living in relative prosperity in the USA or the UK have less risk of contracting an infectious disease causing severe illness or death. However, they are much more likely to suffer a disease related to their lifestyle, caused by overeating, unbalanced eating, lack of exercise, smoking, drinking or the effects of air pollution.

Some of the lifestyle factors that can cause disease, or at least increase the likelihood of suffering a particular disease, are under our control; others are not. Babies and small children have little choice about what they eat, yet the foundations of diet-related illnesses may well be laid in early childhood. You cannot change where you were born and the circumstances of your upbringing, and these early experiences help form many of your lifestyle habits. However, we in the more developed countries of the world are provided with knowledge with which to make lifestyle choices. If we know that exercise is important for a healthy heart, and yet sit slumped in front of the television during our leisure time, then we are choosing to increase our risk of disease. If, with knowledge of healthy eating, we choose to eat too much energy-rich refined carbohydrate and fat and refuse to eat fresh fruit and vegetables, then we cannot be surprised if we suffer ill-effects.

Diet and disease

Across the world, people eat an enormous variety of foods to obtain a balanced diet. It is becoming increasingly recognised that diet can affect our health in a number of ways.

Taking in problems

Lactose intolerance

The food we take into our bodies can cause health problems directly. For example, human infants almost all synthesise the enzyme **lactase** which is needed to break down lactose, the natural sugar in milk. Most mammals stop producing lactase once they are weaned, as they no longer drink milk. However, many human societies keep dairy herds and whilst no longer drinking human milk, many adults drink large quantities of cow's milk.

Some people suffer from severe stomach cramps, wind, diarrhoea and vomiting if they drink milk. They are said to be **lactose intolerant**. There is evidence that the ability of adult humans to digest milk has evolved within the last 5000 years or so, and only in those cultures that have traditionally kept dairy animals, such as in northern Africa, the Near East and Europe. Between 70% and 100% of individuals from these historical dairying regions produce lactase and can digest milk. In traditionally non-dairying regions, the situation is reversed and 70–100% of the population are lactose intolerant. Maintaining the ability to digest lactose must have been an advantage for children and young adults in areas where milk was a readily available source of food.

Figure 7.3.1 Wherever you live, your lifestyle contributes to your pattern of health and disease.

Food allergies

Food allergies are another way in which the food taken into the body can cause a direct, and in some cases very serious, threat to health. **Mast cells** are small oval cells often found in connective tissue. They have immunoglobulin E on their surfaces, which responds to the presence of a foreign particle by stimulating the mast cell to secrete **histamine**. This causes local blood vessels to dilate and changes the permeability of the capillaries. As a result, plasma moves out into the surrounding tissues, causing them to swell. For many people this is a useful defence mechanism, helping them fight off invading infections. However, for increasing numbers of people (more than 35 million Americans alone) the mast cell system seems to be oversensitive, causing allergies to foods such as milk, eggs, wheat, peanuts, shellfish and various fruits. Allergic reactions range from mild breathlessness or a mild rash, through severe rashes and itching or sickness and diarrhoea, to severe wheezing and asthma and even, in extreme cases, death. The main treatment for any food allergy is to avoid the trigger food, but this is not easy as many processed foods contain traces of all sorts of substances which seem unrelated to the main ingredients. A mild allergy can be treated with antihistamine drugs, which counteract the histamine released by the mast cells. For more severe allergies, adrenaline has to be taken to counteract the state of shock which develops and to prevent the closing of the airways.

Food-borne infections

Finally, food can carry pathogenic microorganisms into the body. We have already mentioned salmonellosis and amoebic dysentery in chapter 7.2. Another food-borne disease is listeriosis, caused by *Listeria monocytogenes*. These bacteria may be found in soft ripened cheeses such as Brie and Camembert, in any cheeses made with unpasteurised milk and in pâtés. They have also been found in considerable numbers in prepared cooked and chilled meals which are reheated before eating, and in ready-to-eat poultry. In adults *Listeria* does not usually cause serious disease – mild fever and backache are the usual symptoms. Listeriosis is important because in pregnant women the bacteria can cross the placenta and reach the fetus. If a woman eats *Listeria*-infected food in the early stages of her pregnancy, the most likely outcome is that the fetus will miscarry (abort). If she becomes infected later in the pregnancy, the baby may be born severely ill and either die or be permanently damaged. Treatment with antibiotics can be very successful, but the bacteria do not always respond to the drugs as well as expected. The best policy is to avoid eating those foods that carry the highest risk during pregnancy.

E. coli *hits* Scotland

In the late autumn of 1996 there was a major outbreak of food poisoning in Scotland. Cooked meats and pies supplied by one butcher, John M. Barr and Sons of Wishaw, who had been voted Scottish Butcher of the Year, were distributed around central Scotland. The meat products became contaminated by a strain of *E. coli* normally found in cattle guts, and which can be present in undercooked meat or cooked meat that has been in contact with raw meat. For example, the bacteria were found in gravy supplied by the butcher for a pensioners' lunch in Wishaw.

Figure 7.3.2 The butcher's shop where the fatal outbreak of *E. coli* food poisoning began.

Several hundred people became ill. This infection is particularly dangerous as not only does it cause severe diarrhoea and sickness, but in around 25% of those infected it causes permanent kidney damage. Many sufferers were elderly, although people of all ages were admitted to hospital. Around 20 people died, making it one of the worst known outbreaks of food poisoning in the UK. Afterwards it was recognised that the outbreak had been very badly handled. The butcher had been warned about the products by health inspectors, but continued to sell them for several days. Once the outbreak was confirmed, the Scottish Agriculture, Environment and Fisheries Department prevented publication of the names of the known outlets, so that people continued to eat contaminated products and more became infected. With better management, substantially fewer people would probably have become ill or died. This is an example of the difficult marriage of commercial interests with the interests of public health, demonstrating the need for effective public health legislation.

The human diet

In many parts of the world, there is little choice over what food is eaten or how much is eaten. However, where there is sufficient food available for choices to be made, foods should be chosen in sensible combinations to provide a healthy balance of carbohydrates, fats and proteins as well as minerals, vitamins, plenty of water and fibre (see section 3.3).

Diet can affect health in a multitude of ways – too little food and we starve, too much and we become obese. Minerals and vitamins must be present in the right amounts to avoid deficiency diseases. And increasingly research is suggesting that what we eat affects the development of physical illness in our bodies. It seems that we may be able, to some extent at least, to eat our way to health – or to ill health. One of the clearest demonstrations of this link (along with the deficiency diseases described in section 3.3) is the association between levels of fibre in our diet and certain diseases.

The link between fibre and disease

Fibre is mainly the cellulose cell walls of plant material, along with other indigestible compounds. Plenty of fibre in the diet ensures that the food has sufficient bulk to stretch the walls of the gut and stimulate efficient peristalsis. This keeps the food moving steadily through the gut, ensuring a **throughput time** (the time for the remains of food taken in to reappear as faeces) of under 24 hours, which is desirable for several reasons. If there is insufficient fibre in the diet, the waste material spends a long time in the colon. Here water is removed from the waste, so a long throughput time means that more water is removed. This results in the hard, compacted faeces known as **constipation**. **Haemorrhoids** (piles) often accompany constipation – these are swollen veins in the wall of the rectum and anus. Constipation and haemorrhoids cause many people a great deal of discomfort and unhappiness, and make a large profit for the companies selling laxatives, yet a simple change of diet would solve the majority of such problems. However, a long throughput time can cause problems other than simple constipation.

Diverticulitis is a very painful condition which is particularly common in older, constipated patients. It involves pockets forming in the lining of the colon. These fill with compacted faeces and may become inflamed and extremely painful. If the lining of the pocket perforates, releasing the contents into the body cavity, the condition may cause death.

Much less serious, but still a problem to many people, is **irritable bowel syndrome**. This is also linked to a low-fibre diet, and is more common in women than in men. One symptom is pain, particularly in the lower abdomen but sometimes perceived as being higher up in the chest. Most sufferers have constipation, but they sometimes have diarrhoea. There is no major physical cause for the symptoms except lack of fibre in the diet, and it is thought that irritable bowel syndrome is linked with stress, and that it is partly a psychosomatic illness (involving both the mind and the body). Treated or untreated, the symptoms tend to lessen with age.

One of the most serious conditions currently linked to a low-fibre, high-fat diet is **cancer of the colon**. It is the most common type of gastrointestinal

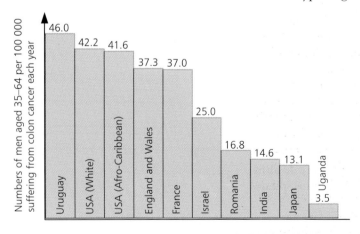

Figure 7.3.3 In many countries in the developing world, the diet is based largely around plant food, which is high in fibre and low in fat. It seems likely that this is the main reason for the low rates of colon cancer seen in such countries, and that highly refined diets are the biggest factor in the high levels of the disease in the developed world.

cancer in the developed world, yet it is seldom seen in developing countries. There may be genetic factors that make the disease more likely in some people, but the major cause seems to be a low-fibre diet leading to long retention of faecal material in the colon. This means that bacterial action takes place for longer, leading to the production of more toxic and possibly carcinogenic waste products which are kept in close contact with the lining of the colon. The constipation that results from a low-fibre diet makes any changes in the working of the bowel more difficult to notice, and so delays detection of the problem. Only 35% of people diagnosed with cancer of the colon will still be alive five years later, because symptoms are often not picked up until the cancer is far advanced. The possibility of screening for bowel cancer has been raised, and better education about dietary matters might also be useful in reducing the problem in years to come.

Diseases of the respiratory system

The respiratory system takes in the oxygen the body needs for cellular respiration, and removes the waste carbon dioxide produced (see section 2.4).

Infectious diseases of the respiratory system can be life threatening – influenza and pneumonia are frequently cited on death certificates as the cause of death. However, in the developed world, infectious diseases of the respiratory system are becoming less of a threat, while respiratory diseases that result from our lifestyle and environment are becoming increasingly common.

Asthma

Asthma is one such condition. The number of cases of asthma is rising each year in the UK. Hundreds of thousands of asthma sufferers live completely normal lives, but around 2000 people die of the disease each year in the UK, many of them children and young people, in spite of improvements in both drug treatments and understanding of the management of the disease. Asthma occurs when the mast cells in the lining of the respiratory tract produce extra histamine (see page 652). This causes the lining to swell and the smooth muscle to contract, narrowing the bronchioles. There is a much increased resistance to air moving in and out of the lungs. This gives rise to the breathlessness and 'wheezing' sounds associated with asthma.

Asthma may be an inherited condition, with several family members suffering the disease. It may occur as an allergic reaction, often to house dust mites and their faeces, or to animals such as cats, dogs or horses. It may be a response to an irritant such as cigarette smoke or to an infection like the common cold. Everyone is capable of developing asthma, but some people are genetically programmed to be more sensitive than others. Some children will need 10 triggers in place before they get breathless with the symptoms of asthma, whilst others need only one trigger before they begin to wheeze.

Management of asthma involves careful observations on how well the lungs are functioning. A machine measures the total volume of air breathed out over a complete exhalation, therefore showing the lung capacity available for use. These machines are usually found in hospitals or doctor's practices. A **peak flow meter** is more portable, and is used by most asthma patients. This is a simple device which is calibrated to give the **peak expiratory flow**, as figure 7.3.4 (page 656) shows. By measuring this twice a day, asthma sufferers can see how their lungs are functioning and tailor their drug intake accordingly.

Another important aspect of asthma management is to remove as many triggers as possible. A home largely free from dust and dust mites, and with no pets, helps reduce the problem for many patients.

Drug treatments for asthma have come a very long way in the last 70 years. **Beta agonists** rapidly relax the smooth muscle of the respiratory tract, dilating the bronchioles and making breathing easier. They are usually taken as an aerosol using an inhaler which delivers a set dose. Beta agonists may be used regularly, or before exercise, or only at the onset of an attack, depending on how badly affected the sufferer is. **Sodium cromoglycate** is a preventive drug which stabilises the mast cells so they produce less histamine. It is particularly useful for allergy-induced asthma and for asthma triggered by exercise. For people who have more severe asthma, daily inhalation of **steroids** can help to prevent attacks.

Why is the incidence of asthma increasing? There is no single answer. Some feel that the disease is being diagnosed more often now that more is known and there are effective treatments. There is some evidence, certainly in adults, that the stress of modern life may play a part. Centrally heated and carpeted houses may provide the house dust mite with many more potential homes. There is evidence that increasing levels of air pollution from traffic may be a major contributor to what is sometimes referred to as 'the asthma epidemic'.

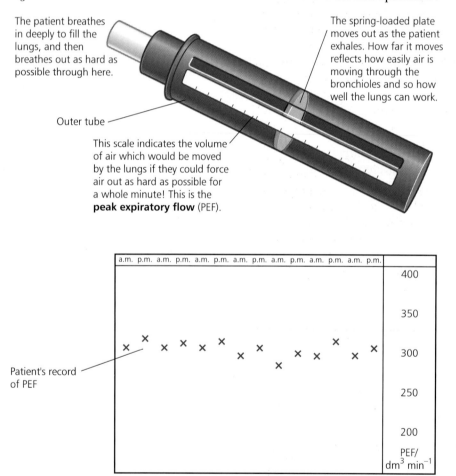

The patient breathes in deeply to fill the lungs, and then breathes out as hard as possible through here.

The spring-loaded plate moves out as the patient exhales. How far it moves reflects how easily air is moving through the bronchioles and so how well the lungs can work.

Outer tube

This scale indicates the volume of air which would be moved by the lungs if they could force air out as hard as possible for a whole minute! This is the **peak expiratory flow** (PEF).

Patient's record of PEF

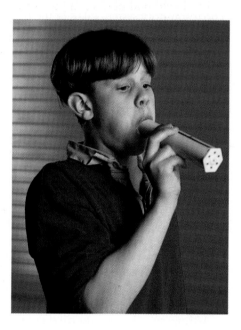

Figure 7.3.4 The peak expiratory flow measured by the peak flow meter is usually lower in the morning than the evening, even in people who do not have asthma.

Pink puffers and blue bloaters

Bronchitis is another disease of the respiratory system that is closely linked with lifestyle and environmental factors. 'Bronchitis' is an umbrella term for a variety of chest conditions, and there are two distinct types. **Acute bronchitis** is an infectious disease which can affect anyone, although it is more common in smokers and their families, in people who work in environments containing irritant particles and in people living in areas of high air pollution. The word acute here describes an illness that comes on quickly and is short term. Acute chest infections are the largest group of serious diseases that turn up in doctors' waiting rooms, and even with modern treatments there is still a 2–3% mortality rate from them.

Chronic bronchitis is more closely linked with environmental factors, particularly smoking. The word **chronic** generally describes a disease that comes on gradually and may last a long time. Someone with chronic bronchitis secretes too much mucus in the airways, causing a persistent cough which does not respond to over-the-counter medicines. Because the airways are permanently irritated, they are vulnerable to infection, and so sufferers from chronic bronchitis are also likely to get infectious bronchitis. The mucus, irritation and frequent infections together cause narrowing of the bronchioles and so chronic shortness of breath. The lungs can be permanently damaged. The diagnosis of bronchitis is aided by measurements of the peak expiratory flow rate, and other lung volumes such as the **vital capacity** and the **expiratory reserve volume**.

The likelihood of developing chronic bronchitis increases with age, and men are more likely to develop it than women, as figure 7.3.5 shows. British studies have shown that chronic bronchitis is also twice as common in urban dwellers as in rural dwellers. Social class affects the death rate from bronchitis – unskilled labourers are four times more likely to die of chronic bronchitis than professional people. Genetic factors and exposure to dust in the workplace increase the risk of chronic bronchitis, but perhaps the major risk factor is smoking. Between 15% and 20% of smokers will develop chronic bronchitis. If an affected smoker stops smoking, any permanent damage that has already occurred will remain, but further damage will be prevented.

Chronic bronchitis can become severe, leading to **emphysema** (see figure 7.3.19, page 672). This condition is particularly common in heavy smokers and people exposed at work to chemicals or particles which irritate the lungs. In emphysema, the structure of the lungs begins to break down, and large air spaces develop which are not effective in gaseous exchange. Sufferers from emphysema breathe heavily and use voluntary actions such as hunching the shoulders to try and get more air into the lungs. The chest becomes barrel shaped and the noisy hyperventilation (fast breathing) often leads to a 'healthy' pink colour developing – hence the term 'pink puffers'.

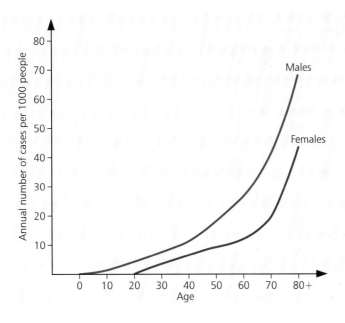

Figure 7.3.5 The occurrence of bronchitis at different ages in the UK.

The other major complication following chronic bronchitis is failure of the right ventricle of the heart. The heart beats rapidly and is substantially enlarged but does not function effectively, giving a bluish colour to the skin due to insufficient oxygen in the blood. This type of patient is often overweight and fluid builds up in the tissues causing swelling – the 'blue bloaters'. The breathing becomes very quiet and shallow.

Severely breathless bronchitics may be given oxygen supplies at home. Up to 15 hours of oxygen therapy is needed at a time. Smoking whilst using oxygen is obviously forbidden, but it is not unknown for heavy smokers to fit in their 40-a-day in the short time when they are not inhaling oxygen! If a patient with severe chronic bronchitis gets an infection, or continues to smoke, he or she runs the risk of total respiratory failure, low blood pressure and eventual circulatory collapse. This can lead rapidly to death, and about 35 000 people each year die from chronic bronchitis in the UK. Of those, 75% are over 65, and 80% are smokers.

Diseases of the cardiovascular system

A healthy adult heart beats about 70 times a minute, pumping the blood to the lungs to pick up oxygen and then on around the body (see section 2.5). However, the cardiovascular system is particularly vulnerable to diseases resulting from lifestyle factors such as diet, smoking and lack of physical fitness. Cardiovascular diseases, including heart attacks and strokes, kill more people than any other group of diseases in the developed world.

Hypertension – high blood pressure

How high is high?

One of the most common conditions of the cardiovascular system is **hypertension** (high blood pressure). This disease is unusual in that most sufferers are unaware of it because unless the blood pressure is very high, hypertension gives no symptoms.

When the blood pressure is measured, a result higher than the expected norm of around 120/80 reveals hypertension. It seems likely that blood pressure is naturally a variable characteristic rather like weight and height, so it is quite difficult to judge whether someone's blood pressure is in fact 'high'. If your blood pressure is naturally very low, then a reading at the high end of the normal range could mean you are suffering from mild hypertension. On the other hand, if your blood pressure is naturally on the high side, a reading just above the normal range could be quite normal for you. Blood pressure is usually higher in urban societies than in rural ones, and differs with ethnic groups – African and Japanese people generally have lower than average blood pressures, while Afro-Americans have higher than average values.

Systolic blood pressure can change rapidly in response to many things, including the stress of having your blood pressure taken. For many years this was regarded as relatively unimportant, although there is now evidence that raised systolic pressure figures should be treated with caution. Instead, a raised diastolic pressure has been taken to indicate hypertension. However, it has now been shown that diastolic pressure too can rise with stress, and 'white coat hypertension' – a raised blood pressure which only exists when a doctor or nurse is taking your blood pressure – is now a recognised state! The level of blood pressure regarded as mild hypertension needing treatment varies from country to country. In Britain it is 140/90, but the figures have been known to alter as different treatments become available.

Using the British figure, about 15% of the entire population have some level of hypertension. For people over 40 the figure rises to 20%, and about 40% of people over 70 have hypertension. The majority (85%) of these people will have only mild hypertension, with diastolic blood pressures of 90–109 mm Hg. These data raise the question whether the mild hypertension being treated is in fact just the higher end of the 'normal' range of blood pressure. The current thinking is moving away from treating these people purely on the strength of the blood pressure reading, as most probably do not need clinical treatment.

The problems of hypertension

The reason for anxiety over hypertension is the diseases associated with it. It can cause kidney damage and blindness, and the risk of a stroke is greatly increased, along with a significantly higher risk of heart disease. A stroke may result from a blocked artery supplying the brain due to atherosclerosis, as described on pages 662–663. The artery may be blocked by a blood clot formed elsewhere in the circulatory system, or a stroke may be caused by a blood vessel rupturing, releasing blood into the brain. A stroke frequently leads to permanent brain damage, paralysis or death.

Figure 7.3.6 Overweight, fatty foods, smoking, little exercise: a lifestyle like this raises your chances of suffering cardiovascular disease.

The role of lifestyle in hypertension

Raised blood pressure is usually due to a narrowing of the blood vessels, which may be the result of fatty deposits in the blood vessels, or of the artery walls losing elasticity, or a response to stress. Smoking causes damage to the endothelial linings of the blood vessels, making the build-up of plaque more likely. Being overweight means there are more capillary networks supplying the adipose tissue, and so increases the peripheral resistance of the circulatory system. Too much salt in the diet affects the water balance of the body, increasing the blood volume. Taking insufficient exercise results in narrowed blood vessels and therefore more resistance to the flow of blood. All of these factors make raised blood pressure more likely. Removing any one of these risk factors – giving up smoking, losing weight, reducing the salt in the diet or exercising more – is likely to lower the blood pressure.

Treatment

When preventive measures such as these fail, hypertension needs to be treated with drugs. There are several alternative approaches.

- **Diuretics** increase the excretion of salt and water in the urine, reducing the blood volume and thus the blood pressure.
- **Beta blockers** slow the heart rate and decrease its output, thus reducing the blood pressure as less blood is forced through the blood vessels (see box overleaf).
- **Calcium antagonists** dilate arteries and arterioles by preventing calcium ions moving into smooth muscle cells. This reduces the resistance to blood flow.
- **Angiotensin-converting enzyme inhibitors** prevent the formation of the peptide hormone angiotensin II. This hormone acts to constrict the arteries, so the inhibitors prevent this constriction.
- A number of drugs dilate the arteries by decreasing sympathetic nervous system activity.

Many of these drugs have side-effects, but untreated high blood pressure increases the risk of cardiovascular disease, so their use is worthwhile. Diuretics and beta blockers are the most commonly used drugs in the battle against hypertension.

Beta blockers

The heart beats rhythmically as a whole organ because of the pacemaker region, as described in section 2.5. The rate and strength of the heartbeat sometimes need to change in response to changes in the body's needs, and these changes in heartbeat are brought about by nervous messages and hormones.

The sympathetic nervous system supplies the heart and releases adrenaline as a neurotransmitter. Adrenaline binds to a protein called a **beta receptor** on the surface of the cardiac muscle cells and stimulates them to contract both more quickly and more strongly, so speeding up the heart rate and increasing the force of pumping. The hormone adrenaline released by the adrenal glands in times of stress has the same effect.

Beta blockers such as propranalol have their effect by interacting with the adrenaline beta receptors. The molecules are a similar shape to adrenaline and fit the beta receptors of the cardiac muscle cells without having a stimulating effect on them. This reduces the number of receptor sites available for the adrenaline to bind to, and so reduces the effect of adrenaline on the heart. One result of this is a reduction in the force of the ventricular contraction, which is very important in the reduction of high blood pressure. Someone using beta blockers will not experience the heart pounding most of us feel when very nervous, and so these drugs are sometimes used to help people cope with extremely stressful situations.

One problem with using beta blockers in the control of high blood pressure is that they block the normal nervous messages carried by adrenaline, as well as the larger outflow of adrenaline during stress. As a result, patients using beta blockers may have impaired circulation to their hands and feet and feel very cold, because their heart rates are slowed and their blood pressure relatively low most of the time.

Low blood pressure

When discussing blood pressure problems, most people automatically think of raised blood pressure. However, lowered blood pressure is also a clinical problem, as the oxygen supply to major organs can become insufficient. Lowered blood pressure is usually the result of the heart either not beating strongly enough or beating too infrequently.

Atherosclerosis

Atherosclerosis (hardening of the arteries) is a build-up of yellowish fatty deposits (**plaque**) on the endothelium inside the arteries. A large abnormal mass of fatty material building up on the arterial wall is called an **atheroma**. Figure 7.3.7 shows how atherosclerosis develops. It may begin as early as late childhood, and continues throughout life. Plaque is particularly likely to form in the arteries of the heart (coronary arteries) and the arteries of the neck (carotid arteries). It may cause the wall of the artery to be severely weakened, which can lead to a balloon-shaped swelling of the artery called an **aneurysm**. This can burst, leading to massive internal bleeding. Aneurysms often happen in the brain or the aorta, and a ruptured aneurysm is usually fatal. More frequently, the plaque blocks the blood vessels, resulting in a blood clot called a **thrombosis**.

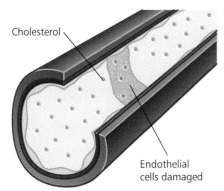

Cholesterol

Endothelial cells damaged

Slight damage to the endothelial cells can lead to an accumulation of lipids – the start of a plaque desposit.

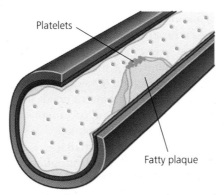

Platelets

Fatty plaque

Blood platelets form a cap over the fatty plaque, narrowing the entire artery.

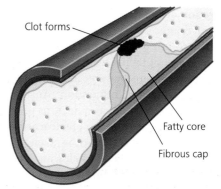

Clot forms

Fatty core

Fibrous cap

If the cap breaks, lipids from the fatty core can combine with clotting factors. A blood clot forms which can block the artery and lead to a stroke or a heart attack.

A thrombosis in the coronary artery causes **coronary heart disease**. A thrombosis in an artery supplying the brain causes a **stroke** – part of the brain is damaged. In America alone, atherosclerosis accounts for half of all adult deaths each year.

Coronary heart disease

Coronary heart disease, the result of blocked or impeded coronary arteries, causes around 27% of all deaths in the countries of the developed world, which means around 160 000 deaths in the UK alone each year. The most common diseases of the heart are **angina** and **myocardial infarction** (heart attack).

Angina

Angina can be seen as a milder form of heart attack. To maintain regular contractions of the heart, the cardiac muscle needs glucose and oxygen, and these are supplied by the blood via the coronary arteries. Atherosclerosis often occurs in the coronary arteries, reducing the supply of blood to the heart. The symptoms become apparent initially during exercise, when the heart rate goes up and more blood is being pumped. The cardiac muscle is working harder and needs more oxygen, but the narrowed coronary arteries cannot supply it. This leads to a gripping pain in the chest, which can extend down into the arms, particularly the left one, and up into the jaw. This is angina. The symptoms subside once exercise stops, but the experience is painful and frightening. Most angina is relatively mild, but up to 20% of patients with severe angina are likely to die within five years. Management involves stopping smoking, a low-fat diet, regular exercise and losing weight. **Glyceryl trinitrate** is taken when symptoms occur, either as a tablet to put under the tongue or a spray. The drug causes rapid dilation of the blood vessels and so improves the supply of oxygen to the cardiac muscle.

If the blockage of the coronary arteries continues to get worse, so will the angina, until it can become impossible even to walk across a room without experiencing severe pain. Treatment then involves calcium antagonists to dilate the blood vessels and beta blockers to reduce the heart rate – these drugs are described in the box opposite for the treatment of hypertension. Drugs cannot solve the problem of severe angina permanently, so at this stage, or earlier, heart bypass surgery may be carried out.

Heart attack

If a branch of the coronary artery becomes completely blocked, part of the heart muscle will be totally starved of oxygen and the patient will suffer a **myocardial**

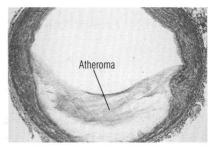

Atheroma

Figure 7.3.7 The development of atherosclerosis, which can begin in childhood.

infarction or **heart attack**. The symptoms are pain in the same areas as angina, but much more severe. It does not go off once exercise stops, and indeed may start when sitting down or in bed. The pain lasts for several hours, and glyceryl nitrate does not help. Death may occur within a few minutes having felt no previous symptoms, or after a few hours of pain, or after several days of feeling 'tired' and suffering 'indigestion'. Anyone with a suspected heart attack needs to be admitted to hospital as quickly as possible, for intensive care and treatment with anti-clotting drugs. An **electrocardiogram** (ECG), a recording of the electrical activity of the heart, is taken to confirm a diagnosis of heart attack. Rapid treatment is needed following a heart attack, as up to 45% of heart attack victims will be dead within five years of their initial attack and most of those will die within a week of the initial attack. For patients who survive this first week after an acute attack, the outlook is much more positive – 75% can expect to be alive five years later.

Heart surgery – the bypass and the transplant

Bypass surgery

Figure 7.3.8 Bypass surgery.

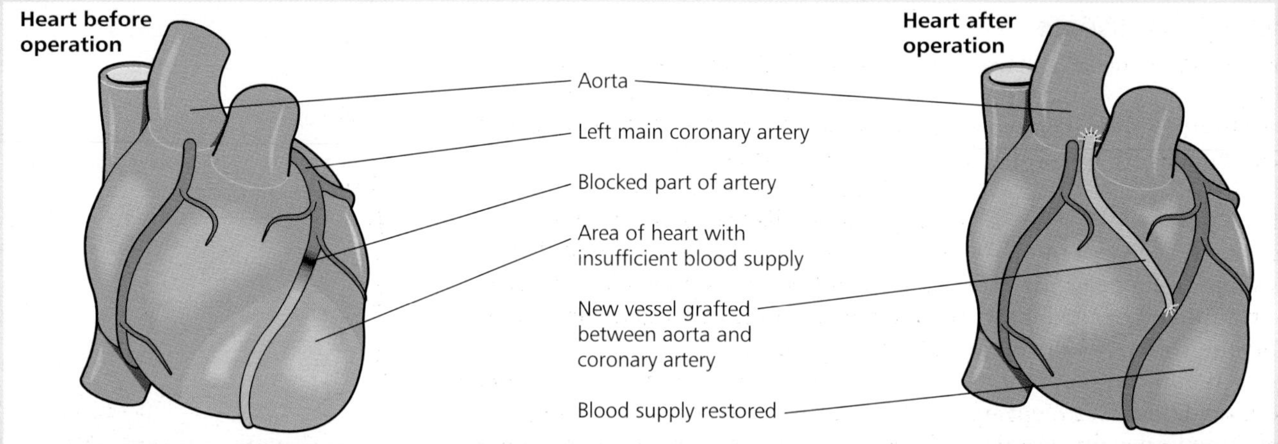

Heart before operation

Heart after operation

Aorta

Left main coronary artery

Blocked part of artery

Area of heart with insufficient blood supply

New vessel grafted between aorta and coronary artery

Blood supply restored

In patients with severe angina, the blood supply to the heart may become very restricted. To overcome this, **bypass surgery** may be carried out in which the diseased parts of the coronary arteries are 'bypassed' using pieces of blood vessels taken from elsewhere in the patient's body. This gives the cardiac muscle a much improved blood supply, and avoids the tissue being rejected. The symptoms of angina are relieved very rapidly and the quality of life is greatly improved.

Heart transplant

If a bypass operation is not suitable, or the heart has been severely damaged by a series of heart attacks, then the only remaining option may be a **heart transplant**. This technique was pioneered in the 1960s by the South African surgeon Christiaan Barnard. Now it is carried out regularly in many countries and most heart transplant patients can expect years rather than months or weeks of life ahead of them.

A heart transplant involves taking the diseased heart out of a patient's body and replacing it with the healthy heart of someone who has died, usually in an accident or from a brain haemorrhage. Once connected, the new heart will pump blood around the body, controlled by a pacemaker. The nervous connections have obviously been severed, so the overriding controls needed to stop the heart slowing down or speeding up have been lost. By imposing a rhythm, the artificial pacemaker overcomes these problems.

One of the major problems of heart transplants is rejection of the new organ by the body of the host. Once the body recognises the new heart as 'non-self' it will rapidly attack and destroy it. To prevent this, recipients have to take a cocktail of immunosuppressant drugs for the remainder of their lives, and this makes them vulnerable to attack by infectious diseases.

The heart transplant programme is hindered by lack of suitable donors. Accident victims who have registered to donate their organs are fewer than the patients needing transplants. Obviously the tissue match must be as close as possible, and there is no guarantee that an available heart will be of the right tissue type. More potential donors are needed, but future developments include the possibility of making entirely artificial hearts, or of using genetically engineered animals to produce 'human' hearts.

A change in lifestyle

Treatments such as bypass surgery and heart transplants raise certain dilemmas. Although some people with coronary heart disease are simply the victims of their own genetics, many patients have contributed to their own ill-health by various factors in their lifestyle. The most frequent contributory factor is smoking, along with eating a high-fat diet and not taking exercise. If a patient is treated without making lifestyle changes, the arteries supplying their cardiac muscle may once again become blocked, and further expensive surgery will be needed in future. In a health service where resources are always at a premium, do doctors have the right to demand that patients change their lifestyle before treatment is made available? Even if a patient does make changes before surgery, such as giving up smoking, old habits die hard and a reformed lifestyle cannot be imposed on an individual once the need for direct medical intervention is past.

Risk factors for cardiovascular disease

The risk factors involved in heart disease break down into two main groups – those we cannot help and those we can do something about. There is a genetic tendency in some families to develop heart disease or hypertension which can bring about heart disease and this we cannot (at present) alter. Age is also an unalterable factor. As we get older, our blood vessels begin to lose their elasticity and to narrow slightly, making us more likely to suffer from heart disease. The final unalterable factor is our gender – men are more likely to suffer from heart disease than women. This difference is particularly marked before the female menopause, as the female hormone oestrogen appears to offer some protection against the build-up of plaque.

Other risk factors for heart disease are aspects of our lifestyles which can be changed, as illustrated in figure 7.3.9. We each have the power to change some or all of these things for ourselves. However, as a society we have less power to prevent heart disease – banning smoking or introducing compulsory exercise for all would be unlikely to win a politician many votes. Health education programmes aimed at all ages can help to make everyone aware of the choices they are making in their lifestyle, and the future implications of those choices. Schools can provide education in healthy eating and in the risks associated with smoking, poor diet and lack of exercise. In the final analysis, everybody has to weigh up the evidence, make their own choices and take their own risks.

Smoking increases the risk of heart disease by damaging the endothelial lining of the blood vessels and encouraging a build-up of plaque. Being overweight puts a greater strain of the heart because of increased peripheral resistance. Eating too much saturated fat increases the risk of fatty deposits building up in the arteries. Saturated fat is found in foods of animal origin, particularly meat and dairy products, and in foods cooked in animal fats. Some plant oils are also bad for the heart – many nut oils are as damaging as animal fats. However, other oils, particularly olive oil, seem to give positive protection from heart disease. Figure 7.3.10 shows the annual death rates from heart disease in a number of countries. Countries such as Italy and Greece where large quantities of olive oil are a regular part of the diet show a significantly lower rate of death from heart disease than countries such as the UK.

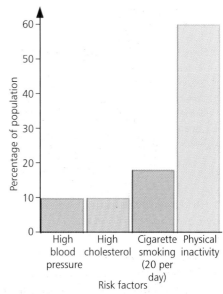

Figure 7.3.9 Percentage of the population of the USA with various risk factors for coronary heart disease.

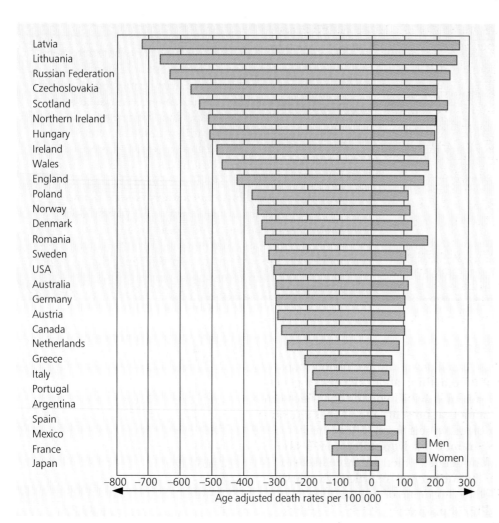

Latvia
Lithuania
Russian Federation
Czechoslovakia
Scotland
Northern Ireland
Hungary
Ireland
Wales
England
Poland
Norway
Denmark
Romania
Sweden
USA
Australia
Germany
Austria
Canada
Netherlands
Greece
Italy
Portugal
Argentina
Spain
Mexico
France
Japan

☐ Men
☐ Women

−800 −700 −600 −500 −400 −300 −200 −100   0   100   200   300

Age adjusted death rates per 100 000

Research done in the USA over ten years followed a group of middle-aged men with raised blood cholesterol levels. **Cholesterol** is a type of fat called a sterol, and it is the main constituent of fatty deposits in blood vessels. The research showed that the incidence of fatty deposits in the arteries, and of heart attacks and strokes that result from this, was lowered if the blood cholesterol level was decreased. In many patients, the blood cholesterol level could be lowered by careful management of the diet. Others needed to take cholesterol-lowering drugs. Diet is evidently a major influence on the risk of developing heart disease for most people. Eating a relatively low-fat diet in which much of the fat comes from foods such as olive oil and oily fish, which actually *lower* the blood cholesterol level, will reduce the likelihood of future heart disease and may even offer some protection against it.

However, blood cholesterol levels also depend on the genetically determined metabolism. Some individuals seem to be able to eat almost unlimited amounts of fatty food with no appreciable effect on their blood cholesterol, whilst others can eat a very low-fat diet and still have raised blood cholesterol levels. One of the most publicised ways of helping to avoid heart disease and increasing overall health is physical fitness. Is it really effective, and if so, why?

Physical fitness can be considered as 'the capacity to meet successfully the present and potential challenges of life'. This means that our body systems are in a condition that meets with the demands of our current way of life and also with any increased demands which may be put upon us. Most animals maintain

Figure 7.3.11 We make our lifestyle choices for many reasons and knowledge about causes of heart disease may not be enough to influence our decisions.

physical fitness simply through their natural way of life. However, this is not always true for humans. In the developed world the average person lives a far more sedentary existence than our evolutionary ancestors, and so needs to make an effort to remain reasonably fit.

Undertaking a single, isolated piece of physical exercise – for example, running for a bus – will be rather stressful in the short term, but in the long term it has no effect on the body. The immediate needs of the body are dealt with as well as possible, and then the systems return to their original functioning. But a regular, sustained programme of exercise brings about modifications in the body systems, having long-term benefits to the overall health of the individual. Athletes take this process to its extremes, and frequently develop a very specific fitness suited to their own particular sport, but physical fitness is a goal which can be achieved by anyone who is prepared to make a regular effort.

The internal environment of the body is maintained in a very stable state. The levels of glucose and other substances in the blood are kept as constant as possible, the core temperature is held within very narrow limits and action is taken as soon as events threaten to disturb the status quo. We shall look at the effects of exercise on three main systems – the heart, the lungs and the skeleton and muscles.

Exercise and the heart

When we begin a period of strenuous exercise our muscles quickly (within about three seconds) use up all their ATP and then rely on creatine phosphate (CP). This has a higher free energy of hydrolysis than ATP, so the breakdown of CP produces energy to make more ATP which allows the muscles to keep working. By the end of about ten seconds we have used up our CP and need oxygen to allow the Krebs' cycle to continue in the cells, to produce more ATP. During exercise the heart pumps blood at a higher rate to supply this oxygen.

At rest in a normal individual the heart beats about 70 times and pumps between 4 and 6 litres of blood each minute. In a trained athlete this blood flow can be increased to around 30 litres a minute during exercise. The increased blood flow is brought about both by an increase in the rate of the heartbeat and by an increase in the amount of blood pumped each time the heart contracts. The response of the heart to exercise is very rapid, and when exercise is anticipated in a fit individual the heart rate will begin to increase before the exercise begins, as shown in figure 7.3.12. The heart rate is controlled by a series of complex interactions which are considered in more detail in section 2.5. At the end of exercise in a fit individual, the heartbeat drops back to normal very rapidly. In those of us who are less fit, the pounding continues for several minutes!

During exercise the distribution of blood around the body can change dramatically. At rest, blood flows to the digestive system, the muscles, the brain, the liver, the skin – all of the body systems are supplied. But in strenuous exercise, automatic systems divert the flow of blood from areas where it is not immediately needed to areas where it is needed in large volumes. The digestive system and liver get a substantially reduced flow of blood, whilst the muscles – for energy – and the skin – for cooling – receive a greatly increased blood flow. The blood supply to the brain, the kidneys and the heart muscle itself remain more or less the same regardless of the activity levels of the rest of the body, since whatever else happens, these organs must continue to function.

As a result of increased exercise, the heart muscle becomes stronger and more efficient and the resting heart rate drops. The coronary arteries become larger and more extensive as a result of the increased blood flows they carry to

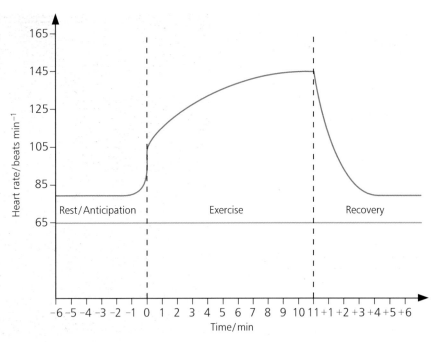

the heart during exercise. Regular exercise has been shown to increase blood levels of **high-density lipoproteins** which help to remove cholesterol from the blood, and also reduce the tendency of fatty deposits to build up on the artery walls. Most studies show that individuals who exercise regularly reduce their likelihood of suffering from heart disease, even if they have a family history of heart problems, smoke or are overweight.

Exercise and the lungs

We have already seen that the oxygen needs of the body increase with exercise. The oxygen is taken into the body through the lungs, and during exercise the breathing rate increases to provide extra oxygen. At rest the average adult breathes around 12 times a minute, taking in and out about 6 litres of air. In fit athletes this can be increased to between 45 and 80 litres in females and 80 and 100 litres in males during exercise. Regular exercise results in increased lung volume and efficiency, and an increase in the capillary blood supply to the lungs.

Although the breathing rate increases with the onset of exercise, it cannot respond quickly enough to the demand for more oxygen. In the first stage of exercise the muscle cells respire **anaerobically** (without oxygen), so that glucose and glycogen are not completely broken down. During this period an **oxygen deficit** builds up, when the oxygen requirement of the body is not fully met. At the end of the period of exercise the oxygen deficit has to be paid off as the **oxygen debt**, and a raised breathing rate continues until this has happened and all the lactic acid produced in anaerobic respiration has been metabolised. The size of the oxygen deficit and the time it takes to make up the oxygen debt are measures of the fitness of an individual. With increasing fitness the respiratory system responds more efficiently to exercise and so the deficit is smaller and is paid off more rapidly.

As part of a training programme an athlete in any sport will work both aerobically and anaerobically. Aerobic exercise is carried out at a rate which allows an adequate supply of oxygen to the muscle cells so aerobic respiration can continue. This builds up stamina, increasing both cardiac output and oxygen transport – more capillaries form and the red cell count increases. Anaerobic training increases the ability to produce short bursts of high speed,

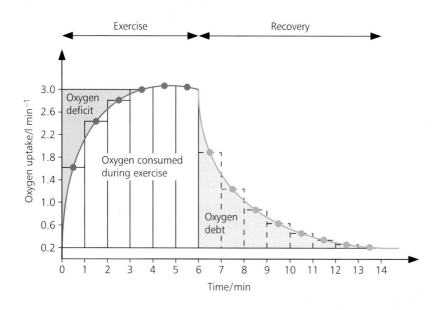

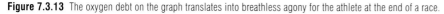

Figure 7.3.13 The oxygen debt on the graph translates into breathless agony for the athlete at the end of a race.

and this type of training builds up levels of creatine phosphate in the muscles, making it possible to work anaerobically for longer.

Exercise and the skeletal system

The complex system of bones and joints that make up the skeleton, along with the muscles needed to move them, are of vital importance in exercise. Vigorous exercise carried out without preparation can damage the skeletal system, but in general exercise is beneficial. The bones of the body are built up and dissolved away continuously. They are built up where stresses on them indicate that more bone mass is needed. When the bones are rarely stressed they are dissolved away. Plenty of exercise therefore tends to increase the overall bone mass. This is of great importance, particularly for women. With age, the bone mass is gradually reduced. If there is insufficient material to begin with, this erosion of the bone may result in crippling disease. Regular exercise helps to prevent this and also, when not carried out to excess, keeps the joints flexible and helps to maintain a full range of movement.

Muscles are used to move the skeleton in exercise. Different types of exercise use different muscles. When muscles are used regularly they get larger and stronger which has the effect of 'toning' the body. The development of the muscles involves an increase in the cross-sectional areas of the muscle fibres, rather than an increase in the numbers of fibres. As the proportion of the body mass made up of muscle increases, the amount of energy used in the basic maintenance of the body increases too. Muscle cells use up more energy than fat cells. This in turn helps to reduce obesity.

Exercise and energy

In 532 BC Milo of Croton won the wrestling competition at the Olympic Games seven years in succession. It was recorded that he trained on a diet of 20lb of bread, 20lb of meat and 18 pints of wine each day. Thus sportsmen attempting to improve their performance with special diets has a very long history. The link between diet and exercise is relatively simple, and certainly for the majority of people attempting to improve their physical fitness the most important factor is that exercise uses up energy.

For an athlete on a very specific training programme, diet is very important. A high protein diet is usually eaten to provide plenty of amino acids for muscle building in the body and heart, for lung tissue development and for new blood vessels and blood cells. During training and before competitions slow-release carbohydrates such as pasta, wholemeal bread and potatoes are also important as a source of energy during exercise.

Compare the energy requirements of a sedentary person with those when exercise is undertaken (see table 7.3.1) and it is easy to see the difference. An hour on the tennis court or a brisk hour's walk demands around 25kJ of energy for every kilogram of body weight. Steady running uses 36.5kJ per hour and a hard game of squash around $50kJkg^{-1}h^{-1}$. It is therefore easy to see that the development of a programme of regular exercise has benefits not only for the fitness of the cardiovascular systems and the skeletal system, but also in the loss of weight and the maintenance of that weight loss.

Is exercise a good thing?

Too much or inappropriate exercise can be very bad for you – several people die each year because they attempt to run marathons without the required training beforehand. Sporting injuries devastate the lives of some individuals each year. But in spite of this the overwhelming body of evidence suggests that moderate exercise, carried out sensibly and with a gentle build-up to fitness, carries many benefits. In addition, exercise produces a feeling of physical well-being because chemicals known as endorphins are released in the brain.

In fact at many leisure/sports centres around the country GPs can now prescribe a 'fitness building' course for their patients. Under close supervision the patients swim and work out in the gym, often with the result of weight loss, improved cardiovascular fitness and reduced blood pressure.

Activity	Energy/kJ h^{-1} kg^{-1}
Lying in bed	4.3
Sitting down, reading	4.45
Standing	5.2
Bowling	12.6
Canoeing	25.2
Cycling for pleasure	18.3
Aerobics	33.6
Golf	21.4
Squash	50.0
Football	42.0
Brisk walking	24.4

Table 7.3.1 The approximate energy costs of a variety of activities

How much exercise is good for you?

It is generally agreed that exercise is good for us, and that few people take enough exercise. There is evidence to suggest that the amount of activity undertaken by a person depends on factors such as their age, economic status and gender. But what exactly is meant by exercise? If you never take exercise, walking to the shops might seem quite strenuous, but an active person might swim 3000 metres each morning before work or school. There is no universal agreement on how much exercise you need to do to benefit your health. However, studies indicate that a level of exercise which uses at least 31.5 kJ of energy per minute with an oxygen uptake of 1.5 litres per minute has a clear health benefit.

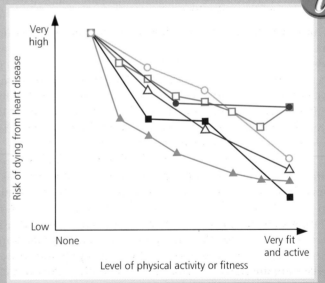

Figure 7.3.14 The graphs show the results of six different studies on the effect of exercise on the risk of dying of a heart attack.

In spite of evidence of this sort, very few people take regular vigorous exercise. However, an increasing body of research suggests that even quite gentle exercise such as walking two or three times a week can have positive health benefits.

Activity	Examples of 'vigorous exercise'
Keep fit	Aerobic exercises
Recreation	Swimming, tennis, dancing, sailing, climbing
Gardening	Digging, clearing scrub, planting bushes
DIY	Building in stone or brick, fencing
Getting around	Brisk walking, running, cycling
Climbing upstairs	500+ stairs daily
Other	Moving snow, heavy car repairs

Table 7.3.2 Some physical activities which use at least 31.5 kJ of energy per minute

The many causes of cancer

Cancer is one of the most common causes of death in the developed world. Cancer is a mass of abnormally growing cells (a **tumour**), which can appear in almost any part of the body. The cancer cells do not respond to the normal mechanisms which control cell growth, and they divide and invade the surrounding tissues. A tumour may split up, releasing small clumps of malignant cells into the blood or lymph systems where they circulate and then lodge in a different area of the body, continuing their uncontrolled division and forming a **secondary tumour**. Cancer is often fatal as it interferes with the functioning of vital organs, and modern medical treatments cannot guarantee a cure. Many of the factors that increase the likelihood of cancer developing are present in our individual environments as part of our lifestyle.

Some people have a genetic make-up programmed with particular genes called **oncogenes** or **protooncogenes** that make them more vulnerable than normal to cell changes, and they obviously have no control over this factor. As we age, our exposure to cancer-triggering stimuli becomes longer, and errors in DNA replication increase, raising the likelihood of a loss of control of cell growth. We cannot avoid ageing, but there are also behavioural factors that can increase our risk of developing certain cancers, including:

- smoking cigarettes
- drinking too much alcohol
- exposure to the ultra-violet light of the Sun
- not eating sufficient fibre and fruit
- promiscuous sex
- eating a diet of highly refined foods containing lots of additives.

These are all aspects of our lifestyle over which we have at least some control.

Screening – an early warning system

Screening means testing people who are apparently healthy to find any early symptoms of disease. We can check our own bodies for some diseases. Women should examine their breasts regularly for signs of a lump developing, which could turn out to be breast cancer. Men should check their testes regularly for any lumps or enlargements that might signal testicular cancer. Both of these cancers can be treated successfully if they are detected early enough. There are also national screening programmes for certain diseases. For example, in the UK all women are offered a regular cervical smear test to pick up precancerous changes in the cells of the cervix. It is then possible to treat the condition simply and cheaply before there is any major risk to health. Blood pressure measurements are taken at regular intervals in adults to screen for hypertension or for abnormally low blood pressure, and blood cholesterol levels are measured in anyone with a family history of heart problems. Considerable amounts of money are being spent on screening large sections of the population, with the assumption that this is cheaper long term than treating more advanced diseases and also paying sickness benefit and pensions to those who become severely ill or die, leaving dependants needing support. Only time will reveal how effective these screening programmes are.

A combination of knowledge, enabling informed choices about lifestyle which minimise the risk of disease, and screening, to pick up many serious diseases early on, may well lead to a society of healthier individuals.

Health is a very precious thing, often not appreciated until it is lost. Yet in countries across the developed world people make conscious lifestyle choices

Figure 7.3.15 Regular breast checks and mammography are offered to women with a family history of breast cancer and to all women from the age of 50 onwards.

which put their health at risk. Increasingly these same disease-causing commodities are spreading across the developing world. As a major cause of a wide range of lifestyle diseases, we will look in some detail at smoking.

Tobacco

Cigarettes contain tobacco leaves which burn to produce smoke, which is inhaled into the lungs. Here the drug **nicotine**, one component of that smoke, is absorbed into the bloodstream and then carried around the body to the brain, where it has its effect. Nicotine is a mild stimulant, although some of its effects are more like a sedative as it causes vasoconstriction (narrowing) of the peripheral blood vessels, as illustrated in figure 7.3.16. The overall effect of the drug is to produce a sensation of calm well-being and 'being able to cope'. The heart rate is slightly raised by the drug, but the peripheral blood flow is reduced, so less blood flows to the skin and areas such as the hands. This in turn leads to a slight increase in blood pressure.

Nicotine is a physically addictive drug, which means there is a physical craving for the drug as the blood nicotine level drops. Also, increasingly high levels of the drug are needed over the years to maintain the same effect, so the number of cigarettes smoked tends to increase over the years. On giving up smoking, nicotine withdrawal symptoms include a craving for the drug (for a cigarette), irritability, difficulty in concentrating, restlessness, hunger and feelings of sadness or depression. In addition, there is a level of psychological addiction to smoking. Smoking gives smokers something to do with their hands and their mouths and it gives comfort and reassurance through a regular ritual. To give up the habit, smokers have to battle with both physical and mental addiction, and it is often the latter which drives them back to smoking months after any physical addiction has been lost.

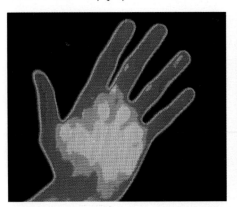 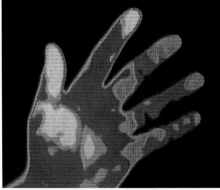

Figure 7.3.16 Pictures taken with a heat-sensitive camera show the effects of smoking on the temperature of the hands. The difference between the hand of the non-smoker (left) and the smoker (right) is the result of vasoconstriction caused by the drug nicotine. (Blue=cool, yellow=warm.)

Tobacco facts

- There are 1.1 billion smokers worldwide.
- In developed countries, on average, 41% of men and 21% of women smoke regularly.
- In developing countries, on average, 50% of men and 8% of women smoke regularly.
- The number of women who smoke is increasing in many countries, and so are the numbers of women with smoking-related diseases.
- Six thousand billion cigarettes are smoked each year.

- Three million deaths a year are a direct result of smoking, with 30% of these in the developing world. In other words, someone dies every 10 seconds as a direct result of smoking.
- If current smoking trends persist, in 30–40 years' time there will be 10 million smoking-related deaths each year, 70% of them in the developing world.
- Smoking currently causes just under 20% of all deaths in developed countries.

Nicotine's companions

Carbon monoxide

If cigarette smoke contained only nicotine, it would still be an addictive drug and would still, with its effects on the cardiovascular system, probably be a bad idea. But there are over 4000 different chemical compounds in the smoke from burning tobacco leaves, and whilst it is the drug nicotine that addicts people to smoking cigarettes, it is largely these other compounds that cause lasting and often fatal damage to the body cells. For example, **carbon monoxide** is one component of cigarette smoke. Carbon monoxide is a poisonous gas for which haemoglobin has a greater affinity than it has for oxygen, as shown in figure 7.3.17.

After smoking a cigarette, up to 10% of the haemoglobin in the blood of a smoker will be carrying carbon monoxide rather than oxygen. This reduction in the oxygenation of the blood can lead to a shortage of oxygen. The effect is most marked in pregnant women. The haemoglobin of a pregnant woman is carrying oxygen for her developing fetus as well as for her respiring tissues. Fetal haemoglobin has a high affinity for oxygen, and it picks up oxygen from the maternal haemoglobin in the placenta and carries it round the fetal circulation, supplying all the developing tissues. If the maternal blood does not contain sufficient oxygen as a result of smoking, the fetus suffers from long-term oxygen deprivation and this can lead to growth problems, reduced development of the brain, and ultimately to premature birth, low birth weight and even stillbirth (the baby is born dead) or death soon after birth.

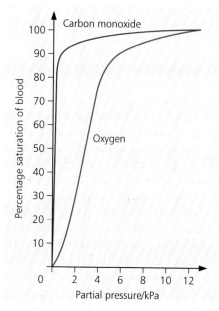

Figure 7.3.17 Carbon monoxide combines more readily with haemoglobin than oxygen does. The gas prevents the haemoglobin from transporting oxygen to the tissues.

Smoking and the cardiovascular system

Smoking increases the risk of cardiovascular disease. The effect is particularly noticable in younger people, but is present throughout all the age ranges. It is estimated that 24% of deaths due to coronary heart disease in men and 11% in women are due to cigarette smoking.

Number of cigarettes smoked per day	Annual death rate from CHD per 100 000	Relative risk
0	572	
1–14	802	1.4
15–24	892	1.6
25+	1025	1.8

Table 7.3.3 The increased risk of coronary heart disease (CHD) caused by smoking

Incidence of atherosclerosis, coronary heart disease and strokes are all raised in smokers. Strokes involve an interference with the blood supply to the brain, particularly the cerebral hemispheres. This may be due to atherosclerosis in the blood vessels leading to the brain, to clot formation or to the walls of a blood vessel thinning and bursting – an aneurism. We still do not understand fully the reasons why smoking increases the incidence of strokes, as there are so many different chemical compounds in tobacco smoke which could be causing the damage.

Two compounds which we know play a part in the raised risk of cardiovascular disease due to smoking are nicotine and carbon monoxide. Nicotine causes peripheral vasoconstriction and raises the heart rate, which results in raised blood pressure, a known risk factor

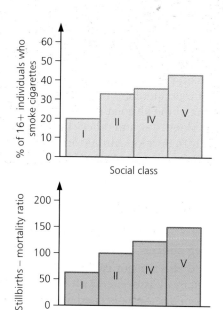

Figure 7.3.18 These graphs suggest a close relationship between incidence of smoking and incidence of stillbirths. Further research has confirmed this link.

for cardiovascular disease. Carbon monoxide binds to some of the haemoglobin, so the blood carries less oxygen. As a result the heart needs to beat faster to maintain an adequate oxygen supply. This again puts stress on the cardiovascular system. The raised blood presssure and increased heartbeat which result from the nicotine and carbon monoxide in cigarette smoke mean that the endothelial linings of the arteries are more likely to be damaged. This makes the vessels more vulnerable to the development of atherosclerosis, and also to the formation of a thrombosis. If these events happen in the coronary vessels supplying the heart, then coronary heart disease will result. If they happen in the vessels supplying the brain, then a stroke is the most likely outcome. Thus nicotine and carbon monoxide – and probably other compounds as well – give smokers a raised risk of cardiovascular disease. All patients who have heart disease or a stroke which they survive are strongly advised to stop smoking. If they stopped earlier, or never started, then the problems might never have arisen.

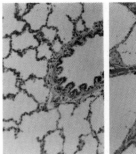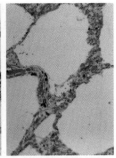

Figure 7.3.19 Chronic bronchitis and emphysema are well known risks of smoking, caused by the build-up of tar and other damaging chemicals from cigarette smoke. This photograph shows normal lung tissue on the left, and emphysemic alveoli on the right – the spaces are much larger.

Tar

Another component of cigarette smoke is **tar**. This is a sticky black substance which is not absorbed into the bloodstream. It simply accumulates in the lungs, discolouring the tissue. The lungs of a young child are bright pink. In most adults in the developed world, that pinkness becomes a little diminished as a result of air pollution – including other people's tobacco smoke. The lungs of a serious smoker are not pink but grey. This is partly due to the effect of tar on the ciliated epithelial cells lining the respiratory system. In a non-smoker, these cilia are constantly active, moving mucus (along with trapped dirt, dust and bacteria from the inhaled air) up the respiratory tract away from the lungs. This mucus is swept either into the throat to be swallowed and digested, or to the nose to be blown out. In a smoker, these cilia are anaesthetised by each cigarette and stop working for a time, allowing dirt down into the lungs. In a heavy smoker the cilia are permanently out of action during the day when smoking is taking place.

Tar accumulates in the lungs and interferes with gas exchange, covering some of the alveolar surface and preventing gases from diffusing through to the blood. Tar and other chemicals from cigarette smoke make smokers more likely to develop chronic bronchitis, described on pages 656–657. Impaired cilial function prevents the extra mucus produced being cleared, so it accumulates and causes coughing. The accumulation of tar and other compounds in the delicate lung tissue, particularly when associated with chronic bronchitis, can lead to a breakdown in alveolar structure, resulting in the large air spaces and inefficient lung functioning of emphysema.

Lung cancer

Tar is also a major **carcinogen** (cancer-causing substance), one of 60 such substances associated with tobacco smoke. **Lung cancer**, perhaps the best known disease associated with smoking cigarettes, results partly from this accumulation of tar. The carcinogenic chemicals found in tobacco smoke also lead to an increased risk of cancers of the tongue and oesophagus in smokers.

Lung cancer is particularly dangerous because it has plenty of space in the lungs to grow unnoticed without causing any symptoms. It is a treatable disease if it is caught early, but in many cases smokers ignore coughs and

Figure 7.3.20 This health education poster from a few years ago provides a graphic illustration of the carcinogenic tar which accumulates in the lungs of every smoker.

breathlessness, or deny the condition to themselves, until the cancer has spread to other parts of the body.

There are several different types of lung cancer. One type occurs regardless of whether or not an individual smokes, but the great majority of lung cancers are found only in the lungs of smokers. Of course not everyone who smokes will develop lung cancer, and a few non-smokers will suffer from the disease, but the epidemiological evidence for the link is extremely strong – up to 90% of all lung cancers are thought to be due to smoking. The link was first noticed by Sir Richard Doll early in the twentieth century, but it has taken many years for the smoking public to accept the link, and even longer for the cigarette manufacturers. Indeed, in spite of carrying out extensive research themselves, many manufacturers have publicly denied both the addictive nature of nicotine and the health risks associated with cigarette smoke for years. In the late

Figure 7.3.21 Epidemiologists use data such as these to identify causal effects for diseases. (a) shows how many of the people dying of lung cancer are smokers – 81% compared with 19% of non-smokers. (b) shows the effect of the number of cigarettes smoked on the risk of dying from lung cancer. As the risk increases when more cigarettes are smoked, this suggests that something in the cigarettes is responsible for the cancers. (c) and (d) show the death rates of different age groups of men from lung cancer and the percentage of the male population who smoke. Analysis of data such as these leads to research intended to confirm or disprove apparent links. (e) summarises the result of work done on cigarette smoke in response to the findings of epidemiologists.

(a) Deaths from lung cancer and smoking

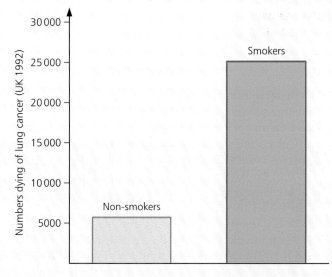

(b) Cigarette consumption and risk of lung cancer death

Number of cigarettes smoked per day	Annual death rate per 100 000	Relative risk
0	14	–
1–14	105	8
15–24	208	15
25+	355	25

(d) Percentage of men smoking (manual + non-manual workers) in Great Britain 1974–94

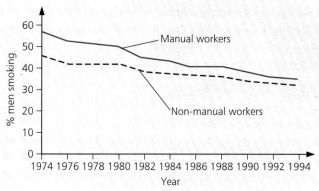

(c) Death rates from lung cancer in men by age group: England and Wales 1974–92

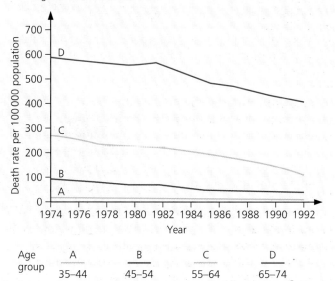

Age group	A	B	C	D
	35–44	45–54	55–64	65–74

(e)

Scientists say they have found the component of cigarette smoke that causes lung cancer. 'We have found a specific component of cigarette smoke, benzo pyrene, to be strongly implicated in lung cancer development,' said Gerd Pfeifer, a researcher at City of Hope Medical Center near Los Angeles. When the benzo pyrene compound was added to a culture of human lungs, a gene called p53 that normally suppresses tumours was damaged. The cells began to divide abnormally. The scientists found the DNA in the cells was damaged at the same specific sites where mutations are found in lung cancer cells.

twentieth century a number of court cases took place. The aim was to force cigarette companies to accept responsibility for the terminal illnesses of smokers who took up smoking at a time when it is claimed the cigarette companies had evidence of both the health and addiction risks of smoking, and yet continued to advertise their products as 'cool' and 'healthy', with no mention of risks.

Passive smoking

In recent years it has been shown that smoking is not simply a personal health risk chosen by an individual. When anyone smokes a cigarette, the majority of the smoke goes not into their lungs, but into the air around them for others to breathe in. This is called **passive smoking**. In the last ten years evidence has accumulated that passive smoking can cause 'smoker's diseases' such as lung cancer in non-smokers. The evidence has led to no-smoking policies in some offices, shops, restaurants and bars. The majority of the population are non-smokers who feel increasingly aggrieved at having to put up with unpleasant-smelling and potentially damaging smoke from other people. However, bans on smoking in public places have raised some interesting issues of human rights and the arguments look set to continue for some time.

Smoking and children

Figure 7.3.22 Much of the evidence for the dangers of passive smoking have come from studies on young children.

In recent years there has been increasing evidence that babies and young children who are exposed to passive smoking have an increased risk of health problems.

As discussed on page 671, maternal smoking can lead to a fetus failing to develop properly, and to the birth of premature, low birth-mass or dead babies. After birth, babies and small children are at risk from **environmental tobacco smoke** (ETS).

Sudden infant death syndrome (SIDS or cot death) is a tragic occurrence when an apparently healthy baby dies in its sleep for no obvious reason. For example, in the UK, although the numbers of cot deaths have been falling steadily, as many as two babies each day die in this way. One contributory factor is the position in which the baby is put to sleep, particularly in very small babies who cannot move themselves about.

Overheating may be involved, and there are sometimes undiagnosed infections. But one of the major factors in cot deaths appears to be if the parents, particularly the mother, smoke. A baby whose mother smokes is twice as likely to die from a cot death as a baby with non-smoking parents. It is estimated that if parents with small babies did not smoke, the life of at least one of the babies that die each day from SIDS would be saved. It is interesting that a UK campaign to change the recommended sleeping position of small infants from their fronts to their backs was very successful, halving the death rate from cot deaths. However, that behaviour cost very little effort from parents. Advice about giving up smoking, which would similarly save the lives of many babies but which involves a far greater sacrifice by the parents, is largely ignored.

The children of smokers are more likely to suffer from respiratory infections such as pneumonia and bronchitis. American data suggest that parental smoking – again mainly that of the mother, who is frequently with the child more often than the father – contributes to 150 000–300 000 cases of lower respiratory tract infections in children under eighteen months old. Up to 15 000 of these cases are serious enough to need hospitalisation. In addition, environmental tobacco smoke increases both the numbers of children suffering from asthma, and the severity and number of attacks they have. Perhaps the most damaging effect of all is that the children of parents who smoke are substantially more likely to smoke themselves than the children of non-smokers.

The economics of cigarette smoking

With all the present evidence of the damage smoking causes to health, it is perhaps surprising that cigarettes are still widely available. The cost to health services in caring for people who suffer and die from smoking-related diseases is immense. Even larger is the personal suffering of people who lose their quality of life and indeed, in many cases, lose their lives, and the suffering of their families. So why are cigarettes still manufactured, advertised and sold?

Tobacco products are very cheap to make, so the companies that manufacture them make very large profits and are extremely powerful as a result. Because tobacco products are addictive, customers are almost guaranteed. However, these highly profitable tobacco companies have persuaded governments to subsidise tobacco growing. Members of the European Union put more money into promoting tobacco production *each day* (US$3.8 million) than the European Commission spends on tobacco control in a year. Tobacco is the most subsidised crop in the European Union. If the Union simply paid all tobacco farmers an amount equal to their net income, on condition that they do not grow any more tobacco, subsidy expenditures would be reduced by 44%.

Policies like these are in direct opposition to the policies of governments to control cigarette smoking. However, cigarettes also bring in a large tax revenue both at the point of sale and from the manufacturers. The economic issues linked to cigarette smoking are massive, complex and often incomprehensible.

Why smoke?

All the scientific and medical evidence shows that cigarette smoking is bad for health. Yet people still smoke in their millions, and young people in particular continue to take up the habit. Why?

The reason why smokers continue to smoke is quite simple. Nicotine is a strongly addictive drug with unpleasant withdrawal symptoms. Many of the people currently ill and dying of smoking-related diseases started smoking and became addicted before the health risks were widely known. But when people start smoking today, particularly in the developed world, they have plenty of information available to them. So why do young people start smoking? Research indicates that most young people start smoking for one of the following reasons:

- it is the social norm within their family or peer group
- advertising
- curiosity to 'see what it is like'
- peer group pressure.

Once the smoking habit is established, the reasons largely change and young people report that smoking gives them pleasure, helps them cope and that they smoke because they can't give up. Once addicted, it is not easy to stop smoking. In one study of a group of American 16–18-year-old smokers, 44% believed that in five years' time they would no longer be smokers. Five years later the researchers did a follow-up study, and almost 75% of the young people who had been sure that they were not long-term smokers were still smoking, and smoking more. In 1992 almost two-thirds of American adolescent smokers reported that they wanted to stop smoking, and 70% said that they would not start smoking if they could choose again.

Most smokers begin their habit as adolescents, so if young people can be persuaded to leave tobacco alone, the habit might die. However, converting the knowledge available to people about the health risks of smoking into sensible lifestyle choices is not an easy task.

Needing a cigarette

In the 1990s Hilary Graham carried out some research into the smoking habits of women of different social groups. She obtained clear evidence showing that in some circumstances people need to smoke not just because of physical addiction but also because smoking helps them to cope with their difficult and chaotic lives. When they sit down to have a cigarette they mark out a few minutes of time for themselves, when they cannot be disturbed by the demands of others. Mothers in the most difficult circumstances, such as women on very low incomes who are single mothers or who have a large number of young dependant children, or a child with specific learning or behavioural difficulties, were most likely to smoke – over 60% of these mothers smoke, compared with 28% of the general female population.

Many women were smoking in spite of awareness of the long-term damage to health. In these circumstances it is not health education but social change that is needed to reduce smoking.

Figure 7.3.23 The tobbaco companies have worked hard to associate smoking with the glamour and excitment of motorsport. In the late1990s there was a move by the British Government to end the sponsership of sporting events by tobacco companies, and this led to much controversy. However, as the cigarette packet shows, no one who can read can claim that they are unaware of the health risks associated with smoking and nicotine addiction.

Alcohol

The effects of alcohol

Ethanol, C_2H_5OH, or 'alcohol' is a commonly used social drug in many parts of the world. It is poisonous, but the human body can detoxify relatively large amounts of it before permanent damage or death results. Alcohol is primarily a depressant drug with a weaker but longer-lasting agitating or irritant effect on the central nervous system. Alcohol is physically addictive.

Following an alcoholic drink, the alcohol is absorbed into the bloodstream from all parts of the gastrointestinal tract, with most absorption taking place in the stomach and small intestine. The peak **blood alcohol level** (BAL) occurs 60–90 minutes after taking in alcohol on an empty stomach. The presence of food in the stomach slows the absorption of alcohol into the blood, although it does not reduce the total amount of alcohol that is absorbed. The standard way of describing the amount of alcohol in the blood is as **grams of alcohol per 100 cm³ of blood**, **g 100 cm⁻³** or **g %**. Once the alcohol is in the blood, it passes into nearly every tissue of the body, because cell membranes are permeable to alcohol and there is always a concentration gradient from blood to cells. Because alcohol passes easily into the brain, brain alcohol levels are very similar to blood alcohol levels.

The intoxicating effects of alcohol are caused by its direct action on the brain and nervous system. The sedative effect of the drug causes slowed thought processes and reflexes, and releases certain areas of the cortex of the brain from inhibition. With high doses of the drug, these sedative effects can lead to coma and death. However, the irritant effect of alcohol lasts up to six times longer than the sedative effect. This is partly why people feel jumpy, irritable and unsettled after a hard night's drinking. The 'hair of the dog' – in other words another drink – can help ease these symptoms because the new intake of alcohol has a more immediate and powerful sedative effect to override the irritant effect left over from the previous day. It is easy to see how this becomes a vicious circle, leading to repeated alcohol intake with virtually no return to the fully sober state.

Research suggests that alcohol affects the cell membranes of nerve cells and their axons and dendrites. Thus it affects the functioning of both the central and peripheral nervous systems, reducing their ability to transmit nerve impulses, which in turn leads to the typical behaviour following drinking.

If too much alcohol is absorbed by the body, the drinker may die of alcohol overdose. On average, 50% of drinkers whose blood alcohol level rises over 0.40 g % will die of acute alcohol poisoning. The drinker passes through phases of staggering and slurred speech, loss of emotional control, stupor, severe respiratory depression, coma and death. The later stages often occur after the drinker has passed out, and he or she will be found dead in bed in the morning. Excess drink can also cause death by triggering the vomiting centres. Vomiting may occur whilst the drinker is in a stupor or a coma, and unless someone sits with them to keep their airways free, they have a high risk of choking or drowning in their own vomit.

Long-term alcohol abuse – alcoholism

Whilst many people drink merely socially, and would suffer no ill effects if they never drank again, many others are addicted to the drug. Some alcoholics need a constant level of alcohol in their system to keep them functioning 'normally' so they may drink first thing in the morning to restore their alcohol levels and continue to drink at intervals throughout the day. This type of alcoholic will be able to maintain a semblance of normal life for some time, in spite of a constant level of intoxication. The drinking is often kept a secret from friends, family and colleagues until their behaviour and health become increasingly affected and so much alcohol is taken that it becomes difficult to hide the evidence. These people are often in complete denial that they have a problem. In another type of alcoholism, the alcoholic does not drink constantly, but has compulsive binges, taking in large amounts of alcohol over a period of several days. This may be followed by a period of remorse about their behaviour and resolutions not to repeat the pattern, until the next craving hits and the drinking starts again. In both patterns of alcoholism the alcoholic risks severe damage to many body systems, but particularly the brain and the liver.

Alcohol has an immediate effect on the functioning of the brain, as already described. In addition, continued excessive alcohol use over a period of years causes long-term damage to the brain. The evidence for this is clear from the post-mortem examinations of the brains of alcoholics compared with those of non-alcoholics. The brains of alcoholics contain fewer nerve cells, fewer synapses (connections between cells), less white and grey matter and larger ventricles. This damage correlates closely with loss of intellectual functions. The damage in some alcoholics is so extensive, with soft, pulpy and deteriorated brains, that almost all the normal brain structures have been lost. The cause of the brain damage seems to be the toxic action of the alcohol on the nerve cells, along with an indirect effect brought about by liver damage.

People who drink very large amounts of alcohol, or who drink heavily for a long time, substantially increase their risk of potentially fatal liver diseases such as **cirrhosis** of the liver and cancer of the liver. The liver tissue is damaged by excess alcohol. In cirrhosis of the liver, hepatocytes (liver cells) are killed and replaced with fibrous scar tissue which cannot carry out the normal metabolic functions of the liver. The damaged liver cannot detoxify many of the poisons taken in as a normal part of the diet, and so toxic compounds such as ammonia are released into the bloodstream. These compounds then cause damage to the nerve cells of the brain and the peripheral nervous system. A cirrhotic liver is smaller than normal with hardened, bumpy areas of scarring and dead tissue. The liver tissue is irreversibly damaged and when liver function drops below a critical level, the patient with cirrhosis of the liver will die. Sadly death is often brought about by continued drinking of alcohol, as the addiction to alcohol is stronger than the fear of death from a diseased liver.

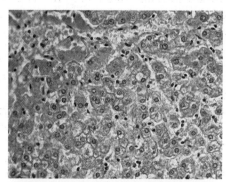
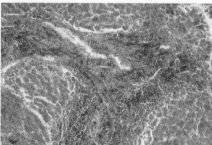

Figure 7.3.24 The damage alcohol causes to the liver can be seen very clearly here in the contrast between a healthy liver (top) and one taken from an individual who died of alcoholism.

Cancers of the mouth and throat are more common than usual in heavy drinkers. The brain and peripheral nervous system are also extremely sensitive to the levels of minerals and vitamins such as magnesium, potassium, phosphorus and thiamine. Alcoholics often do not eat properly as the energy-rich alcoholic drinks suppress their appetite. In addition, alcohol affects the digestive tract, causing inflammation and irritation of the stomach and small intestine. This reduces the ability of the small intestine to absorb minerals and vitamins, and when these nutrient levels fall the nervous tissue slowly deteriorates. Symptoms of peripheral nervous tissue damage include numbness in parts of the fingers, toes and buttocks.

Many alcoholics show few symptoms in the early stages of their addiction. Then gradually there will be conflict and even violence at home, they have difficulty in concentrating and holding down a job and they may stockpile drinks. Alcoholics may suffer blackouts after binge drinking, leaving them with periods of time of which they have no memory, yet during which time they were awake and taking part in society in some way. It is very difficult for a physically dependent alcoholic to give up drinking. The physical symptoms of withdrawal are traumatic and, for severe alcoholics, may even be life threatening if not carefully supervised by medical staff. After withdrawal from the drug an alcoholic will remain an alcoholic for life, just one drink away from a return to the cycle of abuse. Alcoholics who are not abusing the drug need counselling and support to remain alcohol-free and get on with the rest of their lives.

Alcohol withdrawal symptoms

When a physically dependent alcoholic stops drinking, the withdrawal symptoms range from mild to life threatening. Withdrawal symptoms from alcohol addiction are often far more severe and dangerous than those experienced on withdrawal from many other drugs. Symptoms begin within the first 24 alcohol-free hours, reach a peak of intensity after two or three days and disappear within one or two weeks. As alcohol levels begin to drop the symptoms include:

- shakiness
- restlessness and unease
- nausea
- anxiety
- increased heart rate (tachycardia)
- raised blood pressure.

At this point the craving for alcohol will become strong. Within 24 hours of stopping drinking, the second stage of withdrawal symptoms begin:

- hyperventilation (rapid breathing)
- drop in blood pressure
- fever
- delirium, involving disorientation, delusions (irrational beliefs) and hallucinations which are usually visual but may involve the senses of hearing or smell; these hallucinations are usually unpleasant and often frightening
- convulsions and seizures.

Without treatment the delirium, fever and convulsions may continue for several days, getting increasingly severe and causing disturbances of the cardiovascular system. This is the condition often referred to as 'DTs' (delirium tremens). Without medical intervention, a patient with DTs can harm other people or themselves, or die from a heart attack or stroke. The withdrawal symptoms can be controlled with other drugs under medical supervision until the risk of developing DTs has passed.

This chapter has shown that lifestyle – how we eat and drink, exercise, share our lives – has a major effect on our health, in both the long and short term. The facts cannot be denied. But however we live our lives, eventually we will begin to suffer the effects of ageing. There are a variety of conditions which are particularly associated with the ageing of the body.

Ageing and death

Humans have a longer average life span than almost any other mammal, but in common with all other mammals, after a period of maturity we show signs of ageing and eventually die. It is possible to monitor the decline in function of the body by such measures as reduction in running speed, smaller lung capacity and weaker grip, and it is also possible to describe the cellular changes that can be observed as the body ages. What has not been possible so far is to identify a mechanism for ageing. Research into this is driven partly by scientific interest and partly by the search for advances in the treatment of diseases associated with ageing. However, there is also a desire on the part of many people to understand what causes ageing in the hope that it might be possible to stop the clock, or at least delay it!

Theories of ageing

Each individual begins life as a single cell, then enters the world as a tiny newborn baby, after which our physical appearance changes rapidly as we grow and mature. After young adulthood, appearance changes less rapidly, but the changes that do occur are increasingly associated with ageing. Different cultures look on ageing differently. In some cultures age is venerated and thus the signs of ageing are welcomed because they bring added status. Unfortunately, in much of the developed world, the culture values youth and youthful looks, and so changing distribution of body hair (baldness), change in hair colour (going grey) and the appearance of facial wrinkles are often dreaded. It is interesting that within one society the same symptoms can send different messages simply depending on the sex of the individual concerned. In the UK certain signs of maturity such as greying hair and a few wrinkles are regarded as positive and distinguished in men, giving them a level of respect among their peers and in the work place. The same early symptoms of ageing in a woman are often regarded as negative, showing that she is losing her sexual and reproductive appeal.

Ageing does not start at one particular time or continue at a constant rate once it has started. Cellular and tissue changes accumulate over time and become increasingly evident with age. But the rate at which these changes occur varies greatly from individual to individual, depending on genetics, lifestyle and the environment in which an individual has lived. Ageing can be defined as *a progressive, generalised impairment of function resulting from a loss of adaptive responses to stress and resulting in a growing risk of age-related disease*. As we go through life more and more genetic errors are made as cells replicate, there are degenerative changes in cells and the immune system becomes less effective so diseases have a greater effect.

Why do we age? Some people have put forward theories that there is an adaptive advantage to ageing and indeed to death, on the basis that if individuals did not age and die the population would get too large and there would be insufficient resources for the younger, reproductive members of the species. The problem with this argument is that natural selection acts on the individual, not the population. Looking at other animals as well as humans, it would seem to be of little individual advantage to suffer from the disabilities of old age, and even less of an advantage to be dead! It may be that ageing is

Figure 7.3.25 Whilst we may not understand the mechanism for ageing, we can certainly recognise the signs as it takes place.

genetically programmed, but because the damaging 'age' genes do not become apparent until after reproduction has taken place, there is no effective way of removing them from the population. Another idea suggests that some genes may have multiple effects, with favourable effects dominating during early life and the reproductive years which leads to them being passed on, but with harmful ageing effects which only become apparent later in life. Another idea about ageing is that it is inevitable, rather along the same lines that a car or washing machine has built-in obsolescence. In the **disposable soma theory**, resources are not wasted in producing a body capable of eternal life when it is likely to die in some sort of accident anyway. Sufficient resources are used to produce a body which will reproduce and take care of the offspring to adulthood but which is then disposable. All other resources are put into reproductive effort, using a lower level of resources for the body than would be needed for eternal youth.

Observing ageing

Cells and ageing

There are certain changes in cells that seem typical of ageing. Ageing cells can be observed in tissue culture, where they are isolated from all the normal biochemical changes in the body which may affect their behaviour. Alternatively, cells from individuals at different stages of their lives may be compared, though it is difficult to tell which differences are due to lifestyle changes (e.g. taking less exercise) and which are genuinely due to ageing. However, combined evidence from both types of study suggests there are certain changes common to all ageing cells.

The turnover of proteins in normal cells and body fluids provides a good marker of ageing. Proteins are broken down into their constituent amino acids ready for recycling. When this process occurs inefficiently, granules of a yellow fatty substance called **lipofuscin** begin to accumulate in the cells. Protein recycling becomes increasingly inefficient as cells age and so the level of lipofuscin granules offers a measure of cell age. Lipofuscin has the effect of slowing cell metabolism, so as it builds up the cell metabolism becomes slower and less efficient in a vicious circle of ageing.

The number of **lysosomes** (vesicles full of digestive enzymes) in a cell also increases as it ages. Some aged cells die before the organism dies, and in some tissues these cells are not all replaced, leading to a net degeneration of the tissue and to organs working less effectively in older people. New theories suggest that cells are genetically programmed to die unless they are continuously stimulated by chemical signals from other cells. It may well be a failure of these communication systems which leads to cell death as the lysosomes burst.

Most of our organ systems operate with a large amount of overcapacity when we are young. For example, we can manage with only half a kidney functioning instead of the normal two. Much of this **reserve capacity** is lost as we get older. We can continue to operate quite normally for a long time, but are less well equipped to cope with sudden physiological stresses placed on our bodies. This is why diseases or injuries can have more serious consequences in older people. As can be seen in figure 7.3.27, some organs lose a lot of cells and become significantly less efficient as we get older, while other tissues are affected very little. These average figures will vary greatly from individual to individual as well, depending on both genetic and environmental factors.

Another cellular effect of ageing seems to be a reduction in the effectiveness of the immune system when faced with an unknown pathogen. As people get older they usually maintain their immunity to pathogens which they have met during their lifetime. Problems arise when they meet new pathogens for the

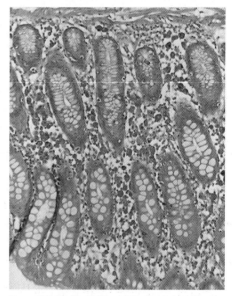

Figure 7.3.26 The build-up of lipofuscin in cells (shown as brown granules in this picture) seems closely associated with ageing and loss of function.

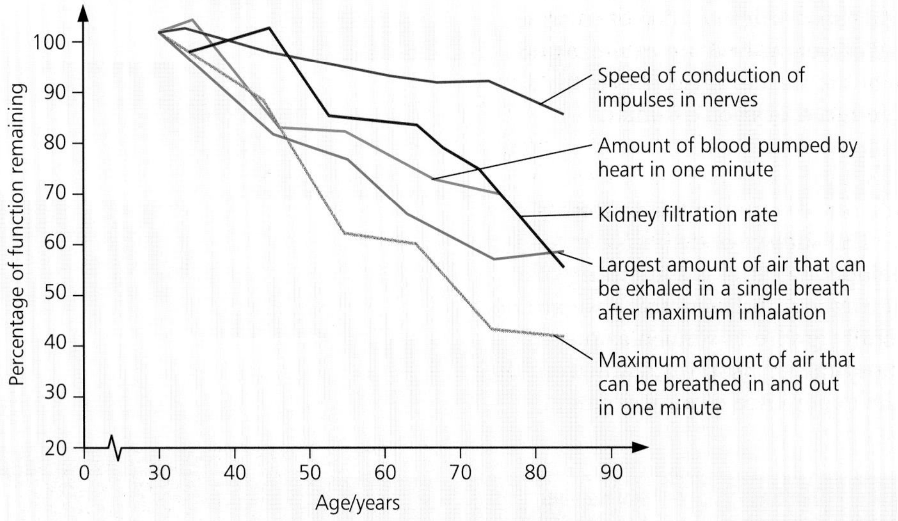

Figure 7.3.27 The decline of a range of body functions with age.

first time. This failure of the immune system is particularly marked with respect to infections of the respiratory system. This vulnerability may be due in part to the effect of a lifetime of breathing in pollutants, particularly tobacco smoke, or it may be partly due to the shallow breathing which is common in older people. As a result of this, parts of the lungs are not inflated properly, providing bacteria with a suitable habitat in which to multiply.

Signs of ageing

A number of changes typically occur during the ageing process in human beings.

- Skin becomes less elastic and wrinkles, hair loses colour and becomes grey and (in males particulary) may fall out.
- The lean body mass reduces – in other words muscle and bone are lost – and there is also a steady reduction in the water content of the body. These changes are the result of a decline in function of a variety of organs.
- After the menopause, women are unable to conceive a baby naturally.
- Problems of the muscles and skeletal system become more common. For example, joints tend to move less freely, bones break more easily and muscles are often weaker.
- The senses tend to deteriorate, leading to poorer sight and hearing. Less obviously, the senses of balance, taste and smell may also be reduced.
- There is increased susceptibility to infectious diseases which seems likely to be the result of the reduced efficiency of the immune system.
- Homeostasis becomes less reliable. For example, the mechanism to maintain a constant body temperature when the surroundings are cold becomes less efficient.
- There is often mental deterioration, with older people finding it difficult to remember recent events.
- Arthritis, cancer and diseases of the cardiovascular system (like heart attacks and strokes) become much more common with age.

The majority of these changes are inevitable, but at what age and to what degree they occur are variable, and in some cases can be delayed with the right lifestyle choices. For example, an increase in the protein collagen in the skin cells, causing some loss of elasticity and wrinkling, is unavoidable with old age, but if we choose to smoke these changes will be speeded up. The blood supply to the skin is reduced with each cigarette and this accelerates the process of ageing. Similarly, if we maintain a high level of weight-bearing exercise and a diet rich in calcium and vitamin D, many of the skeletomuscular changes associated with ageing will be substantially reduced or even avoided.

Dying and death

At the end of the ageing process, if we are fortunate enough to live long enough to experience ageing, comes death. The subject of death is treated very differently in different societies. In the developed world it is something of a taboo subject. Death in the young is a great tragedy, and something we are no longer used to. Death in the elderly is generally ignored as much as possible and in the majority of cases takes place in hospitals or hospices, away from the home environment and so removed from the experience of most younger people (see table 7.3.4).

Year	Deaths in hospital/%	Deaths in hospice, nursing home, etc./%	Deaths in own home/%	Deaths in someone else's home/%	Total number of deaths (100%)
1960	50.0	3.0	42.0	5.0	526 268
1991	65.7	7.6	22.5	4.2	573 096

Table 7.3.4 Places of death in 1960 and 1991, UK

In many other areas of the world, death is frequently seen at first hand. A combination of lack of medical treatment, poverty and malnutrition along with few health and safety regulations in workplaces mean that death is common. There are still many countries where parents can expect at least half the children they bear to die in the early years of life. Women still die in large numbers during childbirth, and many children lose at least one of their parents during their childhood. Old age means living into the 50s rather than the 70s, 80s and even 90s we can expect in the developed world. This means that people are much more familiar with death, and that the care of the dying is much more a part of everyday life. The losses of death are felt just as keenly, but effective strategies for coping with grief have to be in place to make it possible to carry on with life in a meaningful way.

What is death?

The moment of death is when the cellular processes of the living body cease to take place. This is most easily seen when breathing stops and the heart stops beating. Once the blood stops circulating, it is only a matter of about 2–3 minutes before the cells of the brain stop functioning due to lack of oxygen and glucose. In these circumstances, once the brain is dead, so is the entire individual.

However, it is possible for the brain to be effectively dead while the heart carries on beating and respiration continues. In this case the individual cannot respond to the environment, but is in some way alive, although artificial feeding is needed to maintain life. There have been a number of legal cases where, after a patient has been fed artificially in a brain dead state for years, the family have applied to have feeding stopped so that the patient may die in all senses. There is a great deal of discussion about the ethics of this type of decision and the circumstances in which it should be made. In some cases, the functions of the heart and lungs are maintained artificially until the damage to the brain can be assessed. If the patient is shown by repeated tests to be brain dead then the artificial ventilation will be turned off.

For many old people death creeps up very gently as their body systems become increasingly less able to cope with the demands of everyday life. However, many others both old and young have to face up to the knowledge of their own impending death from a terminal illness. This is very difficult for people to come to terms with. The process of acceptance generally has five phases. The first response is denial – 'It can't be me'. This is usually followed by anger at the situation and those involved – 'Why me?' is the most frequently expressed emotion. Many people then go through a stage of bargaining with fate, trying to gain a bit more life, followed by depression as the symptoms of illness increase and physical deterioration becomes more obvious. People often feel very afraid of death and the process of dying at this point. Finally comes an acceptance of the inevitable as the end approaches. Although most death certificates show a specific cause of death, which may be cancer, stroke, heart failure, etc., many people really die of old age after a lengthy and gradual process of physical decline. Death in hospital may be a peaceful event, with the dying person surrounded by the family that they love. But sadly there are many people for whom death in an institution is a very lonely affair, with no one except professional care-givers around. These people may well die alone.

Attitudes to ageing

In addition to the fact that most people want to live as long and healthy a life as possible, our increasing knowledge of the processes of ageing, and our increasing ability to prolong the lives of many people by successful medical intervention, raise many questions for us as a society. As people get older, in general their need for support within the community increases. The life expectation in the population of the UK is increasing, and is predicted to continue increasing well into the next century, as figure 7.3.28 shows.

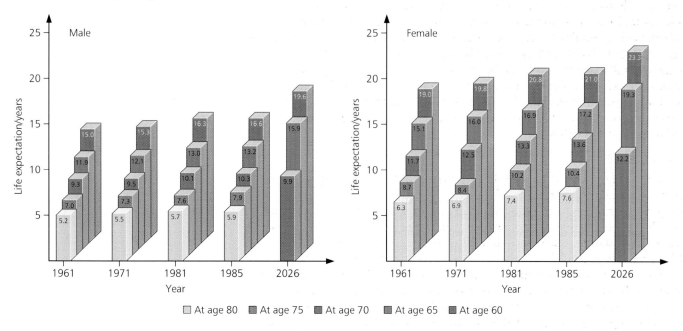

Figure 7.3.28 Predicted patterns of life expectation at different ages in the UK.

Changes in family and social structures in the late twentieth century, such as children living and working in different parts of the country from their parents and increasing numbers of marriages ending in divorce, make it more and more unlikely that ageing individuals will be cared for by their own families. The burden of care for the elderly falls onto society as a whole. At its most intensive (and expensive), support for the elderly involves residential nursing

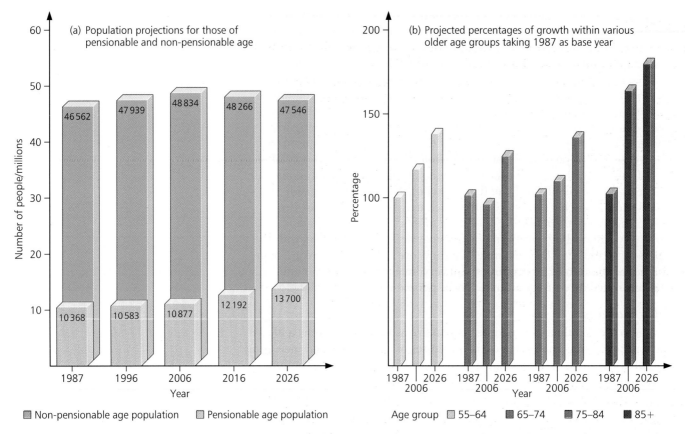

(a) Population projections for those of pensionable and non-pensionable age

Number of people/millions

46 562
47 939
48 834
48 266
47 546

10 368
10 583
10 877
12 192
13 700

1987   1996   2006   2016   2026
Year

■ Non-pensionable age population   □ Pensionable age population

(b) Projected percentages of growth within various older age groups taking 1987 as base year

Percentage

1987 | 2006   1987 | 2006   1987 | 2006   1987 | 2006
2006   2006   2006   2006
Year

Age group   ■ 55–64   ■ 65–74   ■ 75–84   ■ 85+

Figure 7.3.29 Demographic predictions of population trends in the UK. The pensionable age groups will form a larger percentage of the population as a whole, and the numbers in each older age group will rise substantially, particularly those over 85.

care. Other elderly people need residential care once they can no longer manage to cook, shop, wash and clean – in other words, take care of themselves and their homes. Yet others need the support of carers within their own homes. All this support for the elderly population costs a considerable amount of money. As figure 7.3.29 shows, in the UK, demographic trends suggest that the elderly population is set to increase substantially over the next 30 years, whilst the birth rate is falling. A growing ageing population will demand more support from a shrinking young working population.

These data also show that the group predicted to show the greatest percentage increase is the 80+ age group, and they are most likely to need help and support from the community. Thus the main issue for society raised by these trends, which result from years of improved nutrition and health care, is who pays? As society in the developed world moves further and further away from the model in the developing world, where care of elderly relatives falls directly to the younger generation, and parents expect to live with their children when they get old, the problem of how to finance the care of an ageing population is not going to go away.

The whole of the human life span involves a battle between health and disease. As ageing gradually takes place, the odds are stacked higher in favour of disease. And finally, in every human lifetime comes the point of death, when all life processes cease, and the struggle to maintain homeostasis against all the odds finally ends.

SUMMARY

- Many non-infectious diseases are a result of the lifestyle people are either forced or choose to lead – for example, the diet they eat.

- Diseases caused directly by the food eaten include **lactose intolerance** (inability to digest the natural sugar in milk), **food allergies** and **food-borne infections** such as listeriosis.

- Eating insufficient fibre leads to a long throughput time (the time the food stays in the gut). This can cause **constipation** (hard compacted faeces), **haemorrhoids** (swollen veins in the wall of the anus and rectum), **diverticulitis** (pockets forming in the colon), **irritable bowel syndrome** (pain in the lower abdomen) and **cancer of the colon**.

- Eating too much saturated fat in the diet is linked with heart disease, caused by a build-up of cholesterol deposits in the arteries. Some oils, such as olive oil and oily fish, appear to give protection against heart disease.

- Diseases of the respiratory system resulting from lifestyle include **asthma**, which can be triggered by an allergic reaction or an irritant such as cigarette smoke. Too much histamine is produced which causes the bronchioles to contract. This increases the resistance to air moving in and out of the lungs, resulting in breathlessness and wheezing. Asthma is treated with **beta agonists** which relax the smooth muscle and so open up the bronchioles, **sodium chromoglycate** which reduces histamine production and **steroids** which help prevent an attack.

- **Acute bronchitis** is an infection of the respiratory system. **Chronic bronchitis** is the secretion of too much mucus in the airways, leading to a persistent cough, narrowing of the airways and shortness of breath. Smokers and people exposed to irritant particles and traffic pollution are more likely to suffer from bronchitis. **Emphysema** (large air spaces in the lungs) may result from severe chronic bronchitis, as may failure of the right ventricle of the heart.

- **Hypertension** or high blood pressure can be caused by too much fat or salt in the diet, smoking, stress, obesity or insufficient exercise. It can be treated with **diuretics** to increase the excretion of salt and water in the urine, **beta blockers** to slow the heart rate, **calcium antagonists** to prevent constriction of the arteries or **enzyme inhibitors** to block the action of certain enzymes that constrict the arteries.

- **Atherosclerosis** is a build-up of **plaque**, fatty deposits in the arteries. It can lead to a swelling in the artery called an **aneurysm**, which may burst. Plaque can also encourage a clot or **thrombosis** to form, which can block the coronary artery, leading to **coronary heart disease**, or the arteries supplying the brain, leading to a **stroke**.

- Plaque in the coronary artery can cause **angina**, pain in the chest when exercising. The reduced blood supply to the heart muscle cannot supply it with enough glucose and oxygen. **Glyceryl trinitrate** causes dilation of the blood vessels and is taken during an angina attack.

- A **heart attack** or **myocardial infarction** results when the coronary artery is completely blocked by a thrombosis. Part of the heart muscle is starved of oxygen and dies. An **electrocardiogram** (ECG) records the electrical activity of the heart and anti-clotting drugs are given.

- Risk factors in coronary heart disease include smoking, eating too much saturated fat, being overweight and suffering high levels of stress. Regular exercise and physical fitness help reduce the risk of heart disease.

- **Cancer** or a **tumour** is a mass of cells which are dividing out of control. Cells may split off from the tumour and circulate to another part of the body, causing a **secondary tumour**. Some people have genes that make them more likely to develop cancer, but environmental factors include smoking, too much alcohol, ultra-violet light, insufficient fibre and fruit or too many additives in the diet, and promiscuous sex.

- **Screening** – checking all members of a population to find early signs of some diseases – means treatment can be effective at an early stage.

- Ageing is a progressive generalised impairment of function resulting from a loss of adaptive responses to stress and resulting in a growing risk of age-related diseases. There are degenerative changes in cells and the immune system becomes less effective with age.

- Ageing cells accumulate granules of a fatty substance called **lipofuscin**. This slows down cell metabolism. Whole-body changes include wrinkling of the skin, reduction in muscle and bone mass, problems with muscles and joints, deterioration of sight and hearing, increased susceptibility to cold and mental deterioration.

QUESTIONS

1 Many diseases have now been linked to the type of food we eat, or do not eat. Summarise the main ways in which diet and disease are linked.

2 a How does the human respiratory system work?
   b What causes asthma, and how does asthma affect the respiratory system?
   c What is bronchitis?

3 a What are the main signs of ageing?
   b What appear to be the causes of ageing?
   c How might the effects of ageing on the major body systems be reduced or minimised?

Developing Key Skills

Produce a leaflet called 'A healthy heart – lifestyle choices for the future' designed to be placed in sixth form, university and college common rooms, as well as in waiting rooms at doctors' and dentists' surgeries and in leisure centres and fitness clubs. It should inform people in a lively and accessible way about how they can affect their own future health by the choices they make now. The leaflet needs to explain clearly the importance of cardiovascular health and the ways in which it can be compromised or damaged by lifestyle factors.

LOUIS PASTEUR – FATHER OF MICROBIOLOGY

Louis Pasteur was born on 27 December 1822. Although he did not shine at school, his intellect and his interest in science blossomed later and he eventually decided to become a research scientist.

Pasteur's early work was based firmly in chemistry: he studied the optical activity and structures of crystals. In 1854, his direction began to change. There were considerable problems in the local brewing industry at Lille where he now worked, and Pasteur took an interest, increasingly convinced that fermentation was a biological process, not pure chemistry as had been previously believed. Within a relatively short time he had shown that it was the action of living microorganisms – yeast – that brought about the fermentation reactions, and that these microbes worked best if kept at a carefully controlled temperature with their waste products removed regularly.

By the mid-nineteenth century some people were questioning the idea of **spontaneous generation** and in 1860, in a series of elegant experiments, Pasteur showed that moulds growing on sterilised broth were introduced from 'germs' already present in the air. Once this idea became accepted it changed the way people looked at many other things, including disease.

Louis and his wife Marie had five children, four girls and a boy. However, they lost three of their little daughters to the many infectious diseases that were rife at the time. Then in 1868, when he was only 45 years old, Pasteur suffered a severe stroke which left him paralysed down his left side and with badly affected speech. He recovered enough to continue his work but the ideas and experiments he dreamed up were from then on carried out mainly by his trusted assistants.

Louis felt the deaths of his children very keenly, and in 1876, after some highly successful work on silkworm diseases, he moved on to the study and prevention of infectious diseases in farm animals and people.

Figure 1 Until the nineteenth century people believed in the principle of **spontaneous generation** – that mould grew on food, and frogs appeared out of the mud at the bottom of a pond, as result of direct creation by the will of God.

Anthrax and rabies

Anthrax is a disease which in Pasteur's time killed up to 50 per cent of French flocks and herds each year. Pasteur was convinced that it was caused by a microorganism, and he set out to prove this by developing a vaccine that would protect animals from infection. When challenged, Pasteur undertook a very public trial of his methods in the town of Pouilly-Fort. A group of 25 sheep were given Pasteur's anthrax vaccines, and 25 were not. All of the sheep were then infected with anthrax spores. Several days later the public, press and dignitaries arrived to see the results. Of the unvaccinated sheep, 22 were already dead and the rest were dying of anthrax. All of the vaccinated sheep were still alive!

Even whilst working on anthrax, Pasteur was also trying to discover a vaccination against rabies. In the village where he grew up some people had been bitten by a rabid wolf and the eight year old Pasteur had heard the screams as the blacksmith had cauterised the wounds. This was the only available treatment at the time. It was a long struggle to develop a vaccine, but eventually he succeeded in dramatic fashion, saving the lives of two boys bitten by rabid animals.

Pasteur's work affected so many areas of microbiology and biotechnology – the acceptance of the existence of microbes, brewing and winemaking, pasteurisation, antiseptic practice and vaccinations – he is rightly remembered as one of the greatest biologists ever known.

Figure 2 Louis Pasteur dedicated his whole life to his scientific work.

7.4 Biotechnology and food production

About biotechnology

The old and the new

Microorganisms cause human beings many problems in the form of disease and food damage, but they also play very positive roles in the recycling of nutrients and the working of healthy guts. For thousands of years, people have also been harnessing the beneficial power of microbes to their own ends. Using microbes in this way is known as **biotechnology**.

The earliest recorded use of microorganisms by people was around 6000 BC when the Sumerians and Babylonians were using yeast to make beer. By 4000 BC the Egyptians were using yeast to make their bread rise. Wine- and cheese-making also go back into the distant reaches of human history. These are all examples of the development and use over thousands of years of biotechnology. Now one of the fastest growing areas of both industry and biology, biotechnology is often presented as a new and exciting area of biological science. It certainly is exciting, with enormous potential for solving many problems of the future, but it definitely is not new!

What is biotechnology? There are lots of different definitions but perhaps the most straightforward is: *biotechnology is applying biological organisms or enzymes to the synthesis, breakdown or transformation of materials in the service of people*. Biotechnology includes a whole range of processes, from the traditional production of cheese, wine, bread and beer to the latest technologies that manipulate DNA to produce genetically engineered microorganisms which synthesise drugs or other substances for use. Biotechnology involves aspects of microbiology, biochemistry, cell biology and much more. Probably the most commonly used organisms in biotechnological processes are the fungi, particularly the yeasts, followed by bacteria which are particularly useful in the newer technologies of genetic manipulation.

Why use microorganisms?

As we shall explore further in the next chapter, most biotechnology involves using biological catalysts (enzymes) in a manufacturing process. The most stable, convenient and effective way of using enzymes is often by using whole organisms that produce them. This is one reason why microorganisms play such a large part in biotechnology although as cell culture techniques improve it is likely that intact animal and plant cells will play an increasingly large role.

Microorganisms are often ideal for a variety of reasons.

- Although living, they do not have nervous systems and so there are no ethical issues about cruelty to consider – all that is necessary is to provide the optimum conditions for growth.

- There is an enormous range of microorganisms available for use. They share such a vast pool of genetic information that there is a microorganism somewhere capable of carrying out almost any chemical synthesis or degradation that we might need.

Figure 7.4.1 This ancient Egyptian picture shows a nobleman's wife serving him with beer.

- Microbes have an extremely rapid growth rate, as we have already seen, which is far in excess of anything achieved by multicellular plants and animals. This means that, given the right conditions of food, oxygen and temperature, huge quantities of microorganisms can be produced in short periods of time.
- The nutrient requirements of microorganisms are often very simple and relatively cheap. With the added benefits of genetic manipulation it is also becoming possible to modify those nutritional needs so that the microbes can utilise waste materials which would otherwise have to be disposed of.

The products of biotechnology

The desired products of the microorganism vary from process to process. In some cases, we want to make as much microorganism as possible, because that is the product which is to be sold. This is the case in, for example, the production of single cell protein like Quorn, or the manufacture of baker's yeast. In other cases we want substances that are formed as part of the normal biochemical action of the microorganism. Such substances include ethanol (a product of anaerobic respiration in yeast) and ethanoic acid, as well as a range of amino acids and enzymes. They are known as **primary metabolites.** In certain conditions the microorganisms are encouraged to act on the primary metabolites they have produced in a way they would not normally do. This results in further chemicals called **secondary metabolites**. Most antibiotics are secondary metabolites.

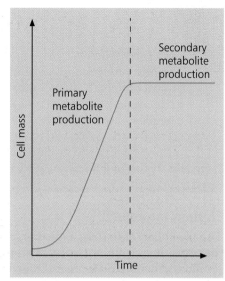

Figure 7.4.2 Primary metabolites are usually formed in the period of active growth, whilst secondary metabolites tend to be formed during the stationary phase of the life of the culture, once the cell mass has reached its maximum. The time at which the culture is 'harvested' will depend on which product we want from the microorganisms.

The process of biotechnology

First choose your microbe …

When a new biotechnological process is being developed, the first task is to find a suitable microorganism to carry out the process. Because the choice of possible microorganisms is very large, it can take a long time to find a suitable candidate. The microorganism must obviously be able to synthesise or break down the chemical required, and it also needs to work reasonably fast and give a good yield of the product. To make the final production process financially worthwhile, it is important that it uses a relatively cheap source of nutrients. It is also important that the microbe does not require extreme (and therefore expensive) conditions and that it does not produce any toxins to contaminate the product. The microorganism must be genetically stable – in other words, unlikely to mutate into forms that do not carry out the required reaction.

Finding the right microorganism

Possible sources of a suitable microorganism are suggested based on knowledge of microbes that carry out the right sort of reactions. For example, soil is often a likely source and so is decaying plant material. Choosing the right microorganism for a particular job usually involves screening thousands of different possibilities. Some of the steps are outlined simply below.

(1) The source material is dried and treated with an insecticide to kill any insects which might be present.
(2) One gram of the source material is shaken with $99\,cm^3$ of sterile water for around 30 minutes.

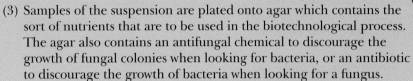

(3) Samples of the suspension are plated onto agar which contains the sort of nutrients that are to be used in the biotechnological process. The agar also contains an antifungal chemical to discourage the growth of fungal colonies when looking for bacteria, or an antibiotic to discourage the growth of bacteria when looking for a fungus.

(4) The plates are incubated at 30 °C for several days until any colonies are well developed. These colonies can then be used to make further cultures in order to produce sufficient amounts of microorganism to be able to look in detail at what they are capable of doing.

... then improve it

The likelihood of finding a microorganism in the wild that exactly fulfils all of the requirements for a particular process is quite remote. The most common result of screening is an organism that carries out the right reaction but too slowly, or too inefficiently. Research scientists then take the best available wild organism and alter its genetic material to develop its useful features. This produces a more 'tailor-made' microorganism, well suited to the process.

Until recently, changes in the genetic material of the microorganism would have been brought about by radiation. A culture of the microbe would be exposed to X-rays, causing mutations (changes) in the DNA. The mutant microorganisms would be given very specialised nutrients to encourage the growth of the most suitable cultures, allowing pure cultures of more efficient microbes to be isolated and grown in large numbers. More recently, recombinant DNA technology or genetic engineering (see chapter 7.5) has been used, making the process of improving microorganisms more effective and reliable.

The development stage

There is a big jump from having a microorganism carrying out a particular chemical reaction in a laboratory under carefully monitored conditions to setting up a massive industrial plant using the same microorganism. The steps in achieving this development process are outlined below.

Once a suitable microorganism has been developed, a pure batch of the microorganisms is grown to provide a **master culture**. This is then dried (often by freeze-drying) and stored, and some kept for reference so it will be possible to compare later cultures with the original culture. Then **stock cultures** are made up from the master culture at regular intervals. Stock cultures are kept going in the laboratory for study and for reference, and as a source of microorganisms for the **working cultures** which are actually used in the biotechnological process.

All of these culture stages are carried out under sterile conditions. Unlikely as it may seem, it was not until the middle of the twentieth century that the need for sterile conditions in the handling of microorganisms was understood. Before then, a few different microorganisms might have been viewed as adding to the flavour of the cheese or beer. It was only when biotechnology began to move on from the production of beer, wine and cheeses into the manufacture of drugs like penicillin that it became apparent how important it is that only the desired microorganism is cultured. Any other strains of bacteria or fungus present may affect the product. Preventing contamination is now a major concern in biotechnological processes. If the master culture or stock cultures become contaminated, they have to be purified and recultured, which is time consuming and therefore expensive. However, if contamination is not detected at this stage and a rogue organism gets into the industrial process, the whole plant has to be stopped, emptied, cleaned, sterilised and then restarted. This costs a company a great deal more money – enough to affect the financial returns for the year – and so it is avoided as far as possible by the enforcement of strict sterile conditions throughout the whole process.

Scaling up

There are practical considerations in taking a microorganism that works well in a laboratory and getting it to function well in a large production process. These are explored and optimised in the process of **scaling up**. Any lack of nutrients or oxygen, build-up of waste products or temperature fluctuations need to be dealt with. The optimum temperature is found for the reactions of the process as well as the limits of temperature, pH and oxygen tolerance. The reactions may produce heat, in which case the process may need to be cooled. A culture of microorganisms which needs no shaking in a laboratory culture will usually need regular stirring when in a massive industrial tank to make sure all the microorganisms get plenty of oxygen. These types of problems are solved at every stage of the scaling up process.

Initially, scaling up is carried out in a series of steps. Each step uses a larger volume, and the optimum conditions for growth and any problems that arise are recorded at each stage. The ideal fermenter size is then chosen based on these studies. This will be the size at which the maximum product yield is gained for the minimum technological input, which may not always be the largest size trialled. For example, if one size of production vessel needs paddles constantly stirring it, oxygen bubbling in at intervals and careful temperature regulation to produce a 30 per cent yield, whilst a smaller reaction vessel gives a 29 per cent yield without any technological input except oxygen bubbling through every 30 minutes, then the smaller vessel might well be chosen. This is because although less product would be made at any one time, overall production costs would be lower.

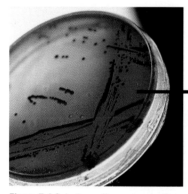 

Figure 7.4.3 In the scaling up process for a potentially useful microorganism, the culture is taken in steps from an agar plate to a fermentation vessel which may hold 1 000 000 dm³.

The main steps in the scaling up process are listed below. The time-scale varies depending on whether the microorganism being trialled is a bacterium or a fungus. For bacteria, each step takes a few days, but for fungi which grow more slowly the same steps will take a few weeks.

1 Freeze-dried cells from the stock culture are grown on an **agar plate** under optimum growth conditions.
2 Successful colonies are used to inoculate a **starter vessel**, also known as a shake flask because the culture is vibrated as it grows. The optimum

conditions of nutrients, oxygen and temperature are noted. The resulting culture is the starter culture, which is used as a working culture in the process.

3 The starter culture is then used in a **seed fermenter** which usually has a capacity of around 50–200 dm³. Conditions are watched carefully to see that optimum growth occurs and any problems due to the increase in size are noted.

4 There may be a **secondary fermenter** in which the culture from the seed fermenter grows even more before being added to the production vessel.

5 The **production vessel** or **bioreactor** is the final vessel into which the culture is poured. Here conditions will again be set up to maximise growth, and any problems of overheating, lack of oxygen or waste build-up will be dealt with before full-scale industrial production can go ahead. This trial run is always needed, though the company would have to be very sure from earlier scaling up tests that the process would work before they invested in a production vessel which may be up to 1 000 000 dm³ in volume.

How do your microbes grow?

Once a microorganism has been chosen and the ideal size and shape of bioreactor found, the organisation of the commercial production has to be decided. There are three main ways of growing microorganisms – **batch culture**, **semicontinuous culture** and **continuous culture**. These are outlined in figure 7.4.4.

Figure 7.4.4 Three different processes for growing microorganisms.

Batch culture:
The microorganisms are inoculated into a fixed volume of medium. As growth takes place nutrients are used up and both biomass and waste products build up. As the culture reaches the stationary phase overall growth ceases but during this phase the microorganisms often carry out biochemical changes to form the desired end products (such as antibiotics and enzymes). The process is stopped before the death phase and the products harvested. The whole system is then cleaned and sterilised and a new batch culture started up.

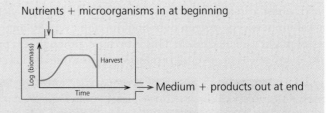

Nutrients + microorganisms in at beginning

Medium + products out at end

Semicontinuous (fed batch) culture:
This is very similar to batch culture, except that the life of the batch is extended by the addition of extra nutrients, allowing the formation of more end product.

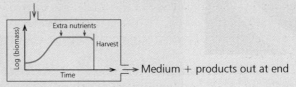

Nutrients + microorganisms in at beginning. Extra nutrients added to extend life + increase the total volume

Medium + products out at end

Continuous culture:
This involves a constant addition of sterile nutrient medium to the culture once it reaches the exponetial start of growth. There is a corresponding withdrawal of culture broth (medium, waste products plus microorganisms), keeping the culture volume in the bioreactor constant. This enables continuous balanced growth, with levels of nutrients, metabolic products and pH kept more or less constant.

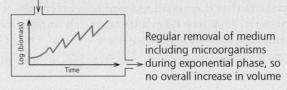

Nutrients + microorganisms in at beginning. Regular addition of nutrients during exponential growth

Regular removal of medium including microorganisms during exponential phase, so no overall increase in volume

Note: log scales allow us to show very small and very large numbers on the same graph.

Each of these different methods of operating a bioreactor can be adjusted to ensure the maximum production either of biomass or of primary or secondary metabolites. On first sight continuous culture, which has been developed relatively recently, would seem to be the best method of operating a bioprocess but in fact the majority of industrial processes use batch or semicontinuous culture. Penicillin, for example, is made in this way. Continuous culture is largely reserved for the production of single cell protein (mycoprotein) and in some waste water treatment processes. This is because, perhaps surprisingly, batch and semicontinuous cultures are much more flexible. Some reasons why they are used are listed below.

- The product may only be needed in small quantities at a time.
- There may be periods of the year when there is little demand for the product.
- It may be necessary to have very high concentrations of product in the broth to be able to extract it economically.
- Some metabolic products are only produced during the stationary phase of the growth cycle.
- Some strains of microorganism are unstable and so they need regular renewal from the stock cultures.
- Continuous processes can present many technical difficulties.

Downstream processing

Whatever type of culture technique is used in a bioreactor, the end result of the process inside is a mixture of unused nutrient broth, microorganisms, primary metabolites, possible secondary metabolites and waste products. The useful component of this mixture has to be separated out from all the rest. This process of extracting and purifying the end-product from the raw output of the bioprocessor is known as **downstream processing**.

As in all industrial processes, the aim of downstream processing is to achieve the purest possible product in the cheapest possible way. Although extracting and purifying the product might sound quite simple compared with the technological achievements inside the bioreactor, it is in fact one of the most difficult parts of the whole process. For example, the giant pharmaceutical company Eli Lilley has a bioprocessing plant for the production of human insulin. About 200 staff are employed at this plant, and more than 90 per cent of them are involved in downstream processing – recovering the pure hormone once it has been made. The percentage of the total cost of a product that is accounted for by downstream processing costs varies between 15 per cent and 40 per cent. The downstream processing of penicillin is described on page 703.

The initial stage of downstream processing is usually to separate the broth from the bioreactor into solid and liquid parts. Further purification is then done to extract the product. Techniques used include distillation, centrifuging, filtration, ultrafiltration, solvent extraction, reverse osmosis and electrophoresis.

Although an extraction process can be devised for almost everything, it may be very expensive in terms of resources and energy. There are several potential applications of biotechnology which have not been developed because the extraction of the end-product would cost so much that the process would be uneconomic.

An added difficulty is that the pure product once extracted needs to be in a stable form so that it does not degrade while being stored. The most common way of making sure that products remain stable is to dry them. Amino acids, organic acids, antibiotics, polysaccharides, enzymes and single cell protein are just some of the products that are marketed in a dried form. Other products need to be sold as liquid preparations, and in this case great care has to be taken to avoid contamination by microbes which could destroy the carefully manufactured product.

Design of bioreactors

The most common processes carried out in bioreactors are fermentation reactions, and so most bioreactors are actually giant fermentation vessels. Bioreactors vary greatly depending on the needs of the microorganisms to be grown. Some are little more than simple containers or vats, which may or may not be stirred. They are not aseptic, as they are open to the air. Simple reactors like this have been in use in one form or another for centuries in the brewing of beer and the making of wine.

Other reactors are much more complicated, designed specifically for the particular process taking place. However, there are some common problems in bioreactors which are often solved in similar ways, as described below.

Temperature

Getting the temperature right is always important in biological reactions and this can be difficult in a large-scale fermentation. If the bioreactor tends to cool down a heating system will be required, usually linked to temperature probes. When the temperature of the broth falls, the heating system switches on to warm it up. A negative feedback system ensures that as the temperature rises the heater is switched off again so that the culture does not get too hot. If the bioreactor tends to overheat because heat is produced by the process inside, then a cooling system is needed to carry heat away from the broth until the temperature is restored to the optimum. Again this is linked to temperature sensors in a negative feeedback system. In some bioreactors the temperature can fluctuate so much that both a heating and a cooling system are necessary. The most common device used for temperature control in bioreactors is a **heat exchanger** controlled by a computer system that automatically monitors and controls the temperature of the broth, as shown in figure 7.4.6.

Figure 7.4.5 People have used the fermentation of yeast in anaerobic conditions to produce ethanol for alcoholic drinks like beer for thousands of years. Although the technology has changed and bigger quantities are now made, the basic principles of brewing remain the same.

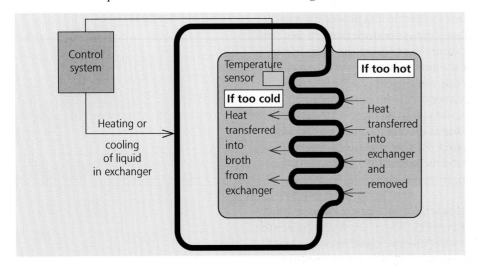

Figure 7.4.6 A heat exchange system in a bioreactor.

Stirring in the nutrients

Another common difficulty to be overcome in bioreactors is making sure that there is enough oxygen and nutrient medium for the growing microorganisms.

Controlled amounts are added to the broth when probes or sample tests indicate that levels are dropping. However, this leads to another difficulty. Inside a bioreactor there is usually a very large volume of liquid, which may be quite thick (viscous) due to the growth of microorganisms. Making sure that the whole mixture is kept to the right temperature, and that all the microorganisms receive enough food and oxygen, cannot be left to simple diffusion. To overcome this problem most bioreactors have a mixing mechanism. This can vary from a simple propeller to a multi-bladed stirrer in a **continuously stirred tank reactor**, or a pumped circulation system may be used in a **recycle** or **loop bioreactor**. Various mixing mechanisms are shown in figure 7.4.7.

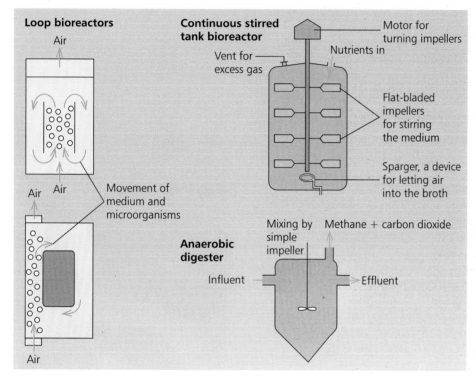

Figure 7.4.7 The design of bioreactors is advancing all the time as new and more sensitive ways of controlling conditions during fermentation processes become available.

Contamination

Most bioreactors are sealed, aseptic units. This prevents contamination of the process by microorganisms from the air or from workers. Also, when the process involves genetically engineered organisms, it is a legal requirement that they should be contained within the biorector and not be released into the environment.

A final general consideration is the material of which the biorector is made. It is important that it resists corrosion, and is non-toxic so that any material that does enter the broth does not poison either the microorganisms or the people or animals that will consume the products. In addition, the material of the bioreactor and associated pipework has to be able to withstand frequent sterilisation with high-pressure steam.

Some products of biotechnology

Biotechnology, or using microorganisms to make end-products that are useful to people, is an ever-growing area of industrial development. The range of materials that can be produced in this way is getting bigger all the time. We shall look at several processes in detail, some which have been part of human culture for thousands of years and others which are relatively new, all of which are continuing to develop.

Breadmaking

Cereals are produced almost all over the world, and often used for making bread of one sort or another. Bread is an example of the simplest sort of biotechnology, in which a microorganism (in Europe usually the yeast *Saccharomyces cerevisiae*) causes a fermentation, and the carbon dioxide produced in the fermentation causes the dough to rise. Flour (usually wheat flour in the UK) is mixed with water or milk, salt, sugar and a variety of other ingredients, and combined with the yeast in a dough. The yeast uses the sugar for respiration and produces carbon dioxide, making the dough expand and stretch. The unique protein gluten in the wheat is extensible and elastic, and allows the bread to rise and keep its shape on cooking. Kneading the dough increases the elasticity, and allows the bread to rise better.

A number of different additives affect the texture of the bread, including reducing agents such as ascorbic acid, which is often added commercially as a flour improver. Fats, oxidising agents and different enzymes are also added to commercially produced bread to improve its mixing, fermentation, baking and storage characteristics.

The fermentation by the yeast plays three main roles in bread making – it leavens the bread, gives it flavour and encourages the texture changes in the dough.

Pickled cabbage?

In European culture, particularly in Germany, the production of sauerkraut has been an important aspect of food technology. Sauerkraut is cabbage which is preserved by a combination of salt and a fermentation process. Shredded cabbage is packed anaerobically (without air) with salt and kept at a relatively low temperature – around 7.5 °C. The salt causes water to be drawn from the cabbage leaves. As a result lactic acid bacteria proliferate. They use the sugar in a fermentation reaction and produce lactic acid as a waste product. This lowers the pH, preventing the growth of putrefying bacteria and preserving the cabbage. The preserved vegetable is then packed and stored in jars or cans. The production of sauerkraut on a large scale in Germany can be traced back to the year AD 800 – it is certainly not a new form of biotechnology!

Preserving beans

The soy bean is an important source of protein in South-East Asia and India. For many years people in these regions have used biotechnology to ferment soy beans. Soy beans alone are relatively indigestible, and they tend to cause a build-up of a lot of intestinal gas and flatulence. Fermenting the beans is another example of the use of microorganisms to modify foods. One of the best known products of soy bean fermentation is soy sauce. Other products include miso, sake and tempeh.

In the production of soy sauce the soy beans are first soaked in water and cooked under pressure for about an hour. Then the cooked soy beans are mixed with wheat flour and both are mixed and fermented with a form of moult (*Aspergillus oryzae*). This fermentation breaks down starches, proteins and pectins, and takes place in solid layers on bamboo trays. For the next fermentation stage, the soy mash is mixed with yeast of the *Candida* family in salt water anaerobic conditions to form a slurry. This is left to ferment in large vats for up to four months. The final stage, the maturation of the product, allows the flavours to develop. The soy sauce is also pasteurised to kill microorganisms, and clarified by adding kaolin to flocculate any particles.

Figure 7.4.8 Sauerkraut – not a common food in the UK but an important foodstuff in Europe for centuries.

Tofu production

Tofu is soy bean curd, made by straining the liquid away from the solid curd part of soy milk, in a way that is similar to the production of cheese from cow's milk. However, it does not involve any biotechnology. Soy milk is made by crushing the beans and soaking them overnight. They are then boiled to break down the enzymes in the soy beans that make them indigestible to humans. The resulting slurry is filtered. The liquid part is soy milk, and the solid can be used to make bread or as animal feed.

A small amount of either calcium sulphate (used in China) or magnesium chloride in salt (used in Japan) is added to the soy milk to make it coagulate. It separates into curds and whey. The curds are put into large containers containing cheese cloth and weighted down so that any whey is strained off. The resulting blocks of creamy white solid curd are tofu, a food high in protein and very low in fat.

Dairy products

Milk production

Milk is the basis of any dairy product. In the developing world dairy foods are generally produced on a very small scale. In the developed world large herds of cows are reared to provide the millions of gallons of milk needed to supply the dairy industry.

Figure 7.4.9 Cows have been selectively bred for years to give large yields of milk per cow – far more than would ever be needed by a calf.

Milk is an emulsion of tiny fat droplets in water, along with protein, carbohydrate in the form of lactose (milk sugar) and many vitamins and minerals dissolved in the water. Milk is a very useful form of food for many people, but it is also a very attractive growth medium for bacteria. Bacterial growth not only causes the milk to go bad so that it is no longer fit for people to drink, but it can also cause disease. In the past people frequently caught tuberculosis from drinking infected milk, before heat treatment of milk (pasteurisation) and careful attention to the health of cattle were introduced. Even now, although milk leaving the udder of a cow is usually sterile, bacteria can sometimes be found in it. *E. coli* and other bacteria found in the gut (coliform bacteria) can cause disease and they find their way into milk from the unwashed hands of farm workers or from cow faeces contaminating the milking equipment.

If untreated milk has been handled correctly there will be fewer than 10 000 microorganisms per cubic centimetre of milk, and less than 700 of them will be coliform bacteria. But if strict hygiene measures are not observed, the numbers of microorganisms present in the milk rise rapidly, and there may be as many as 10 000 coliform bacteria per cubic centimetre as well as millions of others. Because milk is such an ideal medium for the growth of microorganisms, in the developed world it is almost always heat treated before being used for either drinking or for making products like yoghurt or cheese. The most common heat treatment methods are **pasteurisation**, in which the milk is heated to 71.7°C for at least 15 seconds, and **ultraheat treatment (UHT)** (or sterilisation), in which the milk is brought up to 132.2°C for at least one second. After pasteurisation the milk will last for four or five days before going off, whilst UHT milk lasts for several months in a sealed container.

Before milk is used to make dairy products it will be tested carefully for bacteria, for taste and smell, the water and fat content (which can vary a surprising amount) and the antibiotic content (because antibiotic traces in the milk prevent it being used to make products such as yoghurt that are manufactured using bacteria). After all of this, the milk is ready to be used in any one of a number of biotechnological processes.

Using milk 1: making cheese

The origin of using dairy products as human food is lost in the mists of time, but we are fairly certain that foods such as cheese and yoghurt were developed to preserve milk and prevent it going off. Both cheese- and yoghurt-making use bacteria which feed on the milk sugar (lactose) in the milk. The bacteria change the texture and taste of the milk to a form which people enjoy eating, and they inhibit the growth of less desirable bacteria, preserving the milk and preventing it from going off so quickly.

Cheese production is one of the main activities of the dairy industry. About 900 different types of cheese are made around the world, some produced by very small-scale traditional methods and others produced commercially in very large quantities.

Cheese is made by separating the protein **casein** along with the fat of the milk (**curds**) from the liquid part (**whey**), so that cheese is almost a form of dehydrated milk. The first stage in the process is the action of bacteria on the lactose to produce lactic acid, which acidifies the milk. Different starter cultures of bacteria affect the milk slightly differently and result in different cheeses. The acidic conditions produced by the bacteria, often combined with the action of added enzymes that break down protein, cause the milk to curdle and separate into curds and whey in a controlled way. The enzymes used are traditionally from **rennet** (extracted from the stomachs of calves, cows and pigs) which contains the enzyme **chymosin**.

Modern cheese-making is becoming less dependent on enzymes from animals' stomachs to curdle the milk. Chymosin that is almost identical to the animal-derived enzyme can be derived from three different fungal sources, and up to a third of the world's cheese production, particularly in the USA and France, now uses these fungal enzymes. Even more recently, genetic manipulation has resulted in microorganisms that can produce animal chymosin, which works exactly like the real thing, avoiding the problems that occur occasionally when using the fungal enzyme. It seems likely that in the future, almost all cheese will be made using the microbial enzyme.

Early cheese-making

It is believed that some of the earliest cheese-makers were nomadic sheep herders who used animal stomachs for carrying liquids. Milk from sheep, goats or camels carried in this way would be heated up by the sun and would become soured by bacteria in the milk. This souring provided acidic conditions under which any traces of rennet left in the stomach lining would curdle the milk and turn it into curds and whey. People soon realised that if the whey was drained off and the curds were mixed with a little salt, they tasted good and also meant the milk could be used as food long after it would have gone bad without treatment. This method of cheese-making was already old when it was documented by the Romans in Europe.

The milk is incubated with the bacteria for about 24 hours at 18 °C, by which time it has usually formed curds and whey. If the process is to make cottage cheese, the whey is strained off at this stage and the curds are simply cut and packaged. To make solid cheeses the curds and whey are cooked together before the whey is strained off. The whey produced in the manufacture of cheese is not wasted, as it is often used as an animal feed. The curds are cut and perhaps mixed with salt before being packed into steel or wooden containers and either pressed or left to dry naturally. Bacteria continue to act on the cheese, and different cheeses are kept for varying lengths of time, giving each type of cheese a distinctive flavour. Some cheeses are dipped in wine or inoculated with fungi to add to the flavour – well known examples of this are Blue Stilton with its blue veins and Brie with its white outer coating.

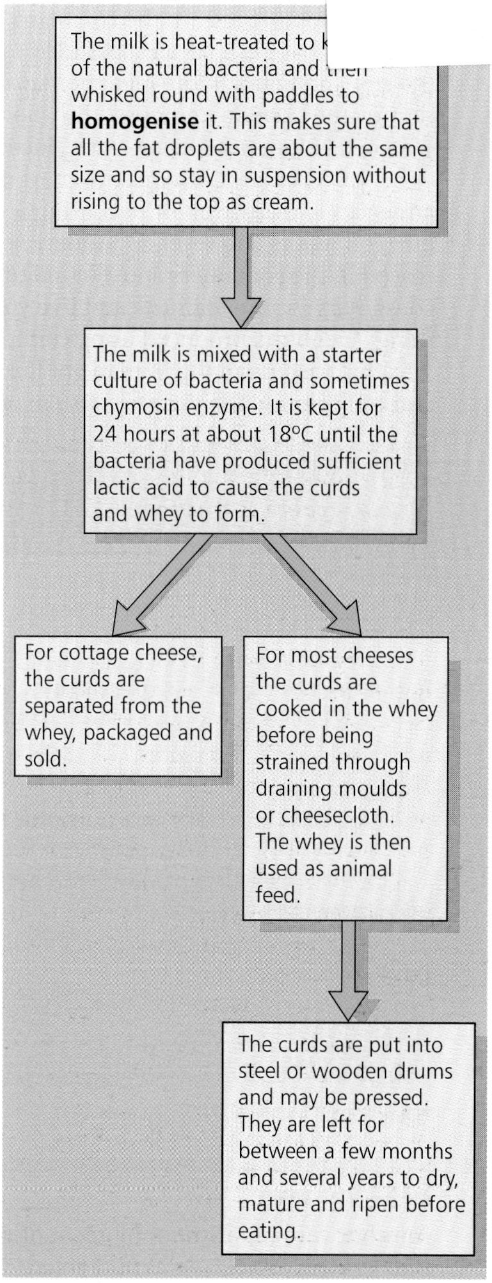

Using milk 2: Making yoghurt

Traditionally yoghurt is fermented whole milk, and yoghurt and other very similar products have a long history in human culture. Like cheese, yoghurt is formed by the action of bacteria on the lactose (milk sugar) in the milk. The most commonly used bacteria in the process are *Lactobacillus bulgaricus* which forms ethanal and *Streptococcus thermophilus* which forms the lactic acid that reduces the pH and gives yoghurt is sharp, tangy taste. Both of these bacteria produce polymers (large molecules) as they react with the milk, giving yoghurt the smooth, thick texture that is so different from that of milk. The growth of these 'yoghurt-forming' bacteria in milk also helps to prevent it going off, which is probably one of the reasons why yoghurt-making has been part of our culture for so long.

Eating yoghurt is becoming increasingly popular: yoghurt is one of the fastest growing food products of the dairy industry, and even of the food industry as a whole. In the developed world yoghurt is now available flavoured by an enormous range of fruits, making it very pleasant to eat, and it is a convenient food both for adults and children. It is also perceived as being a relatively 'healthy' food. Like all dairy products yoghurt is high in calcium, which is important for bone growth in children and for the prevention of osteoporosis in adults. Modern technologies have made it possible to produce palatable yoghurt from skimmed milk, so that the fat content (and therefore the energy content) of some yoghurt is very low. Finally, there is a growing body of opinion that the bacteria in the yoghurt have a beneficial effect on the human gut, helping to maintain a healthy balance of intestinal bacteria.

Yoghurt can be made from the milk of any dairy animal, but cows' milk is the most common source. When yoghurt is made traditionally, a small amount of the previous batch of yoghurt is mixed with a new batch of milk to start the

The milk is heat-treated to k[...] of the natural bacteria and then whisked round with paddles to **homogenise** it. This makes sure that all the fat droplets are about the same size and so stay in suspension without rising to the top as cream.

↓

The milk is mixed with a starter culture of bacteria and sometimes chymosin enzyme. It is kept for 24 hours at about 18°C until the bacteria have produced sufficient lactic acid to cause the curds and whey to form.

For cottage cheese, the curds are separated from the whey, packaged and sold.

For most cheeses the curds are cooked in the whey before being strained through draining moulds or cheesecloth. The whey is then used as animal feed.

The curds are put into steel or wooden drums and may be pressed. They are left for between a few months and several years to dry, mature and ripen before eating.

Figure 7.4.10 A summary of cheese production.

Figure 7.4.11 Yoghurts are marketed in many flavours and styles of packaging.

fermentation process. In the commercial production of yoghurt, a pure inoculation of fresh bacteria is added to each vat to ensure a reliable process. Any trace of antibiotics in the milk, perhaps from the treatment of infected cows, can destroy the bacteria and upset the whole production, so the milk is carefully screened before production starts. Incubation is usually carried out at around either 30 °C or 45 °C. In most yoghurt production the incubation takes place in large vats and any fruit or flavouring is added later before the product is packed into containers. However, to produce set yoghurts, milk inoculated by bacteria is placed in the containers and allowed to ferment there. Increasingly popular with consumers are **bioyoghurts** and **live yoghurts**. They are both basically the same thing – yoghurts produced using cultures of bacteria that increase the balance of 'healthy' bacteria in the human gut flora. The bacteria remain alive in the yoghurt and can colonise the digestive system to some extent after the yoghurt is eaten.

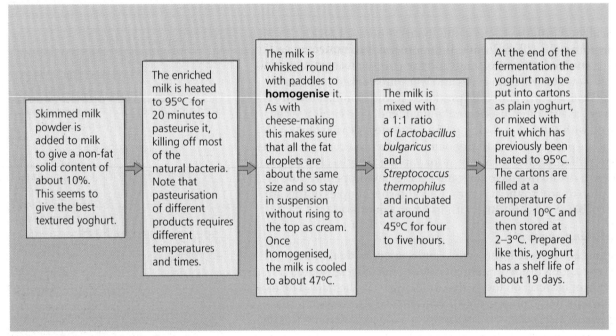

Figure 7.4.12 A summary of yoghurt production.

Brewing beer

Another very old form of biotechnology that plays a large part in modern life is the brewing of beers, ales and lagers. The worldwide production of commercial beers approaches 100 billion dm^3 per year, and this does not take into account all the beer brewed by individuals, the rice beer brewed in India and Asia or the sorghum beer brewed in Africa.

The basis of brewing is to use yeast to break down a carbohydrate source in a largely anaerobic environment, producing ethanol. A balance of conditions has to be achieved in which the yeast grows and makes as much ethanol as possible without making too many unwanted by-products.

Beers generally use starchy cereals such as barley as their carbohydrate source. However, brewing yeasts cannot break down starch themselves, so enzymes are used on the starch-rich cereals to break down the starch into sugars which the yeasts can then respire. The obvious way to achieve this breakdown of starch is to allow the cereals to start germinating, when enzymes are released in the seeds to mobilise the food stores. Thus the first step in beer-making is **malting** – dried barley is soaked in water and then spread out to germinate on the floor of the

Figure 7.4.13 Many individuals all around the world brew beer for themselves, their friends and their families. But brewing is also a multimillion pound industry producing billions of gallons of beer and lager every year.

malthouse or in revolving drums. Once plenty of amylase (starch-hydrolysing) and protease (protein-hydrolysing) enzymes have been produced in the germinating barley grains, the grains are transferred to a kiln where they are slowly heated to about 80 °C. This kills the grains but retains most of the enzyme activity. The resulting cooked barley is known as **malt**.

The malt is mixed with water at around 55–65 °C (known as **mashing**). The enzymes now act to break down the starch to produce sugars such as dextrin and maltose. The mixture also contains protein breakdown products, mineral and vitamins. This mixture or **wort** is used as the nutrient source for the yeasts. Hops of different kinds and in different amounts are added to the wort to give flavour and bitterness. Hops are also slighly antiseptic and so help to prevent the growth of unwanted microorganisms such as bacteria. The wort is then transferred to an open bioreactor system (a tank!) and inoculated with pure strains of yeast.

Traditionally *Saccharomyces cerevisiae* is the most commonly used yeast for fermenting beers, ales and stouts. This strain of yeast works best in a temperature range of around 20–28 °C and is known as a **top fermenter**, as the yeast rises to the top of the fermenter towards the end of the fermentation and can be skimmed off. In the production of lager, **bottom fermenters** are used. These are yeasts such as *Saccharomyces uvarum* which sink to the bottom of the fermenter at the end of the process. The great advantage of bottom fermenters is that they work at lower (and therefore cheaper) temperatures, fermenting at 10–15 °C. Genetically engineered yeasts are now being produced which can ferment beers at lower temperatures. These modern yeast strains also clump together (**flocculate**) at the end of the fermentation, so that they settle to the bottom of the tank, leaving the beer very clear.

Beer fermenters are not aerated or mixed, because it is important that the yeasts respire anaerobically for much of the time so that they produce carbon dioxide and ethanol rather than carbon dioxide and water. In traditional brewing, after the fermentation process is complete and most of the yeast has floated to the top or settled at the bottom and been removed, the beer is stored in wooden casks at around 0 °C for several weeks to allow the final fermentation to take place and improve the flavour. This is known as **conditioning**. The cool temperature and period of resting also allows the beer to clear further as the remaining yeasts settle out and any haze disappears. Isinglass, a fining agent, is often added to make the yeast settle to the bottom of the cask more effectively, helping to clear the beer. In modern large-scale breweries the beer is conditioned in big steel lagering tanks, and the yeast is removed by filtering or centrifuging. The beer is then pasteurised to kill any bacteria. Finally it is put in kegs, bottles or cans, and carbon dioxide is added to get rid of unwanted gases and to give a slight fizz. The alcohol content of beer varies between about 4 per cent and 9 per cent. Some of the yeast is retained to start a new batch brewing – the same strain may be used in a brewery for years – but the rest of the yeast is used to produce yeast extract, rich in B vitamins but very high in added salt as well.

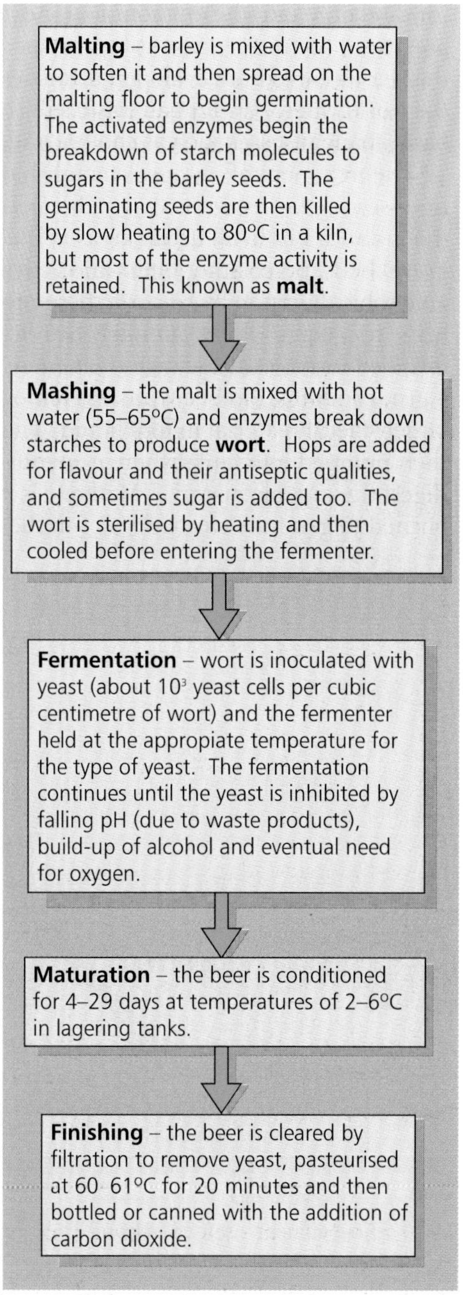

Sewage and waste water treatment

Growth in human populations has been matched, inevitably, by an increase in human waste. This carries great risk of disease, and many years ago we developed sewers to remove the sewage and waste water produced from our towns and cities. Unfortunately for a long time this raw sewage was simply discharged into rivers and the sea. We are now considerably more aware of the environmental damage such dumping can cause, and human sewage is treated in special sewage treatment plants (also known as sewage farms) by microorganisms to make it safe

Malting – barley is mixed with water to soften it and then spread on the malting floor to begin germination. The activated enzymes begin the breakdown of starch molecules to sugars in the barley seeds. The germinating seeds are then killed by slow heating to 80°C in a kiln, but most of the enzyme activity is retained. This known as **malt**.

Mashing – the malt is mixed with hot water (55–65°C) and enzymes break down starches to produce **wort**. Hops are added for flavour and their antiseptic qualities, and sometimes sugar is added too. The wort is sterilised by heating and then cooled before entering the fermenter.

Fermentation – wort is inoculated with yeast (about 10^3 yeast cells per cubic centimetre of wort) and the fermenter held at the appropiate temperature for the type of yeast. The fermentation continues until the yeast is inhibited by falling pH (due to waste products), build-up of alcohol and eventual need for oxygen.

Maturation – the beer is conditioned for 4–29 days at temperatures of 2–6°C in lagering tanks.

Finishing – the beer is cleared by filtration to remove yeast, pasteurised at 60–61°C for 20 minutes and then bottled or canned with the addition of carbon dioxide.

Figure 7.4.14 A summary of the stages of large-scale brewing.

for discharge into the environment. Advances in the treatment of human waste are one of the major reasons for the spectacular improvement in public health that has occurred in developed countries over the last century or so. In areas of the world where raw human waste still contaminates drinking water on a regular basis, many diseases such as cholera and typhoid are still widespread.

The treatment of sewage is mainly biological. In rural areas septic tanks act as mini-sewage farms, with bacteria breaking down the waste in large tanks under the ground. But in all urban areas in the UK sewage is treated through a series of gravel beds, percolating filters and activated sludge processes. Along with anaerobic digestion by bacteria these processes reduce human excrement and urine to a liquid which can safely be released into our rivers. The biotechnology involved in successful sewage treatement is complex. Unwanted inorganic matter – grit, condoms, old beer cans – is removed by filters, leaving a thick sludge of largely faecal material in foul liquid. The solid material is allowed to settle out and then pumped into tanks where it spends up to a month whilst anaerobic microbes digest the organic material. Methane is a by-product of this process and can be burned to generate electricity to run the sewage farm.

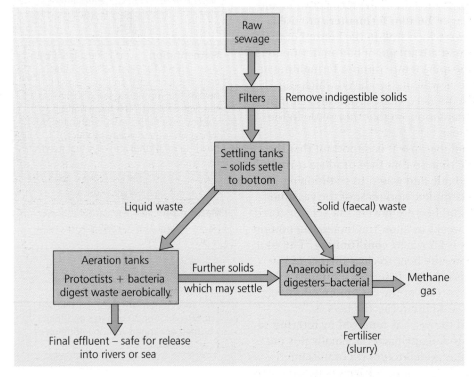

Figure 7.4.15 Sewage farms not only remove vast tonnages of human waste, they also play a major part in reducing disease within the population.

The liquid is treated by protoctists which digest the potentially harmful or disease-causing bacteria present. This takes place in tanks where air is continually pumped through as the protoctists use a lot of oxygen. To maximise the surface area over which digestion takes place the microbes are grown on stones, gravel or plastic sheets. Also as part of the process, mucus produced by the microbes causes any solid particles to clump together (flocculate). After a few hours these clumps are allowed to settle to the bottom of the tank. At this point they too are pumped to the sludge digester tanks, leaving behind relatively clean water, which can be released into the rivers. The sludge can eventually be used as fertiliser, or dumped at sea.

Producing penicillin

The most commonly used and best known antimicrobial drugs are the antibiotics. These can be used against both bacterial and fungal diseases.

Although the French medical student Ernest Duchesne first described penicillin, Alexander Fleming is usually credited with the discovery of the first modern antibiotic. He discovered the mould *Penicillium notatum* infecting his bacterial plates and observed the clear area of agar jelly around the mould where a chemical produced by the mould had destroyed the bacterial culture. However, it was not until 1940 that the Australian Howard Florey and the German Ernst Chain, working in England, developed penicillin as an antibiotic drug. This new drug could be used with almost magical effect to cure patients who were seriously ill with bacterial diseases without harming the patient in the process. Many other antibiotics have been discovered since, but penicillin is still commonly used to combat bacterial infections.

The original *Penicillium* mould discovered by Fleming and the others was of very limited use as a large-scale source of the antibiotic. Every cubic decimetre of fungus yielded only 0.0012 g of active penicillin. Because of this, many patients died whose lives could have been saved by the drug because penicillin was simply not available in large enough amounts. During the Second World War commercial amounts of penicillin were needed to treat soldiers injured in the fighting, and also to keep healthy the large number who contracted sexually transmitted diseases. The drive to manufacture penicillin took a major step forward when a different fungus, *Penicillium chrysogenum*, was tried. This improved the yield to 50 g dm⁻³ so that the larger scale production of penicillin could have a major impact on the health of individuals throughout the world. The production of pencillin and other antibiotics has since become a multi-million pound business.

In recent years different strains of *Penicillium* mould have been produced by mutation and genetic crosses, so that the yield has continued to improve. Purifying the drug during downstream processing has also become easier and cheaper. Commerical production of penicillin takes place in relatively small fermenters (40–200 dm³) with continual central stirring. This is because *Penicillium chrysogenum* is aerobic, and needs relatively high oxygen levels at all stages of growth and during the formation of the secondary metabolites (penicillin). It is difficult to maintain thorough oxygenation in very large bioreactors. The nutrient medium for the growth of *P. chrysogenum* is usually based on either corn steep liquor, a by-product of starch manufacture, or on a commercially produced nitrogen source. In addition, another nitrogen source such as yeast extract and a good carbon source in the form of lactose are often added. The production of penicillin by the mould is very

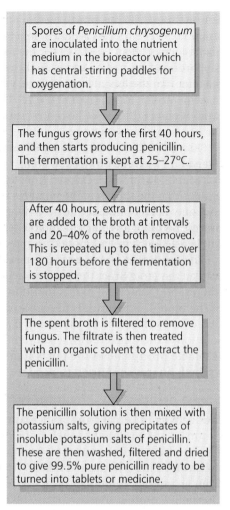

Spores of *Penicillium chrysogenum* are inoculated into the nutrient medium in the bioreactor which has central stirring paddles for oxygenation.

The fungus grows for the first 40 hours, and then starts producing penicillin. The fermentation is kept at 25–27°C.

After 40 hours, extra nutrients are added to the broth at intervals and 20–40% of the broth removed. This is repeated up to ten times over 180 hours before the fermentation is stopped.

The spent broth is filtered to remove fungus. The filtrate is then treated with an organic solvent to extract the penicillin.

The penicillin solution is then mixed with potassium salts, giving precipitates of insoluble potassium salts of penicillin. These are then washed, filtered and dried to give 99.5% pure penicillin ready to be turned into tablets or medicine.

Figure 7.4.16 A summary of the production of penicillin.

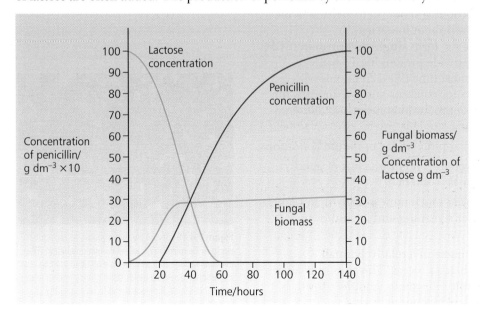

Figure 7.4.17 Graph of fungal biomass production and penicillin concentration with time.

sensitive to pH, so the growth medium also contains a buffer to maintin the pH at around 6.5. The process is quite temperature sensitive and the bioreactors are maintained at about 25–27 °C. For the first 40 hours of the process a large proportion of the carbon source in the medium is used up to produce new fungus, but after that the fungal biomass increases very little and the resources are used to make penicillin, as shown in figure 7.4.17. As the fungal biomass increases, the broth becomes thicker so the central stirring paddles have to be very strong to keep the liquid moving without being broken.

Once penicillin production is well underway, new nutrients are added at regular intervals to keep the production going as long as possible. At the same time 20–40 per cent of the broth is removed from the fermenter. This semicontinous process ensures that the growth of the mould is controlled but that penicillin production continues at an optimum rate for as long as possible. After about 180 hours the process becomes less efficient and the fermentation is stopped. At this point the whole reaction vessel is emptied and sterilised before the process is started again.

The broth that is removed at intervals and the final broth are treated in similar ways to extract the pure penicillin. The penicillin is secreted by the fungus, and almost all of it is found in the liquid broth rather than in the tissue of the mould. The broth is filtered to remove the fungus and then the penicillin is extracted by dissolving in an organic solvent. The penicillin solution is then mixed with a solution of potassium salts, which produces an insoluble precipitate of the potassium salt of penicillin. This salt can then be washed, filtered and dried to produce almost pure penicillin.

Single cell protein – food for the future?

Productivity of cereal crops is increasing all over the world. But as developing countries are tending to switch from a largely plant-based diet to one that relies much more heavily on meat (animal protein), the demand for grain is rocketing. This is because it takes 3–10 kg of grain to produce 1 kg of meat from an animal. A number of major research projects have been looking at alternative protein sources for use both as animal feed and for human consumption. These projects have been driven largely by the need to find new plentiful protein sources to ensure that starvation and malnutrition become less rather than more common as the world population climbs. So far the technology is not wide-spread or cheap enough to tackle the problems of malnutrition and starvation in developing countries, but there are now some promising products on the market. The new protein foods involve microorganisms – bacteria or fungi – hence the term **single cell protein (SCP)**.

Microorganisms are the ideal choice to provide protein for a variety of reasons. They double their mass in a very short time (20–120 minutes compared with 2 weeks for grass, 2–4 weeks for chickens and 1–2 months for cattle). They are more suitable as a source of protein than most conventional animals or plants for the reasons listed below.

● Microorganisms grow and reproduce very rapidly under optimum conditions.

● Microorganisms have a relatively high protein content which is of good nutritional value and they also have a low fat content.

● Microorganisms can be genetically modified much more readily than plants and animals, and can be grown quickly for screening and in studies to develop the best operating conditions.

● Microorganisms can be grown in vast numbers in a relatively small fermenting vessel using a continuous or batch process. This uses only a very small area of land to produce large amounts of protein, and the growth is completely independent of climate, unlike conventional crops.

Figure 7.4.18 One of the major problems facing the world is the massive growth in human population. The ever increasing millions of people all need feeding, and in particular everyone needs good quality protein food to grow to their full potential and to be as healthy as possible.

- Microorganisms can grow on a wide range of raw materials, particularly low value wastes. Some can even grow on cellulose.

SCP has been produced on a wide variety of nutrients. Originally some of these were compounds resulting from the petrochemical industry, but there was concern both about using a non-renewable energy source in the production of food and also about the possibility of traces of carcinogenic chemicals passing into the SCP. More recently various wastes, including molasses (waste syrup from the production of sugar), whey, waste fruits and wood, and the starchy wastes produced when vegetables such as potatoes are processed, have been used in bioreactors to produce SCP.

SCP is usually a very bland foodstuff, with relatively little flavour, so it has easily been incorporated as a high protein feed for animals, allowing more cereals and vegetables to remain available for humans. For some time SCP was not aimed at the human food chain, as microorganisms have a relatively high proportion of DNA and RNA as part of their cell contents and humans are not good at dealing with nucleic acids. Their metabolism produces lots of uric acid, which can cause kidney stones and gout. Before SCP is used as human food it needs additional processing to break down some of the nucleic acids.

So far there is one great success story in the development of SCP as a human food. In the 1960s scientists were predicting that there would be a severe worldwide protein famine as a result of the massive increase in the human population. J Arthur Rank, chair of the massive food production group Rank Hovis MacDougall, set in motion a research programme to develop a new protein food. Although the protein famine has not happened in the way predicted, the SCP food which was developed now forms the basis for a range of very successful products on the UK market, and is set to be marketed across the world. As more of the food is manufactured and the prices fall, it may yet fulfil the original dream.

To begin with, a suitable microorganism had to be found. It was decided that a fungus would be more suitable than a bacterium to make a food which people would like to eat, which would take up flavours easily and which could be shaped and textured in different ways. The initial screening process took a good deal of time, and around 3000 fungi from all over the world were collected and tested. Apart from growing quickly in relatively simple conditions, the fungus had to be safe to eat and the final product had to be high in protein, nutritious and palatable. Eventually, the most suitable fungus turned out to be one found in a Buckinghamshire field just four miles from the company's research laboratories. *Fusarium* grows rapidly in maize syrup, and years of work went into determining the ideal conditions needed in the bioreactors. At this stage ICI joined the project, as the company had considerable experience of manufacturing SCP using methanol, but the methanol had recently become too expensive for the

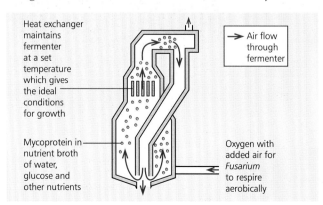

Heat exchanger maintains fermenter at a set temperature which gives the ideal conditions for growth

Air flow through fermenter

Mycoprotein in nutrient broth of water, glucose and other nutrients

Oxygen with added air for *Fusarium* to respire aerobically

Figure 7.4.19 A mycoprotein fermenter. Each fermentation lasts 6–8 weeks, with broth being extracted and new nutrients added throughout the process.

animal feed process to continue. The two industrial giants set up a new company, Marlow Foods, dedicated to the development and manufacture of the new **mycoprotein** (protein from fungus).

The fermentation of *Fusarium* was a completely novel process. Unlike other fungal fermenters, the mycoprotein is produced in a continuous culture system which runs for weeks at a time. All the operating conditions are monitored and controlled by computer. The mycoprotein grows quickly, doubling its mass every 5 hours or so. The broth containing the mycoprotein is harvested regularly and new nutrients added. Once removed from the fermenter, the mycoprotein is separated from the rest of the broth by filtration and then

The high protein, low fat food

The drive behind the development of Quorn was the expected need for a high protein food to feed the world. However, it was important for Quorn to be marketed successfully in the UK first. Not only would it seem very suspect to offer another country a new protein food not eaten in Britain, but also Marlow Foods is a company not a charity. To be able to increase the production of mycoprotein to the levels necessary to have an impact on the international scene, the food had to be a commercial success in the UK.

Unforeseen developments in the productivity of traditional crops have meant that the protein famine has not happened in quite the expected way. However, at the same time, there has been an increasing awareness in developed countries of the need to reduce the levels of fat, particularly animal fat, in the diet. This provided Quorn with a niche in the market. It is now perceived, partly as a result of strong advertising, as 'healthy food' and 'fun, innovative food'. This, combined with a product which tastes good and is very versatile, means Quorn has been very successful, both in the UK and internationally.

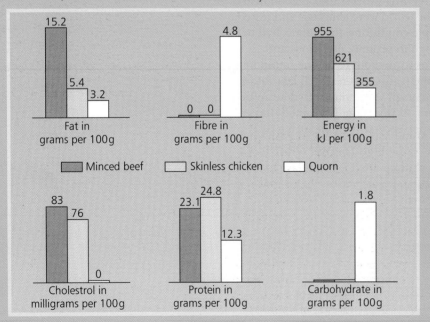

Figure 7.4.20 The nutritional content of Quorn compared with beef and chicken.

subjected to heat treatment to break down most of the nucleic acids. It is then steam washed and filtered again on a horizontal bed to remove the products of RNA and DNA breakdown before being rapidly dried or frozen to prevent contamination by other microorganisms.

The mycoprotein collected at the end of the production process is a pale, creamy yellow paste with just the faintest taste of mushrooms. On its own it has little flavour, but it can be given a wide range of tastes and textures. Mycoprotein is high in protein but low in fat. It is marketed as **Quorn**™, sold both as chunks and as mince for people to use in their own recipes and in a wide range of prepared foods like burgers, sausages, pies, crunchy fillets and kormas. Whether it will ever be possible to manufacture this type of mycoprotein cheaply enough to feed the starving millions of the world population remains to be seen, but Quorn has been a very successful first in the field, and it is certainly possible that as a result of this development in food technology more of the food shortage problems of the world will be met in the future.

The food on the shelves

Part of the process of the mass production of food involves making food which looks good, tastes palatable, does not cost too much and lasts for as long as possible. To make all this possible, food technologists have come up with a range of solutions which often mean adding a little something to the food products before they leave the factory.

For many hundreds of years people have preserved food against the decay caused by microorganisms. Food is kept usable for long periods of time by salting, smoking, pickling, canning, freezing and drying. During the twentieth century, we have gone further in the preservation, production and presentation of food. New chemical **additives** make food last longer, have a more reliable taste and look better on supermarket shelves. Chemicals have been introduced to make food production easier, and to make sure our food has a good texture.

In 1978 the Commission of the European Community issued a directive to member states requiring them to list food additives not only by category ('colour' or 'preservative'), but also by name or **E-number** (for example, 'tartrazine' or 'E102'). All colourings that are permitted to be used in foods in the EC have an E-number that identifies them.

Sweeteners

The majority of people have a sweet tooth, and in the USA and Europe people consume the equivalent of about 57 kg of sucrose per head per year! But nowadays not all of the sweeteners added to our food are glucose and sucrose, and artificial sweeteners are widely used.

In the 1970s, enzyme technology using immobilised enzymes (see Chapter 7.5) made it possible to break down starch to make high fructose syrup. Corn starch is exposed to a mixture of enzymes including amyloglucosidase to break down any branching, and amylase to break the polysaccharide chains down to glucose. Immobilised glucose isomerase is then used to change just over 50 per cent of the glucose into its sweeter isomer, fructose. This sweet syrup adds more sweetness for fewer calories, and so it is widely used in foods today.

There are also a range of artificial sweeteners which are widely used as additives in food. They taste incredibly sweet – far sweeter than the naturally occurring sugars – and they are almost entirely indigestible by the body. In one way they help in controlling the calorie intake, but they do nothing towards re-educating the taste towards less sweet foods. Artifical sweeteners include saccharin, aspartame and most recently thaumatin, the sweetest compound known. There have been a number of health scares about the safety of these

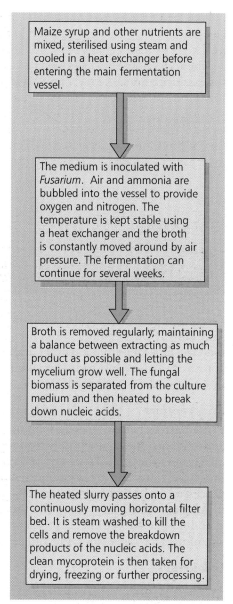

Maize syrup and other nutrients are mixed, sterilised using steam and cooled in a heat exchanger before entering the main fermentation vessel.

The medium is inoculated with *Fusarium*. Air and ammonia are bubbled into the vessel to provide oxygen and nitrogen. The temperature is kept stable using a heat exchanger and the broth is constantly moved around by air pressure. The fermentation can continue for several weeks.

Broth is removed regularly, maintaining a balance between extracting as much product as possible and letting the mycelium grow well. The fungal biomass is separated from the culture medium and then heated to break down nucleic acids.

The heated slurry passes onto a continuously moving horizontal filter bed. It is steam washed to kill the cells and remove the breakdown products of the nucleic acids. The clean mycoprotein is then taken for drying, freezing or further processing.

Figure 7.4.21 A summary of the production of Quorn.

Which is the sweetest one of all?

Table 7.4.1 gives a comparison of the sweetness of a number of commonly used sweeteners in food.

Sweetener	Relative sweetness
Sucrose	1
55 per cent high fructose corn syrup	1.4
Cyclamate	50
Aspartame	150
Saccharin	300
Thaumatin	3000

Table 7.4.1

sweeteners in the diet, and aspartame in particulr was linked to cancer in one scare story. However, these substances have to undergo rigorous testing before they are allowed onto the market: it took ten years for aspartame to be approved. This is only right, because they are used in enormous quantities throughout the food industry.

Preservatives

Preservatives help to prevent food from decaying. Many preservatives work as **antioxidants.** Fats are naturally oxidised, causing them to go rancid which affects both the appearance and the smell of the food. Antioxidants prevent this happening, and are used to extend the shelf life of a wide range of processed foods that contain fats. Examples of antioxidants added to foods include **ascorbic acid** (vitamin C), **tocopherol** (vitamin E), and chemicals such as sodium metabisulphite. This last preservative can case problems, as the chemical can trigger wheezing and asthma in some people.

Colourings

Much of the processed food we buy is highly coloured. Home-prepared food generally looks less 'perfect' and the colours in home-made jams fade with time and exposure to light. Manufacturers want the food they sell always to look the same. Also, many processed foods would have an unappetising colour without a bit of help, so food labels often show lists of colourings. These colourings are some of the more controversial modern additions to processed food. Examples of synthetic colourings include **tartrazine** (E102) **chocolate brown HT** (E155), **sunset yellow** (E110) and **indigo carmine** (E132), which are all coal tar dyes derived from the petrochemical industry. Permitted natural colourings include **beta carotene**, extracted from naturally yellow/orange sources such as carrots, and **cochineal,** which is made from an extract of crushed insects! There is evidence to suggest that some food colourings may have adverse effects on health. Some permitted coal tar dyes have been shown to be carcinogenic (cancer-causing) in laboratory animals. There is evidence to link other permitted colourings to hyperactivity, eczema and asthma in children, and even in some cases to fits.

There has been a wave of public reaction against the use of artificial colourings in food, and in response the food industry has reduced the number of colourings it uses, and switched to using more natural food colourings. In the Food Act 1974 in Britain, recommendations were made that colourings should not be added to food specifically targeted at babies and young children, and the food industry agreed to a voluntary ban on the use of additives in food for children of 18 months and under.

Flavourings

Flavourings are being used in increasing amounts as food manufacturers create more 'new' foods. For example, many desserts which are strawberry or raspberry or banana flavoured contain no real fruit at all – all the flavour comes from additives. Some flavourings are of natural origin, extracted from real fruit or herbs or spices, such as **vanilla**, **quinine** and **menthol**. Many others are synthetic, straight from the chemistry laboratory. There is a whole industry making new flavourings for an enormous range of foods – how many different flavour crisps can you think of?

Flavour enhancers are used in foods that contain artificial flavourings and also in those with only natural flavourings. Probably the oldest known flavour enhancer is salt. Both salt and sugar have been added to foods for centuries, but they need to be used sparingly. Excess salt in the diet can lead to kidney problems and is linked to hypertension (high blood pressure). Excess sugar can lead to tooth decay and obesity. A more modern flavour enhancer is **monosodium glutamate**, which has been linked to hyperactivity in some children and to headaches, nausea and restlessness in adults who eat a lot of it.

Additives and hyperactivity

During the 1970s an American, Dr Feingold, became convinced that many of the hyperactive children he was seeing were being affected by food additives. He devised a diet free of foods containing certain additives, including monosodium glutamate, and although many of his peers criticised his thesis as unscientific and unproven, large numbers of parents with hyperactive children adopted the diet or simplified versions of it and felt that the behaviour of their children was substantially changed. The Feingold diet was taken up in America first, and then in Canada, Australia and New Zealand. In the late 1970s it began to be introduced in Britain, where the link between hyperactive behaviour and food additives is now taken more seriously by many health professionals.

In spite of increasing public awareness that food additives may cause some health problems, the overall consumption of additives continues to soar. The social changes in Britain during the 1980s and 1990s, with increasing numbers of people unemployed or on low wages, and with more women choosing or needing to work, have had an effect on shopping and eating habits. Pre-packed, ready-prepared meals of all sorts are popular, and these often contain large numbers of different additives. It has been estimated that an average British 12-year-old will have consumed around 250g of additives!

Food storage and packaging

Once food has been produced it very often undergoes a period of storage before it arrives in the shops or markets to be sold. Earlier in this book (section 4.5) the changes which take place in fruits after ripening have been described. They continue to change colour, soften and develop sweetness. But because they also continue respiring, water is constantly being lost. Measures which can reduce this water loss – covering the fruit surface with a thin layer of wax, keeping fruit and vegetables in cold storage to slow down respiration – are frequently used. Spoilage by microorganisms is another problem which we have considered before. Food may be dried, or sprayed with antifungal chemicals to try and prevent attack by microbes. Manipulation of the storage atmosphere, with high levels of nitrogen or other gases, also helps to slow ripening and prevent damage by microbes.

Much manufactured food is packaged before it reaches the consumer. This packaging has various functions. To protect the food inside from damage, cardboard and polystyrene containers can be used. To display the food to best advantage, transparent plastic is widely used. The plastic can also help to control the atmosphere around the product: it minimises any diffusion of gases into or out of the package, so it extends shelf-life. In shrink wrapping, the food is wrapped in a film which is then heated briefly, making it shrink to fit exactly round the package. This effectively seals out as much as possible. When food is vacuum packed, either before freezing or simply for display, the air is drawn out of the packaging before it is sealed so that the food is effectively in an anaerobic environment, greatly reducing the likelihood of decay. In some types of packaging the products are placed in a nitrogen atmosphere before the package is sealed, again depriving any microorganisms of the oxygen they need to thrive. Alternatively, food may be frozen, tinned, bottled, salted or even irradiated; all of these methods help to preserve it for as long as possible by destroying or inhibiting microbes. The battle between the food producers and the microbes who, given the chance, would take first pickings, is not going to end in the near future.

SUMMARY

- **Biotechnology** is the use of living organisms, or enzymes derived from them, to carry out processes for people, such as the manufacture or breakdown of a material.

- The desired end-product of the process may be the microorganism itself, or it may be a product of its normal metabolism (a **primary metabolite**), or a product of the organism's action on a primary metabolite (a **secondary metabolite**).

- **Screening** is carried out to find a suitable microorganism for a new biotechnological process.

- Once selected, the microorganism is repeatedly cultured under sterile conditions. The process is **scaled up** and optimum conditions of temperature, pH and oxygen levels are found. Microorganisms may be grown on a large scale by:

  - **batch culture**, in which microorganisms and medium are place in the reactor, allowed to grow and then the reactor is emptied and sterilised and the process is started again

  - **semicontinuous culture**, which is like batch culture except that extra nutrients are added at intervals to extend the life of the culture.

  - **continuous culture**, in which there is a continuous throughput of material, as nutrients are added and medium is removed regularly, keeping the volume constant.

  At the end of the culture, the desired end-product is removed from the resulting mixture of microorganisms, medium and waste products by **downstream processing**.

- **Bread** is made from flour, combined with other ingredients and yeast. Carbon dioxide from the fermentation of the yeast causes the dough to rise, then it is cooked.
- **Sauerkraut** is cabbage preserved by a combination of salt and fermentation.
- **Soy beans** are very indigestible in their raw state, so various methods are used to make more digestible soy products.
  - To produce soy sauce, soy beans are mixed with wheat flour and then undergo two-stage fermentation, first with the mould *Aspergillus oryzae*, then with a yeast from the *Candida* family. The soy sauce is then matured, pasteurised and finally clarified by adding kaolin.
  - To make tofu, soy beans are first soaked, boiled and strained to make soy milk. The curds from soy milk form tofu, a food high in protein and low in fat.
- Milk is treated before consumption or being used to make yoghurt or cheese to help prevent the growth of microorganisms in it by:
  - **pasteurisation** (heating to 71.7 °C for 15 seconds)
  - **ultraheat treatment** (**UHT**) (heating to 132.2 °C for at least 1 second)
- Cheese and yoghurt are the main foods made from milk. Cheese production involves enzymes while yoghurt is made using bacteria.
- In **brewing**, yeast converts the carbohydrate in a cereal such as barley into ethanol. Beer, ale or lager are produced.
- **Penicillin** is produced using the aerobic fungus *Penicillium chrysogenum* in relatively small fermenters which are stirred to keep them aerated.
- In a sewage farm the organic parts of the solid waste are digested by **anaerobic microbes**. (The methane produced by this process can be used as an energy source to run the sewage farm.) The liquid waste is treated by **protoctists** which digest the potentially harmful bacteria. The liquid effluent from a sewage farm is sufficiently clean to be pumped harmlessly into rivers or the sea. The sludge is either used as a fertiliser or dumped at sea.
- **Single cell protein** is food that is high in protein and low in fat, produced by microorganisms in a bioreactor. An example is **mycoprotein** (quorn).
- In order to mass-produce food that looks and tastes good, has a long shelf-life and does not cost too much, the food industry uses the following additives: sweeteners, preservatives, colourings and flavourings.
- The food industry has developed methods of storing and packing foods to lengthen their shelf-life and improve their appearance and convenience. Fresh fruit and vegetables can be protected from water loss by cold storage and by covering them with a thin layer of was. Drying, storage with high levels of nitrogen or spraying with antifungal chemicals helps to protect food from microbes. Food can also be frozen, tinned, bottled, salted, irradiated, shrink-wrapped or vacuum-packed, all methods aimed principally at destroying or inhibiting microbes.

1 a What are the main difficulties of finding a suitable microorganism for a new biotechnological process?

b What are the main factors that need to be controlled in a large scale bioreactor and why do they need such careful control?

c How is control of the different factors brought about?

d What is meant by **downstream processing** and why is it often so expensive?

2 Make a table to summarise the main foodstuffs made as a result of biotechnology, along with the source material (e.g. barley, hops) and the process by which they are made (e.g. anaerobic fermentation by yeast).

3 a Single cell protein (SCP) was developed to overcome a predicted problem in the food supply – what was this problem and did it materialise?

b What is SCP and how is it manufactured?

c What is the major problem for a company introducing a completely new foodstuff?

d What were the advantages of SCP that the manufacturers of Quorn were able to exploit to gain a strong market position for their product?

4 The food industry is worth billions of pounds world-wide and much of the food available has been processed in a variety of ways to make it more profitable for the producer and, in some cases at least, more palatable for the consumer. Explain the reasons for the following additions to the food in our shops.

a sweeteners

b preservatives

c colourings and flavourings

d plastic packaging.

Developing Key Skills

Using the focus material at the beginning of this chapter as your starting point, research into the life and work of Louis Pasteur. Find out as much as you can about the man and his family. At the same time, investigate his contribution to our understanding of microbiology and the role of microorganisms in fermentation, food decay and disease. Produce a short biography that could be used with pupils at the top of KS3 or KS4 to introduce them to both the life and work of a great scientist and also to give them an introduction into the importance of microbiology.

A genetically modified (GM) plant contains genes that have been added to its genome from another organism (a plant or an animal) in the process known as genetic engineering (see pages 725–735). With this technology we can give plants tailor-made genes for a particular property in the space of one generation.

At the very end of the twentieth century the UK press focussed very heavily on the perceived dangers of what they dubbed 'Frankenstein foods'. Public fears were stirred up further when one scientist claimed to have shown that GM potatoes caused cancer in rats (even though many other scientists expressed reservations about the validity of the work). The public, already uneasy about food production after the problems with BSE in cattle and *E. coli* and *Salmonella* food poisoning, became increasingly concerned and food retailers and restaurants began to display notices claiming that they did not stock or use GM food. In response Monsanto, one of the major biotechnology companies involved in the development of GM crops, ran a series of adverts to explain the technology and its advantages and set up an infomative web-site.

Both pro- and anti-GM food lobbies have some valid ethical and scientific points to make, but it is useful to examine them away from the dramatic presentation of the media.

Figure 1 Legislation ensured that GM foods had to be labelled as such in an attempt to give consumers choice.

Pro-GM food/plants	Anti-GM food/plants
• GM crops are kind to the environment – of 27.8 million hectares of GM crops planted in the USA, 71 per cent were resistant to herbicides, others resistant to insects, weeds and diseases, which has led to a reduction in the use of chemical sprays.	• When plants are engineered to produce insecticides, resistant insect strains will soon appear. This can be prevented by planting GM-crop-free refuges – but will this happen?
• Genetic modification has the potential to solve the problem of feeding the world by the development of crops tolerant of drought, poor soil, frost, etc.	• GM crops are expensive – plants modified to survive in extreme environments will be too expensive for those countries to afford. Benefits will always tend to be with the big growers.
• GM crops have the potential to make the food we do produce last longer and therefore go further – for example, genes to prevent over-ripening mean less food is wasted.	• Genetic modification can be used to produce plants which will grow in the developed world conditions but produce commodities usually bought from the developing world, taking trade from where it is needed.
• 'Terminator' genes can be inserted into plants to prevent them producing fertile seeds. This stops fears of the engineered genes 'escaping' into the wild gene pool and 'superweeds' developing.	• The use of 'Terminator' genes to stop superweeds would also force people in developing countries into buying seed every year instead of saving seed from their own crop to replant.
	• It is unnatural – we shouldn't 'play God'. For some people GM food is a step too far.
	• To identify cells which have taken up foreign DNA antibiotic-resistant markers are often used. There are fears that this could increase the spread of antibiotic resistance in humans, animals and microbes.

Table 1

In both cases there are strong ethical arguments. Surely we have a duty to realise the potential benefits of GM food in increasing food production, doing away with hunger around the world and reducing the dependence of agriculture on toxic chemicals? On the other hand, we also have a duty to ensure that any organisms we produce are safe both for ourselves and for the environment, and that any benefits which come from such developments are for the whole of humanity, not just the large multinational companies who are driving the' technology forward. GM food certainly gives us something to chew on!

7.5 Technology and genetic manipulation

Background to enzyme technology

Enzymes are complicated protein molecules made by living cells. They speed up chemical reactions within a cell without changing the conditions in the cytoplasm – in other words, they act as biological catalysts. Most enzymes are highly specific and catalyse only a few reactions, or even just one. Most are highly active – only a tiny amount of enzyme is needed to catalyse the reaction. The catalytic function of an enzyme is largely due to the intricate folding of the protein molecule. Changes in pH or temperature change the three-dimensional structure of a protein, and this is why enzymes are easily inactivated or denatured by such changes.

Many enzymes can be separated out from the contents of the cell and still continue to act as catalysts, and this discovery has led to a rapidly developing **enzyme technology**, the use of enzymes in industrial processes. Enzymes are of great value in biotechnology because their very specific actions can result in relatively pure products with few by-products, needing quite simple purification procedures. Enzymes are also non-toxic and biodegradeable, so they form an environmentally friendly part of the industrial process.

As described in chapter 7.4, microorganisms have been used because of their enzymes for thousands of years in the technologies of beer- and wine-making and in the baking of bread. It is only more recently that enzymes have been used in isolation.

Enzymes and leather

Figure 7.5.1 Tanning in the nineteenth century was an unpleasant and extremely smelly process.

Leather has always been regarded as a useful and important product in Europe. It is made by **tanning** the hide of an animal such as a cow or goat. This means treating the hide with a tanning agent such as a plant extract containing a brown substance called tannin, or with fish oils or formaldehyde. A softening agent is often used on the hide before tanning so that the resulting leather is more supple. However, the original process by which the hides were treated before tanning was particularly revolting, as a mixture of dog faeces and pigeon droppings was rubbed into the hides to soften them. At the very end of the nineteenth century the distinguished German chemist Otto Rohm discovered that it was proteases (enzymes that break down protein) in the dog faeces that had the desired effect on the leather. By 1905 he had developed a method of producing proteases from the pancreases of cows and pigs, and this was used to supply the enzymes for softening hides. He must have earned the undying gratitude of leather workers everywhere!

Microorganisms – living enzyme factories

In the mid-1950s enzyme technology developed rapidly, with microorganisms being used to produce enzymes which were then isolated. Microorganisms are particularly useful as a source of isolated enzymes for all the reasons described in chapter 7.4.

- They carry out many varied biochemical reactions so there is plenty of scope for finding a microorganism that produces any enzyme we might need.
- If the yield of the desired enzyme is low, it can be increased by selection of a suitable strain, by mutation and by the modern techniques of genetic manipulation.
- Microorganisms can be cultured relatively easily in the very large numbers needed to produce sufficient enzyme.
- The nutrients they need are often relatively cheap.
- Microorganisms are a very reliable source material because they can be cultured in bioreactors, so their supply need not be affected by fluctuations in the weather, or by shortages in raw material.

Why isolated enzymes?

Many biotechnological processes still use whole microorganisms as their enzyme source, but there are clear advantages to using isolated enzymes when possible. Whole microorganisms use up a considerable part of the subtstrate simply to grow more microorganisms, converting substrate to biomass rather than to the desired end-product of the reaction catalysed by the enzyme. Isolated enzymes are present in much higher concentrations than they would be as part of the whole organism, so they are much more efficient. There are no unwanted enzymes present when isolated enzymes are used, so no wasteful side reactions take place. Also, using isolated enzymes means the ideal conditions can be used for maximum product formation. These may not be the same as the conditions needed for the maximum growth of the whole microorganism. Finally, when an industrial process involves an isolated enzyme acting on the substrate to give a desired product, downstream processing is often much simpler than when whole microorganisms are involved. With whole microbes there may be a variety of products in the final broth, making isolation and purification of the desired product much more difficult and therefore expensive.

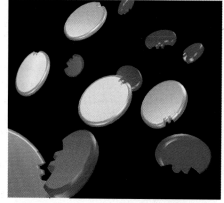

Figure 7.5.2 The shape of the active site gives an enzyme great specificity and makes it an invaluable tool to the biotechnologist.

Intracellular and extracellular enzymes

Microorganisms, like all cells, make two different types of enzymes. **Intracellular enzymes** are made inside the cell and remain there, carrying out all the biochemical reactions of life. **Extracellular enzymes** are also made inside the cell but they are secreted out of the cell into the surrounding medium. Most of the isolated enzymes used in industrial processes are extracellular enzymes produced by microorganisms. There are several reasons why extracellular enzymes are easier and therefore cheaper to use in biotechnological processes than intracellular enzymes.

- Extracellular enzymes are secreted and so are outside the cell, making them easier to isolate and use.
- Any one microorganism secretes relatively few extracellular enzymes, so it is quite easy to identify and isolate the desired enzyme. In contrast, to use an intracellular enzyme involves breaking open cells and then extracting the desired enzyme from the hundreds present in the cytoplasm.
- Intracellular enzymes, which normally work in the very controlled conditions inside the cytoplasm of the cell, are very sensitive to any changes in temperature and pH. Extracellular enzymes, because they have to work

outside the cell where conditions may be much less stable, tend to be more robust and can cope with greater variations in temperature and pH.

However, because there is a much wider range of intracellular enzymes than extracellular ones, some intracellular enzymes are used in industry, such as glucose oxidase for food preservation, asparaginase for cancer treatment and penicillin acylase for antibiotic conversion, and in future their use will probably grow.

Finding the right microorganism

As with any biotechnological process, the first important step is to find the right microorganism. In this case the microorganism must produce the enzyme needed for the industrial process. Bacteria or fungi that carry out the sort of biochemical reaction needed are obviously candidates, as they must produce the enzyme that catalyses the reaction. If the enzyme-catalysed reaction is to be part of a larger manufacturing process, the conditions of temperature, pressure and pH of the rest of the process will need to be considered, and microbes which naturally thrive in these conditions are looked for as well. Once a variety of microorganism has been collected, a process of elimination begins. The microorganisms are subjected to heat or varying levels of pH to eliminate the least likely candidates. Then they are all grown on culture media which mimic the anticipated conditions in the final process, with the anticipated substrate. The medium may contain only very specific nutrients, and may be impregnated with antibacterial or antifungal chemicals so that only a small number of possible micoorganisms go through to the final screening stages.

Now the microorganisms are screened to see if they actually do produce a useful enzyme. The microorganisms are grown on special agar containing the substrate for the desired enzyme. By observing changes in the agar around the colonies as they form, it is possible to detect whether the desired kind of enzyme activity has taken place.

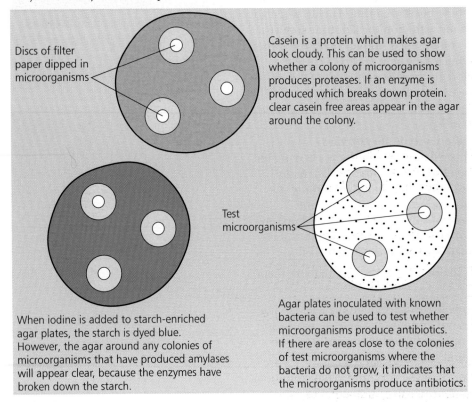

Discs of filter paper dipped in microorganisms

Casein is a protein which makes agar look cloudy. This can be used to show whether a colony of microorganisms produces proteases. If an enzyme is produced which breaks down protein. clear casein free areas appear in the agar around the colony.

Test microorganisms

When iodine is added to starch-enriched agar plates, the starch is dyed blue. However, the agar around any colonies of microorganisms that have produced amylases will appear clear, because the enzymes have broken down the starch.

Agar plates inoculated with known bacteria can be used to test whether microorganisms produce antibiotics. If there are areas close to the colonies of test microorganisms where the bacteria do not grow, it indicates that the microorganisms produce antibiotics.

Figure 7.5.3

Identifying a microorganism that makes the enzyme we are looking for is not the end of the story. The microorganism may only make a very small amount of enzyme, or it may be difficult to extract, or the conditions needed to grow the microbe may be so expensive that the product would not be financially viable. However, genetic engineering has enabled us to solve some of these problems.

If the gene for the particular enzyme protein in the microorganism can be identified, the gene can then be removed and engineered into the DNA of a microorganism that can be grown very easily, such as the mould fungus *Aspergillus oryzae*. The fungus will then produce much larger amounts of the required enzyme much more cheaply than the original microorganism.

Industrial enzyme production

Producing enzymes for use in industry is a commercial enterprise in itself. Although enormous volumes of enzymes are not usually required in industry, the microorganisms that have been selected to secrete them still need to be grown in large cultures to produce enough enzymes to supply industrial needs. The oldest method of culturing microorganisms for enzyme extraction was developed in the nineteenth century by Dr Jokichi Takamine, a Japanese scientist. In his **surface culture** or **solid substrate methods**, trays of moist wheat or rice bran with added nutrients act as the substrate for microorganism growth. The trays are maintained at constant temperature and the microorganisms grow on the surface. This method is still in use today, particularly in Japan and the Far East. It is used for the production of amylases, proteases, pectinases and cellulases of fungal origin.

However, the majority of industrial enzyme preparations are made using **submerged culture techniques**. These techniques use bioreactors similar to those used in antibiotic production, with the microorganisms growing throughout a container of liquid nutrient medium. The choice of fermentation medium is important, because this supplies all the energy needs of the microorganisms as well as providing carbon and nitrogen sources for protein (and therefore enzyme) synthesis. Most enzyme-producing bioreactors are made of stainless steel, with relatively small capacities of around $10\,000$–$50\,000\,dm^3$. Batch fermentation is usually carried out, with each batch taking between 30 and 150 hours to complete. The enzymes formed in the process may be sold as solids or liquids, and they may be highly purified or relatively crude.

The final cost of the enzyme product will depend largely on the cost of the raw materials of the nutrient broth and the cost of the downstream processing that is necesarry before the product is ready for sale. If the enzyme is intracellular, the first stage of the downstream processing is to split open the cells, which is done by either sonic shock or mechanical grinding. From then on, intracellular and extracellular enzymes are treated alike. A range of processes including reverse osmosis, various filters and centrifugation are used to isolate a relatively pure enzyme solution. A summary of the stages in the production of one isolated enzyme is shown in figure 7.5.4.

Just how pure the final enzyme product needs to be will depend on its use. Enzymes for medical use must be very pure, and need a lot of downstream processing. This makes them generally quite expensive, although they are needed in relatively small amounts. On the other hand, enzymes needed in large quantities for industries like the leather industry need not be quite so pure. This means less downstream processing is needed and so the product is less expensive.

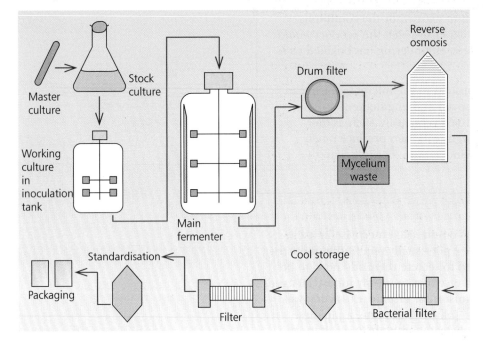

Figure 7.5.4 The main stages in the production of a liquid enzyme preparation, for example the production of proteases for the detergent market.

Producing proteases

The most common of the commercially produced enzymes are the **proteases**, widely used in washing powders and in the food industry. In fact, about 40 per cent of commercial enzyme production results in proteases, which may be from either bacteria or fungi, depending on the intended use. To make sure that the final fermentation is as efficient as possible, there is a scaling up through the industrial process.

1 A stock culture is begun in a relatively small **starter vessel**, which contains nutrient medium and is kept under ideal conditions for growth.

2 Once exponential growth is well underway, the broth is fed into the larger **seed vessel** (inoculation tank). This also contains a nutrient medium designed to encourage continued exponential growth, in order to produce enough microorganisms to introduce into the main vessel.

3 In the **main fermentation vessel** (the largest of the three, with a capacity of around $10\,000$–$50\,000\,dm^3$) rapid growth of the microorganisms continues for a few more days, but then they enter the stationary phase. There is relatively little protein in the nutrient medium in the main fermenter, although all other nutrient needs are met in full. A high level of protease secretion takes place and the microorganisms are maintained in this state for as long as possible by keeping all the conditions apart from the protein concentration at optimum levels.

4 It is very important that all the fermentation vessels are kept scrupulously clean and sterile, because other microorganisms could also grow very well on the medium, not only reducing the growth of the wanted microbes but also contaminating and possibly destroying the desired end-product.

5 Once the fermentation has finished, the enzyme must be extracted from the microbial cells, the nutrient broth and any waste products that have been

produced. A variety of processes may be used in downstream processing depending on how pure the protease needs to be.

Why change the protein concentration?

The microorganisms secrete proteases as extracellular enzymes to break down protein into amino acids. The amino acids are then taken back into the microorganisms and used for growth. During the industrial production of proteases, the starter and seed vessels contain a nutrient medium with a high protein concentration. The medium in the main fermentation vessel has a much lower protein concentration. The reason for this difference lies in what is required of the microorganisms at the different stages of the fermentation process, and the fact that the amount of the extracellular protease enzyme secreted is linked to the amount of amino acids taken in by the microorganism.

In the first two vessels, the main aim is for the microorganisms to grow and replicate as fast as possible. If there is plenty of protein in the medium the microorganisms will not secrete a lot of protease, because they will easily break down protein and absorb the amino acids they need for rapid growth. Thus in the first two protein-rich vessels, there are plenty of nutrients available to encourage exponential growth. However, in the main vessel the aim is to encourage a stationary growth phase with microorganisms producing as much enzyme as possible. By having a low protein medium, the microorganisms need to secrete a lot of extracellular protease to make sure of a good supply of amino acids, thus providing a good harvest of protein-digesting enzyme at the end of the process.

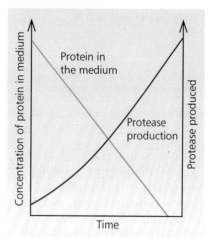

Figure 7.5.5 Relationship between protein in the medium and protease production

Industrial uses of enzymes

The enzymes produced and isolated are used in a wide variety of industrial applications. Table 7.5.1 shows some of the more important ones.

Industrial applications	Enzymes used
Biological detergents – to digest the protein dirt in clothes and on plates, occasionally to digest fat or to digest the 'bobbles' on clothing	Mainly extracellular proteases produced by bacteria Some amylases and lipases
Baking industry – catalysing the breakdown of the starch in flour to sugar, which can be used by yeast	α-amylase enzymes produced by fungi for the breakdown of starch, destroyed during baking at temperatures higher than 50 °C
Lowering the protein level in flour for biscuit manufacture	Proteases

Table 7.5.1 Industrial applications of some enzymes produced by biotechnology

Table 7.5.1 continued

Industrial applications	Enzymes used
Brewing industry – hydrolysing starches into sugars which can be used by yeast to form alcohol, and hydrolysing proteins Improving the filtration characteristics and removing cloudiness in the beer, the production of low-calorie beer	Amylases and proteases from germinating barley Industrially produced enzymes such as amylase, β-glucanase
Dairy industry – used in the manufacture of cheese, ripening of blue cheeses and breakdown of lactose to glucose and galactose	Rennin from calves' and lambs' stomachs rennin from genetically engineered microbes, enzymes such as lipase and lactase from industrial fermentations
Starch industry – converting starch into glucose and various syrups, particularly high fructose syrup	Amylases, glucose isomerase and immobilised enzymes (used a lot in the USA and Japan but restricted in the EU to protect sugar beet farmers)
Textile industry – used to remove starch on threads of certain fabrics (starch is used as 'size' to prevent damage during weaving)	Bacterial amylases
Leather industry – used to soften leather by removing certain properties and to remove hair from hides	Trypsin produced by microorganisms
Food technology – e.g. clarifying fruit juices and grape juice before wine production, producing olive oil, tenderising meat by beginning protein digestion	Pectinases produced by fungi such as *Aspergillus niger* Proteases
Medical and pharmaceutical uses – dissolving blood clots, helping digestion, as diagnostic tools	Trypsin from microorganisms and a wide range of other very pure and specialised enzymes

Biological washing powders

Commercial production and use of enzymes first started in the 1960s with the introduction of enzymes into detergents – the arrival of **biological washing powders**. There were two big advantages to these detergents. The proteases digested the protein-based dirt in the clothes, washing them cleaner, and the washes could be carried out – even *should* be carried out – at relatively low temperatures, so saving energy. Once people realised that boiling clothes was no longer necessary – in fact it made the powders work less well as the enzymes were denatured – biological washing powders became very popular. Between 1965 and 1969 sales soared. However, between 1969 and 1970 there were a number of cases of alleged allergy problems among both customers of biological washing powders and the factory workers involved in their production. These stories received a lot of media coverage and enzymes were removed from detergents. A series of precautions to protect staff in detergent factories was introduced. It was shown that it was enzyme powder touching the skin of the workers or being inhaled that was causing the problem. The enzymes were immobilised (see pages 722–723) by being put in capsules, and this reduced problems for both workers and consumer. In fact, no adverse effects on either the environment or individuals were shown once the enzymes were in capsules, and so enzymes were gradually reintroduced into detergents.

The protease enzymes used in detergents are made by bacteria. The enzymes work best in an alkaline environment and they can withstand a wider range of temperatures than the free enzymes did. This means that the enzymes will break down protein more or less regardless of the temperature chosen. Today proteases are not the only enzymes found in biological detergents – lipases (to digest fatty and oily stains) and amylases (to remove starch) are also added. The most recent addition is cellulase, which is there not to digest stains but to remove broken strands and fuzziness of the fabric.

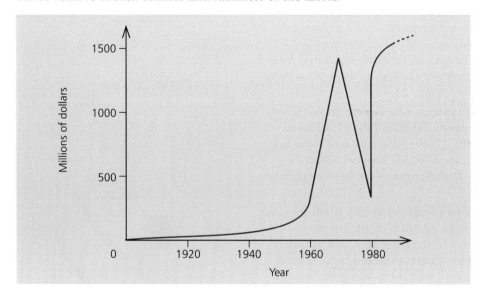

Figure 7.5.6 The fall in sales of protease enzymes was reversed by immobilising the enzymes. Trapping the enzymes in tiny capsules prevents them from being inhaled, so the proteases do not damage or irritate the respiratory systems of either factory workers or consumers.

Enzymes in food production

Enzymes are also very important in food production. Apart from the use of enzymes in the baking and brewing industries described in section 7.4, there is also a relatively big market (1 per cent of all industrial enzyme production) for pectinases. Pectin molecules are a naturally occurring part of plant walls, particularly in fruits. They have a branching structure which readily traps water to form a gel. We use this property when we make jam, but if we want to make fruit juice or wine the pectin holds the juice in the gel, and the fruit or grape juice which is extracted appears very cloudy. Pectinase enzymes are added to crushed fruit to hydrolyse the pectin molecules and make it easier to extract the juice. Pectinase is also added to cloudy fruit juice, where it again breaks down the pectin molecules and leaves clear juice. This is particularly important in making wine – a pectin haze in the grape juice will continue throughout the process and result in cloudy wine unless steps are taken along the way. Pectinases are also used in the production of olive oil, both to soften the olives and make the extraction of the oil easier, and to help make sure the olive oil is clear of pectin haze.

Biosensors

Enzymes are used in medical diagnosis in the form of **biosensors**. A biosensor may be used to find out information about the body without actually entering it. They are ideal for detecting the presence of chemicals in samples of body fluid such as blood and urine. The enzymes are extremely specific in their actions, making the results of such tests very reliable. They also act rapidly, so that results can be given to patients without long delays, and treatment can start immediately when it is needed (see page 724).

Immobilised enzymes

Holding enzymes in place

Most industrial processes which use enzymes are very wasteful. Enzymes are quite expensive to produce, but at the end of the process that uses them enzymes cannot usually be recovered and so they are simply lost. One of the newest areas of enzyme technology tackles this problem by **immobilising** the enzymes on inert and insoluble polymers. The enzymes are held stationary while they catalyse the reaction, and can then be recovered from the reaction mixture at the end of the process and reused time after time. This ability to use the enzyme repeatedly makes the process more economical, and enzymes do not contaminate the end-product.

Apart from the fact that immobilised enzymes can easily be separated from the reactants and products of the reaction they are catalysing, there seem to be other advantages too.

1 There is a high degree of control over the process when using immobilised enzymes, which are usually considerably more stable and therefore more reliable than soluble enzymes. This stability comes about because there is a microenvironment around the enzyme in its insoluble support where conditions such as pH change very little, so the enzymes are kept near their optimum conditions.

2 Many enzymes appear to be much more temperature tolerant when they are immobilised. Not only are they denatured by heat less easily, but they work at optimum levels over a much wider range of temperature. Again this is good news in an industrial process, because temperature tolerance means the reactor needs to be less tightly controlled, so it is less expensive to run.

3 The catalytic properties of immobilised enzymes can be altered to fit a particular process more easily than when using free enzymes. For example, immobilised glucose isomerase can be used continuously for over 1000 hours at temperatures of 60–65 °C. Being able to keep the bioreactors running continuously for long periods without regularly emptying and cleaning them helps to keep running costs low.

How are enzymes immobilised?

Enzymes can be immobilised by either physical or chemical means. **Physically** immobilised enzymes can be trapped in a gel, absorbed onto an insoluble matrix or encapsulated in either a microcapsule (like proteases for detergent use) or behind a selectively permeable membrane. **Chemical** immobilisation involves cross-linking the enzymes or covalently bonding them to solid supports.

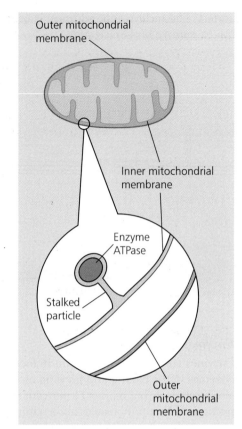

Figure 7.5.7 The stalked particles on the inner mitochondrial membrane inside the cell appear to hold the enzymes needed for ATP synthesis. Immobilising enzymes is a case of technology mimicking nature – enzymes in cells are usually bound to membranes where they carry out their catalysis repeatedly, and a similar arrangement seems to be the way forward for the industrial use of enzymes.

Method of immobilising the enzymes	Advantages	Disadvantages
Cross-linking and covalent bonding to inorganic carriers	Enzymes are unaffected by conditions such as pH and substrate concentration. They are strongly bound and therefore unlikely to be lost	Expensive Active site of the enzyme may be modified, making it less effective
Entrapment in gel and encapsulation	Enzyme activity not affected	Diffusion of the substrate to and product from the active site can be slow, holding up the reaction
Adsorption onto insoluble matrix	Relatively cheap Regeneration possible No modification of the enzyme Easy for enzyme to come into contact with substrate	Changes in ionic concentration can affect enzyme activity

Table 7.5.2 Summary of different ways of immobilising enzymes

In some cases whole microorganisms rather than enzymes may be immobilised. This has many of the same advantages but avoids the time-consuming and expensive process of extracting the pure enzyme.

There is a range of forms of immobilised enzymes – enzyme beads, enzyme capsules, enzyme membranes and enzyme columns. The bioreactors used with such immobilised enzyme systems differ from those used with free enzymes. Only a relatively small number have so far been developed on an industrial scale, but it seems certain that many more will be seen in the future.

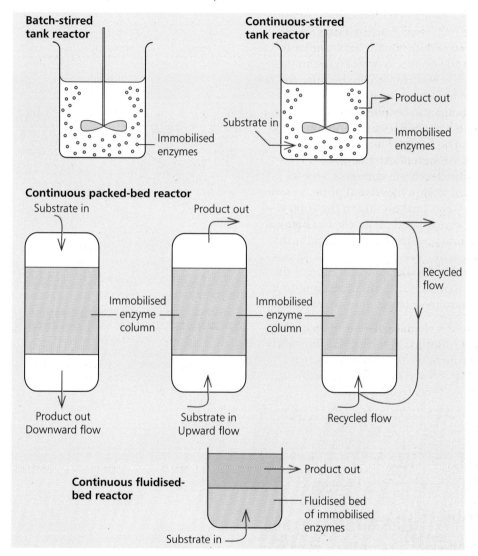

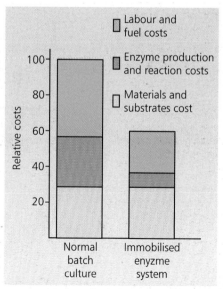

Figure 7.5.8 Some of the types of reactors used with immobilised enzymes.

Figure 7.5.9 Comparison of the industrial costs of a process using batch culture and an immobilised enzyme system.

There are some disadvantages to using immobilised enzymes, mainly related to the high initial costs of setting up new types of bioreactors and to the fact that the cost of immobilised enzymes is higher than the cost of free enzymes. However, the immobilised enzymes, unlike free enzymes, do not need to be replaced frequently. Because the reactors which use immobilised enzymes are more complicated than those using free enzymes, they have more parts that can go wrong, and they can get blocked by substrate. As with any bioreactor, contamination by unwanted microorganisms is a serious problem: it is particularly difficult to decontaminate the immobilised enzymes. But by and large the advantages of using immobilised enzymes far outweigh the disadvantages, as the graph of the relative costs in figure 7.5.9 shows.

Uses of immobilised enzymes

Immobilised enzymes are very useful if large quantities of product are needed, because they allow continuous production. In Europe, immobilised penicillin acylase is used to make penicillin derivatives from naturally produced penicillin V. These derivative drugs are important in the fight against bacterial infections that are resistant to penicillin, or that respond better to a modified penicillin molecule. Perhaps the most widely used immobilised enzyme is glucose isomerase, which is used in Japan, the USA and Europe to produce high-fructose syrups from starch-containing raw material. Thousands of tonnes of high-fructose syrup are made in this way each year. Fructose tastes much sweeter than glucose and the syrup produced is nutritionally very similar to sucrose ('sugar'), so the syrup finds a multitude of uses as a sweetener in the food industry. Glucose produced form starch is relatively cheap because the raw material is cheap. This glucose is converted to fructose by glucose isomerase.

Immobilised enzymes and microbial cells are also becoming increasingly important as diagnostic tools in medicine (see pages 616–617) and also in pharmacology – the manufacture of drugs. The fungus *Rhizopus arrhizus* is immobilised and used in the production of the steroid drug cortisone.

Biosensors are used to monitor accurately the levels of substances such as glucose, urea, amino acids, ethanol and lactic acid in blood and urine, as well as in the monitoring of waste treatment, in water analysis and in the control of complex chemical processes. Such biosensors are based on an electrochemical sensor in close proximity to an enzyme membrane. The enzymes react with a specific substrate and the products of the reaction are detected by the sensor. Because the magnitude of the response is related to the concentration of the substrate, these sensors can be very sensitive in their measurements and so may be used (for example) by diabetics, to measure their blood glucose levels and so judge the insulin dose they need.

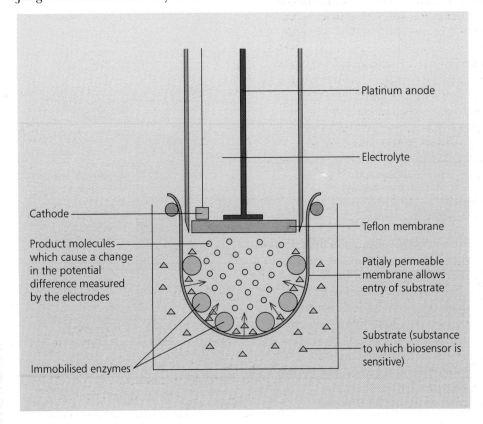

Platinum anode

Electrolyte

Cathode

Teflon membrane

Product molecules which cause a change in the potential difference measured by the electrodes

Patialy permeable membrane allows entry of substrate

Substrate (substance to which biosensor is sensitive)

Immobilised enzymes

Figure 7.5.10 Generalised diagram of a biosensor.

Genetic engineering

As biotechnology has raced forward over the last decades, one of the most exciting developments has been the ability to change the genetic material of microorganisms so that they will synthesise a chemical that we want, but that they would not naturally produce.

What is genetic engineering?

Genetic engineering is the term used to describe the process of moving genes from one genome to another – it enables an aspect of the biological functioning of an organism to be changed by altering its genetic material (usually DNA). The techniques of genetic engineering have made it possible to create new genomes which can express human genes and make human proteins.

Genetic engineering involves locating a desirable gene, isolating it and then moving it into the genome of another organism where it will be expressed. The proteins produced in response to the new piece of DNA may either have a useful effect in the host cell, or may be harvested for use elsewhere. The principles involved in genetic engineering are the same whether applied to animals, plants or bacteria.

The techniques used in genetic engineering are complex. Sometimes artificial genes are made. If the mRNA molecule transcribed from the required gene can be isolated, then it can be used to produce a gene by effectively reversing the transcription process. Using the enzyme **reverse transcriptase**, the DNA sequence of the gene can be made from the mRNA. The DNA made from mRNA by these reverse transcriptase enzymes is known as **complementary DNA** or **cDNA**, and it can act as an artificial gene. It will be shorter than natural genes because it is stripped of introns. Artificial genes are useful when very specific proteins are formed, for example, insulin production in the islets of Langerhans in the pancreas makes it possible to extract the mRNA for insulin from those cells and create artificial insulin genes for insertion into bacteria.

Special enzymes called **restriction endonucleases** chop up DNA strands, cutting them at specific sites. These enzymes, discovered in the 1970s, get the DNA into small pieces which can be handled more easily. They are naturally produced by bacteria as a protection against bacteriophages. Each type of endonuclease will only cut DNA at specific sites within a particular DNA sequence – the endonucleases are restricted in their action, and this is why they are known as restriction endonucleases. Some restriction endonucleases are particularly useful, cutting the DNA at sites where the base sequence is identical on both strands. This leaves small sticking out regions of DNA known as **sticky ends**, at which it is relatively easy to attach new pieces of DNA.

The polymerase chain reaction

One of the most important developments in DNA technology has been the **polymerase chain reaction**. It allows the amplification of a tiny fragment of DNA, making millions of copies in a few hours. It has uses in genetic engineering, diagnosis of genetic diseases, DNA fingerprinting and archaeology, and new applications are being found all the time. There are three main steps.

- The double-stranded DNA is heated (95–98 °C) making it separate into two complementary strands, which act as templates.
- Primers (short pieces of synthetic DNA) are added, and bind to the original strands acting as a signal to start copying.
- In a medium rich in nucleotides, DNA polymerase is added. The enzyme synthesises new DNA strands complementary to the template strands.

This cycle is repeated over a few hours, leading to the formation of large amounts of the desired DNA.

Even using sticky ends, the new DNA does not join tightly into the original DNA on its own. Fortunately genetic engineers found some enzymes known as **DNA ligases** which act as 'genetic glue' and join pieces of DNA together. In this way the required fragment of DNA cut from the chromosome of one organism is pasted into another piece of DNA which will carry it into the host cell. **Plasmids**, the circular strands of DNA found in bacteria, are often used as vectors to carry the DNA into the host cell. They often have specific marker genes which make it easy to show that the process has been successful. Once the plasmid is incorporated into the host nucleus it becomes part of the new **recombinant DNA** of the genetically engineered or **transformed** organism. Successfully transformed cells can be identified, isolated and cultivated on an industrial scale so that the proteins they make can be harvested for human use.

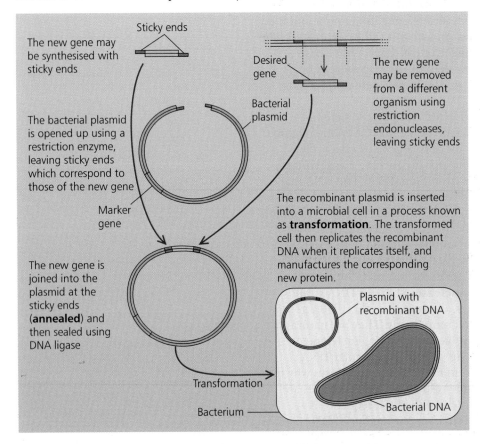

Figure 7.5.11 The main stages involved in inserting a new gene into a bacterium.

Microorganisms – the genetic engineer's friends

Microorganisms are the most commonly used organisms in genetic engineering because they are relatively easy, cheap and quick to culture. They reproduce so rapidly that a transferred gene is copied many times, very quickly, when the microbes are allowed to replicate in ideal conditions.

It is very important to be able to tell which bacteria contain the desired recombinant piece of DNA. Many plasmids contain special **marker genes** which make it easy to pick out those microbes in which a successful transformation has taken place. These markers may be characteristics such as antibiotic resistance. If the bacteria are cultured on agar containing the relevant antibiotic, then the microorganisms containing the marked genetically engineered plasmid will be easily identified because they will be the only ones able to grow. The bacteria identified in this way can then be cultured on a large scale in industrial fermenters, and the proteins which they make can be harvested.

Applications of genetic engineering

An ever-growing range of chemicals is being manufactured by genetically engineered organisms, including antibiotics such as penicillin, hormones such as growth hormone, and many enzymes. Chemicals produced by biotechnology are not always used directly on humans. For example, the cattle hormone **bovine somatotrophin** (BST) is made in large quantities and can be given to dairy cattle to increase their milk yield. There has been some controversy over whether traces of the hormone might pass into the milk and affect the health of people, particularly children, who drink a lot of milk. There was particular concern when the hormone was first used that people could not choose whether they used the milk from such cows – all the milk was simply mixed together and bottled with no information given on the label. Cows given BST have been shown to be more likely to develop mastitis, an inflammation and infection of the udder. In the USA BST is used regularly, but in the EC its use is now banned, probably more for political reasons (as there is already too much milk) than for sound scientific reasons.

Microbes and human insulin

Most people make the hormone insulin in the pancreas. Insulin is vital in maintaining a fairly steady blood glucose concentration in the body. Insulin enables glucose to get into the cells of the body, where it is used in cellular respiration to provide energy, and enables excess glucose to be converted to glycogen for storage. Insulin therefore causes glucose to be removed from the blood. When the concentration of glucose in the blood goes up, the insulin concentration rises, which in turn causes the blood glucose concentration to fall again. As the blood glucose concentration falls, so does the insulin concentration.

There are people of all ages who have problems making insulin – they suffer from **diabetes**. People with diabetes can and usually do live normal healthy lives, provided they have regular injections of insulin. Although this is not a perfect solution, it generally works very well.

The insulin for injections used to come from the pancreases of slaughtered pigs, sheep and cattle. Although the insulin from these animals is very similar to human insulin, it is not quite the same, and this caused problems for some diabetic patients. Also the supply of insulin was not always reliable, because it depended on how many animals of which type were slaughtered.

It seemed sensible to use biotechnology to develop a way of manufacturing human insulin using microorganisms. The process was difficult because the insulin molecule is made up of two polypeptide chains. To tackle this problem, scientists in the 1980s managed to introduce a synthesised gene for each chain into different bacteria, and then culture them in huge numbers. Downstream processing gave two pure chains which were then oxidised to join them together. The resulting chemical, often referred to as humulin, appears to function exactly like human insulin. Its purity is guaranteed, making it easier to calculate doses accurately. It has been a great advantage for the majority of diabetics, over 83 per cent of whom now use it. Even more recently, a synthetic gene has been developed which mimics the normal human gene for insulin and allows a molecule called **proinsulin** to be made by engineered bacteria. At the end of the process, enzymes convert proinsulin to insulin. Using microorganisms in this way solves the problems of uncertain supply and provides a constant, convenient and pure source of a human hormone. This is a clear example of the way genetic engineering and the new biotechnology have had a positive effect in human medicine.

The answer – but too late

For most parents, the birth of a baby is followed by years of pleasure mixed with amazement at the way their offspring grow and develop. But a few babies fail to grow properly. There is of course an enormous range of growth which is regarded as 'normal', but some children grow so slowly it needs to be investigated. For some of those children the cause is a lack of **growth hormone (GH)** or **somatotrophin**, the hormone secreted by the pituitary gland which stimulates growth.

For many years the problem was at least partly overcome by giving children regular injections of pituitary extract. This was made from pituitary glands taken from human corpses. The extract was very expensive and always in short supply. Genetic engineering has solved the problem of supply by producing the hormone in commercial amounts using genetically engineered microbes.

However, the solution came too late for some unfortunate children. Some of the pituitary extract had been contaminated by brain tissue from individuals who had died as a result of the very rare Creutzfeldt-Jakob disease. This is a fatal disease that affects the brain, the same disease that appears to be linked to BSE in cattle. Sadly a number of people were treated with contaminated pituitary extract before the new hormone was produced, and they died of the disease.

Biotechnology and genetic engineering – a wider view

Biotechnology does not only concern work with microorganisms. Increasingly genetic engineering is being carried out on the cells of multicellular organisms. The techniques are being applied not only to solve issues of human health, but also to improve food crops and domestic animals. In addition, 'old' biotechnology is being looked at in new ways, sometimes in conjunction with genetic engineering to try and solve some of the pressing problems facing people at the beginning of the twenty-first century.

Artificial selection

Human beings have interfered with the breeding of animals and plants since the earliest times of human civilisation. Farmers and breeders select animals or plants with a particularly useful or desirable trait and use those organisms as their breeding stock rather than other less well endowed specimens. For a selective breeding programme to work, the characteristics selected for must be heritable – if it is not genetic then the process is doomed to failure.

Selective breeding in plants has successfully produced an enormous range of cereal crops that are distantly related to original wild grasses. To produce or improve a strain of wheat is, however, a complicated and time consuming process. Apart from anything else, improving one characteristic may affect another useful feature about the plant, for example altering the protein content of the wheat seed may affect the overall yield. If a breeder wished to introduce a gene for fungal resistance into a strain of wheat, he or she might cross the wheat with a wild grass plant that is resistant to the fungus. This cross would be brought about by the transfer of pollen from the grass to the wheat in a closed environment, so no pollen from other plants could get in. The anthers of the wheat flowers would be removed to prevent self pollination. The plants

Figure 7.5.12 Selective breeding is a slow and somewhat hit-and-miss method of changing agricultural and domestic animals. It has taken hundreds of years to breed a horse like an Arab (bottom) from original wild stock probably similar to the Przewalski's horse (top).

resulting from this cross might have the resistance gene, but they would also have a large number of other undesirable genes from the grass parent. The breeder would then need to do a series of back crosses to the original wheat parent. At each stage the breeder would need to test the progeny and only continue to breed from those that still maintained the resistance gene. In this way, eventually, a plant with all the positive attributes of the original wheat plant along with the fungal resistance of the grass would be obtained, and could be used as the parent strain from then on.

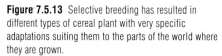

Figure 7.5.13 Selective breeding has resulted in different types of cereal plant with very specific adaptations suiting them to the parts of the world where they are grown.

Rice is a swamp plant. It has a hollow aerenchyma to support it in the water, and a tolerance to the lactic acid produced by anaerobic respiration beneath the water.

Sorghum grows in very hot, dry conditions. It has a number of xerophytic adaptations: an extensive root system to reach water deep underground, a thick cuticle and a reduced number of sunken stomata to reduce water loss, and a high temperature tolerance in both the adult and the embryo plant.

Maize is a tropical plant. It uses C_4 photosynthesis (see page 193) which is very efficient at high temperatures and is adapted to cope with low carbon dioxide concentrations.

Selective breeding of animals has resulted in the breeds of cattle, sheep and pigs that we take for granted as the farm animals of today. For example, the milk yield of Friesian dairy cattle has been greatly increased by the selection of cows with a high milk yield and bulls from strains with a high milk yield in the females. These days a farmer does not have to own such a bull: semen from an appropriate bull can be obtained in the process of artificial insemination (AI). Over time, cows with bigger yields have become the norm.

One problem with selective breeding in both plants and animals is that it can lead to **inbreeding**. This eventually results in increased genetic disorders, reduced resistance to disease and general weakness of the strain. To avoid these problems, regular outbreeding is needed – the introduction of new genetic material from a different strain of animals or plants. This ensures that hybrid vigour continues. Hybridisation in plants almost always leads to an increase in yield. The only problem is that the progeny rarely breed true, and new hybrids from the original parent strains have to be produced each year.

Genetic engineering aims both to speed up artificial selection and to make it much more targeted, changing only one gene at a time. The impact of genetic engineering on our crop plants and domestic animals is only just beginning to be seen. The potential is enormous but some would say the risks are great.

Artificial insemination

Artificial insemination is increasingly used in the breeding of cattle. Keeping a bull on a farm is often not a convenient option because:

- bulls are very large and powerful animals, and they need careful handling.

- the bull cannot remain out in the field with the cows all the time, because the farmer needs to control when matings take place in order to achieve year-round milk yield
- to introduce new genetic material, AI is a great deal easier than buying or borrowing a new bull.

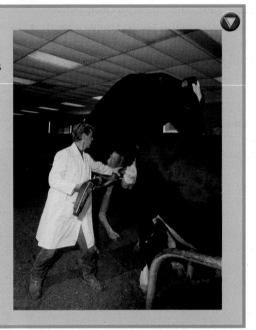

Figure 7.5.14 In AI, sperm from only the best stud males is selected and offered for sale. Bull semen is collected by persuading the bull to mount and mate with an artificial 'cow' and the semen collected can be divided into a number of different packages and frozen.

Artificial insemination allows farmers to select the characteristics they want to introduce to their stock. The disadvantages include the fact that, as the farmers do not know the bull concerned they do not know his temperament, and so risk a more aggressive or difficult temperament in their calves. Also, if a bull carries a mutation it can be a long time before this is picked up, as a farmer may only use sperm from that bull once. A recessive problem can be incorporated into a herd long before it is recognised. However, on the whole AI in cattle has been very successful. There are still plenty of bulls around servicing their cows, but the option of more selective breeding is there for any farmer who chooses to use it.

Genetic engineering of plants against insect pests

One aim of manipulating genes in agriculture is to produce biological control agents for pests and thus remove the need for crop spraying. The work is very much concentrated on pathogens that attack the pests. Gene manipulation is used on existing pathogens that act on known pest species, creating 'super-pathogens' which are much more effective against the pests. Other genetic engineering work is designed to extend the range of pest organisms affected by the pathogen. Another thrust of genetic engineering is to introduce genes from insect pathogens into plants, so that when an insect has a meal from its food plant, it also gets a dose of toxin. Genes from *Bacillus thurigiensis* (BT) have been introduced into various crop plants including cotton, potatoes and tomatoes to protect them from insect pests. Although this has been very effective, a problem has arisen in that the insects are developing resistance to the toxin.

Herbicide resistance and enhanced vegetable oils

Genetic engineering has been used to develop crop plants that are particularly resistant to herbicides. This means that the more environmentally friendly, **broad-spectrum** herbicides (that act on a wide range of plant species) can be used on crop fields to treat weeds. These herbicides are rapidly degraded by soil organisms, but previously would have killed the crop as well as the weeds. This technique has been effective in potatoes and oil seed rape. Other useful characteristics are also being enhanced by genetic engineering – for example, modification of oil-producing plants such as soya beans and rape is not only giving higher yields of oil, but also changing the composition of the oil so that it is useful for particular purposes, such as cosmetic production or lubricants.

Increased life of vegetables

During storage and transport, as much as 40 per cent of crops can be lost in the USA and Europe, and as much as 80 per cent in other areas of the world. Some of this loss is due to pests and fungi, but much is due to natural changes such as softening and ripening. This is another area where biotechnology is having a noticeable effect. For example, in tomatoes the enzyme polygalacturonase breaks down the cell walls during ripening, making the fruit soften. This softening is quite independent of the colour change as the tomato ripens. Tomatoes called 'Flavr Savr' which have an improved flavour have been engineered in the USA, but more importantly commercially, they also have an improved shelf life because the softening enzyme is inhibited by genes inserted into the DNA of the plant.

Figure 7.5.15 Engineered rape fields – or not? One of the disconcerting things about many genetically engineered crops is that there is no way for the ordinary person to tell whether the plants they see and eat are genetically engineered, because they do not usually look any different.

Making transgenic plants

Introducing genes from one type of plant into another, or even from an animal into a plant, is brought about using a particular bacterium, *Agrobacterium tumefaciens*. *A. tumefaciens* causes tumours known as crown galls in plants. It contains a plasmid called the Ti plasmid which transfers information directly into the plant DNA, usually causing abnormal growth of the plant cells. Biotechnologists have found that modified plasmids can be used instead, allowing beneficial genes into the plant genome. By the process of plant cloning, the modified transgenic cells can then be used to produce whole new transgenic plants.

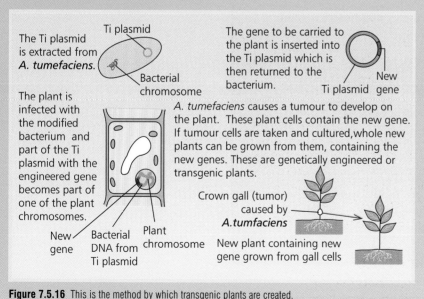

Figure 7.5.16 This is the method by which transgenic plants are created.

Genetically modified animals

Some of the most exciting recent research in genetic engineering has involved inserting human genes into the tissues of sheep and cattle to produce **transgenic animals**. Although microbes have been extremely successful at making human proteins such as insulin, prokaryotes simply do not possess the biochemistry to make some of the more complex human proteins. Work has therefore moved on to introduce desirable human genes into other eukaryotic cells. Yeast is often used, but in recent years more and more work has been done using mammals.

It is very difficult to transfer new DNA into eukaryotic cells (see information box below) but there have already been some notable successes. In 1991 the first transgenic sheep was born, a ewe called Tracey who produced the human protein alpha-1-antitrypsin in her milk. The production of proteins using transgenic animals involves the microinjection of a copy of a human gene which codes for the desired protein into the genetic material of an egg of a different animal species. As well as the gene for the specific protein there is also a promoter sequence which makes sure the gene will be expressed in the mammary gland of the lactating female. The fertilised and transgenic embryo is then replaced inside a surrogate mother. When the resulting offspring has grown to maturity and produces milk, that milk is harvested, purified and the human protein extracted.

Making transgenic animals

Getting new DNA into eukaryotic cells, particularly mammalian cells, is very difficult. A number of techniques are being tried, with varying degrees of success. The difficulty is to get the new DNA through the cell membrane and into the cytoplasm – or nucleus – where it can be accepted and incorporated into the host cell DNA. The current methods are listed below.

- **Microinjection (DNA injection)**. This involves the direct injection of DNA into a cell through a very fine micropipette. This is manipulated using a micromanipulator, because the steadiest hand would tremble enough to destroy the cell. This method is rather unreliable: many cells have to be injected before one takes up the DNA successfully. However, this method has resulted in many of the best known transgenic animals.
- **Microprojectiles**. DNA is 'shot' into the cell at high speed, carried on minute gold or tungsten pellets. A few of the cells recover from the bombardment and accept the DNA.
- **A harmless virus** can be engineered to carry a desirable gene and then used to infect the animal cells, carrying the DNA with it.
- **Liposome wrapping**. The gene to be inserted is wrapped in liposomes (spheres formed from a lipid bilayer). These fuse with the cell membrane and can pass through it to deliver the DNA into the cytoplasm.

So far transgenic sheep, cows, pigs, rabbits and mice have been produced, all capable of producing human proteins in their milk. Using large animals such as cows and sheep, large volumes of milk – and therefore of human proteins – can be achieved, and the number of animals can be increased by breeding or cloning.

More than 20 different human proteins have been produced so far using genetically modified animals, and some of them are already in therapeutic use or are being trialled. Factor VII and Factor IX are both important components of the human blood-clotting cascade which can be missing in haemophiliacs and those with other blood-clotting diseases. These factors are being harvested from transgenic milk. The protein alpha-1-antitrypsin (as produced by Tracey) seems to offer a major benefit to sufferers of cystic fibrosis and emphysema, alleviating many of their symptoms. Trials of a treatment using the transgenic protein are already underway. The milk of Tracey and others like her contains up to 35 g of the human protein in every litre of milk, a very high yield which makes the milk very expensive – it costs several thousand pounds per litre. But as the numbers of transgenic animals increase, the price will eventually come down. Activated protein C for treating deep vein thrombosis and modified milk for people with lactose and other intolerances are also being tested. The New Zealand government has agreed to the setting up of two farms running up to 10 000 transgenic sheep, which will enable a new source of human medicine to become a reality. As we unravel the mysteries of the human genome, we should come to know the genetic sequence of every chemical in our body. If many of our faulty molecules can be made for us by transgenic animals, the impact on future health and medicine could be enormous.

(See also Focus 1.6 on the use of transgenic animals in human transplantation.)

Gene therapy

One of the most exciting opportunities offered by genetic engineering is the development of **gene therapy**. A number of human genetic diseases are brought about by the presence of faulty genes inherited from the parents, and genetic engineering offers the hope that in the not-too-distant future it will be possible to replace those faulty genes with healthy copies. The disease where this is closest to becoming a reality is **cystic fibrosis** (see page 458).

A normal individual makes a protein known as **cystic fibrosis transmembrane regulator (CFTR)**. This membrane protein is involved in the transport of chloride ions out of epithelial cells and into mucus. Sodium ions

Germ line therapy

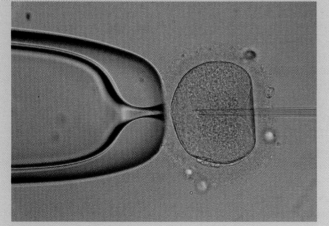

Figure 7.5.17 A human egg being microinjected: germ line engineering is for ever.

Gene therapy such as that described for cystic fibrosis offers great potential benefits to the individual sufferer. However, it does not alter the fact that their offspring will receive their faulty genes, and may even have affected children themselves, depending on the genotype of their partner. So the obvious next step is to alter the germ cells – the reproductive cells of the body – so that the faulty genes are no longer passed on. The most obvious place to carry out this intervention would be in the very early embryo immediately after *in vitro* fertilisation. The individuals developing from such embryos would then be free from the disease, and free from the risk of passing it on to their offspring. At first sight this seems a very positive idea, and there are some who would argue that when the technology is available it should be used, but there are many others who would sound a note of caution.

No-one is yet sure what effect such an invasive intervention would have on an early embryo, and the impact might not become clear until years into the life of the individual. In addition, such manipulation of the human genome is seen as a Pandora's box. Whilst attempting to remove the risk of genetic diseases seems a very positive aim, it would be difficult to know where to draw the line and some people may be prepared to pay a great deal of money to have the line moved a little. If it became possible not simply to remedy disease but to enhance longevity, change skin colour, increase adult height or reduce adult weight by gene therapy, people would be tempted to try it. At the moment most aspects of germ line research are banned in the UK, most European countries and the USA. But sooner or later, someone somewhere will start the ball rolling. We need to decide which way we are going to jump before we are put on the spot.

Health and safety and genetically engineered organisms

Genetically engineered organisms are still a very new phenomenon. Careful legislation is in place to make sure that the risk from any newly engineered organism is kept to a minimum.

Physical containment of the organisms is important. In laboratories where genetic engineering work is carried out, people have to take precautions to ensure that they do not release their experimental material into the outside world. Similarly there are tight restrictions on the manufacturing plants that make drugs and vaccines using genetically engineered organisms, not only in the fermentation process but also in the downstream processing.

Biological containment is also important. For example, microbial pesticides have to be sprayed onto fields of crops so physical containment is inappropriate. In this situation scientists engineer organisms with suicide genes, or genes that prevent them from growing without a particular chemical. Alternatively organisms can be engineered which are effective even when they are dead through toxins they have produced, so only killed cells need to be released.

There are also concerns about certain aspects of the process of genetic engineering, such as the use of antibiotic-resistance markers in bacteria, and scientists are working all the time to ensure that the new biotechnologies are not only beneficial, but also safe.

follow the chloride ions, changing the osmotic potential so that water too moves out into the mucus by osmosis. This keeps the mucus thin and runny so it can be moved about by the cilia on the epithelial cells. Individuals suffering from cystic fibrosis inherit two recessive genes, one from each parent, and this results in a mutant form of CFTR. It is only one amino acid different from the normal form, but that is enough to interfere with chloride transport. Without the chloride movement there is no sodium flow either, and no osmotic water movement. As a result the mucus in the airways, gut and other areas of the body is almost solid, and cannot be moved naturally, so patients rely on physiotherapy and antibiotics to help them overcome the infections to which they are prone.

Genetic engineering offers the opportunity of putting right the defects, in the lungs at least. The idea is to isolate and clone healthy CFTR genes. These

Figure 7.5.18 The future of the Earth is in the hands of the people who live on her. Biotechnology will play a major part in that future.

will then be introduced to the lung epithelial cells using either harmless viruses or lipid encapsulaton. Once inside the lung epithelial cells the healthy genes should be transcribed, producing the normal, active protein and relieving the symptoms. Cystic fibrosis looks set to be the first of many human complaints that may be relieved by the application of gene therapy.

What does the future hold?

No-one can gaze into a crystal ball and see what will happen to the world in the future. We do know there are many problems to be solved. Changes in our energy sources will be forced upon us in the next century or two by the depletion of the stocks of fossil fuels.

Using biotechnology to develop biomass may well have a role in their replacement. The production of sufficient food for everyone on the planet, the manufacture of appropriate drugs in large enough quantities to cope with all the diseases spread across the world, dealing with the massive problems of an overcrowded planet – there are so many major problems which biotechnology will surely help us solve. Whether this will be using modifications of the fermentation and genetic engineering techniques we know today, or some new biotechnology as yet undiscovered, we must wait and find out. Only time will tell.

SUMMARY

- **Enzymes** are proteins made by living cells that act as specific biological catalysts. **Enzyme technology** is the use of **isolated** enzymes (instead of whole microorganisms) to carry out particular reactions.

- Enzymes may be produced by a microorganism and act inside the cell (**intracellular enzymes**), or they may be secreted by the cell (**extracellular enzymes**). Extracellular enzymes are easier to isolate and are generally more tolerant of temperature and pH changes, but intracellular enzymes are used in biotechnological processes if they are the only ones available to catalyse the desired reaction.

- A microorganism that produces the desired enzyme is found by screening. It is then grown in large numbers either by **surface** or **solid substrate culture** (on large trays of solid medium) or by a **submerged culture technique** in which the microorganism grows throughout a liquid medium in a batch process. The enzyme is separated from the medium by various methods during **downstream processing**.

- **Proteases** are enzymes that break down proteins. They are produced by bacteria for use in biological washing powders, the food industry and brewing. Proteases in washing powders allow protein-based stains to be digested at low washing temperatures. The enzymes are enclosed in tiny capsules to prevent allergy problems.

- **Amylases** are used in the baking, brewing and textiles industries to break down starch into sugar. **Trypsin** is used in the leather industry and for medical uses. **Pectinases** are enzymes used to clear cloudy wine or olive oil by breaking down pectin molecules.

- Enzymes are used in **biosensors**, devices that detect the presence of chemicals in samples of blood or urine. Biosensors can detect the presence of glucose in the blood, a condition which might indicate diabetes.

- Enzymes may be **immobilised** on inert polymers, so that they can be re-used many times. Immobilised enzymes can easily be removed from the reaction mixture and are more stable and reliable than soluble enzymes. **Physically immobilised enzymes** may be trapped in a gel, adsorbed onto an insoluble matrix or encapsulated behind a membrane. **Chemically immobilised** enzymes are cross-linked or covalently bonded to solid supports.

- In **genetic engineering**, a desirable gene is removed from its chromosome by enzymes called **restriction endonucleases**. It is joined into the DNA of another organism, for example into a bacterial plasmid, by enzymes called **DNA ligases**. The resulting recombinant DNA is inserted into a host cell.

- The host cell is often a microorganism, which can be cultured and will produce large quantities of the desired product coded for by the recombinant DNA. The plasmid containing the altered DNA is often marked with other genes, for example antibiotic resistance markers.

- The **polymerase chain reaction** allows the amplification and fast replication of tiny fragments of DNA: it is a very important development in genetic engineering.

- The products of genetically engineered microorganisms include penicillin, hormones such as human growth hormone and insulin, and many enzymes. There are many safety precautions that have to be observed when working with genetically engineered organisms, to avoid releasing a potentially dangerous organism into the outside world.

- Farmers have traditionally used **artificial selection** to improve plant and animal breeds.

- **Artificial insemination** allows cattle farmers relatively easy access to sperm from the best stud bulls. AI is a way of facilitating selective breeding.

- Altering the genetic make-up of plants and animals by genetic engineering is much quicker and more effective than selective breeding: the desired change can be achieved in the space of one generation.

- Genetic engineering is being developed on larger organisms including insects and plants.

- **Transgenic plants** are created by using the Ti plasmid of the bacterium *A. tumefaciens* to transfer information directly into the plant DNA. This causes a tumour to develop made up of plant cells containing the desired DNA. These cells can then be cultured, and from them whole plants are grown with the desirable trait.

- **Genetically modified animals** have so far been created mainly to produce ▼ particular human proteins that cannot be synthesised by microbes. It is difficult to introduce new DNA to eukaryotic cells, but **microinjection**, **microprojectiles**, **invasion by a harmless virus** carrying the desired gene, and **wrapping the gene in liposomes** have all produced some degree of success.

- **Gene therapy** means the replacement of faulty genes in an individual with healthy copies.

- **Germ line therapy** means altering the reproductive cells of the body so that faulty genes are not passed on to the next generation.

QUESTIONS

1 a What are the advantages of using isolated enzymes in biotechnological processes?

  b How are the enzymes obtained from whole cells?

  c The use of immobilised enzymes is becoming increasingly common. What are the advantages of this over free isolated enzymes, and how are the enzymes immobilised?

2 Summarise the main types of isolated enzymes used in biotechnology and what they are used for.

3 a How does genetic engineering differ from artificial selection?

  b How is genetic engineering carried out in:
  i bacteria
  ii plants
  iii animals.

Developing Key Skills

Genetic engineering is a relatively new technology that offers many potential benefits to human beings but which also carries a number of potential risks. Produce two newspaper articles for the same paper (choose any national newspaper and write your articles in an appropriate style for your readership). In the first article present the positive face of genetic engineering – food, farming and health benefits. Present any scientific evidence you can find and produce an article that is both exciting and reassuring.

In the second article present the negative side of genetic engineering. Highlight the concerns and potential problems that could arise from this new technology. Again present any scientific evidence you can find and produce an article that would turn people against the new technology. In both articles make sure that your scientific facts are correct, along with any data or evidence you present.

1 An investigation was carried out to determine the number of bacteria in a sample of stale milk. The method (shown in the diagram below) involved making serial dilutions of the stale milk with sterile distilled water. Then 1 cm³ of each diluted sample was transferred to a separate nutrient agar plate and incubated for 24 hours. The number of colonies counted is recorded in the table.

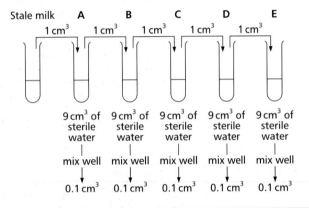

	A	B	C	D	E
Number of colonies	Too many to count	Too many to count	480	63	3

a Give **two** precautions for the aseptic transfer of a sample to an agar plate. **(2 marks)**

b **i** Using the results from test tube **C**, calculate the number of bacteria per cm³ of the stale milk. Show your working. **(2 marks)**

ii Explain why the total cell count per cm³ would produce a different result from that obtained in **b i**. **(2 marks)**

(AQA specimen 2000)

2 The diagram below shows the structure of a human immunodeficiency virus (HIV).

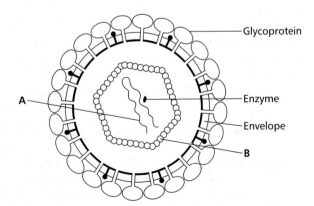

a Name the parts of the virus labelled **A** and **B**. **(2 marks)**

b Describe **two** ways in which viruses may cause disease. **(2 marks)**

c Explain why diseases caused by viruses are difficult to treat using drugs. **(2 marks)**

(AQA specimen 2000)

3 Read the following passage.
Many industrial processes involve the synthesis or breakdown of organic compounds. Methods which involve enzymes are rapidly being adopted by industry. The commonest sources of enzymes are bacteria, yeasts and filamentous fungi. The enzymes produced are often immobilised. Although this involves extra cost, it has a number of advantages.

a Explain why microorganisms are particularly useful as sources of enzymes. **(3 marks)**

b **i** What is meant by an immobilised enzyme? **(2 marks)**

ii Give **two** advantages of using immobilised enzymes. **(2 marks)**

c Explain how an enzyme speed up a chemical reaction. **(2 marks)**

(AQA specimen 2000)

4 The diagram shows a bacterial cell with the site of action of two antibiotics.

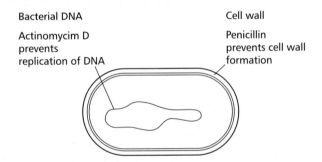

a Explain why penicillin is effective against bacteria but has very little effect on animal cells. **(1 mark)**

b Suggest an explanation for the fact that actinomycin D is too toxic to humans to be used as an antibiotic against bacterial infections. **(1 mark)**

c Explain why frequent treatment with penicillin can lead to the appearance of large numbers of bacteria which have resistance to antibiotics. **(3 marks)**

(AQA specimen 2000)

5 *Streptomyces* are bacteria that produce the antibiotic neomycin. The changes in pH in a culture of *Streptomyces* are shown in the graph below. The table records the concentration of neomycin in the medium.

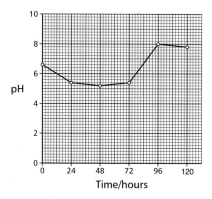

Concentration of neomycin/μg cm^{-3}

Time / hours	24	48	72	96	120
Concentration of neomycin / μg cm^{-3}	0	150	450	1800	2000

a Plot the data from the table on the graph. **(2 marks)**
b i Calculate the rate of increase in the concentration of neomycin between 72 and 96 hours.
ii Suggest an explanation for the relationship between pH and the concentration of neomycin between 72 and 96 hours. **(2 marks)**

(AQA specimen 2000)

6 The figure shows a biosensor that makes use of the enzyme urease to measure urea in either blood or urine.

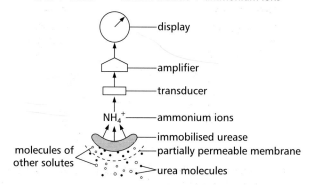

urease
urea + water ⟶ carbon dioxide + ammonium ions

display
amplifier
transducer
NH$_4^+$ — ammonium ions
immobilised urease
molecules of other solutes — partially permeable membrane
urea molecules

a i Suggest a substance that could be used to immobilise the enzyme. **(1 mark)**
ii Explain the presence of the partially permeable membrane. **(1 mark)**
iii Explain why other solutes do not affect the results. **(2 marks)**
iv Describe the function of the transducer. **(2 marks)**
b State **two** advantages of using a biosensor, rather than a chemical method, to measure the concentration of urea. **(2 marks)**
c Discuss the use of a biosensor in the monitoring of blood glucose. (*In this question, 1 mark is available for the quality of written communication.*) **(8 marks)**

(OCR specimen 2000)

7 a Describe the methods of transmission and the symptoms of Salmonella food poisoning. Explain the methods by which its incidence might be reduced. **(5 marks)**
b Antibodies can be used to give protection against infection by some pathogenic microbes. Explain how a bacterium could be genetically engineered to produce an anitbody. **(5 marks)**

(AQA specimen 2000)

8 a i Describe how the lungs of a patient with emphysema differ from those of a healthy person. **(1 mark)**
ii Explain why the lungs of an emphysema patient cannot supply the body with sufficient oxygen. **(2 marks)**
b The table below shows the results of a study of 83 patients relating the occurrence of black particles in the lungs and emphysema to the number of cigarettes smoked per day.

		Number of cigarettes smoked per day	Severity of emphysema/ arbitrary scale			
			0	1	2	3
Amount of black particles in lungs / abitrary scale	1	0	11	3	0	1
		1 – 15	1	5	0	0
		16 or more	5	7	3	2
	2	0	1	2	1	1
		1 – 15	1	1	1	0
		16 or more	0	7	11	9
		0	0	0	0	0
	3	1 – 15	0	0	0	0
		16 or more	0	1	3	6

Calculate the percentage of people who smoked 16 or more cigarettes per day who had:
i severe emphysema (a value of 3 on the scale) **(1 mark)**
ii a large amount of black particles in the lungs (a value of 3 on the scale). **(1 mark)**

(AQA specimen 2000)

9 The table shows the results of a blood test carried out on a patient who had suffered a heart attack. All units are arbitrary units.

Substance	Concentrations in patient's blood	Normal range
Cholesterol	8.2	3.6 – 3.7
Glucose	13.6	Less than 7
Aspartate transaminase	235	5 – 40
Lactate dehydrogenase	2265	300 – 650

a i Explain the link between high blood cholesterol and heart attacks. **(3 marks)**
ii Explain why it is not possible to say that the high cholesterol concentration in the blood of this patient caused the heart attack. **(2 marks)**
b Aspartate transaminase and lactate dehydrogenase are enzymes that are normally found inside muscle cells. Suggest why measurement of the concentration of these enzymes in the blood can be used to confirm that a person has had a heart attack. **(2 marks)**

(AQA specimen 2000)

10 a The graph shows changes in the birth and death rates in the UK from 1700 to the present day.

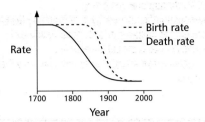

Sketch a line on the graph axes below to show how the population size would have changed over the period shown.
(1 mark)

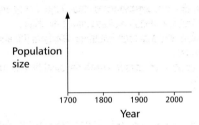

b Suggest:
i **two** features which contributed to the fall in death rate which started at around 1750 **(2 marks)**
ii **two** reasons to explain why the birth rate fell from about 1870 **(2 marks)**
iii **one different** reason to explain why the birth rate has continued to fall since 1950. **(1 mark)**

c Deaths from colon cancer are increasing. There are several genes that control the division of cells. One type of gene, called a tumour suppressor gene, prevents uncontrolled cell division. Colon cancer may result if these tumour suppressor genes are prevented from working normally. Another gene, called the p53 gene, has been found to activate transcription in a tumour suppressor gene. In tumour cells from cancer of the colon, this p53 gene is often found to have mutated.
i Explain what is meant by mutation of a gene. **(2 marks)**
ii Use the information above to draw a flow diagram to show how mutation of the p53 gene could result in the development of colon cancer. **(2 marks)**

(AQA specimen 2000)

11 a Explain the meaning of the following terms as they apply to infectious diseases: *endemic* and *epidemic*. **(2 marks)**
The table shows the diseases which cause death in developing and developed countries.

Developing countries		Developed countries	
Disease	**Percentage deaths**	**Disease**	**Percentage deaths**
Diarrhoea	42	Heart diseases	32
Respiratory infections e.g. tuberculosis (TB)	25	Cancers	23
Malnutrition	10	Strokes	12
Malaria	7	Bronchitis	6
Measles	5	Pneumonia	5
Others	11	Others	22

b With reference to the table:
i explain why infectious diseases are leading causes of death in developing countries **(4 marks)**
ii explain why degenerative diseases are leading causes of death in developed countries. **(4 marks)**

(OCR specimen 2000

12 a Complete the table below to show **two** differences between active and passive immunity.

	Active immunity	**Passive immunity**
1	....	....
2	....	....

(4 marks)

b Complete the table below by describing how each type of immunity is acquired.

Type of immunity	**How acquired**
Natural active	....
Artificial passive	....
Natural passive	....
Artificial passive	....

(4 marks)

c Explain, in terms of the structure of antibody molecules, how the immune system is able to produce large numbers of different types of antibodies.
(In this question, 1 mark is available for the quality of written communication.) **(7 marks)**

(OCR specimen 2000)

13 The bacterium, *Vibrio cholerae*, is the causative agent of cholera. The El Tor strain of *V. cholerae* originally occurred only in Indonesia. In 1961, this strain began to spread replacing existing strains in other parts of Asia. El Tor is now widespread throughout Asia, the Middle East, Africa and parts of Eastern Europe, but has never established itself in Western Europe. El Tor is hardier than the strain it replaced and the bacteria may continue to appear in the faeces for up to three months after patients have recovered. The bacteria may persist in water for up to fourteen days.

a State **two** ways in which *V. cholerae* is transmitted from infected to uninfected people. **(2 marks)**

Some people infected with cholera have mild symptoms, or none at all, and are carriers of the disease.

b Suggest how laboratory tests could identify carriers of cholera. **(2 marks)**

c Suggest **four** reasons why El Tor has not become established in Western Europe. **(4 marks)**

The United Nations, recognising that most of the outbreaks of cholera were the result of polluted water supplies, set up a 'Decade of Water' in 1981. Its aim was to provide safe water for everyone. Over the decade 1981/1990, the number of people lacking a safe water supply in developing countries dropped from 1800 million to 1200 million.

d Explain why cholera continues to be a worldwide problem, in spite of the 'Decade of Water' campaign.
(*In this question, 1 mark is available for the quality of written communication.*) **(8 marks)**

The antibiotic tetracycline is sometimes used as a treatment for cholera.

e i Suggest **two** ways in which tetracycline can affect *V. cholerae*. **(2 marks)**

ii Explain why tetracycline should not be used routinely for all cases of cholera. **(1 mark)**

(OCR specimen 2000)

14 a State **three** components of a balanced diet which provide energy. **(3 marks)**

Four investigations of the energy intake of 14 and 15 year old boys and girls have been carried out in the UK since the 1930s. These studies show that the average intake of energy has decreased, while the average body masses of both boys and girls have remained the same. The results of these investigations are shown in the table below.

Investigation	Average energy intake / kJ per day	
	boys	girls
1930s	12 873	11 088
1960s	11 739	9 534
1970s	10 962	8 484
1980s	10 478	8 316

b i Calculate the percentage decrease in energy intake for boys between the 1930s and the 1980s. Show your working. **(3 marks)**

ii Suggest **two** reasons for the fact that the intake of energy has decreased between the 1930s and the 1980s while the average body mass has remained constant. **(2 marks)**

iii Explain why the energy intake of girls is lower than that for boys of the same age. **(1 mark)**

In 1991, the British Government's Committee on Medical Aspects of Food Policy (COMA) published dietary reference values (DRVs). The Estimated Average Requirement (EAR) is the dietary reference value for energy intake. EARs for different age groups are calculated from basal metabolic rates, the amount of energy needed to support growth and the amount of physical activity.

c Explain the value of publishing EARs for dietary energy. **(3 marks)**

d Suggest **two** problems that might be encountered in calculating the EAR for any one age group. **(2 marks)**

The overconsumption of energy-rich food can lead to obesity, which can increase the chances of becoming seriously ill.

e i Explain what is meant by *obesity*. **(1 mark)**

ii Suggest **three** ways in which obesity may lead to serious illness. **(3 marks)**

(OCR specimen 2000)

15 During strenuous exercise, such as long distance running, changes occur as muscles use their stores of glycogen and fat to supply energy. Glycogen can be respired both aerobically and anaerobically whilst fat is respired aerobically.

a Describe and explain the changes that occur within muscle during the first few minutes of strenuous exercise. **(5 marks)**

b Explain why a person breathes deeply at the end of strenuous exercise. **(4 marks)**

c Describe **four** ways in which physical fitness may benefit the body. **(4 marks)**

(OCR specimen 2000)

16 The figure shows the death rates from coronary heart disease (CHD) for men aged 35 to 74 between 1968 and 1992 for four countries, Finland, UK, Australia and Japan.

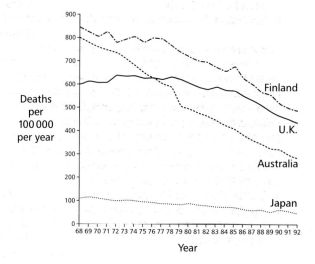

a With reference to the figure, compare the death rates from CHD in the UK with those in Australia over the period between 1968 and 1992. **(5 marks)**

b Suggest **four** reasons for the difference between death rates from CHD in Finland and Japan. **(4 marks)**

Two of the main targets in the British Government's health strategy are the reduction in the prevalence of smoking and the reduction in the number of cases of CHD.

c Explain how smoking contributes to the development of CHD. **(6 marks)**

(OCR specimen 2000)

17 The figure shows a labelled diagram of a bacteriophage.

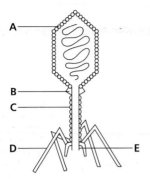

a Name the group of microorganisms which includes
bacteriophages. **(1 mark)**
b Using the letters on the figure, identify the region:
   i involved in the attachment to bacteria **(1 mark)**
   ii involved in penetrating bacterial cells **(1 mark)**
   iii containing genetic information. **(1 mark)**
c Describe the life cycle of a **named** bacteriophage.
   (*In this question, 1 mark is available for the quality of written
   communication.*) **(9 marks)**

The number of bacteriophages in a liquid medium can be
determined by serial dilution of the medium, followed by plating a
small volume, 0.5 cm³, on to an agar plate that has been covered in
bacteria. Each bacteriophage is capable of infecting a bacterium.
When the agar plates are incubated, a bacterial lawn results in which
there are clear areas known as plaques. A plaque is produced when
a single bacteriophage infects a bacterium, and eventually results in
the death of a large number of bacteria. The clear areas are due to
lysis of these bacteria. The number of plaques produced from a
serial dilution of the medium on two sets of plates, inoculated with
the same bacterium, are shown in the table below.

	Dilution		
	10^{-6}	**10^{-7}**	**10^{-8}**
Number of	956	98	7
plaques	948	94	3

d With reference to the table:
   i suggest why the values at the dilutions of 10^{-6} and 10^{-8} are
   inaccurate and should not be used to estimate bacteriophage
   numbers **(5 marks)**
   ii estimate the number of bacteriophage particles per cm³ in the
   original liquid medium. Show your working. **(3 marks)**

(OCR specimen 2000)

18 For many years, Britain has disposed of much of its domestic waste
in landfill sites. Occasionally there have been reports of explosions.
These have been due to the production of gases in the buried waste.
a Explain the sequence of events that may have led to these
explosions. **(4 marks)**
b **i** Explain how the gas produced might be used. **(3 marks)**
   ii Suggest why the gas produced is only likely to be used
   locally. **(1 mark)**
   iii Suggest **two** areas of human activity for which the production
   and use of biogas might be an advantage. **(2 marks)**

(OCR specimen 2000)

19 a Explain why microorganisms are particularly useful for industrial
processes. **(4 marks)**
b Astaxanthin is a pigment which can be added to the food of
salmon grown in fish-farms, to make their flesh pinker. The
pigment is made by a species of yeast, *Phaffia rhodozyma*. The
graph shows the results of a laboratory fermentation in which the
pigment was produced from a yeast culture.

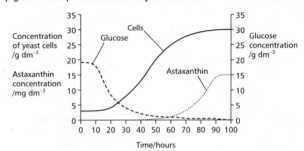

Use the data to explain whether astaxanthin is a primary or a
secondary metabolite. **(4 marks)**
c Describe and explain **two** problems involved in scaling up from a
laboratory fermentation by microorganisms to full scale industrial
production. **(4 marks)**

(AQA summer 1999)

20 The figure shows a large scale fermenter of a type that might be
used in the production of an antibiotic.

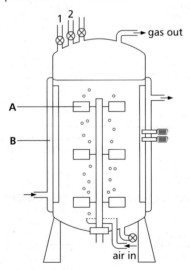

a **i** Name parts **A** and **B**. **(2 marks)**
   ii Suggest **two** substances that might be added through taps **1**
   and **2** during a fermentation. **(2 marks)**
   iii Explain the function of part **B**. **(2 marks)**
b Describe how the fermenter and substrates are prepared
before use. **(5 marks)**
   The antibiotic penicillin is produced in batch fermenters.
c Explain how a *batch* fermentation differs from a *continuous*
fermentation. **(3 marks)**

(OCR specimen 2000)

INDEX

courtship behaviour 365
cranium 490
Craspedecusia 487
creatine, phosphagens 477
creatinine secretion 322
Creutzfeldt–Jakob disease 728
Crick, Francis 36, 39
crista, mammalian ear 269, 273
cristae, mitochondria 11
critical temperature, low/high 337
crocodiles 491
crop rotation 531, 544
crossing over
    chromosomes 368–9, 370, 378
    crossover value 442–3, 448
crown gall, transgenes 731
crustaceans, exoskeletons 157, 489
crypts of Leiberkuhn 205, 221
crystallins, eye 266
culture 599–600
    batch culture 692
    master culture 690
    pure 603–4, 610
    semicontinuous/continuous
        culture 692–3
    stock/working cultures 690–1
    submerged culture 717
    surface/solid substrate culture
        717
    total viable cell count 602, 609
    see also microorganisms
culture media 599–600
    indicator media 604
    MacConkey's agar 698
    screening microbes 716
cupula 269, 273
curare, acetylcholine action 252
cuticle
    leaves 108–9
    stem 104, 106, 109
    transpiration 117
cutin 107, 109, 110, 112
cyanide
    chemical death 178
    enzyme irreversible inhibition 69
cyanobacteria 481, 520
cyclic AMP 295, 297
cystic fibrosis 16, 450, 458, 462–4,
    466, 615
    gene therapy 733–5
cytochrome c, apoptosis 224
cytochrome oxidase 71
    electron transfer chain 179, 181
cytokinesis see mitosis
cytokinins 298, 306–8, 313
cytoplasm see cell cytoplasm
cytosine 35, 44
cytoskeleton 11–12, 15
    eukaryotic cells 11
    function 11

dandelions, protandry 385
Danielli, JF 52
dark field illumination,
    microscopy 5
Darwin, Charles 301, 475–6, 492
Darwin, Francis 301
Davson, H 52
day length, courtship behaviour
    365
day-neutral plants 310, 313

DDT 546–7, 562
de Vries, Hugo 438
deamination of urea 331, 343
death
    and ageing 679–84, 686
    defined 682–3
    and dying 682–5
death phase 596
death rate 525, 537
decarboxylases 230
decline phase 526, 537, 596
decomposers 220, 483, 514, 521,
    598
defences, non-specific and specific
    immune system 631–4
deficiency diseases 211, 222, 615,
    647
deflected succession 511
deforestation 570–2, 580
degrees of freedom, chi-squared
    test 446
dehydrogenases 230
delirium tremens (DTs) 678
denaturing of proteins 27, 67
dendrites, Nissl's granules 243, 254
dendron, sensory neurones 243,
    254
dengue 632
density-dependent/independent
    factors, population growth
    527–8, 537
dentition (teeth) 199, 201–2, 221
deoxygenated blood 143
deoxyribonucleic acid see DNA
deoxyribose 34
depression 614
dermatitis, vitamin PP deficiency
    211
desertification 570–2, 580
deserts 314, 340, 509, 521
    net primary production 517
destarched plants 185
detergents 63
    use of protease enzymes 720–1
detoxified organisms, vaccines 80
detritivores 220
development pattern, human 400
diabetes insipidus 323
diabetes mellitus 291–2, 727
diaphragm
    contraception 422, 428
    respiratory system 127, 128,
        129, 137
diarrhoea 209, 632, 646
    cholera 646
    typhoid 646
    vitamin PP deficiency 211
diastema 199
diastole 144, 154
diastolic blood pressure 148, 658
dicotyledons 94, 381–2, 385, 393,
    493
    anatomy 382
    energy stores 386, 388
    germination 388, 394
    synthetic auxins 305
    see also flowering plants; leaf;
        root; stem
dietary reference values (DRVs)
    215–17

differential centrifugation,
    organelle separation 9
differential survival and fertility,
    evolution 476
differentiation 74, 404
diffusion 53–7, 61
    absorption of digested food 208
    capillary system 143
    concentration gradient 53
    expiratory surfaces 132
    facilitated 57, 58, 61–2
    Fick's law 53, 131
    fish 135–6
    see also osmosis
digestion 199, 200, 221
digestive enzymes 199, 206, 221–2
    saliva 202, 221, 271
    in small intestine 206–7, 222
    in stomach 203–5
digestive system see gut
diglycerides 22
dihybrid crosses 438–40, 448
dihydroxyacetone phosphate 228
dilution plating 602, 609
dinitrophenol, sodium ion
    removal 246
dinoflagellates 482
dioecious plants 367, 377, 381
dipeptides 25, 31
diphtheria, /tetanus/pertussis
    (DTP) vaccine 641–2
diploblastic structure 487
diploid cells 356, 363, 366
diploid number (of chromosomes)
    363
Diplopoda 489, 494
dipole, in water 46
direct drilling 541
directional selection 501–2, 505
disaccharides 18, 19, 31, 206,
    207, 222
discontinuous variation 376, 378
disease 615, 647, 650–86
    aetiology (causes) 614, 620
        bacterial 584
        degenerative 615, 647
        diet-related 651–5
        heart disease 139
        hypertension association
            659, 685
        viral 590
        water quality 611
    communicable 631, 647
    control 635–43, 640, 648
    defined 612–13, 647
    detection 616–23, 647
    elimination 640, 649
    eradication 640
    inherited disease 615, 647
    morbidity and mortality 620,
        647
    multifactorial 450
    outbreak 631
    person-to-person contact 631
    point source 631
    and population size 535, 537
    prevention 643
    spread by ingestion, inhalation
        632, 648
    symptoms and signs 613
    see also bacteria

disinfectants 605, 610, 637
displacement behaviour 285
disposable soma theory 680
disruptive selection 502–3, 505
distribution of species see
    population distributions
distribution studies 477, 492
diuretics, hypertensive treatment
    659, 685
divergence, light rays 263
divergent evolution 477
diversifying selection see
    disruptive selection
diversity index 513
diverticulitis 654, 685
diving mammals 152–3, 155
dizygotic twins 413, 427
dizziness 269
DNA 34–44
    animal cells 9
    cell role 1, 39
    complementary (cDNA) 725–6
    control of cell division 39
    core units 33
    double helix 33, 35, 36
    gyrase inhibitors 638
    hypervariable regions 33
    microprojectiles, transgenes 732
    non-overlapping code 40
    nucleotide production 206
    recombinant DNA 726–7
    replication 37–8, 44, 357
        conservative and
            semiconservative 38
    structure 34–6
    transcription 41
    translation 42
    triple code 29, 39
DNA fingerprinting 33
DNA injection, transgenes 732
DNA ligases 726
DNA profiling 33
DNA viruses 588
DNA–RNA hybridisation 461
DNA-directed RNA polymerase 41
dogs
    faeces, leather production 63
    hybrid vigour 503
    skin problems 3
Doll, Sir Richard 620, 673
Dolly the cloned sheep 352–4, 584
Domagk, Gerhard 605, 637
dominant alleles 431, 447
dormancy, seeds 387–8, 393
dorsal root ganglion 258
double circulation 40, 153
Down's syndrome 452–4, 465, 615
downstream processing 693
Drosophila
    ecdysone effects 296
    genetic experiments 371–2,
        430, 434, 438
        outcome probabilities 439
    sex-linked chromosomes 444
drug abuse 615
drugs, and pregnancy risks 410,
    416
dry mass, growth measurement
    360, 363, 603, 609
Dryopteris 485

gastric pits 204, 221
gastric ulcers, autodigestion 204
gastrin 204
gastrodermis, cnidarians 487
gastrointestinal infections 594
Gastropoda 489, 494
Gazania flower 381
Gearhart, John 349
gender, and health 620, 647, 663
gene banks, International Potato
    Centre, Peru 542
gene flow effect 499–500, 505
gene frequencies 496–8, 505
gene pool 496, 505
gene probes 461
gene therapy 465, 466, 733–5
    cystic fibrosis 733–5
generation time 595
generative nucleus 384
generator current 259
generator potential 259
genes 430, 447
    lethal 436–8, 448
    linkage 441–3, 448
    pleiotropy 459–60, 466
    sex-linked 443–4
genetic code 39–40
genetic counselling 464
genetic crosses 431–40, 432–40,
    448
    map units 442
    outcome probabilities 439
    values 442–3, 448
genetic disease 452–64, 465, 615,
    647
    sex-linked 451–2, 465
genetic engineering 367, 464–5,
    466, 584, 725–35
    applications 727–8
    bacteria (vaccines) 641
    gene therapy 733–5
    genetic modification 713
    marker genes 726
    pest control 551–2, 730
    restriction endonucleases 725–6
    transgenic animals and plants
    731–3
genetic fingerprinting 33
genetic testing and screening,
    ethical issues 461–4, 466
genetically modified (GM) foods
    713
genetics 429–49, 450–66
    epistasis 443
    experimental species 434
    history 436
    Mendel's laws 440–7, 451
    population genetics 496–505
genome 438, 451
genotype 430, 447
genus, defined 479, 493
geotaxis 281
geotropism 96, 300, 303–4, 312
germ cells, spermatogenesis 398,
    404
germ line therapy 733–4
germ warfare 634
German measles 642
    pregnancy risks 410
germination 385, 387–8, 393, 394
gestation see pregnancy
giant axons 244, 254

giant chromosomes 296
gibberellins 304, 306, 312, 313
    chemical structure and
        functions 308
GIFT see gamete intra-fallopian
    transfer
gill arch and filaments 135–7
gill slits 490
gills
    fish 135–7, 316
    molluscs 489
glands 633
glass, recycling 577–8, 580
global conservation 577
globular proteins 26–7, 32
    see also enzymes; haemoglobin;
        immunoglobulins
glomerular filtrate, composition
    320
glomerulus 317–18, 326
glottis 128
glucagon 289, 290
    alpha cells 292
    insulin interaction 292
glucocorticoids 289
glucose 18, 120, 206
    alpha- and beta-fructose 19
    blood level control 290
    conversion to fructose 707, 724
    insulin action 727
    see also glycolysis
glucose isomerase 707, 724
glucose oxidase, urine testing 63,
    616
gluten 696
glyceraldehyde 3-phosphate
    (GALP) 191, 196, 228–9,
    232, 234
glyceraldehyde
    respiration biochemistry 18
    stereoisomerism 18
glycerate 3-phosphate (GP) 191,
    196
glycerol 21, 206, 207, 222
glyceryl trinitrate 661, 685
glycogen 20, 209, 233, 234, 271
    liver storage 332, 343
glycolysis 226, 228–30, 234
glycopeptides 638
glycoproteins 26, 52, 76, 84
    formation 10, 15
glycosidic link, formation 19
goitre, simple 293
Golgi apparatus 9–10, 15,
    329–30, 343
Golgi, Camillo 9
gonadotrophins 289, 295
gonads
    gamete formation 367, 377
    see also ovaries; testes
gonorrhoea 632
Gorter 52
Gould, Stephen Jay 500
Graham, Hilary 675
Gram, Hans Christian 592
Gram's stain, bacteria 592–3, 608
grana 13
granulocytes 149, 154
grasses 381
gravity
    perception 268–9, 273

plant geotropism 96, 300,
    303–4, 312
gravity receptors 256
greenhouse, environment control
    554–5, 561
greenhouse gases 567–9, 580
Grendel 52
grey matter 258, 275–7, 285
growth
    chemical messages, plants 299
    defined 299, 359
    embryos 361, 363
    measurement 360–3
        dry mass 360, 363, 603, 609
    meristems 388–9, 394
    patterns 360–1, 363
    populations 524–8, 537
    puberty 361
    shoots/stems 390, 394
growth curves 360
    exponential 524–6, 537, 596
    populations 527–8, 537
growth hormone 289, 295
    antagonism 307–8, 313
    failure 728
    synergism 307, 313
guanine 35, 44
guard cells 108–9, 110, 112
guinea worm 611
Gusella, Dr James 459
gut 201–9
    autodigestion protection 204
    blood vessels 141
    defense mechanism 633
    digestion 199, 201, 221
    exocrine glands 288
    structure 218, 223
    see also specific named parts
guttation 119
gymnosperms 390

habitat, defined 496, 505, 508, 521
habitat niche 5–9
Habitats Directive, EU
    conservation measures
    576–7
habituation 284, 286
haem 71, 155
haemocytometer 601, 609
haemoglobin 149, 150–1, 154
    breakdown in liver 332, 343
    fetal 151, 155
    globular proteins 27
    sickle cell anaemia 459–60, 466
haemoglobinic acid 152, 155
haemophilia 150, 456–7, 466
    Factor VII and IX, transgenes
    733
    genetic screening 463
Haemophilus influenzae 594
    Hib vaccine 642
haemorrhoids, dietary fibre 212,
    654, 685
hair
    blow-drying and perming 28
    mammals 491
    in thermoregulation 336
hair loss 3
Haldane, JBS 472
halophytes 325, 327
Hanson, Jean 164

haploid cells 356, 366–7, 371
Harden, Arthur 230
Hardy, GH 497
Hardy-Weinberg equation 497–9,
    505
harelip 452
harvest index 540–1, 560
harvesting 542
harvestmen (insects) 489
Harvey, William 140
Hatch, Hal 193
Hatch–Slack pathway 193, 195
haustoria 597
haversian canal 161, 165
HCG see human chorionic
    gonadotrophin
head-foots 489, 494
health
    defined 612, 647
    qualitative/quantitative
        measures 612
health regulations 627
hearing 256
heart 144–8, 154
    birth changes 139, 418, 419, 428
    bypass surgery 662–3
    control 146
    exercise response 139, 147,
        665–6
    'hole in heart' 139, 419
    intrinsic rhythmicity 146
    in pregnancy 415
    structure 144, 145, 154
heart attack see myocardial
    infarction
heart disease 139
heart rate 144–6, 147, 154, 271
    diving mammals 152, 155
heart transplant 662–3
heat exchange, bioreactors 694
heat gain/loss centre 338
heavy metal ions 564–5, 579
hedgerows 539
helminths 487, 493, 629, 647
helper T-cells 625
hemicelluloses 13
hepatic artery 329–30, 343
hepatic portal vein 208, 222,
    329–30, 343
hepatic vein 208, 222, 329–30, 343
Hepaticae see liverworts
hepatitis A 632
hepatitis B 632
    vaccine 641
hepatocytes 329–30, 343
    deamination 331, 343
herbicides 252, 298, 502, 546, 560
    resistance by crop plants 730–1
herbivores
    cellulose digestion 20, 198, 221
    energy source 173
    gut structure 218, 223
    microorganism symbiotic
        relationships 218, 223
    vision 265
herd effect, vaccination 641
hermaphrodite 367, 377, 488
heroin, pregnancy risks 416
herpes, genital 639
heterogametic organisms 172,
    443, 591

myosin 163, 164, 165
myxomatosis 502

NAD *see* nicotinamide adenine
    dinucleotide
nasal cavity, respiratory system
    128
nastic responses, plants 305, 312
natality *see* birth rate
National Nature Reserves (NNRs)
    574, 580
National Parks 575–6, 580
Natura 2000, EU conservation
    measures 576–7, 580
natural active/passive immunity
    79, 84
natural defences 631–4
natural killer cells 76, 84, 625,
    634, 648
natural selection 475, 492, 500–5
    classic type 501
nature conservation organisations
    574–7, 580
nature *vs* nurture 429
navigation, birds 523
necrosis 224
nectar 382
negative feedback loop 290, 291,
    293, 400
Neisseria gonorrhoeae 634
Neisseria meningitidis 594
nematoblasts 242, 487
nematocyst 242
Nematoda 488, 494
neo-Darwinism 476, 492
nephridia 488
nephrons 318, 326
nerve cells/fibres *see* neurones
nerve cord 490
nerve gases
    cholinesterase inactivation 252
    enzyme irreversible inhibition
        69–70
nerve impulses 242, 248, 254
    defined 244
    investigation 247
    mechanism evidence 246
nervous control 242–55
    vs endocrine control 289
    see also nervous system
nervous stimulation, small
    intestine secretions 207, 222
nervous system
    insects 275, 285
    invertebrates 244, 254
    mammals 256–73
    organisation 242–3
net primary production (NPP)
    517, 522, 540
neuromuscular junctions 251–2,
    255
neurones 242–4, 254
    accommodation 253, 255
    coordination and control 252,
        255
    fatigued 253, 255
    giant axons 244, 254
    intermediate 257, 271
    polarisation/depolarisation
        245, 254
    reflex arc 257, 271
    relay 258

resting potential 245, 254
    sensory 258
    threshold 248, 254
    transmission speed 244
    see also motor and sensory
        neurones; synapses
neurosecretory cells 294, 297
neutrophils 149, 154
niche, ecological 508, 521
Nicholson, Garth 51, 52
nicotinamide adenine
    dinucleotide (NAD) 71
    electron transfer chain 178–9,
        181, 228–9, 234
nicotine
    acetylcholine mimicking 252
    vasoconstriction 670
    nicotinic acid, vitamin PP 211
Nissl's granules, protein synthesis
    243, 254
nitrifying bacteria 520
Nitrobacter 520
nitrogen
    dietary 210
    mutualism 220
nitrogen cycle 520–1, 522
nitrogen-fixing plants 520, 522
nitrogenous waste, excretio 332
Nitrosomonas 520
nodes of Ranvier 243, 254
nomenclature, binomial system
    479, 493
non-infectious disease 615, 647
nondisjunction 452, 465
noradrenaline 270–1, 289
    vertebrate nerves 251
normal distribution curve 376
Northrop, J 65
notochord 490
nucellus 387
nuclear membrane
    animal cells 9
    mitosis 358–9, 363
nuclease 206
nucleic acids 34–44, 206
    animal cells 9
    pentose sugars 18
nucleoid 14, 15
nucleolus, animal cells 9
nucleoplasm, animal cells 9
nucleosomes 356
nucleotidases 206
nucleotides 34, 35, 44
nucleus
    animal cell 7, 8–9, 14
    endosperm, triploid 385, 393
    eukaryotic cells 14
    plant cells 111, 385
    spermatozoa 399, 404
nuptial pads, frogs 374
nurse cells *see* Sertoli (nurse) cells
nutrient media 600, 609
nutrition 209–14, 653–5
    absorption of food 200
    balanced diet 212–14
    deficiencies 615
    and disease 651–5
    and exercise 667–8
    food allergies 652, 685
    food energy values 214–17
    minerals 156, 210
    overnutrition 215, 223

recommended nutritional
    guidelines 215–17
reference nutrient intake 216
refined food, cancer risk 669,
    686
saprobiotic nutrition 220, 598,
    609
saprotrophic 198, 199, 220
nymph 490

obesity 212–13
    coronary heart disease 663
    hypertension 659, 685
obligate aerobes 595, 608
obligate anaerobes 226, 234, 595,
    608
obligate outbreeders 374
occupation, health effects 622–3
octopuses 489
oesophagus, digestive system
    202–3, 221
oestrogen 289, 399, 404
    see also hormone replacement
        therapy
oestrus 403, 407, 427
Ohm, George 244
oil pollution 565–6
oils *see* fats and oils
olive oil 663
ommatidia, compound eyes 266
omnivores
    energy source 173
    gut structure 218, 223
*On the Origin of Species by Natural
    Selection, or the Preservation of
    Favoured Races in the Struggle
    for Life* 475
onchocerciasis 630
oncogenes, protooncogenes 362,
    669
oocyte *see* egg (oocyte)
oogonia 373
Oomycetes 482
Oomycota 493
Oparin, Aleksander 472
open ocean communities
    aquatic biomes 510
    net primary production 517
operant learning 285, 286
operculum, fish 135, 136, 137, 490
opportunist species 510, 521
opsin, rhodopsin formation 272
optic lobes 275
optic nerve 262, 272
optical (light) microscope 4–5
orbit, eye 262
order (taxon) 480, 493
organ of Corti 268, 273
organ system 74–5
organelles
    animal cells 7, 8–9
    lysosome destruction of 10
    plant cells 12–14
    separation, differential
        centrifugation 9
organic compounds 17, 31
organic farming 552–3
organophosphorus compounds,
    cholinesterase inactivation
    252
organs for transplantation 73
ornithine cycle 331, 343

osmoreceptors 323, 326
osmoregulation
    animals 315–24, 326, 340
    fish 316, 326
    mammals 317–24
    plants 324–5
osmosis 13, 53–7, 61
    defined 54
    living cells 55–7
    osmotic pressure 55
    role in phloem transport 121–2
    role in transpiration 117–19
    terminology 54–5
    water movement in root 95–100
osmotic concentration 54
osmotic habitats, plants 324–5
ossicles 256, 267–8, 272
Osteichthyes 490, 494
osteoarthritis 156, 613, 615
osteoblasts/osteoclasts 161, 165
osteocytes 161, 165
osteogenesis imperfecta (brittle
    bone disease) 16
osteomalacia, vitamin D deficiency
    211
osteoporosis 156, 403, 615
    diet 156
    HRT 403
otoliths 268, 273
outbreeding 375, 378
    obligate outbreeders 374
oval window, cochlea 267–8, 272
ovary
    mammal 368, 377, 399, 400,
        404
    plant 368, 377, 382, 393
overnutrition 215, 223
Overton, E 52
ovulation 396, 401, 404
ovules, plants 368, 377, 382, 384,
    393
ovum *see* egg (oocyte)
oxaloacetic acid 193, 195
oxidation, defined 178
oxidative phosphorylation 178,
    179, 181
oxygen
    altitude 153, 155
    availability, and population size
        530, 537
    biological demand 564
    cellular respiration 126
    electron transfer chain 179, 181
    Krebs cycle 226, 231, 234
    ozone layer 570
    photosynthesis 126, 185
    requirements of plants 125–6
    transport in blood 141, 142,
        148, 149–51
    uptake curve and Bohr shift
        151, 155
    see also gaseous exchange
oxygen deficit/debt 163, 229, 666
oxyhaemoglobin 150, 155
oxyntic cells, HCl production
    204, 221
oxytocin 42, 289, 295, 408, 417,
    420
oysters 489
    directional selection 501–2
ozone layer 570

Acknowledgements
The authors and publishers would like to thank the following for permission to use photographs:

Cover photos: Oxford Scientific Films

p2 University of Belfast/SPL; **p3 T** Oxford Scientific Films, **B** RSPCA; **p6 L** SPL/ Dr Jeremy Burgess, **R** SPL/Professor P Motta; **p8 T** SPL/Manfred Kage, **B** SPL/Moredun Animal Health Limited; **p11** SPL/CNRI; **p12 T** SPL/CNRI, **M** SPL/Professor P Motta; **BR** Biophoto Associates, **BL** Geoscience Features Picture Library/Dr B Booth; **p13** SPL/Dr Jeremy Burgess; **p16 T** Tony Stone, **B** Mirror Syndication; **p20 T** SPL/CNRI, **B** SPL/Dr Jeremy Burgess; **p21 L** Barnaby's PictureLibrary, **M** J Allan Cash Ltd, **R** SPL/Alex Bartel; **p27** SPL/Ken Edward; **p29** SPL/Peter Menzel; **p33 T** SPL/Peter Menzel, **B** Press Association; **p36 L** SPL/James King-Holmes/OCMS; **R** SPLPhilippe Plailly; **p45** Oxford Scientific Films; **p48** SPL/Claude Nuridsany and Maria Perennou; **p51** Biophoto Associates; **p52** SPL/ Dr Don Fawcett; **p56 T** SPL/Bill Longcove, **second to top, BL and M** Microscopix/Andrew Syred, **BR** SPL/CNRI; **p60** SPL/Biology Media; **p63 T** Mary Evans, **B** Andrew Syred; **p65** SPL/Magreth Photography; **p71** SPL/Oxford Molecular Biophysics; **p73 T** SPL/Kevin Beebe/Custom Medical Stock Photo, **B** RSPCA; **p75 T** SPL/Eric Grave, **M** SPL/Bruce Iverson, **B** NHPA/George Gainsbrugh; **p76** SPL/ James Stevenson; **p79** Andes Press Agency/Carlos Reyes; **p80** Barnaby's Picture Library; **p90** SPL/Martin Dohrn/Royal College of Surgeons; **p91** Corbis UK; **p92** SPL/Dr Jeremy Burgess; **p102 T** Oxford Scientific Films, **B** David Muench/Corbis; **p103** NHPA/Laurie Campbell; **p107 L** NHPA/Dave Currey, **M** NHPA/ G I Bernard, **R** NHPA/ David Woodfall; **p113 T** Robert Harding, **B** Oxford Scientific Films; **p115 L** UKEA **R** Microscopix/Andrew Syred; **p116** Biophoto Associates; **p119 T** Mary Evans Picture Library, **B** SPL/Tony Craddock; **p121** Microscopix/Andrew Syred; **p124 T** Tony Stone **B** SPL/James Stevenson; **p125** NHPA/Philip Sharpe; **p126 both** Biophoto Associates; **p139 T** Photodisc, **B** Wellcome Trust; **p141** SPL/Manfred Kage; **p142** Biophoto Associates; **p137:** SPL/Manfred Kage; **p145 L** Peter Gould, **R** SPL; **p148** Pictor; **p149** SPL; **p150** SPL/NIBSC; **p152** FLPA; **p153** Andes Press Agency/Carlos Reyes; **p156 T** Arthritis Research Campaign, **B** Wellcome Trust Medical Library; **p157 T** Natural History Museum; **M** Frank Lane Picture Agency; **p159** SPL/Alexander Tsiaras; **p160** SPL/Astrid and Hanns – Frieder Michler; **p161 T** SPL/Professor P Motta, **M** SPL/Eric Grave, **B** SPL/Astrid and Hanns – Frieder Michler; **p163** Biophoto Associates; **p155:** Sporting Pictures (UK) Ltd; **p158:** Biophoto Associates; **p170 and contents** Photodisc; **p171** Image Bank, **B** Panos Pictures;; **p173** Hutchison Library; **p174 T and M** Frank Lane Picture Agency; **B** Robert Harding Picture Library; **p175** Panos Pictures; **p176 T** Panos Pictures; **B** Frank Lane Picture Agency; **p179** Biophoto Associates; **p180** Hulton Deutsch Collection; **p183** Holt Studios; **p184** Holt Studios; **p186 both** Peter Gould; **p197** Culumus Digital/Malcolm Cross; **p198 T** Hutchison Library, **M** Oxford Scientific Films/Katie Atkinson, **B** Biophoto Associates; **p199 both** Frank Lane Picture Agency; **p201** Biophoto Associates; **p203** SPL/John Burbridge; **p204** SPL/Sinclair Stammers; **p205 T** SPL/Manfred Kage, **B** SPL/Fawcett/Hirokawa/Heuser; **p213 T** Syndication International, **BL and R** Panos Pictures; **p219** Eye of Science/Science Photo Library; **p220** SPL/Adam Hart-Davis; **p224 T** SPL/Dr Gopal Murti, **B** SPL/Blair Seitz; **p226 T** NHPA/Manfred Daaanegger, **B** SPL/CNRI; **p229** Barnaby's Picture Library; **p240** NHPA/Nigel J Dennis; **p241 T and M** Lupe Cunha Photos, **B** Anna Clopet/Corbis; **p243** Juergen Berger, Max-Planck Institute/SPL; **p244** Jeffrey L Rotman/Corbis; **p256 T** Kevin Schafer/Corbis, **B** Dr Andrew King; **p257** Lupe Cunha Photos; **p266** Frank Lane Picture Agency; **p274** RSPCA Photo Library, **B** Bruce Coleman Collection; **p275** Oxford Scientific Films/Scott Camazine; **p280** Sylvia Cordiay Photo Library; **p281 L** Frank Lane Picture Agency; **R** NHPA; **p283** Corbis; **p284 both** Ardea London Ltd; **p287 T** Bruce Coleman Collection, **B** Ken Gibson/Garden Matters; **p290** Biophoto Associates/SPL; **p298** Holt Studios International; **p299** Holt Studios International; **p303 TR** A–Z Botanical Collection, **L** Frank Lane Picture Agency, **BM** SPL/Adam Hart-Davies; **p304** Biophoto Associates; **p306** NHPA; **p314 both** Oxford Scientific Films; **p319 T** SPL/Brad Nelson, **B** SPL/Prof. P M Motta; **p320** Biophoto Associates; **p325 both** Biophoto Associates; **p328 T** Bubbles/Dr Hercules Robinson, **B** Roger Antrobus/Corbis; **p330** Biophoto Associates; **p331 T** SPL/Richard Kirby/David Spears; **B** Philip Parkhouse; **p334 both** Frank Lane Picture Agency; **p336** SPL/Manfred Kage; **p339** SPL/Jim Amos; **p340** Frank Lane Picture Agency; **p341 both** Frank Lane Picture Agency; **p342 T** NHPA; **B** Holt Studios International; **p348:** SPL; **p349T** PA Photos **B** Dr Yorgos Nikas/SPL; **p350** NHPA; **p351** Biophoto Associates; **p354** PA News; **p355 L** NHPA/B Jones and M Shimlock, **both M** Frank Lane Picture Agency, **R** SPL/Petit Format/Nestle; **p357** SPL/Manfred Kage; **p358** SPL/Dr Keith Porter; **p359 L** SPL/Dr Jeremy Burgess, **TM** SPL/Chris Priest and Mark Clarke, **BM, T and BR** Philip Parkhouse; **p365 T** Oxford Scientific Films **B** Roger Wilmshurst, FLPA/Corbis; **p367 T** NHPA/E J Cambridge; **M and B**

A–Z Botanical Collection; **p374** Frank Lane Picture Agency; **p375** Robert Harding; **p380 both** Royal Botanic Gardens, Kew; **p381 L** NHPA/R Pearse, **M** A–Z Botanical Collection, **R** NHPA/Stephen Dalton; **p384** SPL/David Scharf; **p386 L** SPL/Jonathan Watts, **M** NHPA, **R** A–Z Botanical Collection; **p387** Heather Angel; **p391** Frank Lane Picture Agency; **p392** SPL/John Burbidge; **p395** Scimat/SPL; **p404** Holt Studios International; **p406** Wellcome Library; **p409** SPL/D Phillips; **p410 T and M** SPL/Alexander Tsiaras; **B** SPL/Petit Format/CSI; **p414** Hattie Young/SPL; **p415** Bubbles/Frans Rombout; **p420** Sally and Richard Greenhill; **p429** Last Resort Picture Library; **p430 L** Bridgeman Art Library/ Linley Library, RHS London, **M** SPL/John Heseltine, **R** A–Z Botanical Collection; **p433 T and B** Sally Anne Thompson Animal Photography, **M** Tony Stone Worldwide; **p436 both** NHPA/Gerard Lacz; **p446** Dr Kari Iounatmaa/SPL; **p450** BTA/ETB; **p451** Sally and Richard Greenhill; **p458** Mark Clarke/SPL; **p459** SPL/Science Source; **p464** University of Pennsylvania, Phildalphia/SPL; R L Brinster and R E Hammer, School of Veterinary Medicine; **p470** Bruce Coleman Collection; **p471 T** Niall Benvie/Corbis, **B** Moviestore; **p472** Frank Lane Picture Agency; **p475** Punch Publications; **p477 T** The Natural History Museum, **M** NHPA/Jany Sauvanet, **B** NHPA/Anthony Bannister; **p479 T** Frank Lane Picture Agency, **M** NHPA/Stephen Dalton, **B** NHPA/Trevor McDonald; **p481 T** SPL **B** SPL/Andrew Syred; **482 T** SPL/Eric Grave, **B** NHPA/Norbert Wu; **p484** Frank Lane Picture Agency; **p485** Frank Lane Picture Agency; **p487** NHPA/Roy Waller; **p488** SSPL/J C Revy; **p489 T** NHPA/Jones and Shimlock; **B** Oxford Scientific Films/Fred Baverdam; **p490 T** NHPA, **B** NHPA/Kevin Schafer; **p491** NHPA/Anthony Bannister; **p492 L** Bruce Coleman Collection, **R** NHPA/Joe Blossom; **p496 T and M** Frank Lane Picture Agency, **B** Sally and Richard Greenhill; **p498** Sally and Richard Greenhill; **p500 T** NHPA/Alan Williams, **B** Frank Lane Picture Agency/H Hautala; p501 **L** NHPA/Michael Tweedie, **R** Bruce Coleman/Kim Taylor; **p506 T** The Natural History Museum, **B** Bruce Collection/Fritz Prenzel; **p507 T** SPL/European Space Agency; **B** NHPA/James Carmichael Jr; **p509** NHPA/Stephen J Krasemann; **p510** NHPA/Norbert Wu; **p511** SPL/Rick Goff; **TM** NHPA/L Campbell; **TR and B** Frank Lane Picture Agency; **p516** SPL/Andrew Syred; **p523** Holt Studios; **p528 T** NHPA/Laurie Campbell; **B** NHPA/David Woodfall; **p529 M** NHPA/Stephen Dalton; **B** Frank Lane Picture Agency; **p532** Frank Lane Picture Agency /W Wisniewski; **p533** NHPA/Mandal Ranjit; **p535 both** J Allan Cash; **p536** SPL/Alex Bartel; **p539 both** Holt Studios; **p540** Holt Studios; **p541** Holt Studios; **p542** Andrew Syred/Microscopix; **p543** Holt Studios; **p544** Holt Studios; **p545** Holt Studios; **p553** Garden & Wildlife Matters; **p554** Holt Studios; **p555** Holt Studios; **p556 T** Holt Studios, **B** Holt Studios/Bob Gibbons; **p557** Holt Studios; **p558** Jeffrey L Rotman/Corbis; **p562 T** NHPA/Anthony Bannister, **B** NHPA/Daryl Balfour; **p564** Holt Studios; **p566** Garden & Wildlife Matters; p570 SPL/NASA; **p571** Holt Studios; **p573** ARDEA; **p574** National Trust/Joe Cornish; **p575 both** Holt Studios; **p576** Ecoscene/Ian Harwood; **p577** Kevin Schafer/Corbis; **p578** Wildlife Matters; **p579 L** Alan Sheppard, Hanson Aggregates, **R** University of Georgia/China Clay Producers Association; **p584** PA News; **p585** Hulton Getty Picture Collection; **p587** SPL/Eye of Science; p589 SPL/Eye of Science; **p595** SPL/Dr Linda Stannard; **p597** Wellcome Trust Medical Photographic Library/Dr D W Gregory, University of Aberdeen; **p604** SPL/Geoff Tompkinson; **p607** SPL/Hank Morgan/John Durham; **p611 T** NHPA/Daniel Heuchlin; **B** Holt Studios; **p612 all** Sally and Richard Greenhill; **p614** PA News; **p615 T** SPL; **B** Mirror Syndication; **p616** SPL; **p618 both** SPL; **p619** SPL; **p624** SPL; **p628 T** National Medical Slide Bank, **B** SPL; **p632** SPL; **p634** PA Photos; **p635** SPL; **p637** Hulton Getty Picture Collection/Keystone; **p638** Mary Evans; **p640** Ann Fullick; **p641** Panos/R Gilling; **p644** SPL; **p650** Roger Scruton; **p651 T** Ace Photos, **B** Still Pictures; **p653** PA News; **p654** Panos/P Tweedie; **p658** Sally and Richard Greenhill; **p664 both** Sally and Richard Greenhill; **p667** Sporting Pictures; **p669** SPL; **p670** SPL; **p672T** Biophoto Associates, **B** Health Education Authority; **p674** Sally and Richard Greenhill; **p676 L** Roger Scruton, **R** Colorsport; **p677** SPL; **p679 T** Ace Photos, **B** Sally and Richard Greenhill; **p680** Biophoto Associates; **p687 T** Frank Lane Picture Agency /Roger Tidman; **B** Hulton Getty Picture Collection; **p688** Ancient Art & Architecture Collection; **p691** SPL/Hank Morgan/TEK Image; **p694** Barnaby's Picture Library; **p696** ©Food Features; **p697** Roger Scruton; **p706** Robert Harding/Paul van Riel; **p707** Still Pictures/John Isaac; **p713** Holt Studios; **p714** Mary Evans; **p728** Ardea/Kit Houghton; **p729 all** Holt Studios; **p730** Corbis; **p731** Holt Studios; **p733** SPL/CC Studio; **p735** Bruce Coleman Collection/Atlantide.

The publishers have made every effort to trace the copyright holders, but if they have inadvertently overlooked any they will be pleased to make the necessary arrangements at the first opportunity.

The authors and publishers would like to thank the AQA, Edexel and OCR Examination Boards for permission to reproduce their material.